W9-API-510

# Probability, Statistics, and Random Processes for Electrical Engineering

## Third Edition

Alberto Leon-Garcia

University of Toronto

Upper Saddle River, NJ 07458

**Library of Congress Cataloging-in-Publication Data on file**

**NOTICE:**
This work is protected by U.S. copyright laws and is provided solely for the use of college instructors in reviewing course materials for classroom use. Dissemination or sale of this work, or any part (including on the World Wide Web), is not permitted.

Vice President and Editorial Director, ECS: *Marcia J. Horton*
Associate Editor: *Alice Dworkin*
Editorial Assistant: *William Opaluch*
Senior Managing Editor: *Scott Disanno*
Production Editor: *Craig Little*
Art Director: *Jayen Conte*
Cover Designer: *Bruce Kenselaar*
Art Editor: *Greg Dulles*
Manufacturing Manager: *Alan Fischer*
Manufacturing Buyer: *Lisa McDowell*
Marketing Manager: *Tim Galligan*

© 2008 Pearson Education, Inc.
Pearson Prentice Hall
Pearson Education, Inc.
Upper Saddle River, NJ 07458

All rights reserved. No part of this book may be reproduced, in any form or by any means, without permission in writing from the publisher.

Pearson Prentice Hall™ is a trademark of Pearson Education, Inc. MATLAB is a registered trademark of The Math Works, Inc. All other product or brand names are trademarks or registered trademarks of their respective holders.

The author and publisher of this book have used their best efforts in preparing this book. These efforts include the development, research, and testing of the theories and programs to determine their effectiveness. The author and publisher make no warranty of any kind, expressed or implied, with regard to the material contained in this book. The author and publisher shall not be liable in any event for incidental or consequential damages in connection with, or arising out of, the furnishing, performance, or use of this material.

Printed in the United States of America

10  9  8  7  6  5  4  3  2  1

**ISBN 0-13-601641-3**

Pearson Education Ltd., *London*
Pearson Education Australia Pty. Ltd., *Sydney*
Pearson Education Singapore, Pte. Ltd.
Pearson Education North Asia Ltd., *Hong Kong*
Pearson Education Canada, Inc., *Toronto*
Pearson Educación de Mexico, S.A. de C.V.
Pearson Education—Japan, *Tokyo*
Pearson Education Malaysia, Pte. Ltd.
Pearson Education, *Upper Saddle River, New Jersey*

TO KAREN, CARLOS, MARISA, AND MICHAEL.

# Contents

**Preface**    **ix**

**CHAPTER 1**    Probability Models in Electrical
and Computer Engineering    1

1.1    Mathematical Models as Tools in Analysis and Design    2
1.2    Deterministic Models    4
1.3    Probability Models    4
1.4    A Detailed Example: A Packet Voice Transmission System    9
1.5    Other Examples    11
1.6    Overview of Book    16
Summary    17
Problems    18

**CHAPTER 2**    Basic Concepts of Probability Theory    21

2.1    Specifying Random Experiments    21
2.2    The Axioms of Probability    30
*2.3    Computing Probabilities Using Counting Methods    41
2.4    Conditional Probability    47
2.5    Independence of Events    53
2.6    Sequential Experiments    59
*2.7    Synthesizing Randomness: Random Number Generators    67
*2.8    Fine Points: Event Classes    70
*2.9    Fine Points: Probabilities of Sequences of Events    75
Summary    79
Problems    80

**CHAPTER 3**    Discrete Random Variables    96

3.1    The Notion of a Random Variable    96
3.2    Discrete Random Variables and Probability Mass Function    99
3.3    Expected Value and Moments of Discrete Random Variable    104
3.4    Conditional Probability Mass Function    111
3.5    Important Discrete Random Variables    115
3.6    Generation of Discrete Random Variables    127
Summary    129
Problems    130

**CHAPTER 4**    One Random Variable    141

4.1    The Cumulative Distribution Function    141
4.2    The Probability Density Function    148
4.3    The Expected Value of $X$    155
4.4    Important Continuous Random Variables    163
4.5    Functions of a Random Variable    174
4.6    The Markov and Chebyshev Inequalities    181
4.7    Transform Methods    184
4.8    Basic Reliability Calculations    189
4.9    Computer Methods for Generating Random Variables    194
*4.10    Entropy    202
         Summary    213
         Problems    215

**CHAPTER 5**    Pairs of Random Variables    233

5.1    Two Random Variables    233
5.2    Pairs of Discrete Random Variables    236
5.3    The Joint cdf of $X$ and $Y$    242
5.4    The Joint pdf of Two Continuous Random Variables    248
5.5    Independence of Two Random Variables    254
5.6    Joint Moments and Expected Values of a Function of Two Random
         Variables    257
5.7    Conditional Probability and Conditional Expectation    261
5.8    Functions of Two Random Variables    271
5.9    Pairs of Jointly Gaussian Random Variables    278
5.10    Generating Independent Gaussian Random Variables    284
         Summary    286
         Problems    288

**CHAPTER 6**    Vector Random Variables    303

6.1    Vector Random Variables    303
6.2    Functions of Several Random Variables    309
6.3    Expected Values of Vector Random Variables    318
6.4    Jointly Gaussian Random Vectors    325
6.5    Estimation of Random Variables    332
6.6    Generating Correlated Vector Random Variables    342
         Summary    346
         Problems    348

**CHAPTER 7    Sums of Random Variables and Long-Term Averages    359**

7.1    Sums of Random Variables    360
7.2    The Sample Mean and the Laws of Large Numbers    365
       Weak Law of Large Numbers    367
       Strong Law of Large Numbers    368
7.3    The Central Limit Theorem    369
       Central Limit Theorem    370
*7.4    Convergence of Sequences of Random Variables    378
*7.5    Long-Term Arrival Rates and Associated Averages    387
7.6    Calculating Distribution's Using the Discrete Fourier
          Transform    392
       Summary    400
       Problems    402

**CHAPTER 8    Statistics    411**

8.1    Samples and Sampling Distributions    411
8.2    Parameter Estimation    415
8.3    Maximum Likelihood Estimation    419
8.4    Confidence Intervals    430
8.5    Hypothesis Testing    441
8.6    Bayesian Decision Methods    455
8.7    Testing the Fit of a Distribution to Data    462
       Summary    469
       Problems    471

**CHAPTER 9    Random Processes    487**

9.1    Definition of a Random Process    488
9.2    Specifying a Random Process    491
9.3    Discrete-Time Processes: Sum Process, Binomial Counting Process,
          and Random Walk    498
9.4    Poisson and Associated Random Processes    507
9.5    Gaussian Random Processes, Wiener Process
          and Brownian Motion    514
9.6    Stationary Random Processes    518
9.7    Continuity, Derivatives, and Integrals of Random Processes    529
9.8    Time Averages of Random Processes and Ergodic Theorems    540
*9.9    Fourier Series and Karhunen-Loeve Expansion    544
9.10    Generating Random Processes    550
       Summary    554
       Problems    557

**CHAPTER 10**    Analysis and Processing of Random Signals    577

10.1    Power Spectral Density    577
10.2    Response of Linear Systems to Random Signals    587
10.3    Bandlimited Random Processes    597
10.4    Optimum Linear Systems    605
*10.5    The Kalman Filter    617
*10.6    Estimating the Power Spectral Density    622
10.7    Numerical Techniques for Processing Random Signals    628
        Summary    633
        Problems    635

**CHAPTER 11**    Markov Chains    647

11.1    Markov Processes    647
11.2    Discrete-Time Markov Chains    650
11.3    Classes of States, Recurrence Properties, and Limiting
        Probabilities    660
11.4    Continuous-Time Markov Chains    673
*11.5    Time-Reversed Markov Chains    686
11.6    Numerical Techniques for Markov Chains    692
        Summary    700
        Problems    702

**CHAPTER 12**    Introduction to Queueing Theory    713

12.1    The Elements of a Queueing System    714
12.2    Little's Formula    715
12.3    The M/M/1 Queue    718
12.4    Multi-Server Systems: M/M/$c$, M/M/$c$/$c$, And M/M/$\infty$    727
12.5    Finite-Source Queueing Systems    734
12.6    M/G/1 Queueing Systems    738
12.7    M/G/1 Analysis Using Embedded Markov Chains    745
12.8    Burke's Theorem: Departures From M/M/$c$ Systems    754
12.9    Networks of Queues: Jackson's Theorem    758
12.10   Simulation and Data Analysis of Queueing Systems    771
        Summary    782
        Problems    784

**Appendices**

A.    Mathematical Tables    797
B.    Tables of Fourier Transforms    800
C.    Matrices and Linear Algebra    802

**Index**    805

# Preface

This book provides a carefully motivated, accessible, and interesting introduction to probability, statistics, and random processes for electrical and computer engineers. The complexity of the systems encountered in engineering practice calls for an understanding of probability concepts and a facility in the use of probability tools. The goal of the introductory course should therefore be to teach both the basic theoretical concepts and techniques for solving problems that arise in practice. The third edition of this book achieves this goal by retaining the proven features of previous editions:

- Relevance to engineering practice
- Clear and accessible introduction to probability
- Computer exercises to develop intuition for randomness
- Large number and variety of problems
- Curriculum flexibility through rich choice of topics
- Careful development of random process concepts.

This edition also introduces two major new features:

- Introduction to statistics
- Extensive use of MATLAB©/Octave.

## RELEVANCE TO ENGINEERING PRACTICE

Motivating students is a major challenge in introductory probability courses. Instructors need to respond by showing students the relevance of probability theory to engineering practice. Chapter 1 addresses this challenge by discussing the role of probability models in engineering design. Practical current applications from various areas of electrical and computer engineering are used to show how averages and relative frequencies provide the proper tools for handling the design of systems that involve randomness. These application areas include wireless and digital communications, digital media and signal processing, system reliability, computer networks, and Web systems. These areas are used in examples and problems throughout the text.

## ACCESSIBLE INTRODUCTION TO PROBABILITY THEORY

Probability theory is an inherently mathematical subject so concepts must be presented carefully, simply, and gradually. The axioms of probability and their corollaries are developed in a clear and deliberate manner. The model-building aspect is introduced through the assignment of probability laws to discrete and continuous sample spaces. The notion of a single discrete random variable is developed in its entirety, allowing the student to focus on the basic probability concepts without analytical complications. Similarly, pairs of random variables and vector random variables are discussed in separate chapters.

The most important random variables and random processes are developed in systematic fashion using model-building arguments. For example, a systematic development of concepts can be traced across every chapter from the initial discussions on coin tossing and Bernoulli trials, through the Gaussian random variable, central limit theorem, and confidence intervals in the middle chapters, and on to the Wiener process and the analysis of simulation data at the end of the book. The goal is to teach the student not only the fundamental concepts and methods of probability, but to also develop an awareness of the key models and their interrelationships.

## COMPUTER EXERCISES TO DEVELOP INTUITION FOR RANDOMNESS

A true understanding of probability requires developing an intuition for variability and randomness. The development of an intuition for randomness can be aided by the presentation and analysis of random data. Where applicable, important concepts are motivated and reinforced using empirical data. Every chapter introduces one or more numerical or simulation techniques that enable the student to apply and validate the concepts. Topics covered include: Generation of random numbers, random variables, and random vectors; linear transformations and application of FFT; application of statistical tests; simulation of random processes, Markov chains, and queueing models; statistical signal processing; and analysis of simulation data.

The sections on computer methods are optional. However, we have found that computer generated data is very effective in motivating each new topic and that the computer methods can be incorporated into existing lectures. The computer exercises can be done using MATLAB or Octave. We opted to use Octave in the examples because it is sufficient to perform our exercises and it is free and readily available on the Web. Students with access can use MATLAB instead.

## STATISTICS TO LINK PROBABILITY MODELS TO THE REAL WORLD

Statistics plays the key role of bridging probability models to the real world, and for this reason there is a trend in introductory undergraduate probability courses to include an introduction to statistics. This edition includes a new chapter that covers all the main topics in an introduction to statistics: Sampling distributions, parameter estimation, maximum likelihood estimation, confidence intervals, hypothesis testing, Bayesian decision methods and goodness of fit tests. The foundation of random variables from earlier chapters allows us to develop statistical methods in a rigorous manner rather than present them in "cookbook" fashion. In this chapter MATLAB/Octave prove extremely useful in the generation of random data and the application of statistical methods.

## EXAMPLES AND PROBLEMS

Numerous examples in every section are used to demonstrate analytical and problem-solving techniques, develop concepts using simplified cases, and illustrate applications. The text includes 1200 problems, nearly double the number in the previous edition. A large number of new problems involve the use of MATLAB or Octave to obtain numerical or simulation results. Problems are identified by section to help the instructor select homework problems. Additional problems requiring cumulative knowledge are provided at the end of each chapter. Answers to selected problems are included in the book website. A **Student Solutions Manual** accompanies this text to develop problem-solving skills. A sampling of 25% of carefully worked out problems has been selected to help students understand concepts presented in the text. An **Instructor Solutions Manual** with complete solutions is also available on the book website.

http://www.prenhall.com/leongarcia

## FROM RANDOM VARIABLES TO RANDOM PROCESSES

Discrete-time random processes provide a crucial "bridge" in going from random variables to continuous-time random processes. Care is taken in the first seven chapters to lay the proper groundwork for this transition. Thus sequences of dependent experiments are discussed in Chapter 2 as a preview of Markov chains. In Chapter 6, emphasis is placed on how a joint distribution generates a consistent family of marginal distributions. Chapter 7 introduces sequences of independent identically distributed (iid) random variables. Chapter 8 uses the sum of an iid sequence to develop important examples of random processes.

The traditional introductory course in random processes has focused on applications from linear systems and random signal analysis. However, many courses now also include an introduction to Markov chains and some examples from queueing theory. We provide sufficient material in both topic areas to give the instructor leeway in striking a balance between these two areas. Here we continue our systematic development of related concepts. Thus, the development of random signal analysis includes a discussion of the sampling theorem which is used to relate discrete-time signal processing to continuous-time signal processing. In a similar vein, the embedded chain formulation of continuous-time Markov chains is emphasized and later used to develop simulation models for continuous-time queueing systems.

## FLEXIBILITY THROUGH RICH CHOICE OF TOPICS

The textbook is designed to allow the instructor maximum flexibility in the selection of topics. In addition to the standard topics taught in introductory courses on probability, random variables, statistics and random processes, the book includes sections on modeling, computer simulation, reliability, estimation and entropy, as well as chapters that provide introductions to Markov chains and queueing theory.

## SUGGESTED SYLLABI

A variety of syllabi for undergraduate and graduate courses are supported by the text. The flow chart above shows the basic chapter dependencies, and the table of contents provides a detailed description of the sections in each chapter.

The first five chapters (without the starred or optional sections) form the basis for a one-semester undergraduate introduction to probability. A course on probability and statistics would proceed from Chapter 5 to the first three sections of Chapter 7 and then

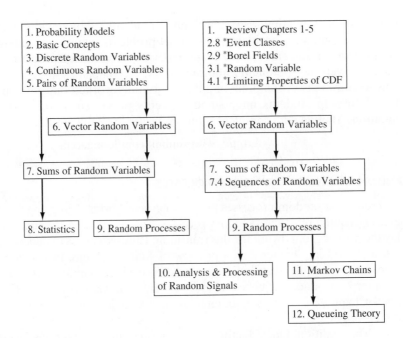

to Chapter 8. A first course on probability with a brief introduction to random processes would go from Chapter 5 to Sections 6.1, 7.1 – 7.3, and then the first few sections in Chapter 9, as time allows. Many other syllabi are possible using the various optional sections.

A first-level graduate course in random processes would begin with a quick review of the axioms of probability and the notion of a random variable, including the starred sections on event classes (2.8), Borel fields and continuity of probability (2.9), the formal definition of a random variable (3.1), and the limiting properties of the cdf (4.1). The material in Chapter 6 on vector random variables, their joint distributions, and their transformations would be covered next. The discussion in Chapter 7 would include the central limit theorem and convergence concepts. The course would then cover Chapters 9, 10, and 11. A statistical signal processing emphasis can be given to the course by including the sections on estimation of random variables (6.5), maximum likelihood estimation and Cramer-Rao lower bound (8.3) and Bayesian decision methods (8.6). An emphasis on queueing models is possible by including renewal processes (7.5) and Chapter 12. We note in particular that the last section in Chapter 12 provides an introduction to simulation models and output data analysis not found in most textbooks.

## CHANGES IN THE THIRD EDITION

This edition of the text has undergone several major changes:

- The introduction to the notion of a random variable is now carried out in two phases: discrete random variables (Chapter 3) and continuous random variables (Chapter 4).

- Pairs of random variables and vector random variables are now covered in separate chapters (Chapters 5 and 6). More advanced topics have been placed in Chapter 6, e.g., general transformations, joint characteristic functions.

- Chapter 8, a new chapter, provides an introduction to all of the standard topics on statistics.

- Chapter 9 now provides separate and more detailed development of the random walk, Poisson, and Wiener processes.

- Chapter 10 has expanded the coverage of discrete-time linear systems, and the link between discrete-time and continuous-time processing is bridged through the discussion of the sampling theorem.

- Chapter 11 now provides a complete coverage of discrete-time Markov chains before introducing continuous-time Markov chains. A new section shows how transient behavior can be investigated through numerical and simulation techniques.

- Chapter 12 now provides detailed discussions on the simulation of queueing systems and the analysis of simulation data.

## ACKNOWLEDGMENTS

I would like to acknowledge the help of several individuals in the preparation of the third edition. First and foremost, I must thank the users of the first two editions, both professors and students, who provided many of the suggestions incorporated into this edition. I would especially like to thank the many students whom I have met around the world over the years and who provided the positive comments that encouraged me to undertake this revision. I would also like to thank my graduate and post-graduate students for providing feedback and help in various ways, especially Nadeem Abji, Hadi Bannazadeh, Ramy Farha, Khash Khavari, Ivonne Olavarrieta, Shad Sharma, and Ali Tizghadam, and Dr. Yu Cheng. My colleagues in the Communications Group, Professors Frank Kschischang, Pas Pasupathy, Sharokh Valaee, Parham Aarabi, Elvino Sousa and T.J. Lim, provided useful comments and suggestions. Delbert Dueck provided particularly useful and insightful comments. I am especially thankful to Professor Ben Liang for providing detailed and valuable feedback on the manuscript.

The following reviewers aided me with their suggestions and comments in this third edition: William Bard (University of Texas at Austin), In Soo Ahn (Bradley University), Harvey Bruce (Florida A&M University and Florida State University College of Engineering), V. Chandrasekar (Colorado State University), YangQuan Chen (Utah State University), Suparna Datta (Northeastern University), Sohail Dianat (Rochester Institute of Technology), Petar Djuric (Stony Brook University), Ralph Hippenstiel (University of Texas at Tyler), Fan Jiang (Tuskegee University), Todd Moon (Utah State University), Steven Nardone (University of Massachusetts), Martin Plonus (Northwestern University), Jim Ritcey (University of Washington), Robert W. Scharstein (University of Alabama), Frank Severance (Western Michigan University), John Shea (University of Florida), Surendra Singh (The University of Tulsa), and Xinhui Zhang (Wright State University).

I thank Scott Disanno, Craig Little, and the entire production team at the composition house Laserwords for their tremendous efforts in getting this book to print on time. Most of all I would like to thank my partner, Karen Carlyle, for her love, support, and partnership. This book would not be possible without her help.

# Probability Models in Electrical and Computer Engineering

Electrical and computer engineers have played a central role in the design of modern information and communications systems. These highly successful systems work reliably and predictably in highly variable and chaotic environments:

- Wireless communication networks provide voice and data communications to mobile users in severe interference environments.
- The vast majority of media signals, voice, audio, images, and video are processed digitally.
- Huge Web server farms deliver vast amounts of highly specific information to users.

Because of these successes, designers today face even greater challenges. The systems they build are unprecedented in scale and the chaotic environments in which they must operate are untrodden terrritory:

- Web information is created and posted at an accelerating rate; future search applications must become more discerning to extract the required response from a vast ocean of information.
- Information-age scoundrels hijack computers and exploit these for illicit purposes, so methods are needed to identify and contain these threats.
- Machine learning systems must move beyond browsing and purchasing applications to real-time monitoring of health and the environment.
- Massively distributed systems in the form of peer-to-peer and grid computing communities have emerged and changed the nature of media delivery, gaming, and social interaction; yet we do not understand or know how to control and manage such systems.

Probability models are one of the tools that enable the designer to make sense out of the chaos and to successfully build systems that are efficient, reliable, and cost effective. This book is an introduction to the theory underlying probability models as well as to the basic techniques used in the development of such models.

This chapter introduces probability models and shows how they differ from the deterministic models that are pervasive in engineering. The key properties of the notion of probability are developed, and various examples from electrical and computer engineering, where probability models play a key role, are presented. Section 1.6 gives an overview of the book.

## 1.1    MATHEMATICAL MODELS AS TOOLS IN ANALYSIS AND DESIGN

The design or modification of any complex system involves the making of choices from various feasible alternatives. Choices are made on the basis of criteria such as cost, reliability, and performance. The quantitative evaluation of these criteria is seldom made through the actual implementation and experimental evaluation of the alternative configurations. Instead, decisions are made based on estimates that are obtained using models of the alternatives.

A **model** is an approximate representation of a physical situation. A model attempts to explain observed behavior using a set of simple and understandable rules. These rules can be used to predict the outcome of experiments involving the given physical situation. A *useful* model explains all relevant aspects of a given situation. Such models can be used instead of experiments to answer questions regarding the given situation. Models therefore allow the engineer to avoid the costs of experimentation, namely, labor, equipment, and time.

**Mathematical models** are used when the observational phenomenon has measurable properties. A mathematical model consists of a set of assumptions about how a system or physical process works. These assumptions are stated in the form of mathematical relations involving the important parameters and variables of the system. The conditions under which an experiment involving the system is carried out determine the "givens" in the mathematical relations, and the solution of these relations allows us to predict the measurements that would be obtained if the experiment were performed.

Mathematical models are used extensively by engineers in guiding system design and modification decisions. Intuition and rules of thumb are not always reliable in predicting the performance of complex and novel systems, and experimentation is not possible during the initial phases of a system design. Furthermore, the cost of extensive experimentation in existing systems frequently proves to be prohibitive. The availability of adequate models for the components of a complex system combined with a knowledge of their interactions allows the scientist and engineer to develop an overall mathematical model for the system. It is then possible to quickly and inexpensively answer questions about the performance of complex systems. Indeed, computer programs for obtaining the solution of mathematical models form the basis of many computer-aided analysis and design systems.

In order to be useful, a model must fit the facts of a given situation. Therefore the process of developing and validating a model necessarily consists of a series of experiments and model modifications as shown in Fig. 1.1. Each experiment investigates a certain aspect of the phenomenon under investigation and involves the taking of observations and measurements under a specified set of conditions. The model is used to predict the outcome of the experiment, and these predictions are compared with the actual observations that result when the experiment is carried out. If there is a

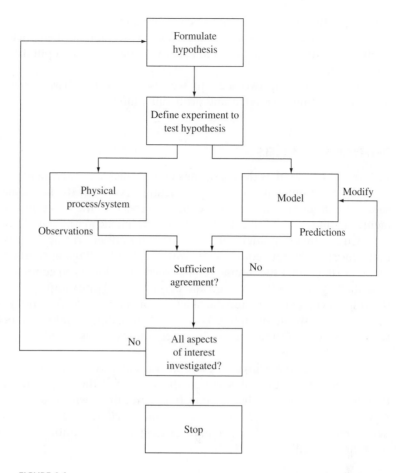

**FIGURE 1.1**
The modeling process.

significant discrepancy, the model is then modified to account for it. The modeling process continues until the investigator is satisfied that the behavior of all relevant aspects of the phenomenon can be predicted to within a desired accuracy. It should be emphasized that the decision of when to stop the modeling process depends on the immediate objectives of the investigator. Thus a model that is adequate for one application may prove to be completely inadequate in another setting.

The predictions of a mathematical model should be treated as hypothetical until the model has been validated through a comparison with experimental measurements. A dilemma arises in a system design situation: The model cannot be validated experimentally because the real system does not exist. Computer simulation models play a useful role in this situation by presenting an alternative means of predicting system behavior, and thus a means of checking the predictions made by a mathematical model. A **computer simulation model** consists of a computer program that simulates or mimics the dynamics of a system. Incorporated into the program are instructions that "measure" the relevant performance parameters. In general, simulation models are capable of representing systems in greater detail than mathematical models. However, they tend to be less flexible and usually require more computation time than mathematical models.

In the following two sections we discuss the two basic types of mathematical models, deterministic models and probability models.

## 1.2    DETERMINISTIC MODELS

In **deterministic models** the conditions under which an experiment is carried out determine the exact outcome of the experiment. In deterministic mathematical models, the solution of a set of mathematical equations specifies the exact outcome of the experiment. Circuit theory is an example of a deterministic mathematical model.

Circuit theory models the interconnection of electronic devices by ideal circuits that consist of discrete components with idealized voltage-current characteristics. The theory assumes that the interaction between these idealized components is completely described by Kirchhoff's voltage and current laws. For example, Ohm's law states that the voltage-current characteristic of a resistor is $I = V/R$. The voltages and currents in any circuit consisting of an interconnection of batteries and resistors can be found by solving a system of simultaneous linear equations that is found by applying Kirchhoff's laws and Ohm's law.

If an experiment involving the measurement of a set of voltages is repeated a number of times under the same conditions, circuit theory predicts that the observations will always be exactly the same. In practice there will be some variation in the observations due to measurement errors and uncontrolled factors. Nevertheless, this deterministic model will be adequate as long as the deviation about the predicted values remains small.

## 1.3    PROBABILITY MODELS

Many systems of interest involve phenomena that exhibit unpredictable variation and randomness. We define a **random experiment** to be an experiment in which the outcome varies in an unpredictable fashion when the experiment is repeated under the same conditions. Deterministic models are not appropriate for random experiments since they predict the same outcome for each repetition of an experiment. In this section we introduce probability models that are intended for random experiments.

As an example of a random experiment, suppose a ball is selected from an urn containing three identical balls, labeled 0, 1, and 2. The urn is first shaken to randomize the position of the balls, and a ball is then selected. The number of the ball is noted, and the ball is then returned to the urn. The **outcome** of this experiment is a number from the set $S = \{0, 1, 2\}$. We call the set $S$ of all possible outcomes the **sample space**. Figure 1.2 shows the outcomes in 100 repetitions (trials) of a computer simulation of this urn experiment. It is clear that the outcome of this experiment cannot consistently be predicted correctly.

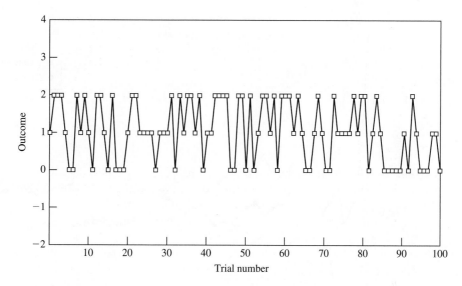

**FIGURE 1.2**
Outcomes of urn experiment.

### 1.3.1    Statistical Regularity

In order to be useful, a model must enable us to make predictions about the future behavior of a system, and in order to be predictable, a phenomenon must exhibit regularity in its behavior. Many probability models in engineering are based on the fact that averages obtained in long sequences of repetitions (trials) of random experiments consistently yield approximately the same value. This property is called **statistical regularity**.

Suppose that the above urn experiment is repeated $n$ times under identical conditions. Let $N_0(n)$, $N_1(n)$, and $N_2(n)$ be the number of times in which the outcomes are balls 0, 1, and 2, respectively, and let the **relative frequency** of outcome $k$ be defined by

$$f_k(n) = \frac{N_k(n)}{n}. \tag{1.1}$$

By statistical regularity we mean that $f_k(n)$ varies less and less about a constant value as $n$ is made large, that is,

$$\lim_{n \to \infty} f_k(n) = p_k. \tag{1.2}$$

The constant $p_k$ is called the **probability** of the outcome $k$. Equation (1.2) states that the probability of an outcome is the long-term proportion of times it arises in a long sequence of trials. We will see throughout the book that Eq. (1.2) provides the key connection in going from the measurement of physical quantities to the probability models discussed in this book.

Figures 1.3 and 1.4 show the relative frequencies for the three outcomes in the above urn experiment as the number of trials $n$ is increased. It is clear that all the relative

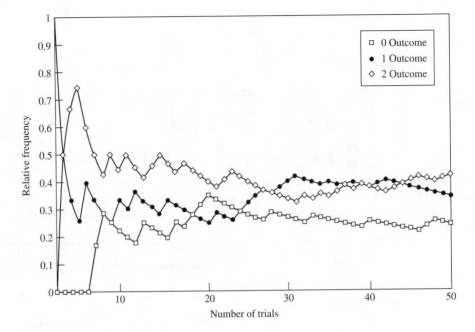

**FIGURE 1.3**
Relative frequencies in urn experiment.

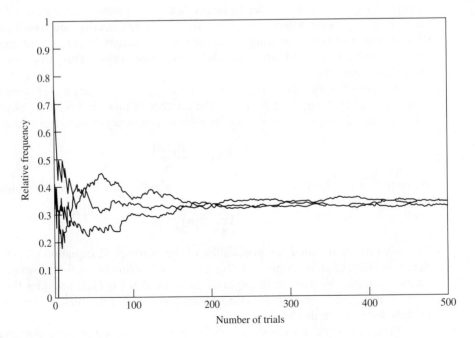

**FIGURE 1.4**
Relative frequencies in urn experiment.

frequencies are converging to the value 1/3. This is in agreement with our intuition that the three outcomes are equiprobable.

Suppose we alter the above urn experiment by placing in the urn a fourth identical ball with the number 0. The probability of the outcome 0 is now 2/4 since two of the four balls in the urn have the number 0. The probabilities of the outcomes 1 and 2 would be reduced to 1/4 each. This demonstrates a key property of probability models, namely, *the conditions under which a random experiment is performed determine the probabilities of the outcomes of an experiment.*

### 1.3.2    Properties of Relative Frequency

We now present several properties of relative frequency. Suppose that a random experiment has $K$ possible outcomes, that is, $S = \{1, 2, \ldots, K\}$. Since the number of occurrences of any outcome in $n$ trials is a number between zero and $n$, we have that

$$0 \le N_k(n) \le n \qquad \text{for } k = 1, 2, \ldots, K,$$

and thus dividing the above equation by $n$, we find that the relative frequencies are a number between zero and one:

$$0 \le f_k(n) \le 1 \qquad \text{for } k = 1, 2, \ldots, K. \tag{1.3}$$

The sum of the number of occurrences of all possible outcomes must be $n$:

$$\sum_{k=1}^{K} N_k(n) = n.$$

If we divide both sides of the above equation by $n$, we find that the sum of all the relative frequencies equals one:

$$\sum_{k=1}^{K} f_k(n) = 1. \tag{1.4}$$

Sometimes we are interested in the occurrence of **events** associated with the outcomes of an experiment. For example, consider the event "an even-numbered ball is selected" in the above urn experiment. What is the relative frequency of this event? The event will occur whenever the number of the ball is 0 or 2. The number of experiments in which the outcome is an even-numbered ball is therefore $N_E(n) = N_0(n) + N_2(n)$. The relative frequency of the event is thus

$$f_E(n) = \frac{N_E(n)}{n} = \frac{N_0(n) + N_2(n)}{n} = f_0(n) + f_2(n).$$

This example shows that the relative frequency of an event is the sum of the relative frequencies of the associated outcomes. More generally, let $C$ be the event "$A$ or $B$ occurs," where $A$ and $B$ are two events that cannot occur simultaneously, then the number of times when $C$ occurs is $N_C(n) = N_A(n) + N_B(n)$,  so

$$f_C(n) = f_A(n) + f_B(n). \tag{1.5}$$

Equations (1.3), (1.4), and (1.5) are the three basic properties of relative frequency from which we can derive many other useful results.

### 1.3.3    The Axiomatic Approach to a Theory of Probability

Equation (1.2) suggests that we define the probability of an event by its long-term relative frequency. There are problems with using this definition of probability to develop a mathematical theory of probability. First of all, it is not clear when and in what mathematical sense the limit in Eq. (1.2) exists. Second, we can never perform an experiment an infinite number of times, so we can never know the probabilities $p_k$ exactly. Finally, the use of relative frequency to define probability would rule out the applicability of probability theory to situations in which an experiment cannot be repeated. Thus it makes practical sense to develop a mathematical theory of probability that is not tied to any particular application or to any particular notion of what probability means. On the other hand, we must insist that, when appropriate, the theory should allow us to use our intuition and interpret probability as relative frequency.

In order to be consistent with the relative frequency interpretation, any definition of "probability of an event" must satisfy the properties in Eqs. (1.3) through (1.5). The modern theory of probability begins with a construction of a set of axioms that specify that probability assignments must satisfy these properties. It supposes that: (1) a random experiment has been defined, and a set $S$ of all possible outcomes has been identified; (2) a class of subsets of $S$ called events has been specified; and (3) each event $A$ has been assigned a number, $P[A]$, in such a way that the following axioms are satisfied:

1.  $0 \leq P[A] \leq 1$.
2.  $P[S] = 1$.
3.  If $A$ and $B$ are events that cannot occur simultaneously,
    then $P[A \text{ or } B] = P[A] + P[B]$.

The correspondence between the three axioms and the properties of relative frequency stated in Eqs. (1.3) through (1.5) is apparent. These three axioms lead to many useful and powerful results. Indeed, we will spend the remainder of this book developing many of these results.

Note that the theory of probability does not concern itself with how the probabilities are obtained or with what they mean. Any assignment of probabilities to events that satisfies the above axioms is legitimate. It is up to the user of the theory, the model builder, to determine what the probability assignment should be and what interpretation of probability makes sense in any given application.

### 1.3.4    Building a Probability Model

Let us consider how we proceed from a real-world problem that involves randomness to a **probability model** for the problem. The theory requires that we identify the elements in the above axioms. This involves (1) defining the random experiment inherent in the application, (2) specifying the set $S$ of all possible outcomes and the events of interest, and (3) specifying a probability assignment from which the probabilities of all events of interest can be computed. The challenge is to develop the simplest model that explains all the relevant aspects of the real-world problem.

As an example, suppose that we test a telephone conversation to determine whether a speaker is currently speaking or silent. We know that on the average the typical speaker is active only 1/3 of the time; the rest of the time he is listening to the other party or pausing between words and phrases. We can model this physical situation as an urn experiment in which we select a ball from an urn containing two white balls (silence) and one black ball (active speech). We are making a great simplification here; not all speakers are the same, not all languages have the same silence-activity behavior, and so forth. The usefulness and power of this simplification becomes apparent when we begin asking questions that arise in system design, such as: What is the probability that more than 24 speakers out of 48 independent speakers are active at the same time? This question is equivalent to: What is the probability that more than 24 black balls are selected in 48 independent repetitions of the above urn experiment? By the end of Chapter 2 you will be able to answer the latter question *and* all the real-world problems that can be reduced to it!

## 1.4    A DETAILED EXAMPLE: A PACKET VOICE TRANSMISSION SYSTEM

In the beginning of this chapter we claimed that probability models provide a tool that enables the designer to successfully design systems that must operate in a random environment, but that nevertheless are efficient, reliable, and cost effective. In this section, we present a detailed example of such a system. Our objective here is to convince you of the power and usefulness of probability theory. The presentation intentionally draws upon your intuition. Many of the derivation steps that may appear nonrigorous now will be made precise later in the book.

Suppose that a communication system is required to transmit 48 simultaneous conversations from site A to site B using "packets" of voice information. The speech of each speaker is converted into voltage waveforms that are first digitized (i.e., converted into a sequence of binary numbers) and then bundled into packets of information that correspond to 10-millisecond (ms) segments of speech. A source and destination address is appended to each voice packet before it is transmitted (see Fig. 1.5).

The simplest design for the communication system would transmit 48 packets every 10 ms in each direction. This is an inefficient design, however, since it is known that on the average about 2/3 of all packets contain silence and hence no speech information. In other words, on the average the 48 speakers only produce about $48/3 = 16$ active (nonsilence) packets per 10-ms period. We therefore consider another system that transmits only $M < 48$ packets every 10 ms.

Every 10 ms, the new system determines which speakers have produced packets with active speech. Let the outcome of this random experiment be $A$, the number of active packets produced in a given 10-ms segment. The quantity $A$ takes on values in the range from 0 (all speakers silent) to 48 (all speakers active). If $A \leq M$, then all the active packets are transmitted. However, if $A > M$, then the system is unable to transmit all the active packets, so $A - M$ of the active packets are selected at random and discarded. The discarding of active packets results in the loss of speech, so we would like to keep the fraction of discarded active packets at a level that the speakers do not find objectionable.

First consider the relative frequencies of $A$. Suppose the above experiment is repeated $n$ times. Let $A(j)$ be the outcome in the $j$th trial. Let $N_k(n)$ be the number of trials in which the number of active packets is $k$. The relative frequency of the outcome $k$ in the first $n$ trials is then $f_k(n) = N_k(n)/n$, which we suppose converges to a probability $p_k$:

$$\lim_{n \to \infty} f_k(n) = p_k \qquad 0 \leq k \leq 48. \tag{1.6}$$

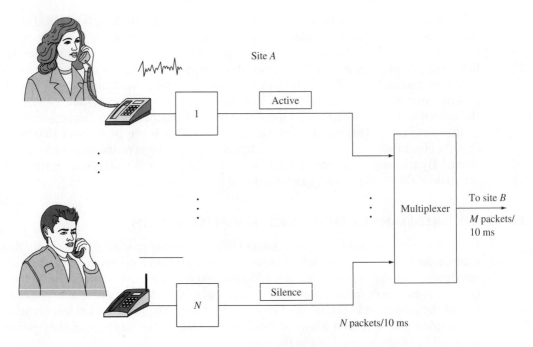

**FIGURE 1.5**
A packet voice transmission system.

In Chapter 2 we will derive the probability $p_k$ that $k$ speakers are active. Figure 1.6 shows $p_k$ versus $k$. It can be seen that the most frequent number of active speakers is 16 and that the number of active speakers is seldom above 24 or so.

Next consider the rate at which active packets are produced. The average number of active packets produced per 10-ms interval is given by the **sample mean** of the number of active packets:

$$\langle A \rangle_n = \frac{1}{n}\sum_{j=1}^{n} A(j) \tag{1.7}$$

$$= \frac{1}{n}\sum_{k=0}^{48} k N_k(n). \tag{1.8}$$

The first expression adds the number of active packets produced in the first $n$ trials in the order in which the observations were recorded. The second expression counts how many of these observations had $k$ active packets for each possible value of $k$, and then computes the total.[1] As $n$ gets large, the ratio $N_k(n)/n$ in the second expression approaches $p_k$. Thus the average number of active packets produced per 10-ms segment approaches

$$\langle A \rangle_n \to \sum_{k=0}^{48} k p_k \triangleq E[A]. \tag{1.9}$$

---

[1] Suppose you pull out the following change from your pocket: 1 quarter, 1 dime, 1 quarter, 1 nickel. Equation (1.7) says your total is $25 + 10 + 25 + 5 = 65$ cents. Equation (1.8) says your total is $(1)5 + (1)10 + (2)(25) = 65$ cents.

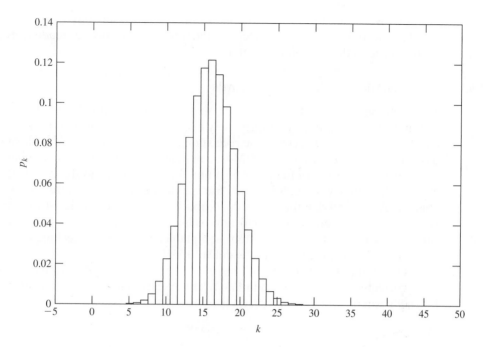

**FIGURE 1.6**
Probabilities for number of active speakers in a group of 48.

The expression on the right-hand side will be defined as the **expected value of $A$** in Section 3.3. $E[A]$ is completely determined by the probabilities $p_k$ and in Chapter 3 we will show that $E[A] = 48 \times 1/3 = 16$. Equation (1.9) states that the long-term average number of active packets produced per 10-ms period is $E[A] = 16$ speakers per 10 ms.

The information provided by the probabilities $p_k$ allows us to design systems that are efficient and that provide good voice quality. For example, we can reduce the transmission capacity in half to 24 packets per 10-ms period, while discarding an imperceptible number of active packets.

Let us summarize what we have done in this section. We have presented an example in which the system behavior is intrinsically random, and in which the system performance measures are stated in terms of long-term averages. We have shown how these long-term measures lead to expressions involving the probabilities of the various outcomes. Finally we have indicated that, in some cases, probability theory allows us to derive these probabilities. We are then able to predict the long-term averages of various quantities of interest and proceed with the system design.

## 1.5    OTHER EXAMPLES

In this section we present further examples from electrical and computer engineering, where probability models are used to design systems that work in a random environment. Our intention here is to show how probabilities and long-term averages arise naturally as performance measures in many systems. We hasten to add, however, that this book is intended to present the basic concepts of probability theory and not detailed applications. For the interested reader, references for further reading are provided at the end of this and other chapters.

### 1.5.1 Communication over Unreliable Channels

Many communication systems operate in the following way. Every $T$ seconds, the transmitter accepts a binary input, namely, a 0 or a 1, and transmits a corresponding signal. At the end of the $T$ seconds, the receiver makes a decision as to what the input was, based on the signal it has received. Most communications systems are unreliable in the sense that the decision of the receiver is not always the same as the transmitter input. Figure 1.7(a) models systems in which transmission errors occur at random with probability $\varepsilon$. As indicated in the figure, the output is not equal to the input with probability $\varepsilon$. Thus $\varepsilon$ is the long-term proportion of bits delivered in error by the receiver. In situations where this error rate is not acceptable, error-control techniques are introduced to reduce the error rate in the delivered information.

One method of reducing the error rate in the delivered information is to use error-correcting codes as shown in Fig. 1.7(b). As a simple example, consider a repetition code where each information bit is transmitted three times:

$$0 \rightarrow 000$$
$$1 \rightarrow 111.$$

If we suppose that the decoder makes a decision on the information bit by taking a majority vote of the three bits output by the receiver, then the decoder will make the wrong decision only if two or three of the bits are in error. In Example 2.37, we show that this occurs with probability $3\varepsilon^2 - 2\varepsilon^3$. Thus if the bit error rate of the channel without coding is $10^{-3}$, then the delivered bit error with the above simple code will be $3 \times 10^{-6}$, a reduction of three orders of magnitude! This improvement is obtained at a

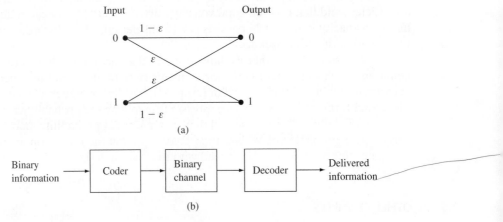

(a)

(b)

**FIGURE 1.7**
(a) A model for a binary communication channel. (b) Error control system.

cost, however: The rate of transmission of information has been slowed down to 1 bit every $3T$ seconds. By going to longer, more complicated codes, it is possible to obtain reductions in error rate without the drastic reduction in transmission rate of this simple example.

Error detection and correction methods play a key role in making reliable communications possible over radio and other noisy channels. Probability plays a role in determining the error patterns that are likely to occur and that hence must be corrected.

### 1.5.2    Compression of Signals

The outcome of a random experiment need not be a single number, but can also be an entire function of time. For example, the outcome of an experiment could be a voltage waveform corresponding to speech or music. In these situations we are interested in the properties of a signal and of processed versions of the signal.

For example, suppose we are interested in compressing a music signal $S(t)$. This involves representing the signal by a sequence of bits. Compression techniques provide efficient representations by using prediction, where the next value of the signal is predicted using past encoded values. Only the error in the prediction needs to be encoded so the number of bits can be reduced.

In order to work, prediction systems require that we know how the signal values are correlated with each other. Given this correlation structure we can then design optimum prediction systems. Probability plays a key role in solving these problems. Compression systems have been highly successful and are found in cell phones, digital cameras, and camcorders.

### 1.5.3    Reliability of Systems

Reliability is a major concern in the design of modern systems. A prime example is the system of computers and communication networks that support the electronic transfer of funds between banks. It is of critical importance that this system continues operating even in the face of subsystem failures. The key question is, How does one build reliable systems from unreliable components? Probability models provide us with the tools to address this question in a quantitative way.

The operation of a system requires the operation of some or all of its components. For example, Fig. 1.8(a) shows a system that functions only when all of its components are functioning, and Fig. 1.8(b) shows a system that functions as long as at least one of its components is functioning. More complex systems can be obtained as combinations of these two basic configurations.

We all know from experience that it is not possible to predict exactly when a component will fail. Probability theory allows us to evaluate measures of reliability such as the average *time to failure* and the probability that a component is still functioning after a certain time has elapsed. Furthermore, we will see in Chapters 2 and 4 that probability theory enables us to determine these averages and probabilities for an entire system in terms of the probabilities and averages of its components. This allows

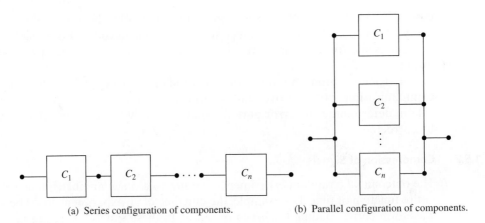

(a)  Series configuration of components.          (b)  Parallel configuration of components.

**FIGURE 1.8**
Systems with $n$ components.

us to evaluate system configurations in terms of their reliability, and thus to select system designs that are reliable.

### 1.5.4    Resource-Sharing Systems

Many applications involve sharing resources that are subject to unsteady and random demand. Clients intersperse demands for short periods of service between relatively long idle periods. The demands of the clients can be met by dedicating sufficient resources to each individual client, but this approach can be wasteful because the resources go unused when a client is idle. A better approach is to configure systems where client demands are met through dynamic sharing of resources.

For example, many Web server systems operate as shown in Fig. 1.9. These systems allow up to $c$ clients to be connected to a server at any given time. Clients submit queries to the server. The query is placed in a waiting line and then processed by the server. After receiving the response from the server, each client spends some time

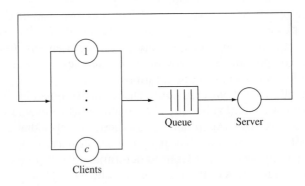

**FIGURE 1.9**
Simple model for Web server system.

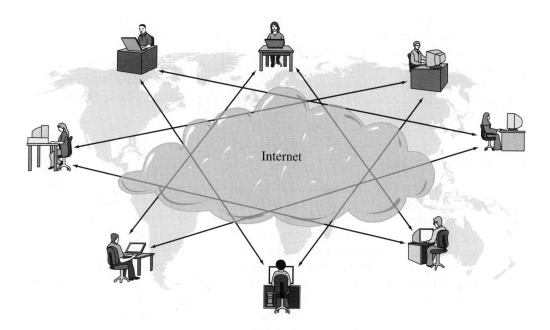

**FIGURE 1.10**
A large community of users interacting across the Internet.

thinking before placing the next query. The system closes an existing client's connection after a timeout period, and replaces it with a new client.

The system needs to be configured to provide rapid responses to clients, to avoid premature closing of connections, and to utilize the computing resources effectively. This requires the probabilistic characterization of the query processing time, the number of clicks per connection, and the time between clicks (think time). These parameters are then used to determine the optimum value of $c$ as well as the timeout value.

### 1.5.5    Internet Scale Systems

One of the major current challenges today is the design of Internet-scale systems as the client-server systems of Fig. 1.9 evolve into massively distributed systems, as in Fig. 1.10. In these new systems the number of users who are online at the same time can be in the tens of thousands and in the case of peer-to-peer systems in the millions.

The interactions among users of the Internet are much more complex than those of clients accessing a server. For example, the links in Web pages that point to other Web pages create a vast web of interconnected documents. The development of graphing and mapping techniques to represent these logical relationships is key to understanding user behavior. A variety of Web crawling techniques have been developed to produce such graphs [Broder]. Probabilistic techniques can assess the relative importance of nodes in these graphs and, indeed, play a central role in the operation of search engines. New applications, such as peer-to-peer file sharing and content distribution, create new communities with their own interconnectivity patterns and graphs. The behavior of users in these communities can have dramatic impact on the volume, patterns, and dynamics of traffic flows in the Internet. Probabilistic methods are playing an important role in understanding these systems and in developing methods to manage and control resources so that they operate in reliable and predictable fashion [15].

## 1.6    OVERVIEW OF BOOK

In this chapter we have discussed the important role that probability models play in the design of systems that involve randomness. *The principal objective of this book is to introduce the student to the basic concepts of probability theory that are required to understand probability models used in electrical and computer engineering.* The book is not intended to cover applications per se; there are far too many applications, with each one requiring its own detailed discussion. On the other hand, we do attempt to keep the examples relevant to the intended audience by drawing from relevant application areas.

*Another objective of the book is to present some of the basic techniques required to develop probability models.* The discussion in this chapter has made it clear that the probabilities used in a model must be determined experimentally. *Statistical techniques* are required to do this, so we have included an introduction to the basic but essential statistical techniques. We have also alluded to the usefulness of *computer simulation models* in validating probability models. Most chapters include a section that presents some useful computer method. These sections are optional and can be skipped without loss of continuity. However, the student is encouraged to explore these techniques. They are fun to play with, and they will provide insight into the nature of randomness. The remainder of the book is organized as follows:

- Chapter 2 presents the basic concepts of probability theory. We begin with the axioms of probability that were stated in Section 1.3 and discuss their implications. Several basic probability models are introduced in Chapter 2.

- In general, probability theory does not require that the outcomes of random experiments be numbers. Thus the outcomes can be objects (e.g., black or white balls) or conditions (e.g., computer system up or down). However, we are usually interested in experiments where the outcomes are numbers. The notion of a random variable addresses this situation. Chapters 3 and 4 discuss experiments where the outcome is a single number from a discrete set or a continuous set, respectively. In these two chapters we develop several extremely useful problem-solving techniques.

- Chapter 5 discusses pairs of random variables and introduces methods for describing the correlation of interdependence between random variables. Chapter 6 extends these methods to vector random variables.

- Chapter 7 presents mathematical results (limit theorems) that answer the question of what happens in a very long sequence of independent repetitions of an experiment. The results presented will justify our extensive use of relative frequency to motivate the notion of probability.

- Chapter 8 provides an introduction to basic statistical methods.
- Chapter 9 introduces the notion of a random or stochastic process, which is simply an experiment in which the outcome is a function of time.
- Chapter 10 introduces the notion of the power spectral density and its use in the analysis and processing of random signals.
- Chapter 11 discusses Markov chains, which are random processes that allow us to model sequences of nonindependent experiments.
- Chapter 12 presents an introduction to queueing theory and various applications.

## SUMMARY

- Mathematical models relate important system parameters and variables using mathematical relations. They allow system designers to predict system performance by using equations when experimentation is not feasible or too costly.
- Computer simulation models are an alternative means of predicting system performance. They can be used to validate mathematical models.
- In deterministic models the conditions under which an experiment is performed determine the *exact* outcome. The equations in deterministic models predict an exact outcome.
- In probability models the conditions under which a random experiment is performed determine the *probabilities* of the possible outcomes. The solution of the equations in probability models yields the probabilities of outcomes and events as well as various types of averages.
- The probabilities and averages for a random experiment can be found experimentally by computing relative frequencies and sample averages in a large number of repetitions of a random experiment.
- The performance measures in many systems of practical interest involve relative frequencies and long-term averages. Probability models are used in the design of these systems.

## CHECKLIST OF IMPORTANT TERMS

Deterministic model
Event
Expected value
Probability
Probability model

Random experiment
Relative frequency
Sample mean
Sample space
Statistical regularity

## ANNOTATED REFERENCES

References [1] through [5] discuss probability models in an engineering context. References [6] and [7] are classic works, and they contain excellent discussions on the foundations of probability models. Reference [8] is an introduction to error control. Reference [9] discusses random signal analysis in the context of communication systems, and references [10] and [11] discuss various aspects of random signal analysis. References [12] and [13] are introductions to performance aspects of computer communications.

1. A. Papoulis and S. U. Pillai, *Probability, Random Variables, and Stochastic Processes*, 4th ed., McGraw-Hill, New York, 2002.
2. D. P. Bertsekas and J. N. Tsitsiklis, *Introduction to Probability*, Athena Scientific, Belmont, MA, 2002.
3. T. L. Fine, *Probability and Probabilistic Reasoning for Electrical Engineering*, Prentice Hall, Upper Saddle River, N.J., 2006.
4. H. Stark and J. W. Woods, *Probability and Random Processes with Applications to Signal Processing*, 3d ed., Prentice Hall, Upper Saddle River, N.J., 2002.
5. R. D. Yates and D. J. Goodman, *Probability and Stochastic Processes*, Wiley, New York, 2005.
6. H. Cramer, *Mathematical Models of Statistics*, Princeton University Press, Princeton, N.J., 1946.
7. W. Feller, *An Introduction to Probability Theory and Its Applications*, Wiley, New York, 1968.
8. S. Lin and R. Costello, *Error Control Coding: Fundamentals and Applications*, Prentice Hall, Upper Saddle River, N.J., 2005.
9. S. Haykin, *Communications Systems*, 4th ed., Wiley, New York, 2000.
10. A. V. Oppenheim, R. W. Schafer, and J. R. Buck, *Discrete-Time Signal Processing*, 2d ed., Prentice Hall, Upper Saddle River, N.J., 1999.
11. J. Gibson, T. Berger, and T. Lookabough, *Digital Compression and Multimedia*, Morgan Kaufmann Publishers, San Francisco, 1998.
12. L. Kleinrock, *Queueing Theory, Volume 1: Theory*, Wiley, New York, 1975.
13. D. Bertsekas and R. G. Gallager, *Data Networks*, Prentice Hall, Upper Saddle River, N.J., 1987.
14. Broder et al., "Graph Structure in the Web," *Proceedings of the 9th international World Wide Web conference on Computer networks: the international journal of computer and telecommunications networking*, North-Holland, The Netherlands, 2000.
15. P. Baldi et al., *Modeling the Internet and the Web*, Wiley, Hoboken, N.J., 2003.

## PROBLEMS

1.1. Consider the following three random experiments:
Experiment 1: Toss a coin.
Experiment 2: Toss a die.
Experiment 3: Select a ball at random from an urn containing balls numbered 0 to 9.

(a) Specify the sample space of each experiment.

(b) Find the relative frequency of each outcome in each of the above experiments in a large number of repetitions of the experiment. Explain your answer.

**1.2.** Explain how the following experiments are equivalent to random urn experiments:

(a) Flip a fair coin twice.

(b) Toss a pair of fair dice.

(c) Draw two cards from a deck of 52 distinct cards, with replacement after the first draw; without replacement after the first draw.

**1.3.** Explain under what conditions the following experiments are equivalent to a random coin toss. What is the probability of heads in the experiment?

(a) Observe a pixel (dot) in a scanned black-and-white document.

(b) Receive a binary signal in a communication system.

(c) Test whether a device is working.

(d) Determine whether your friend Joe is online.

(e) Determine whether a bit error has occurred in a transmission over a noisy communication channel.

**1.4.** An urn contains three electronically labeled balls with labels 00, 01, 10. Lisa, Homer, and Bart are asked to characterize the random experiment that involves selecting a ball at random and reading the label. Lisa's label reader works fine; Homer's label reader has the most significant digit stuck at 1; Bart's label reader's least significant digit is stuck at 0.

(a) What is the sample space determined by Lisa, Homer, and Bart?

(b) What are the relative frequencies observed by Lisa, Homer, and Bart in a large number of repetitions of the experiment?

**1.5.** A random experiment has sample space $S = \{1, 2, 3, 4\}$ with probabilities $p_1 = 1/2$, $p_2 = 1/4$, $p_3 = 1/8$, $p_4 = 1/8$.

(a) Describe how this random experiment can be simulated using tosses of a fair coin.

(b) Describe how this random experiment can be simulated using an urn experiment.

(c) Describe how this experiment can be simulated using a deck of 52 distinct cards.

**1.6.** A random experiment consists of selecting two balls in succession from an urn containing two black balls and and one white ball.

(a) Specify the sample space for this experiment.

(b) Suppose that the experiment is modified so that the ball is immediately put back into the urn after the first selection. What is the sample space now?

(c) What is the relative frequency of the outcome (white, white) in a large number of repetitions of the experiment in part a? In part b?

(d) Does the outcome of the second draw from the urn depend in any way on the outcome of the first draw in either of these experiments?

**1.7.** Let $A$ be an event associated with outcomes of a random experiment, and let the event $B$ be defined as "event $A$ does not occur." Show that $f_B(n) = 1 - f_A(n)$.

**1.8.** Let $A$, $B$, and $C$ be events that cannot occur simultaneously as pairs or triplets, and let $D$ be the event "$A$ or $B$ or $C$ occurs." Show that

$$f_D(n) = f_A(n) + f_B(n) + f_C(n).$$

**1.9.** The *sample mean* for a series of numerical outcomes $X(1)$, $X(2), \ldots, X(n)$ of a sequence of random experiments is defined by

$$\langle X \rangle_n = \frac{1}{n} \sum_{j=1}^{n} X(j).$$

Show that the sample mean satisfies the recursion formula:

$$\langle X \rangle_n = \langle X \rangle_{n-1} + \frac{X(n) - \langle X \rangle_{n-1}}{n}, \qquad \langle X \rangle_0 = 0.$$

**1.10.** Suppose that the signal $2 \cos 2\pi t$ is sampled at random instants of time.

(a) Find the long-term sample mean.

(b) Find the long-term relative frequency of the events "voltage is positive"; "voltage is less than $-2$."

(c) Do the answers to parts a and b change if the sampling times are periodic and taken every $\tau$ seconds?

**1.11.** In order to generate a random sequence of random numbers you take a column of telephone numbers and output a "0" if the last digit in the telephone number is even and a "1" if the digit is odd. Discuss how one could determine if the resulting sequence is "random." What test would you apply to the relative frequencies of single outcomes? Of pairs of outcomes?

# Basic Concepts of Probability Theory

This chapter presents the basic concepts of probability theory. In the remainder of the book, we will usually be further developing or elaborating the basic concepts presented here. You will be well prepared to deal with the rest of the book if you have a good understanding of these basic concepts when you complete the chapter.

The following basic concepts will be presented. First, set theory is used to specify the sample space and the events of a random experiment. Second, the axioms of probability specify rules for computing the probabilities of events. Third, the notion of conditional probability allows us to determine how partial information about the outcome of an experiment affects the probabilities of events. Conditional probability also allows us to formulate the notion of "independence" of events and of experiments. Finally, we consider "sequential" random experiments that consist of performing a sequence of simple random subexperiments. We show how the probabilities of events in these experiments can be derived from the probabilities of the simpler subexperiments. Throughout the book it is shown that complex random experiments can be analyzed by decomposing them into simple subexperiments.

## 2.1 SPECIFYING RANDOM EXPERIMENTS

A random experiment is an experiment in which the outcome varies in an unpredictable fashion when the experiment is repeated under the same conditions. *A random experiment is specified by stating an experimental procedure and a set of one or more measurements or observations.*

### Example 2.1

*Experiment $E_1$:* Select a ball from an urn containing balls numbered 1 to 50. Note the number of the ball.

*Experiment $E_2$:* Select a ball from an urn containing balls numbered 1 to 4. Suppose that balls 1 and 2 are black and that balls 3 and 4 are white. Note the number and color of the ball you select.

*Experiment $E_3$:* Toss a coin three times and note the sequence of heads and tails.

*Experiment $E_4$:* Toss a coin three times and note the number of heads.

*Experiment $E_5$:* Count the number of voice packets containing only silence produced from a group of $N$ speakers in a 10-ms period.

*Experiment $E_6$:* A block of information is transmitted repeatedly over a noisy channel until an error-free block arrives at the receiver. Count the number of transmissions required.
*Experiment $E_7$:* Pick a number at random between zero and one.
*Experiment $E_8$:* Measure the time between page requests in a Web server.
*Experiment $E_9$:* Measure the lifetime of a given computer memory chip in a specified environment.
*Experiment $E_{10}$:* Determine the value of an audio signal at time $t_1$.
*Experiment $E_{11}$:* Determine the values of an audio signal at times $t_1$ and $t_2$.
*Experiment $E_{12}$:* Pick two numbers at random between zero and one.
*Experiment $E_{13}$:* Pick a number $X$ at random between zero and one, then pick a number $Y$ at random between zero and $X$.
*Experiment $E_{14}$:* A system component is installed at time $t = 0$. For $t \geq 0$ let $X(t) = 1$ as long as the component is functioning, and let $X(t) = 0$ after the component fails.

The specification of a random experiment must include an unambiguous statement of exactly what is measured or observed. For example, random experiments may consist of the same procedure but differ in the observations made, as illustrated by $E_3$ and $E_4$.

A random experiment may involve more than one measurement or observation, as illustrated by $E_2, E_3, E_{11}, E_{12}$, and $E_{13}$. A random experiment may even involve a continuum of measurements, as shown by $E_{14}$.

Experiments $E_3, E_4, E_5, E_6, E_{12}$, and $E_{13}$ are examples of sequential experiments that can be viewed as consisting of a sequence of simple subexperiments. Can you identify the subexperiments in each of these? Note that in $E_{13}$ the second subexperiment depends on the outcome of the first subexperiment.

## 2.1.1 The Sample Space

Since random experiments do not consistently yield the same result, it is necessary to determine the set of possible results. We define an **outcome** or **sample point** of a random experiment as a result that cannot be decomposed into other results. When we perform a random experiment, one and only one outcome occurs. Thus outcomes are mutually exclusive in the sense that they cannot occur simultaneously. The **sample space** $S$ of a random experiment is defined as the set of all possible outcomes.

We will denote an outcome of an experiment by $\zeta$, where $\zeta$ is an element or point in $S$. Each performance of a random experiment can then be viewed as the selection at random of a single point (outcome) from $S$.

The sample space $S$ can be specified compactly by using set notation. It can be visualized by drawing tables, diagrams, intervals of the real line, or regions of the plane. There are two basic ways to specify a set:

**1.** *List all the elements*, separated by commas, inside a pair of braces:

$$A = \{0, 1, 2, 3\},$$

**2.** *Give a property* that specifies the elements of the set:

$$A = \{x : x \text{ is an integer such that } 0 \leq x \leq 3\}.$$

Note that the order in which items are listed does not change the set, e.g., $\{0, 1, 2, 3\}$ and $\{1, 2, 3, 0\}$ are the same set.

## Example 2.2

The sample spaces corresponding to the experiments in Example 2.1 are given below using set notation:

$$S_1 = \{1, 2, \ldots, 50\}$$

$$S_2 = \{(1, b), (2, b), (3, w), (4, w)\}$$

$$S_3 = \{\text{HHH, HHT, HTH, THH, TTH, THT, HTT, TTT}\}$$

$$S_4 = \{0, 1, 2, 3\}$$

$$S_5 = \{0, 1, 2, \ldots, N\}$$

$$S_6 = \{1, 2, 3, \ldots\}$$

$$S_7 = \{x : 0 \leq x \leq 1\} = [0, 1] \quad \text{See Fig. 2.1(a).}$$

$$S_8 = \{t : t \geq 0\} = [0, \infty)$$

$$S_9 = \{t : t \geq 0\} = [0, \infty) \quad \text{See Fig. 2.1(b).}$$

$$S_{10} = \{v : -\infty < v < \infty\} = (-\infty, \infty)$$

$$S_{11} = \{(v_1, v_2) : -\infty < v_1 < \infty \text{ and } -\infty < v_2 < \infty\}$$

$$S_{12} = \{(x, y) : 0 \leq x \leq 1 \text{ and } 0 \leq y \leq 1\} \quad \text{See Fig. 2.1(c).}$$

$$S_{13} = \{(x, y) : 0 \leq y \leq x \leq 1\} \quad \text{See Fig. 2.1(d).}$$

$S_{14} =$ set of functions $X(t)$ for which $X(t) = 1$ for $0 \leq t < t_0$ and $X(t) = 0$ for $t \geq t_0$,

where $t_0 > 0$ is the time when the component fails.

Random experiments involving the same experimental procedure may have different sample spaces as shown by Experiments $E_3$ and $E_4$. Thus the purpose of an experiment affects the choice of sample space.

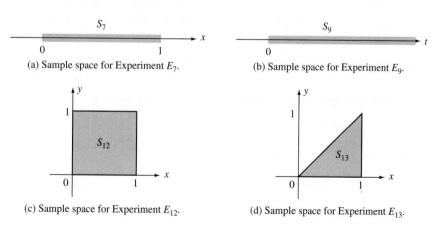

(a) Sample space for Experiment $E_7$.

(b) Sample space for Experiment $E_9$.

(c) Sample space for Experiment $E_{12}$.

(d) Sample space for Experiment $E_{13}$.

**FIGURE 2.1**
Sample spaces for Experiments $E_7, E_9, E_{12}$, and $E_{13}$.

There are three possibilities for the number of outcomes in a sample space. A sample space can be finite, countably infinite, or uncountably infinite. We call $S$ a **discrete sample space** if $S$ is countable; that is, its outcomes can be put into one-to-one correspondence with the positive integers. We call $S$ a **continuous sample space** if $S$ is not countable. Experiments $E_1$, $E_2$, $E_3$, $E_4$, and $E_5$ have finite discrete sample spaces. Experiment $E_6$ has a countably infinite discrete sample space. Experiments $E_7$ through $E_{13}$ have continuous sample spaces.

Since an outcome of an experiment can consist of one or more observations or measurements, the sample space $S$ can be multi-dimensional. For example, the outcomes in Experiments $E_2$, $E_{11}$, $E_{12}$, and $E_{13}$ are two-dimensional, and those in Experiment $E_3$ are three-dimensional. In some instances, the sample space can be written as the Cartesian product of other sets.[1] For example, $S_{11} = R \times R$, where $R$ is the set of real numbers, and $S_3 = S \times S \times S$, where $S = \{H, T\}$.

It is sometimes convenient to let the sample space include outcomes that are impossible. For example, in Experiment $E_9$ it is convenient to define the sample space as the positive real line, even though a device cannot have an infinite lifetime.

### 2.1.2    Events

We are usually not interested in the occurrence of specific outcomes, but rather in the occurrence of some event (i.e., whether the outcome satisfies certain conditions). This requires that we consider subsets of $S$. We say that $A$ is a subset of $B$ if every element of $A$ also belongs to $B$. For example, in Experiment $E_{10}$, which involves the measurement of a voltage, we might be interested in the event "signal voltage is negative." The conditions of interest define a subset of the sample space, namely, the set of points $\zeta$ from $S$ that satisfy the given conditions. For example, "voltage is negative" corresponds to the set $\{\zeta: -\infty < \zeta < 0\}$. The event occurs if and only if the outcome of the experiment $\zeta$ is in this subset. For this reason **events** correspond to subsets of $S$.

Two events of special interest are the **certain event**, $S$, which consists of all outcomes and hence always occurs, and the **impossible** or **null event**, $\varnothing$, which contains no outcomes and hence never occurs.

---

### Example 2.3

In the following examples, $A_k$ refers to an event corresponding to Experiment $E_k$ in Example 2.1.

$E_1$: "An even-numbered ball is selected," $A_1 = \{2, 4, \ldots, 48, 50\}$.
$E_2$: "The ball is white and even-numbered," $A_2 = \{(4, w)\}$.
$E_3$: "The three tosses give the same outcome," $A_3 = \{HHH, TTT\}$.
$E_4$: "The number of heads equals the number of tails," $A_4 = \varnothing$.
$E_5$: "No active packets are produced," $A_5 = \{0\}$.

---

[1]The Cartesian product of the sets $A$ and $B$ consists of the set of all ordered pairs $(a, b)$, where the first element is taken from $A$ and the second from $B$.

$E_6$:  "Fewer than 10 transmissions are required," $A_6 = \{1, \ldots, 9\}$.

$E_7$:  "The number selected is nonnegative," $A_7 = S_7$.

$E_8$:  "Less than $t_0$ seconds elapse between page requests," $A_8 = \{t: 0 \le t < t_0\} = [0, t_0)$.

$E_9$:  "The chip lasts more than 1000 hours but fewer than 1500 hours," $A_9 = \{t: 1000 < t < 1500\}$
$= (1000, 1500)$.

$E_{10}$:  "The absolute value of the voltage is less than 1 volt," $A_{10} = \{v: -1 < v < 1\} = (-1, 1)$.

$E_{11}$:  "The two voltages have opposite polarities," $A_{11} = \{(v_1, v_2): (v_1 < 0$ and $v_2 > 0)$ or $(v_1 > 0$ and $v_2 < 0)\}$.

$E_{12}$:  "The two numbers differ by less than 1/10," $A_{12} = \{(x, y): (x, y)$ in $S_{12}$ and $|x - y| < 1/10\}$.

$E_{13}$:  "The two numbers differ by less than 1/10," $A_{13} = \{(x, y): (x, y)$ in $S_{13}$ and $|x - y| < 1/10\}$.

$E_{14}$:  "The system is functioning at time $t_1$," $A_{14} =$ subset of $S_{14}$ for which $X(t_1) = 1$.

An event may consist of a single outcome, as in $A_2$ and $A_5$. An event from a *discrete* sample space that consists of a single outcome is called an **elementary event**. Events $A_2$ and $A_5$ are elementary events. An event may also consist of the entire sample space, as in $A_7$. The null event, $\varnothing$, arises when none of the outcomes satisfy the conditions that specify a given event, as in $A_4$.

## 2.1.3   Review of Set Theory

In random experiments we are interested in the occurrence of events that are represented by sets. We can combine events using set operations to obtain other events. We can also express complicated events as combinations of simple events. Before proceeding with further discussion of events and random experiments, we present some essential concepts from set theory.

A set is a collection of objects and will be denoted by capital letters $S, A, B, \ldots$. We define $U$ as the **universal set** that consists of all possible objects of interest in a given setting or application. In the context of random experiments we refer to the universal set as the sample space. For example, the universal set in Experiment $E_6$ is $U = \{1, 2, \ldots\}$. A **set** $A$ is a collection of objects from $U$, and these objects are called the **elements** or **points** of the set $A$ and will be denoted by lowercase letters, $\zeta, a, b, x, y, \ldots$. We use the notation:

$$x \in A \qquad \text{and} \qquad x \notin A$$

to indicate that "$x$ is an element of $A$" or "$x$ is not an element of $A$," respectively.

We use Venn diagrams when discussing sets. A Venn diagram is an illustration of sets and their interrelationships. The universal set $U$ is usually represented as the set of all points within a rectangle as shown in Fig. 2.2(a). The set $A$ is then the set of points within an enclosed region inside the rectangle.

We say $A$ is a **subset** of $B$ if every element of $A$ also belongs to $B$, that is, if $x \in A$ implies $x \in B$. We say that "$A$ is contained in $B$" and we write:

$$A \subset B.$$

If $A$ is a subset of $B$, then the Venn diagram shows the region for $A$ to be inside the region for $B$ as shown in Fig. 2.2(e).

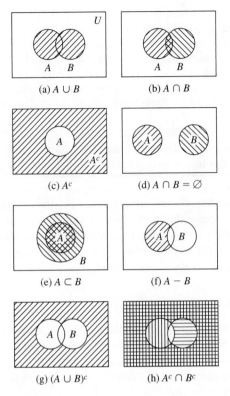

**FIGURE 2.2**
Set operations and set relations.

---

### Example 2.4

In Experiment $E_6$ three sets of interest might be $A = \{x : x \geq 10\} = \{10, 11, \dots\}$, that is, 10 or more transmissions are required; $B = \{2, 4, 6, \dots\}$, the number of transmissions is an even number; and $C = \{x : x \geq 20\} = \{20, 21, \dots\}$. Which of these sets are subsets of the others?

Clearly, $C$ is a subset of $A$ ($C \subset A$). However, $C$ is not a subset of $B$, and $B$ is not a subset of $C$, because both sets contain elements the other set does not contain. Similarly, $B$ is not a subset of $A$, and $A$ is not a subset of $B$.

---

The **empty set** $\varnothing$ is defined as the set with no elements. The empty set $\varnothing$ is a subset of every set, that is, for any set $A, \varnothing \subset A$.

We say sets **$A$ and $B$ are equal** if they contain the same elements. Since every element in $A$ is also in $B$, then $x \in A$ implies $x \in B$, so $A \subset B$. Similarly every element in $B$ is also in $A$, so $x \in B$ implies $x \in A$ and so $B \subset A$. Therefore:

$$A = B \quad \text{if and only if} \quad A \subset B \quad \text{and} \quad B \subset A.$$

The standard method to show that two sets, $A$ and $B$, are equal is to show that $A \subset B$ and $B \subset A$. A second method is to list all the items in $A$ and all the items in $B$, and to show that the items are the same. A variation of this second method is to use a

Venn diagram to identify the region that corresponds to $A$ and to then show that the Venn diagram for $B$ occupies the same region. We provide examples of both methods shortly.

We will use three basic operations on sets. The *union* and the *intersection* operations are applied to two sets and produce a third set. The *complement* operation is applied to a single set to produce another set.

The **union** of two sets $A$ and $B$ is denoted by $A \cup B$ and is defined as the set of outcomes that are either in $A$ or in $B$, or both:

$$A \cup B = \{x : x \in A \quad \text{or} \quad x \in B\}.$$

The operation $A \cup B$ corresponds to the logical "or" of the properties that define set $A$ and set $B$, that is, $x$ is in $A \cup B$ if $x$ satisfies the property that defines $A$, or $x$ satisfies the property that defines $B$, or both. The Venn diagram for $A \cup B$ consists of the shaded region in Fig. 2.2(a).

The **intersection** of two sets $A$ and $B$ is denoted by $A \cap B$ and is defined as the set of outcomes that are in both $A$ and $B$:

$$A \cap B = \{x : x \in A \quad \text{and} \quad x \in B\}.$$

The operation $A \cap B$ corresponds to the logical "and" of the properties that define set $A$ and set $B$. The Venn diagram for $A \cap B$ consists of the double shaded region in Fig. 2.2(b). Two sets are said to be **disjoint** or **mutually exclusive** if their intersection is the null set, $A \cap B = \varnothing$. Figure 2.2(d) shows two mutually exclusive sets $A$ and $B$.

The **complement** of a set $A$ is denoted by $A^c$ and is defined as the set of all elements not in $A$:

$$A^c = \{x : x \notin A\}.$$

The operation $A^c$ corresponds to the logical "not" of the property that defines set $A$. Figure 2.2(c) shows $A^c$. Note that $S^c = \varnothing$ and $\varnothing^c = S$.

The **relative complement** or **difference** of sets $A$ and $B$ is the set of elements in $A$ that are not in $B$:

$$A - B = \{x : x \in A \text{ and } x \notin B\}.$$

$A - B$ is obtained by removing from $A$ all the elements that are also in $B$, as illustrated in Fig. 2.2(f). Note that $A - B = A \cap B^c$. Note also that $B^c = S - B$.

---

### Example 2.5

Let $A$, $B$, and $C$ be the events from Experiment $E_6$ in Example 2.4. Find the following events: $A \cup B$, $A \cap B$, $A^c$, $B^c$, $A - B$, and $B - A$.

$$A \cup B = \{2, 4, 6, 8, 10, 11, 12, \dots\};$$

$$A \cap B = \{10, 12, 14, \dots\};$$

$$A^c = \{x : x < 10\} = \{1, 2, \dots, 9\};$$

$$B^c = \{1, 3, 5, \dots\};$$

$$A - B = \{11, 13, 15, \ldots\};$$

$$\text{and } B - A = \{2, 4, 6, 8\}.$$

The three basic set operations can be combined to form other sets. The following properties of set operations are useful in deriving new expressions for combinations of sets:

*Commutative properties:*

$$A \cup B = B \cup A \quad \text{and} \quad A \cap B = B \cap A. \tag{2.1}$$

*Associative properties:*

$$A \cup (B \cup C) = (A \cup B) \cup C \quad \text{and} \quad A \cap (B \cap C) = (A \cap B) \cap C. \tag{2.2}$$

*Distributive properties:*

$$A \cup (B \cap C) = (A \cup B) \cap (A \cup C) \quad \text{and}$$

$$A \cap (B \cup C) = (A \cap B) \cup (A \cap C). \tag{2.3}$$

By applying the above properties we can derive new identities. DeMorgan's rules provide an important such example:

*DeMorgan's rules:*

$$(A \cup B)^c = A^c \cap B^c \quad \text{and} \quad (A \cap B)^c = A^c \cup B^c \tag{2.4}$$

## Example 2.6

Prove DeMorgan's rules by using Venn diagrams and by demonstrating set equality.

First we will use a Venn diagram to show the first equality. The shaded region in Fig. 2.2(g) shows the complement of $A \cup B$, the left-hand side of the equation. The cross-hatched region in Fig. 2.2(h) shows the intersection of $A^c$ and $B^c$. The two regions are the same and so the sets are equal. Try sketching the Venn diagrams for the second equality in Eq. (2.4).

Next we prove DeMorgan's rules by proving set equality. The proof has two parts: First we show that $(A \cup B)^c \subset A^c \cap B^c$; then we show that $A^c \cap B^c \subset (A \cup B)^c$. Together these results imply $(A \cup B)^c = A^c \cap B^c$.

First, suppose that $x \in (A \cup B)^c$, then $x \notin A \cup B$. In particular, we have $x \notin A$, which implies $x \in A^c$. Similarly, we have $x \notin B$, which implies $x \in B^c$. Hence $x$ is in both $A^c$ and $B^c$, that is, $x \in A^c \cap B^c$. We have shown that $(A \cup B)^c \subset A^c \cap B^c$.

To prove inclusion in the other direction, suppose that $x \in A^c \cap B^c$. This implies that $x \in A^c$, so $x \notin A$. Similarly, $x \in B^c$ and so $x \notin B$. Therefore, $x \notin (A \cup B)$ and so $x \in (A \cup B)^c$. We have shown that $A^c \cap B^c \subset (A \cup B)^c$. This proves that $(A \cup B)^c = A^c \cap B^c$.

To prove the second DeMorgan rule, apply the first DeMorgan rule to $A^c$ and $B^c$ to obtain:

$$(A^c \cup B^c)^c = (A^c)^c \cap (B^c)^c = A \cap B,$$

where we used the identity $A = (A^c)^c$. Now take complements of both sides of the above equation:

$$A^c \cup B^c = (A \cap B)^c.$$

**Example 2.7**

For Experiment $E_{10}$, let the sets $A$, $B$, and $C$ be defined by

$$A = \{v: |v| > 10\}, \quad \text{"magnitude of } v \text{ is greater than 10 volts,"}$$
$$B = \{v: v < -5\}, \quad \text{"} v \text{ is less than } -5 \text{ volts,"}$$
$$C = \{v: v > 0\}, \quad \text{"} v \text{ is positive."}$$

You should then verify that

$$A \cup B = \{v: v < -5 \text{ or } v > 10\},$$
$$A \cap B = \{v: v < -10\},$$
$$C^c = \{v: v \leq 0\},$$
$$(A \cup B) \cap C = \{v: v > 10\},$$
$$A \cap B \cap C = \varnothing, \text{ and}$$
$$(A \cup B)^c = \{v: -5 \leq v \leq 10\}.$$

The union and intersection operations can be repeated for an arbitrary number of sets. Thus the union of $n$ sets

$$\bigcup_{k=1}^{n} A_k = A_1 \cup A_2 \cup \cdots \cup A_n \tag{2.5}$$

is the set that consists of all elements that are in $A_k$ for at least one value of $k$. The same definition applies to the union of a countably infinite sequence of sets:

$$\bigcup_{k=1}^{\infty} A_k. \tag{2.6}$$

The intersection of $n$ sets

$$\bigcap_{k=1}^{n} A_k = A_1 \cap A_2 \cap \cdots \cap A_n \tag{2.7}$$

is the set that consists of elements that are in *all* of the sets $A_1, \ldots, A_n$. The same definition applies to the intersection of a countably infinite sequence of sets:

$$\bigcap_{k=1}^{\infty} A_k. \tag{2.8}$$

We will see that countable unions and intersections of sets are essential in dealing with sample spaces that are not finite.

### 2.1.4    Event Classes

We have introduced the sample space $S$ as the set of all possible outcomes of the random experiment. We have also introduced events as subsets of $S$. Probability theory also requires that we state the *class* $\mathcal{F}$ of events of interest. Only events in this class are assigned probabilities. We expect that any set operation on events in $\mathcal{F}$ will produce a set that is also an event in $\mathcal{F}$. In particular, we insist that complements, as well as countable unions and intersections of events in $\mathcal{F}$, i.e., Eqs. (2.1) and (2.5) through (2.8), result in events in $\mathcal{F}$. When the sample space $S$ is finite or countable, we simply let $\mathcal{F}$ consist of all subsets of $S$ and we can proceed without further concerns about $\mathcal{F}$. However, when $S$ is the real line $R$ (or an interval of the real line), we cannot let $\mathcal{F}$ be all possible subsets of $R$ and still satisfy the axioms of probability. Fortunately, we can obtain all the events of practical interest by letting $\mathcal{F}$ be of the class of events obtained as complements and countable unions and intersections of intervals of the real line, e.g., $(a, b]$ or $(-\infty, b]$. We will refer to this class of events as the *Borel field*. In the remainder of the book, we will refer to the event class $\mathcal{F}$ from time to time. For the introductory-level course in probability you will not need to know more than what is stated in this paragraph.

When we speak of a class of events we are referring to a collection (set) of events (sets), that is, we are speaking of a "set of sets." We refer to the collection of sets as a class to remind us that the elements of the class are sets. We use script capital letters to refer to a class, e.g., $\mathcal{C}, \mathcal{F}, \mathcal{G}$. If the class $\mathcal{C}$ consists of the collection of sets $A_1, \ldots, A_k$, then we write $\mathcal{C} = \{A_1, \ldots, A_k\}$.

---

### Example 2.8

Let $S = \{\text{T}, \text{H}\}$ be the outcome of a coin toss. Let every subset of $S$ be an event. Find all possible events of $S$.

An event is a subset of $S$, so we need to find all possible subsets of $S$. These are:

$$S = \{\varnothing, \{\text{H}\}, \{\text{T}\}, \{\text{H}, \text{T}\}\}.$$

Note that $S$ includes both the empty set and $S$. Let $i_\text{T}$ and $i_\text{H}$ be binary numbers where $i = 1$ indicates that the corresponding element of $S$ is in a given subset. We generate all possible subsets by taking all possible values of the pair $i_\text{T}$ and $i_\text{H}$. Thus $i_\text{T} = 0, i_\text{H} = 1$ corresponds to the set $\{\text{H}\}$. Clearly there are $2^2$ possible subsets as listed above.

---

For a *finite sample space*, $S = \{1, 2, \ldots, k\}$,[2] we usually allow all subsets of $S$ to be events. This class of events is called the **power set of $S$** and we will denote it by $\mathcal{S}$. We can index all possible subsets of $S$ with binary numbers $i_1, i_2, \ldots, i_k$, and we find that the power set of $S$ has $2^k$ members. Because of this, the power set is also denoted by $\mathcal{S} = 2^S$.

Section 2.8 discusses some of the fine points on event classes.

## 2.2    THE AXIOMS OF PROBABILITY

Probabilities are numbers assigned to events that indicate how "likely" it is that the events will occur when an experiment is performed. A **probability law** for a random experiment is a rule that assigns probabilities to the events of the experiment that belong to the event class $\mathcal{F}$. Thus a probability law is a function that assigns a number to sets (events). In Section 1.3 we found a number of properties of relative frequency that any definition of probability should satisfy. The axioms of probability formally state that a

---

[2]The discussion applies to any finite sample space with arbitrary objects $S = \{x_1, \ldots, x_k\}$, but we consider $\{1, 2, \ldots, k\}$ for notational simplicity.

probability law must satisfy these properties. In this section, we develop a number of results that follow from this set of axioms.

Let $E$ be a random experiment with sample space $S$ and event class $\mathcal{F}$. A *probability law* for the experiment $E$ is a rule that assigns to each event $A \in \mathcal{F}$ a number $P[A]$, called the **probability of $A$**, that satisfies the following axioms:

| | |
|---|---|
| *Axiom I* | $0 \le P[A]$ |
| *Axiom II* | $P[S] = 1$ |
| *Axiom III* | If $A \cap B = \varnothing$, then $P[A \cup B] = P[A] + P[B]$. |
| *Axiom III'* | If $A_1, A_2, \ldots$ is a sequence of events such that $A_i \cap A_j = \varnothing$ for all $i \neq j$, then |

$$P\left[\bigcup_{k=1}^{\infty} A_k\right] = \sum_{k=1}^{\infty} P[A_k].$$

Axioms I, II, and III are enough to deal with experiments with finite sample spaces. In order to handle experiments with infinite sample spaces, Axiom III needs to be replaced by Axiom III'. Note that Axiom III' includes Axiom III as a special case, by letting $A_k = \varnothing$ for $k \ge 3$. Thus we really only need Axioms I, II, and III'. Nevertheless we will gain greater insight by starting with Axioms I, II, and III.

The axioms allow us to view events as objects possessing a property (i.e., their probability) that has attributes similar to physical mass. Axiom I states that the probability (mass) is nonnegative, and Axiom II states that there is a fixed total amount of probability (mass), namely 1 unit. Axiom III states that the total probability (mass) in two disjoint objects is the sum of the individual probabilities (masses).

The axioms provide us with a set of consistency rules that any valid probability assignment must satisfy. We now develop several properties stemming from the axioms that are useful in the computation of probabilities.

The first result states that if we partition the sample space into two mutually exclusive events, $A$ and $A^c$, then the probabilities of these two events add up to one.

---

### Corollary 1

$P[A^c] = 1 - P[A]$

*Proof:* Since an event $A$ and its complement $A^c$ are mutually exclusive, $A \cap A^c = \varnothing$, we have from Axiom III that

$$P[A \cup A^c] = P[A] + P[A^c].$$

Since $S = A \cup A^c$, by Axiom II,

$$1 = P[S] = P[A \cup A^c] = P[A] + P[A^c].$$

The corollary follows after solving for $P[A^c]$.

---

The next corollary states that the probability of an event is always less than or equal to one. Corollary 2 combined with Axiom I provide good checks in problem solving: If your probabilities are negative or are greater than one, you have made a mistake somewhere!

---

### Corollary 2

$P[A] \leq 1$

*Proof:* From Corollary 1,

$$P[A] = 1 - P[A^c] \leq 1,$$

since $P[A^c] \geq 0$.

---

Corollary 3 states that the impossible event has probability zero.

---

### Corollary 3

$P[\varnothing] = 0$

*Proof:* Let $A = S$ and $A^c = \varnothing$ in Corollary 1:

$$P[\varnothing] = 1 - P[S] = 0.$$

---

Corollary 4 provides us with the standard method for computing the probability of a complicated event $A$. The method involves decomposing the event $A$ into the union of disjoint events $A_1, A_2, \ldots, A_n$. The probability of $A$ is the sum of the probabilities of the $A_k$'s.

---

### Corollary 4

If $A_1, A_2, \ldots, A_n$ are pairwise mutually exclusive, then

$$P\left[\bigcup_{k=1}^{n} A_k\right] = \sum_{k=1}^{n} P[A_k] \qquad \text{for } n \geq 2.$$

*Proof:* We use mathematical induction. Axiom III implies that the result is true for $n = 2$. Next we need to show that if the result is true for some $n$, then it is also true for $n + 1$. This, combined with the fact that the result is true for $n = 2$, implies that the result is true for $n \geq 2$.

Suppose that the result is true for some $n > 2$; that is,

$$P\left[\bigcup_{k=1}^{n} A_k\right] = \sum_{k=1}^{n} P[A_k], \tag{2.9}$$

and consider the $n + 1$ case

$$P\left[\bigcup_{k=1}^{n+1} A_k\right] = P\left[\left\{\bigcup_{k=1}^{n} A_k\right\} \cup A_{n+1}\right] = P\left[\bigcup_{k=1}^{n} A_k\right] + P[A_{n+1}], \tag{2.10}$$

where we have applied Axiom III to the second expression after noting that the union of events $A_1$ to $A_n$ is mutually exclusive with $A_{n+1}$. The distributive property then implies

$$\left\{\bigcup_{k=1}^{n} A_k\right\} \cap A_{n+1} = \bigcup_{k=1}^{n} \{A_k \cap A_{n+1}\} = \bigcup_{k=1}^{n} \varnothing = \varnothing.$$

Substitution of Eq. (2.9) into Eq. (2.10) gives the $n + 1$ case

$$P\left[\bigcup_{k=1}^{n+1} A_k\right] = \sum_{k=1}^{n+1} P[A_k].$$

Corollary 5 gives an expression for the union of two events that are not necessarily mutually exclusive.

### Corollary 5

$P[A \cup B] = P[A] + P[B] - P[A \cap B]$

*Proof:* First we decompose $A \cup B$, $A$, and $B$ as unions of disjoint events. From the Venn diagram in Fig. 2.3,

$$P[A \cup B] = P[A \cap B^c] + P[B \cap A^c] + P[A \cap B]$$

$$P[A] = P[A \cap B^c] + P[A \cap B]$$

$$P[B] = P[B \cap A^c] + P[A \cap B]$$

By substituting $P[A \cap B^c]$ and $P[B \cap A^c]$ from the two lower equations into the top equation, we obtain the corollary.

By looking at the Venn diagram in Fig. 2.3, you will see that the sum $P[A] + P[B]$ counts the probability (mass) of the set $A \cap B$ twice. The expression in Corollary 5 makes the appropriate correction.

Corollary 5 is easily generalized to three events,

$$P[A \cup B \cup C] = P[A] + P[B] + P[C] - P[A \cap B]$$
$$- P[A \cap C] - P[B \cap C] + P[A \cap B \cap C], \quad (2.11)$$

and in general to $n$ events, as shown in Corollary 6.

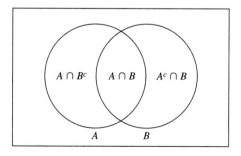

**FIGURE 2.3**
Decomposition of $A \cup B$ into three disjoint sets.

**Corollary 6**

$$P\left[\bigcup_{k=1}^{n}A_k\right] = \sum_{j=1}^{n}P[A_j] - \sum_{j<k}P[A_j \cap A_k] + \cdots$$

$$+ (-1)^{n+1}P[A_1 \cap \cdots \cap A_n].$$

*Proof* is by induction (see Problems 2.26 and 2.27).

Since probabilities are nonnegative, Corollary 5 implies that the probability of the union of two events is no greater than the sum of the individual event probabilities

$$P[A \cup B] \leq P[A] + P[B]. \tag{2.12}$$

The above inequality is a special case of the fact that a subset of another set must have smaller probability. This result is frequently used to obtain upper bounds for probabilities of interest. In the typical situation, we are interested in an event $A$ whose probability is difficult to find; so we find an event $B$ for which the probability can be found and that includes $A$ as a subset.

**Corollary 7**

If $A \subset B$, then $P[A] \leq P[B]$.

*Proof:* In Fig. 2.4, $B$ is the union of $A$ and $A^c \cap B$, thus

$$P[B] = P[A] + P[A^c \cap B] \geq P[A],$$

since $P[A^c \cap B] \geq 0$.

The axioms together with the corollaries provide us with a set of rules for computing the probability of certain events in terms of other events. However, we still need an **initial probability assignment** for some basic set of events from which the probability of all other events can be computed. This problem is dealt with in the next two subsections.

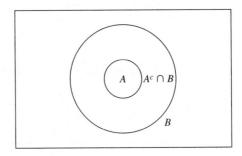

**FIGURE 2.4**
If $A \subset B$, then $P(A) \leq P(B)$.

### 2.2.1    Discrete Sample Spaces

In this section we show that *the probability law for an experiment with a countable sample space can be specified by giving the probabilities of the elementary events.* First, suppose that the sample space is finite, $S = \{a_1, a_2, \ldots, a_n\}$ and let $\mathcal{F}$ consist of all subsets of $S$. All distinct elementary events are mutually exclusive, so by Corollary 4 the probability of any event $B = \{a'_1, a'_2, \ldots, a'_m\}$ is given by

$$P[B] = P[\{a'_1, a'_2, \ldots, a'_m\}]$$
$$= P[\{a'_1\}] + P[\{a'_2\}] + \cdots + P[\{a'_m\}]; \tag{2.13}$$

that is, the probability of an event is equal to the sum of the probabilities of the outcomes in the event. Thus we conclude that the probability law for a random experiment with a finite sample space is specified by giving the probabilities of the elementary events.

If the sample space has $n$ elements, $S = \{a_1, \ldots, a_n\}$, a probability assignment of particular interest is the case of **equally likely outcomes**. The probability of the elementary events is

$$P[\{a_1\}] = P[\{a_2\}] = \cdots = P[\{a_n\}] = \frac{1}{n}. \tag{2.14}$$

The probability of any event that consists of $k$ outcomes, say $B = \{a'_1, \ldots, a'_k\}$, is

$$P[B] = P[\{a'_1\}] + \cdots + P[\{a'_k\}] = \frac{k}{n}. \tag{2.15}$$

Thus *if outcomes are equally likely, then the probability of an event is equal to the number of outcomes in the event divided by the total number of outcomes in the sample space.* Section 2.3 discusses counting methods that are useful in finding probabilities in experiments that have equally likely outcomes.

Consider the case where the sample space is countably infinite, $S = \{a_1, a_2, \ldots\}$. Let the event class $\mathcal{F}$ be the class of all subsets of $S$. Note that $\mathcal{F}$ must now satisfy Eq. (2.8) because events can consist of countable unions of sets. Axiom III$'$ implies that the probability of an event such as $D = \{b_1, b_2, b_3, \ldots\}$ is given by

$$P[D] = P[\{b'_1, b'_2, b'_3, \ldots\}] = P[\{b'_1\}] + P[\{b'_2\}] + P[\{b'_3\}] + \ldots$$

The probability of an event with a countably infinite sample space is determined from the probabilities of the elementary events.

---

### Example 2.9

An urn contains 10 identical balls numbered $0, 1, \ldots, 9$. A random experiment involves selecting a ball from the urn and noting the number of the ball. Find the probability of the following events:

$$A = \text{``number of ball selected is odd,''}$$

$$B = \text{``number of ball selected is a multiple of 3,''}$$

$$C = \text{``number of ball selected is less than 5,''}$$

and of $A \cup B$ and $A \cup B \cup C$.

The sample space is $S = \{0, 1, \ldots, 9\}$, so the sets of outcomes corresponding to the above events are

$$A = \{1, 3, 5, 7, 9\}, \qquad B = \{3, 6, 9\}, \qquad \text{and} \qquad C = \{0, 1, 2, 3, 4\}.$$

If we assume that the outcomes are equally likely, then

$$P[A] = P[\{1\}] + P[\{3\}] + P[\{5\}] + P[\{7\}] + P[\{9\}] = \frac{5}{10}.$$

$$P[B] = P[\{3\}] + P[\{6\}] + P[\{9\}] = \frac{3}{10}.$$

$$P[C] = P[\{0\}] + P[\{1\}] + P[\{2\}] + P[\{3\}] + P[\{4\}] = \frac{5}{10}.$$

From Corollary 5,

$$P[A \cup B] = P[A] + P[B] - P[A \cap B] = \frac{5}{10} + \frac{3}{10} - \frac{2}{10} = \frac{6}{10},$$

where we have used the fact that $A \cap B = \{3, 9\}$, so $P[A \cap B] = 2/10$. From Corollary 6,

$$P[A \cup B \cup C] = P[A] + P[B] + P[C] - P[A \cap B]$$
$$- P[A \cap C] - P[B \cap C] + P[A \cap B \cap C]$$
$$= \frac{5}{10} + \frac{3}{10} + \frac{5}{10} - \frac{2}{10} - \frac{2}{10} - \frac{1}{10} + \frac{1}{10}$$
$$= \frac{9}{10}.$$

You should verify the answers for $P[A \cup B]$ and $P[A \cup B \cup C]$ by enumerating the outcomes in the events.

---

Many probability models can be devised for the same sample space and events by varying the probability assignment; in the case of finite sample spaces all we need to do is come up with $n$ nonnegative numbers that add up to one for the probabilities of the elementary events. Of course, in any particular situation, the probability assignment should be selected to reflect experimental observations to the extent possible. The following example shows that situations can arise where there is more than one "reasonable" probability assignment and where experimental evidence is required to decide on the appropriate assignment.

---

### Example 2.10

Suppose that a coin is tossed three times. If we observe the sequence of heads and tails, then there are eight possible outcomes $S_3 = \{HHH, HHT, HTH, THH, TTH, THT, HTT, TTT\}$. If we assume that the outcomes of $S_3$ are equiprobable, then the probability of each of the eight elementary events is 1/8. This probability assignment implies that the probability of obtaining two heads in three tosses is, by Corollary 3,

$$P[\text{"2 heads in 3 tosses"}] = P[\{HHT, HTH, THH\}]$$

$$= P[\{HHT\}] + P[\{HTH\}] + P[\{THH\}] = \frac{3}{8}.$$

Now suppose that we toss a coin three times but we count the number of heads in three tosses instead of observing the sequence of heads and tails. The sample space is now $S_4 = \{0, 1, 2, 3\}$. If we assume the outcomes of $S_4$ to be equiprobable, then each of the elementary events of $S_4$ has probability 1/4. This second probability assignment predicts that the probability of obtaining two heads in three tosses is

$$P[\text{``2 heads in 3 tosses''}] = P[\{2\}] = \frac{1}{4}.$$

The first probability assignment implies that the probability of two heads in three tosses is 3/8, and the second probability assignment predicts that the probability is 1/4. Thus the two assignments are not consistent with each other. As far as the theory is concerned, either one of the assignments is acceptable. It is up to us to decide which assignment is more appropriate. Later in the chapter we will see that only the first assignment is consistent with the assumption that the coin is fair and that the tosses are "independent." This assignment correctly predicts the relative frequencies that would be observed in an actual coin tossing experiment.

Finally we consider an example with a countably infinite sample space.

**Example 2.11**

A fair coin is tossed repeatedly until the first heads shows up; the outcome of the experiment is the number of tosses required until the first heads occurs. Find a probability law for this experiment.

It is conceivable that an arbitrarily large number of tosses will be required until heads occurs, so the sample space is $S = \{1, 2, 3, \dots\}$. Suppose the experiment is repeated $n$ times. Let $N_j$ be the number of trials in which the $j$th toss results in the first heads. If $n$ is very large, we expect $N_1$ to be approximately $n/2$ since the coin is fair. This implies that a second toss is necessary about $n - N_1 \approx n/2$ times, and again we expect that about half of these—that is, $n/4$—will result in heads, and so on, as shown in Fig. 2.5. Thus for large $n$, the relative frequencies are

$$f_j \approx \frac{N_j}{n} = \left(\frac{1}{2}\right)^j \qquad j = 1, 2, \dots.$$

We therefore conclude that a reasonable probability law for this experiment is

$$P[\,j \text{ tosses till first heads}] = \left(\frac{1}{2}\right)^j \qquad j = 1, 2, \dots. \tag{2.16}$$

We can verify that these probabilities add up to one by using the geometric series with $\alpha = 1/2$:

$$\sum_{j=1}^{\infty} \alpha^j = \frac{\alpha}{1 - \alpha}\bigg|_{\alpha = 1/2} = 1.$$

### 2.2.2    Continuous Sample Spaces

Continuous sample spaces arise in experiments in which the outcomes are numbers that can assume a continuum of values, so we let the sample space $S$ be the entire real line $R$ (or some interval of the real line). We could consider letting the event class consist of all subsets of $R$. But it turns out that this class is "too large" and it is impossible

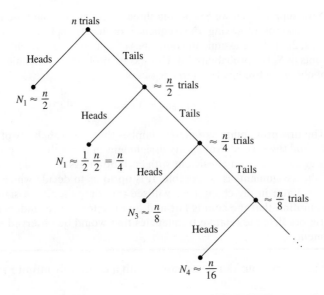

**FIGURE 2.5**
In $n$ trials heads comes up in the first toss approximately $n/2$ times, in the second toss approximately $n/4$ times, and so on.

to assign probabilities to all the subsets of $R$. Fortunately, it is possible to assign probabilities to all events in a smaller class that includes all events of practical interest. This class denoted by $\mathcal{B}$, is called the **Borel field** and it contains all open and closed intervals of the real line as well as all events that can be obtained as countable unions, intersections, and complements.[3] Axiom III' is once again the key to calculating probabilities of events. Let $A_1$, $A_2$,... be a sequence of mutually exclusive events that are represented by intervals of the real line, then

$$P\left[\bigcup_{k=1}^{\infty} A_k\right] = \sum_{k=1}^{\infty} P[A_k]$$

where each $P[A_k]$ is specified by the probability law. *For this reason, probability laws in experiments with continuous sample spaces specify a rule for assigning numbers to intervals of the real line.*

---

**Example 2.12**

Consider the random experiment "pick a number $x$ at random between zero and one." The sample space $S$ for this experiment is the unit interval $[0, 1]$, which is uncountably infinite. If we suppose that all the outcomes $S$ are equally likely to be selected, then we would guess that the probability that the outcome is in the interval $[0, 1/2]$ is the same as the probability that the outcome is in the interval $[1/2, 1]$. We would also guess that the probability of the outcome being exactly equal to $1/2$ would be zero since there are an uncountably infinite number of equally likely outcomes.

[3]Section 2.9 discusses $\mathcal{B}$ in more detail.

Consider the following probability law: "The probability that the outcome falls in a subinterval of $S$ is equal to the length of the subinterval," that is,

$$P[[a, b]] = (b - a) \qquad \text{for } 0 \le a \le b \le 1, \tag{2.17}$$

where by $P[[a, b]]$ we mean the probability of the event corresponding to the interval $[a, b]$. Clearly, Axiom I is satisfied since $b \ge a \ge 0$. Axiom II follows from $S = [a, b]$ with $a = 0$ and $b = 1$.

We now show that the probability law is consistent with the previous guesses about the probabilities of the events $[0, 1/2], [1/2, 1]$, and $\{1/2\}$:

$$P[[0, 0.5]] = 0.5 - 0 = .5$$

$$P[[0.5, 1]] = 1 - 0.5 = .5$$

In addition, if $x_0$ is any point in $S$, then $P[[x_0, x_0]] = 0$ since individual points have zero width.

Now suppose that we are interested in an event that is the union of several intervals; for example, "the outcome is at least 0.3 away from the center of the unit interval," that is, $A = [0, 0.2] \cup [0.8, 1]$. Since the two intervals are disjoint, we have by Axiom III

$$P[A] = P[[0, 0.2]] + P[[0.8, 1]] = .4.$$

---

The next example shows that an initial probability assignment that specifies the probability of semi-infinite intervals also suffices to specify the probabilities of all events of interest.

---

### Example 2.13

Suppose that the lifetime of a computer memory chip is measured, and we find that "the proportion of chips whose lifetime exceeds $t$ decreases exponentially at a rate $\alpha$." Find an appropriate probability law.

Let the sample space in this experiment be $S = (0, \infty)$. If we interpret the above finding as "the probability that a chip's lifetime exceeds $t$ decreases exponentially at a rate $\alpha$," we then obtain the following assignment of probabilities to events of the form $(t, \infty)$:

$$P[(t, \infty)] = e^{-\alpha t} \qquad \text{for } t > 0, \tag{2.18}$$

where $\alpha > 0$. Note that the exponential is a number between 0 and 1 for $t > 0$, so Axiom I is satisfied. Axiom II is satisfied since

$$P[S] = P[(0, \infty)] = 1.$$

The probability that the lifetime is in the interval $(r, s]$ is found by noting in Fig. 2.6 that $(r, s] \cup (s, \infty) = (r, \infty)$, so by Axiom III,

$$P[(r, \infty)] = P[(r, s]] + P[(s, \infty)].$$

**FIGURE 2.6**
$(r, \infty) = (r, s] \cup (s, \infty)$.

By rearranging the above equation we obtain

$$P[(r, s]] = P[(r, \infty)] - P[(s, \infty)] = e^{-\alpha r} - e^{-\alpha s}.$$

We thus obtain the probability of arbitrary intervals in $S$.

---

In both Example 2.12 and Example 2.13, the probability that the outcome takes on a specific value is zero. You may ask: If an outcome (or event) has probability zero, doesn't that mean it cannot occur? And you may then ask: How can all the outcomes in a sample space have probability zero? We can explain this paradox by using the relative frequency interpretation of probability. An event that occurs only once in an infinite number of trials will have relative frequency zero. Hence the fact that an event or outcome has relative frequency zero does not imply that it cannot occur, but rather that it occurs *very infrequently*. In the case of continuous sample spaces, the set of possible outcomes is so rich that all outcomes occur infrequently enough that their relative frequencies are zero.

We end this section with an example where the events are regions in the plane.

---

### Example 2.14

Consider Experiment $E_{12}$, where we picked two numbers $x$ and $y$ at random between zero and one. The sample space is then the unit square shown in Fig. 2.7(a). If we suppose that all pairs of numbers in the unit square are equally likely to be selected, then it is reasonable to use a probability assignment in which the probability of any region $R$ inside the unit square is equal to the area of $R$. Find the probability of the following events: $A = \{x > 0.5\}$, $B = \{y > 0.5\}$, and $C = \{x > y\}$.

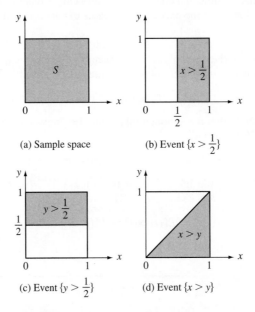

(a) Sample space     (b) Event $\{x > \frac{1}{2}\}$

(c) Event $\{y > \frac{1}{2}\}$     (d) Event $\{x > y\}$

**FIGURE 2.7**
A two-dimensional sample space and three events.

Figures 2.7(b) through 2.7(d) show the regions corresponding to the events $A$, $B$, and $C$. Clearly each of these regions has area 1/2. Thus

$$P[A] = \frac{1}{2}, \qquad P[B] = \frac{1}{2}, \qquad P[C] = \frac{1}{2}.$$

We reiterate how to proceed from a problem statement to its probability model. The problem statement implicitly or explicitly defines a random experiment, which specifies an experimental procedure and a set of measurements and observations. These measurements and observations determine the set of all possible outcomes and hence the sample space $S$.

An initial probability assignment that specifies the probability of certain events must be determined next. This probability assignment must satisfy the axioms of probability. If $S$ is discrete, then it suffices to specify the probabilities of elementary events. If $S$ is continuous, it suffices to specify the probabilities of intervals of the real line or regions of the plane. The probability of other events of interest can then be determined from the initial probability assignment and the axioms of probability and their corollaries. Many probability assignments are possible, so the choice of probability assignment must reflect experimental observations and/or previous experience.

## *2.3    COMPUTING PROBABILITIES USING COUNTING METHODS[4]

In many experiments with finite sample spaces, the outcomes can be assumed to be equiprobable. The probability of an event is then the ratio of the number of outcomes in the event of interest to the total number of outcomes in the sample space (Eq. (2.15)). The calculation of probabilities reduces to counting the number of outcomes in an event. In this section, we develop several useful counting (combinatorial) formulas.

Suppose that a multiple-choice test has $k$ questions and that for question $i$ the student must select one of $n_i$ possible answers. What is the total number of ways of answering the entire test? The answer to question $i$ can be viewed as specifying the $i$th component of a $k$-tuple, so the above question is equivalent to: How many distinct ordered $k$-tuples $(x_1, \ldots, x_k)$ are possible if $x_i$ is an element from a set with $n_i$ distinct elements?

Consider the $k = 2$ case. If we arrange all possible choices for $x_1$ and for $x_2$ along the sides of a table as shown in Fig. 2.8, we see that there are $n_1 n_2$ distinct ordered pairs. For triplets we could arrange the $n_1 n_2$ possible pairs $(x_1, x_2)$ along the vertical side of the table and the $n_3$ choices for $x_3$ along the horizontal side. Clearly, the number of possible triplets is $n_1 n_2 n_3$.

In general, *the number of distinct ordered $k$-tuples $(x_1, \ldots, x_k)$ with components $x_i$ from a set with $n_i$ distinct elements is*

$$\text{number of distinct ordered } k\text{-tuples} = n_1 n_2 \ldots n_k. \tag{2.19}$$

Many counting problems can be posed as sampling problems where we select "balls" from "urns" or "objects" from "populations." We will now use Eq. (2.19) to develop combinatorial formulas for various types of sampling.

[4]This section and all sections marked with an asterisk may be skipped without loss of continuity.

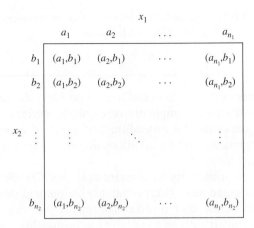

**FIGURE 2.8**
If there are $n_1$ distinct choices for $x_1$ and $n_2$ distinct choices for $x_2$, then there are $n_1 n_2$ distinct ordered pairs $(x_1, x_2)$.

### 2.3.1    Sampling with Replacement and with Ordering

Suppose we choose $k$ objects from a set $A$ that has $n$ distinct objects, with replacement—that is, after selecting an object and noting its identity in an ordered list, the object is placed back in the set before the next choice is made. We will refer to the set $A$ as the "population." The experiment produces an ordered $k$-tuple

$$(x_1, \dots, x_k),$$

where $x_i \in A$ and $i = 1, \dots, k$. Equation (2.19) with $n_1 = n_2 = \cdots = n_k = n$ implies that

$$\text{number of distinct ordered } k\text{-tuples} = n^k. \qquad (2.20)$$

---

**Example 2.15**

An urn contains five balls numbered 1 to 5. Suppose we select two balls from the urn with replacement. How many distinct *ordered* pairs are possible? What is the probability that the two draws yield the same number?

Equation (2.20) states that the number of ordered pairs is $5^2 = 25$. Table 2.1 shows the 25 possible pairs. Five of the 25 outcomes have the two draws yielding the same number; if we suppose that all pairs are equiprobable, then the probability that the two draws yield the same number is $5/25 = .2$.

---

### 2.3.2    Sampling without Replacement and with Ordering

Suppose we choose $k$ objects in succession without replacement from a population $A$ of $n$ distinct objects. Clearly, $k \leq n$. The number of possible outcomes in the first draw is $n_1 = n$; the number of possible outcomes in the second draw is $n_2 = n - 1$, namely all $n$ objects except the one selected in the first draw; and so on, up to $n_k = n - (k - 1)$ in the final draw. Equation (2.19) then gives

$$\text{number of distinct ordered } k\text{-tuples} = n(n - 1)\dots(n - k + 1). \qquad (2.21)$$

---

**TABLE 2.1**   Enumeration of possible outcomes in various types of sampling of two balls from an urn containing five distinct balls.

---

(a) Ordered pairs for sampling with replacement.

| | | | | |
|---|---|---|---|---|
| (1, 1) | (1, 2) | (1, 3) | (1, 4) | (1, 5) |
| (2, 1) | (2, 2) | (2, 3) | (2, 4) | (2, 5) |
| (3, 1) | (3, 2) | (3, 3) | (3, 4) | (3, 5) |
| (4, 1) | (4, 2) | (4, 3) | (4, 4) | (4, 5) |
| (5, 1) | (5, 2) | (5, 3) | (5, 4) | (5, 5) |

(b) Ordered pairs for sampling without replacement.

| | | | | |
|---|---|---|---|---|
| | (1, 2) | (1, 3) | (1, 4) | (1, 5) |
| (2, 1) | | (2, 3) | (2, 4) | (2, 5) |
| (3, 1) | (3, 2) | | (3, 4) | (3, 5) |
| (4, 1) | (4, 2) | (4, 3) | | (4, 5) |
| (5, 1) | (5, 2) | (5, 3) | (5, 4) | |

(c) Pairs for sampling without replacement or ordering.

| | | | |
|---|---|---|---|
| (1, 2) | (1, 3) | (1, 4) | (1, 5) |
| | (2, 3) | (2, 4) | (2, 5) |
| | | (3, 4) | (3, 5) |
| | | | (4, 5) |

---

## Example 2.16

An urn contains five balls numbered 1 to 5. Suppose we select two balls in succession without replacement. How many distinct *ordered* pairs are possible? What is the probability that the first ball has a number larger than that of the second ball?

Equation (2.21) states that the number of ordered pairs is $5(4) = 20$. The 20 possible ordered pairs are shown in Table 2.1(b). Ten ordered pairs in Tab. 2.1(b) have the first number larger than the second number; thus the probability of this event is $10/20 = 1/2$.

---

## Example 2.17

An urn contains five balls numbered $1, 2, \ldots, 5$. Suppose we draw three balls with replacement. What is the probability that all three balls are different?

From Eq. (2.20) there are $5^3 = 125$ possible outcomes, which we will suppose are equiprobable. The number of these outcomes for which the three draws are different is given by Eq. (2.21): $5(4)(3) = 60$. Thus the probability that all three balls are different is $60/125 = .48$.

---

### 2.3.3   Permutations of *n* Distinct Objects

Consider sampling without replacement with $k = n$. This is simply drawing objects from an urn containing $n$ distinct objects until the urn is empty. Thus, the number of possible orderings (arrangements, permutations) of $n$ distinct objects is equal to the number of ordered $n$-tuples in sampling without replacement with $k = n$. From Eq. (2.21), we have

$$\text{number of permutations of } n \text{ objects} = n(n - 1)\ldots(2)(1) \triangleq n!. \qquad (2.22)$$

We refer to $n!$ as **$n$ factorial**.

We will see that $n!$ appears in many of the combinatorial formulas. For large $n$, **Stirling's formula** is very useful:

$$n! \sim \sqrt{2\pi}\, n^{n+1/2}e^{-n}, \qquad (2.23)$$

where the sign $\sim$ indicates that the ratio of the two sides tends to unity as $n \to \infty$ [Feller, p. 52].

---

### Example 2.18

Find the number of permutations of three distinct objects $\{1, 2, 3\}$. Equation (2.22) gives $3! = 3(2)(1) = 6$. The six permutations are

$$123 \quad 312 \quad 231 \quad 132 \quad 213 \quad 321.$$

---

### Example 2.19

Suppose that 12 balls are placed at random into 12 cells, where more than 1 ball is allowed to occupy a cell. What is the probability that all cells are occupied?

The placement of each ball into a cell can be viewed as the selection of a cell number between 1 and 12. Equation (2.20) implies that there are $12^{12}$ possible placements of the 12 balls in the 12 cells. In order for all cells to be occupied, the first ball selects from any of the 12 cells, the second ball from the remaining 11 cells, and so on. Thus the number of placements that occupy all cells is $12!$. If we suppose that all $12^{12}$ possible placements are equiprobable, we find that the probability that all cells are occupied is

$$\frac{12!}{12^{12}} = \left(\frac{12}{12}\right)\left(\frac{11}{12}\right)\ldots\left(\frac{1}{12}\right) = 5.37(10^{-5}).$$

This answer is surprising if we reinterpret the question as follows. Given that 12 airplane crashes occur at random in a year, what is the probability that there is exactly 1 crash each month? The above result shows that this probability is very small. Thus a model that assumes that crashes occur randomly in time does *not* predict that they tend to occur uniformly over time [Feller, p. 32].

---

## 2.3.4  Sampling without Replacement and without Ordering

Suppose we pick $k$ objects from a set of $n$ distinct objects without replacement and that we record the result without regard to order. (You can imagine putting each selected object into another jar, so that when the $k$ selections are completed we have no record of the order in which the selection was done.) We call the resulting subset of $k$ selected objects a "combination of size $k$."

From Eq. (2.22), there are $k!$ possible orders in which the $k$ objects in the second jar could have been selected. Thus if $C_k^n$ denotes the number of combinations of size $k$

from a set of size $n$, then $C_k^n k!$ must be the total number of distinct ordered samples of $k$ objects, which is given by Eq. (2.21). Thus

$$C_k^n k! = n(n-1)\dots(n-k+1), \tag{2.24}$$

and the *number of different combinations of size k from a set of size n, $k \le n$, is*

$$C_k^n = \frac{n(n-1)\dots(n-k+1)}{k!} = \frac{n!}{k!\,(n-k)!} \triangleq \binom{n}{k}. \tag{2.25}$$

The expression $\binom{n}{k}$ is called a **binomial coefficient** and is read "$n$ choose $k$."

Note that choosing $k$ objects out of a set of $n$ is equivalent to choosing the $n - k$ objects that are to be left out. It then follows that (also see Problem 2.60):

$$\binom{n}{k} = \binom{n}{n-k}.$$

---

### Example 2.20

Find the number of ways of selecting two objects from $A = \{1, 2, 3, 4, 5\}$ without regard to order.
    Equation (2.25) gives

$$\binom{5}{2} = \frac{5!}{2!\,3!} = 10.$$

Table 2.1(c) gives the 10 pairs.

---

### Example 2.21

Find the number of distinct permutations of $k$ white balls and $n - k$ black balls.
    This problem is equivalent to the following sampling problem: Put $n$ tokens numbered 1 to $n$ in an urn, where each token represents a position in the arrangement of balls; pick a combination of $k$ tokens and put the $k$ white balls in the corresponding positions. Each combination of size $k$ leads to a distinct arrangement (permutation) of $k$ white balls and $n - k$ black balls. Thus the number of distinct permutations of $k$ white balls and $n - k$ black balls is $C_k^n$.
    As a specific example let $n = 4$ and $k = 2$. The number of combinations of size 2 from a set of four distinct objects is

$$\binom{4}{2} = \frac{4!}{2!\,2!} = \frac{4(3)}{2(1)} = 6.$$

The 6 distinct permutations with 2 whites (zeros) and 2 blacks (ones) are

$$1100 \quad 0110 \quad 0011 \quad 1001 \quad 1010 \quad 0101.$$

---

### Example 2.22    Quality Control

A batch of 50 items contains 10 defective items. Suppose 10 items are selected at random and tested. What is the probability that exactly 5 of the items tested are defective?

The number of ways of selecting 10 items out of a batch of 50 is the number of combinations of size 10 from a set of 50 objects:

$$\binom{50}{10} = \frac{50!}{10!\,40!}.$$

The number of ways of selecting 5 defective and 5 nondefective items from the batch of 50 is the product $N_1 N_2$, where $N_1$ is the number of ways of selecting the 5 items from the set of 10 defective items, and $N_2$ is the number of ways of selecting 5 items from the 40 nondefective items. Thus the probability that exactly 5 tested items are defective is

$$\frac{\binom{10}{5}\binom{40}{5}}{\binom{50}{10}} = \frac{10!\,40!\,10!\,40!}{5!\,5!\,35!\,5!\,50!} = .016.$$

---

Example 2.21 shows that sampling without replacement and without ordering is equivalent to partitioning the set of $n$ distinct objects into two sets: $B$, containing the $k$ items that are picked from the urn, and $B^c$, containing the $n - k$ left behind. Suppose we partition a set of $n$ distinct objects into $\mathcal{J}$ subsets $B_1, B_2, \ldots, B_{\mathcal{J}}$, where $B_{\mathcal{J}}$ is assigned $k_{\mathcal{J}}$ elements and $k_1 + k_2 + \cdots + k_{\mathcal{J}} = n$.

In Problem 2.61, it is shown that the number of distinct partitions is

$$\frac{n!}{k_1!\,k_2!\ldots k_{\mathcal{J}}!}. \tag{2.26}$$

Equation (2.26) is called the **multinomial coefficient**. The binomial coefficient is the $\mathcal{J} = 2$ case of the multinomial coefficient.

---

### Example 2.23

A six-sided die is tossed 12 times. How many distinct sequences of faces (numbers from the set $\{1, 2, 3, 4, 5, 6\}$) have each number appearing exactly twice? What is the probability of obtaining such a sequence?

The number of distinct sequences in which each face of the die appears exactly twice is the same as the number of partitions of the set $\{1, 2, \ldots, 12\}$ into 6 subsets of size 2, namely

$$\frac{12!}{2!\,2!\,2!\,2!\,2!\,2!} = \frac{12!}{2^6} = 7{,}484{,}400.$$

From Eq. (2.20) we have that there are $6^{12}$ possible outcomes in 12 tosses of a die. If we suppose that all of these have equal probabilities, then the probability of obtaining a sequence in which each face appears exactly twice is

$$\frac{12!/2^6}{6^{12}} = \frac{7{,}484{,}400}{2{,}176{,}782{,}336} \simeq 3.4(10^{-3}).$$

---

## 2.3.5 Sampling with Replacement and without Ordering

Suppose we pick $k$ objects from a set of $n$ distinct objects with replacement and we record the result without regard to order. This can be done by filling out a form which has $n$ columns, one for each distinct object. Each time an object is selected, an "x" is placed in the corresponding column. For example, if we are picking 5 objects from 4 distinct objects, one possible form would look like this:

| *Object 1* | | *Object 2* | | *Object 3* | | *Object 4* |
|---|---|---|---|---|---|---|
| xx | / | | / | x | / | xx |

where the slash symbol ("/") is used to separate the entries for different columns. Note that this form can be summarized by the sequence

$$\text{xx//x/xx}$$

where the $n - 1$ /'s indicate the lines between columns, and where nothing appears between consecutive /'s if the corresponding object was not selected. Each different arrangement of 5 x's and 3 /'s leads to a distinct form. If we identify x's with "white balls" and /'s with "black balls," then this problem was considered in Example 2.21, and the number of different arrangements is given by $\binom{8}{3}$.

In the general case the form will involve $k$ x's and $n - 1$ /'s. Thus the *number of different ways of picking $k$ objects from a set of $n$ distinct objects with replacement and without ordering* is given by

$$\binom{n - 1 + k}{k} = \binom{n - 1 + k}{n - 1}.$$

## 2.4 CONDITIONAL PROBABILITY

Quite often we are interested in determining whether two events, $A$ and $B$, are related in the sense that knowledge about the occurrence of one, say $B$, alters the likelihood of occurrence of the other, $A$. This requires that we find the **conditional probability**, $P[A \mid B]$, of event $A$ given that event $B$ has occurred. The conditional probability is defined by

$$P[A \mid B] = \frac{P[A \cap B]}{P[B]} \qquad \text{for } P[B] > 0. \tag{2.27}$$

Knowledge that event $B$ has occurred implies that the outcome of the experiment is in the set $B$. In computing $P[A \mid B]$ we can therefore view the experiment as now having the reduced sample space $B$ as shown in Fig. 2.9. The event $A$ occurs in the reduced sample space if and only if the outcome $\zeta$ is in $A \cap B$. Equation (2.27) simply renormalizes the probability of events that occur jointly with $B$. Thus if we let $A = B$, Eq. (2.27) gives $P[B \mid B] = 1$, as required. It is easy to show that $P[A \mid B]$, for fixed $B$, satisfies the axioms of probability. (See Problem 2.74.)

If we interpret probability as relative frequency, then $P[A \mid B]$ should be the relative frequency of the event $A \cap B$ in experiments where $B$ occurred. Suppose that the experiment is performed $n$ times, and suppose that event $B$ occurs $n_B$ times, and that

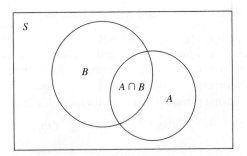

**FIGURE 2.9**
If $B$ is known to have occurred, then $A$ can occur only
if $A \cap B$ occurs.

event $A \cap B$ occurs $n_{A \cap B}$ times. The relative frequency of interest is then

$$\frac{n_{A \cap B}}{n_B} = \frac{n_{A \cap B}/n}{n_B/n} \rightarrow \frac{P[A \cap B]}{P[B]},$$

where we have implicitly assumed that $P[B] > 0$. This is in agreement with Eq. (2.27).

---

**Example 2.24**

A ball is selected from an urn containing two black balls, numbered 1 and 2, and two white balls, numbered 3 and 4. The number and color of the ball is noted, so the sample space is $\{(1, b), (2, b), (3, w), (4, w)\}$. Assuming that the four outcomes are equally likely, find $P[A \mid B]$ and $P[A \mid C]$, where $A, B,$ and $C$ are the following events:

$A = \{(1, b), (2, b)\}$, "black ball selected,"

$B = \{(2, b), (4, w)\}$, "even-numbered ball selected," and

$C = \{(3, w), (4, w)\}$, "number of ball is greater than 2."

Since $P[A \cap B] = P[(2, b)]$ and $P[A \cap C] = P[\varnothing] = 0$, Eq. (2.24) gives

$$P[A \mid B] = \frac{P[A \cap B]}{P[B]} = \frac{.25}{.5} = .5 = P[A]$$

$$P[A \mid C] = \frac{P[A \cap C]}{P[C]} = \frac{0}{.5} = 0 \neq P[A].$$

In the first case, knowledge of $B$ did not alter the probability of $A$. In the second case, knowledge of $C$ implied that $A$ had not occurred.

---

If we multiply both sides of the definition of $P[A \mid B]$ by $P[B]$ we obtain

$$P[A \cap B] = P[A \mid B]P[B]. \tag{2.28a}$$

Similarly we also have that

$$P[A \cap B] = P[B \mid A]P[A]. \tag{2.28b}$$

In the next example we show how this equation is useful in finding probabilities in sequential experiments. The example also introduces a **tree diagram** that facilitates the calculation of probabilities.

---

**Example 2.25**

An urn contains two black balls and three white balls. Two balls are selected at random from the urn without replacement and the sequence of colors is noted. Find the probability that both balls are black.

This experiment consists of a sequence of two subexperiments. We can imagine working our way down the tree shown in Fig. 2.10 from the topmost node to one of the bottom nodes: We reach node 1 in the tree if the outcome of the first draw is a black ball; then the next subexperiment consists of selecting a ball from an urn containing one black ball and three white balls. On the other hand, if the outcome of the first draw is white, then we reach node 2 in the tree and the second subexperiment consists of selecting a ball from an urn that contains two black balls and two white balls. Thus if we know which node is reached after the first draw, then we can state the probabilities of the outcome in the next subexperiment.

Let $B_1$ and $B_2$ be the events that the outcome is a black ball in the first and second draw, respectively. From Eq. (2.28b) we have

$$P[B_1 \cap B_2] = P[B_2 \mid B_1]P[B_1].$$

In terms of the tree diagram in Fig. 2.10, $P[B_1]$ is the probability of reaching node 1 and $P[B_2 \mid B_1]$ is the probability of reaching the leftmost bottom node from node 1. Now $P[B_1] = 2/5$ since the first draw is from an urn containing two black balls and three white balls; $P[B_2 \mid B_1] = 1/4$ since, given $B_1$, the second draw is from an urn containing one black ball and three white balls. Thus

$$P[B_1 \cap B_2] = \frac{1}{4}\frac{2}{5} = \frac{1}{10}.$$

In general, the probability of any sequence of colors is obtained by multiplying the probabilities corresponding to the node transitions in the tree in Fig. 2.10.

---

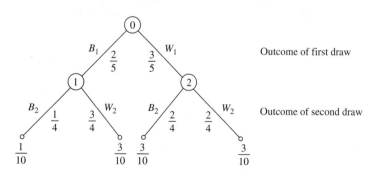

**FIGURE 2.10**

The paths from the top node to a bottom node correspond to the possible outcomes in the drawing of two balls from an urn without replacement. The probability of a path is the product of the probabilities in the associated transitions.

### Example 2.26   Binary Communication System

Many communication systems can be modeled in the following way. First, the user inputs a 0 or a 1 into the system, and a corresponding signal is transmitted. Second, the receiver makes a decision about what was the input to the system, based on the signal it received. Suppose that the user sends 0s with probability $1 - p$ and 1s with probability $p$, and suppose that the receiver makes random decision errors with probability $\varepsilon$. For $i = 0, 1$, let $A_i$ be the event "input was $i$," and let $B_i$ be the event "receiver decision was $i$." Find the probabilities $P[A_i \cap B_j]$ for $i = 0, 1$ and $j = 0, 1$.

The tree diagram for this experiment is shown in Fig. 2.11. We then readily obtain the desired probabilities

$$P[A_0 \cap B_0] = (1 - p)(1 - \varepsilon),$$

$$P[A_0 \cap B_1] = (1 - p)\varepsilon,$$

$$P[A_1 \cap B_0] = p\varepsilon, \text{ and}$$

$$P[A_1 \cap B_1] = p(1 - \varepsilon).$$

---

Let $B_1, B_2, \ldots, B_n$ be mutually exclusive events whose union equals the sample space $S$ as shown in Fig. 2.12. We refer to these sets as a **partition** of $S$. Any event $A$ can be represented as the union of mutually exclusive events in the following way:

$$A = A \cap S = A \cap (B_1 \cup B_2 \cup \cdots \cup B_n)$$

$$= (A \cap B_1) \cup (A \cap B_2) \cup \cdots \cup (A \cap B_n).$$

(See Fig. 2.12.) By Corollary 4, the probability of $A$ is

$$P[A] = P[A \cap B_1] + P[A \cap B_2] + \cdots + P[A \cap B_n].$$

By applying Eq. (2.28a) to each of the terms on the right-hand side, we obtain the **theorem on total probability**:

$$P[A] = P[A \mid B_1]P[B_1] + P[A \mid B_2]P[B_2] + \cdots + P[A \mid B_n]P[B_n]. \qquad (2.29)$$

This result is particularly useful when the experiments can be viewed as consisting of a sequence of two subexperiments as shown in the tree diagram in Fig. 2.10.

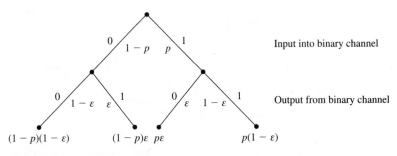

**FIGURE 2.11**
Probabilities of input-output pairs in a binary transmission system.

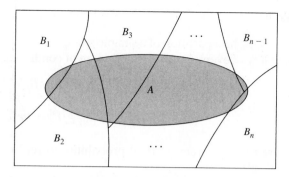

**FIGURE 2.12**
A partition of $S$ into $n$ disjoint sets.

---

### Example 2.27

In the experiment discussed in Example 2.25, find the probability of the event $W_2$ that the second ball is white.

The events $B_1 = \{(b, b), (b, w)\}$ and $W_1 = \{(w, b), (w, w)\}$ form a partition of the sample space, so applying Eq. (2.29) we have

$$P[W_2] = P[W_2 | B_1]P[B_1] + P[W_2 | W_1]P[W_1]$$

$$= \frac{3}{4}\frac{2}{5} + \frac{1}{2}\frac{3}{5} = \frac{3}{5}.$$

It is interesting to note that this is the same as the probability of selecting a white ball in the first draw. The result makes sense because we are computing the probability of a white ball in the second draw under the assumption that we have no knowledge of the outcome of the first draw.

---

### Example 2.28

A manufacturing process produces a mix of "good" memory chips and "bad" memory chips. The lifetime of good chips follows the exponential law introduced in Example 2.13, with a rate of failure $\alpha$. The lifetime of bad chips also follows the exponential law, but the rate of failure is $1000\alpha$. Suppose that the fraction of good chips is $1 - p$ and of bad chips, $p$. Find the probability that a randomly selected chip is still functioning after $t$ seconds.

Let $C$ be the event "chip still functioning after $t$ seconds," and let $G$ be the event "chip is good," and $B$ the event "chip is bad." By the theorem on total probability we have

$$P[C] = P[C|G]P[G] + P[C|B]P[B]$$

$$= P[C|G](1 - p) + P[C|B]p$$

$$= (1 - p)e^{-\alpha t} + pe^{-1000\alpha t},$$

where we used the fact that $P[C|G] = e^{-\alpha t}$ and $P[C|B] = e^{-1000\alpha t}$.

### 2.4.1 Bayes' Rule

Let $B_1, B_2, \ldots, B_n$ be a partition of a sample space $S$. Suppose that event $A$ occurs; what is the probability of event $B_j$? By the definition of conditional probability we have

$$P[B_j|A] = \frac{P[A \cap B_j]}{P[A]} = \frac{P[A|B_j]P[B_j]}{\sum_{k=1}^{n} P[A|B_k]P[B_k]}, \tag{2.30}$$

where we used the theorem on total probability to replace $P[A]$. Equation (2.30) is called **Bayes' rule**.

Bayes' rule is often applied in the following situation. We have some random experiment in which the events of interest form a partition. The "a priori probabilities" of these events, $P[B_j]$, are the probabilities of the events before the experiment is performed. Now suppose that the experiment is performed, and we are informed that event $A$ occurred; the "a posteriori probabilities" are the probabilities of the events in the partition, $P[B_j|A]$, given this additional information. The following two examples illustrate this situation.

---

### Example 2.29 Binary Communication System

In the binary communication system in Example 2.26, find which input is more probable given that the receiver has output a 1. Assume that, a priori, the input is equally likely to be 0 or 1.

Let $A_k$ be the event that the input was $k, k = 0, 1$, then $A_0$ and $A_1$ are a partition of the sample space of input-output pairs. Let $B_1$ be the event "receiver output was a 1." The probability of $B_1$ is

$$P[B_1] = P[B_1|A_0]P[A_0] + P[B_1|A_1]P[A_1]$$

$$= \varepsilon\left(\frac{1}{2}\right) + (1 - \varepsilon)\left(\frac{1}{2}\right) = \frac{1}{2}.$$

Applying Bayes' rule, we obtain the a posteriori probabilities

$$P[A_0|B_1] = \frac{P[B_1|A_0]P[A_0]}{P[B_1]} = \frac{\varepsilon/2}{1/2} = \varepsilon$$

$$P[A_1|B_1] = \frac{P[B_1|A_1]P[A_1]}{P[B_1]} = \frac{(1 - \varepsilon)/2}{1/2} = (1 - \varepsilon).$$

Thus, if $\varepsilon$ is less than 1/2, then input 1 is more likely than input 0 when a 1 is observed at the output of the channel.

---

### Example 2.30 Quality Control

Consider the memory chips discussed in Example 2.28. Recall that a fraction $p$ of the chips are bad and tend to fail much more quickly than good chips. Suppose that in order to "weed out" the bad chips, every chip is tested for $t$ seconds prior to leaving the factory. The chips that fail are discarded and the remaining chips are sent out to customers. Find the value of $t$ for which 99% of the chips sent out to customers are good.

Let $C$ be the event "chip still functioning after $t$ seconds," and let $G$ be the event "chip is good," and $B$ be the event "chip is bad." The problem requires that we find the value of $t$ for which

$$P[G|C] = .99.$$

We find $P[G|C]$ by applying Bayes' rule:

$$P[G|C] = \frac{P[C|G]P[G]}{P[C|G]P[G] + P[C|B]P[B]}$$

$$= \frac{(1 - p)e^{-\alpha t}}{(1 - p)e^{-\alpha t} + pe^{-\alpha 1000t}}$$

$$= \frac{1}{1 + \dfrac{pe^{-\alpha 1000t}}{(1 - p)e^{-\alpha t}}} = .99.$$

The above equation can then be solved for $t$:

$$t = \frac{1}{999\alpha} \ln\left(\frac{99p}{1 - p}\right).$$

For example, if $1/\alpha = 20{,}000$ hours and $p = .10$, then $t = 48$ hours.

---

## 2.5   INDEPENDENCE OF EVENTS

If knowledge of the occurrence of an event $B$ does not alter the probability of some other event $A$, then it would be natural to say that event $A$ is independent of $B$. In terms of probabilities this situation occurs when

$$P[A] = P[A|B] = \frac{P[A \cap B]}{P[B]}.$$

The above equation has the problem that the right-hand side is not defined when $P[B] = 0$.

We will define two events $A$ and $B$ to be **independent** if

$$P[A \cap B] = P[A]P[B]. \tag{2.31}$$

Equation (2.31) then implies both

$$P[A|B] = P[A] \tag{2.32a}$$

and

$$P[B|A] = P[B] \tag{2.32b}$$

Note also that Eq. (2.32a) implies Eq. (2.31) when $P[B] \neq 0$ and Eq. (2.32b) implies Eq. (2.31) when $P[A] \neq 0$.

**Example 2.31**

A ball is selected from an urn containing two black balls, numbered 1 and 2, and two white balls, numbered 3 and 4. Let the events $A, B,$ and $C$ be defined as follows:

$A = \{(1, b), (2, b)\}$, "black ball selected";

$B = \{(2, b), (4, w)\}$, "even-numbered ball selected"; and

$C = \{(3, w), (4, w)\}$, "number of ball is greater than 2."

Are events $A$ and $B$ independent? Are events $A$ and $C$ independent?

First, consider events $A$ and $B$. The probabilities required by Eq. (2.31) are

$$P[A] = P[B] = \frac{1}{2},$$

and

$$P[A \cap B] = P[\{(2, b)\}] = \frac{1}{4}.$$

Thus

$$P[A \cap B] = \frac{1}{4} = P[A]P[B],$$

and the events $A$ and $B$ are independent. Equation (2.32b) gives more insight into the meaning of independence:

$$P[A|B] = \frac{P[A \cap B]}{P[B]} = \frac{P[\{(2, b)\}]}{P[\{(2, b), (4, w)\}]} = \frac{1/4}{1/2} = \frac{1}{2}$$

$$P[A] = \frac{P[A]}{P[S]} = \frac{P[\{(1, b), (2, b)\}]}{P[\{(1, b), (2, b), (3, w), (4, w)\}]} = \frac{1/2}{1}.$$

These two equations imply that $P[A] = P[A|B]$ because *the proportion of outcomes in S that lead to the occurrence of A is equal to the proportion of outcomes in B that lead to A.* Thus knowledge of the occurrence of $B$ does not alter the probability of the occurrence of $A$.

Events $A$ and $C$ are not independent since $P[A \cap C] = P[\varnothing] = 0$ so

$$P[A|C] = 0 \neq P[A] = .5.$$

In fact, $A$ and $C$ are mutually exclusive since $A \cap C = \varnothing$, so the occurrence of $C$ implies that $A$ has definitely not occurred.

---

In general if two events have nonzero probability and are mutually exclusive, then they cannot be independent. For suppose they were independent *and* mutually exclusive; then

$$0 = P[A \cap B] = P[A]P[B],$$

which implies that at least one of the events must have zero probability.

**Example 2.32**

Two numbers $x$ and $y$ are selected at random between zero and one. Let the events $A$, $B$, and $C$ be defined as follows:

$$A = \{x > 0.5\}, \qquad B = \{y > 0.5\}, \qquad \text{and } C = \{x > y\}.$$

Are the events $A$ and $B$ independent? Are $A$ and $C$ independent?

    Figure 2.13 shows the regions of the unit square that correspond to the above events. Using Eq. (2.32a), we have

$$P[A|B] = \frac{P[A \cap B]}{P[B]} = \frac{1/4}{1/2} = \frac{1}{2} = P[A],$$

so events $A$ and $B$ are independent. Again we have that the "proportion" of outcomes in $S$ leading to $A$ is equal to the "proportion" in $B$ that lead to $A$.

    Using Eq. (2.32b), we have

$$P[A|C] = \frac{P[A \cap C]}{P[C]} = \frac{3/8}{1/2} = \frac{3}{4} \neq \frac{1}{2} = P[A],$$

so events $A$ and $C$ are not independent. Indeed from Fig. 2.13(b) we can see that knowledge of the fact that $x$ is greater than $y$ increases the probability that $x$ is greater than 0.5.

---

    What conditions should three events $A$, $B$, and $C$ satisfy in order for them to be independent? First, they should be pairwise independent, that is,

$$P[A \cap B] = P[A]P[B], P[A \cap C] = P[A]P[C], \text{ and } P[B \cap C] = P[B]P[C].$$

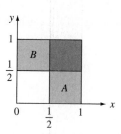

(a) Events $A$ and $B$ are independent.

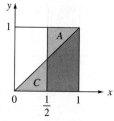

(b) Events $A$ and $C$ are not independent.

**FIGURE 2.13**
Examples of independent and nonindependent events.

In addition, knowledge of the joint occurrence of any two, say $A$ and $B$, should not affect the probability of the third, that is,

$$P[C|A \cap B] = P[C].$$

In order for this to hold, we must have

$$P[C|A \cap B] = \frac{P[A \cap B \cap C]}{P[A \cap B]} = P[C].$$

This in turn implies that we must have

$$P[A \cap B \cap C] = P[A \cap B]P[C] = P[A]P[B]P[C],$$

where we have used the fact that $A$ and $B$ are pairwise independent. Thus we conclude that *three events A, B, and C are independent if the probability of the intersection of any pair or triplet of events is equal to the product of the probabilities of the individual events.*

The following example shows that if three events are pairwise independent, it does not necessarily follow that $P[A \cap B \cap C] = P[A]P[B]P[C]$.

---

**Example 2.33**

Consider the experiment discussed in Example 2.32 where two numbers are selected at random from the unit interval. Let the events $B$, $D$, and $F$ be defined as follows:

$$B = \left\{ y > \frac{1}{2} \right\}, \qquad D = \left\{ x < \frac{1}{2} \right\}$$

$$F = \left\{ x < \frac{1}{2} \text{ and } y < \frac{1}{2} \right\} \cup \left\{ x > \frac{1}{2} \text{ and } y > \frac{1}{2} \right\}.$$

The three events are shown in Fig. 2.14. It can be easily verified that any pair of these events is independent:

$$P[B \cap D] = \frac{1}{4} = P[B]P[D],$$

$$P[B \cap F] = \frac{1}{4} = P[B]P[F], \text{ and}$$

$$P[D \cap F] = \frac{1}{4} = P[D]P[F].$$

However, the three events are not independent, since $B \cap D \cap F = \varnothing$, so

$$P[B \cap D \cap F] = P[\varnothing] = 0 \neq P[B]P[D]P[F] = \frac{1}{8}.$$

---

In order for a set of $n$ events to be independent, the probability of an event should be unchanged when we are given the joint occurrence of any subset of the other events. This requirement naturally leads to the following definition of independence. *The events $A_1, A_2, \ldots, A_n$ are said to be **independent** if for $k = 2, \ldots, n$,*

$$P[A_{i_1} \cap A_{i_2} \cap \cdots \cap A_{i_k}] = P[A_{i_1}]P[A_{i_2}] \ldots P[A_{i_k}], \qquad (2.33)$$

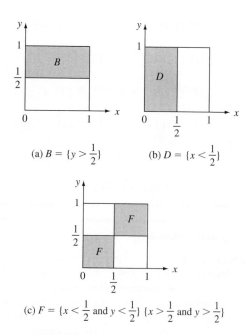

**FIGURE 2.14**

Events $B$, $D$, and $F$ are pairwise independent, but the triplet $B$, $D$, $F$ are not independent events.

where $1 \leq i_1 < i_2 < \cdots < i_k \leq n$. For a set of $n$ events we need to verify that the probabilities of all $2^n - n - 1$ possible intersections factor in the right way.

The above definition of independence appears quite cumbersome because it requires that so many conditions be verified. However, the most common application of the independence concept is in making the assumption that the events of separate experiments are independent. We refer to such experiments as **independent experiments**. For example, it is common to assume that the outcome of a coin toss is independent of the outcomes of all prior and all subsequent coin tosses.

## Example 2.34

Suppose a fair coin is tossed three times and we observe the resulting sequence of heads and tails. Find the probability of the elementary events.

The sample space of this experiment is $S = \{$HHH, HHT, HTH, THH, TTH, THT, HTT, TTT$\}$. The assumption that the coin is fair means that the outcomes of a single toss are equiprobable, that is, $P[\text{H}] = P[\text{T}] = 1/2$. If we assume that the outcomes of the coin tosses are independent, then

$$P[\{\text{HHH}\}] = P[\{\text{H}\}]P[\{\text{H}\}]P[\{\text{H}\}] = \frac{1}{8},$$

$$P[\{\text{HHT}\}] = P[\{\text{H}\}]P[\{\text{H}\}]P[\{\text{T}\}] = \frac{1}{8},$$

$$P[\{HTH\}] = P[\{H\}]P[\{T\}]P[\{H\}] = \frac{1}{8},$$

$$P[\{THH\}] = P[\{T\}]P[\{H\}]P[\{H\}] = \frac{1}{8},$$

$$P[\{TTH\}] = P[\{T\}]P[\{T\}]P[\{H\}] = \frac{1}{8},$$

$$P[\{THT\}] = P[\{T\}]P[\{H\}]P[\{T\}] = \frac{1}{8},$$

$$P[\{HTT\}] = P[\{H\}]P[\{T\}]P[\{T\}] = \frac{1}{8}, \text{ and}$$

$$P[\{TTT\}] = P[\{T\}]P[\{T\}]P[\{T\}] = \frac{1}{8}.$$

---

### Example 2.35    System Reliability

A system consists of a controller and three peripheral units. The system is said to be "up" if the controller and at least two of the peripherals are functioning. Find the probability that the system is up, assuming that all components fail independently.

Define the following events: $A$ is "controller is functioning" and $B_i$ is "peripheral $i$ is functioning" where $i = 1, 2, 3$. The event $F$, "two or more peripheral units are functioning," occurs if all three units are functioning or if exactly two units are functioning. Thus

$$F = (B_1 \cap B_2 \cap B_3^c) \cup (B_1 \cap B_2^c \cap B_3)$$

$$\cup (B_1^c \cap B_2 \cap B_3) \cup (B_1 \cap B_2 \cap B_3).$$

Note that the events in the above union are mutually exclusive. Thus

$$P[F] = P[B_1]P[B_2]P[B_3^c] + P[B_1]P[B_2^c]P[B_3]$$

$$+ P[B_1^c]P[B_2]P[B_3] + P[B_1]P[B_2]P[B_3]$$

$$= 3(1 - a)^2 a + (1 - a)^3,$$

where we have assumed that each peripheral fails with probability $a$, so that $P[B_i] = 1 - a$ and $P[B_i^c] = a$.

The event "system is up" is then $A \cap F$. If we assume that the controller fails with probability $p$, then

$$P[\text{"system up"}] = P[A \cap F] = P[A]P[F]$$

$$= (1 - p)P[F]$$

$$= (1 - p)\{3(1 - a)^2 a + (1 - a)^3\}.$$

Let $a = 10\%$, then all three peripherals are functioning $(1 - a)^3 = 72.9\%$ of the time and two are functioning and one is "down" $3(1 - a)^2 a = 24.3\%$ of the time. Thus two or more peripherals are functioning 97.2% of the time. Suppose that the controller is not very reliable, say $p = 20\%$, then the system is up only 77.8% of the time, mostly because of controller failures.

Suppose a second identical controller with $p = 20\%$ is added to the system, and that the system is "up" if at least one of the controllers is functioning and if two or more of the peripherals are functioning. In Problem 2.94, you are asked to show that at least one of the controllers is functioning 96% of the time, and that the system is up 93.3% of the time. This is an increase of 16% over the system with a single controller.

## 2.6    SEQUENTIAL EXPERIMENTS

Many random experiments can be viewed as sequential experiments that consist of a sequence of simpler subexperiments. These subexperiments may or may not be independent. In this section we discuss methods for obtaining the probabilities of events in sequential experiments.

### 2.6.1    Sequences of Independent Experiments

Suppose that a random experiment consists of performing experiments $E_1, E_2, \ldots, E_n$. The outcome of this experiment will then be an $n$-tuple $s = (s_1, \ldots, s_n)$, where $s_k$ is the outcome of the $k$th subexperiment. The sample space of the sequential experiment is defined as the set that contains the above $n$-tuples and is denoted by the Cartesian product of the individual sample spaces $S_1 \times S_2 \times \cdots \times S_n$.

We can usually determine, because of physical considerations, when the subexperiments are independent, in the sense that the outcome of any given subexperiment cannot affect the outcomes of the other subexperiments. Let $A_1, A_2, \ldots, A_n$ be events such that $A_k$ concerns only the outcome of the $k$th subexperiment. If the subexperiments are independent, then it is reasonable to assume that the above events $A_1, A_2, \ldots, A_n$ are independent. Thus

$$P[A_1 \cap A_2 \cap \cdots \cap A_n] = P[A_1]P[A_2]\ldots P[A_n]. \tag{2.34}$$

This expression allows us to compute all probabilities of events of the sequential experiment.

---

### Example 2.36

Suppose that 10 numbers are selected at random from the interval $[0, 1]$. Find the probability that the first 5 numbers are less than 1/4 and the last 5 numbers are greater than 1/2. Let $x_1, x_2, \ldots, x_{10}$ be the sequence of 10 numbers, then the events of interest are

$$A_k = \left\{ x_k < \frac{1}{4} \right\} \qquad \text{for } k = 1, \ldots, 5$$

$$A_k = \left\{ x_k > \frac{1}{2} \right\} \qquad \text{for } k = 6, \ldots, 10.$$

If we assume that each selection of a number is independent of the other selections, then

$$P[A_1 \cap A_2 \cap \cdots \cap A_{10}] = P[A_1]P[A_2]\ldots P[A_{10}]$$

$$= \left(\frac{1}{4}\right)^5 \left(\frac{1}{2}\right)^5.$$

---

We will now derive several important models for experiments that consist of sequences of independent subexperiments.

### 2.6.2    The Binomial Probability Law

A **Bernoulli trial** involves performing an experiment once and noting whether a particular event $A$ occurs. The outcome of the Bernoulli trial is said to be a "success" if $A$ occurs and a "failure" otherwise. In this section we are interested in finding the probability of $k$ successes in $n$ independent repetitions of a Bernoulli trial.

We can view the outcome of a single Bernoulli trial as the outcome of a toss of a coin for which the probability of heads (success) is $p = P[A]$. The probability of $k$ successes in $n$ Bernoulli trials is then equal to the probability of $k$ heads in $n$ tosses of the coin.

---

### Example 2.37

Suppose that a coin is tossed three times. If we assume that the *tosses are independent* and the probability of heads is $p$, then the probability for the sequences of heads and tails is

$$P[\{HHH\}] = P[\{H\}]P[\{H\}]P[\{H\}] = p^3,$$

$$P[\{HHT\}] = P[\{H\}]P[\{H\}]P[\{T\}] = p^2(1 - p),$$

$$P[\{HTH\}] = P[\{H\}]P[\{T\}]P[\{H\}] = p^2(1 - p),$$

$$P[\{THH\}] = P[\{T\}]P[\{H\}]P[\{H\}] = p^2(1 - p),$$

$$P[\{TTH\}] = P[\{T\}]P[\{T\}]P[\{H\}] = p(1 - p)^2,$$

$$P[\{THT\}] = P[\{T\}]P[\{H\}]P[\{T\}] = p(1 - p)^2,$$

$$P[\{HTT\}] = P[\{H\}]P[\{T\}]P[\{T\}] = p(1 - p)^2, \text{ and}$$

$$P[\{TTT\}] = P[\{T\}]P[\{T\}]P[\{T\}] = (1 - p)^3$$

where we used the fact that the tosses are independent. Let $k$ be the number of heads in three trials, then

$$P[k = 0] = P[\{TTT\}] = (1 - p)^3,$$

$$P[k = 1] = P[\{TTH, THT, HTT\}] = 3p(1 - p)^2,$$

$$P[k = 2] = P[\{HHT, HTH, THH\}] = 3p^2(1 - p), \text{ and}$$

$$P[k = 3] = P[\{HHH\}] = p^3.$$

---

The result in Example 2.37 is the $n = 3$ case of the binomial probability law.

---

### Theorem

Let $k$ be the number of successes in $n$ independent Bernoulli trials, then the probabilities of $k$ are given by the **binomial probability law**:

$$p_n(k) = \binom{n}{k}p^k(1 - p)^{n-k} \qquad \text{for} \qquad k = 0, \ldots, n, \tag{2.35}$$

where $p_n(k)$ is the probability of $k$ successes in $n$ trials, and

$$\binom{n}{k} = \frac{n!}{k!\,(n-k)!} \tag{2.36}$$

is the binomial coefficient.

---

The term $n!$ in Eq. (2.36) is called $n$ factorial and is defined by $n! = n(n-1)\ldots$ $(2)(1)$. By definition $0!$ is equal to 1.

We now prove the above theorem. Following Example 2.34 we see that each of the sequences with $k$ successes and $n-k$ failures has the same probability, namely $p^k(1-p)^{n-k}$. Let $N_n(k)$ be the number of distinct sequences that have $k$ successes and $n-k$ failures, then

$$p_n(k) = N_n(k)p^k(1-p)^{n-k}. \tag{2.37}$$

The expression $N_n(k)$ is the number of ways of picking $k$ positions out of $n$ for the successes. It can be shown that[5]

$$N_n(k) = \binom{n}{k}. \tag{2.38}$$

The theorem follows by substituting Eq. (2.38) into Eq. (2.37).

---

### Example 2.38

Verify that Eq. (2.35) gives the probabilities found in Example 2.37.

In Example 2.37, let "toss results in heads" correspond to a "success," then

$$p_3(0) = \frac{3!}{0!\,3!}p^0(1-p)^3 = (1-p)^3,$$

$$p_3(1) = \frac{3!}{1!\,2!}p^1(1-p)^2 = 3p(1-p)^2,$$

$$p_3(2) = \frac{3!}{2!\,1!}p^2(1-p)^1 = 3p^2(1-p), \text{ and}$$

$$p_3(3) = \frac{3!}{0!\,3!}p^3(1-p)^0 = p^3,$$

which are in agreement with our previous results.

---

You were introduced to the binomial coefficient in an introductory calculus course when the **binomial theorem** was discussed:

$$(a+b)^n = \sum_{k=0}^{n}\binom{n}{k}a^k b^{n-k}. \tag{2.39a}$$

[5]See Example 2.21.

If we let $a = b = 1$, then

$$2^n = \sum_{k=0}^{n} \binom{n}{k} = \sum_{k=0}^{n} N_n(k),$$

which is in agreement with the fact that there are $2^n$ distinct possible sequences of successes and failures in $n$ trials. If we let $a = p$ and $b = 1 - p$ in Eq. (2.39a), we then obtain

$$1 = \sum_{k=0}^{n} \binom{n}{k} p^k (1 - p)^{n-k} = \sum_{k=0}^{n} p_n(k), \qquad (2.39b)$$

which confirms that the probabilities of the binomial probabilities sum to 1.

The term $n!$ grows very quickly with $n$, so numerical problems are encountered for relatively small values of $n$ if one attempts to compute $p_n(k)$ directly using Eq. (2.35). The following recursive formula avoids the direct evaluation of $n!$ and thus extends the range of $n$ for which $p_n(k)$ can be computed before encountering numerical difficulties:

$$p_n(k + 1) = \frac{(n - k)p}{(k + 1)(1 - p)} p_n(k). \qquad (2.40)$$

Later in the book, we present two approximations for the binomial probabilities for the case when $n$ is large.

### Example 2.39

Let $k$ be the number of active (nonsilent) speakers in a group of eight noninteracting (i.e., independent) speakers. Suppose that a speaker is active with probability 1/3. Find the probability that the number of active speakers is greater than six.

For $i = 1, \dots, 8$, let $A_i$ denote the event "$i$th speaker is active." The number of active speakers is then the number of successes in eight Bernoulli trials with $p = 1/3$. Thus the probability that more than six speakers are active is

$$P[k = 7] + P[k = 8] = \binom{8}{7}\left(\frac{1}{3}\right)^7\left(\frac{2}{3}\right) + \binom{8}{8}\left(\frac{1}{3}\right)^8$$

$$= .00244 + .00015 = .00259.$$

### Example 2.40   Error Correction Coding

A communication system transmits binary information over a channel that introduces random bit errors with probability $\varepsilon = 10^{-3}$. The transmitter transmits each information bit three times, and a decoder takes a majority vote of the received bits to decide on what the transmitted bit was. Find the probability that the receiver will make an incorrect decision.

The receiver can correct a single error, but it will make the wrong decision if the channel introduces two or more errors. If we view each transmission as a Bernoulli trial in which a "success" corresponds to the introduction of an error, then the probability of two or more errors in three Bernoulli trials is

$$P[k \geq 2] = \binom{3}{2}(.001)^2(.999) + \binom{3}{3}(.001)^3 \simeq 3(10^{-6}).$$

### 2.6.3 The Multinomial Probability Law

The binomial probability law can be generalized to the case where we note the occurrence of more than one event. Let $B_1, B_2, \ldots, B_M$ be a partition of the sample space $S$ of some random experiment and let $P[B_j] = p_j$. The events are mutually exclusive, so

$$p_1 + p_2 + \cdots + p_M = 1.$$

Suppose that $n$ independent repetitions of the experiment are performed. Let $k_j$ be the number of times event $B_j$ occurs, then the vector $(k_1, k_2, \ldots, k_M)$ specifies the number of times each of the events $B_j$ occurs. The probability of the vector $(k_1, \ldots, k_M)$ satisfies the **multinomial probability law**:

$$P[(k_1, k_2, \ldots, k_M)] = \frac{n!}{k_1!\, k_2! \ldots k_M!}\, p_1^{k_1} p_2^{k_2} \cdots p_M^{k_M}, \tag{2.41}$$

where $k_1 + k_2 + \cdots + k_M = n$. The binomial probability law is the $M = 2$ case of the multinomial probability law. The derivation of the multinomial probabilities is identical to that of the binomial probabilities. We only need to note that the number of different sequences with $k_1, k_2, \ldots, k_M$ instances of the events $B_1, B_2, \ldots, B_M$ is given by the multinomial coefficient in Eq. (2.26).

---

### Example 2.41

A dart is thrown nine times at a target consisting of three areas. Each throw has a probability of .2, .3, and .5 of landing in areas 1, 2, and 3, respectively. Find the probability that the dart lands exactly three times in each of the areas.

This experiment consists of nine independent repetitions of a subexperiment that has three possible outcomes. The probability for the number of occurrences of each outcome is given by the multinomial probabilities with parameters $n = 9$ and $p_1 = .2$, $p_2 = .3$, and $p_3 = .5$:

$$P[(3, 3, 3)] = \frac{9!}{3!\, 3!\, 3!}(.2)^3(.3)^3(.5)^3 = .04536.$$

---

### Example 2.42

Suppose we pick 10 telephone numbers at random from a telephone book and note the last digit in each of the numbers. What is the probability that we obtain each of the integers from 0 to 9 only once?

The probabilities for the number of occurrences of the integers is given by the multinomial probabilities with parameters $M = 10$, $n = 10$, and $p_j = 1/10$ if we assume that the 10 integers in the range 0 to 9 are equiprobable. The probability of obtaining each integer once in 10 draws is then

$$\frac{10!}{1!\, 1! \ldots 1!}(.1)^{10} \simeq 3.6(10^{-4}).$$

---

### 2.6.4 The Geometric Probability Law

Consider a sequential experiment in which we repeat independent Bernoulli trials until the occurrence of the first success. Let the outcome of this experiment be $m$, the number of trials carried out until the occurrence of the first success. The sample space for this experiment is the set of positive integers. The probability, $p(m)$, that $m$ trials are required is found by noting that this can only happen if the first $m - 1$ trials result in failures and the $m$th trial in success.[6] The probability of this event is

$$p(m) = P[A_1^c A_2^c \dots A_{m-1}^c A_m] = (1 - p)^{m-1} p \qquad m = 1, 2, \dots, \qquad (2.42a)$$

where $A_i$ is the event "success in $i$th trial." The probability assignment specified by Eq. (2.42a) is called the **geometric probability law**.

The probabilities in Eq. (2.42a) sum to 1:

$$\sum_{m=1}^{\infty} p(m) = p \sum_{m=1}^{\infty} q^{m-1} = p \frac{1}{1 - q} = 1, \qquad (2.42b)$$

where $q = 1 - p$, and where we have used the formula for the summation of a geometric series. The probability that more than $K$ trials are required before a success occurs has a simple form:

$$P[\{m > K\}] = p \sum_{m=K+1}^{\infty} q^{m-1} = pq^K \sum_{j=0}^{\infty} q^j$$

$$= pq^K \frac{1}{1 - q}$$

$$= q^K. \qquad (2.43)$$

---

### Example 2.43   Error Control by Retransmission

Computer $A$ sends a message to computer $B$ over an unreliable radio link. The message is encoded so that $B$ can detect when errors have been introduced into the message during transmission. If $B$ detects an error, it requests $A$ to retransmit it. If the probability of a message transmission error is $q = .1$, what is the probability that a message needs to be transmitted more than two times?

Each transmission of a message is a Bernoulli trial with probability of success $p = 1 - q$. The Bernoulli trials are repeated until the first success (error-free transmission). The probability that more than two transmissions are required is given by Eq. (2.43):

$$P[m > 2] = q^2 = 10^{-2}.$$

---

### 2.6.5   Sequences of Dependent Experiments

In this section we consider a sequence or "chain" of subexperiments in which the outcome of a given subexperiment determines which subexperiment is performed next. We first give a simple example of such an experiment and show how diagrams can be used to specify the sample space.

---

### Example 2.44

A sequential experiment involves repeatedly drawing a ball from one of two urns, noting the number on the ball, and replacing the ball in its urn. Urn 0 contains a ball with the number 1 and two balls with the number 0, and urn 1 contains five balls with the number 1 and one ball

---

[6]See Example 2.11 in Section 2.2 for a relative frequency interpretation of how the geometric probability law comes about.

with the number 0. The urn from which the first draw is made is selected at random by flipping a fair coin. Urn 0 is used if the outcome is heads and urn 1 if the outcome is tails. Thereafter the urn used in a subexperiment corresponds to the number on the ball selected in the previous subexperiment.

The sample space of this experiment consists of sequences of 0s and 1s. Each possible sequence corresponds to a path through the "trellis" diagram shown in Fig. 2.15(a). The nodes in the diagram denote the urn used in the $n$th subexperiment, and the labels in the branches denote the outcome of a subexperiment. Thus the path 0011 corresponds to the sequence: The coin toss was heads so the first draw was from urn 0; the outcome of the first draw was 0, so the second draw was from urn 0; the outcome of the second draw was 1, so the third draw was from urn 1; and the outcome from the third draw was 1, so the fourth draw is from urn 1.

Now suppose that we want to compute the probability of a particular sequence of outcomes, say $s_0, s_1, s_2$. Denote this probability by $P[\{s_0\} \cap \{s_1\} \cap \{s_2\}]$. Let $A = \{s_2\}$ and $B = \{s_0\} \cap \{s_1\}$, then since $P[A \cap B] = P[A|B]P[B]$ we have

$$P[\{s_0\} \cap \{s_1\} \cap \{s_2\}] = P[\{s_2\}|\{s_0\} \cap \{s_1\}]P[\{s_0\} \cap \{s_1\}]$$

$$= P[\{s_2\}|\{s_0\} \cap \{s_1\}]P[\{s_1\}|\{s_0\}]P[\{s_0\}]. \qquad (2.44)$$

Now note that in the above urn example the probability $P[\{s_n\}|\{s_0\} \cap \cdots \cap \{s_{n-1}\}]$ depends only on $\{s_{n-1}\}$ since the most recent outcome determines which subexperiment is performed:

$$P[\{s_n\}|\{s_0\} \cap \cdots \cap \{s_{n-1}\}] = P[\{s_n\}|\{s_{n-1}\}]. \qquad (2.45)$$

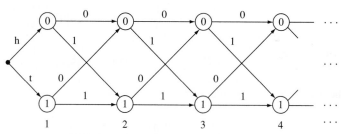

(a) Each sequence of outcomes corresponds
to a path through this trellis diagram.

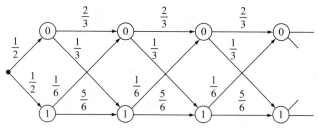

(b) The probability of a sequence of outcomes is the
product of the probabilities along the associated path.

**FIGURE 2.15**
Trellis diagram for a Markov chain.

Therefore for the sequence of interest we have that

$$P[\{s_0\} \cap \{s_1\} \cap \{s_2\}] = P[\{s_2\}|\{s_1\}]P[\{s_1\}|\{s_0\}]P[\{s_0\}]. \qquad (2.46)$$

Sequential experiments that satisfy Eq. (2.45) are called **Markov chains**. For these experiments, the probability of a sequence $s_0, s_1, \ldots, s_n$ is given by

$$P[s_0, s_1, \ldots, s_n] = P[s_n|s_{n-1}]P[s_{n-1}|s_{n-2}] \ldots P[s_1|s_0]P[s_0] \qquad (2.47)$$

where we have simplified notation by omitting braces. Thus the probability of the sequence $s_0, \ldots, s_n$ is given by the product of the probability of the first outcome $s_0$ and the probabilities of all subsequent transitions, $s_0$ to $s_1$, $s_1$ to $s_2$, and so on. Chapter 11 deals with Markov chains.

---

### Example 2.45

Find the probability of the sequence 0011 for the urn experiment introduced in Example 2.44.

Recall that urn 0 contains two balls with label 0 and one ball with label 1, and that urn 1 contains five balls with label 1 and one ball with label 0. We can readily compute the probabilities of sequences of outcomes by labeling the branches in the trellis diagram with the probability of the corresponding transition as shown in Fig. 2.15(b). Thus the probability of the sequence 0011 is given by

$$P[0011] = P[1|1]P[1|0]P[0|0]P[0],$$

where the transition probabilities are given by

$$P[1|0] = \frac{1}{3} \quad \text{and} \quad P[0|0] = \frac{2}{3}$$

$$P[1|1] = \frac{5}{6} \quad \text{and} \quad P[0|1] = \frac{1}{6},$$

and the initial probabilities are given by

$$P(0) = \frac{1}{2} = P[1].$$

If we substitute these values into the expression for $P[0011]$, we obtain

$$P[0011] = \left(\frac{5}{6}\right)\left(\frac{1}{3}\right)\left(\frac{2}{3}\right)\left(\frac{1}{2}\right) = \frac{5}{54}.$$

---

The two-urn experiment in Examples 2.44 and 2.45 is the simplest example of the Markov chain models that are discussed in Chapter 11. The two-urn experiment discussed here is used to model situations in which there are only two outcomes, and in which the outcomes tend to occur in bursts. For example, the two-urn model has been used to model the "bursty" behavior of the voice packets generated by a single speaker where bursts of active packets are separated by relatively long periods of silence. The model has also been used for the sequence of black and white dots that result from scanning a black and white image line by line.

*2.7 **A COMPUTER METHOD FOR SYNTHESIZING RANDOMNESS: RANDOM NUMBER GENERATORS**

This section introduces the basic method for generating sequences of "random" numbers using a computer. Any computer simulation of a system that involves randomness must include a method for generating sequences of random numbers. These random numbers must satisfy long-term average properties of the processes they are simulating. In this section we focus on the problem of generating random numbers that are "uniformly distributed" in the interval $[0, 1]$. In the next chapter we will show how these random numbers can be used to generate numbers with arbitrary probability laws.

The first problem we must confront in generating a random number in the interval $[0, 1]$ is the fact that there are an uncountably infinite number of points in the interval, but the computer is limited to representing numbers with finite precision only. We must therefore be content with generating equiprobable numbers from some finite set, say $\{0, 1, \ldots, M - 1\}$ or $\{1, 2, \ldots, M\}$. By dividing these numbers by $M$, we obtain numbers in the unit interval. These numbers can be made increasingly dense in the unit interval by making $M$ very large.

The next step involves finding a mechanism for generating random numbers. The direct approach involves performing random experiments. For example, we can generate integers in the range 0 to $2^m - 1$ by flipping a fair coin $m$ times and replacing the sequence of heads and tails by 0s and 1s to obtain the binary representation of an integer. Another example would involve drawing a ball from an urn containing balls numbered 1 to $M$. Computer simulations involve the generation of long sequences of random numbers. If we were to use the above mechanisms to generate random numbers, we would have to perform the experiments a large number of times and store the outcomes in computer storage for access by the simulation program. It is clear that this approach is cumbersome and quickly becomes impractical.

### 2.7.1 Pseudo-Random Number Generation

The preferred approach for the computer generation of random numbers involves the use of recursive formulas that can be implemented easily and quickly. These **pseudo-random number generators** produce a sequence of numbers that appear to be random but that in fact repeat after a very long period. The currently preferred pseudo-random number generator is the so-called Mersenne Twister, which is based on a matrix linear recurrence over a binary field. This algorithm can yield sequences with an extremely long period of $2^{19937} - 1$. The Mersenne Twister generates 32-bit integers, so $M = 2^{32} - 1$ in terms of our previous discussion. We obtain a sequence of numbers in the unit interval by dividing the 32-bit integers by $2^{32}$. The sequence of such numbers should be equally distributed over unit cubes of very high dimensionality. The Mersenne Twister has been shown to meet this condition up to 632-dimensionality. In addition, the algorithm is fast and efficient in terms of storage.

Software implementations of the Mersenne Twister are widely available and incorporated into numerical packages such as MATLAB® and Octave.[7] Both MATLAB and Octave provide a means to generate random numbers from the unit interval using the

---

[7]MATLAB® and Octave are interactive computer programs for numerical computations involving matrices. MATLAB® is a commercial product sold by The Mathworks, Inc. Octave is a free, open-source program that is mostly compatible with MATLAB in terms of computation. Long [9] provides an introduction to Octave.

rand command. The `rand` (n, m) operator returns an *n* row by *m* column matrix with elements that are random numbers from the interval $[0, 1)$. This operator is the starting point for generating all types of random numbers.

### Example 2.46 Generation of Numbers from the Unit Interval

First, generate 6 numbers from the unit interval. Next, generate 10,000 numbers from the unit interval. Plot the histogram and empirical distribution function for the sequence of 10,000 numbers.

The following command results in the generation of six numbers from the unit interval.

```
>rand(1,6)
ans =
Columns 1 through 6:
0.642667 0.147811 0.317465 0.512824 0.710823 0.406724
```

The following set of commands will generate 10000 numbers and produce the histogram shown in Fig. 2.16.

```
>X-rand(10000,1);            % Return result in a 10,000-element column vector X.

>K=0.005:0.01;0.995;         % Produce column vector K consisting of the mid points
                             % for 100 bins of width 0.01 in the unit interval.

>Hist(X,K)                   % Produce the desired histogram in Fig 2.16.

>plot(K,empirical_cdf(K,X))  % Plot the proportion of elements in the array X less
                             % than or equal to k, where k is an element of K.
```

The empirical cdf is shown in Fig. 2.17. It is evident that the array of random numbers is uniformly distributed in the unit interval.

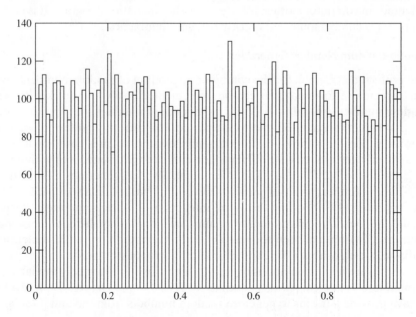

**FIGURE 2.16**
Histogram resulting from experiment to generate 10,000 numbers in the unit interval.

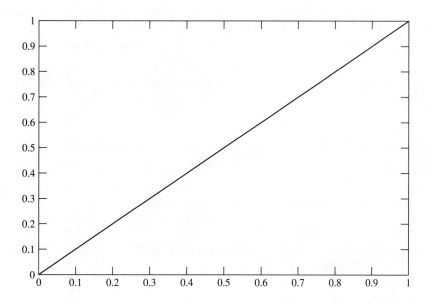

**FIGURE 2.17**
Empirical cdf of experiment that generates 10,000 numbers.

## 2.7.2    Simulation of Random Experiments

MATLAB® and Octave provide functions that are very useful in carrying out numerical evaluation of probabilities involving the most common distributions. Functions are also provided for the generation of random numbers with specific probability distributions. In this section we consider Bernoulli trials and binomial distributions. In Chapter 3 we consider experiments with discrete sample spaces.

---

### Example 2.47    Bernoulli Trials and Binomial Probabilities

First, generate the outcomes of eight Bernoulli trials. Next, generate the outcomes of 100 repetitions of a random experiment that counts the number of successes in 16 Bernoulli trials with probability of success $1/2$. Plot the histogram of the outcomes in the 100 experiments and compare to the binomial probabilities with $n = 16$ and $p = 1/2$.

The following command will generate the outcomes of eight Bernoulli trials, as shown by the answer that follows.

```
>X=rand(1,8)<0.5;              % Generate 1 row of Bernoulli trials with p = 0.5

X =
 0 1 1 0 0 0 1 1
```

If the number produced by rand for a given Bernoulli trial is less than $p = 0.5$, then the outcome of the Bernoulli trial is 1.

Next we show the set of commands to generate the outcomes of 100 repetitions of random experiments where each involves 16 Bernoulli trials.

| | |
|---|---|
| `>X=rand(100,16)<0.5;` | % Generate 100 rows of 16 Bernoulli trials with<br>% $p = 0.5$. |
| `>Y=sum(X,2);` | % Add the results of each row to obtain the number of<br>% successes in each experiment. $Y$ contains the 100<br>% outcomes. |
| `>K=0:16;` | |
| `>Z=empirical_pdf(K,Y));` | % Find the relative frequencies of the outcomes in $Y$. |
| `>Bar(K,Z)` | % Produce a bar graph of the relative frequencies. |
| `>hold on` | % Retains the graph for next command. |
| `>stem(K,binomial_pdf(K,16,0.5))` | % Plot the binomial probabilities along<br>% with the corresponding relative frequencies. |

Figure 2.18 shows that there is good agreement between the relative frequencies and the binomial probabilities.

## *2.8    FINE POINTS: EVENT CLASSES[8]

If the sample space $S$ is discrete, then the event class can consist of all subsets of $S$. There are situations where we may wish or are compelled to let the event class $\mathcal{F}$ be a smaller class of subsets of $S$. In these situations, only the subsets that belong to this class are considered events. In this section we explain how these situations arise.

Let $C$ be the class of events of interest in a random experiment. It is reasonable to expect that any set operation on events in $C$ will produce a set that is also an event in $C$. We can then ask any question regarding events of the random experiment, express it using set operations, and obtain an event that is in $C$. Mathematically, we require that $C$ be a field.

A collection of sets $\mathcal{F}$ is called a **field** if it satisfies the following conditions:

(i)   $\varnothing \in \mathcal{F}$                                                           (2.48a)

(ii)  if $A \in \mathcal{F}$ and $B \in \mathcal{F}$, then $A \cup B \in \mathcal{F}$               (2.48b)

(iii) if $A \in \mathcal{F}$ then $A^c \in \mathcal{F}$.                                    (2.48c)

Using DeMorgan's rule we can show that (ii) and (iii) imply that if $A \in \mathcal{F}$ and $B \in \mathcal{F}$, then $A \cap B \in \mathcal{F}$. Conditions (ii) and (iii) then imply that any finite union or intersection of events in $\mathcal{F}$ will result in an event that is also in $\mathcal{F}$.

### Example 2.48

Let $S = \{T, H\}$. Find the field generated by set operations on the class consisting of elementary events of $S : C = \{\{H\}, \{T\}\}$.

---

[8]The "Fine Points" sections elaborate on concepts and distinctions that are not required in an introductory course. The material in these sections is not necessarily more mathematical, but rather is not usually covered in a first course in probability.

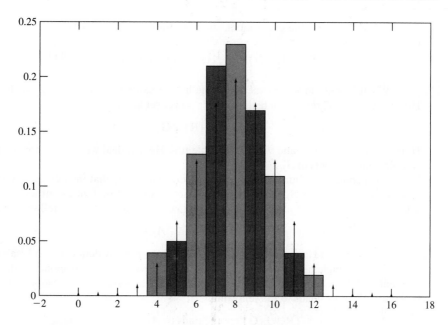

**FIGURE 2.18**
Relative frequencies from 100 binomial experiments and corresponding binomial probabilities.

Let $\mathcal{F}$ be the class generated by $C$. First note that $\{H\} \cup \{T\} = \{H, T\} = S$, which implies that $S$ is in $\mathcal{F}$. Next we find that $S^c = \varnothing$ which implies that $\varnothing \in \mathcal{F}$. Any other set operations will not yield events that are not already in $\mathcal{F}$. Therefore

$$\mathcal{F} = \{\varnothing, \{H\}, \{T\}, \{H, T\}\} = \mathcal{S}.$$

Note that we have generated the power set of $S$ and shown that it is a field.

The above example can be generalized to any finite or countably infinite set $S$. We can generate the power set $\mathcal{S}$ by taking all possible unions of elementary events and their complements, and $S$ forms a field. Note that in Example 2.1, this includes the random experiments $E_1, E_2, E_3, E_4,$ and $E_5$. *Classical probability deals with finite sample spaces and so taking the class of events of interest as the power set is sufficient to proceed to the final step in specifying a probability model, namely, to provide a rule for assigning probabilities to events.*

The following example shows that in some situations the field $\mathcal{F}$ of events of interest need *not* include all subsets of the sample space $S$. In this case only those subsets of $S$ that are in $\mathcal{F}$ are considered valid events. *For this reason, we will restrict the use of the term "event" to sets that are in the field $\mathcal{F}$ that is associated with a given random experiment.*

### Example 2.49   Lisa and Homer's Urn Experiment

An urn contains three white balls. One ball has a red dot, another ball has a green dot, and the third ball has a teal dot. The experiment consists of selecting a ball at random and noting the color of the ball.

When Lisa does the experiment, she has sample space $S_L = \{r, g, t\}$, and her power set has $2^3 = 8$ events:

$$\mathcal{S_L} = \{\varnothing, \{r\}, \{g\}, \{t\}, \{r, g\}, \{r, t\}, \{g, t\}, \{r, g, t\}\}.$$

When Homer does the experiment, he has a smaller sample space $S_H = \{R, G\}$ because Homer cannot tell green from teal! Homer's power set has 4 events:

$$\mathcal{S_H} = \{\varnothing, \{R\}, \{G\}, \{R, G\}\}.$$

Homer does not understand what the problem is. He can deal with any union, intersection, or complement of events in $\mathcal{S_H}$.

The problem of course is that Lisa is interested in sets that include questions about teal. Homer's class of events $\mathcal{S_H}$ cannot handle these questions. Lisa figures out what's happened as follows. She notes that Homer has partitioned Lisa's sample space $S_L$ as follows (see Fig. 2.19b):

$$A_1 = \{r\} \quad \text{and} \quad A_2 = \{g, t\}.$$

Each event in Homer's experiment is related to an equivalent event in Lisa's experiment. Every union, complement, or intersection in Homer's event class corresponds to the union, complement, or intersection of the corresponding $A_k$'s in the partition. For example, the event "the outcome is R or G" leads to the following:

$$\{R\} \cup \{G\} \quad \text{corresponds to} \quad A_1 \cup A_2 = \{r, g, t\}.$$

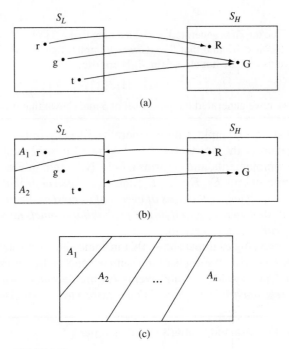

**FIGURE 2.19**
(a) Homer's mapping; (b) Partition of Lisa's sample space;
(c) Partitioning of a sample space.

You can try any combination of unions, intersections, and complements of events in Homer's experiment and the corresponding operations on $A_1$ and/or $A_2$ will result in events in the field:

$$\mathcal{F} = \{\varnothing, \{r\}, \{r, g\}, \{r, g, t\}\}.$$

The field $\mathcal{F}$ does not contain all of the events in Lisa's power set $\mathcal{S}_{\mathcal{L}}$. The field $\mathcal{F}$ suffices to address events that only involve the outcomes in $S_H$. Questions that involve distinguishing between teal and green lead to subsets of $S_L$, such as $\{r, t\}$, that are not events in $\mathcal{F}$ and hence are outside the scope of the experiment.

Lisa explains it all to Homer, and, predictably, his response is "D'oh!"

---

The sets in the field $\mathcal{F}$ that specify the events of interest are said to be *measurable*. Any subset of $S$ that is not in $\mathcal{F}$ is not measurable. In the above example, the set $\{r, t\}$ is not measurable with respect to $\mathcal{F}$. The situation in the above example occurs very frequently in practice, where a decision is made to restrict the scope of questions about a random experiment. Indeed this is part of the modeling process!

In the general case, the sample space $S$ in the original random experiment is divided into mutually exclusive events $A_1, \ldots, A_n$, where $A_i \cap A_j = \varnothing$ for $i \neq j$ and

$$S = A_1 \cup A_2 \cup \cdots \cup A_n,$$

as shown in Fig. 2.19(c). The collection of events $A_1, \ldots, A_n$ are said to form a **partition** of $S$. When the experiment is performed, we observe which event in the partition occurs and not the specific outcome $\zeta$. All questions (events) that involve unions, intersections, or complements of the events in the partition can be answered from this observation. The events in the partition are like elementary events. We can obtain the field $\mathcal{F}$ generated by the events in the partition by taking unions of all distinct combinations of the $A_1, \ldots, A_n$ and their complements. In this case, the subsets of $S$ that are not in $\mathcal{F}$ are not measurable and thus are not considered to be events.

---

**Example 2.50**

In Experiment $E_3$ a coin is tossed three times and the sequence of heads and tails is recorded. The sample space is $S_3 = \{TTT, TTH, THT, HTT, HHT, HTH, THH, HHH\}$ and the corresponding power set $\mathcal{S}_3$ has $2^8 = 256$ events:

$$\mathcal{S}_3 = \{\varnothing, \{TTT\}, \{TTH\}, \ldots, \{HHH\}, \{TTT, TTH\}, \ldots, \{THH, HHH\}, \ldots, S_3\}.$$

In Experiment $E_4$ the coin is tossed three times but only the number of heads is recorded. The sample space is $S_4 = \{0, 1, 2, 3\}$ and the corresponding power set $\mathcal{S}_4$ has $2^4 = 16$ events:

$$\mathcal{S}_4 = \left\{ \begin{array}{l} \varnothing, \{0\}, \{1\}, \{2\}, \{3\}, \{0, 1\}, \{0, 2\}, \{0, 3\}, \{1, 2\}, \{1, 3\}, \\ \{2, 3\}, \{0, 1, 2\}, \{0, 1, 3\}, \{0, 2, 3\} \{1, 2, 3\}, S_4 \end{array} \right\}.$$

Experiment $E_4$ divides the sample space $S_3$ into the following partition:

$$A_0 = \{TTT\}, A_1 = \{TTH, THT, HTT\},$$

$$A_2 = \{THH, HTH, HHT\}, A_3 = \{HHH\}.$$

All the events in $S_4$ correspond to unions, intersections, and complements of $A_0, A_1, A_2$, and $A_3$. The field $\mathcal{F}$ generated by unions, intersections, and complements of these four events has 16 events and addresses all questions associated with Experiment $E_4$.

We see that the event space is greatly simplified and reduced in size by restricting the events of interest to those that only involve the total number of heads and not details about the sequence of heads and tails. The simplification is even more marked as we increase the number of tosses. For example if we extend $E_3$ to 100 coin tosses, then $S_3$ has $2^{100}$ outcomes, a huge number, whereas $S_4$ has only 101 outcomes.

---

Now suppose that $S$ is countably infinite. For example in Experiment $E_6$ we have $S = \{1, 2, \dots\}$ and we might be interested in the condition "number of transmissions is greater than 10." This condition corresponds to the set $\{10, 11, 12, \dots\}$, which is a countable union of elementary sets. It is clear that for events in our class of interest, we should now require that a countable union of events should also be an event, that is:

**(i)** $\varnothing \in \mathcal{F}$      (2.49a)

**(ii)** if $A_1 A_2, \dots \in \mathcal{F}$ then $\displaystyle\bigcup_{k=1}^{\infty} A_k \in \mathcal{F}$      (2.49b)

**(iii)** if $A \in \mathcal{F}$ then $A^c \in \mathcal{F}$.      (2.49c)

A class of sets $\mathcal{F}$ that satisfies Eqs. (2.49a)–(2.49c) is called a **sigma field**. As before, equations (ii) and (iii) and DeMorgan's rule imply that countable intersections of events $\bigcap_{k=1}^{\infty} A_k$ are also in $\mathcal{F}$.

Next consider the case where the sample space $S$ is not countable, as in the unit interval in the real line in Experiment $E_7$, or the unit square in the real plane in $E_{12}$. (See Figs. 2.1(a) and (c).) The probability that the outcome of the experiment is exactly a single point in $S_{12}$ is clearly zero. But this result is not very useful. Instead, we can say that the probability of the event "the outcome $(x, y)$ satisfies $x > y$" is 1/2, by noting that half of $S_{12}$ satisfies the condition of the event. Similarly, the probability of any event that corresponds to a rectangle within $S_{12}$ is simply the area of the rectangle. Taking the set of events that are rectangles within $S$, we can build a field of events by forming countable unions, intersections, and complements. From your previous experience using integrals to calculate areas in the plane, you know that we can approximate any reasonable shape, i.e., event, by taking the union of a sequence of increasingly fine rectangles as shown in Fig. 2.20(a). Clearly there is a strong relationship between calculating integrals, measuring areas, and assigning probabilities to events.

We can finally explain (qualitatively) why we cannot allow all subsets of $S$ to be events when the sample space is uncountably infinite. In essence, there are subsets that are so irregular (see Fig. 2.20b) that it is impossible to define integrals to measure them. We say that these subsets are not measurable. Advanced math is required to show this and we will not deal with this any further. The good news is that we *can* build a sigma field from the countable unions, intersections, and complements of intervals in $R$, or rectangles in $R^2$ that have well-behaved integrals and to which we can assign probabilities. This is familiar territory. In the remainder of this text, we will refer to these sigma fields over $R$ and $R^2$ as the **Borel fields**.

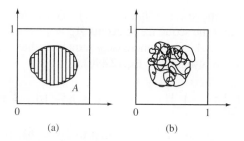

**FIGURE 2.20**
If $A \subset B$, then $P(A) \leq P(B)$.

## *2.9    FINE POINTS: PROBABILITIES OF SEQUENCES OF EVENTS

In this optional section, we discuss the Borel field in more detail and show how sequences of intervals can generate many events of practical interest. We then present a result on the continuity of the probability function for a sequence of events. We show how this result is applied to find the probability of the limit of a sequence of Borel events.

### 2.9.1    The Borel Field of Events

Let $S$ be the real line $R$. Consider events that are semi-infinite intervals of the real line:

$$(-\infty, b] = \{x : -\infty < x \leq b\}.$$

We are interested in the **Borel field** $\mathcal{B}$, which is the sigma field generated by countable unions, countable intersections and complements of events of the form $(-\infty, b]$. We will show that events of the following form are also in $\mathcal{B}$:

$$(a, b), [a, b], (a, b], [a, b), [a, \infty), (a, \infty), (-\infty, b), \{b\}.$$

Since $(-\infty, b] \in \mathcal{B}$, then its complement is in $\mathcal{B}$:

$$(-\infty, b]^c = (b, \infty) \in \mathcal{B}.$$

The following intersection must then be in $\mathcal{B}$:

$$(a, \infty) \cap (-\infty, b] = (a, b] \quad \text{for} \quad a < b.$$

We claim for now that $(-\infty, b) \in \mathcal{B}$. Then the following complements and intersections are also in $\mathcal{B}$:

$$(-\infty, b)^c = [b, \infty) \text{ and } (a, \infty) \cap (-\infty, b) = (a, b) \text{ for } a < b,$$

$$[a, \infty) \cap (-\infty, b] = [a, b] \text{ and } [a, \infty) \cap (-\infty, b) = [a, b) \text{ for } a < b,$$

$$\text{and } [b, \infty) \cap (-\infty, b] = \{b\}.$$

Furthermore, $\mathcal{B}$ contains all complements, countable unions, and intersections of events of the above forms. Note in particular that $\mathcal{B}$ contains all singleton sets (elementary events) $\{b\}$ and therefore all the events for discrete and countable sample spaces of real numbers.

Let's prove the above claim that $(-\infty, b) \in \mathcal{B}$. By definition, all events of the form $(-\infty, b] \in \mathcal{B}$. Consider the sequence of events $A_n = (-\infty, b - 1/n] = \{x : -\infty < x \leq b - 1/n\}$. Note that the $A_n$ are an increasing sequence, that is, $A_n \subset A_{n+1}$. All $A_n \in \mathcal{B}$, so their countable union is also in $\mathcal{B}$ by Eq. (2.49b):

$$\bigcup_{n=1}^{\infty} A_n = \bigcup_{n=1}^{\infty} \{x : -\infty < x \leq b - 1/n\} = (-\infty, b).$$

We claim that this countable union is equal to $(-\infty, b)$. To show equality of the two rightmost sets, first assume that $x \in \bigcup_{n=1}^{\infty} A_n$. We can find a sufficiently large index $n$ so that $x < b - 1/n < b$ (that is, $x$ is strictly less than $b$), which implies that $x \in (-\infty, b)$. Thus we have shown that $\bigcup_{n=1}^{\infty} A_n \subset (-\infty, b)$.

Now assume that $x \in (-\infty, b)$, then $x < b$. We can therefore find an integer $n_0$ such that $x < b - 1/n_0 < b$, so $x \in A_{n_0}$ and so $x \in \bigcup_{n=1}^{\infty} A_n$. Thus $(-\infty, b) \subset \bigcup_{n=1}^{\infty} A_n$. We conclude that $\bigcup_{n=1}^{\infty} A_n = (-\infty, b)$. Therefore $(-\infty, b) \in \mathcal{B}$.

### 2.9.2    Continuity of Probability

Axiom III′ provides the key property that allows us to assign probabilities to events through the addition of the probabilities of mutually exclusive events. In this section we present two consequences of the Axiom III′ that are very useful in finding the probabilities of sequences of events.

Let $A_1, A_2, \ldots$ be a sequence of events from a sigma field, such that,

$$A_1 \subset A_2 \subset \ldots \subset A_n \ldots$$

The sequence is said to be an **increasing sequence of events**. For example, the sequence of intervals $[a, b - 1/n]$ with $a < b - 1$ is an increasing sequence. The sequence $(-n, a]$ is also increasing. We define the limit of an increasing sequence as the union of all the events in the sequence:

$$\lim_{n \to \infty} A_n = \bigcup_{n=1}^{\infty} A_n.$$

The union contains all elements of all events in the sequence and no other elements. Note that the countable union of events is also in the sigma field.

We say that the sequence $A_1, A_2, \ldots$ is a **decreasing sequence of events** if

$$A_1 \supset A_2 \supset \ldots \supset A_n \ldots$$

For example, the sequence of intervals $(a - 1/n, a + 1/n)$ is a decreasing sequence, as is the sequence $(-\infty, a + 1/n]$. We define the limit of a decreasing sequence as the intersection of all the events in the sequence:

$$\lim_{n \to \infty} A_n = \bigcap_{n=1}^{\infty} A_n.$$

The intersection contains all elements that are in all the events of the sequence and no other elements. If all the events in the sequence are in a sigma field, then the countable intersection will also be in the sigma field.

---

**Corollary 8 Continuity of Probability Function**

Let $A_1, A_2, \ldots$ be an increasing or decreasing sequences of events in $\mathcal{F}$, then:

$$\lim_{n \to \infty} P[A_n] = P[\lim_{n \to \infty} A_n]. \tag{2.50}$$

---

We first show how the continuity result is applied in problems that involve events from the Borel field.

---

**Example 2.51**

Find an expression for the probabilities of the following sequences of events from the Borel field: $[a, b - 1/n], (-n, a], (a - 1/n, a + 1/n), (-\infty, a + 1/n]$.

$$\lim_{n \to \infty} P[\{x : a \leq x \leq b - 1/n\}] = P[\lim_{n \to \infty} \{x : a \leq x \leq b - 1/n\}] = P[\{x : a \leq x < b\}].$$

$$\lim_{n \to \infty} P[\{x : -n < x \leq a\}] = P[\lim_{n \to \infty} \{x : -n < x \leq a\}] = P[\{x : -\infty < x \leq a\}].$$

$$\lim_{n \to \infty} P[\{x : a - 1/n < x < a + 1/n\}] = P[\lim_{n \to \infty} \{x : a - 1/n < x < a + 1/n\}] = P[\{x = a\}].$$

$$\lim_{n \to \infty} P[\{x : -\infty < x \leq a + 1/n\}] = P[\lim_{n \to \infty} \{x : -\infty < x \leq a + 1/n\}]$$

$$= P[\{x : -\infty < x \leq a\}].$$

---

To prove the continuity property for an increasing sequence of events, form the following sequence of mutually exclusive events:

$$B_1 = A_1, B_2 = A_2 - A_1, \ldots, B_n = A_n - A_{n-1}, \ldots. \tag{2.51a}$$

The event $B_n$ contains the set of outcomes in $A_n$ not already present in $A_1, A_2, \ldots A_{n-1}$ as illustrated in Fig. 2.21, so it is easy to show that $B_j \cap B_k = \varnothing$ and that

$$\bigcup_{j=1}^{n} B_j = \bigcup_{j=1}^{n} A_j \quad \text{for } n = 1, 2, \ldots \tag{2.51b}$$

as well as

$$\bigcup_{j=1}^{\infty} B_j = \bigcup_{j=1}^{\infty} A_j. \tag{2.51c}$$

Since the sequence is expanding, we also have that:

$$A_n = \bigcup_{j=1}^{n} A_j. \tag{2.51d}$$

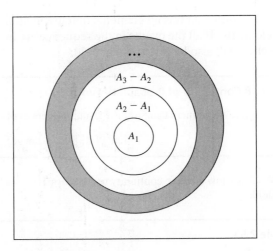

**FIGURE 2.21**
Increasing sequence of events.

The proof of continuity applies Axiom III′ to Eq (2.51c):

$$P\left[\bigcup_{j=1}^{\infty} A_j\right] = P\left[\bigcup_{j=1}^{\infty} B_j\right] = \sum_{j=1}^{\infty} P[B_j].$$

We express the summation as a limit and apply Axiom II:

$$\sum_{j=1}^{\infty} P[B_j] = \lim_{n\to\infty} \sum_{j=1}^{n} P[B_j] = \lim_{n\to\infty} P\left[\bigcup_{j=1}^{n} B_j\right].$$

Finally we use Eqs. (2.51b) and (2.51d):

$$\lim_{n\to\infty} P\left[\bigcup_{j=1}^{n} B_j\right] = \lim_{n\to\infty} P\left[\bigcup_{j=1}^{n} A_j\right] = \lim_{n\to\infty} P[A_n].$$

This proves continuity for increasing sequences:

$$\lim_{n\to\infty} P[A_n] = P\left[\bigcup_{n=1}^{\infty} A_n\right] = P[\lim_{n\to\infty} A_n].$$

For decreasing sequences, we note that the sequence of complements of the decreasing sequences is an increasing sequence. We therefore apply the continuity result to the complement of the decreasing sequence $A_n$:

$$P\left[\bigcup_{j=1}^{\infty} A_j^c\right] = \lim_{n\to\infty} P[A_n^c]. \tag{2.52a}$$

Next we apply DeMorgan's rule:

$$\left(\bigcup_{j=1}^{\infty} A_j^c\right)^c = \bigcap_{j=1}^{\infty} (A_j^c)^c = \bigcap_{j=1}^{\infty} A_j$$

and Corollary 1 to obtain:

$$1 - P\left[\bigcap_{j=1}^{\infty} A_j\right] = P\left[\bigcup_{j=1}^{\infty} A_j^c\right].$$

We now use Eq. (2.52a):

$$1 - P\left[\bigcap_{j=1}^{\infty} A_j\right] = P\left[\bigcup_{j=1}^{\infty} A_j^c\right] = \lim_{n\to\infty} P\left[A_n^c\right] = \lim_{n\to\infty}\left(1 - P[A_n]\right)$$

which gives the desired result:

$$P\left[\bigcap_{j=1}^{\infty} A_j\right] = \lim_{n\to\infty}[A_n]. \tag{2.52b}$$

## SUMMARY

- A probability model is specified by identifying the sample space $S$, the event class of interest, and an initial probability assignment, a "probability law," from which the probability of all events can be computed.

- The sample space $S$ specifies the set of all possible outcomes. If it has a finite or countable number of elements, $S$ is discrete; $S$ is continuous otherwise.

- Events are subsets of $S$ that result from specifying conditions that are of interest in the particular experiment. When $S$ is discrete, events consist of the union of elementary events. When $S$ is continuous, events consist of the union or intersection of intervals in the real line.

- The axioms of probability specify a set of properties that must be satisfied by the probabilities of events. The corollaries that follow from the axioms provide rules for computing the probabilities of events in terms of the probabilities of other related events.

- An initial probability assignment that specifies the probability of certain events must be determined as part of the modeling. If $S$ is discrete, it suffices to specify the probabilities of the elementary events. If $S$ is continuous, it suffices to specify the probabilities of intervals or of semi-infinite intervals.

- Combinatorial formulas are used to evaluate probabilities in experiments that have an equiprobable, finite number of outcomes.

- A conditional probability quantifies the effect of partial knowledge about the outcome of an experiment on the probabilities of events. It is particularly useful in sequential experiments where the outcomes of subexperiments constitute the "partial knowledge."

- Bayes' rule gives the a posteriori probability of an event given that another event has been observed. It can be used to synthesize decision rules that attempt to determine the most probable "cause" in light of an observation.

- Two events are independent if knowledge of the occurrence of one does not alter the probability of the other. Two experiments are independent if all of their respective events are independent. The notion of independence is useful for computing probabilities in experiments that involve noninteracting subexperiments.

- Many experiments can be viewed as consisting of a sequence of independent subexperiments. In this chapter we presented the binomial, the multinomial, and the geometric probability laws as models that arise in this context.
- A Markov chain consists of a sequence of subexperiments in which the outcome of a subexperiment determines which subexperiment is performed next. The probability of a sequence of outcomes in a Markov chain is given by the product of the probability of the first outcome and the probabilities of all subsequent transitions.
- Computer simulation models use recursive equations to generate sequences of pseudo-random numbers.

## CHECKLIST OF IMPORTANT TERMS

Axioms of Probability
Bayes' rule
Bernoulli trial
Binomial coefficient
Binomial theorem
Certain event
Conditional probability
Continuous sample space
Discrete sample space
Elementary event
Event
Event class
Independent events

Independent experiments
Initial probability assignment
Markov chain
Mutually exclusive events
Null event
Outcome
Partition
Probability law
Sample space
Set operations
Theorem on total probability
Tree diagram

## ANNOTATED REFERENCES

There are dozens of introductory books on probability and statistics. The books listed here are some of my favorites. They start from the very beginning, they draw on intuition, they point out where mysterious complications lie below the surface, and they are fun to read! Reference [9] presents an introduction ot Octave and [10] gives an excellent introduction to computer simulation methods of random systems. Reference [11] is an online tutorial for Octave.

1. Y. A. Rozanov, *Probability Theory: A Concise Course*, Dover Publications, New York, 1969.
2. P. L. Meyer, *Introductory Probability and Statistical Applications*, Addison-Wesley, Reading, Mass., 1970.
3. K. L. Chung, *Elementary Probability Theory*, Springer-Verlag, New York, 1974.
4. Robert B. Ash, *Basic Probability Theory*, Wiley, New York, 1970.
5. L. Breiman, *Probability and Stochastic Processes*, Houghton Mifflin, Boston, 1969.
6. Terrence L. Fine, *Probability and Probabilistic Reasoning for Electrical Engineering*, Prentice Hall, Upper Saddle River, N.J., 2006.

**7.** W. Feller, *An Introduction to Probability Theory and Its Applications*, 3d ed., Wiley, New York, 1968.

**8.** A. N. Kolmogorov and S. V. Fomin, *Introductory Real Analysis*, Dover Publications, New York, 1970.

**9.** P. J. G. Long, "Introduction to Octave," University of Cambridge, September 2005, available online.

**10.** A. M. Law and W. D. Kelton, *Simulation Modeling and Analysis*, McGraw-Hill, New York, 2000.

## PROBLEMS

### Section 2.1:  Specifying Random Experiments

**2.1.** The (loose) minute hand in a clock is spun hard and the hour at which the hand comes to rest is noted.

(a) What is the sample space?

(b) Find the sets corresponding to the events: $A$ = "hand is in first 4 hours"; $B$ = "hand is between 2nd and 8th hours inclusive"; and $D$ = "hand is in an odd hour."

(c) Find the events: $A \cap B \cap D$, $A^c \cap B$, $A \cup (B \cap D^c)$, $(A \cup B) \cap D^c$.

**2.2.** A die is tossed twice and the number of dots facing up in each toss is counted and noted in the order of occurrence.

(a) Find the sample space.

(b) Find the set $A$ corresponding to the event "number of dots in first toss is not less than number of dots in second toss."

(c) Find the set $B$ corresponding to the event "number of dots in first toss is 6."

(d) Does $A$ imply $B$ or does $B$ imply $A$?

(e) Find $A \cap B^c$ and describe this event in words.

(f) Let $C$ correspond to the event "number of dots in dice differs by 2." Find $A \cap C$.

**2.3.** Two dice are tossed and the magnitude of the difference in the number of dots facing up in the two dice is noted.

(a) Find the sample space.

(b) Find the set $A$ corresponding to the event "magnitude of difference is 3."

(c) Express each of the elementary events in this experiment as the union of elementary events from Problem 2.2.

**2.4.** A binary communication system transmits a signal $X$ that is either a $+2$ voltage signal or a $-2$ voltage signal. A malicious channel reduces the magnitude of the received signal by the number of heads it counts in two tosses of a coin. Let $Y$ be the resulting signal.

(a) Find the sample space.

(b) Find the set of outcomes corresponding to the event "transmitted signal was definitely $+2$."

(c) Describe in words the event corresponding to the outcome $Y = 0$.

**2.5.** A desk drawer contains six pens, four of which are dry.

(a) The pens are selected at random one by one until a good pen is found. The sequence of test results is noted. What is the sample space?

**(b)** Suppose that only the number, and not the sequence, of pens tested in part a is noted. Specify the sample space.

**(c)** Suppose that the pens are selected one by one and tested until both good pens have been identified, and the sequence of test results is noted. What is the sample space?

**(d)** Specify the sample space in part c if only the number of pens tested is noted.

**2.6.** Three friends (Al, Bob, and Chris) put their names in a hat and each draws a name from the hat. (Assume Al picks first, then Bob, then Chris.)

**(a)** Find the sample space.

**(b)** Find the sets $A$, $B$, and $C$ that correspond to the events "Al draws his name," "Bob draws his name," and "Chris draws his name."

**(c)** Find the set corresponding to the event, "no one draws his own name."

**(d)** Find the set corresponding to the event, "everyone draws his own name."

**(e)** Find the set corresponding to the event, "one or more draws his own name."

**2.7.** Let $M$ be the number of message transmissions in Experiment $E_6$.

**(a)** What is the set $A$ corresponding to the event "$M$ is even"?

**(b)** What is the set $B$ corresponding to the event "$M$ is a multiple of 3"?

**(c)** What is the set $C$ corresponding to the event "6 or fewer transmissions are required"?

**(d)** Find the sets $A \cap B$, $A - B$, $A \cap B \cap C$ and describe the corresponding events in words.

**2.8.** A number $U$ is selected at random from the unit interval. Let the events $A$ and $B$ be: $A =$ "$U$ differs from 1/2 by more than 1/4" and $B =$ "$1 - U$ is less than 1/2." Find the events $A \cap B$, $A^c \cap B$, $A \cup B$.

**2.9.** The sample space of an experiment is the real line. Let the events $A$ and $B$ correspond to the following subsets of the real line: $A = (-\infty, r]$ and $B = (-\infty, s]$, where $r \leq s$. Find an expression for the event $C = (r, s]$ in terms of $A$ and $B$. Show that $B = A \cup C$ and $A \cap C = \emptyset$.

**2.10.** Use Venn diagrams to verify the set identities given in Eqs. (2.2) and (2.3). You will need to use different colors or different shadings to denote the various regions clearly.

**2.11.** Show that:

**(a)** If event $A$ implies $B$, and $B$ implies $C$, then $A$ implies $C$.

**(b)** If event $A$ implies $B$, then $B^c$ implies $A^c$.

**2.12.** Show that if $A \cup B = A$ and $A \cap B = A$ then $A = B$.

**2.13.** Let $A$ and $B$ be events. Find an expression for the event "exactly one of the events $A$ and $B$ occurs." Draw a Venn diagram for this event.

**2.14.** Let $A$, $B$, and $C$ be events. Find expressions for the following events:

**(a)** Exactly one of the three events occurs.

**(b)** Exactly two of the events occur.

**(c)** One or more of the events occur.

**(d)** Two or more of the events occur.

**(e)** None of the events occur.

**2.15.** Figure P2.1 shows three systems of three components, $C_1$, $C_2$, and $C_3$. Figure P2.1(a) is a "series" system in which the system is functioning only if all three components are functioning. Figure 2.1(b) is a "parallel" system in which the system is functioning as long as at least one of the three components is functioning. Figure 2.1(c) is a "two-out-of-three" system in which the system is functioning as long as at least two components are functioning. Let $A_k$ be the event "component $k$ is functioning." For each of the three system configurations, express the event "system is functioning" in terms of the events $A_k$.

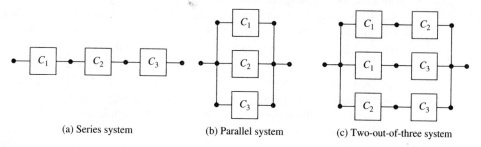

(a) Series system        (b) Parallel system        (c) Two-out-of-three system

**FIGURE P2.1**

**2.16.** A system has two key subsystems. The system is "up" if both of its subsystems are functioning. Triple redundant systems are configured to provide high reliability. The overall system is operational as long as one of three systems is "up." Let $A_{jk}$ correspond to the event "unit $k$ in system $j$ is functioning," for $j = 1, 2, 3$ and $k = 1, 2$.

(a) Write an expression for the event "overall system is up."

(b) Explain why the above problem is equivalent to the problem of having a connection in the network of switches shown in Fig. P2.2.

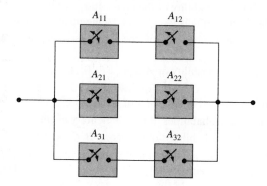

**FIGURE P2.2**

**2.17.** In a specified 6-AM-to-6-AM 24-hour period, a student wakes up at time $t_1$ and goes to sleep at some later time $t_2$.

(a) Find the sample space and sketch it on the $x$-$y$ plane if the outcome of this experiment consists of the pair $(t_1, t_2)$.

(b) Specify the set $A$ and sketch the region on the plane corresponding to the event "student is asleep at noon."

(c) Specify the set $B$ and sketch the region on the plane corresponding to the event "student sleeps through breakfast (7–9 AM)."

(d) Sketch the region corresponding to $A \cap B$ and describe the corresponding event in words.

**2.18.** A road crosses a railroad track at the top of a steep hill. The train cannot stop for oncoming cars and cars, cannot see the train until it is too late. Suppose a train begins crossing the road at time $t_1$ and that the car begins crossing the track at time $t_2$, where $0 < t_1 < T$ and $0 < t_2 < T$.

   **(a)** Find the sample space of this experiment.

   **(b)** Suppose that it takes the train $d_1$ seconds to cross the road and it takes the car $d_2$ seconds to cross the track. Find the set that corresponds to a collision taking place.

   **(c)** Find the set that corresponds to a collision is missed by 1 second or less.

**2.19.** A random experiment has sample space $S = \{-1, 0, +1\}$.

   **(a)** Find all the subsets of $S$.

   **(b)** The outcome of a random experiment consists of pairs of outcomes from S where the elements of the pair cannot be equal. Find the sample space $S'$ of this experiment. How many subsets does $S'$ have?

**2.20.** **(a)** A coin is tossed twice and the sequence of heads and tails is noted. Let S be the sample space of this experiment. Find all subsets of S.

   **(b)** A coin is tossed twice and the number of heads is noted. Let S? be the sample space of this experiment. Find all subsets of $S'$.

   **(c)** Consider parts a and b if the coin is tossed 10 times. How many subsets do S and $S'$ have? How many bits are needed to assign a binary number to each possible subset?

### Section 2.2: The Axioms of Probability

**2.21.** A die is tossed and the number of dots facing up is noted.

   **(a)** Find the probability of the elementary events under the assumption that all faces of the die are equally likely to be facing up after a toss.

   **(b)** Find the probability of the events: $A = \{$more than 3 dots$\}$; $B = \{$odd number of dots$\}$.

   **(c)** Find the probability of $A \cup B$, $A \cap B$, $A^c$.

**2.22.** In Problem 2.2, a die is tossed twice and the number of dots facing up in each toss is counted and noted in the order of occurrence.

   **(a)** Find the probabilities of the elementary events.

   **(b)** Find the probabilities of events $A$, $B$, $C$, $A \cap B^c$, and $A \cap C$ defined in Problem 2.2.

**2.23.** A random experiment has sample space $S = \{a, b, c, d\}$. Suppose that $P[\{c, d\}] = 3/8$, $P[\{b, c\}] = 6/8$, and $P[\{d\}] = 1/8$, $P[\{c, d\}] = 3/8$. Use the axioms of probability to find the probabilities of the elementary events.

**2.24.** Find the probabilities of the following events in terms of $P[A]$, $P[B]$, and $P[A \cap B]$:

   **(a)** $A$ occurs and $B$ does not occur; $B$ occurs and $A$ does not occur.

   **(b)** Exactly one of $A$ or $B$ occurs.

   **(c)** Neither $A$ nor $B$ occur.

**2.25.** Let the events $A$ and $B$ have $P[A] = x$, $P[B] = y$, and $P[A \cup B] = z$. Use Venn diagrams to find $P[A \cap B]$, $P[A^c \cap B^c]$, $P[A^c \cup B^c]$, $P[A \cap B^c]$, $P[A^c \cup B]$.

**2.26.** Show that
$$P[A \cup B \cup C] = P[A] + P[B] + P[C] - P[A \cap B] - P[A \cap C] - P[B \cap C]$$
$$+ P[A \cap B \cap C].$$

**2.27.** Use the argument from Problem 2.26 to prove Corollary 6 by induction.

**2.28.** A hexadecimal character consists of a group of three bits. Let $A_i$ be the event "$i$th bit in a character is a 1."

    **(a)** Find the probabilities for the following events: $A_1, A_1 \cap A_3, A_1 \cap A_2 \cap A_3$ and $A_1 \cup A_2 \cup A_3$. Assume that the values of bits are determined by tosses of a fair coin.

    **(b)** Repeat part a if the coin is biased.

**2.29.** Let $M$ be the number of message transmissions in Problem 2.7. Find the probabilities of the events $A, B, C, C^c, A \cap B, A - B, A \cap B \cap C$. Assume the probability of successful transmission is 1/2.

**2.30.** Use Corollary 7 to prove the following:

    **(a)** $P[A \cup B \cup C] \le P[A] + P[B] + P[C]$.

    **(b)** $P\left[\bigcup_{k=1}^{n} A_k\right] \le \sum_{k=1}^{n} P[A_k]$.

    **(c)** $P\left[\bigcap_{k=1}^{n} A_k\right] \ge 1 - \sum_{k=1}^{n} P[A_k^c]$.

    The second expression is called the **union bound**.

**2.31.** Let $p$ be the probability that a single character appears incorrectly in this book. Use the union bound for the probability of there being any errors in a page with $n$ characters.

**2.32.** A die is tossed and the number of dots facing up is noted.

    **(a)** Find the probability of the elementary events if faces with an even number of dots are twice as likely to come up as faces with an odd number.

    **(b)** Repeat parts b and c of Problem 2.21.

**2.33.** Consider Problem 2.1 where the minute hand in a clock is spun. Suppose that we now note the *minute* at which the hand comes to rest.

    **(a)** Suppose that the minute hand is very loose so the hand is equally likely to come to rest anywhere in the clock. What are the probabilities of the elementary events?

    **(b)** Now suppose that the minute hand is somewhat sticky and so the hand is 1/2 as likely to land in the second minute than in the first, 1/3 as likely to land in the third minute as in the first, and so on. What are the probabilities of the elementary events?

    **(c)** Now suppose that the minute hand is very sticky and so the hand is 1/2 as likely to land in the second minute than in the first, 1/2 as likely to land in the third minute as in the second, and so on. What are the probabilities of the elementary events?

    **(d)** Compare the probabilities that the hand lands in the last minute in parts a, b, and c.

**2.34.** A number $x$ is selected at random in the interval $[-1, 2]$. Let the events $A = \{x < 0\}$, $B = \{|x - 0.5| < 0.5\}$, and $C = \{x > 0.75\}$.

    **(a)** Find the probabilities of $A, B, A \cap B$, and $A \cap C$.

    **(b)** Find the probabilities of $A \cup B, A \cup C$, and $A \cup B \cup C$, first, by directly evaluating the sets and then their probabilities, and second, by using the appropriate axioms or corollaries.

**2.35.** A number $x$ is selected at random in the interval $[-1, 2]$. Numbers from the subinterval $[0, 2]$ occur half as frequently as those from $[-1, 0)$.

    **(a)** Find the probability assignment for an interval completely within $[-1, 0)$; completely within $[0, 2]$; and partly in each of the above intervals.

    **(b)** Repeat Problem 2.34 with this probability assignment.

**2.36.** The lifetime of a device behaves according to the probability law $P[(t, \infty)] = 1/t$ for $t > 1$. Let $A$ be the event "lifetime is greater than 4," and $B$ the event "lifetime is greater than 8."

   **(a)** Find the probability of $A \cap B$, and $A \cup B$.

   **(b)** Find the probability of the event "lifetime is greater than 6 but less than or equal to 12."

**2.37.** Consider an experiment for which the sample space is the real line. A probability law assigns probabilities to subsets of the form $(-\infty, r]$.

   **(a)** Show that we must have $P[(-\infty, r]] \le P[(-\infty, s]]$ when $r < s$.

   **(b)** Find an expression for $P[(r, s]]$ in terms of $P[(-\infty, r]]$ and $P[(-\infty, s]]$

   **(c)** Find an expression for $P[(s, \infty)]$.

**2.38.** Two numbers $(x, y)$ are selected at random from the interval $[0, 1]$.

   **(a)** Find the probability that the pair of numbers are inside the unit circle.

   **(b)** Find the probability that $y > 2x$.

## *Section 2.3: Computing Probabilities Using Counting Methods

**2.39.** The combination to a lock is given by three numbers from the set $\{0, 1, \dots, 59\}$. Find the number of combinations possible.

**2.40.** How many seven-digit telephone numbers are possible if the first number is not allowed to be 0 or 1?

**2.41.** A pair of dice is tossed, a coin is flipped twice, and a card is selected at random from a deck of 52 distinct cards. Find the number of possible outcomes.

**2.42.** A lock has two buttons: a "0" button and a "1" button. To open a door you need to push the buttons according to a preset 8-bit sequence. How many sequences are there? Suppose you press an arbitrary 8-bit sequence; what is the probability that the door opens? If the first try does not succeed in opening the door, you try another number; what is the probability of success?

**2.43.** A Web site requires that users create a password with the following specifications:

   • Length of 8 to 10 characters
   • Includes at least one special character $\{!, @, \#, \$, \%, \wedge, \&, *, (, ), +, =, \{, \}, |, <, >,$
     $\backslash, —, -, [, ], /, ?\}$
   • No spaces
   • May contain numbers (0–9), lower and upper case letters (a–z, A–Z)
   • Is case-sensitive.

   How many passwords are there? How long would it take to try all passwords if a password can be tested in 1 microsecond?

**2.44.** A multiple choice test has 10 questions with 3 choices each. How many ways are there to answer the test? What is the probability that two papers have the same answers?

**2.45.** A student has five different t-shirts and three pairs of jeans ("brand new," "broken in," and "perfect").

   **(a)** How many days can the student dress without repeating the combination of jeans and t-shirt?

   **(b)** How many days can the student dress without repeating the combination of jeans and t-shirt and without wearing the same t-shirt on two consecutive days?

**2.46.** Ordering a "deluxe" pizza means you have four choices from 15 available toppings. How many combinations are possible if toppings can be repeated? If they cannot be repeated? Assume that the order in which the toppings are selected does not matter.

**2.47.** A lecture room has 60 seats. In how many ways can 45 students occupy the seats in the room?

**2.48.** List all possible permutations of two distinct objects; three distinct objects; four distinct objects. Verify that the number is $n!$.

**2.49.** A toddler pulls three volumes of an encyclopedia from a bookshelf and, after being scolded, places them back in random order. What is the probability that the books are in the correct order?

**2.50.** Five balls are placed at random in five buckets. What is the probability that each bucket has a ball?

**2.51.** List all possible combinations of two objects from two distinct objects; three distinct objects; four distinct objects. Verify that the number is given by the binomial coefficient.

**2.52.** A dinner party is attended by four men and four women. How many unique ways can the eight people sit around the table? How many unique ways can the people sit around the table with men and women alternating seats?

**2.53.** A hot dog vendor provides onions, relish, mustard, ketchup, Dijon ketchup, and hot peppers for your hot dog. How many variations of hot dogs are possible using one condiment? Two condiments? None, some, or all of the condiments?

**2.54.** A lot of 100 items contains $k$ defective items. $M$ items are chosen at random and tested.

   **(a)** What is the probability that $m$ are found defective? This is called the *hypergeometric distribution*.

   **(b)** A lot is accepted if 1 or fewer of the $M$ items are defective. What is the probability that the lot is accepted?

**2.55.** A park has $N$ raccoons of which eight were previously captured and tagged. Suppose that 20 raccoons are captured. Find the probability that four of these are found to be tagged. Denote this probability, which depends on $N$, by $p(N)$. Find the value of $N$ that maximizes this probability. *Hint:* Compare the ratio $p(N)/p(N-1)$ to unity.

**2.56.** A lot of 50 items has 40 good items and 10 bad items.

   **(a)** Suppose we test five samples from the lot, with replacement. Let $X$ be the number of defective items in the sample. Find $P[X = k]$.

   **(b)** Suppose we test five samples from the lot, without replacement. Let $Y$ be the number of defective items in the sample. Find $P[Y = k]$.

**2.57.** How many distinct permutations are there of four red balls, two white balls, and three black balls?

**2.58.** A hockey team has 6 forwards, 4 defensemen, and 2 goalies. At any time, 3 forwards, 2 defensemen, and 1 goalie can be on the ice. How many combinations of players can a coach put on the ice?

**2.59.** Find the probability that in a class of 28 students exactly four were born in each of the seven days of the week.

**2.60.** Show that

$$\binom{n}{k} = \binom{n}{n-k}$$

**2.61.** In this problem we derive the multinomial coefficient. Suppose we partition a set of $n$ distinct objects into $J$ subsets $B_1, B_2, \ldots, B_J$ of size $k_1, \ldots, k_J$, respectively, where $k_i \geq 0$, and $k_1 + k_2 + \ldots + k_J = n$.

   **(a)** Let $N_i$ denote the number of possible outcomes when the $i$th subset is selected. Show that

$$N_1 = \binom{n}{k_1}, \quad N_2 = \binom{n-k_1}{k_2}, \ldots, N_{J-1} = \binom{n-k_1-\cdots-k_{J-2}}{k_{J-1}}.$$

**(b)** Show that the number of partitions is then:

$$N_1 N_2 \ldots N_{J-1} = \frac{n!}{k_1! \, k_2! \ldots k_J!}.$$

## Section 2.4: Conditional Probability

**2.62.** A die is tossed twice and the number of dots facing up is counted and noted in the order of occurrence. Let $A$ be the event "number of dots in first toss is not less than number of dots in second toss," and let $B$ be the event "number of dots in first toss is 6." Find $P[A|B]$ and $P[B|A]$.

**2.63.** Use conditional probabilities and tree diagrams to find the probabilities for the elementary events in the random experiments defined in parts a to d of Problem 2.5.

**2.64.** In Problem 2.6 (name in hat), find $P[B \cap C|A]$ and $P[C|A \cap B]$.

**2.65.** In Problem 2.29 (message transmissions), find $P[B|A]$ and $P[A|B]$.

**2.66.** In Problem 2.8 (unit interval), find $P[B|A]$ and $P[A|B]$.

**2.67.** In Problem 2.36 (device lifetime), find $P[B|A]$ and $P[A|B]$.

**2.68.** In Problem 2.33, let $A = \{$hand rests in last 10 minutes$\}$ and $B = \{$hand rests in last 5 minutes$\}$. Find $P[B|A]$ for parts a, b, and c.

**2.69.** A number $x$ is selected at random in the interval $[-1, 2]$. Let the events $A = \{x < 0\}$, $B = \{|x - 0.5| < 0.5\}$, and $C = \{x > 0.75\}$. Find $P[A|B]$, $P[B|C]$, $P[A|C^c]$, $P[B|C^c]$.

**2.70.** In Problem 2.36, let $A$ be the event "lifetime is greater than $t$," and $B$ the event "lifetime is greater than $2t$." Find $P[B|A]$. Does the answer depend on $t$? Comment.

**2.71.** Find the probability that two or more students in a class of 20 students have the same birthday. *Hint:* Use Corollary 1. How big should the class be so that the probability that two or more students have the same birthday is 1/2?

**2.72.** A cryptographic hash takes a message as input and produces a fixed-length string as output, called the digital fingerprint. A brute force attack involves computing the hash for a large number of messages until a pair of distinct messages with the same hash is found. Find the number of attempts required so that the probability of obtaining a match is 1/2. How many attempts are required to find a matching pair if the digital fingerprint is 64 bits long? 128 bits long?

**2.73.** **(a)** Find $P[A|B]$ if $A \cap B = \emptyset$; if $A \subset B$; if $A \supset B$.

**(b)** Show that if $P[A|B] > P[A]$, then $P[B|A] > P[B]$.

**2.74.** Show that $P[A|B]$ satisfies the axioms of probability.

    **(i)** $0 \le P[A|B] \le 1$

    **(ii)** $P[S|B] = 1$

    **(iii)** If $A \cap C = \emptyset$, then $P[A \cup C|B] = P[A|B] + P[C|B]$.

**2.75.** Show that $P[A \cap B \cap C] = P[A|B \cap C]P[B|C]P[C]$.

**2.76.** In each lot of 100 items, two items are tested, and the lot is rejected if either of the tested items is found defective.

**(a)** Find the probability that a lot with $k$ defective items is accepted.

**(b)** Suppose that when the production process malfunctions, 50 out of 100 items are defective. In order to identify when the process is malfunctioning, how many items should be tested so that the probability that one or more items are found defective is at least 99%?

**2.77.** A nonsymmetric binary communications channel is shown in Fig. P2.3. Assume the input is "0" with probability $p$ and "1" with probability $1 - p$.

**(a)** Find the probability that the output is 0.

**(b)** Find the probability that the input was 0 given that the output is 1. Find the probability that the input is 1 given that the output is 1. Which input is more probable?

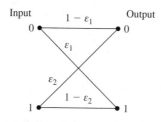

**FIGURE P2.3**

**2.78.** The transmitter in Problem 2.4 is equally likely to send $X = +2$ as $X = -2$. The malicious channel counts the number of heads in two tosses of a fair coin to decide by how much to reduce the magnitude of the input to produce the output $Y$.

**(a)** Use a tree diagram to find the set of possible input-output pairs.

**(b)** Find the probabilities of the input-output pairs.

**(c)** Find the probabilities of the output values.

**(d)** Find the probability that the input was $X = +2$ given that $Y = k$.

**2.79.** One of two coins is selected at random and tossed three times. The first coin comes up heads with probability $p_1$ and the second coin with probability $p_2 = 2/3 > p_1 = 1/3$.

**(a)** What is the probability that the number of heads is $k$?

**(b)** Find the probability that coin 1 was tossed given that $k$ heads were observed, for $k = 0, 1, 2, 3$.

**(c)** In part b, which coin is more probable when $k$ heads have been observed?

**(d)** Generalize the solution in part b to the case where the selected coin is tossed $m$ times. In particular, find a threshold value $T$ such that when $k > T$ heads are observed, coin 1 is more probable, and when $k < T$ are observed, coin 2 is more probable.

**(e)** Suppose that $p_2 = 1$ (that is, coin 2 is two-headed) and $0 < p_1 < 1$. What is the probability that we do not determine with certainty whether the coin is 1 or 2?

**2.80.** A computer manufacturer uses chips from three sources. Chips from sources A, B, and C are defective with probabilities .005, .001, and .010, respectively. If a randomly selected chip is found to be defective, find the probability that the manufacturer was A; that the manufacturer was C. Assume that the proportions of chips from A, B, and C are 0.5, 0.1, and 0.4, respectively.

**2.81.** A ternary communication system is shown in Fig. P2.4. Suppose that input symbols 0, 1, and 2 occur with probability 1/3 respectively.

**(a)** Find the probabilities of the output symbols.

**(b)** Suppose that a 1 is observed at the output. What is the probability that the input was 0? 1? 2?

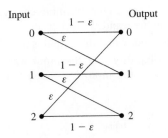

**FIGURE P2.4**

## Section 2.5: Independence of Events

**2.82.** Let $S = \{1, 2, 3, 4\}$ and $A = \{1, 2\}, B = \{1, 3\}, C = \{1, 4\}$. Assume the outcomes are equiprobable. Are $A$, $B$, and $C$ independent events?

**2.83.** Let $U$ be selected at random from the unit interval. Let $A = \{0 < U < 1/2\}$, $B = \{1/4 < U < 3/4\}$, and $C = \{1/2 < U < 1\}$. Are any of these events independent?

**2.84.** Alice and Mary practice free throws at the basketball court after school. Alice makes free throws with probability $p_a$ and Mary makes them with probability $p_m$. Find the probability of the following outcomes when Alice and Mary each take one shot: Alice scores a basket; Either Alice or Mary scores a basket; both score; both miss.

**2.85.** Show that if $A$ and $B$ are independent events, then the pairs $A$ and $B^c$, $A^c$ and $B$, and $A^c$ and $B^c$ are also independent.

**2.86.** Show that events $A$ and $B$ are independent if $P[A|B] = P[A|B^c]$.

**2.87.** Let $A$, $B$, and $C$ be events with probabilities $P[A], P[B]$, and $P[C]$.
   **(a)** Find $P[A \cup B]$ if $A$ and $B$ are independent.
   **(b)** Find $P[A \cup B]$ if $A$ and $B$ are mutually exclusive.
   **(c)** Find $P[A \cup B \cup C]$ if $A$, $B$, and $C$ are independent.
   **(d)** Find $P[A \cup B \cup C]$ if $A$, $B$, and $C$ are pairwise mutually exclusive.

**2.88.** An experiment consists of picking one of two urns at random and then selecting a ball from the urn and noting its color (black or white). Let $A$ be the event "urn 1 is selected" and $B$ the event "a black ball is observed." Under what conditions are $A$ and $B$ independent?

**2.89.** Find the probabilities in Problem 2.14 assuming that events $A$, $B$, and $C$ are independent.

**2.90.** Find the probabilities that the three types of systems are "up" in Problem 2.15. Assume that all units in the system fail independently and that a type $k$ unit fails with probability $p_k$.

**2.91.** Find the probabilities that the system is "up" in Problem 2.16. Assume that all units in the system fail independently and that a type $k$ unit fails with probability $p_k$.

**2.92.** A random experiment is repeated a large number of times and the occurrence of events $A$ and $B$ is noted. How would you test whether events $A$ and $B$ are independent?

**2.93.** Consider a very long sequence of hexadecimal characters. How would you test whether the relative frequencies of the four bits in the hex characters are consistent with independent tosses of coin?

**2.94.** Compute the probability of the system in Example 2.35 being "up" when a second controller is added to the system.

**2.95.** In the binary communication system in Example 2.26, find the value of $\varepsilon$ for which the input of the channel is independent of the output of the channel. Can such a channel be used to transmit information?

**2.96.** In the ternary communication system in Problem 2.81, is there a choice of $\varepsilon$ for which the input of the channel is independent of the output of the channel?

## Section 2.6: Sequential Experiments

**2.97.** A block of 100 bits is transmitted over a binary communication channel with probability of bit error $p = 10^{-2}$.

**(a)** If the block has 1 or fewer errors then the receiver accepts the block. Find the probability that the block is accepted.

**(b)** If the block has more than 1 error, then the block is retransmitted. Find the probability that $M$ retransmissions are required.

**2.98.** A fraction $p$ of items from a certain production line is defective.

**(a)** What is the probability that there is more than one defective item in a batch of $n$ items?

**(b)** During normal production $p = 10^{-3}$ but when production malfunctions $p = 10^{-1}$. Find the size of a batch that should be tested so that if any items are found defective we are 99% sure that there is a production malfunction.

**2.99.** A student needs eight chips of a certain type to build a circuit. It is known that 5% of these chips are defective. How many chips should he buy for there to be a greater than 90% probability of having enough chips for the circuit?

**2.100.** Each of $n$ terminals broadcasts a message in a given time slot with probability $p$.

**(a)** Find the probability that exactly one terminal transmits so the message is received by all terminals without collision.

**(b)** Find the value of $p$ that maximizes the probability of successful transmission in part a.

**(c)** Find the asymptotic value of the probability of successful transmission as $n$ becomes large.

**2.101.** A system contains eight chips. The lifetime of each chip has a Weibull probability law: with parameters $\lambda$ and $k = 2$: $P[(t, \infty)] = e^{-(\lambda t)^k}$ for $t \geq 0$. Find the probability that at least two chips are functioning after $2/\lambda$ seconds.

**2.102.** A machine makes errors in a certain operation with probability $p$. There are two types of errors. The fraction of errors that are type 1 is $\alpha$, and type 2 is $1 - \alpha$.

**(a)** What is the probability of $k$ errors in $n$ operations?

**(b)** What is the probability of $k_1$ type 1 errors in $n$ operations?

**(c)** What is the probability of $k_2$ type 2 errors in $n$ operations?

**(d)** What is the joint probability of $k_1$ and $k_2$ type 1 and 2 errors, respectively, in $n$ operations?

**2.103.** Three types of packets arrive at a router port. Ten percent of the packets are "expedited forwarding (EF)," 30 percent are "assured forwarding (AF)," and 60 percent are "best effort (BE)."

**(a)** Find the probability that $k$ of $N$ packets are not expedited forwarding.

**(b)** Suppose that packets arrive one at a time. Find the probability that $k$ packets are received before an expedited forwarding packet arrives.

**(c)** Find the probability that out of 20 packets, 4 are EF packets, 6 are AF packets, and 10 are BE.

**2.104.** A run-length coder segments a binary information sequence into strings that consist of either a "run" of $k$ "zeros" punctuated by a "one", for $k = 0, \ldots, m - 1$, or a string of $m$ "zeros." The $m = 3$ case is:

| String | Run-length $k$ |
|--------|----------------|
| 1      | 0              |
| 01     | 1              |
| 001    | 2              |
| 000    | 3              |

Suppose that the information is produced by a sequence of Bernoulli trials with $P[\text{"one"}] = P[\text{success}] = p$.

(a) Find the probability of run-length $k$ in the $m = 3$ case.

(b) Find the probability of run-length $k$ for general $m$.

**2.105.** The amount of time cars are parked in a parking lot follows a geometric probability law with $p = 1/2$. The charge for parking in the lot is \$1 for each half-hour or less.

(a) Find the probability that a car pays $k$ dollars.

(b) Suppose that there is a maximum charge of \$6. Find the probability that a car pays $k$ dollars.

**2.106.** A biased coin is tossed repeatedly until heads has come up three times. Find the probability that $k$ tosses are required. *Hint:* Show that $\{\text{"}k \text{ tosses are required"}\} = A \cap B$, where $A = \{\text{"}k\text{th toss is heads"}\}$ and $B = \{\text{"2 heads occurs in } k - 1 \text{ tosses"}\}$.

**2.107.** An urn initially contains two black balls and two white balls. The following experiment is repeated indefinitely: A ball is drawn from the urn; if the color of the ball is the same as the majority of balls remaining in the urn, then the ball is put back in the urn. Otherwise the ball is left out.

(a) Draw the trellis diagram for this experiment and label the branches by the transition probabilities.

(b) Find the probabilities for all sequences of outcomes of length 2 and length 3.

(c) Find the probability that the urn contains no black balls after three draws; no white balls after three draws.

(d) Find the probability that the urn contains two black balls after $n$ trials; two white balls after $n$ trials.

**2.108.** In Example 2.45, let $p_0(n)$ and $p_1(n)$ be the probabilities that urn 0 or urn 1 is used in the $n$th subexperiment.

(a) Find $p_0(1)$ and $p_1(1)$.

(b) Express $p_0(n + 1)$ and $p_1(n + 1)$ in terms of $p_0(n)$ and $p_1(n)$.

(c) Evaluate $p_0(n)$ and $p_1(n)$ for $n = 2, 3, 4$.

(d) Find the solution to the recursion in part b with the initial conditions given in part a.

(e) What are the urn probabilities as $n$ approaches infinity?

## *Section 2.7: Synthesizing Randomness: Number Generators

**2.109.** An urn experiment is to be used to simulate a random experiment with sample space $S = \{1, 2, 3, 4, 5\}$ and probabilities $p_1 = 1/3$, $p_2 = 1/5$, $p_3 = 1/4$, $p_4 = 1/7$, and $p_5 = 1 - (p_1 + p_2 + p_3 + p_4)$. How many balls should the urn contain? Generalize the result to show that an urn experiment can be used to simulate any random experiment with finite sample space and with probabilities given by rational numbers.

**2.110.** Suppose we are interested in using tosses of a fair coin to simulate a random experiment in which there are six equally likely outcomes, where $S = \{0, 1, 2, 3, 4, 5\}$. The following version of the "rejection method" is proposed:

    **1.** Toss a fair coin three times and obtain a binary number by identifying heads with zero and tails with one.

    **2.** If the outcome of the coin tosses in step 1 is the binary representation for a number in $S$, output the number. Otherwise, return to step 1.

**(a)** Find the probability that a number is produced in step 2.

**(b)** Show that the numbers that are produced in step 2 are equiprobable.

**(c)** Generalize the above algorithm to show how coin tossing can be used to simulate any random urn experiment.

**2.111.** Use the `rand` function in Octave to generate 1000 pairs of numbers in the unit square. Plot an $x$-$y$ scattergram to confirm that the resulting points are uniformly distributed in the unit square.

**2.112.** Apply the rejection method introduced above to generate points that are uniformly distributed in the $x > y$ portion of the unit square. Use the `rand` function to generate a pair of numbers in the unit square. If $x > y$, accept the number. If not, select another pair. Plot an $x$-$y$ scattergram for the pair of accepted numbers and confirm that the resulting points are uniformly distributed in the $x > y$ region of the unit square.

**2.113.** The *sample mean-squared value* of the numerical outcomes $X(1), X(2), \ldots X(n)$ of a series of $n$ repetitions of an experiment is defined by

$$\langle X^2 \rangle_n = \frac{1}{n}\sum_{j=1}^{n} X^2(j).$$

**(a)** What would you expect this expression to converge to as the number of repetitions $n$ becomes very large?

**(b)** Find a recursion formula for $\langle X^2 \rangle_n$ similar to the one found in Problem 1.9.

**2.114.** The *sample variance* is defined as the mean-squared value of the variation of the samples about the sample mean

$$\langle V^2 \rangle_n = \frac{1}{n}\sum_{j=1}^{n} \{X(j) - \langle X \rangle_n\}^2.$$

Note that the $\langle X \rangle_n$ also depends on the sample values. (It is customary to replace the $n$ in the denominator with $n - 1$ for technical reasons that will be discussed in Chapter 8. For now we will use the above definition.)

**(a)** Show that the sample variance satisfies the following expression:

$$\langle V^2 \rangle_n = \langle X^2 \rangle_n - \langle X \rangle_n^2.$$

**(b)** Show that the sample variance satisfies the following recursion formula:

$$\langle V^2 \rangle_n = \left(1 - \frac{1}{n}\right)\langle V^2 \rangle_{n-1} + \frac{1}{n}\left(1 - \frac{1}{n}\right)(X(n) - \langle X \rangle_{n-1})^2,$$

with $\langle V^2 \rangle_0 = 0$.

**2.115.** Suppose you have a program to generate a sequence of numbers $U_n$ that is uniformly distributed in $[0, 1]$. Let $Y_n = \alpha U_n + \beta$.

(a) Find $\alpha$ and $\beta$ so that $Y_n$ is uniformly distributed in the interval $[a, b]$.

(b) Let $a = -5$ and $b = 15$. Use Octave to generate $Y_n$ and to compute the sample mean and sample variance in 1000 repetitions. Compare the sample mean and sample variance to $(a + b)/2$ and $(b - a)^2/12$, respectively.

**2.116.** Use Octave to simulate 100 repetitions of the random experiment where a coin is tossed 16 times and the number of heads is counted.

(a) Confirm that your results are similar to those in Figure 2.18.

(b) Rerun the experiment with $p = 0.25$ and $p = 0.75$. Are the results as expected?

**\*Section 2.8:  Fine Points: Event Classes**

**2.117.** In Example 2.49, Homer maps the outcomes from Lisa's sample space $S_L = \{r, g, t\}$ into a smaller sample space $S_H = \{R, G\} : f(r) = R, f(g) = G,$ and $f(t) = G$.

Define the inverse image events as follows:

$$f^{-1}(\{R\}) = A_1 = \{r\} \quad \text{and} \quad f^{-1}(\{G\}) = A_2 = \{g, t\}.$$

Let $A$ and $B$ be events in Homer's sample space.

(a) Show that $f^{-1}(A \cup B) = f^{-1}(A) \cup f^{-1}(B)$.

(b) Show that $f^{-1}(A \cap B) = f^{-1}(A) \cap f^{-1}(B)$.

(c) Show that $f^{-1}(A^c) = f^{-1}(A)^c$.

(d) Show that the results in parts a, b, and c hold for a general mapping $f$ from a sample space $S$ to a set $S'$.

**2.118.** Let $f$ be a mapping from a sample space $S$ to a finite set $S' = \{y_1, y_2, \ldots, y_n\}$.

(a) Show that the set of inverse images $A_k = f^{-1}(\{y_k\})$ forms a partition of $S$.

(b) Show that any event $B$ of $S'$ can be related to a union of $A_k$'s.

**2.119.** Let $A$ be any subset of $S$. Show that the class of sets $\{\emptyset, A, A^c, S\}$ is a field.

**\*Section 2.9:  Fine Points: Probabilities of Sequences of Events**

**2.120.** Find the countable union of the following sequences of events:

(a) $A_n = [a + 1/n, b - 1/n]$.

(b) $B_n = (-n, b - 1/n]$.

(c) $C_n = [a + 1/n, b)$.

**2.121.** Find the countable intersection of the following sequences of events:

(a) $A_n = (a - 1/n, b + 1/n)$.

(b) $B_n = [a, b + 1/n)$.

(c) $C_n = (a - 1/n, b]$.

**2.122.** (a) Show that the Borel field can be generated from the complements and countable intersections and unions of open sets $(a, b)$.

(b) Suggest other classes of sets that can generate the Borel field.

**2.123.** Find expressions for the probabilities of the events in Problem 2.120.

**2.124.** Find expressions for the probabilities of the events in Problem 2.121.

## Problems Requiring Cumulative Knowledge

**2.125.** Compare the binomial probability law and the hypergeometric law introduced in Problem 2.54 as follows.

   **(a)** Suppose a lot has 20 items of which five are defective. A batch of ten items is tested without replacement. Find the probability that $k$ are found defective for $k = 0, \dots, 10$. Compare this to the binomial probabilities with $n = 10$ and $p = 5/20 = .25$.

   **(b)** Repeat but with a lot of 1000 items of which 250 are defective. A batch of ten items is tested without replacement. Find the probability that $k$ are found defective for $k = 0, \dots, 10$. Compare this to the binomial probabilities with $n = 10$ and $p = 5/20 = .25$.

**2.126.** Suppose that in Example 2.43, computer A sends each message to computer B simultaneously over two unreliable radio links. Computer B can detect when errors have occurred in either link. Let the probability of message transmission error in link 1 and link 2 be $q_1$ and $q_2$ respectively. Computer B requests retransmissions until it receives an error-free message on either link.

   **(a)** Find the probability that more than $k$ transmissions are required.

   **(b)** Find the probability that in the last transmission, the message on link 2 is received free of errors.

**2.127.** In order for a circuit board to work, seven identical chips must be in working order. To improve reliability, an additional chip is included in the board, and the design allows it to replace any of the seven other chips when they fail.

   **(a)** Find the probability $p_b$ that the board is working in terms of the probability $p$ that an individual chip is working.

   **(b)** Suppose that $n$ circuit boards are operated in parallel, and that we require a 99.9% probability that at least one board is working. How many boards are needed?

**2.128.** Consider a well-shuffled deck of cards consisting of 52 distinct cards, of which four are aces and four are kings.

   **(a)** Find the probability of obtaining an ace in the first draw.

   **(b)** Draw a card from the deck and look at it. What is the probability of obtaining an ace in the second draw? Does the answer change if you had not observed the first draw?

   **(c)** Suppose we draw seven cards from the deck. What is the probability that the seven cards include three aces? What is the probability that the seven cards include two kings? What is the probability that the seven cards include three aces and/or two kings?

   **(d)** Suppose that the entire deck of cards is distributed equally among four players. What is the probability that each player gets an ace?

# CHAPTER 3

# Discrete Random Variables

In most random experiments we are interested in a numerical attribute of the outcome of the experiment. A random variable is defined as a function that assigns a numerical value to the outcome of the experiment. In this chapter we introduce the concept of a random variable and methods for calculating probabilities of events involving a random variable. We focus on the simplest case, that of discrete random variables, and introduce the probability mass function. We define the expected value of a random variable and relate it to our intuitive notion of an average. We also introduce the conditional probability mass function for the case where we are given partial information about the random variable. These concepts and their extension in Chapter 4 provide us with the tools to evaluate the probabilities and averages of interest in the design of systems involving randomness.

Throughout the chapter we introduce important random variables and discuss typical applications where they arise. We also present methods for generating random variables. These methods are used in computer simulation models that predict the behavior and performance of complex modern systems.

## 3.1 THE NOTION OF A RANDOM VARIABLE

The outcome of a random experiment need not be a number. However, we are usually interested not in the outcome itself, but rather in some measurement or numerical attribute of the outcome. For example, in $n$ tosses of a coin, we may be interested in the total number of heads and not in the specific order in which heads and tails occur. In a randomly selected Web document, we may be interested only in the length of the document. In each of these examples, *a measurement assigns a numerical value to the outcome of the random experiment.* Since the outcomes are random, the results of the measurements will also be random. Hence it makes sense to talk about the probabilities of the resulting numerical values. The concept of a random variable formalizes this notion.

A **random variable** $X$ is a function that assigns a real number, $X(\zeta)$, to each outcome $\zeta$ in the sample space of a random experiment. Recall that a function is simply a rule for assigning a numerical value to each element of a set, as shown pictorially in

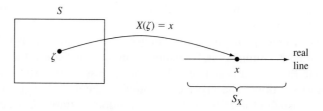

**FIGURE 3.1**
A random variable assigns a number $X(\zeta)$ to each outcome $\zeta$ in the sample space $S$ of a random experiment.

Fig. 3.1. The specification of a measurement on the outcome of a random experiment defines a function on the sample space, and hence a random variable. The sample space $S$ is the *domain* of the random variable, and the set $S_X$ of all values taken on by $X$ is the *range* of the random variable. Thus $S_X$ is a subset of the set of all real numbers. We will use the following notation: capital letters denote random variables, e.g., $X$ or $Y$, and lower case letters denote possible values of the random variables, e.g., $x$ or $y$.

---

### Example 3.1    Coin Tosses

A coin is tossed three times and the sequence of heads and tails is noted. The sample space for this experiment is $S = \{HHH, HHT, HTH, HTT, THH, THT, TTH, TTT\}$. Let $X$ be the number of heads in the three tosses. $X$ assigns each outcome $\zeta$ in $S$ a number from the set $S_X = \{0, 1, 2, 3\}$. The table below lists the eight outcomes of $S$ and the corresponding values of $X$.

| $\zeta$: | HHH | HHT | HTH | THH | HTT | THT | TTH | TTT |
|---|---|---|---|---|---|---|---|---|
| $X(\zeta)$: | 3 | 2 | 2 | 2 | 1 | 1 | 1 | 0 |

$X$ is then a random variable taking on values in the set $S_X = \{0, 1, 2, 3\}$.

---

### Example 3.2    A Betting Game

A player pays \$1.50 to play the following game: A coin is tossed three times and the number of heads $X$ is counted. The player receives \$1 if $X = 2$ and \$8 if $X = 3$, but nothing otherwise. Let $Y$ be the reward to the player. $Y$ is a function of the random variable $X$ and its outcomes can be related back to the sample space of the underlying random experiment as follows:

| $\zeta$: | HHH | HHT | HTH | THH | HTT | THT | TTH | TTT |
|---|---|---|---|---|---|---|---|---|
| $X(\zeta)$: | 3 | 2 | 2 | 2 | 1 | 1 | 1 | 0 |
| $Y(\zeta)$: | 8 | 1 | 1 | 1 | 0 | 0 | 0 | 0 |

$Y$ is then a random variable taking on values in the set $S_Y = \{0, 1, 8\}$.

The above example shows that a function of a random variable produces another random variable.

For random variables, the function or rule that assigns values to each outcome is fixed and deterministic, as, for example, in the rule "count the total number of dots facing up in the toss of two dice." The randomness in the experiment is complete as soon as the toss is done. The process of counting the dots facing up is deterministic. Therefore the distribution of the values of a random variable $X$ is determined by the probabilities of the outcomes $\zeta$ in the random experiment. In other words, the randomness in the observed values of $X$ is *induced* by the underlying random experiment, and we should therefore be able to compute the probabilities of the observed values of $X$ in terms of the probabilities of the underlying outcomes.

---

### Example 3.3    Coin Tosses and Betting

Let $X$ be the number of heads in three independent tosses of a fair coin. Find the probability of the event $\{X = 2\}$. Find the probability that the player in Example 3.2 wins \$8.

Note that $X(\zeta) = 2$ if and only if $\zeta$ is in $\{HHT, HTH, THH\}$. Therefore

$$P[X = 2] = P[\{HHT, HTH, HHT\}]$$

$$= P[\{HHT\}] + P[\{HTH\}] + P[\{HHT\}]$$

$$= 3/8.$$

The event $\{Y = 8\}$ occurs if and only if the outcome $\zeta$ is HHH, therefore

$$P[Y = 8] = P[\{HHH\}] = 1/8.$$

---

Example 3.3 illustrates a general technique for finding the probabilities of events involving the random variable $X$. Let the underlying random experiment have sample space $S$ and event class $\mathcal{F}$. To find the probability of a subset $B$ of $R$, e.g., $B = \{x_k\}$, we need to find the outcomes in $S$ that are mapped to $B$, that is,

$$A = \{\zeta : X(\zeta) \in B\} \tag{3.1}$$

as shown in Fig. 3.2. If event $A$ occurs then $X(\zeta) \in B$, so event $B$ occurs. Conversely, if event $B$ occurs, then the value $X(\zeta)$ implies that $\zeta$ is in $A$, so event $A$ occurs. Thus the probability that $X$ is in $B$ is given by:

$$P[X \in B] = P[A] = P[\{\zeta : X(\zeta) \in B\}]. \tag{3.2}$$

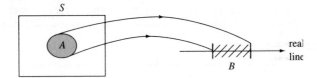

**FIGURE 3.2**
$P[X \text{ in } B] = P[\zeta \text{ in } A]$

We refer to $A$ and $B$ as **equivalent events**.

In some random experiments the outcome $\zeta$ is already the numerical value we are interested in. In such cases we simply let $X(\zeta) = \zeta$, that is, the identity function, to obtain a random variable.

### *3.1.1   Fine Point: Formal Definition of a Random Variable

In going from Eq. (3.1) to Eq. (3.2) we actually need to check that the event $A$ is in $\mathcal{F}$, because only events in $\mathcal{F}$ have probabilities assigned to them. The formal definition of a random variable in Chapter 4 will explicitly state this requirement.

If the event class $\mathcal{F}$ consists of all subsets of $S$, then the set $A$ will always be in $\mathcal{F}$, and any function from $S$ to $R$ will be a random variable. However, if the event class $\mathcal{F}$ does not consist of all subsets of $S$, then some functions from $S$ to $R$ may not be random variables, as illustrated by the following example.

---

### Example 3.4   A Function That Is Not a Random Variable

This example shows why the definition of a random variable requires that we check that the set $A$ is in $\mathcal{F}$. An urn contains three balls. One ball is electronically coded with a label 00. Another ball is coded with 01, and the third ball has a 10 label. The sample space for this experiment is $S = \{00, 01, 10\}$. Let the event class $\mathcal{F}$ consist of all unions, intersections, and complements of the events $A_1 = \{00, 10\}$ and $A_2 = \{01\}$. In this event class, the outcome 00 cannot be distinguished from the outcome 10. For example, this could result from a faulty label reader that cannot distinguish between 00 and 10. The event class has four events $\mathcal{F} = \{\varnothing, \{00, 10\}, \{01\}, \{00, 01, 10\}\}$. Let the probability assignment for the events in $\mathcal{F}$ be $P[\{00, 10\}] = 2/3$ and $P[\{01\}] = 1/3$.

Consider the following function $X$ from $S$ to $R$: $X(00) = 0$, $X(01) = 1$, $X(10) = 2$. To find the probability of $\{X = 0\}$, we need the probability of $\{\zeta: X(\zeta) = 0\} = \{00\}$. However, $\{00\}$ is not in the class $\mathcal{F}$, and so $X$ is not a random variable because we cannot determine the probability that $X = 0$.

---

## 3.2   DISCRETE RANDOM VARIABLES AND PROBABILITY MASS FUNCTION

A **discrete random variable** $X$ is defined as a random variable that assumes values from a countable set, that is, $S_X = \{x_1, x_2, x_3, \dots\}$. A discrete random variable is said to be **finite** if its range is finite, that is, $S_X = \{x_1, x_2, \dots, x_n\}$. We are interested in finding the probabilities of events involving a discrete random variable $X$. Since the sample space $S_X$ is discrete, we only need to obtain the probabilities for the events $A_k = \{\zeta: X(\zeta) = x_k\}$ in the underlying random experiment. The probabilities of all events involving $X$ can be found from the probabilities of the $A_k$'s.

The **probability mass function (pmf) of a discrete random variable** $X$ is defined as:

$$p_X(x) = P[X = x] = \mathrm{P}[\{\zeta: X(\zeta) = x\}] \quad \text{for } x \text{ a real number.} \tag{3.3}$$

Note that $p_X(x)$ is a function of $x$ over the real line, and that $p_X(x)$ can be nonzero only at the values $x_1, x_2, x_3, \dots$. For $x_k$ in $S_X$, we have $p_X(x_k) = P[A_k]$.

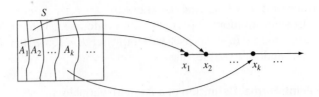

**FIGURE 3.3**
Partition of sample space $S$ associated with a discrete random variable.

The events $A_1, A_2, \ldots$ form a partition of $S$ as illustrated in Fig. 3.3. To see this, we first show that the events are disjoint. Let $j \neq k$, then

$$A_j \cap A_k = \{\zeta : X(\zeta) = x_j \text{ and } X(\zeta) = x_k\} = \varnothing$$

since each $\zeta$ is mapped into one and only one value in $S_X$. Next we show that $S$ is the union of the $A_k$'s. Every $\zeta$ in $S$ is mapped into some $x_k$ so that every $\zeta$ belongs to an event $A_k$ in the partition. Therefore:

$$S = A_1 \cup A_2 \cup \ldots.$$

All events involving the random variable $X$ can be expressed as the union of events $A_k$'s. For example, suppose we are interested in the event $X$ in $B = \{x_2, x_5\}$, then

$$P[X \text{ in } B] = P[\{\zeta : X(\zeta) = x_2\} \cup \{\zeta : X(\zeta) = x_5\}]$$
$$= P[A_2 \cup A_5] = P[A_2] + P[A_5]$$
$$= p_X(2) + p_X(5).$$

The pmf $p_X(x)$ satisfies three properties that provide all the information required to calculate probabilities for events involving the discrete random variable $X$:

**(i)** $p_X(x) \geq 0$ for all $x$ \hfill (3.4a)

**(ii)** $\displaystyle\sum_{x \in S_X} p_X(x) = \sum_{\text{all } k} p_X(x_k) = \sum_{\text{all } k} P[A_k] = 1$ \hfill (3.4b)

**(iii)** $P[X \text{ in } B] = \displaystyle\sum_{x \in B} p_X(x)$ where $B \subset S_X$. \hfill (3.4c)

Property (i) is true because the pmf values are defined as a probability, $p_X(x) = P[X = x]$. Property (ii) follows because the events $A_k = \{X = x_k\}$ form a partition of $S$. Note that the summations in Eqs. (3.4b) and (3.4c) will have a finite or infinite number of terms depending on whether the random variable is finite or not. Next consider property (iii). Any event $B$ involving $X$ is the union of elementary events, so by Axiom III$'$ we have:

$$P[X \text{ in } B] = P[\bigcup_{x \in B} \{\zeta : X(\zeta) = x\}] = \sum_{x \in B} P[X = x] = \sum_{x \in B} p_X(x).$$

The pmf of $X$ gives us the probabilities for all the elementary events from $S_X$. The probability of any subset of $S_X$ is obtained from the sum of the corresponding elementary events. In fact we have everything required to specify a probability law for the outcomes in $S_X$. If we are only interested in events concerning $X$, then we can forget about the underlying random experiment and its associated probability law and just work with $S_X$ and the pmf of $X$.

---

### Example 3.5   Coin Tosses and Binomial Random Variable

Let $X$ be the number of heads in three independent tosses of a coin. Find the pmf of $X$.
Proceeding as in Example 3.3, we find:

$$p_0 = P[X = 0] = P[\{TTT\}] = (1 - p)^3,$$
$$p_1 = P[X = 1] = P[\{HTT\}] + P[\{THT\}] + P[\{TTH\}] = 3(1 - p)^2 p,$$
$$p_2 = P[X = 2] = P[\{HHT\}] + P[\{HTH\}] + P[\{THH\}] = 3(1 - p)p^2,$$
$$p_3 = P[X = 3] = P[\{HHH\}] = p^3.$$

Note that $p_X(0) + p_X(1) + p_X(2) + p_X(3) = 1$.

---

### Example 3.6   A Betting Game

A player receives \$1 if the number of heads in three coin tosses is 2, \$8 if the number is 3, but nothing otherwise. Find the pmf of the reward $Y$.

$$p_Y(0) = P[\zeta \in \{TTT, TTH, THT, HTT\}] = 4/8 = 1/2$$
$$p_Y(1) = P[\zeta \in \{THH, HTH, HHT\}] = 3/8$$
$$p_Y(8) = P[\zeta \in \{HHH\}] = 1/8.$$

Note that $p_Y(0) + p_Y(1) + p_Y(8) = 1$.

---

Figures 3.4(a) and (b) show the graph of $p_X(x)$ versus $x$ for the random variables in Examples 3.5 and 3.6, respectively. In general, the graph of the pmf of a discrete random variable has vertical arrows of height $p_X(x_k)$ at the values $x_k$ in $S_X$. We may view the total probability as one unit of mass and $p_X(x)$ as the amount of probability mass that is placed at each of the discrete points $x_1, x_2, \ldots$. The relative values of pmf at different points give an indication of the relative likelihoods of occurrence.

---

### Example 3.7   Random Number Generator

A random number generator produces an integer number $X$ that is equally likely to be any element in the set $S_X = \{0, 1, 2, \ldots, M - 1\}$. Find the pmf of $X$.
For each $k$ in $S_X$, we have $p_X(k) = 1/M$. Note that

$$p_X(0) + p_X(1) + \ldots + p_X(M - 1) = 1.$$

We call $X$ the **uniform random variable** in the set $\{0, 1, \ldots, M - 1\}$.

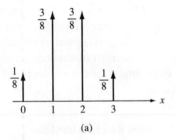

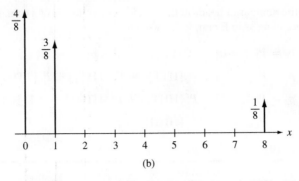

**FIGURE 3.4**
(a) Graph of pmf in three coin tosses; (b) Graph of pmf in betting game.

---

## Example 3.8    Bernoulli Random Variable

Let $A$ be an event of interest in some random experiment, e.g., a device is not defective. We say that a "success" occurs if $A$ occurs when we perform the experiment. The Bernoulli random variable $I_A$ is equal to 1 if $A$ occurs and zero otherwise, and is given by the *indicator function for $A$*:

$$I_A(\zeta) = \begin{cases} 0 & \text{if } \zeta \text{ not in } A \\ 1 & \text{if } \zeta \text{ in } A. \end{cases} \tag{3.5a}$$

Find the pmf of $I_A$.

$I_A(\zeta)$ is a finite discrete random variable with values from $S_I = \{0, 1\}$, with pmf:

$$p_I(0) = P[\{\zeta : \zeta \in A^c\}] = 1 - p$$

$$p_I(1) = P[\{\zeta : \zeta \in A\}] = p. \tag{3.5b}$$

We call $I_A$ the **Bernoulli random variable**. Note that $p_I(1) + p_I(2) = 1$.

---

## Example 3.9    Message Transmissions

Let $X$ be the number of times a message needs to be transmitted until it arrives correctly at its destination. Find the pmf of $X$. Find the probability that $X$ is an even number.

$X$ is a discrete random variable taking on values from $S_X = \{1, 2, 3, \ldots\}$. The event $\{X = k\}$ occurs if the underlying experiment finds $k - 1$ consecutive erroneous transmissions ("failures") followed by a error-free one ("success"):

$$p_X(k) = P[X = k] = P[00\ldots01] = (1 - p)^{k-1}p = q^{k-1}p \quad k = 1, 2, \ldots. \quad (3.6)$$

We call $X$ the **geometric random variable**, and we say that $X$ is geometrically distributed. In Eq. (2.42b), we saw that the sum of the geometric probabilities is 1.

$$P[X \text{ is even}] = \sum_{k=1}^{\infty} p_X(2k) = p\sum_{k=1}^{\infty} q^{2k-1} = p\frac{1}{1 - q^2} = \frac{1}{1 + q}.$$

---

### Example 3.10 Transmission Errors

A binary communications channel introduces a bit error in a transmission with probability $p$. Let $X$ be the number of errors in $n$ independent transmissions. Find the pmf of $X$. Find the probability of one or fewer errors.

$X$ takes on values in the set $S_X = \{0, 1, \ldots, n\}$. Each transmission results in a "0" if there is no error and a "1" if there is an error, $P["1"] = p$ and $P["0"] = 1 - p$. The probability of $k$ errors in $n$ bit transmissions is given by the probability of an error pattern that has $k$ 1's and $n - k$ 0's:

$$p_X(k) = P[X = k] = \binom{n}{k}p^k(1 - p)^{n-k} \quad k = 0, 1, \ldots, n. \quad (3.7)$$

We call $X$ the **binomial random variable**, with parameters $n$ and $p$. In Eq. (2.39b), we saw that the sum of the binomial probabilities is 1.

$$P[X \le 1] = \binom{n}{0}p^0(1 - p)^{n-0} + \binom{n}{1}p^1(1 - p)^{n-1} = (1 - p)^n + np(1 - p)^{n-1}.$$

---

Finally, let's consider the relationship between relative frequencies and the pmf $p_X(x_k)$. Suppose we perform $n$ independent repetitions to obtain $n$ observations of the discrete random variable $X$. Let $N_k(n)$ be the number of times the event $X = x_k$ occurs and let $f_k(n) = N_k(n)/n$ be the corresponding relative frequency. As $n$ becomes large we expect that $f_k(n) \to p_X(x_k)$. Therefore the graph of relative frequencies should approach the graph of the pmf. Figure 3.5(a) shows the graph of relative

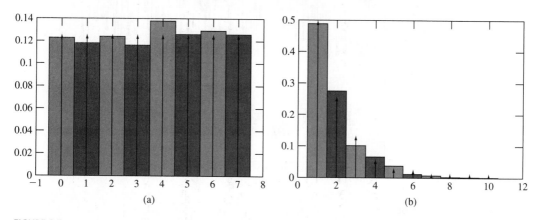

**FIGURE 3.5**

(a) Relative frequencies and corresponding uniform pmf; (b) Relative frequencies and corresponding geometric pmf.

frequencies for 1000 repetitions of an experiment that generates a uniform random variable from the set $\{0, 1, \ldots, 7\}$ and the corresponding pmf. Figure 3.5(b) shows the graph of relative frequencies and pmf for a geometric random variable with $p = 1/2$ and $n = 1000$ repetitions. In both cases we see that the graph of relative frequencies approaches that of the pmf.

## 3.3 EXPECTED VALUE AND MOMENTS OF DISCRETE RANDOM VARIABLE

In order to completely describe the behavior of a discrete random variable, an entire function, namely $p_X(x)$, must be given. In some situations we are interested in a few parameters that summarize the information provided by the pmf. For example, Fig. 3.6 shows the results of many repetitions of an experiment that produces two random variables. The random variable $Y$ varies about the value 0, whereas the random variable $X$ varies around the value 5. It is also clear that $X$ is more spread out than $Y$. In this section we introduce parameters that quantify these properties.

The **expected value** or **mean** of a **discrete random variable** $X$ is defined by

$$m_X = E[X] = \sum_{x \in S_X} x p_X(x) = \sum_k x_k p_X(x_k). \tag{3.8}$$

The expected value $E[X]$ is defined if the above sum converges absolutely, that is,

$$E[|X|] = \sum_k |x_k| p_X(x_k) < \infty. \tag{3.9}$$

There are random variables for which Eq. (3.9) does not converge. In such cases, we say that the expected value does not exist.

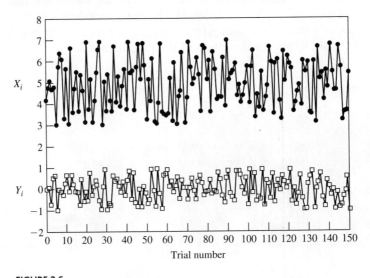

**FIGURE 3.6**
The graphs show 150 repetitions of the experiments yielding $X$ and $Y$. It is clear that $X$ is centered about the value 5 while $Y$ is centered about 0. It is also clear that $X$ is more spread out than $Y$.

If we view $p_X(x)$ as the distribution of mass on the points $x_1, x_2, \ldots$ in the real line, then $E[X]$ represents the center of mass of this distribution. For example, in Fig. 3.5(a), we can see that the pmf of a discrete random variable that is uniformly distributed in $\{0, \ldots, 7\}$ has a center of mass at 3.5.

---

### Example 3.11    Mean of Bernoulli Random Variable

Find the expected value of the Bernoulli random variable $I_A$.

From Example 3.8, we have

$$E[I_A] = 0p_I(0) + 1p_I(1) = p.$$

where $p$ is the probability of success in the Bernoulli trial.

---

### Example 3.12    Three Coin Tosses and Binomial Random Variable

Let $X$ be the number of heads in three tosses of a fair coin. Find $E[X]$.

Equation (3.8) and the pmf of $X$ that was found in Example 3.5 gives:

$$E[X] = \sum_{k=0}^{3} kp_X(k) = 0\left(\frac{1}{8}\right) + 1\left(\frac{3}{8}\right) + 2\left(\frac{3}{8}\right) + 3\left(\frac{1}{8}\right) = 1.5.$$

Note that the above is the $n = 3$, $p = 1/2$ case of a binomial random variable, which we will see has $E[X] = np$.

---

### Example 3.13    Mean of a Uniform Discrete Random Variable

Let $X$ be the random number generator in Example 3.7. Find $E[X]$.

From Example 3.5 we have $p_X(j) = 1/M$ for $j = 0, \ldots, M - 1$, so

$$E[X] = \sum_{k=0}^{M-1} k\frac{1}{M} = \frac{1}{M}\{0 + 1 + 2 + \cdots + M - 1\} = \frac{(M - 1)M}{2M} = \frac{(M - 1)}{2}$$

where we used the fact that $1 + 2 + \cdots + L = (L + 1)L/2$. Note that for $M = 8$, $E[X] = 3.5$, which is consistent with our observation of the center of mass in Fig. 3.5(a).

---

The use of the term "expected value" does not mean that we expect to observe $E[X]$ when we perform the experiment that generates $X$. For example, the expected value of a Bernoulli trial is $p$, but its outcomes are always either 0 or 1.

$E[X]$ corresponds to the "average of $X$" in a large number of observations of $X$. Suppose we perform $n$ independent repetitions of the experiment that generates $X$, and we record the observed values as $x(1), x(2), \ldots, x(n)$, where $x(j)$ is the observation in the $j$th experiment. Let $N_k(n)$ be the number of times $x_k$ is observed, and let $f_k(n) = N_k(n)/n$ be the corresponding relative frequency. The arithmetic average, or **sample mean**, of the observations, is:

$$\langle X \rangle_n = \frac{x(1) + x(2) + \cdots + x(n)}{n} = \frac{x_1 N_1(n) + x_2 N_2(n) + \cdots + x_k N_k(n) + \cdots}{n}$$

$$= x_1 f_1(n) + x_2 f_2(n) + \cdots + x_k f_k(n) + \cdots$$

$$= \sum_k x_k f_k(n). \tag{3.10}$$

The first numerator adds the observations in the order in which they occur, and the second numerator counts how many times each $x_k$ occurs and then computes the total. As n becomes large, we expect relative frequencies to approach the probabilities $p_X(x_k)$:

$$\lim_{n \to \infty} f_k(n) = p_X(x_k) \quad \text{for all } k. \tag{3.11}$$

Equation (3.10) then implies that:

$$\langle X \rangle_n = \sum_k x_k f_k(n) \to \sum_k x_k p_X(x_k) = E[X]. \tag{3.12}$$

Thus we expect the sample mean to converge to E[X] as n becomes large.

---

### Example 3.14    A Betting Game

A player at a fair pays \$1.50 to toss a coin three times. The player receives \$1 if the number of heads is 2, \$8 if the number is 3, but nothing otherwise. Find the expected value of the reward Y. What is the expected value of the gain?

The expected reward is:

$$E[Y] = 0p_Y(0) + 1p_Y(1)) + 8p_Y(8) = 0\left(\frac{4}{8}\right) + 1\left(\frac{3}{8}\right) + 8\left(\frac{1}{8}\right) = \left(\frac{11}{8}\right).$$

The expected gain is:

$$E[Y - 1.5] = \frac{11}{8} - \frac{12}{8} = -\frac{1}{8}.$$

Players lose 12.5 cents on average per game, so the house makes a nice profit over the long run. In Example 3.18 we will see that some engineering designs also "bet" that users will behave a certain way.

---

### Example 3.15    Mean of a Geometric Random Variable

Let $X$ be the number of bytes in a message, and suppose that $X$ has a geometric distribution with parameter $p$. Find the mean of $X$.

$X$ can take on arbitrarily large values since $S_X = \{1, 2, \dots\}$. The expected value is:

$$E[X] = \sum_{k=1}^{\infty} kpq^{k-1} = p\sum_{k=1}^{\infty} kq^{k-1}.$$

This expression is readily evaluated by differentiating the series

$$\frac{1}{1-x} = \sum_{k=0}^{\infty} x^k \tag{3.13}$$

to obtain

$$\frac{1}{(1-x)^2} = \sum_{k=0}^{\infty} kx^{k-1}. \tag{3.14}$$

Letting $x = q$, we obtain

$$E[X] = p\frac{1}{(1-q)^2} = \frac{1}{p}. \tag{3.15}$$

We see that $X$ has a finite expected value as long as $p > 0$.

---

For certain random variables large values occur sufficiently frequently that the expected value does not exist, as illustrated by the following example.

---

### Example 3.16    St. Petersburg Paradox

A fair coin is tossed repeatedly until a tail comes up. If $X$ tosses are needed, then the casino pays the gambler $Y = 2^X$ dollars. How much should the gambler be willing to pay to play this game?

 If the gambler plays this game a large number of times, then the payoff should be the expected value of $Y = 2^X$. If the coin is fair, $P[X = k] = (1/2)^k$ and $P[Y = 2^k] = (1/2)^k$, so:

$$E[Y] = \sum_{k=1}^{\infty} 2^k p_Y(2^k) = \sum_{k=1}^{\infty} 2^k \left(\frac{1}{2}\right)^k = 1 + 1 + \cdots = \infty.$$

This game does indeed appear to offer the gambler a sweet deal, and so the gambler should be willing to pay any amount to play the game! The paradox is that a sane person would not pay a lot to play this game. Problem 3.34 discusses ways to resolve the paradox.

---

 Random variables with unbounded expected value are not uncommon and appear in models where outcomes that have extremely large values are not that rare. Examples include the sizes of files in Web transfers, frequencies of words in large bodies of text, and various financial and economic problems.

### 3.3.1    Expected Value of Functions of a Random Variable

Let $X$ be a discrete random variable, and let $Z = g(X)$. Since $X$ is discrete, $Z = g(X)$ will assume a countable set of values of the form $g(x_k)$ where $x_k \in S_X$. Denote the set of values assumed by $g(X)$ by $\{z_1, z_2, \dots\}$. One way to find the expected value of $Z$ is to use Eq. (3.8), which requires that we first find the pmf of $Z$. Another way is to use the following result:

$$E[Z] = E[g(X)] = \sum_{k} g(x_k) p_X(x_k). \qquad (3.16)$$

To show Eq. (3.16) group the terms $x_k$ that are mapped to each value $z_j$:

$$\sum_{k} g(x_k) p_X(x_k) = \sum_{j} z_j \left\{ \sum_{x_k : g(x_k) = z_j} p_X(x_k) \right\} = \sum_{j} z_j p_Z(z_j) = E[Z].$$

The sum inside the braces is the probability of all terms $x_k$ for which $g(x_k) = z_j$, which is the probability that $Z = z_j$, that is, $p_Z(z_j)$.

---

### Example 3.17    Square-Law Device

Let $X$ be a noise voltage that is uniformly distributed in $S_X = \{-3, -1, +1, +3\}$ with $p_X(k) = 1/4$ for $k$ in $S_X$. Find $E[Z]$ where $Z = X^2$.

 Using the first approach we find the pmf of $Z$:

$$p_Z(9) = P[X \in \{-3, +3\}] = p_X(-3) + p_X(3) = 1/2$$

$$p_Z(1) = p_X(-1) + p_X(1) = 1/2$$

and so

$$E[Z] = 1\left(\frac{1}{2}\right) + 9\left(\frac{1}{2}\right) = 5.$$

The second approach gives:

$$E[Z] = E[X^2] = \sum_k k^2 p_X(k) = \frac{1}{4}\{(-3)^2 + (-1)^2 + 1^2 + 3^2\} = \frac{20}{4} = 5.$$

Equation 3.16 implies several very useful results. Let $Z$ be the function

$$Z = ag(X) + bh(X) + c$$

where $a$, $b$, and $c$ are real numbers, then:

$$E[Z] = aE[g(X)] + bE[h(X)] + c. \qquad (3.17a)$$

From Eq. (3.16) we have:

$$E[Z] = E[ag(X) + bh(X) + c] = \sum_k (ag(x_k) + bh(x_k) + c)p_X(x_k)$$

$$= a\sum_k g(x_k)p_X(x_k) + b\sum_k h(x_k)p_X(x_k) + c\sum_k p_X(x_k)$$

$$= aE[g(X)] + bE[h(X)] + c.$$

Equation (3.17a), by setting $a$, $b$, and/or $c$ to 0 or 1, implies the following expressions:

$$E[g(X) + h(X)] = E[g(X)] + E[h(X)]. \qquad (3.17b)$$

$$E[aX] = aE[X]. \qquad (3.17c)$$

$$E[X + c] = E[X] + c. \qquad (3.17d)$$

$$E[c] = c. \qquad (3.17e)$$

---

### Example 3.18   Square-Law Device

The noise voltage $X$ in the previous example is amplified and shifted to obtain $Y = 2X + 10$, and then squared to produce $Z = Y^2 = (2X + 10)^2$. Find $E[Z]$.

$$E[Z] = E[(2X + 10)^2] = E[4X^2 + 40X + 100]$$

$$= 4E[X^2] + 40E[X] + 100 = 4(5) + 40(0) + 100 = 120.$$

---

### Example 3.19   Voice Packet Multiplexer

Let $X$ be the number of voice packets containing active speech produced by $n = 48$ independent speakers in a 10-millisecond period as discussed in Section 1.4. $X$ is a binomial random variable with parameter $n$ and probability $p = 1/3$. Suppose a packet multiplexer transmits up to $M = 20$ active packets every 10 ms, and any excess active packets are discarded. Let $Z$ be the number of packets discarded. Find $E[Z]$.

The number of packets discarded every 10 ms is the following function of $X$:

$$Z = (X - M)^+ \triangleq \begin{cases} 0 & \text{if } X \le M \\ X - M & \text{if } X > M. \end{cases}$$

$$E[Z] = \sum_{k=20}^{48} (k - 20)\binom{48}{k}\left(\frac{1}{3}\right)^k\left(\frac{2}{3}\right)^{48-k} = 0.182.$$

Every 10 ms $E[X] = np = 16$ active packets are produced on average, so the fraction of active packets discarded is $0.182/16 = 1.1\%$, which users will tolerate. This example shows that engineered systems also play "betting" games where favorable statistics are exploited to use resources efficiently. In this example, the multiplexer transmits 20 packets per period instead of 48 for a reduction of $28/48 = 58\%$.

---

### 3.3.2    Variance of a Random Variable

The expected value $E[X]$, by itself, provides us with limited information about $X$. For example, if we know that $E[X] = 0$, then it could be that $X$ is zero all the time. However, it is also possible that $X$ can take on extremely large positive and negative values. We are therefore interested not only in the mean of a random variable, but also in the extent of the random variable's variation about its mean. Let the deviation of the random variable $X$ about its mean be $X - E[X]$, which can take on positive and negative values. Since we are interested in the magnitude of the variations only, it is convenient to work with the square of the deviation, which is always positive, $D(X) = (X - E[X])^2$. The expected value is a constant, so we will denote it by $m_X = E[X]$. The **variance of the random variable** $X$ is defined as the expected value of $D$:

$$\sigma_X^2 = \text{VAR}[X] = E[(X - m_X)^2]$$

$$= \sum_{x \in S_X} (x - m_X)^2 p_X(x) = \sum_{k=1}^{\infty} (x_k - m_X)^2 p_X(x_k). \tag{3.18}$$

The **standard deviation of the random variable** $X$ is defined by:

$$\sigma_X = \text{STD}[X] = \text{VAR}[X]^{1/2}. \tag{3.19}$$

By taking the square root of the variance we obtain a quantity with the same units as $X$. An alternative expression for the variance can be obtained as follows:

$$\text{VAR}[X] = E[(X - m_X)^2] = E[X^2 - 2m_X X + m_X^2]$$

$$= E[X^2] - 2m_X E[X] + m_X^2$$

$$= E[X^2] - m_X^2. \tag{3.20}$$

$E[X^2]$ is called the **second moment of** $X$. The $n$th moment of $X$ is defined as $E[X^n]$.

Equations (3.17c), (3.17d), and (3.17e) imply the following useful expressions for the variance. Let $Y = X + c$, then

$$\text{VAR}[X + c] = E[(X + c - (E[X] + c)])^2]$$

$$= E[(X - E[X])^2] = \text{VAR}[X]. \tag{3.21}$$

Adding a constant to a random variable does not affect the variance. Let $Z = cX$, then:

$$\text{VAR}[cX] = E[(cX - cE[X])^2] = E[c^2(X - E[X])^2] = c^2\,\text{VAR}[X]. \quad (3.22)$$

Scaling a random variable by $c$ scales the variance by $c^2$ and the standard deviation by $|c|$.
Now let $X = c$, a random variable that is equal to a constant with probability 1, then

$$\text{VAR}[X] = E[(X - c)^2] = E[0] = 0. \quad (3.23)$$

A constant random variable has zero variance.

---

### Example 3.20    Three Coin Tosses

Let $X$ be the number of heads in three tosses of a fair coin. Find $\text{VAR}[X]$.

$$E[X^2] = 0\left(\frac{1}{8}\right) + 1^2\left(\frac{3}{8}\right) + 2^2\left(\frac{3}{8}\right) + 3^2\left(\frac{1}{8}\right) = 3 \quad \text{and}$$

$$\text{VAR}[X] = E[X^2] - m_X^2 = 3 - 1.5^2 = 0.75.$$

Recall that this is an $n = 3$, $p = 1/2$ binomial random variable. We see later that variance for the binomial random variable is $npq$.

---

### Example 3.21    Variance of Bernoulli Random Variable

Find the variance of the Bernoulli random variable $I_A$.

$$E[I_A^2] = 0p_I(0) + 1^2 p_I(1) = p \quad \text{and so}$$

$$\text{VAR}[I_A] = p - p^2 = p(1 - p) = pq. \quad (3.24)$$

---

### Example 3.22    Variance of Geometric Random Variable

Find the variance of the geometric random variable.
Differentiate the term $(1 - x^2)^{-1}$ in Eq. (3.14) to obtain

$$\frac{2}{(1 - x)^3} = \sum_{k=0}^{\infty} k(k - 1)x^{k-2}.$$

Let $x = q$ and multiply both sides by $pq$ to obtain:

$$\frac{2pq}{(1 - q)^3} = pq\sum_{k=0}^{\infty} k(k - 1)q^{k-2}$$

$$= \sum_{k=0}^{\infty} k(k - 1)pq^{k-1} = E[X^2] - E[X].$$

So the second moment is

$$E[X^2] = \frac{2pq}{(1 - q)^3} + E[X] = \frac{2q}{p^2} + \frac{1}{p} = \frac{1 + q}{p^2}$$

and the variance is

$$\text{VAR}[X] = E[X^2] - E[X]^2 = \frac{1+q}{p^2} - \frac{1}{p^2} = \frac{q}{p^2}.$$

---

## 3.4 CONDITIONAL PROBABILITY MASS FUNCTION

In many situations we have partial information about a random variable $X$ or about the outcome of its underlying random experiment. We are interested in how this information changes the probability of events involving the random variable. The conditional probability mass function addresses this question for discrete random variables.

### 3.4.1 Conditional Probability Mass Function

Let $X$ be a discrete random variable with pmf $p_X(x)$, and let $C$ be an event that has nonzero probability, $P[C] > 0$. See Fig. 3.7. The **conditional probability mass function** of $X$ is defined by the conditional probability:

$$p_X(x|C) = P[X = x|C] \qquad \text{for } x \text{ a real number.} \tag{3.25}$$

Applying the definition of conditional probability we have:

$$p_X(x|C) = \frac{P[\{X = x\} \cap C]}{P[C]}. \tag{3.26}$$

The above expression has a nice intuitive interpretation: The conditional probability of the event $\{X = x_k\}$ is given by the probabilities of outcomes $\zeta$ for which *both* $X(\zeta) = x_k$ *and* $\zeta$ are in $C$, normalized by $P[C]$.

The conditional pmf satisfies Eqs. (3.4a) – (3.4c). Consider Eq. (3.4b). The set of events $A_k = \{X = x_k\}$ is a partition of $S$, so

$$C = \bigcup_k (A_k \cap C), \quad \text{and}$$

$$\sum_{x_k \in S_X} p_X(x_k|C) = \sum_{\text{all } k} p_X(x_k|C) = \sum_{\text{all } k} \frac{P[\{X = x_k\} \cap C]}{P[C]}$$

$$= \frac{1}{P[C]} \sum_{\text{all } k} P[A_k \cap C] = \frac{P[C]}{P[C]} = 1.$$

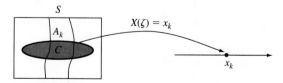

**FIGURE 3.7**
Conditional pmf of $X$ given event $C$.

Similarly we can show that:

$$P[X \text{ in } B|C] = \sum_{x \in B} p_X(x|C) \text{ where } B \subset S_X.$$

---

### Example 3.23    A Random Clock

The minute hand in a clock is spun and the outcome $\zeta$ is the minute where the hand comes to rest. Let $X$ be the hour where the hand comes to rest. Find the pmf of $X$. Find the conditional pmf of $X$ given $B = \{\text{first 4 hours}\}$; given $D = \{1 < \zeta \le 11\}$.

We assume that the hand is equally likely to rest at any of the minutes in the range $S = \{1, 2, \dots, 60\}$, so $P[\zeta = k] = 1/60$ for $k$ in $S$. $X$ takes on values from $S_X = \{1, 2, \dots, 12\}$ and it is easy to show that $p_X(j) = 1/12$ for $j$ in $S_X$. Since $B = \{1, 2, 3, 4\}$:

$$p_X(j|B) = \frac{P[\{X = j\} \cap B]}{P[B]} = \frac{P[X \in \{j\} \cap \{1, 2, 3, 4\}]}{P[X \in \{1, 2, 3, 4\}]}$$

$$= \begin{cases} \dfrac{P[X = j]}{1/3} = \dfrac{1}{4} & \text{if } j \in \{1, 2, 3, 4\} \\ 0 & \text{otherwise.} \end{cases}$$

The event $B$ above involves $X$ only. The event $D$, however, is stated in terms of the outcomes in the underlying experiment (i.e., minutes not hours), so the probability of the intersection has to be expressed accordingly:

$$p_X(j|D) = \frac{P[\{X = j\} \cap D]}{P[D]} = \frac{P[\zeta : X(\zeta) = j \text{ and } \zeta \in \{2, \dots, 11\}]}{P[\zeta \in \{2, \dots, 11\}]}$$

$$= \begin{cases} \dfrac{P[\zeta \in \{2, 3, 4, 5\}]}{10/60} = \dfrac{4}{10} & \text{for } j = 1 \\[2mm] \dfrac{P[\zeta \in \{6, 7, 8, 9, 10\}]}{10/60} = \dfrac{5}{10} & \text{for } j = 2 \\[2mm] \dfrac{P[\zeta \in \{11\}]}{10/60} = \dfrac{1}{10} & \text{for } j = 3. \end{cases}$$

Most of the time the event $C$ is defined in terms of $X$, for example $C = \{X > 10\}$ or $C = \{a \le X \le b\}$. For $x_k$ in $S_X$, we have the following general result:

$$p_X(x_k|C) = \begin{cases} \dfrac{p_X(x_k)}{P[C]} & \text{if } x_k \in C \\ 0 & \text{if } x_k \notin C. \end{cases} \tag{3.27}$$

The above expression is determined entirely by the pmf of $X$.

---

### Example 3.24    Residual Waiting Times

Let $X$ be the time required to transmit a message, where $X$ is a uniform random variable with $S_X = \{1, 2, \dots, L\}$. Suppose that a message has already been transmitting for $m$ time units, find the probability that the remaining transmission time is $j$ time units.

We are given $C = \{X > m\}$, so for $m + 1 \le m + j \le L$:

$$p_X(m + j | X > m) = \frac{P[X = m + j]}{P[X > m]}$$

$$= \frac{\dfrac{1}{L}}{\dfrac{L - m}{L}} = \frac{1}{L - m} \qquad \text{for } m + 1 \le m + j \le L. \qquad (3.28)$$

$X$ is equally likely to be any of the remaining $L - m$ possible values. As $m$ increases, $1/(L - m)$ increases implying that the end of the message transmission becomes increasingly likely.

Many random experiments have natural ways of partitioning the sample space $S$ into the union of disjoint events $B_1, B_2, \ldots, B_n$. Let $p_X(x | B_i)$ be the conditional pmf of $X$ given event $B_i$. The theorem on total probability allows us to find the pmf of $X$ in terms of the conditional pmf's:

$$p_X(x) = \sum_{i=1}^{n} p_X(x | B_i) P[B_i]. \qquad (3.29)$$

---

**Example 3.25   Device Lifetimes**

A production line yields two types of devices. Type 1 devices occur with probability $\alpha$ and work for a relatively short time that is geometrically distributed with parameter $r$. Type 2 devices work much longer, occur with probability $1 - \alpha$, and have a lifetime that is geometrically distributed with parameter $s$. Let $X$ be the lifetime of an arbitrary device. Find the pmf of $X$.

The random experiment that generates $X$ involves selecting a device type and then observing its lifetime. We can partition the sets of outcomes in this experiment into event $B_1$, consisting of those outcomes in which the device is type 1, and $B_2$, consisting of those outcomes in which the device is type 2. The conditional pmf's of $X$ given the device type are:

$$p_{X|B_1}(k) = (1 - r)^{k-1} r \qquad \text{for } k = 1, 2, \ldots$$

and

$$p_{X|B_2}(k) = (1 - s)^{k-1} s \qquad \text{for } k = 1, 2, \ldots.$$

We obtain the pmf of $X$ from Eq. (3.29):

$$p_X(k) = p_X(k | B_1) P[B_1] + p_X(k | B_2) P[B_2]$$

$$= (1 - r)^{k-1} r\alpha + (1 - s)^{k-1} s(1 - \alpha) \qquad \text{for } k = 1, 2, \ldots.$$

---

### 3.4.2   Conditional Expected Value

Let $X$ be a discrete random variable, and suppose that we know that event $B$ has occurred. The **conditional expected value of $X$ given $B$** is defined as:

$$m_{X|B} = E[X | B] = \sum_{x \in S_X} x p_X(x | B) = \sum_{k} x_k p_X(x_k | B) \qquad (3.30)$$

where we apply the absolute convergence requirement on the summation. The **conditional variance of $X$ given $B$** is defined as:

$$\text{VAR}[X|B] = E[(X - m_{X|B})^2|B] = \sum_{k=1}^{\infty}(x_k - m_{X|B})^2 p_X(x_k|B)$$

$$= E[X^2|B] - m_{X|B}^2.$$

Note that the variation is measured with respect to $m_{X|B}$, not $m_X$.

Let $B_1, B_2, ..., B_n$ be the partition of $S$, and let $p_X(x|B_i)$ be the conditional pmf of $X$ given event $B_i$. $E[X]$ can be calculated from the conditional expected values $E[X|B]$:

$$E[X] = \sum_{i=1}^{n} E[X|B_i]P[B_i]. \tag{3.31a}$$

By the theorem on total probability we have:

$$E[X] = \sum_{k} k p_X(x_k) = \sum_{k} k \left\{ \sum_{i=1}^{n} p_X(x_k|B_i)P[B_i] \right\}$$

$$= \sum_{i=1}^{n} \left\{ \sum_{k} k p_X(x_k|B_i) \right\} P[B_i] = \sum_{i=1}^{n} E[X|B_i]P[B_i],$$

where we first express $p_X(x_k)$ in terms of the conditional pmf's, and we then change the order of summation. Using the same approach we can also show

$$E[g(X)] = \sum_{i=1}^{n} E[g(X)|B_i]P[B_i]. \tag{3.31b}$$

---

**Example 3.26    Device Lifetimes**

Find the mean and variance for the devices in Example 3.25.

The conditional mean and second moment of each device type is that of a geometric random variable with the corresponding parameter:

$$m_{X|B_1} = 1/r \quad E[X^2|B_1] = (1 + r)/r^2$$

$$m_{X|B_2} = 1/s \quad E[X^2|B_2] = (1 + s)/s^2.$$

The mean and the second moment of $X$ are then:

$$m_X = m_{X|B_1}\alpha + m_{X|B_2}(1 - \alpha) = \alpha/r + (1 - \alpha)/s$$

$$E[X^2] = E[X^2|B_1]\alpha + E[X^2|B_2](1 - \alpha) = \alpha(1 + r)/r^2 + (1 - \alpha)(1 + s)/s^2.$$

Finally, the variance of $X$ is:

$$\text{VAR}[X] = E[X^2] - m_X^2 = \frac{\alpha(1 + r)}{r^2} + \frac{(1 - \alpha)(1 + s)}{s^2} - \left(\frac{\alpha}{r} + \frac{(1 - \alpha)}{s}\right)^2.$$

---

Note that we do *not* use the conditional variances to find VAR[$Y$] because Eq. (3.31b) does not apply to conditional variances. (See Problem 3.40.) However, the equation does apply to the conditional second moments.

## 3.5   IMPORTANT DISCRETE RANDOM VARIABLES

Certain random variables arise in many diverse, unrelated applications. The pervasiveness of these random variables is due to the fact that they model fundamental mechanisms that underlie random behavior. In this section we present the most important of the discrete random variables and discuss how they arise and how they are interrelated. Table 3.1 summarizes the basic properties of the discrete random variables discussed in this section. By the end of this chapter, most of these properties presented in the table will have been introduced.

---

**TABLE 3.1**   Discrete random variables

---

**Bernoulli Random Variable**

---

$S_X = \{0, 1\}$

$p_0 = q = 1 - p \qquad p_1 = p \qquad 0 \le p \le 1$

$E[X] = p \quad \text{VAR}[X] = p(1 - p) \qquad G_X(z) = (q + pz)$

*Remarks:* The Bernoulli random variable is the value of the indicator function $I_A$ for some event $A$; $X = 1$ if $A$ occurs and 0 otherwise.

---

**Binomial Random Variable**

---

$S_X = \{0, 1, \ldots, n\}$

$p_k = \binom{n}{k} p^k (1 - p)^{n-k} \qquad k = 0, 1, \ldots, n$

$E[X] = np \quad \text{VAR}[X] = np(1 - p) \qquad G_X(z) = (q + pz)^n$

*Remarks:* $X$ is the number of successes in $n$ Bernoulli trials and hence the sum of $n$ independent, identically distributed Bernoulli random variables.

---

**Geometric Random Variable**

---

*First Version:* $S_X = \{0, 1, 2, \ldots\}$

$p_k = p(1 - p)^k \qquad k = 0, 1, \ldots$

$E[X] = \dfrac{1 - p}{p} \qquad \text{VAR}[X] = \dfrac{1 - p}{p^2} \qquad G_X(z) = \dfrac{p}{1 - qz}$

*Remarks:* $X$ is the number of failures before the first success in a sequence of independent Bernoulli trials. The geometric random variable is the only discrete random variable with the memoryless property.

---

*Second Version:* $S_{X'} = \{1, 2, \ldots\}$

$p_k = p(1 - p)^{k-1} \qquad k = 1, 2, \ldots$

$E[X'] = \dfrac{1}{p} \qquad \text{VAR}[X'] = \dfrac{1 - p}{p^2} \qquad G_{X'}(z) = \dfrac{pz}{1 - qz}$

*Remarks:* $X' = X + 1$ is the number of trials until the first success in a sequence of independent Bernoulli trials.

---

*(Continued)*

**TABLE 3.1** (*Continued*)

**Negative Binomial Random Variable**

$S_X = \{r, r + 1, \dots\}$ where $r$ is a positive integer

$$p_k = \binom{k - 1}{r - 1} p^r (1 - p)^{k-r} \quad k = r, r + 1, \dots$$

$$E[X] = \frac{r}{p} \quad \text{VAR}[X] = \frac{r(1 - p)}{p^2} \quad G_X(z) = \left(\frac{pz}{1 - qz}\right)^r$$

*Remarks:* $X$ is the number of trials until the $r$th success in a sequence of independent Bernoulli trials.

**Poisson Random Variable**

$S_X = \{0, 1, 2, \dots\}$

$$p_k = \frac{\alpha^k}{k!} e^{-\alpha} \quad k = 0, 1, \dots \quad \text{and } \alpha > 0$$

$$E[X] = \alpha \quad \text{VAR}[X] = \alpha \quad G_X(z) = e^{\alpha(z-1)}$$

*Remarks:* $X$ is the number of events that occur in one time unit when the time between events is exponentially distributed with mean $1/\alpha$.

**Uniform Random Variable**

$S_X = \{1, 2, \dots, L\}$

$$p_k = \frac{1}{L} \quad k = 1, 2, \dots, L$$

$$E[X] = \frac{L + 1}{2} \quad \text{VAR}[X] = \frac{L^2 - 1}{12} \quad G_X(z) = \frac{z}{L} \frac{1 - z^L}{1 - z}$$

*Remarks:* The uniform random variable occurs whenever outcomes are equally likely. It plays a key role in the generation of random numbers.

**Zipf Random Variable**

$S_X = \{1, 2, \dots, L\}$ where $L$ is a positive integer

$$p_k = \frac{1}{c_L} \frac{1}{k} \quad k = 1, 2, \dots, L \text{ where } c_L \text{ is given by Eq. (3.45)}$$

$$E[X] = \frac{L}{c_L} \quad \text{VAR}[X] = \frac{L(L + 1)}{2c_L} - \frac{L^2}{c_L^2}$$

*Remarks:* The Zipf random variable has the property that a few outcomes occur frequently but most outcomes occur rarely.

Discrete random variables arise mostly in applications where counting is involved. We begin with the Bernoulli random variable as a model for a single coin toss. By counting the outcomes of multiple coin tosses we obtain the binomial, geometric, and Poisson random variables.

### 3.5.1    The Bernoulli Random Variable

Let $A$ be an event related to the outcomes of some random experiment. The Bernoulli random variable $I_A$ (defined in Example 3.8) equals one if the event $A$ occurs, and zero otherwise. $I_A$ is a discrete random variable since it assigns a number to each outcome of $S$. It is a discrete random variable with range $= \{0, 1\}$, and its pmf is

$$p_I(0) = 1 - p \quad \text{and} \quad p_I(1) = p, \tag{3.32}$$

where $P[A] = p$.

In Example 3.11 we found the mean of $I_A$:

$$m_I = E[I_A] = p.$$

The sample mean in $n$ independent Bernoulli trials is simply the relative frequency of successes and converges to $p$ as $n$ increases:

$$\langle I_A \rangle_n = \frac{0N_0(n) + 1N_1(n)}{n} = f_1(n) \to p.$$

In Example 3.21 we found the variance of $I_A$:

$$\sigma_I^2 = \text{VAR}[I_A] = p(1 - p) = pq.$$

The variance is quadratic in $p$, with value zero at $p = 0$ and $p = 1$ and maximum at $p = 1/2$. This agrees with intuition since values of $p$ close to 0 or to 1 imply a preponderance of successes or failures and hence less variability in the observed values. The maximum variability occurs when $p = 1/2$ which corresponds to the case that is most difficult to predict.

Every Bernoulli trial, regardless of the event $A$, is equivalent to the tossing of a biased coin with probability of heads $p$. In this sense, coin tossing can be viewed as representative of a fundamental mechanism for generating randomness, and the Bernoulli random variable is the model associated with it.

### 3.5.2    The Binomial Random Variable

Suppose that a random experiment is repeated $n$ independent times. Let $X$ be the number of times a certain event $A$ occurs in these $n$ trials. $X$ is then a random variable with range $S_X = \{0, 1, \ldots, n\}$. For example, $X$ could be the number of heads in $n$ tosses of a coin. If we let $I_j$ be the indicator function for the event $A$ in the $j$th trial, then

$$X = I_1 + I_2 + \ldots + I_n,$$

that is, $X$ is the sum of the Bernoulli random variables associated with each of the $n$ independent trials.

In Section 2.6, we found that $X$ has probabilities that depend on $n$ and $p$:

$$P[X = k] = p_X(k) = \binom{n}{k} p^k (1 - p)^{n-k} \quad \text{for } k = 0, \ldots, n. \tag{3.33}$$

$X$ is called the **binomial random variable**. Figure 3.8 shows the pdf of $X$ for $n = 24$ and $p = .2$ and $p = .5$. Note that $P[X = k]$ is maximum at $k_{\max} = [(n + 1)p]$, where $[x]$

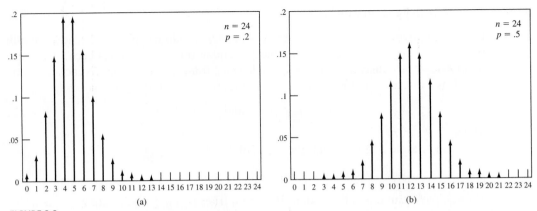

**FIGURE 3.8**
Probability mass functions of binomial random variable (a) $p = 0.2$; (b) $p = 0.5$.

denotes the largest integer that is smaller than or equal to $x$. When $(n + 1)p$ is an integer, then the maximum is achieved at $k_{\max}$ and $k_{\max} - 1$. (See Problem 3.50.)

The factorial terms grow large very quickly and cause overflow problems in the calculation of $\binom{n}{k}$. We can use Eq. (2.40) for the ratio of successive terms in the pmf allows us to calculate $p_X(k + 1)$ in terms of $p_X(k)$ and delays the onset of overflows:

$$\frac{p_X(k + 1)}{p_X(k)} = \frac{n - k}{k + 1}\frac{p}{1 - p} \quad \text{where } p_X(0) = (1 - p)^n. \quad (3.34)$$

The binomial random variable arises in applications where there are two types of objects (i.e., heads/tails, correct/erroneous bits, good/defective items, active/silent speakers), and we are interested in the number of type 1 objects in a randomly selected batch of size $n$, where the type of each object is independent of the types of the other objects in the batch. Examples involving the binomial random variable were given in Section 2.6.

---

**Example 3.27    Mean of a Binomial Random Variable**

The expected value of $X$ is:

$$E[X] = \sum_{k=0}^{n} k p_X(k) = \sum_{k=0}^{n} k \binom{n}{k} p^k (1 - p)^{n-k} = \sum_{k=1}^{n} k \frac{n!}{k!(n - k)!} p^k (1 - p)^{n-k}$$

$$= np \sum_{k=1}^{n} \frac{(n - 1)!}{(k - 1)!(n - k)!} p^{k-1} (1 - p)^{n-k}$$

$$= np \sum_{j=0}^{n-1} \frac{(n - 1)!}{j!(n - 1 - j)!} p^j (1 - p)^{n-1-j} = np, \quad (3.35)$$

where the first line uses the fact that the $k = 0$ term in the sum is zero, the second line cancels out the $k$ and factors $np$ outside the summation, and the last line uses the fact that the summation is equal to one since it adds all the terms in a binomial pmf with parameters $n - 1$ and $p$.

The expected value $E[X] = np$ agrees with our intuition since we expect a fraction $p$ of the outcomes to result in success.

---

### Example 3.28    Variance of a Binomial Random Variable

To find $E[X^2]$ below, we remove the $k = 0$ term and then let $k' = k - 1$:

$$E[X^2] = \sum_{k=0}^{n} k^2 \frac{n!}{k!(n-k)!} p^k (1-p)^{n-k} = \sum_{k=1}^{n} k \frac{n!}{(k-1)!(n-k)!} p^k (1-p)^{n-k}$$

$$= np \sum_{k'=0}^{n-1} (k'+1) \binom{n-1}{k'} p^{k'} (1-p)^{n-1-k}$$

$$= np \left\{ \sum_{k'=0}^{n-1} k' \binom{n-1}{k'} p^{k'} (1-p)^{n-1-k} + \sum_{k'=0}^{n-1} 1 \binom{n-1}{k'} p^{k'} (1-p)^{n-1-k'} \right\}$$

$$= np \{ (n-1)p + 1 \} = np(np + q).$$

In the third line we see that the first sum is the mean of a binomial random variable with parameters $(n-1)$ and $p$, and hence equal to $(n-1)p$. The second sum is the sum of the binomial probabilities and hence equal to 1.

We obtain the variance as follows:

$$\sigma_X^2 = E[X^2] - E[X]^2 = np(np + q) - (np)^2 = npq = np(1-p).$$

We see that the variance of the binomial is $n$ times the variance of a Bernoulli random variable. We observe that values of $p$ close to 0 or to 1 imply smaller variance, and that the maximum variability is when $p = 1/2$.

---

### Example 3.29    Redundant Systems

A system uses triple redundancy for reliability: Three microprocessors are installed and the system is designed so that it operates as long as one microprocessor is still functional. Suppose that the probability that a microprocessor is still active after $t$ seconds is $p = e^{-\lambda t}$. Find the probability that the system is still operating after $t$ seconds.

Let $X$ be the number of microprocessors that are functional at time $t$. $X$ is a binomial random variable with parameter $n = 3$ and $p$. Therefore:

$$P[X \geq 1] = 1 - P[X = 0] = 1 - (1 - e^{-\lambda t})^3.$$

---

### 3.5.3    The Geometric Random Variable

The geometric random variable arises when we count the number $M$ of independent Bernoulli trials until the first occurrence of a success. $M$ is called the geometric random variable and it takes on values from the set $\{1, 2, \dots\}$. In Section 2.6, we found that the pmf of $M$ is given by

$$P[M = k] = p_M(k) = (1-p)^{k-1} p \quad k = 1, 2, \dots, \tag{3.36}$$

where $p = P[A]$ is the probability of "success" in each Bernoulli trial. Figure 3.5(b) shows the geometric pmf for $p = 1/2$. Note that $P[M = k]$ decays geometrically with $k$, and that the ratio of consecutive terms is $p_M(k+1)/p_M(k) = (1-p) = q$. As $p$ increases, the pmf decays more rapidly.

The probability that $M \leq k$ can be written in closed form:

$$P[M \leq k] = \sum_{j=1}^{k} pq^{j-1} = p\sum_{j'=0}^{k-1} q^{j'} = p\frac{1 - q^k}{1 - q} = 1 - q^k. \tag{3.37}$$

Sometimes we are interested in $M' = M - 1$, the number of *failures* before a success occurs. We also refer to $M'$ as a geometric random variable. Its pmf is:

$$P[M' = k] = P[M = k + 1] = (1 - p)^k p \quad k = 0, 1, 2, \ldots. \tag{3.38}$$

In Examples 3.15 and 3.22, we found the mean and variance of the geometric random variable:

$$m_M = E[M] = 1/p \quad \mathrm{VAR}[M] = \frac{1 - p}{p^2}.$$

We see that the mean and variance increase as $p$, the success probability, decreases.

The geometric random variable is the only discrete random variable that satisfies the memoryless property:

$$P[M \geq k + j \mid M > j] = P[M \geq k] \quad \text{for all } j, k > 1.$$

(See Problems 3.54 and 3.55.) The above expression states that if a success has not occurred in the first $j$ trials, then the probability of having to perform at least $k$ more trials is the same as the probability of initially having to perform at least $k$ trials. Thus, each time a failure occurs, the system "forgets" and begins anew as if it were performing the first trial.

The geometric random variable arises in applications where one is interested in the time (i.e., number of trials) that elapses between the occurrence of events in a sequence of independent experiments, as in Examples 2.11 and 2.43. Examples where the modified geometric random variable $M'$ arises are: number of customers awaiting service in a queueing system; number of white dots between successive black dots in a scan of a black-and-white document.

### 3.5.4   The Poisson Random Variable

In many applications, we are interested in counting the number of occurrences of an event in a certain time period or in a certain region in space. The Poisson random variable arises in situations where the events occur "completely at random" in time or space. For example, the Poisson random variable arises in counts of emissions from radioactive substances, in counts of demands for telephone connections, and in counts of defects in a semiconductor chip.

The pmf for the **Poisson random variable** is given by

$$P[N = k] = p_N(k) = \frac{\alpha^k}{k!}e^{-\alpha} \quad \text{for } k = 0, 1, 2, \ldots, \tag{3.39}$$

where $\alpha$ is the average number of event occurrences in a specified time interval or region in space. Figure 3.9 shows the Poisson pmf for several values of $\alpha$. For $\alpha < 1$, $P[N = k]$ is maximum at $k = 0$; for $\alpha > 1$, $P[N = k]$ is maximum at $[\alpha]$; if $\alpha$ is a positive integer, the $P[N = k]$ is maximum at $k = \alpha$ and at $k = \alpha - 1$.

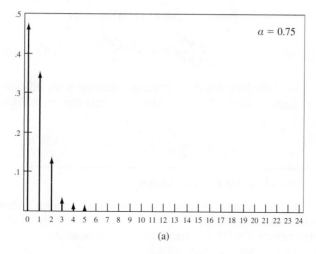

(a)

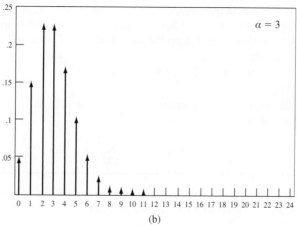

(b)

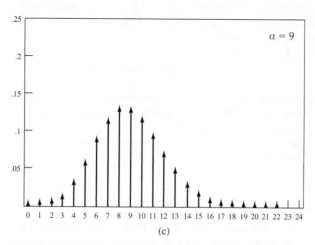

(c)

**FIGURE 3.9**
Probability mass functions of Poisson random variable (a) $\alpha = 0.75$;
(b) $\alpha = 3$; (c) $\alpha = 9$.

The pmf of the Poisson random variable sums to one, since

$$\sum_{k=0}^{\infty} \frac{\alpha^k}{k!} e^{-\alpha} = e^{-\alpha} \sum_{k=0}^{\infty} \frac{\alpha^k}{k!} = e^{-\alpha} e^{\alpha} = 1,$$

where we used the fact that the second summation is the infinite series expansion for $e^{\alpha}$.

It is easy to show that the mean and variance of a Poisson random variable is given by:

$$E[N] = \alpha \quad \text{and} \quad \sigma_N^2 = \text{VAR}[N] = \alpha.$$

---

### Example 3.30 Queries at a Call Center

The number $N$ of queries arriving in $t$ seconds at a call center is a Poisson random variable with $\alpha = \lambda t$ where $\lambda$ is the average arrival rate in queries/second. Assume that the arrival rate is four queries per minute. Find the probability of the following events: (a) more than 4 queries in 10 seconds; (b) fewer than 5 queries in 2 minutes.

The arrival rate in queries/second is $\lambda = 4$ queries/60 sec = 1/15 queries/sec. In part a, the time interval is 10 seconds, so we have a Poisson random variable with $\alpha = $ (1/15 queries/sec) * 10 seconds = 10/15 queries. The probability of interest is evaluated numerically:

$$P[N > 4] = 1 - P[N \le 4] = 1 - \sum_{k=0}^{4} \frac{(2/3)^k}{k!} e^{-2/3} = 6.33(10^{-4}).$$

In part b, the time interval of interest is $t = 120$ seconds, so $\alpha = 1/15 * 120$ seconds = 8. The probability of interest is:

$$P[N \le 5] = \sum_{k=0}^{5} \frac{(8)^k}{k!} e^{-8} = 0.10.$$

---

### Example 3.31 Arrivals at a Packet Multiplexer

The number $N$ of packet arrivals in $t$ seconds at a multiplexer is a Poisson random variable with $\alpha = \lambda t$ where $\lambda$ is the average arrival rate in packets/second. Find the probability that there are no packet arrivals in $t$ seconds.

$$P[N = 0] = \frac{\alpha^0}{0!} e^{-\lambda t} = e^{-\lambda t}.$$

This equation has an interesting interpretation. Let $Z$ be the time until the first packet arrival. Suppose we ask, "What is the probability that $X > t$, that is, the next arrival occurs $t$ or more seconds later?" Note that $\{N = 0\}$ implies $\{Z > t\}$ and vice versa, so $P[Z > t] = e^{-\lambda t}$. The probability of no arrival decreases exponentially with $t$.

Note that we can also show that

$$P[N(t) \ge n] = 1 - P[N(t) < n] = 1 - \sum_{k=0}^{n-1} \frac{(\lambda t)^k}{k!} e^{-\lambda t}.$$

---

One of the applications of the Poisson probabilities in Eq. (3.39) is to approximate the binomial probabilities in the case where $p$ is very small and $n$ is very large, that is, where the event $A$ of interest is very rare but the number of Bernoulli trials is very large. We show that *if $\alpha = np$ is fixed*, then as $n$ becomes *large*:

$$p_k = \binom{n}{k} p^k (1 - p)^{n-k} \simeq \frac{\alpha^k}{k!} e^{-\alpha} \qquad \text{for } k = 0, 1, \ldots . \tag{3.40}$$

Equation (3.40) is obtained by taking the limit $n \to \infty$ in the expression for $p_k$, while keeping $\alpha = np$ fixed. First, consider the probability that no events occur in $n$ trials:

$$p_0 = (1 - p)^n = \left(1 - \frac{\alpha}{n}\right)^n \to e^{-\alpha} \quad \text{as } n \to \infty, \tag{3.41}$$

where the limit in the last expression is a well known result from calculus. Consider the ratio of successive binomial probabilities:

$$\frac{p_{k+1}}{p_k} = \frac{(n - k)p}{(k + 1)q} = \frac{(1 - k/n)\alpha}{(k + 1)(1 - \alpha/n)}$$

$$\to \frac{\alpha}{k + 1} \quad \text{as } n \to \infty.$$

Thus the limiting probabilities satisfy

$$p_{k+1} = \frac{\alpha}{k + 1} p_k = \left(\frac{\alpha}{k + 1}\right)\left(\frac{\alpha}{k}\right) \cdots \left(\frac{\alpha}{1}\right) p_0 = \frac{\alpha^k}{k!} e^{-\alpha}. \tag{3.42}$$

Thus the Poisson pmf can be used to approximate the binomial pmf for large $n$ and small $p$, using $\alpha = np$.

---

### Example 3.32 Errors in Optical Transmission

An optical communication system transmits information at a rate of $10^9$ bits/second. The probability of a bit error in the optical communication system is $10^{-9}$. Find the probability of five or more errors in 1 second.

    Each bit transmission corresponds to a Bernoulli trial with a "success" corresponding to a bit error in transmission. The probability of $k$ errors in $n = 10^9$ transmissions (1 second) is then given by the binomial probability with $n = 10^9$ and $p = 10^{-9}$. The Poisson approximation uses $\alpha = np = 10^9 (10^{-9}) = 1$. Thus

$$P[N \geq 5] = 1 - P[N < 5] = 1 - \sum_{k=0}^{4} \frac{\alpha^k}{k!} e^{-\alpha}$$

$$= 1 - e^{-1}\left\{1 + \frac{1}{1!} + \frac{1}{2!} + \frac{1}{3!} + \frac{1}{4!}\right\} = .00366.$$

---

    The Poisson random variable appears in numerous physical situations because many models are very large in scale and involve very rare events. For example, the Poisson pmf gives an accurate prediction for the relative frequencies of the number of particles emitted by a radioactive mass during a fixed time period. This correspondence can be explained as follows. A radioactive mass is composed of a large number of atoms, say $n$. In a fixed time interval each atom has a very small probability $p$ of disintegrating and emitting a radioactive particle. If atoms disintegrate independently of

**FIGURE 3.10**
Event occurrences in $n$ subintervals of $[0, T]$.

other atoms, then the number of emissions in a time interval can be viewed as the number of successes in $n$ trials. For example, one microgram of radium contains about $n = 10^{16}$ atoms, and the probability that a single atom will disintegrate during a one-millisecond time interval is $p = 10^{-15}$ [Rozanov, p. 58]. Thus it is an understatement to say that the conditions for the approximation in Eq. (3.40) hold: $n$ is so large and $p$ so small that one could argue that the limit $n \to \infty$ has been carried out and that the number of emissions is *exactly* a Poisson random variable.

The Poisson random variable also comes up in situations where we can imagine a sequence of Bernoulli trials taking place in time or space. Suppose we count the number of event occurrences in a $T$-second interval. Divide the time interval into a very large number, $n$, of subintervals as shown in Fig. 3.10. A pulse in a subinterval indicates the occurrence of an event. Each subinterval can be viewed as one in a sequence of independent Bernoulli trials if the following conditions hold: (1) At most one event can occur in a subinterval, that is, the probability of more than one event occurrence is negligible; (2) the outcomes in different subintervals are independent; and (3) the probability of an event occurrence in a subinterval is $p = \alpha/n$, where $\alpha$ is the average number of events observed in a 1-second interval. The number $N$ of events in 1 second is a binomial random variable with parameters $n$ and $p = \alpha/n$. Thus as $n \to \infty$, $N$ becomes a Poisson random variable with parameter $\alpha$. In Chapter 9 we will revisit this result when we discuss the Poisson random process.

### 3.5.5 The Uniform Random Variable

The discrete uniform random variable $Y$ takes on values in a set of consecutive integers $S_Y = \{j + 1, \ldots, j + L\}$ with equal probability:

$$p_Y(k) = \frac{1}{L} \quad \text{for} \quad k \in \{j + 1, \ldots, j + L\}. \tag{3.43}$$

This humble random variable occurs whenever outcomes are equally likely, e.g., toss of a fair coin or a fair die, spinning of an arrow in a wheel divided into equal segments, selection of numbers from an urn. It is easy to show that the mean and variance are:

$$E[Y] = j + \frac{L+1}{2} \quad \text{and VAR}[Y] = \frac{L^2 - 1}{12}.$$

---

**Example 3.33    Discrete Uniform Random Variable in Unit Interval**

Let $X$ be a uniform random variable in $S_X = \{0, 1, \ldots, L - 1\}$. We define the discrete uniform random variable in the unit interval by

$$U = \frac{X}{L} \quad \text{so} \quad S_U = \left\{0, \frac{1}{L}, \frac{2}{L}, \frac{3}{L}, \ldots, 1 - \frac{1}{L}\right\}.$$

$U$ has pmf:

$$p_U\left(\frac{k}{L}\right) = \frac{1}{L} \qquad \text{for } k = 0, 2, \ldots, L - 1.$$

The pmf of $U$ puts equal probability mass $1/L$ on equally spaced points $x_k = k/L$ in the unit interval. The probability of a subinterval of the unit interval is equal to the number of points in the subinterval multiplied by $1/L$. As $L$ becomes very large, this probability is essentially the length of the subinterval.

### 3.5.6   The Zipf Random Variable

The Zipf random variable is named for George Zipf who observed that the frequency of words in a large body of text is proportional to their rank. Suppose that words are ranked from most frequent, to next most frequent, and so on. Let $X$ be the rank of a word, then $S_X = \{1, 2, \ldots, L\}$ where $L$ is the number of distinct words. The pmf of $X$ is:

$$p_X(k) = \frac{1}{c_L}\frac{1}{k} \qquad \text{for } k = 1, 2, \ldots, L. \tag{3.44}$$

where $c_L$ is a normalization constant. The second word has $1/2$ the frequency of occurrence as the first, the third word has $1/3$ the frequency of the first, and so on. The normalization constant $c_L$ is given by the sum:

$$c_L = \sum_{j=1}^{L} \frac{1}{j} = 1 + \frac{1}{2} + \frac{1}{3} + \ldots + \frac{1}{L} \tag{3.45}$$

The constant $c_L$ occurs frequently in calculus and is called the $L$th harmonic mean and increases approximately as $\ln L$. For example, for $L = 100, c_L = 5.187378$ and $c_L - \ln(L) = 0.582207$. It can be shown that as $L \to \infty, c_L - \ln L \to 0.57721 \ldots$. The mean of $X$ is given by:

$$E[X] = \sum_{j=1}^{L} j p_X(j) = \sum_{j=1}^{L} j \frac{1}{c_L j} = \frac{L}{c_L}. \tag{3.46}$$

The second moment and variance of $X$ are:

and

$$E[X^2] = \sum_{j=1}^{L} j^2 \frac{1}{c_L j} = \frac{1}{c_L}\sum_{j=1}^{L} j = \frac{L(L + 1)}{2c_L}$$

$$\text{VAR}[X] = \frac{L(L + 1)}{2c_L} - \frac{L^2}{c_L^2}. \tag{3.47}$$

The Zipf and related random variables have gained prominence with the growth of the Internet where they have been found in a variety of measurement studies involving Web page sizes, Web access behavior, and Web page interconnectivity. These random variables had previously been found extensively in studies on the distribution of wealth and, not surprisingly, are now found in Internet video rentals and book sales.

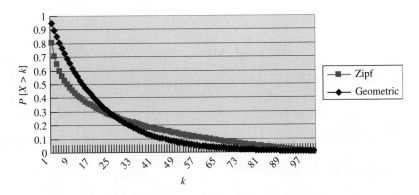

**FIGURE 3.11**
Zipf distribution and its long tail.

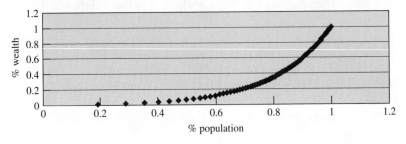

**FIGURE 3.12**
Lorenz curve for Zipf random variable with $L = 100$.

---

### Example 3.34    Rare Events and Long Tails

The Zipf random variable $X$ has the property that a few outcomes (words) occur frequently but most outcomes occur rarely. Find the probability of words with rank higher than $m$.

$$P[X > m] = 1 - P[X \leq m] = 1 - \frac{1}{c_L}\sum_{j=1}^{m}\frac{1}{j} = 1 - \frac{c_m}{c_L} \quad \text{for } m \leq L. \quad (3.48)$$

We call $P[X > m]$ the probability of the tail of the distribution of $X$. Figure 3.11 shows the $P[X > m]$ with $L = 100$ which has $E[X] = 100/c_{100} = 19.28$. Figure 3.12 also shows $P[Y > m]$ for a geometric random variable with the same mean, that is, $1/p = 19.28$. It can be seen that $P[Y > m]$ for the geometric random variable drops off much more quickly than $P[X > m]$. The Zipf distribution is said to have a "long tail" because rare events are more likely to occur than in traditional probability models.

---

### Example 3.35    80/20 Rule and the Lorenz Curve

Let $X$ correspond to a level of wealth and $p_X(k)$ be the proportion of a population that has wealth $k$. Suppose that $X$ is a Zipf random variable. Thus $p_X(1)$ is the proportion of the population with wealth 1, $p_X(2)$ the proportion with wealth 2, and so on. The long tail of the Zipf distribution suggests that very rich individuals are not very rare. We frequently hear statements such as "20% of the population owns 80% of the wealth." The *Lorenz curve* plots the proportion of wealth owned by the poorest fraction $x$ of the population, as the $x$ varies from 0 to 1. Find the Lorenz curve for $L = 100$.

For $k$ in $\{1, 2, \ldots, L\}$, the fraction of the population with wealth $k$ or less is:

$$F_k = P[X \le k] = \frac{1}{c_L} \sum_{j=1}^{k} \frac{1}{j} = \frac{c_k}{c_L}. \tag{3.49}$$

The proportion of wealth owned by the population that has wealth $k$ or less is:

$$W_k = \frac{\displaystyle\sum_{j=1}^{k} j p_X(j)}{\displaystyle\sum_{i=1}^{L} i p_X(i)} = \frac{\dfrac{1}{c_L} \displaystyle\sum_{j=1}^{k} j \dfrac{1}{j}}{\dfrac{1}{c_L} \displaystyle\sum_{i=1}^{L} i \dfrac{1}{i}} = \frac{k}{L}. \tag{3.50}$$

The denominator in the above expression is the total wealth of the entire population. The Lorenz curve consists of the plot of points $(F_k, W_k)$ which is shown in Fig. 3.12 for $L = 100$. In the graph the 70% poorest proportion of the population own only 20% of the total wealth, or conversely, the 30% wealthiest fraction of the population owns 80% of the wealth. See Problem 3.75 for a discussion of what the Lorenz curve should look like in the cases of extreme fairness and extreme unfairness.

---

The explosive growth in the Internet has led to systems of huge scale. For probability models this growth has implied random variables that can attain very large values. Measurement studies have revealed many instances of random variables with long tail distributions.

If we try to let $L$ approach infinity in Eq. (3.45), $c_L$ grows without bound since the series does not converge. However, if we make the pmf proportional to $(1/k)^\alpha$ then the series converges as long as $\alpha > 1$. We define the **Zipf or zeta random variable** with range $\{1, 2, 3, \ldots\}$ to have pmf:

$$p_Z(k) = \frac{1}{z_\alpha} \frac{1}{k^\alpha} \qquad \text{for } k = 1, 2, \ldots, \tag{3.51}$$

where $z_\alpha$ is a normalization constant given by the zeta function which is defined by:

$$z_\alpha = \sum_{j=1}^{\infty} \frac{1}{j^\alpha} = 1 + \frac{1}{2^\alpha} + \frac{1}{3^\alpha} + \cdots \qquad \text{for } \alpha > 1. \tag{3.52}$$

The convergence of the above series is discussed in standard calculus books.

The mean of $Z$ is given by:

$$E[Z] = \sum_{j=1}^{L} j p_Z(j) = \sum_{j=1}^{L} j \frac{1}{z_\alpha j^\alpha} = \frac{1}{z_\alpha} \sum_{j=1}^{L} \frac{1}{j^{\alpha-1}} = \frac{z_{\alpha-1}}{z_\alpha} \qquad \text{for } \alpha > 2,$$

where the sum of the sequence $1/j^{\alpha-1}$ converges only if $\alpha - 1 > 1$, that is, $\alpha > 2$. We can similarly show that the second moment (and hence the variance) exists only if $\alpha > 3$.

## 3.6    GENERATION OF DISCRETE RANDOM VARIABLES

Suppose we wish to generate the outcomes of a random experiment that has sample space $S = \{a_1, a_2, \ldots, a_n\}$ with probability of elementary events $p_j = P[\{a_j\}]$. We divide the unit interval into $n$ subintervals. The $j$th subinterval has length $p_j$ and

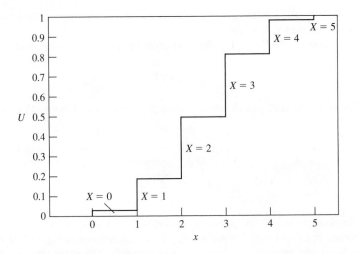

**FIGURE 3.13**
Generating a binomial random variable with $n = 5, p = 1/2$.

corresponds to outcome $a_j$. Each trial of the experiment first uses `rand` to obtain a number $U$ in the unit interval. The outcome of the experiment is $a_j$ if $U$ is in the $j$th subinterval. Figure 3.13 shows the portioning of the unit interval according to the pmf of an $n = 5$, $p = 0.5$ binomial random variable.

The Octave function `discrete_rnd` implements the above method and can be used to generate random numbers with desired probabilities. Functions to generate random numbers with common distributions are also available. For example, `poisson_rnd (lambda, r, c)` can be used to generate an array of Poisson-distributed random numbers with rate lambda.

---

**Example 3.36    Generation of Tosses of a Die**

Use `discrete_rnd` to generate 20 samples of a toss of a die.

| | |
|---|---|
| `> V=1:6;` | % Define $S_X = \{1, 2, 3, 4, 5, 6\}$. |
| `> P=[1/6, 1/6, 1/6, 1/6, 1/6, 1/6];` | % Set all the pmf values for $X$ to 1/6. |
| `> discrete_rnd (20, V, P)` | % Generate 20 samples from $S_X$ with pmf $P$. |

```
ans =

   6  2  2  6  5  2  6  1  3  6  3  1  6  3  4  2  5  3  4  1
```

---

**Example 3.37    Generation of Poisson Random Variable**

Use the built-in function to generate 20 samples of a Poisson random variable with $\alpha = 2$.

| | |
|---|---|
| `> Poisson_rnd (2,1,20)` | % Generate a $1 \times 20$ array of samples of a Poisson % random variable with $\alpha = 2$. |

```
ans =

   4  3  0  2  3  2  1  2  1  4  0  1  2  2  3  4  0  1  3
```

The problems at the end of the chapter elaborate on the rich set of experiments that can be simulated using these basic capabilities of MATLAB or Octave. In the remainder of this book, we will use Octave in examples because it is freely available.

## SUMMARY

- A random variable is a function that assigns a real number to each outcome of a random experiment. A random variable is defined if the outcome of a random experiment is a number, or if a numerical attribute of an outcome is of interest.
- The notion of an equivalent event enables us to derive the probabilities of events involving a random variable in terms of the probabilities of events involving the underlying outcomes.
- A random variable is discrete if it assumes values from some countable set. The probability mass function is sufficient to calculate the probability of all events involving a discrete random variable.
- The probability of events involving discrete random variable $X$ can be expressed as the sum of the probability mass function $p_X(x)$.
- If $X$ is a random variable, then $Y = g(X)$ is also a random variable.
- The mean, variance, and moments of a discrete random variable summarize some of the information about the random variable $X$. These parameters are useful in practice because they are easier to measure and estimate than the pmf.
- The conditional pmf allows us to calculate the probability of events given partial information about the random variable $X$.
- There are a number of methods for generating discrete random variables with prescribed pmf's in terms of a random variable that is uniformly distributed in the unit interval.

## CHECKLIST OF IMPORTANT TERMS

Discrete random variable
Equivalent event
Expected value of $X$
Function of a random variable
$n$th moment of $X$

Probability mass function
Random variable
Standard deviation of $X$
Variance of $X$

## ANNOTATED REFERENCES

Reference [1] is the standard reference for electrical engineers for the material on random variables. Reference [2] discusses some of the finer points regarding the concepts of a random variable at a level accessible to students of this course. Reference [3] is a classic text, rich in detailed examples. Reference [4] presents detailed discussions of the various methods for generating random numbers with specified distributions. Reference [5] is entirely focused on discrete random variables.

1. A. Papoulis and S. U. Pillai, *Probability, Random Variables, and Stochastic Processes*, 4th ed., McGraw-Hill, New York, 2002.
2. K. L. Chung, *Elementary Probability Theory*, Springer-Verlag, New York, 1974.
3. W. Feller, *An Introduction to Probability Theory and Its Applications*, Wiley, New York, 1968.

4. A. M. Law and W. D. Kelton, *Simulation Modeling and Analysis*, McGraw-Hill, New York, 2000.

5. N. L. Johnson, A. W. Kemp, and S. Kotz, *Univariate Discrete Distributions*, Wiley, New York, 2005.

6. Y. A. Rozanov, *Probability Theory: A Concise Course*, Dover Publications, New York, 1969.

## PROBLEMS

### Section 3.1: The Notion of a Random Variable

**3.1.** Let $X$ be the maximum of the number of heads obtained when Carlos and Michael each flip a fair coin twice.

   **(a)** Describe the underlying space $S$ of this random experiment and specify the probabilities of its elementary events.

   **(b)** Show the mapping from $S$ to $S_X$, the range of $X$.

   **(c)** Find the probabilities for the various values of $X$.

**3.2.** A die is tossed and the random variable $X$ is defined as the number of full pairs of dots in the face showing up.

   **(a)** Describe the underlying space $S$ of this random experiment and specify the probabilities of its elementary events.

   **(b)** Show the mapping from $S$ to $S_X$, the range of $X$.

   **(c)** Find the probabilities for the various values of $X$.

   **(d)** Repeat parts a, b, and c, if $Y$ is the number of full or partial pairs of dots in the face showing up.

   **(e)** Explain why $P[X = 0]$ and $P[Y = 0]$ are not equal.

**3.3.** The loose minute hand of a clock is spun hard. The coordinates $(x, y)$ of the point where the tip of the hand comes to rest is noted. $Z$ is defined as the sgn function of the product of $x$ and $y$, where sgn$(t)$ is 1 if $t > 0$, 0 if $t = 0$, and $-1$ if $t < 0$.

   **(a)** Describe the underlying space $S$ of this random experiment and specify the probabilities of its events.

   **(b)** Show the mapping from $S$ to $S_X$, the range of $X$.

   **(c)** Find the probabilities for the various values of $X$.

**3.4.** A data source generates hexadecimal characters. Let $X$ be the integer value corresponding to a hex character. Suppose that the four binary digits in the character are independent and each is equally likely to be 0 or 1.

   **(a)** Describe the underlying space $S$ of this random experiment and specify the probabilities of its elementary events.

   **(b)** Show the mapping from $S$ to $S_X$, the range of $X$.

   **(c)** Find the probabilities for the various values of $X$.

   **(d)** Let $Y$ be the integer value of a hex character but suppose that the most significant bit is three times as likely to be a "0" as a "1". Find the probabilities for the values of $Y$.

**3.5.** Two transmitters send messages through bursts of radio signals to an antenna. During each time slot each transmitter sends a message with probability 1/2. Simultaneous transmissions result in loss of the messages. Let $X$ be the number of time slots until the first message gets through.

(a) Describe the underlying sample space $S$ of this random experiment and specify the probabilities of its elementary events.

(b) Show the mapping from $S$ to $S_X$, the range of $X$.

(c) Find the probabilities for the various values of $X$.

**3.6.** An information source produces binary triplets $\{000, 111, 010, 101, 001, 110, 100, 011\}$ with corresponding probabilities $\{1/4, 1/4, 1/8, 1/8, 1/16, 1/16, 1/16, 1/16\}$. A binary code assigns a codeword of length $-\log_2 p_k$ to triplet $k$. Let $X$ be the length of the string assigned to the output of the information source.

(a) Show the mapping from $S$ to $S_X$, the range of $X$.

(b) Find the probabilities for the various values of $X$.

**3.7.** An urn contains 9 \$1 bills and one \$50 bill. Let the random variable $X$ be the total amount that results when two bills are drawn from the urn without replacement.

(a) Describe the underlying space $S$ of this random experiment and specify the probabilities of its elementary events.

(b) Show the mapping from $S$ to $S_X$, the range of $X$.

(c) Find the probabilities for the various values of $X$.

**3.8.** An urn contains 9 \$1 bills and one \$50 bill. Let the random variable $X$ be the total amount that results when two bills are drawn from the urn *with* replacement.

(a) Describe the underlying space $S$ of this random experiment and specify the probabilities of its elementary events.

(b) Show the mapping from $S$ to $S_X$, the range of $X$.

(c) Find the probabilities for the various values of $X$.

**3.9.** A coin is tossed $n$ times. Let the random variable $Y$ be the difference between the number of heads and the number of tails in the $n$ tosses of a coin. Assume $P[\text{heads}] = p$.

(a) Describe the sample space of $S$.

(b) Find the probability of the event $\{Y = 0\}$.

(c) Find the probabilities for the other values of $Y$.

**3.10.** An $m$-bit password is required to access a system. A hacker systematically works through all possible $m$-bit patterns. Let $X$ be the number of patterns tested until the correct password is found.

(a) Describe the sample space of $S$.

(b) Show the mapping from $S$ to $S_X$, the range of $X$.

(c) Find the probabilities for the various values of $X$.

## Section 3.2: Discrete Random Variables and Probability Mass Function

**3.11.** Let $X$ be the maximum of the coin tosses in Problem 3.1.

(a) Compare the pmf of $X$ with the pmf of $Y$, the number of heads in two tosses of a fair coin. Explain the difference.

(b) Suppose that Carlos uses a coin with probability of heads $p = 3/4$. Find the pmf of $X$.

**3.12.** Consider an information source that produces binary pairs that we designate as $S_X = \{1, 2, 3, 4\}$. Find and plot the pmf in the following cases:

(a) $p_k = p_1/k$ for all $k$ in $S_X$.

(b) $p_{k+1} = p_k/2$ for $k = 2, 3, 4$.

**(c)** $p_{k+1} = p_k/2^k$ for $k = 2, 3, 4$.

**(d)** Can the random variables in parts a, b, and c be extended to take on values in the set $\{1, 2, \dots\}$? If yes, specify the pmf of the resulting random variables. If no, explain why not.

**3.13.** Let $X$ be a random variable with pmf $p_k = c/k^2$ for $k = 1, 2, \dots$.

**(a)** Estimate the value of $c$ numerically. Note that the series converges.

**(b)** Find $P[X > 4]$.

**(c)** Find $P[6 \le X \le 8]$.

**3.14.** Compare $P[X \ge 8]$ and $P[Y \ge 8]$ for outputs of the data source in Problem 3.4.

**3.15.** In Problem 3.5 suppose that terminal 1 transmits with probability 1/2 in a given time slot, but terminal 2 transmits with probability $p$.

**(a)** Find the pmf for the number of transmissions $X$ until a message gets through.

**(b)** Given a successful transmission, find the probability that terminal 2 transmitted.

**3.16. (a)** In Problem 3.7 what is the probability that the amount drawn from the urn is more than $2? More than $50?

**(b)** Repeat part a for Problem 3.8.

**3.17.** A modem transmits a +2 voltage signal into a channel. The channel adds to this signal a noise term that is drawn from the set $\{0, -1, -2, -3\}$ with respective probabilities $\{4/10, 3/10, 2/10, 1/10\}$.

**(a)** Find the pmf of the output $Y$ of the channel.

**(b)** What is the probability that the output of the channel is equal to the input of the channel?

**(c)** What is the probability that the output of the channel is positive?

**3.18.** A computer reserves a path in a network for 10 minutes. To extend the reservation the computer must successfully send a "refresh" message before the expiry time. However, messages are lost with probability 1/2. Suppose that it takes 10 seconds to send a refresh request and receive an acknowledgment. When should the computer start sending refresh messages in order to have a 99% chance of successfully extending the reservation time?

**3.19.** A modem transmits over an error-prone channel, so it repeats every "0" or "1" bit transmission five times. We call each such group of five bits a "codeword." The channel changes an input bit to its complement with probability $p = 1/10$ and it does so independently of its treatment of other input bits. The modem receiver takes a majority vote of the five received bits to estimate the input signal. Find the probability that the receiver makes the wrong decision.

**3.20.** Two dice are tossed and we let $X$ be the difference in the number of dots facing up.

**(a)** Find and plot the pmf of $X$.

**(b)** Find the probability that $|X| \le k$ for all $k$.

## Section 3.3: Expected Value and Moments of Discrete Random Variable

**3.21. (a)** In Problem 3.11, compare $E[Y]$ to $E[X]$ where $X$ is the maximum of coin tosses.

**(b)** Compare VAR$[X]$ and VAR$[Y]$.

**3.22.** Find the expected value and variance of the output of the information sources in Problem 3.12, parts a, b, and c.

**3.23. (a)** Find $E[X]$ for the hex integers in Problem 3.4.

**(b)** Find VAR$[X]$.

**3.24.** Find the mean codeword length in Problem 3.6. How can this average be interpreted in a very large number of encodings of binary triplets?

**3.25.** **(a)** Find the mean and variance of the amount drawn from the urn in Problem 3.7.

**(b)** Find the mean and variance of the amount drawn from the urn in Problem 3.8.

**3.26.** Find $E[Y]$ and VAR$[Y]$ for the difference between the number of heads and tails in Problem 3.9. In a large number of repetitions of this random experiment, what is the meaning of $E[Y]$?

**3.27.** Find $E[X]$ and VAR$[X]$ in Problem 3.13.

**3.28.** Find the expected value and variance of the modem signal in Problem 3.17.

**3.29.** Find the mean and variance of the time that it takes to renew the reservation in Problem 3.18.

**3.30.** The modem in Problem 3.19 transmits 1000 5-bit codewords. What is the average number of codewords in error? If the modem transmits 1000 bits individually without repetition, what is the average number of bits in error? Explain how error rate is traded off against transmission speed.

**3.31.** **(a)** Suppose a fair coin is tossed $n$ times. Each coin toss costs $d$ dollars and the reward in obtaining $X$ heads is $aX^2 + bX$. Find the expected value of the net reward.

**(b)** Suppose that the reward in obtaining $X$ heads is $a^X$, where $a > 0$. Find the expected value of the reward.

**3.32.** Let $g(X) = I_A$, where $A = \{X > 10\}$.

**(a)** Find $E[g(X)]$ for $X$ as in Problem 3.12a with $S_X = \{1, 2, \ldots, 15\}$.

**(b)** Repeat part a for $X$ as in Problem 3.12b with $S_X = \{1, 2, \ldots, 15\}$.

**(c)** Repeat part a for $X$ as in Problem 3.12c with $S_X = \{1, 2, \ldots, 15\}$.

**3.33.** Let $g(X) = (X - 10)^+$ (see Example 3.19).

**(a)** Find $E[X]$ for $X$ as in Problem 3.12a with $S_X = \{1, 2, \ldots, 15\}$.

**(b)** Repeat part a for $X$ as in Problem 3.12b with $S_X = \{1, 2, \ldots, 15\}$.

**(c)** Repeat part a for $X$ as in Problem 3.12c with $S_X = \{1, 2, \ldots, 15\}$.

**3.34.** Consider the St. Petersburg Paradox in Example 3.16. Suppose that the casino has a total of $M = 2^m$ dollars, and so it can only afford a finite number of coin tosses.

**(a)** How many tosses can the casino afford?

**(b)** Find the expected payoff to the player.

**(c)** How much should a player be willing to pay to play this game?

## Section 3.4: Conditional Probability Mass Function

**3.35.** **(a)** In Problem 3.11a, find the conditional pmf of $X$, the maximum of coin tosses, given that $X > 0$.

**(b)** Find the conditional pmf of $X$ given that Michael got one head in two tosses.

**(c)** Find the conditional pmf of $X$ given that Michael got one head in the first toss.

**(d)** In Problem 3.11b, find the probability that Carlos got the maximum given that $X = 2$.

**3.36.** Find the conditional pmf for the quaternary information source in Problem 3.12, parts a, b, and c given that $X < 4$.

**3.37.** **(a)** Find the conditional pmf of the hex integer $X$ in Problem 3.4 given that $X < 8$.

**(b)** Find the conditional pmf of $X$ given that the first bit is 0.

**(c)** Find the conditional pmf of $X$ given that the 4th bit is 0.

**3.38.** **(a)** Find the conditional pmf of $X$ in Problem 3.5 given that no message gets through in time slot 1.

**(b)** Find the conditional pmf of $X$ given that the first transmitter transmitted in time slot 1.

**3.39.** **(a)** Find the conditional expected value of $X$ in Problem 3.5 given that no message gets through in the first time slot. Show that $E[X \mid X > 1] = E[X] + 1$.

**(b)** Find the conditional expected value of $X$ in Problem 3.5 given that a message gets through in the first time slot.

**(c)** Find $E[X]$ by using the results of parts a and b.

**(d)** Find $E[X^2]$ and VAR[$X$] using the approach in parts b and c.

**3.40.** Explain why Eq. (3.31b) can be used to find $E[X^2]$, but it cannot be used to directly find VAR[$X$].

**3.41.** **(a)** Find the conditional pmf for $X$ in Problem 3.7 given that the first draw produced $k$ dollars.

**(b)** Find the conditional expected value corresponding to part a.

**(c)** Find $E[X]$ using the results from part b.

**(d)** Find $E[X^2]$ and VAR[$X$] using the approach in parts b and c.

**3.42.** Find $E[Y]$ and VAR[$Y$] for the difference between the number of heads and tails in $n$ tosses in Problem 3.9. *Hint:* Condition on the number of heads.

**3.43.** **(a)** In Problem 3.10 find the conditional pmf of $X$ given that the password has not been found after $k$ tries.

**(b)** Find the conditional expected value of $X$ given $X > k$.

**(c)** Find $E[X]$ from the results in part b.

## Section 3.5: Important Discrete Random Variables

**3.44.** Indicate the value of the indicator function for the event $A$, $I_A(\zeta)$, for each $\zeta$ in the sample space $S$. Find the pmf and expected of $I_A$.

**(a)** $S = \{1, 2, 3, 4, 5\}$ and $A = \{\zeta > 3\}$.

**(b)** $S = [0, 1]$ and $A = \{0.3 < \zeta \le 0.7\}$.

**(c)** $S = \{\zeta = (x, y) : 0 < x < 1, 0 < y < 1\}$ and
$A = \{\zeta = (x, y) : 0.25 < x + y < 1.25\}$.

**(d)** $S = (-\infty, \infty)$ and $A = \{\zeta > a\}$.

**3.45.** Let $A$ and $B$ be events for a random experiment with sample space $S$. Show that the Bernoulli random variable satisfies the following properties:

**(a)** $I_S = 1$ and $I_\varnothing = 0$.

**(b)** $I_{A \cap B} = I_A I_B$ and $I_{A \cup B} = I_A + I_B - I_A I_B$.

**(c)** Find the expected value of the indicator functions in parts a and b.

**3.46.** Heat must be removed from a system according to how fast it is generated. Suppose the system has eight components each of which is active with probability 0.25, independently of the others. The design of the heat removal system requires finding the probabilities of the following events:

**(a)** None of the systems is active.

**(b)** Exactly one is active.

**(c)** More than four are active.

**(d)** More than two and fewer than six are active.

**3.47.** Eight numbers are selected at random from the unit interval.

**(a)** Find the probability that the first four numbers are less than 0.25 and the last four are greater than 0.25.

**(b)** Find the probability that four numbers are less than 0.25 and four are greater than 0.25.

**(c)** Find the probability that the first three numbers are less than 0.25, the next two are between 0.25 and 0.75, and the last three are greater than 0.75.

**(d)** Find the probability that three numbers are less than 0.25, two are between 0.25 and 0.75, and three are greater than 0.75.

**(e)** Find the probability that the first four numbers are less than 0.25 and the last four are greater than 0.75.

**(f)** Find the probability that four numbers are less than 0.25 and four are greater than 0.75.

**3.48. (a)** Plot the pmf of the binomial random variable with $n = 4$ and $n = 5$, and $p = 0.10$, $p = 0.5$, and $p = 0.90$.

**(b)** Use Octave to plot the pmf of the binomial random variable with $n = 100$ and $p = 0.10$, $p = 0.5$, and $p = 0.90$.

**3.49.** Let $X$ be a binomial random variable that results from the performance of $n$ Bernoulli trials with probability of success $p$.

**(a)** Suppose that $X = 1$. Find the probability that the single event occurred in the $k$th Bernoulli trial.

**(b)** Suppose that $X = 2$. Find the probability that the two events occurred in the $j$th and $k$th Bernoulli trials where $j < k$.

**(c)** In light of your answers to parts a and b in what sense are the successes distributed "completely at random" over the $n$ Bernoulli trials?

**3.50.** Let $X$ be the binomial random variable.

**(a)** Show that

$$\frac{p_X(k + 1)}{p_X(k)} = \frac{n - k}{k + 1}\frac{p}{1 - p} \qquad \text{where} \qquad p_X(0) = (1 - p)^n.$$

**(b)** Show that part a implies that: (1) $P[X = k]$ is maximum at $k_{max} = [(n + 1)p]$, where $[x]$ denotes the largest integer that is smaller than or equal to $x$; and (2) when $(n + 1)p$ is an integer, then the maximum is achieved at $k_{max}$ and $k_{max} - 1$.

**3.51.** Consider the expression $(a + b + c)^n$.

**(a)** Use the binomial expansion for $(a + b)$ and $c$ to obtain an expression for $(a + b + c)^n$.

**(b)** Now expand all terms of the form $(a + b)^k$ and obtain an expression that involves the multinomial coefficient for $M = 3$ mutually exclusive events, $A_1, A_2, A_3$.

**(c)** Let $p_1 = P[A_1]$, $p_2 = P[A_2]$, $p_3 = P[A_3]$. Use the result from part b to show that the multinomial probabilities add to one.

**3.52.** A sequence of characters is transmitted over a channel that introduces errors with probability $p = 0.01$.

**(a)** What is the pmf of $N$, the number of error-free characters between erroneous characters?

**(b)** What is $E[N]$?

**(c)** Suppose we want to be 99% sure that at least 1000 characters are received correctly before a bad one occurs. What is the appropriate value of $p$?

**3.53.** Let $N$ be a geometric random variable with $S_N = \{1, 2, \dots\}$.

**(a)** Find $P[N = k | N \leq m]$.

**(b)** Find the probability that $N$ is odd.

**3.54.** Let $M$ be a geometric random variable. Show that $M$ satisfies the memoryless property: $P[M \geq k + j | M \geq j + 1] = P[M \geq k]$ for all $j, k > 1$.

**3.55.** Let $X$ be a discrete random variable that assumes only nonnegative integer values and that satisfies the memoryless property. Show that $X$ must be a geometric random variable. *Hint:* Find an equation that must be satisfied by $g(m) = P[M \geq m]$.

**3.56.** An audio player uses a low-quality hard drive. The initial cost of building the player is $50. The hard drive fails after each month of use with probability 1/12. The cost to repair the hard drive is $20. If a 1-year warranty is offered, how much should the manufacturer charge so that the probability of losing money on a player is 1% or less? What is the average cost per player?

**3.57.** A Christmas fruitcake has Poisson-distributed independent numbers of sultana raisins, iridescent red cherry bits, and radioactive green cherry bits with respective averages 48, 24, and 12 bits per cake. Suppose you politely accept 1/12 of a slice of the cake.

**(a)** What is the probability that you get lucky and get no green bits in your slice?

**(b)** What is the probability that you get really lucky and get no green bits and two or fewer red bits in your slice?

**(c)** What is the probability that you get extremely lucky and get no green or red bits and more than five raisins in your slice?

**3.58.** The number of orders waiting to be processed is given by a Poisson random variable with parameter $\alpha = \lambda/n\mu$, where $\lambda$ is the average number of orders that arrive in a day, $\mu$ is the number of orders that can be processed by an employee per day, and $n$ is the number of employees. Let $\lambda = 5$ and $\mu = 1$. Find the number of employees required so the probability that more than four orders are waiting is less than 90%. What is the probability that there are no orders waiting?

**3.59.** The number of page requests that arrive at a Web server is a Poisson random variable with an average of 6000 requests per minute.

**(a)** Find the probability that there are no requests in a 100-ms period.

**(b)** Find the probability that there are between 5 and 10 requests in a 100-ms period.

**3.60.** Use Octave to plot the pmf of the Poisson random variable with $\alpha = 0.1, 0.75, 2, 20$.

**3.61.** Find the mean and variance of a Poisson random variable.

**3.62.** For the Poisson random variable, show that for $\alpha < 1$, $P[N = k]$ is maximum at $k = 0$; for $\alpha > 1$, $P[N = k]$ is maximum at $[\alpha]$; and if $\alpha$ is a positive integer, then $P[N = k]$ is maximum at $k = \alpha$, and at $k = \alpha - 1$. *Hint:* Use the approach of Problem 3.50.

**3.63.** Compare the Poisson approximation and the binomial probabilities for $k = 0, 1, 2, 3$ and $n = 10, p = 0.1$; $n = 20$ and $p = 0.05$; and $n = 100$ and $p = 0.01$.

**3.64.** At a given time, the number of households connected to the Internet is a Poisson random variable with mean 50. Suppose that the transmission bit rate available for the household is 20 Megabits per second.

**(a)** Find the probability of the distribution of the transmission bit rate per user.

**(b)** Find the transmission bit rate that is available to a user with probability 90% or higher.

**(c)** What is the probability that a user has a share of 1 Megabit per second or higher?

**3.65.** An LCD display has $1000 \times 750$ pixels. A display is accepted if it has 15 or fewer faulty pixels. The probability that a pixel is faulty coming out of the production line is $10^{-5}$. Find the proportion of displays that are accepted.

**3.66.** A data center has 10,000 disk drives. Suppose that a disk drive fails in a given day with probability $10^{-3}$.

   **(a)** Find the probability that there are no failures in a given day.

   **(b)** Find the probability that there are fewer than 10 failures in two days.

   **(c)** Find the number of spare disk drives that should be available so that all failures in a day can be replaced with probability 99%.

**3.67.** A binary communication channel has a probability of bit error of $10^{-6}$. Suppose that transmissions occur in blocks of 10,000 bits. Let $N$ be the number of errors introduced by the channel in a transmission block.

   **(a)** Find $P[N = 0]$, $P[N \le 3]$.

   **(b)** For what value of $p$ will the probability of 1 or more errors in a block be 99%?

**3.68.** Find the mean and variance of the uniform discrete random variable that takes on values in the set $\{1, 2, \ldots, L\}$ with equal probability. You will need the following formulas:

$$\sum_{i=1}^{n} i = \frac{n(n+1)}{2} \qquad \sum_{i=1}^{n} i^2 = \frac{n(n+1)(2n+1)}{6}.$$

**3.69.** A voltage $X$ is uniformly distributed in the set $\{-3, \ldots, 3, 4\}$.

   **(a)** Find the mean and variance of $X$.

   **(b)** Find the mean and variance of $Y = -2X^2 + 3$.

   **(c)** Find the mean and variance of $W = \cos(\pi X/8)$.

   **(d)** Find the mean and variance of $Z = \cos^2(\pi X/8)$.

**3.70.** Ten news Web sites are ranked in terms of popularity, and the frequency of requests to these sites are known to follow a Zipf distribution.

   **(a)** What is the probability that a request is for the top-ranked site?

   **(b)** What is the probability that a request is for one of the bottom five sites?

**3.71.** A collection of 1000 words is known to have a Zipf distribution.

   **(a)** What is the probability of the 10 top-ranked words?

   **(b)** What is the probability of the 10 lowest-ranked words?

**3.72.** What is the shape of the log of the Zipf probability vs. the log of the rank?

**3.73.** Plot the mean and variance of the Zipf random variable for $L = 1$ to $L = 100$.

**3.74.** An online video store has 10,000 titles. In order to provide fast response, the store caches the most popular titles. How many titles should be in the cache so that with probability 99% an arriving video request will be in the cache?

**3.75.** **(a)** Income distribution is perfectly equal if every individual has the same income. What is the Lorenz curve in this case?

   **(b)** In a perfectly unequal income distribution, one individual has all the income and all others have none. What is the Lorenz curve in this case?

**3.76.** Let $X$ be a geometric random variable in the set $\{1, 2, \ldots\}$.

   **(a)** Find the pmf of $X$.

   **(b)** Find the Lorenz curve of $X$. Assume $L$ is infinite.

   **(c)** Plot the curve for $p = 0.1, 0.5, 0.9$.

**3.77.** Let $X$ be a zeta random variable with parameter $\alpha$.

   **(a)** Find an expression for $P[X \le k]$.

**(b)** Plot the pmf of $X$ for $\alpha = 1.5, 2$, and 3.

**(c)** Plot $P[X \leq k]$ for $\alpha = 1.5, 2$, and 3.

## Section 3.6: Generation of Discrete Random Variables

**3.78.** Octave provides function calls to evaluate the pmf of important discrete random variables. For example, the function `Poisson_pdf`$(x, lambda)$ computes the pmf at $x$ for the Poisson random variable.

**(a)** Plot the Poisson pmf for $\lambda = 0.5, 5, 50$, as well as $P[X \leq k]$ and $P[X > k]$.

**(b)** Plot the binomial pmf for $n = 48$ and $p = 0.10, 0.30, 0.50, 0.75$, as well as $P[X \leq k]$ and $P[X > k]$.

**(c)** Compare the binomial probabilities with the Poisson approximation for $n = 100$, $p = 0.01$.

**3.79.** The `discrete_pdf` function in Octave makes it possible to specify an arbitrary pmf for a specified $S_X$.

**(a)** Plot the pmf for Zipf random variables with $L = 10, 100, 1000$, as well as $P[X \leq k]$ and $P[X > k]$.

**(b)** Plot the pmf for the reward in the St. Petersburg Paradox for $m = 20$ in Problem 3.34, as well as $P[X \leq k]$ and $P[X > k]$. (You will need to use a log scale for the values of $k$.)

**3.80.** Use Octave to plot the Lorenz curve for the Zipf random variables in Problem 3.79a.

**3.81.** Repeat Problem 3.80 for the binomial random variable with $n = 100$ and $p = 0.1, 0.5$, and 0.9.

**3.82.** **(a)** Use the `discrete_rnd` function in Octave to simulate the urn experiment discussed in Section 1.3. Compute the relative frequencies of the outcomes in 1000 draws from the urn.

**(b)** Use the `discrete_pdf` function in Octave to specify a pmf for a binomial random variable with $n = 5$ and $p = 0.2$. Use `discrete_rnd` to generate 100 samples and plot the relative frequencies.

**(c)** Use `binomial_rnd` to generate the 100 samples in part b.

**3.83.** Use the `discrete_rnd` function to generate 200 samples of the Zipf random variable in Problem 3.79a. Plot the sequence of outcomes as well as the overall relative frequencies.

**3.84.** Use the `discrete_rnd` function to generate 200 samples of the St. Petersburg Paradox random variable in Problem 3.79b. Plot the sequence of outcomes as well as the overall relative frequencies.

**3.85.** Use Octave to generate 200 pairs of numbers, $(X_i, Y_i)$, in which the components are independent, and each component is uniform in the set $\{1, 2, \ldots, 9, 10\}$.

**(a)** Plot the relative frequencies of the $X$ and $Y$ outcomes.

**(b)** Plot the relative frequencies of the random variable $Z = X + Y$. Can you discern the pmf of $Z$?

**(c)** Plot the relative frequencies of $W = XY$. Can you discern the pmf of $Z$?

**(d)** Plot the relative frequencies of $V = X/Y$. Is the pmf discernable?

**3.86.** Use Octave function `binomial_rnd` to generate 200 pairs of numbers, $(X_i, Y_i)$, in which the components are independent, and where $X_i$ are binomial with parameter $n = 8, p = 0.5$ and $Y_i$ are binomial with parameter $n = 4, p = 0.5$.

(a) Plot the relative frequencies of the $X$ and $Y$ outcomes.

(b) Plot the relative frequencies of the random variable $Z = X + Y$. Does this correspond to the pmf you would expect? Explain.

**3.87.** Use Octave function `Poisson_rnd` to generate 200 pairs of numbers, $(X_i, Y_i)$, in which the components are independent, and where $X_i$ are the number of arrivals to a system in one second and $Y_i$ are the number of arrivals to the system in the next two seconds. Assume that the arrival rate is five customers per second.

(a) Plot the relative frequencies of the $X$ and $Y$ outcomes.

(b) Plot the relative frequencies of the random variable $Z = X + Y$. Does this correspond to the pmf you would expect? Explain.

## Problems Requiring Cumulative Knowledge

**3.88.** The fraction of defective items in a production line is $p$. Each item is tested and defective items are identified correctly with probability $a$.

(a) Assume nondefective items always pass the test. What is the probability that $k$ items are tested until a defective item is identified?

(b) Suppose that the identified defective items are removed. What proportion of the remaining items is defective?

(c) Now suppose that nondefective items are identified as defective with probability $b$. Repeat part b.

**3.89.** A data transmission system uses messages of duration $T$ seconds. After each message transmission, the transmitter stops and waits $T$ seconds for a reply from the receiver. The receiver immediately replies with a message indicating that a message was received correctly. The transmitter proceeds to send a new message if it receives a reply within $T$ seconds; otherwise, it retransmits the previous message. Suppose that messages can be completely garbled while in transit and that this occurs with probability $p$. Find the maximum possible rate at which messages can be successfully transmitted from the transmitter to the receiver.

**3.90.** An inspector selects every $n$th item in a production line for a detailed inspection. Suppose that the time between item arrivals is an exponential random variable with mean 1 minute, and suppose that it takes 2 minutes to inspect an item. Find the smallest value of $n$ such that with a probability of 90% or more, the inspection is completed before the arrival of the next item that requires inspection.

**3.91.** The number $X$ of photons counted by a receiver in an optical communication system is a Poisson random variable with rate $\lambda_1$ when a signal is present and a Poisson random variable with rate $\lambda_0 < \lambda_1$ when a signal is absent. Suppose that a signal is present with probability $p$.

(a) Find $P[\text{signal present} \mid X = k]$ and $P[\text{signal absent} \mid X = k]$.

(b) The receiver uses the following decision rule:

If $P[\text{signal present} \mid X = k] > P[\text{signal absent} \mid X = k]$, decide signal present; otherwise, decide signal absent.

Show that this decision rule leads to the following threshold rule:

If $X > T$, decide signal present; otherwise, decide signal absent.

(c) What is the probability of error for the above decision rule?

**3.92.** A binary information source (e.g., a document scanner) generates very long strings of 0's followed by occasional 1's. Suppose that symbols are independent and that $p = P[\text{symbol} = 0]$ is very close to one. Consider the following scheme for encoding the run $X$ of 0's between consecutive 1's:

1. If $X = n$, express $n$ as a multiple of an integer $M = 2^m$ and a remainder $r$, that is, find $k$ and $r$ such that $n = kM + r$, where $0 \le r < M - 1$;

2. The binary codeword for $n$ then consists of a prefix consisting of $k$ 0's followed by a 1, and a suffix consisting of the $m$-bit representation of the remainder $r$. The decoder can deduce the value of $n$ from this binary string.

(a) Find the probability that the prefix has $k$ zeros, assuming that $p^M = 1/2$.

(b) Find the average codeword length when $p^M = 1/2$.

(c) Find the compression ratio, which is defined as the ratio of the average run length to the average codeword length when $p^M = 1/2$.

# One Random Variable

In Chapter 3 we introduced the notion of a random variable and we developed methods for calculating probabilities and averages for the case where the random variable is discrete. In this chapter we consider the general case where the random variable may be discrete, continuous, or of mixed type. We introduce the cumulative distribution function which is used in the formal definition of a random variable, and which can handle all three types of random variables. We also introduce the probability density function for continuous random variables. The probabilities of events involving a random variable can be expressed as integrals of its probability density function. The expected value of continuous random variables is also introduced and related to our intuitive notion of average. We develop a number of methods for calculating probabilities and averages that are the basic tools in the analysis and design of systems that involve randomness.

## 4.1    THE CUMULATIVE DISTRIBUTION FUNCTION

The probability mass function of a discrete random variable was defined in terms of events of the form $\{X = b\}$. The cumulative distribution function is an alternative approach which uses events of the form $\{X \leq b\}$. The cumulative distribution function has the advantage that it is not limited to discrete random variables and applies to all types of random variables. We begin with a formal definition of a random variable.

> **Definition:** Consider a random experiment with sample space $S$ and event class $\mathcal{F}$. A **random variable** $X$ is a function from the sample space $S$ to $R$ with the property that the set $A_b = \{\zeta : X(\zeta) \leq b\}$ is in $\mathcal{F}$ for every $b$ in $R$.

The definition simply requires that every set $A_b$ have a well defined probability in the underlying random experiment, and this is not a problem in the cases we will consider. Why does the definition use sets of the form $\{\zeta : X(\zeta) \leq b\}$ and not $\{\zeta : X(\zeta) = x_b\}$? We will see that all events of interest in the real line can be expressed in terms of sets of the form $\{\zeta : X(\zeta) \leq b\}$.

The **cumulative distribution function** (cdf) of a random variable $X$ is defined as the probability of the event $\{X \leq x\}$:

$$F_X(x) = P[X \leq x] \qquad \text{for } -\infty < x < +\infty, \qquad (4.1)$$

that is, it is the probability that the random variable $X$ takes on a value in the set $(-\infty, x]$. In terms of the underlying sample space, the cdf is the probability of the event $\{\zeta: X(\zeta) \leq x\}$. The event $\{X \leq x\}$ and its probability vary as $x$ is varied; in other words, $F_X(x)$ is a function of the variable $x$.

The cdf is simply a convenient way of specifying the probability of all semi-infinite intervals of the real line of the form $(-\infty, b]$. The events of interest when dealing with numbers are intervals of the real line, and their complements, unions, and intersections. We show below that the probabilities of all of these events can be expressed in terms of the cdf.

The cdf has the following interpretation in terms of relative frequency. Suppose that the experiment that yields the outcome $\zeta$, and hence $X(\zeta)$, is performed a large number of times. $F_X(b)$ is then the long-term proportion of times in which $X(\zeta) \leq b$.

Before developing the general properties of the cdf, we present examples of the cdfs for three basic types of random variables.

---

### Example 4.1    Three Coin Tosses

Figure 4.1(a) shows the cdf $X$, the number of heads in three tosses of a fair coin. From Example 3.1 we know that $X$ takes on only the values $0, 1, 2$, and $3$ with probabilities $1/8, 3/8, 3/8$, and $1/8$, respectively, so $F_X(x)$ is simply the sum of the probabilities of the outcomes from $\{0, 1, 2, 3\}$ that are less than or equal to $x$. The resulting cdf is seen to be a nondecreasing staircase function that grows from 0 to 1. The cdf has jumps at the points $0, 1, 2, 3$ of magnitudes $1/8, 3/8, 3/8$, and $1/8$, respectively.

---

Let us take a closer look at one of these discontinuities, say, in the vicinity of $x = 1$. For $\delta$ a small positive number, we have

$$F_X(1 - \delta) = P[X \leq 1 - \delta] = P\{0 \text{ heads}\} = \frac{1}{8}$$

so the limit of the cdf as $x$ approaches 1 from the left is 1/8. However,

$$F_X(1) = P[X \leq 1] = P[0 \text{ or } 1 \text{ heads}] = \frac{1}{8} + \frac{3}{8} = \frac{1}{2},$$

and furthermore the limit from the right is

$$F_X(1 + \delta) = P[X \leq 1 + \delta] = P[0 \text{ or } 1 \text{ heads}] = \frac{1}{2}.$$

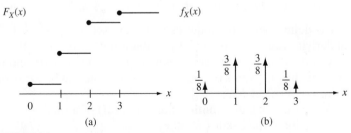

**FIGURE 4.1**
cdf (a) and pdf (b) of a discrete random variable.

Thus the cdf is continuous from the right and equal to 1/2 at the point $x = 1$. Indeed, we note the magnitude of the jump at the point $x = 1$ is equal to $P[X = 1] = 1/2 - 1/8 = 3/8$. Henceforth we will use dots in the graph to indicate the value of the cdf at the points of discontinuity.

The cdf can be written compactly in terms of the unit step function:

$$u(x) = \begin{cases} 0 & \text{for } x < 0 \\ 1 & \text{for } x \geq 0, \end{cases} \tag{4.2}$$

then

$$F_X(x) = \frac{1}{8}u(x) + \frac{3}{8}u(x - 1) + \frac{3}{8}u(x - 2) + \frac{1}{8}u(x - 3).$$

---

### Example 4.2    Uniform Random Variable in the Unit Interval

Spin an arrow attached to the center of a circular board. Let $\theta$ be the final angle of the arrow, where $0 < \theta \leq 2\pi$. The probability that $\theta$ falls in a subinterval of $(0, 2\pi]$ is proportional to the length of the subinterval. The random variable $X$ is defined by $X(\theta) = \theta/2\pi$. Find the cdf of $X$:

As $\theta$ increases from 0 to $2\pi$, $X$ increases from 0 to 1. No outcomes $\theta$ lead to values $x \leq 0$, so

$$F_X(x) = P[X \leq x] = P[\emptyset] = 0 \qquad \text{for } x < 0.$$

For $0 < x \leq 1$, $\{X \leq x\}$ occurs when $\{\theta \leq 2\pi x\}$ so

$$F_X(x) = P[X \leq x] = P[\{\theta \leq 2\pi x\}] = 2\pi x/2\pi = x \qquad 0 < x \leq 1. \tag{4.3}$$

Finally, for $x > 1$, all outcomes $\theta$ lead to $\{X(\theta) \leq 1 < x\}$, therefore:

$$F_X(x) = P[X \leq x] = P[0 < \theta \leq 2\pi] = 1 \qquad \text{for } x > 1.$$

We say that $X$ is a **uniform random variable** in the unit interval. Figure 4.2(a) shows the cdf of the general uniform random variable $X$. We see that $F_X(x)$ is a nondecreasing continuous function that grows from 0 to 1 as $x$ ranges from its minimum values to its maximum values.

---

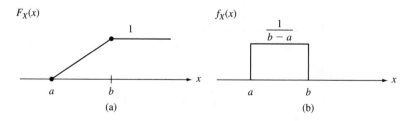

(a)    (b)

**FIGURE 4.2**
cdf (a) and pdf (b) of a continuous random variable.

## Example 4.3

The waiting time $X$ of a customer at a taxi stand is zero if the customer finds a taxi parked at the stand, and a uniformly distributed random length of time in the interval $[0, 1]$ (in hours) if no taxi is found upon arrival. The probability that a taxi is at the stand when the customer arrives is $p$. Find the cdf of $X$.

The cdf is found by applying the theorem on total probability:

$$F_X(x) = P[X \leq x] = P[X \leq x \,|\, \text{find taxi}]p + P[X \leq x \,|\, \text{no taxi}](1 - p).$$

Note that $P[X \leq x \,|\, \text{find taxi}] = 1$ when $x \geq 0$ and 0 otherwise. Furthermore $P[X \leq x \,|\, \text{no taxi}]$ is given by Eq. (4.3), therefore

$$F_X(x) = \begin{cases} 0 & x < 0 \\ p + (1 - p)x & 0 \leq x \leq 1 \\ 1 & x > 1. \end{cases}$$

The cdf, shown in Fig. 4.3(a), combines some of the properties of the cdf in Example 4.1 (discontinuity at 0) and the cdf in Example 4.2 (continuity over intervals). Note that $F_X(x)$ can be expressed as the sum of a step function with amplitude $p$ and a continuous function of $x$.

---

We are now ready to state the basic properties of the cdf. The axioms of probability and their corollaries imply that the cdf has the following properties:

**(i)** $0 \leq F_X(x) \leq 1$.

**(ii)** $\displaystyle\lim_{x \to \infty} F_X(x) = 1$.

**(iii)** $\displaystyle\lim_{x \to -\infty} F_X(x) = 0$.

**(iv)** $F_X(x)$ is a nondecreasing function of $x$, that is, if $a < b$, then $F_X(a) \leq F_X(b)$.

**(v)** $F_X(x)$ is continuous from the right, that is, for $h > 0$, $F_X(b) = \displaystyle\lim_{h \to 0} F_X(b + h)$
$= F_X(b^+)$.

These five properties confirm that, in general, the cdf is a nondecreasing function that grows from 0 to 1 as $x$ increases from $-\infty$ to $\infty$. We already observed these properties in Examples 4.1, 4.2, and 4.3. Property (v) implies that at points of discontinuity, the cdf

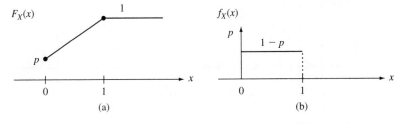

**FIGURE 4.3**
cdf (a) and pdf (b) of a random variable of mixed type.

is equal to the limit from the right. We observed this property in Examples 4.1 and 4.3. In Example 4.2 the cdf is continuous for all values of $x$, that is, the cdf is continuous both from the right and from the left for all $x$.

The cdf has the following properties which allow us to calculate the probability of events involving intervals and single values of $X$:

**(vi)** $P[a < X \leq b] = F_X(b) - F_X(a)$.

**(vii)** $P[X = b] = F_X(b) - F_X(b^-)$.

**(viii)** $P[X > x] = 1 - F_X(x)$.

Property (vii) states that the probability that $X = b$ is given by the magnitude of the jump of the cdf at the point $b$. This implies that *if the cdf is continuous at a point $b$, then* $P[X = b] = 0$. Properties (vi) and (vii) can be combined to compute the probabilities of other types of intervals. For example, since $\{a \leq X \leq b\} = \{X = a\} \cup \{a < X \leq b\}$, then

$$P[a \leq X \leq b] = P[X = a] + P[a < X \leq b]$$
$$= F_X(a) - F_X(a^-) + F_X(b) - F_X(a) = F_X(b) - F_X(a^-). \quad (4.4)$$

If the cdf is continuous at the endpoints of an interval, then the endpoints have zero probability, and therefore they can be included in, or excluded from, the interval without affecting the probability.

---

**Example 4.4**

Let $X$ be the number of heads in three tosses of a fair coin. Use the cdf to find the probability of the events $A = \{1 < X \leq 2\}$, $B = \{0.5 \leq X < 2.5\}$, and $C = \{1 \leq X < 2\}$.

From property (vi) and Fig. 4.1 we have

$$P[1 < X \leq 2] = F_X(2) - F_X(1) = 7/8 - 1/2 = 3/8.$$

The cdf is continuous at $x = 0.5$ and $x = 2.5$, so

$$P[0.5 \leq X < 2.5] = F_X(2.5) - F_X(0.5) = 7/8 - 1/8 = 6/8.$$

Since $\{1 \leq X < 2\} \cup \{X = 2\} = \{1 \leq X \leq 2\}$, from Eq. (4.4) we have

$$P\{1 \leq X < 2\} + P[X = 2] = F_X(2) - F_X(1^-),$$

and using property (vii) for $P[X = 2]$:

$$P\{1 \leq X < 2\} = F_X(2) - F_X(1^-) - P[X = 2] = F_X(2) - F_X(1^-) - (F_X(2) - F_X(2^-))$$
$$= F_X(2^-) - F_X(1^-) = 4/8 - 1/8 = 3/8.$$

---

**Example 4.5**

Let $X$ be the uniform random variable from Example 4.2. Use the cdf to find the probability of the events $\{-0.5 < X < 0.25\}$, $\{0.3 < X < 0.65\}$, and $\{|X - 0.4| > 0.2\}$.

The cdf of $X$ is continuous at every point so we have:

$$P[-0.5 < X \leq 0.25] = F_X(0.25) - F_X(-0.5) = 0.25 - 0 = 0.25,$$

$$P[0.3 < X < 0.65] = F_X(0.65) - F_X(0.3) = 0.65 - 0.3 = 0.35,$$

$$P[|X - 0.4| > 0.2] = P[\{X < 0.2\} \cup \{X > 0.6\}] = P[X < 0.2] + P[X > 0.6]$$

$$= F_X(0.2) + (1 - F_X(0.6)) = 0.2 + 0.4 = 0.6.$$

We now consider the proof of the properties of the cdf.

- Property (i) follows from the fact that the cdf is a probability and hence must satisfy Axiom I and Corollary 2.
- To obtain property (iv), we note that the event $\{X \leq a\}$ is a subset of $\{X \leq b\}$, and so it must have smaller or equal probability (Corollary 7).
- To show property (vi), we note that $\{X \leq b\}$ can be expressed as the union of mutually exclusive events: $\{X \leq a\} \cup \{a < X \leq b\} = \{X \leq b\}$, and so by Axiom III, $F_X(a) + P[a < X \leq b] = F_X(b)$.
- Property (viii) follows from $\{X > x\} = \{X \leq x\}^c$ and Corollary 1.

While intuitively clear, properties (ii), (iii), (v), and (vii) require more advanced limiting arguments that are discussed at the end of this section.

### 4.1.1   The Three Types of Random Variables

The random variables in Examples 4.1, 4.2, and 4.3 are typical of the three most basic types of random variable that we are interested in.

**Discrete random variables** have a cdf that is a right-continuous, staircase function of $x$, with jumps at a countable set of points $x_0, x_1, x_2, \ldots$. The random variable in Example 4.1 is a typical example of a discrete random variable. The cdf $F_X(x)$ of a discrete random variable is the sum of the probabilities of the outcomes less than $x$ and can be written as the weighted sum of unit step functions as in Example 4.1:

$$F_X(x) = \sum_{x_k \leq x} p_X(x_k) = \sum_k p_X(x_k) u(x - x_k), \tag{4.5}$$

where the pmf $p_X(x_k) = P[X = x_k]$ gives the magnitude of the jumps in the cdf. We see that the pmf can be obtained from the cdf and vice versa.

A **continuous random variable** is defined as a random variable whose cdf $F_X(x)$ is continuous everywhere, and which, in addition, is sufficiently smooth that it can be written as an integral of some nonnegative function $f(x)$:

$$F_X(x) = \int_{-\infty}^{x} f(t) \, dt. \tag{4.6}$$

The random variable discussed in Example 4.2 can be written as an integral of the function shown in Fig. 4.2(b). The continuity of the cdf and property (vii) implies that continuous random variables have $P[X = x] = 0$ for all $x$. Every possible outcome has probability zero! An immediate consequence is that the pmf cannot be used to characterize the probabilities of $X$. A comparison of Eqs. (4.5) and (4.6) suggests how we can proceed to characterize continuous random variables. For discrete random variables, (Eq. 4.5), we calculate probabilities as summations of probability masses at discrete points. For continuous random variables, (Eq. 4.6), we calculate probabilities as integrals of "probability densities" over intervals of the real line.

A **random variable of mixed type** is a random variable with a cdf that has jumps on a countable set of points $x_0, x_1, x_2, \ldots$, but that also increases continuously over at least one interval of values of $x$. The cdf for these random variables has the form

$$F_X(x) = pF_1(x) + (1 - p)F_2(x),$$

where $0 < p < 1$, and $F_1(x)$ is the cdf of a discrete random variable and $F_2(x)$ is the cdf of a continuous random variable. The random variable in Example 4.3 is of mixed type.

Random variables of mixed type can be viewed as being produced by a two-step process: A coin is tossed; if the outcome of the toss is heads, a discrete random variable is generated according to $F_1(x)$; otherwise, a continuous random variable is generated according to $F_2(x)$.

## *4.1.2   Fine Point: Limiting properties of cdf

Properties (ii), (iii), (v), and (vii) require the continuity property of the probability function discussed in Section 2.9. For example, for property (ii), we consider the sequence of events $\{X \leq n\}$ which increases to include all of the sample space $S$ as $n$ approaches $\infty$, that is, all outcomes lead to a value of $X$ less than infinity. The continuity property of the probability function (Corollary 8) implies that:

$$\lim_{n \to \infty} F_X(n) = \lim_{n \to \infty} P[X \leq n] = P[\lim_{n \to \infty} \{X \leq n\}] = P[S] = 1.$$

For property (iii), we take the sequence $\{X \leq -n\}$ which decreases to the empty set $\varnothing$, that is, no outcome leads to a value of $X$ less than $-\infty$:

$$\lim_{n \to \infty} F_X(-n) = \lim_{n \to \infty} P[X \leq -n] = P[\lim_{n \to \infty} \{X \leq -n\}] = P[\varnothing] = 0.$$

For property (v), we take the sequence of events $\{X \leq x + 1/n\}$ which decreases to $\{X \leq x\}$ from the right:

$$\lim_{n \to \infty} F_X(x + 1/n) = \lim_{n \to \infty} P[X \leq x + 1/n]$$

$$= P[\lim_{n \to \infty} \{X \leq x + 1/n\}] = P[\{X \leq x\}] = F_X(x).$$

Finally, for property (vii), we take the sequence of events, $\{b - 1/n < X \leq b\}$ which decreases to $\{b\}$ from the left:

$$\lim_{n \to \infty} (F_X(b) - F_X(b - 1/n)) = \lim_{n \to \infty} P[b - 1/n < X \leq b]$$

$$= P[\lim_{n \to \infty} \{b - 1/n < X \leq b\}] = P[X = b].$$

## 4.2    THE PROBABILITY DENSITY FUNCTION

The **probability density function of $X$** (pdf), if it exists, is defined as the derivative of $F_X(x)$:

$$f_X(x) = \frac{dF_X(x)}{dx}. \tag{4.7}$$

In this section we show that the pdf is an alternative, and more useful, way of specifying the information contained in the cumulative distribution function.

The pdf represents the "density" of probability at the point $x$ in the following sense: The probability that $X$ is in a small interval in the vicinity of $x$—that is, $\{x < X \le x + h\}$—is

$$P[x < X \le x + h] = F_X(x + h) - F_X(x)$$

$$= \frac{F_X(x + h) - F_X(x)}{h}h. \tag{4.8}$$

If the cdf has a derivative at $x$, then as $h$ becomes very small,

$$P[x < X \le x + h] \simeq f_X(x)h. \tag{4.9}$$

Thus $f_X(x)$ represents the "density" of probability at the point $x$ in the sense that the probability that $X$ is in a small interval in the vicinity of $x$ is approximately $f_X(x)h$. The derivative of the cdf, when it exists, is positive since the cdf is a nondecreasing function of $x$, thus

**(i)** $f_X(x) \ge 0.$ $\hspace{5cm}$ (4.10)

Equations (4.9) and (4.10) provide us with an alternative approach to specifying the probabilities involving the random variable $X$. We can begin by stating a nonnegative function $f_X(x)$, called the probability density function, which specifies the probabilities of events of the form "$X$ falls in a small interval of width $dx$ about the point $x$," as shown in Fig. 4.4(a). The probabilities of events involving $X$ are then expressed in terms of the pdf by adding the probabilities of intervals of width $dx$. As the widths of the intervals approach zero, we obtain an integral in terms of the pdf. For example, the probability of an interval $[a, b]$ is

**(ii)** $P[a \le X \le b] = \displaystyle\int_a^b f_X(x)\,dx.$ $\hspace{4cm}$ (4.11)

*The probability of an interval is therefore the area under $f_X(x)$ in that interval*, as shown in Fig. 4.4(b). The probability of any event that consists of the union of disjoint intervals can thus be found by adding the integrals of the pdf over each of the intervals.

The cdf of $X$ can be obtained by integrating the pdf:

**(iii)** $F_X(x) = \displaystyle\int_{-\infty}^x f_X(t)\,dt.$ $\hspace{4cm}$ (4.12)

In Section 4.1, we defined a *continuous random variable* as a random variable $X$ whose cdf was given by Eq. (4.12). Since the probabilities of all events involving $X$ can be written in terms of the cdf, it then follows that these probabilities can be written in

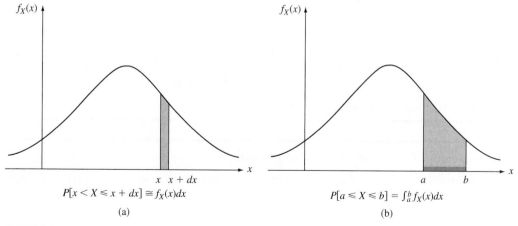

**FIGURE 4.4**
(a) The probability density function specifies the probability of intervals of infinitesimal width. (b) The probability of an interval [a, b] is the area under the pdf in that interval.

terms of the pdf. Thus *the pdf completely specifies the behavior of continuous random variables*.

By letting $x$ tend to infinity in Eq. (4.12), we obtain a *normalization* condition for pdf's:

**(iv)**  $$1 = \int_{-\infty}^{+\infty} f_X(t)\, dt.$$  (4.13)

The pdf reinforces the intuitive notion of probability as having attributes similar to "physical mass." Thus Eq. (4.11) states that the probability "mass" in an interval is the integral of the "density of probability mass" over the interval. Equation (4.13) states that the total mass available is one unit.

*A valid pdf can be formed from any nonnegative, piecewise continuous function g(x) that has a finite integral:*

$$\int_{-\infty}^{\infty} g(x)\, dx = c < \infty.$$  (4.14)

By letting $f_X(x) = g(x)/c$, we obtain a function that satisfies the normalization condition. Note that the pdf must be defined for all real values of $x$; if $X$ does not take on values from some region of the real line, we simply set $f_X(x) = 0$ in the region.

---

**Example 4.6   Uniform Random Variable**

The pdf of the uniform random variable is given by:

$$f_X(x) = \begin{cases} \dfrac{1}{b - a} & a \le x \le b \\ 0 & x < a \quad \text{and} \quad x > b \end{cases}$$  (4.15a)

and is shown in Fig. 4.2(b). The cdf is found from Eq. (4.12):

$$F_X(x) = \begin{cases} 0 & x < a \\ \dfrac{x - a}{b - a} & a \le x \le b \\ 1 & x > b. \end{cases} \qquad (4.15b)$$

The cdf is shown in Fig. 4.2(a).

---

**Example 4.7    Exponential Random Variable**

The transmission time $X$ of messages in a communication system has an exponential distribution:

$$P[X > x] = e^{-\lambda x} \qquad x > 0.$$

Find the cdf and pdf of $X$.
    The cdf is given by $F_X(x) = 1 - P[X > x]$

$$F_X(x) = \begin{cases} 0 & x < 0 \\ 1 - e^{-\lambda x} & x \ge 0. \end{cases} \qquad (4.16a)$$

The pdf is obtained by applying Eq. (4.7):

$$f_X(x) = F'_X(x) = \begin{cases} 0 & x < 0 \\ \lambda e^{-\lambda x} & x \ge 0. \end{cases} \qquad (4.16b)$$

---

**Example 4.8    Laplacian Random Variable**

The pdf of the samples of the amplitude of speech waveforms is found to decay exponentially at a rate $\alpha$, so the following pdf is proposed:

$$f_X(x) = ce^{-\alpha|x|} \qquad -\infty < x < \infty. \qquad (4.17)$$

Find the constant $c$, and then find the probability $P[|X| < v]$.
    We use the normalization condition in (iv) to find $c$:

$$1 = \int_{-\infty}^{\infty} ce^{-\alpha|x|}\, dx = 2\int_{0}^{\infty} ce^{-\alpha x}\, dx = \frac{2c}{\alpha}.$$

Therefore $c = \alpha/2$. The probability $P[|X| < v]$ is found by integrating the pdf:

$$P[|X| < v] = \frac{\alpha}{2}\int_{-v}^{v} e^{-\alpha|x|}\, dx = 2\left(\frac{\alpha}{2}\right)\int_{0}^{v} e^{-\alpha x}\, dx = 1 - e^{-\alpha v}.$$

---

## 4.2.1    pdf of Discrete Random Variables

The derivative of the cdf does not exist at points where the cdf is not continuous. Thus the notion of pdf as defined by Eq. (4.7) does not apply to discrete random variables at the points where the cdf is discontinuous. We can generalize the definition of the probability density function by noting the relation between the unit step function and the delta function. The **unit step function** is defined as

$$u(x) = \begin{cases} 0 & x < 0 \\ 1 & x \geq 0. \end{cases} \quad (4.18a)$$

The **delta function** $\delta(t)$ is related to the unit step function by the following equation:

$$u(x) = \int_{-\infty}^{x} \delta(t) \, dt. \quad (4.18b)$$

A translated unit step function is then:

$$u(x - x_0) = \int_{-\infty}^{x-x_0} \delta(t) \, dt = \int_{-\infty}^{x} \delta(t' - x_0) \, dt'. \quad (4.18c)$$

Substituting Eq. (4.18c) into the cdf of a discrete random variables:

$$F_X(x) = \sum_k p_X(x_k) u(x - x_k) = \sum_k p_X(x_k) \int_{-\infty}^{x} \delta(t - x_k) \, dt$$

$$= \int_{-\infty}^{x} \sum_k p_X(x_k) \delta(t - x_k) \, dt. \quad (4.19)$$

This suggests that we define the **pdf for a discrete random variable** by

$$f_X(x) = \frac{d}{dx} F_X(x) = \sum_k p_X(x_k) \delta(x - x_k). \quad (4.20)$$

Thus the generalized definition of pdf places a delta function of weight $P[X = x_k]$ at the points $x_k$ where the cdf is discontinuous.

To provide some intuition on the delta function, consider a narrow rectangular pulse of unit area and width $\Delta$ centered at $t = 0$:

$$\pi_\Delta(t) = \begin{cases} 1/\Delta & -\Delta/2 \leq t \leq \Delta/2 \\ 0 & |t| > \Delta. \end{cases}$$

Consider the integral of $\pi_\Delta(t)$:

$$\int_{-\infty}^{x} \pi_\Delta(t) \, dt = \begin{cases} \int_{-\infty}^{x} \pi_\Delta(t) \, dt = \int_{-\infty}^{x} 0 \, dt = 0 & \text{for } x < -\Delta/2 \\ \int_{-\infty}^{x} \pi_\Delta(t) \, dt = \int_{-\Delta/2}^{\Delta/2} 1/\Delta \, dt = 1 & \text{for } x > \Delta/2 \end{cases} \to u(x). \quad (4.21)$$

As $\Delta \to 0$, we see that the integral of the narrow pulse approaches the unit step function. For this reason, we visualize the delta function $\delta(t)$ as being zero everywhere except at $x = 0$ where it is unbounded. The above equation does not apply at the value $x = 0$. To maintain the right continuity in Eq. (4.18a), we use the convention:

$$u(0) = 1 = \int_{-\infty}^{0} \delta(t) \, dt.$$

If we replace $\pi_\Delta(t)$ in the above derivation with $g(t)\pi_\Delta(t)$, we obtain the "sifting" property of the delta function:

$$g(0) = \int_{-\infty}^{\infty} g(t)\delta(t) \, dt \quad \text{and} \quad g(x_0) = \int_{-\infty}^{\infty} g(t)\delta(t - x_0) \, dt. \qquad (4.22)$$

The delta function is viewed as sifting through $x$ and picking out the value of $g$ at the point where the delta functions is centered, that is, $g(x_0)$ for the expression on the right.

The pdf for the discrete random variable discussed in Example 4.1 is shown in Fig. 4.1(b). The pdf of a random variable of mixed type will also contain delta functions at the points where its cdf is not continuous. The pdf for the random variable discussed in Example 4.3 is shown in Fig. 4.3(b).

---

### Example 4.9

Let $X$ be the number of heads in three coin tosses as in Example 4.1. Find the pdf of $X$. Find $P[1 < X \le 2]$ and $P[2 \le X < 3]$ by integrating the pdf.

In Example 4.1 we found that the cdf of $X$ is given by

$$F_X(x) = \frac{1}{8}u(x) + \frac{3}{8}u(x - 1) + \frac{3}{8}u(x - 2) + \frac{1}{8}u(x - 3).$$

It then follows from Eqs. (4.18) and (4.19) that

$$f_X(x) = \frac{1}{8}\delta(x) + \frac{3}{8}\delta(x - 1) + \frac{3}{8}\delta(x - 2) + \frac{1}{8}\delta(x - 3).$$

When delta functions appear in the limits of integration, we must indicate whether the delta functions are to be included in the integration. Thus in $P[1 < X \le 2] = P[X \text{ in } (1, 2]]$, the delta function located at 1 is excluded from the integral and the delta function at 2 is included:

$$P[1 < X \le 2] = \int_{1+}^{2+} f_X(x) \, dx = \frac{3}{8}.$$

Similarly, we have that

$$P[2 \le X < 3] = \int_{2-}^{3-} f_X(x) \, dx = \frac{3}{8}.$$

---

### 4.2.2    Conditional cdf's and pdf's

Conditional cdf's can be defined in a straightforward manner using the same approach we used for conditional pmf's. Suppose that event $C$ is given and that $P[C] > 0$. The **conditional cdf of $X$ given $C$** is defined by

$$F_X(x|C) = \frac{P[\{X \le x\} \cap C]}{P[C]} \quad \text{if } P[C] > 0. \qquad (4.23)$$

It is easy to show that $F_X(x|C)$ satisfies all the properties of a cdf. (See Problem 4.29.) The **conditional pdf of $X$ given $C$** is then defined by

$$f_X(x|C) = \frac{d}{dx}F_X(x|C). \tag{4.24}$$

---

### Example 4.10

The lifetime $X$ of a machine has a continuous cdf $F_X(x)$. Find the conditional cdf and pdf given the event $C = \{X > t\}$ (i.e., "machine is still working at time $t$").

The conditional cdf is

$$F_X(x|X > t) = P[X \le x \,|\, X > t] = \frac{P[\{X \le x\} \cap \{X > t\}]}{P[X > t]}.$$

The intersection of the two events in the numerator is equal to the empty set when $x < t$ and to $\{t < X \le x\}$ when $x \ge t$. Thus

$$F_X(x|X > t) = \begin{cases} 0 & x \le t \\ \dfrac{F_X(x) - F_X(t)}{1 - F_X(t)} & x > t. \end{cases}$$

The conditional pdf is found by differentiating with respect to $x$:

$$f_X(x \,|\, X > t) = \frac{f_X(x)}{1 - F_X(t)} \quad x \ge t.$$

---

Now suppose that we have a partition of the sample space $S$ into the union of disjoint events $B_1, B_2, \dots, B_n$. Let $F_X(x|B_i)$ be the conditional cdf of $X$ given event $B_i$. The theorem on total probability allows us to find the cdf of $X$ in terms of the conditional cdf's:

$$F_X(x) = P[X \le x] = \sum_{i=1}^{n} P[X \le x \,|\, B_i]P[B_i] = \sum_{i=1}^{n} F_X(x \,|\, B_i)P[B_i]. \tag{4.25}$$

The pdf is obtained by differentiation:

$$f_X(x) = \frac{d}{dx}F_X(x) = \sum_{i=1}^{n} f_X(x \,|\, B_i)P[B_i]. \tag{4.26}$$

---

### Example 4.11

A binary transmission system sends a "0" bit by transmitting a $-v$ voltage signal, and a "1" bit by transmitting a $+v$. The received signal is corrupted by Gaussian noise and given by:

$$Y = X + N$$

where $X$ is the transmitted signal, and $N$ is a noise voltage with pdf $f_N(x)$. Assume that $P["1"] = p = 1 - P["0"]$. Find the pdf of $Y$.

Let $B_0$ be the event "0" is transmitted and $B_1$ be the event "1" is transmitted, then $B_0, B_1$ form a partition, and

$$F_Y(x) = F_Y(x|B_0)[B_0] + F_Y(x|B_1)[B_1]$$

$$= P[Y \le x|X = -v](1 - p) + P[Y \le x|X = v]p.$$

Since $Y = X + N$, the event $\{Y < x|X = v\}$ is equivalent to $\{v + N < x\}$ and $\{N < x - v\}$, and the event $\{Y < x|X = -v\}$ is equivalent to $\{N < x + v\}$. Therefore the conditional cdf's are:

$$F_Y(x|B_0) = P[N \le x + v] = F_N(x + v)$$

and

$$F_Y(x|B_1) = P[N \le x - v] = F_N(x - v).$$

The cdf is:

$$F_Y(x) = F_N(x + v)(1 - p) + F_N(x - v)p.$$

The pdf of $N$ is then:

$$f_Y(x) = \frac{d}{dx}F_Y(x)$$

$$= \frac{d}{dx}F_N(x + v)(1 - p) + \frac{d}{dx}F_N(x - v)p$$

$$= f_N(x + v)(1 - p) + f_N(x - v)p.$$

The Gaussian random variable has pdf:

$$f_N(x) = \frac{1}{\sqrt{2\pi\sigma^2}}e^{-x^2/2\sigma^2} \qquad -\infty < x < \infty.$$

The conditional pdfs are:

$$f_Y(x|B_0) = f_N(x + v) = \frac{1}{\sqrt{2\pi\sigma^2}}e^{-(x+v)^2/2\sigma^2}$$

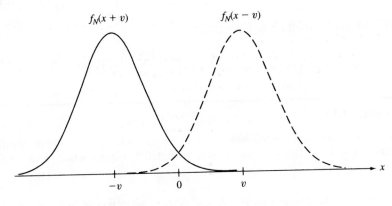

**FIGURE 4.5**
The conditional pdfs given the input signal

and

$$f_Y(x|B_1) = f_N(x - v) = \frac{1}{\sqrt{2\pi\sigma^2}}e^{-(x-v)^2/2\sigma^2}.$$

The pdf of the received signal $Y$ is then:

$$f_Y(x) = \frac{1}{\sqrt{2\pi\sigma^2}}e^{-(x+v)^2/2\sigma^2}(1 - p) + \frac{1}{\sqrt{2\pi\sigma^2}}e^{-(x-v)^2/2\sigma^2}p.$$

Figure 4.5 shows the two conditional pdfs. We can see that the transmitted signal $X$ shifts the center of mass of the Gaussian pdf.

---

## 4.3    THE EXPECTED VALUE OF $X$

We discussed the expected value for discrete random variables in Section 3.3, and found that the sample mean of independent observations of a random variable approaches $E[X]$. Suppose we perform a series of such experiments for continuous random variables. Since continuous random variables have $P[X = x] = 0$ for any specific value of $x$, we divide the real line into small intervals and count the number of times $N_k(n)$ the observations fall in the interval $\{x_k < X < x_k + \Delta\}$. As $n$ becomes large, then the relative frequency $f_k(n) = N_k(n)/n$ will approach $f_X(x_k)\Delta$, the probability of the interval. We calculate the sample mean in terms of the relative frequencies and let $n \to \infty$:

$$\langle X \rangle_n = \sum_k x_k f_k(n) \to \sum_k x_k f_X(x_k)\Delta.$$

The expression on the right-hand side approaches an integral as we decrease $\Delta$.

The **expected value** or **mean** of a random variable $X$ is defined by

$$E[X] = \int_{-\infty}^{+\infty} t f_X(t)\, dt. \tag{4.27}$$

The expected value $E[X]$ is defined if the above integral converges absolutely, that is,

$$E[|X|] = \int_{-\infty}^{+\infty} |t| f_X(t)\, dt \qquad < \infty.$$

If we view $f_X(x)$ as the distribution of mass on the real line, then $E[X]$ represents the center of mass of this distribution.

We already discussed $E[X]$ for discrete random variables in detail, but it is worth noting that the definition in Eq. (4.27) is applicable if we express the pdf of a discrete random variable using delta functions:

$$E[X] = \int_{-\infty}^{+\infty} t \sum_k p_X(x_k)\delta(t - x_k)\, dt$$

$$= \sum_k p_X(x_k) \int_{-\infty}^{+\infty} t \sum_k \delta(t - x_k)\, dt$$

$$= \sum_k p_X(x_k)x_k.$$

## Example 4.12    Mean of a Uniform Random Variable

The mean for a uniform random variable is given by

$$E[X] = (b - a)^{-1} \int_a^b t \, dt = \frac{a + b}{2},$$

which is exactly the midpoint of the interval $[a, b]$. The results shown in Fig. 3.6 were obtained by repeating experiments in which outcomes were random variables $Y$ and $X$ that had uniform cdf's in the intervals $[-1, 1]$ and $[3, 7]$, respectively. The respective expected values, 0 and 5, correspond to the values about which $X$ and $Y$ tend to vary.

The result in Example 4.12 could have been found immediately by noting that $E[X] = m$ when the pdf is symmetric about a point $m$. That is, if

$$f_X(m - x) = f_X(m + x) \qquad \text{for all } x,$$

then, assuming that the mean exists,

$$0 = \int_{-\infty}^{+\infty} (m - t)f_X(t) \, dt = m - \int_{-\infty}^{+\infty} tf_X(t) \, dt.$$

The first equality above follows from the symmetry of $f_X(t)$ about $t = m$ and the odd symmetry of $(m - t)$ about the same point. We then have that $E[X] = m$.

## Example 4.13    Mean of a Gaussian Random Variable

The pdf of a Gaussian random variable is symmetric about the point $x = m$. Therefore $E[X] = m$.

The following expressions are useful when $X$ is a nonnegative random variable:

$$E[X] = \int_0^\infty (1 - F_X(t)) \, dt \qquad \text{if } X \text{ continuous and nonnegative} \qquad (4.28)$$

and

$$E[X] = \sum_{k=0}^\infty P[X > k] \qquad \text{if } X \text{ nonnegative, integer-valued.} \qquad (4.29)$$

The derivation of these formulas is discussed in Problem 4.47.

## Example 4.14    Mean of Exponential Random Variable

The time $X$ between customer arrivals at a service station has an exponential distribution. Find the mean interarrival time.

Substituting Eq. (4.17) into Eq. (4.27) we obtain

$$E[X] = \int_0^\infty t\lambda e^{-\lambda t} \, dt.$$

We evaluate the integral using integration by parts ($\int u\,dv = uv - \int v\,du$), with $u = t$ and $dv = \lambda e^{-\lambda t}\,dt$:

$$E[X] = -te^{-\lambda t}\Big|_0^\infty + \int_0^\infty e^{-\lambda t}\,dt$$

$$= \lim_{t \to \infty} te^{-\lambda t} - 0 + \left\{\frac{-e^{-\lambda t}}{\lambda}\right\}_0^\infty$$

$$= \lim_{t \to \infty}\frac{-e^{-\lambda t}}{\lambda} + \frac{1}{\lambda} = \frac{1}{\lambda},$$

where we have used the fact that $e^{-\lambda t}$ and $te^{-\lambda t}$ go to zero as $t$ approaches infinity.

For this example, Eq. (4.28) is much easier to evaluate:

$$E[X] = \int_0^\infty e^{-\lambda t}\,dt = \frac{1}{\lambda}.$$

Recall that $\lambda$ is the customer arrival rate in *customers per second*. The result that the mean inter-arrival time $E[X] = 1/\lambda$ *seconds per customer* then makes sense intuitively.

---

### 4.3.1    The Expected Value of $Y = g(X)$

Suppose that we are interested in finding the expected value of $Y = g(X)$. As in the case of discrete random variables (Eq. (3.16)), $E[Y]$ can be found directly in terms of the pdf of $X$:

$$E[Y] = \int_{-\infty}^\infty g(x)f_X(x)\,dx. \tag{4.30}$$

To see how Eq. (4.30) comes about, suppose that we divide the $y$-axis into intervals of length $h$, we index the intervals with the index $k$ and we let $y_k$ be the value in the center of the $k$th interval. The expected value of $Y$ is approximated by the following sum:

$$E[Y] \simeq \sum_k y_k f_Y(y_k)h.$$

Suppose that $g(x)$ is strictly increasing, then the $k$th interval in the $y$-axis has a unique corresponding equivalent event of width $h_k$ in the $x$-axis as shown in Fig. 4.6. Let $x_k$ be the value in the $k$th interval such that $g(x_k) = y_k$, then since $f_Y(y_k)h = f_X(x_k)h_k$,

$$E[Y] \simeq \sum_k g(x_k)f_X(x_k)h_k.$$

By letting $h$ approach zero, we obtain Eq. (4.30). This equation is valid even if $g(x)$ is not strictly increasing.

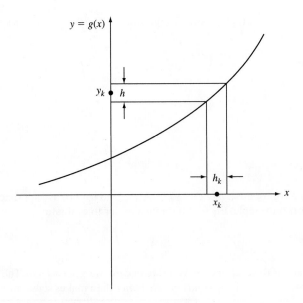

**FIGURE 4.6**
Two infinitesimal equivalent events.

## Example 4.15    Expected Values of a Sinusoid with Random Phase

Let $Y = a \cos(\omega t + \Theta)$ where $a$, $\omega$, and $t$ are constants, and $\Theta$ is a uniform random variable in the interval $(0, 2\pi)$. The random variable $Y$ results from sampling the amplitude of a sinusoid with random phase $\Theta$. Find the expected value of $Y$ and expected value of the power of $Y$, $Y^2$.

$$E[Y] = E[a \cos(\omega t + \Theta)]$$

$$= \int_0^{2\pi} a \cos(\omega t + \theta) \frac{d\theta}{2\pi} = -a \sin(\omega t + \theta) \Big|_0^{2\pi}$$

$$= -a \sin(\omega t + 2\pi) + a \sin(\omega t) = 0.$$

The average power is

$$E[Y^2] = E[a^2 \cos^2(\omega t + \Theta)] = E\left[\frac{a^2}{2} + \frac{a^2}{2} \cos(2\omega t + 2\Theta)\right]$$

$$= \frac{a^2}{2} + \frac{a^2}{2} \int_0^{2\pi} \cos(2\omega t + \theta) \frac{d\theta}{2\pi} = \frac{a^2}{2}.$$

Note that these answers are in agreement with the time averages of sinusoids: the time average ("dc" value) of the sinusoid is zero; the time-average power is $a^2/2$.

**Example 4.16    Expected Values of the Indicator Function**

Let $g(X) = I_C(X)$ be the indicator function for the event $\{X \text{ in } C\}$, where $C$ is some interval or union of intervals in the real line:

$$g(X) = \begin{cases} 0 & X \text{ not in } C \\ 1 & X \text{ in } C, \end{cases}$$

then

$$E[Y] = \int_{-\infty}^{+\infty} g(X)f_X(x)\,dx = \int_C f_X(x)\,dx = P[X \text{ in } C].$$

Thus the expected value of the indicator of an event is equal to the probability of the event.

---

It is easy to show that Eqs. (3.17a)–(3.17e) hold for continuous random variables using Eq. (4.30). For example, let $c$ be some constant, then

$$E[c] = \int_{-\infty}^{\infty} cf_X(x)\,dx = c\int_{-\infty}^{\infty} f_X(x)\,dx = c \tag{4.31}$$

and

$$E[cX] = \int_{-\infty}^{\infty} cxf_X(x)\,dx = c\int_{-\infty}^{\infty} xf_X(x)\,dx = cE[X]. \tag{4.32}$$

The expected value of a sum of functions of a random variable is equal to the sum of the expected values of the individual functions:

$$E[Y] = E\left[\sum_{k=1}^{n} g_k(X)\right]$$

$$= \int_{-\infty}^{\infty}\sum_{k=1}^{n} g_k(x)f_X(x)\,dx = \sum_{k=1}^{n}\int_{-\infty}^{\infty} g_k(x)f_X(x)\,dx$$

$$= \sum_{k=1}^{n} E[g_k(X)]. \tag{4.33}$$

---

**Example 4.17**

Let $Y = g(X) = a_0 + a_1X + a_2X^2 + \cdots + a_nX^n$, where $a_k$ are constants, then

$$E[Y] = E[a_0] + E[a_1X] + \cdots + E[a_nX^n]$$

$$= a_0 + a_1E[X] + a_2E[X^2] + \cdots + a_nE[X^n],$$

where we have used Eq. (4.33), and Eqs. (4.31) and (4.32). A special case of this result is that

$$E[X + c] = E[X] + c,$$

that is, *we can shift the mean of a random variable by adding a constant to it.*

### 4.3.2 Variance of X

The **variance of the random variable** $X$ is defined by

$$\text{VAR}[X] = E[(X - E[X])^2] = E[X^2] - E[X]^2 \tag{4.34}$$

The **standard deviation of the random variable** $X$ is defined by

$$\text{STD}[X] = \text{VAR}[X]^{1/2}. \tag{4.35}$$

---

#### Example 4.18 Variance of Uniform Random Variable

Find the variance of the random variable $X$ that is uniformly distributed in the interval $[a, b]$.
Since the mean of $X$ is $(a + b)/2$,

$$\text{VAR}[X] = \frac{1}{b - a} \int_a^b \left( x - \frac{a + b}{2} \right)^2 dx.$$

Let $y = (x - (a + b)/2)$,

$$\text{VAR}[X] = \frac{1}{b - a} \int_{-(b-a)/2}^{(b-a)/2} y^2 \, dy = \frac{(b - a)^2}{12}.$$

The random variables in Fig. 3.6 were uniformly distributed in the interval $[-1, 1]$ and $[3, 7]$, respectively. Their variances are then 1/3 and 4/3. The corresponding standard deviations are 0.577 and 1.155.

---

#### Example 4.19 Variance of Gaussian Random Variable

Find the variance of a Gaussian random variable.
First multiply the integral of the pdf of $X$ by $\sqrt{2\pi}\,\sigma$ to obtain

$$\int_{-\infty}^{\infty} e^{-(x-m)^2/2\sigma^2} \, dx = \sqrt{2\pi}\,\sigma.$$

Differentiate both sides with respect to $\sigma$:

$$\int_{-\infty}^{\infty} \left( \frac{(x - m)^2}{\sigma^3} \right) e^{-(x-m)^2/2\sigma^2} \, dx = \sqrt{2\pi}.$$

By rearranging the above equation, we obtain

$$\text{VAR}[X] = \frac{1}{\sqrt{2\pi}\,\sigma} \int_{-\infty}^{\infty} (x - m)^2 e^{-(x-m)^2/2\sigma^2} \, dx = \sigma^2.$$

This result can also be obtained by direct integration. (See Problem 4.46.) Figure 4.7 shows the Gaussian pdf for several values of $\sigma$; it is evident that the "width" of the pdf increases with $\sigma$.

---

The following properties were derived in Section 3.3:

$$\text{VAR}[c] = 0 \tag{4.36}$$

$$\text{VAR}[X + c] = \text{VAR}[X] \tag{4.37}$$

$$\text{VAR}[cX] = c^2 \text{VAR}[X], \tag{4.38}$$

where $c$ is a constant.

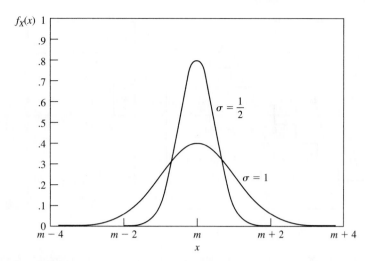

**FIGURE 4.7**
Probability density function of Gaussian random variable.

The mean and variance are the two most important parameters used in summarizing the pdf of a random variable. Other parameters are occasionally used. For example, the skewness defined by $E[(X - E[X])^3]/\text{STD}[X]^3$ measures the degree of asymmetry about the mean. It is easy to show that if a pdf is symmetric about its mean, then its skewness is zero. The point to note with these parameters of the pdf is that each involves the expected value of a higher power of $X$. Indeed we show in a later section that, under certain conditions, a pdf is completely specified if the expected values of all the powers of $X$ are known. These expected values are called the moments of $X$.

The **$n$th moment of the random variable $X$** is defined by

$$E[X^n] = \int_{-\infty}^{\infty} x^n f_X(x)\, dx. \tag{4.39}$$

The mean and variance can be seen to be defined in terms of the first two moments, $E[X]$ and $E[X^2]$.

---

## *Example 4.20    Analog-to-Digital Conversion: A Detailed Example

A quantizer is used to convert an analog signal (e.g., speech or audio) into digital form. A quantizer maps a random voltage $X$ into the nearest point $q(X)$ from a set of $2^R$ representation values as shown in Fig. 4.8(a). The value $X$ is then approximated by $q(X)$, which is identified by an $R$-bit binary number. In this manner, an "analog" voltage $X$ that can assume a continuum of values is converted into an $R$-bit number.

The quantizer introduces an error $Z = X - q(X)$ as shown in Fig. 4.8(b). Note that $Z$ is a function of $X$ and that it ranges in value between $-d/2$ and $d/2$, where $d$ is the quantizer step size. Suppose that $X$ has a uniform distribution in the interval $[-x_{\max}, x_{\max}]$, that the quantizer has $2^R$ levels, and that $2x_{\max} = 2^R d$. It is easy to show that $Z$ is uniformly distributed in the interval $[-d/2, d/2]$ (see Problem 4.93).

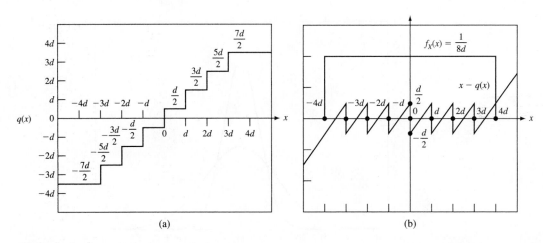

**FIGURE 4.8**
(a) A uniform quantizer maps the input $x$ into the closest point from the set $\{\pm d/2, \pm 3d/2, \pm 5d/2, \pm 7d/2\}$. (b) The uniform quantizer error for the input $x$ is $x - q(x)$.

Therefore from Example 4.12,

$$E[Z] = \frac{d/2 - d/2}{2} = 0.$$

The error $Z$ thus has mean zero.

By Example 4.18,

$$\mathrm{VAR}[Z] = \frac{(d/2 - (-d/2))^2}{12} = \frac{d^2}{12}.$$

This result is approximately correct for any pdf that is approximately flat over each quantizer interval. This is the case when $2^R$ is large.

The approximation $q(x)$ can be viewed as a "noisy" version of $X$ since

$$Q(X) = X - Z,$$

where $Z$ is the quantization error $Z$. The measure of goodness of a quantizer is specified by the SNR ratio, which is defined as the ratio of the variance of the "signal" $X$ to the variance of the distortion or "noise" $Z$:

$$\mathrm{SNR} = \frac{\mathrm{VAR}[X]}{\mathrm{VAR}[Z]} = \frac{\mathrm{VAR}[X]}{d^2/12}$$

$$= \frac{\mathrm{VAR}[X]}{x_{\mathrm{max}}^2/3} 2^{2R},$$

where we have used the fact that $d = 2x_{\mathrm{max}}/2^R$. When $X$ is nonuniform, the value $x_{\mathrm{max}}$ is selected so that $P[|X| > x_{\mathrm{max}}]$ is small. A typical choice is $x_{\mathrm{max}} = 4\,\mathrm{STD}[X]$. The SNR is then

$$\mathrm{SNR} = \frac{3}{16} 2^{2R}.$$

This important formula is often quoted in decibels:

$$\mathrm{SNR\ dB} = 10 \log_{10} \mathrm{SNR} = 6R - 7.3\ \mathrm{dB}.$$

The SNR increases by a factor of 4 (6 dB) with each additional bit used to represent $X$. This makes sense since each additional bit doubles the number of quantizer levels, which in turn reduces the step size by a factor of 2. The variance of the error should then be reduced by the square of this, namely $2^2 = 4$.

## 4.4    IMPORTANT CONTINUOUS RANDOM VARIABLES

We are always limited to measurements of finite precision, so in effect, every random variable found in practice is a discrete random variable. Nevertheless, there are several compelling reasons for using continuous random variable models. First, in general, continuous random variables are easier to handle analytically. Second, the limiting form of many discrete random variables yields continuous random variables. Finally, there are a number of "families" of continuous random variables that can be used to model a wide variety of situations by adjusting a few parameters. In this section we continue our introduction of important random variables. Table 4.1 lists some of the more important continuous random variables.

### 4.4.1    The Uniform Random Variable

The uniform random variable arises in situations where all values in an interval of the real line are equally likely to occur. The uniform random variable $U$ in the interval $[a, b]$ has pdf:

$$f_U(x) = \begin{cases} \dfrac{1}{b - a} & a \le x \le b \\ 0 & x < a \quad \text{and} \quad x > b \end{cases} \tag{4.40}$$

and cdf

$$F_U(x) = \begin{cases} 0 & x < a \\ \dfrac{x - a}{b - a} & a \le x \le b \\ 1 & x > b. \end{cases} \tag{4.41}$$

See Figure 4.2. The mean and variance of $U$ are given by:

$$E[U] = \frac{a + b}{2} \quad \text{and} \quad \text{VAR}[X] = \frac{(b - a)^2}{2}. \tag{4.42}$$

The uniform random variable appears in many situations that involve equally likely continuous random variables. Obviously $U$ can only be defined over intervals that are finite in length. We will see in Section 4.9 that the uniform random variable plays a crucial role in generating random variables in computer simulation models.

### 4.4.2    The Exponential Random Variable

The exponential random variable arises in the modeling of the time between occurrence of events (e.g., the time between customer demands for call connections), and in the modeling of the lifetime of devices and systems. The **exponential random variable** $X$ with parameter $\lambda$ has pdf

**TABLE 4.1** Continuous random variables.

**Uniform Random Variable**

$S_X = [a, b]$

$f_X(x) = \dfrac{1}{b-a} \quad a \le x \le b$

$E[X] = \dfrac{a+b}{2} \qquad \text{VAR}[X] = \dfrac{(b-a)^2}{12} \qquad \Phi_X(\omega) = \dfrac{e^{j\omega b} - e^{j\omega a}}{j\omega(b-a)}$

**Exponential Random Variable**

$S_X = [0, \infty)$

$f_X(x) = \lambda e^{-\lambda x} \qquad x \ge 0 \quad \text{and} \quad \lambda > 0$

$E[X] = \dfrac{1}{\lambda} \qquad \text{VAR}[X] = \dfrac{1}{\lambda^2} \qquad \Phi_X(\omega) = \dfrac{\lambda}{\lambda - j\omega}$

*Remarks:* The exponential random variable is the only continuous random variable with the memoryless property.

**Gaussian (Normal) Random Variable**

$S_X = (-\infty, +\infty)$

$f_X(x) = \dfrac{e^{-(x-m)^2/2\sigma^2}}{\sqrt{2\pi}\sigma} \qquad -\infty < x < +\infty \quad \text{and} \quad \sigma > 0$

$E[X] = m \qquad \text{VAR}[X] = \sigma^2 \qquad \Phi_X(\omega) = e^{jm\omega - \sigma^2\omega^2/2}$

*Remarks:* Under a wide range of conditions $X$ can be used to approximate the sum of a large number of independent random variables.

**Gamma Random Variable**

$S_X = (0, +\infty)$

$f_X(x) = \dfrac{\lambda(\lambda x)^{\alpha-1} e^{-\lambda x}}{\Gamma(\alpha)} \qquad x > 0 \quad \text{and} \quad \alpha > 0, \lambda > 0$

where $\Gamma(z)$ is the gamma function (Eq. 4.56).

$E[X] = \alpha/\lambda \qquad \text{VAR}[X] = \alpha/\lambda^2 \qquad \Phi_X(\omega) = \dfrac{1}{(1 - j\omega/\lambda)^\alpha}$

*Special Cases of Gamma Random Variable*

$m$-Erlang Random Variable: $\alpha = m$, a positive integer

$f_X(x) = \dfrac{\lambda e^{-\lambda x}(\lambda x)^{m-2}}{(m-1)!} \qquad x > 0 \qquad \Phi_X(\omega) = \left(\dfrac{1}{1 - j\omega/\lambda}\right)^m$

*Remarks:* An $m$-Erlang random variable is obtained by adding $m$ independent exponentially distributed random variables with parameter $\lambda$.

Chi-Square Random Variable with $k$ degrees of freedom: $\alpha = k/2$, $k$ a positive integer, and $\lambda = 1/2$

$f_X(x) = \dfrac{x^{(k-2)/2} e^{-x/2}}{2^{k/2}\Gamma(k/2)} \qquad x > 0 \qquad \Phi_X(\omega) = \left(\dfrac{1}{1 - 2j\omega}\right)^{k/2}$

*Remarks:* The sum of $k$ mutually independent, squared zero-mean, unit-variance Gaussian random variables is a chi-square random variable with $k$ degrees of freedom.

## Laplacian Random Variable

$S_X = (-\infty, \infty)$

$f_X(x) = \dfrac{\alpha}{2} e^{-\alpha|x|}$ $\quad -\infty < x < +\infty$ $\quad$ and $\quad \alpha > 0$

$E[X] = 0$ $\quad$ VAR$[X] = 2/\alpha^2$ $\quad \Phi_X(\omega) = \dfrac{\alpha^2}{\omega^2 + \alpha^2}$

## Rayleigh Random Variable

$S_X = [0, \infty)$

$f_X(x) = \dfrac{x}{\alpha^2} e^{-x^2/2\alpha^2}$ $\quad x \geq 0$ $\quad$ and $\quad \alpha > 0$

$E[X] = \alpha\sqrt{\pi/2}$ $\quad$ VAR$[X] = (2 - \pi/2)\alpha^2$

## Cauchy Random Variable

$S_X = (-\infty, +\infty)$

$f_X(x) = \dfrac{\alpha/\pi}{x^2 + \alpha^2}$ $\quad -\infty < x < +\infty$ $\quad$ and $\quad \alpha > 0$

Mean and variance do not exist. $\quad \Phi_X(\omega) = e^{-\alpha|\omega|}$

## Pareto Random Variable

$S_X = [x_m, \infty)x_m > 0$.

$f_X(x) = \begin{cases} 0 & x < x_m \\ \alpha\dfrac{x_m^{\alpha}}{x^{\alpha+1}} & x \geq x_m \end{cases}$

$E[X] = \dfrac{\alpha x_m}{\alpha - 1}$ $\quad$ for $\alpha > 1$ $\quad$ VAR$[X] = \dfrac{\alpha x_m^2}{(\alpha - 2)(\alpha - 1)^2}$ $\quad$ for $\alpha > 2$

*Remarks:* The Pareto random variable is the most prominent example of random variables with "long tails," and can be viewed as a continuous version of the Zipf discrete random variable.

## Beta Random Variable

$f_X(x) = \begin{cases} \dfrac{\Gamma(\alpha + \beta)}{\Gamma(\alpha)\,\Gamma(\beta)} x^{\alpha-1}(1 - x)^{\beta-1} & 0 < x < 1 \quad \text{and} \quad \alpha > 0, \beta > 0 \\ 0 & \text{otherwise} \end{cases}$

$E[X] = \dfrac{\alpha}{\alpha + \beta}$ $\quad$ VAR$[X] = \dfrac{\alpha\beta}{(\alpha + \beta)^2(\alpha + \beta + 1)}$

*Remarks:* The beta random variable is useful for modeling a variety of pdf shapes for random variables that range over finite intervals.

$$f_X(x) = \begin{cases} 0 & x < 0 \\ \lambda e^{-\lambda x} & x \geq 0 \end{cases} \tag{4.43}$$

and cdf

$$F_X(x) = \begin{cases} 0 & x < 0 \\ 1 - e^{-\lambda x} & x \geq 0. \end{cases} \tag{4.44}$$

The cdf and pdf of $X$ are shown in Fig. 4.9.

The parameter $\lambda$ is the rate at which events occur, so in Eq. (4.44) the probability of an event occurring by time $x$ increases at the rate $\lambda$ increases. Recall from Example 3.31 that the interarrival times between events in a Poisson process (Fig. 3.10) is an exponential random variable.

The mean and variance of $X$ are given by:

$$E[U] = \frac{1}{\lambda} \quad \text{and} \quad VAR[X] = \frac{1}{\lambda^2}. \tag{4.45}$$

In event interarrival situations, $\lambda$ is in units of events/second and $1/\lambda$ is in units of seconds per event interarrival.

The exponential random variable satisfies the **memoryless property**:

$$P[X > t + h \mid X > t] = P[X > h]. \tag{4.46}$$

The expression on the left side is the probability of having to wait at least $h$ additional seconds given that one has already been waiting $t$ seconds. The expression on the right side is the probability of waiting at least $h$ seconds when one first begins to wait. Thus the probability of waiting at least an additional $h$ seconds is the same regardless of how long one has already been waiting! We see later in the book that the memoryless property of the exponential random variable makes it the cornerstone for the theory of

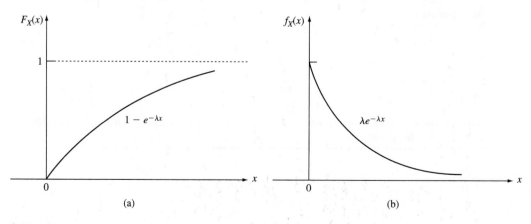

**FIGURE 4.9**
An example of a continuous random variable—the exponential random variable. Part (a) is the cdf and part (b) is the pdf.

Markov chains, which is used extensively in evaluating the performance of computer systems and communications networks.

We now prove the memoryless property:

$$P[X > t + h | X > t] = \frac{P[\{X > t + h\} \cap \{X > t\}]}{P[X > t]} \qquad \text{for } h > 0$$

$$= \frac{P[X > t + h]}{P[X > t]} = \frac{e^{-\lambda(t+h)}}{e^{-\lambda t}}$$

$$= e^{-\lambda h} = P[X > h].$$

It can be shown that the exponential random variable is the only continuous random variable that satisfies the memoryless property.

Examples 2.13, 2.28, and 2.30 dealt with the exponential random variable.

### 4.4.3   The Gaussian (Normal) Random Variable

There are many situations in manmade and in natural phenomena where one deals with a random variable $X$ that consists of the sum of a large number of "small" random variables. The exact description of the pdf of $X$ in terms of the component random variables can become quite complex and unwieldy. However, one finds that under very general conditions, as the number of components becomes large, the cdf of $X$ approaches that of the **Gaussian (normal) random variable.**[1] This random variable appears so often in problems involving randomness that it has come to be known as the "normal" random variable.

The pdf for the Gaussian random variable $X$ is given by

$$f_X(x) = \frac{1}{\sqrt{2\pi}\sigma} e^{-(x-m)^2/2\sigma^2} \qquad -\infty < x < \infty, \tag{4.47}$$

where $m$ and $\sigma > 0$ are real numbers, which we showed in Examples 4.13 and 4.19 to be the mean and standard deviation of $X$. Figure 4.7 shows that the Gaussian pdf is a "bell-shaped" curve centered and symmetric about $m$ and whose "width" increases with $\sigma$.

The cdf of the Gaussian random variable is given by

$$P[X \le x] = \frac{1}{\sqrt{2\pi}\sigma} \int_{-\infty}^{x} e^{-(x'-m)^2/2\sigma^2} \, dx'. \tag{4.48}$$

The change of variable $t = (x' - m)/\sigma$ results in

$$F_X(x) = \frac{1}{\sqrt{2\pi}} \int_{-\infty}^{(x-m)/\sigma} e^{-t^2/2} \, dt$$

$$= \Phi\left(\frac{x - m}{\sigma}\right) \tag{4.49}$$

where $\Phi(x)$ is the cdf of a Gaussian random variable with $m = 0$ and $\sigma = 1$:

$$\Phi(x) = \frac{1}{\sqrt{2\pi}} \int_{-\infty}^{x} e^{-t^2/2} \, dt. \tag{4.50}$$

---

[1]This result, called the central limit theorem, will be discussed in Chapter 7.

Therefore any probability involving an arbitrary Gaussian random variable can be expressed in terms of $\Phi(x)$.

---

**Example 4.21**

Show that the Gaussian pdf integrates to one. Consider the square of the integral of the pdf:

$$\left[ \frac{1}{\sqrt{2\pi}} \int_{-\infty}^{\infty} e^{-x^2/2} \, dx \right]^2 = \frac{1}{2\pi} \int_{-\infty}^{\infty} e^{-x^2/2} \, dx \int_{-\infty}^{\infty} e^{-y^2/2} \, dy$$

$$= \frac{1}{2\pi} \int_{-\infty}^{\infty} \int_{-\infty}^{\infty} e^{-(x^2+y^2)/2} \, dx \, dy.$$

Let $x = r \cos \theta$ and $y = r \sin \theta$ and carry out the change from Cartesian to polar coordinates, then we obtain:

$$\frac{1}{2\pi} \int_0^{\infty} \int_0^{2\pi} e^{-r^2/2} r \, dr \, d\theta = \int_0^{\infty} r e^{-r^2/2} \, dr$$

$$= [-e^{-r^2/2}]_0^{\infty}$$

$$= 1.$$

---

In electrical engineering it is customary to work with the $Q$-function, which is defined by

$$Q(x) = 1 - \Phi(x) \tag{4.51}$$

$$= \frac{1}{\sqrt{2\pi}} \int_x^{\infty} e^{-t^2/2} \, dt. \tag{4.52}$$

$Q(x)$ is simply the probability of the "tail" of the pdf. The symmetry of the pdf implies that

$$Q(0) = 1/2 \quad \text{and} \quad Q(-x) = 1 - Q(x). \tag{4.53}$$

The integral in Eq. (4.50) does not have a closed-form expression. Traditionally the integrals have been evaluated by looking up tables that list $Q(x)$ or by using approximations that require numerical evaluation [Ross]. The following expression has been found to give good accuracy for $Q(x)$ over the entire range $0 < x < \infty$:

$$Q(x) \simeq \left[ \frac{1}{(1-a)x + a\sqrt{x^2 + b}} \right] \frac{1}{\sqrt{2\pi}} e^{-x^2/2}, \tag{4.54}$$

where $a = 1/\pi$ and $b = 2\pi$ [Gallager]. Table 4.2 shows $Q(x)$ and the value given by the above approximation. In some problems, we are interested in finding the value of $x$ for which $Q(x) = 10^{-k}$. Table 4.3 gives these values for $k = 1, \ldots, 10$.

The Gaussian random variable plays a very important role in communication systems, where transmission signals are corrupted by noise voltages resulting from the thermal motion of electrons. It can be shown from physical principles that these voltages will have a Gaussian pdf.

**TABLE 4.2**   Comparison of $Q(x)$ and approximation given by Eq. (4.54).

| $x$ | $Q(x)$ | Approximation | $x$ | $Q(x)$ | Approximation |
|-----|--------|---------------|-----|--------|---------------|
| 0 | 5.00E-01 | 5.00E-01 | 2.7 | 3.47E-03 | 3.46E-03 |
| 0.1 | 4.60E-01 | 4.58E-01 | 2.8 | 2.56E-03 | 2.55E-03 |
| 0.2 | 4.21E-01 | 4.17E-01 | 2.9 | 1.87E-03 | 1.86E-03 |
| 0.3 | 3.82E-01 | 3.78E-01 | 3.0 | 1.35E-03 | 1.35E-03 |
| 0.4 | 3.45E-01 | 3.41E-01 | 3.1 | 9.68E-04 | 9.66E-04 |
| 0.5 | 3.09E-01 | 3.05E-01 | 3.2 | 6.87E-04 | 6.86E-04 |
| 0.6 | 2.74E-01 | 2.71E-01 | 3.3 | 4.83E-04 | 4.83E-04 |
| 0.7 | 2.42E-01 | 2.39E-01 | 3.4 | 3.37E-04 | 3.36E-04 |
| 0.8 | 2.12E-01 | 2.09E-01 | 3.5 | 2.33E-04 | 2.32E-04 |
| 0.9 | 1.84E-01 | 1.82E-01 | 3.6 | 1.59E-04 | 1.59E-04 |
| 1.0 | 1.59E-01 | 1.57E-01 | 3.7 | 1.08E-04 | 1.08E-04 |
| 1.1 | 1.36E-01 | 1.34E-01 | 3.8 | 7.24E-05 | 7.23E-05 |
| 1.2 | 1.15E-01 | 1.14E-01 | 3.9 | 4.81E-05 | 4.81E-05 |
| 1.3 | 9.68E-02 | 9.60E-02 | 4.0 | 3.17E-05 | 3.16E-05 |
| 1.4 | 8.08E-02 | 8.01E-02 | 4.5 | 3.40E-06 | 3.40E-06 |
| 1.5 | 6.68E-02 | 6.63E-02 | 5.0 | 2.87E-07 | 2.87E-07 |
| 1.6 | 5.48E-02 | 5.44E-02 | 5.5 | 1.90E-08 | 1.90E-08 |
| 1.7 | 4.46E-02 | 4.43E-02 | 6.0 | 9.87E-10 | 9.86E-10 |
| 1.8 | 3.59E-02 | 3.57E-02 | 6.5 | 4.02E-11 | 4.02E-11 |
| 1.9 | 2.87E-02 | 2.86E-02 | 7.0 | 1.28E-12 | 1.28E-12 |
| 2.0 | 2.28E-02 | 2.26E-02 | 7.5 | 3.19E-14 | 3.19E-14 |
| 2.1 | 1.79E-02 | 1.78E-02 | 8.0 | 6.22E-16 | 6.22E-16 |
| 2.2 | 1.39E-02 | 1.39E-02 | 8.5 | 9.48E-18 | 9.48E-18 |
| 2.3 | 1.07E-02 | 1.07E-02 | 9.0 | 1.13E-19 | 1.13E-19 |
| 2.4 | 8.20E-03 | 8.17E-03 | 9.5 | 1.05E-21 | 1.05E-21 |
| 2.5 | 6.21E-03 | 6.19E-03 | 10.0 | 7.62E-24 | 7.62E-24 |
| 2.6 | 4.66E-03 | 4.65E-03 | | | |

## Example 4.22

A communication system accepts a positive voltage $V$ as input and outputs a voltage $Y = \alpha V + N$, where $\alpha = 10^{-2}$ and $N$ is a Gaussian random variable with parameters $m = 0$ and $\sigma = 2$. Find the value of $V$ that gives $P[Y < 0] = 10^{-6}$.

The probability $P[Y < 0]$ is written in terms of $N$ as follows:

$$P[Y < 0] = P[\alpha V + N < 0]$$

$$= P[N < -\alpha V] = \Phi\left(\frac{-\alpha V}{\sigma}\right) = Q\left(\frac{\alpha V}{\sigma}\right) = 10^{-6}.$$

From Table 4.3 we see that the argument of the $Q$-function should be $\alpha V/\sigma = 4.753$. Thus $V = (4.753)\sigma/\alpha = 950.6$.

**TABLE 4.3** $Q(x) = 10^{-k}$

| $k$ | $x = Q^{-1}(10^{-k})$ |
|-----|------------------------|
| 1 | 1.2815 |
| 2 | 2.3263 |
| 3 | 3.0902 |
| 4 | 3.7190 |
| 5 | 4.2649 |
| 6 | 4.7535 |
| 7 | 5.1993 |
| 8 | 5.6120 |
| 9 | 5.9978 |
| 10 | 6.3613 |

### 4.4.4 The Gamma Random Variable

The gamma random variable is a versatile random variable that appears in many applications. For example, it is used to model the time required to service customers in queueing systems, the lifetime of devices and systems in reliability studies, and the defect clustering behavior in VLSI chips.

The pdf of the **gamma random variable** has two parameters, $\alpha > 0$ and $\lambda > 0$, and is given by

$$f_X(x) = \frac{\lambda(\lambda x)^{\alpha-1}e^{-\lambda x}}{\Gamma(\alpha)} \qquad 0 < x < \infty, \tag{4.55}$$

where $\Gamma(z)$ is the gamma function, which is defined by the integral

$$\Gamma(z) = \int_0^\infty x^{z-1}e^{-x}\,dx \qquad z > 0. \tag{4.56}$$

The gamma function has the following properties:

$$\Gamma\left(\frac{1}{2}\right) = \sqrt{\pi},$$

$\Gamma(z + 1) = z\Gamma(z)$      for $z > 0$, and
$\Gamma(m + 1) = m!$      for $m$ a nonnegative integer.

The versatility of the gamma random variable is due to the richness of the gamma function $\Gamma(z)$. The pdf of the gamma random variable can assume a variety of shapes as shown in Fig. 4.10. By varying the parameters $\alpha$ and $\lambda$ it is possible to fit the gamma pdf to many types of experimental data. In addition, many random variables are special cases of the gamma random variable. The exponential random variable is obtained by letting $\alpha = 1$. By letting $\lambda = 1/2$ and $\alpha = k/2$, where $k$ is a positive integer, we obtain the **chi-square random variable**, which appears in certain statistical problems. The **$m$-Erlang random variable** is obtained when $\alpha = m$, a positive integer. The $m$-Erlang random variable is used in the system reliability models and in queueing systems models. Both of these random variables are discussed in later examples.

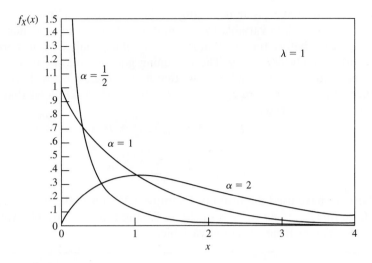

**FIGURE 4.10**
Probability density function of gamma random variable.

---

**Example 4.23**

Show that the pdf of a gamma random variable integrates to one.

The integral of the pdf is

$$\int_0^\infty f_X(x)\,dx = \int_0^\infty \frac{\lambda(\lambda x)^{\alpha-1}e^{-\lambda x}}{\Gamma(\alpha)}\,dx$$

$$= \frac{\lambda^\alpha}{\Gamma(\alpha)}\int_0^\infty x^{\alpha-1}e^{-\lambda x}\,dx.$$

Let $y = \lambda x$, then $dx = dy/\lambda$ and the integral becomes

$$\frac{\lambda^\alpha}{\Gamma(\alpha)\lambda^\alpha}\int_0^\infty y^{\alpha-1}e^{-y}\,dy = 1,$$

where we used the fact that the integral equals $\Gamma(\alpha)$.

---

In general, the cdf of the gamma random variable does not have a closed-form expression. We will show that the special case of the $m$-Erlang random variable does have a closed-form expression for the cdf by using its close interrelation with the exponential and Poisson random variables. The cdf can also be obtained by integration of the pdf (see Problem 4.74).

Consider once again the limiting procedure that was used to derive the Poisson random variable. Suppose that we observe the time $S_m$ that elapses until the occurrence of the $m$th event. The times $X_1, X_2, \ldots, X_m$ between events are exponential random variables, so we must have

$$S_m = X_1 + X_2 + \cdots + X_m.$$

We will show that $S_m$ is an $m$-Erlang random variable. To find the cdf of $S_m$, let $N(t)$ be the Poisson random variable for the number of events in $t$ seconds. Note that the $m$th event occurs before time $t$—that is, $S_m \le t$—if and only if $m$ or more events occur in $t$ seconds, namely $N(t) \ge m$. The reasoning goes as follows. If the $m$th event has occurred before time $t$, then it follows that $m$ or more events will occur in time $t$. On the other hand, if $m$ or more events occur in time $t$, then it follows that the $m$th event occurred by time $t$. Thus

$$F_{S_m}(t) = P[S_m \le t] = P[N(t) \ge m] \tag{4.57}$$

$$= 1 - \sum_{k=0}^{m-1} \frac{(\lambda t)^k}{k!} e^{-\lambda t}, \tag{4.58}$$

where we have used the result of Example 3.31. If we take the derivative of the above cdf, we finally obtain the pdf of the $m$-Erlang random variable. Thus we have shown that $S_m$ is an $m$-Erlang random variable.

---

**Example 4.24**

A factory has two spares of a critical system component that has an average lifetime of $1/\lambda = 1$ month. Find the probability that the three components (the operating one and the two spares) will last more than 6 months. Assume the component lifetimes are exponential random variables.

    The remaining lifetime of the component in service is an exponential random variable with rate $\lambda$ by the memoryless property. Thus, the total lifetime $X$ of the three components is the sum of three exponential random variables with parameter $\lambda = 1$. Thus $X$ has a 3-Erlang distribution with $\lambda = 1$. From Eq. (4.58) the probability that $X$ is greater than 6 is

$$P[X > 6] = 1 - P[X \le 6]$$

$$= \sum_{k=0}^{2} \frac{6^k}{k!} e^{-6} = .06197.$$

---

### 4.4.5    The Beta Random Variable

The beta random variable $X$ assumes values over a closed interval and has pdf:

$$f_X(x) = cx^{a-1}(1 - x)^{b-1} \qquad \text{for } 0 < x < 1 \tag{4.59}$$

where the normalization constant is the reciprocal of the beta function

$$\frac{1}{c} = B(a, b) = \int_0^1 x^{a-1}(1 - x)^{b-1}\, dx$$

and where the beta function is related to the gamma function by the following expression:

$$B(a, b) = \frac{\Gamma(a)\Gamma(b)}{\Gamma(a + b)}.$$

When $a = b = 1$, we have the uniform random variable. Other choices of $a$ and $b$ give pdfs over finite intervals that can differ markedly from the uniform. See Problem 4.75. If

$a = b > 1$, then the pdf is symmetric about $x = 1/2$ and is concentrated about $x = 1/2$ as well. When $a = b < 1$, then the pdf is symmetric but the density is concentrated at the edges of the interval. When $a < b$ (or $a > b$) the pdf is skewed to the right (or left).

The mean and variance are given by:

$$E[X] = \frac{a}{a + b} \quad \text{and} \quad \text{VAR}[X] = \frac{ab}{(a + b)^2(a + b + 1)}. \tag{4.60}$$

The versatility of the pdf of the beta random variable makes it useful to model a variety of behaviors for random variables that range over finite intervals. For example, in a Bernoulli trial experiment, the probability of success $p$ could itself be a random variable. The beta pdf is frequently used to model $p$.

### 4.4.6    The Cauchy Random Variable

The Cauchy random variable $X$ assumes values over the entire real line and has pdf:

$$f_X(x) = \frac{1/\pi}{1 + x^2}. \tag{4.61}$$

It is easy to verify that this pdf integrates to 1. However, $X$ does not have any moments since the associated integrals do not converge. The Cauchy random variable arises as the tangent of a uniform random variable in the unit interval.

### 4.4.7    The Pareto Random Variable

The Pareto random variable arises in the study of the distribution of wealth where it has been found to model the tendency for a small portion of the population to own a large portion of the wealth. Recently the Pareto distribution has been found to capture the behavior of many quantities of interest in the study of Internet behavior, e.g., sizes of files, packet delays, audio and video title preferences, session times in peer-to-peer networks, etc. The Pareto random variable can be viewed as a continuous version of the Zipf discrete random variable.

The Pareto random variable $X$ takes on values in the range $x > x_m$, where $x_m$ is a positive real number. $X$ has complementary cdf with shape parameter $\alpha > 0$ given by:

$$P[X > x] = \begin{cases} 1 & x < x_m \\ \dfrac{x_m^{\alpha}}{x^{\alpha}} & x \geq x_m. \end{cases} \tag{4.62}$$

The tail of $X$ decays algebraically with $x$ which is rather slower in comparison to the exponential and Gaussian random variables. The Pareto random variable is the most prominent example of random variables with "long tails."

The cdf and pdf of $X$ are:

$$F_X(x) = \begin{cases} 0 & x < x_m \\ 1 - \dfrac{x_m^{\alpha}}{x^{\alpha}} & x \geq x_m. \end{cases} \tag{4.63}$$

Because of its long tail, the cdf of $X$ approaches 1 rather slowly as $x$ increases.

$$f_X(x) = \begin{cases} 0 & x < x_m \\ \alpha \dfrac{x_m^\alpha}{x^{\alpha+1}} & x \geq x_m. \end{cases} \tag{4.64}$$

---

### Example 4.25   Mean and Variance of Pareto Random Variable

Find the mean and variance of the Pareto random variable.

$$E[X] = \int_{x_m}^\infty t\alpha \frac{x_m^\alpha}{t^{\alpha+1}}\, dt = \int_{x_m}^\infty \alpha \frac{x_m^\alpha}{t^\alpha}\, dt = \frac{\alpha}{\alpha-1}\frac{x_m^\alpha}{x_m^{\alpha-1}} = \frac{\alpha x_m}{\alpha-1} \qquad \text{for } \alpha > 1 \tag{4.65}$$

where the integral is defined for $\alpha > 1$, and

$$E[X^2] = \int_{x_m}^\infty t^2\alpha \frac{x_m^\alpha}{t^{\alpha+1}}\, dt = \int_{x_m}^\infty \alpha \frac{x_m^\alpha}{t^{\alpha-1}}\, dt = \frac{\alpha}{\alpha-2}\frac{x_m^\alpha}{x_m^{\alpha-2}} = \frac{\alpha x_m^2}{\alpha-2} \qquad \text{for } \alpha > 2$$

where the second moment is defined for $\alpha > 2$.

The variance of $X$ is then:

$$\text{VAR}[X] = \frac{\alpha x_m^2}{\alpha-2} - \left(\frac{\alpha x_m^2}{\alpha-1}\right)^2 = \frac{\alpha x_m^2}{(\alpha-2)(\alpha-1)^2} \qquad \text{for } \alpha > 2. \tag{4.66}$$

---

## 4.5     FUNCTIONS OF A RANDOM VARIABLE

Let $X$ be a random variable and let $g(x)$ be a real-valued function defined on the real line. Define $Y = g(X)$, that is, $Y$ is determined by evaluating the function $g(x)$ at the value assumed by the random variable $X$. Then $Y$ is also a random variable. The probabilities with which $Y$ takes on various values depend on the function $g(x)$ as well as the cumulative distribution function of $X$. In this section we consider the problem of finding the cdf and pdf of $Y$.

---

### Example 4.26

Let the function $h(x) = (x)^+$ be defined as follows:

$$(x)^+ = \begin{cases} 0 & \text{if } x < 0 \\ x & \text{if } x \geq 0. \end{cases}$$

For example, let $X$ be the number of active speakers in a group of $N$ speakers, and let $Y$ be the number of active speakers in excess of $M$, then $Y = (X - M)^+$. In another example, let $X$ be a voltage input to a halfwave rectifier, then $Y = (X)^+$ is the output.

**Example 4.27**

Let the function $q(x)$ be defined as shown in Fig. 4.8(a), where the set of points on the real line are mapped into the nearest representation point from the set $S_Y = \{-3.5d, -2.5d, -1.5d, -0.5d, 0.5d, 1.5d, 2.5d, 3.5d\}$. Thus, for example, all the points in the interval $(0, d)$ are mapped into the point $d/2$. The function $q(x)$ represents an eight-level uniform quantizer.

**Example 4.28**

Consider the linear function $c(x) = ax + b$, where $a$ and $b$ are constants. This function arises in many situations. For example, $c(x)$ could be the cost associated with the quantity $x$, with the constant $a$ being the cost per unit of $x$, and $b$ being a fixed cost component. In a signal processing context, $c(x) = ax$ could be the amplified version (if $a > 1$) or attenuated version (if $a < 1$) of the voltage $x$.

The probability of an event $C$ involving $Y$ is equal to the probability of the equivalent event $B$ of values of $X$ such that $g(X)$ is in $C$:

$$P[Y \text{ in } C] = P[g(X) \text{ in } C] = P[X \text{ in } B].$$

Three types of equivalent events are useful in determining the cdf and pdf of $Y = g(X)$: (1) The event $\{g(X) = y_k\}$ is used to determine the magnitude of the jump at a point $y_k$ where the cdf of $Y$ is known to have a discontinuity; (2) the event $\{g(X) \le y\}$ is used to find the cdf of $Y$ directly; and (3) the event $\{y < g(X) \le y + h\}$ is useful in determining the pdf of $Y$. We will demonstrate the use of these three methods in a series of examples.

The next two examples demonstrate how the pmf is computed in cases where $Y = g(X)$ is discrete. In the first example, $X$ is discrete. In the second example, $X$ is continuous.

**Example 4.29**

Let $X$ be the number of active speakers in a group of $N$ independent speakers. Let $p$ be the probability that a speaker is active. In Example 2.39 it was shown that $X$ has a binomial distribution with parameters $N$ and $p$. Suppose that a voice transmission system can transmit up to $M$ voice signals at a time, and that when $X$ exceeds $M$, $X - M$ randomly selected signals are discarded. Let $Y$ be the number of signals discarded, then

$$Y = (X - M)^+.$$

$Y$ takes on values from the set $S_Y = \{0, 1, \ldots, N - M\}$. $Y$ will equal zero whenever $X$ is less than or equal to $M$, and $Y$ will equal $k > 0$ when $X$ is equal to $M + k$. Therefore

$$P[Y = 0] = P[X \text{ in } \{0, 1, \ldots, M\}] = \sum_{j=0}^{M} p_j$$

and

$$P[Y = k] = P[X = M + k] = p_{M+k} \qquad 0 < k \le N - M,$$

where $p_j$ is the pmf of $X$.

---

**Example 4.30**

Let $X$ be a sample voltage of a speech waveform, and suppose that $X$ has a uniform distribution in the interval $[-4d, 4d]$. Let $Y = q(X)$, where the quantizer input-output characteristic is as shown in Fig. 4.10. Find the pmf for $Y$.

The event $\{Y = q\}$ for $q$ in $S_Y$ is equivalent to the event $\{X \text{ in } I_q\}$, where $I_q$ is an interval of points mapped into the representation point $q$. The pmf of $Y$ is therefore found by evaluating

$$P[Y = q] = \int_{I_q} f_X(t)\, dt.$$

It is easy to see that the representation point has an interval of length $d$ mapped into it. Thus the eight possible outputs are equiprobable, that is, $P[Y = q] = 1/8$ for $q$ in $S_Y$.

---

In Example 4.30, each constant section of the function $q(X)$ produces a delta function in the pdf of $Y$. In general, if the function $g(X)$ is constant during certain intervals and if the pdf of $X$ is nonzero in these intervals, then the pdf of $Y$ will contain delta functions. $Y$ will then be either discrete or of mixed type.

The cdf of $Y$ is defined as the probability of the event $\{Y \le y\}$. In principle, it can always be obtained by finding the probability of the equivalent event $\{g(X) \le y\}$ as shown in the next examples.

---

**Example 4.31    A Linear Function**

Let the random variable $Y$ be defined by

$$Y = aX + b,$$

where $a$ is a nonzero constant. Suppose that $X$ has cdf $F_X(x)$, then find $F_Y(y)$.

The event $\{Y \le y\}$ occurs when $A = \{aX + b \le y\}$ occurs. If $a > 0$, then $A = \{X \le (y - b)/a\}$ (see Fig. 4.11), and thus

$$F_Y(y) = P\left[X \le \frac{y - b}{a}\right] = F_X\left(\frac{y - b}{a}\right) \qquad a > 0.$$

On the other hand, if $a < 0$, then $A = \{X \ge (y - b)/a\}$, and

$$F_Y(y) = P\left[X \ge \frac{y - b}{a}\right] = 1 - F_X\left(\frac{y - b}{a}\right) \qquad a < 0.$$

We can obtain the pdf of $Y$ by differentiating with respect to $y$. To do this we need to use the chain rule for derivatives:

$$\frac{dF}{dy} = \frac{dF}{du}\frac{du}{dy},$$

where $u$ is the argument of $F$. In this case, $u = (y - b)/a$, and we then obtain

$$f_Y(y) = \frac{1}{a}f_X\left(\frac{y - b}{a}\right) \qquad a > 0$$

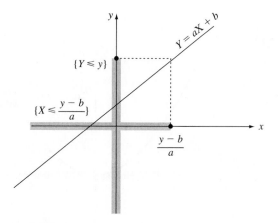

**FIGURE 4.11**
The equivalent event for $\{Y \le y\}$ is the event
$\{X \le (y - b)/a\}$, if a > 0.

and

$$f_Y(y) = \frac{1}{-a} f_X\left(\frac{y-b}{a}\right) \qquad a < 0.$$

The above two results can be written compactly as

$$f_Y(y) = \frac{1}{|a|} f_X\left(\frac{y-b}{a}\right). \tag{4.67}$$

## Example 4.32 A Linear Function of a Gaussian Random Variable

Let $X$ be a random variable with a Gaussian pdf with mean $m$ and standard deviation $\sigma$:

$$f_X(x) = \frac{1}{\sqrt{2\pi}\,\sigma} e^{-(x-m)^2/2\sigma^2} \qquad -\infty < x < \infty. \tag{4.68}$$

Let $Y = aX + b$, then find the pdf of $Y$.
    Substitution of Eq. (4.68) into Eq. (4.67) yields

$$f_Y(y) = \frac{1}{\sqrt{2\pi}|a\sigma|} e^{-(y-b-am)^2/2(a\sigma)^2}.$$

Note that $Y$ also has a Gaussian distribution with mean $b + am$ and standard deviation $|a|\,\sigma$.
Therefore *a linear function of a Gaussian random variable is also a Gaussian random variable.*

## Example 4.33

Let the random variable $Y$ be defined by

$$Y = X^2,$$

where $X$ is a continuous random variable. Find the cdf and pdf of $Y$.

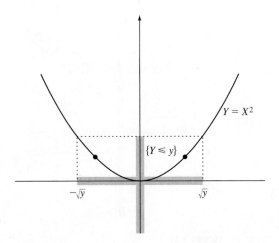

**FIGURE 4.12**
The equivalent event for $\{Y \leq y\}$ is the event
$\{-\sqrt{y} \leq X \leq \sqrt{y}\}$, if $y \geq 0$.

The event $\{Y \leq y\}$ occurs when $\{X^2 \leq y\}$ or equivalently when $\{-\sqrt{y} \leq X \leq \sqrt{y}\}$ for $y$ nonnegative; see Fig. 4.12. The event is null when $y$ is negative. Thus

$$F_Y(y) = \begin{cases} 0 & y < 0 \\ F_X(\sqrt{y}) - F_X(-\sqrt{y}) & y > 0 \end{cases}$$

and differentiating with respect to $y$,

$$f_Y(y) = \frac{f_X(\sqrt{y})}{2\sqrt{y}} - \frac{f_X(-\sqrt{y})}{-2\sqrt{y}} \qquad y > 0$$

$$= \frac{f_X(\sqrt{y})}{2\sqrt{y}} + \frac{f_X(-\sqrt{y})}{2\sqrt{y}}. \tag{4.69}$$

---

### Example 4.34    A Chi-Square Random Variable

Let $X$ be a Gaussian random variable with mean $m = 0$ and standard deviation $\sigma = 1$. $X$ is then said to be a standard normal random variable. Let $Y = X^2$. Find the pdf of $Y$.

Substitution of Eq. (4.68) into Eq. (4.69) yields

$$f_Y(y) = \frac{e^{-y/2}}{\sqrt{2y\pi}} \qquad y \geq 0. \tag{4.70}$$

From Table 4.1 we see that $f_Y(y)$ is the pdf of a *chi-square random variable with one degree of freedom*.

---

The result in Example 4.33 suggests that if the equation $y_0 = g(x)$ has $n$ solutions, $x_0, x_1, \ldots, x_n$, then $f_Y(y_0)$ will be equal to $n$ terms of the type on the right-hand

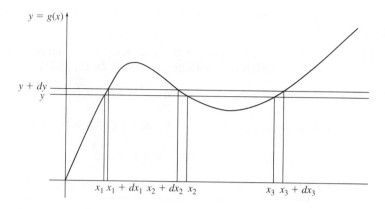

**FIGURE 4.13**
The equivalent event of $\{y < Y < y + dy\}$ is $\{x_1 < X < x_1 + dx_1\}$ $\cup \{x_2 + dx_2 < X < x_2\} \cup \{x_3 < X < x_3 + dx_3\}$.

side of Eq. (4.69). We now show that this is generally true by using a method for directly obtaining the pdf of $Y$ in terms of the pdf of $X$.

Consider a nonlinear function $Y = g(X)$ such as the one shown in Fig. 4.13. Consider the event $C_y = \{y < Y < y + dy\}$ and let $B_y$ be its equivalent event. For $y$ indicated in the figure, the equation $g(x) = y$ has three solutions $x_1$, $x_2$, and $x_3$, and the equivalent event $B_y$ has a segment corresponding to each solution:

$$B_y = \{x_1 < X < x_1 + dx_1\} \cup \{x_2 + dx_2 < X < x_2\}$$

$$\cup \{x_3 < X < x_3 + dx_3\}.$$

The probability of the event $C_y$ is approximately

$$P[C_y] = f_Y(y)|dy|, \tag{4.71}$$

where $|dy|$ is the length of the interval $y < Y \le y + dy$. Similarly, the probability of the event $B_y$ is approximately

$$P[B_y] = f_X(x_1)|dx_1| + f_X(x_2)|dx_2| + f_X(x_3)|dx_3|. \tag{4.72}$$

Since $C_y$ and $B_y$ are equivalent events, their probabilities must be equal. By equating Eqs. (4.71) and (4.72) we obtain

$$f_Y(y) = \sum_k \frac{f_X(x)}{|dy/dx|}\bigg|_{x=x_k} \tag{4.73}$$

$$= \sum_k f_X(x)\left|\frac{dx}{dy}\right|\bigg|_{x=x_k}. \tag{4.74}$$

It is clear that if the equation $g(x) = y$ has $n$ solutions, the expression for the pdf of $Y$ at that point is given by Eqs. (4.73) and (4.74), and contains $n$ terms.

### Example 4.35

Let $Y = X^2$ as in Example 4.34. For $y \geq 0$, the equation $y = x^2$ has two solutions, $x_0 = \sqrt{y}$ and $x_1 = -\sqrt{y}$, so Eq. (4.73) has two terms. Since $dy/dx = 2x$, Eq. (4.73) yields

$$f_Y(y) = \frac{f_X(\sqrt{y})}{2\sqrt{y}} + \frac{f_X(-\sqrt{y})}{2\sqrt{y}}.$$

This result is in agreement with Eq. (4.69). To use Eq. (4.74), we note that

$$\frac{dx}{dy} = \frac{d}{dy} \pm \sqrt{y} = \pm\frac{1}{2\sqrt{y}},$$

which when substituted into Eq. (4.74) then yields Eq. (4.69) again.

### Example 4.36    Amplitude Samples of a Sinusoidal Waveform

Let $Y = \cos(X)$, where $X$ is uniformly distributed in the interval $(0, 2\pi]$. $Y$ can be viewed as the sample of a sinusoidal waveform at a random instant of time that is uniformly distributed over the period of the sinusoid. Find the pdf of $Y$.

It can be seen in Fig. 4.14 that for $-1 < y < 1$ the equation $y = \cos(x)$ has two solutions in the interval of interest, $x_0 = \cos^{-1}(y)$ and $x_1 = 2\pi - x_0$. Since (see an introductory calculus textbook)

$$\left.\frac{dy}{dx}\right|_{x_0} = -\sin(x_0) = -\sin(\cos^{-1}(y)) = -\sqrt{1 - y^2},$$

and since $f_X(x) = 1/2\pi$ in the interval of interest, Eq. (4.73) yields

$$f_Y(y) = \frac{1}{2\pi\sqrt{1 - y^2}} + \frac{1}{2\pi\sqrt{1 - y^2}}$$

$$= \frac{1}{\pi\sqrt{1 - y^2}} \qquad \text{for } -1 < y < 1.$$

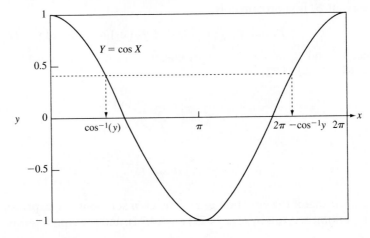

**FIGURE 4.14**
$y = \cos x$ has two roots in the interval $(0, 2\pi)$.

The cdf of $Y$ is found by integrating the above:

$$F_Y(y) = \begin{cases} 0 & y < -1 \\ \dfrac{1}{2} + \dfrac{\sin^{-1} y}{\pi} & -1 \le y \le 1 \\ 1 & y > 1. \end{cases}$$

$Y$ is said to have the **arcsine distribution**.

## 4.6    THE MARKOV AND CHEBYSHEV INEQUALITIES

In general, the mean and variance of a random variable do not provide enough information to determine the cdf/pdf. However, the mean and variance of a random variable $X$ do allow us to obtain bounds for probabilities of the form $P[|X| \ge t]$. Suppose first that $X$ is a nonnegative random variable with mean $E[X]$. The **Markov inequality** then states that

$$P[X \ge a] \le \frac{E[X]}{a} \qquad \text{for } X \text{ nonnegative.} \tag{4.75}$$

We obtain Eq. (4.75) as follows:

$$E[X] = \int_0^a t f_X(t)\, dt + \int_a^\infty t f_X(t)\, dt \ge \int_a^\infty t f_X(t)\, dt$$

$$\ge \int_a^\infty a f_X(t)\, dt = a P[X \ge a].$$

The first inequality results from discarding the integral from zero to $a$; the second inequality results from replacing $t$ with the smaller number $a$.

### Example 4.37

The mean height of children in a kindergarten class is 3 feet, 6 inches. Find the bound on the probability that a kid in the class is taller than 9 feet. The Markov inequality gives $P[H \ge 9] \le 42/108 = .389$.

The bound in the above example appears to be ridiculous. However, a bound, by its very nature, must take the worst case into consideration. One can easily construct a random variable for which the bound given by the Markov inequality is exact. The reason we know that the bound in the above example is ridiculous is that we have knowledge about the variability of the children's height about their mean.

Now suppose that the mean $E[X] = m$ and the variance $\text{VAR}[X] = \sigma^2$ of a random variable are known, and that we are interested in bounding $P[|X - m| \ge a]$. The **Chebyshev inequality** states that

$$P[|X - m| \ge a] \le \frac{\sigma^2}{a^2}. \tag{4.76}$$

The Chebyshev inequality is a consequence of the Markov inequality. Let $D^2 = (X - m)^2$ be the squared deviation from the mean. Then the Markov inequality applied to $D^2$ gives

$$P[D^2 \geq a^2] \leq \frac{E[(X - m)^2]}{a^2} = \frac{\sigma^2}{a^2}.$$

Equation (4.76) follows when we note that $\{D^2 \geq a^2\}$ and $\{|X - m| \geq a\}$ are equivalent events.

Suppose that a random variable $X$ has zero variance; then the Chebyshev inequality implies that

$$P[X = m] = 1, \tag{4.77}$$

that is, the random variable is equal to its mean with probability one. In other words, $X$ is equal to the constant $m$ in almost all experiments.

---

### Example 4.38

The mean response time and the standard deviation in a multi-user computer system are known to be 15 seconds and 3 seconds, respectively. Estimate the probability that the response time is more than 5 seconds from the mean.

The Chebyshev inequality with $m = 15$ seconds, $\sigma = 3$ seconds, and $a = 5$ seconds gives

$$P[|X - 15| \geq 5] \leq \frac{9}{25} = .36.$$

---

### Example 4.39

If $X$ has mean $m$ and variance $\sigma^2$, then the Chebyshev inequality for $a = k\sigma$ gives

$$P[|X - m| \geq k\sigma] \leq \frac{1}{k^2}.$$

Now suppose that we know that $X$ is a Gaussian random variable, then for $k = 2$, $P[|X - m| \geq 2\sigma] = .0456$, whereas the Chebyshev inequality gives the upper bound .25.

---

### Example 4.40    Chebyshev Bound Is Tight

Let the random variable $X$ have $P[X = -v] = P[X = v] = 0.5$. The mean is zero and the variance is $\text{VAR}[X] = E[X^2] = (-v)^2 0.5 + v^2 0.5 = v^2$.

Note that $P[|X| \geq v] = 1$. The Chebyshev inequality states:

$$P[|X| \geq v] \leq 1 - \frac{\text{VAR}[X]}{v^2} = 1.$$

We see that the bound and the exact value are in agreement, so the bound is tight.

We see from Example 4.38 that for certain random variables, the Chebyshev inequality can give rather loose bounds. Nevertheless, the inequality is useful in situations in which we have no knowledge about the distribution of a given random variable other than its mean and variance. In Section 7.2, we will use the Chebyshev inequality to prove that the arithmetic average of independent measurements of the same random variable is highly likely to be close to the expected value of the random variable when the number of measurements is large. Problems 4.100 and 4.101 give examples of this result.

If more information is available than just the mean and variance, then it is possible to obtain bounds that are tighter than the Markov and Chebyshev inequalities. Consider the Markov inequality again. The region of interest is $A = \{t \geq a\}$, so let $I_A(t)$ be the indicator function, that is, $I_A(t) = 1$ if $t \in A$ and $I_A(t) = 0$ otherwise. The key step in the derivation is to note that $t/a \geq 1$ in the region of interest. In effect we bounded $I_A(t)$ by $t/a$ as shown in Fig. 4.15. We then have:

$$P[X \geq a] = \int_0^\infty I_A(t)f_X(t)\,dt \leq \int_0^\infty \frac{t}{a}f_X(t)\,dt = \frac{E[X]}{a}.$$

By changing the upper bound on $I_A(t)$, we can obtain different bounds on $P[X \geq a]$. Consider the bound $I_A(t) \leq e^{s(t-a)}$, also shown in Fig. 4.15, where $s > 0$. The resulting bound is:

$$P[X \geq a] = \int_0^\infty I_A(t)f_X(t)\,dt \leq \int_0^\infty e^{s(t-a)}f_X(t)\,dt$$

$$= e^{-sa}\int_0^\infty e^{st}f_X(t)\,dt = e^{-sa}E[e^{sX}]. \tag{4.78}$$

This bound is called the **Chernoff bound**, which can be seen to depend on the expected value of an exponential function of $X$. This function is called the moment generating function and is related to the transforms that are introduced in the next section. We develop the Chernoff bound further in the next section.

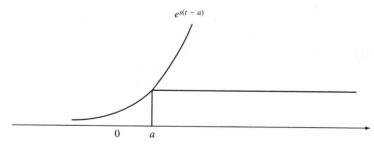

**FIGURE 4.15**
Bounds on indicator function for $A = \{t \geq a\}$.

## 4.7    TRANSFORM METHODS

In the old days, before calculators and computers, it was very handy to have logarithm tables around if your work involved performing a large number of multiplications. If you wanted to multiply the numbers $x$ and $y$, you looked up $\log(x)$ and $\log(y)$, *added* $\log(x)$ and $\log(y)$, and then looked up the inverse logarithm of the result. You probably remember from grade school that longhand multiplication is more tedious and error-prone than addition. Thus logarithms were very useful as a computational aid.

Transform methods are extremely useful computational aids in the solution of equations that involve derivatives and integrals of functions. In many of these problems, the solution is given by the convolution of two functions: $f_1(x) * f_2(x)$. We will define the convolution operation later. For now, all you need to know is that finding the convolution of two functions can be more tedious and error-prone than longhand multiplication! In this section we introduce transforms that map the function $f_k(x)$ into another function $\mathscr{F}_k(\omega)$, and that satisfy the property that $\mathscr{F}[f_1(x) * f_2(x)] = \mathscr{F}_1(\omega)\mathscr{F}_2(\omega)$. In other words, the transform of the convolution is equal to the product of the individual transforms. Therefore transforms allow us to replace the convolution operation by the much simpler multiplication operation. The transform expressions introduced in this section will prove very useful when we consider sums of random variables in Chapter 7.

### 4.7.1    The Characteristic Function

The **characteristic function** of a random variable $X$ is defined by

$$\Phi_X(\omega) = E[e^{j\omega X}] \tag{4.79a}$$

$$= \int_{-\infty}^{\infty} f_X(x)e^{j\omega x}\, dx, \tag{4.79b}$$

where $j = \sqrt{-1}$ is the imaginary unit number. The two expressions on the right-hand side motivate two interpretations of the characteristic function. In the first expression, $\Phi_X(\omega)$ can be viewed as the expected value of a function of $X$, $e^{j\omega X}$, in which the parameter $\omega$ is left unspecified. In the second expression, $\Phi_X(\omega)$ is simply the Fourier transform of the pdf $f_X(x)$ (with a reversal in the sign of the exponent). Both of these interpretations prove useful in different contexts.

If we view $\Phi_X(\omega)$ as a Fourier transform, then we have from the Fourier transform inversion formula that the pdf of $X$ is given by

$$f_X(x) = \frac{1}{2\pi} \int_{-\infty}^{\infty} \Phi_X(\omega)e^{-j\omega x}\, d\omega. \tag{4.80}$$

It then follows that every pdf and its characteristic function form a unique Fourier transform pair. Table 4.1 gives the characteristic function of some continuous random variables.

**Example 4.41  Exponential Random Variable**

The characteristic function for an exponentially distributed random variable with parameter $\lambda$ is given by

$$\Phi_X(\omega) = \int_0^\infty \lambda e^{-\lambda x} e^{j\omega x}\, dx = \int_0^\infty \lambda e^{-(\lambda - j\omega)x}\, dx$$

$$= \frac{\lambda}{\lambda - j\omega}.$$

If $X$ is a discrete random variable, substitution of Eq. (4.20) into the definition of $\Phi_X(\omega)$ gives

$$\Phi_X(\omega) = \sum_k p_X(x_k) e^{j\omega x_k} \qquad \text{discrete random variables.}$$

Most of the time we deal with discrete random variables that are integer-valued. The characteristic function is then

$$\Phi_X(\omega) = \sum_{k=-\infty}^{\infty} p_X(k) e^{j\omega k} \qquad \text{integer-valued random variables.} \qquad (4.81)$$

Equation (4.81) is the **Fourier transform of the sequence** $p_X(k)$. Note that the Fourier transform in Eq. (4.81) is a periodic function of $\omega$ with period $2\pi$, since $e^{j(\omega+2\pi)k} = e^{j\omega k} e^{jk2\pi}$ and $e^{jk2\pi} = 1$. Therefore the characteristic function of integer-valued random variables is a periodic function of $\omega$. The following inversion formula allows us to recover the probabilities $p_X(k)$ from $\Phi_X(\omega)$:

$$p_X(k) = \frac{1}{2\pi} \int_0^{2\pi} \Phi_X(\omega) e^{-j\omega k}\, d\omega \qquad k = 0, \pm 1, \pm 2, \ldots \qquad (4.82)$$

Indeed, a comparison of Eqs. (4.81) and (4.82) shows that the $p_X(k)$ are simply the coefficients of the Fourier series of the periodic function $\Phi_X(\omega)$.

**Example 4.42  Geometric Random Variable**

The characteristic function for a geometric random variable is given by

$$\Phi_X(\omega) = \sum_{k=0}^{\infty} pq^k e^{j\omega k} = p \sum_{k=0}^{\infty} (qe^{j\omega})^k$$

$$= \frac{p}{1 - qe^{j\omega}}.$$

Since $f_X(x)$ and $\Phi_X(\omega)$ form a transform pair, we would expect to be able to obtain the moments of $X$ from $\Phi_X(\omega)$. The **moment theorem** states that the moments of

*X* are given by

$$E[X^n] = \frac{1}{j^n} \frac{d^n}{d\omega^n} \Phi_X(\omega) \Big|_{\omega=0}. \tag{4.83}$$

To show this, first expand $e^{j\omega x}$ in a power series in the definition of $\Phi_X(\omega)$:

$$\Phi_X(\omega) = \int_{-\infty}^{\infty} f_X(x) \left\{ 1 + j\omega X + \frac{(j\omega X)^2}{2!} + \cdots \right\} dx.$$

Assuming that all the moments of *X* are finite and that the series can be integrated term by term, we obtain

$$\Phi_X(\omega) = 1 + j\omega E[X] + \frac{(j\omega)^2 E[X^2]}{2!} + \cdots + \frac{(j\omega)^n E[X^n]}{n!} + \cdots.$$

If we differentiate the above expression once and evaluate the result at $\omega = 0$ we obtain

$$\frac{d}{d\omega} \Phi_X(\omega) \Big|_{\omega=0} = jE[X].$$

If we differentiate *n* times and evaluate at $\omega = 0$, we finally obtain

$$\frac{d^n}{d\omega^n} \Phi_X(\omega) \Big|_{\omega=0} = j^n E[X^n],$$

which yields Eq. (4.83).

Note that when the above power series converges, the characteristic function and hence the pdf by Eq. (4.80) are completely determined by the moments of *X*.

---

### Example 4.43

To find the mean of an exponentially distributed random variable, we differentiate $\Phi_X(\omega) = \lambda(\lambda - j\omega)^{-1}$ once, and obtain

$$\Phi'_X(\omega) = \frac{\lambda j}{(\lambda - j\omega)^2}.$$

The moment theorem then implies that $E[X] = \Phi'_X(0)/j = 1/\lambda$.

If we take two derivatives, we obtain

$$\Phi''_X(\omega) = \frac{-2\lambda}{(\lambda - j\omega)^3},$$

so the second moment is then $E[X^2] = \Phi''_X(0)/j^2 = 2/\lambda^2$. The variance of *X* is then given by

$$\text{VAR}[X] = E[X^2] - E[X]^2 = \frac{2}{\lambda^2} - \frac{1}{\lambda^2} = \frac{1}{\lambda^2}.$$

---

### Example 4.44    Chernoff Bound for Gaussian Random Variable

Let $X$ be a Gaussian random variable with mean $m$ and variance $\sigma^2$. Find the Chernoff bound for $X$.

The Chernoff bound (Eq. 4.78) depends on the moment generating function:

$$E[e^{sX}] = \Phi_X(-js).$$

In terms of the characteristic function the bound is given by:

$$P[X \geq a] \leq e^{-sa}\Phi_X(-js) \quad \text{for} \quad s \geq 0.$$

The parameter $s$ can be selected to minimize the upper bound.

The bound for the Gaussian random variable is:

$$P[X \geq a] \leq e^{-sa}e^{ms+\sigma^2s^2/2} = e^{-s(a-m)+\sigma^2s^2/2} \quad \text{for} \quad s \geq 0.$$

We minimize the upper bound by minimizing the exponent:

$$0 = \frac{d}{ds}(-s(a-m) + \sigma^2s^2/2) \quad \text{which implies} \quad s = \frac{a-m}{\sigma^2}.$$

The resulting upper bound is:

$$P[X \geq a] = Q\left(\frac{a-m}{\sigma}\right) \leq e^{-(a-m)^2/2\sigma^2}.$$

This bound is much better than the Chebyshev bound and is similar to the estimate given in Eq. (4.54).

### 4.7.2    The Probability Generating Function

In problems where random variables are nonnegative, it is usually more convenient to use the $z$-transform or the Laplace transform. The **probability generating function** $G_N(z)$ of a nonnegative integer-valued random variable $N$ is defined by

$$G_N(z) = E[z^N] \tag{4.84a}$$

$$= \sum_{k=0}^{\infty} p_N(k)z^k. \tag{4.84b}$$

The first expression is the expected value of the function of $N$, $z^N$. The second expression is the $z$-transform of the pmf (with a sign change in the exponent). Table 3.1 shows the probability generating function for some discrete random variables. Note that the characteristic function of $N$ is given by $\Phi_N(\omega) = G_N(e^{j\omega})$.

Using a derivation similar to that used in the moment theorem, it is easy to show that the pmf of $N$ is given by

$$p_N(k) = \frac{1}{k!}\frac{d^k}{dz^k}G_N(z)\Big|_{z=0}. \tag{4.85}$$

This is why $G_N(z)$ is called the probability generating function. By taking the first two derivatives of $G_N(z)$ and evaluating the result at $z = 1$, it is possible to find the first two moments of $X$:

$$\left.\frac{d}{dz}G_N(z)\right|_{z=1} = \left.\sum_{k=0}^{\infty}p_N(k)kz^{k-1}\right|_{z=1} = \sum_{k=0}^{\infty}kp_N(k) = E[N]$$

and

$$\left.\frac{d^2}{dz^2}G_N(z)\right|_{z=1} = \left.\sum_{k=0}^{\infty}p_N(k)k(k-1)z^{k-2}\right|_{z=1}$$

$$= \sum_{k=0}^{\infty}k(k-1)p_N(k) = E[N(N-1)] = E[N^2] - E[N].$$

Thus the mean and variance of $X$ are given by

$$E[N] = G'_N(1) \tag{4.86}$$

and

$$\text{VAR}[N] = G''_N(1) + G'_N(1) - (G'_N(1))^2. \tag{4.87}$$

---

**Example 4.45    Poisson Random Variable**

The probability generating function for the Poisson random variable with parameter $\alpha$ is given by

$$G_N(z) = \sum_{k=0}^{\infty}\frac{\alpha^k}{k!}e^{-\alpha}z^k = e^{-\alpha}\sum_{k=0}^{\infty}\frac{(\alpha z)^k}{k!}$$

$$= e^{-\alpha}e^{\alpha z} = e^{\alpha(z-1)}.$$

The first two derivatives of $G_N(z)$ are given by

$$G'_N(z) = \alpha e^{\alpha(z-1)}$$

and

$$G''_N(z) = \alpha^2 e^{\alpha(z-1)}.$$

Therefore the mean and variance of the Poisson are

$$E[N] = \alpha$$

$$\text{VAR}[N] = \alpha^2 + \alpha - \alpha^2 = \alpha.$$

---

### 4.7.3    The Laplace Transform of the pdf

In queueing theory one deals with service times, waiting times, and delays. All of these are nonnegative continuous random variables. It is therefore customary to work with the **Laplace transform** of the pdf,

$$X^*(s) = \int_0^{\infty} f_X(x)e^{-sx}\,dx = E[e^{-sX}]. \tag{4.88}$$

Note that $X^*(s)$ can be interpreted as a Laplace transform of the pdf or as an expected value of a function of $X$, $e^{-sX}$.

The moment theorem also holds for $X*(s)$:

$$E[X^n] = (-1)^n \frac{d^n}{ds^n} X*(s) \bigg|_{s=0} . \tag{4.89}$$

---

**Example 4.46    Gamma Random Variable**

The Laplace transform of the gamma pdf is given by

$$X*(s) = \int_0^\infty \frac{\lambda^\alpha x^{\alpha-1} e^{-\lambda x} e^{-sx}}{\Gamma(\alpha)} dx = \frac{\lambda^\alpha}{\Gamma(\alpha)} \int_0^\infty x^{\alpha-1} e^{-(\lambda+s)x} dx$$

$$= \frac{\lambda^\alpha}{\Gamma(\alpha)} \frac{1}{(\lambda+s)^\alpha} \int_0^\infty y^{\alpha-1} e^{-y} dy = \frac{\lambda^\alpha}{(\lambda+s)^\alpha},$$

where we used the change of variable $y = (\lambda + s)x$. We can then obtain the first two moments of $X$ as follows:

$$E[X] = -\frac{d}{ds} \frac{\lambda^\alpha}{(\lambda+s)^\alpha} \bigg|_{s=0} = \frac{\alpha \lambda^\alpha}{(\lambda+s)^{\alpha+1}} \bigg|_{s=0} = \frac{\alpha}{\lambda}$$

and

$$E[X^2] = \frac{d^2}{ds^2} \frac{\lambda^\alpha}{(\lambda+s)^\alpha} \bigg|_{s=0} = \frac{\alpha(\alpha+1)\lambda^\alpha}{(\lambda+s)^{\alpha+2}} \bigg|_{s=0} = \frac{\alpha(\alpha+1)}{\lambda^2} .$$

Thus the variance of $X$ is

$$\text{VAR}(X) = E[X^2] - E[X]^2 = \frac{\alpha}{\lambda^2}.$$

---

## 4.8    BASIC RELIABILITY CALCULATIONS

In this section we apply some of the tools developed so far to the calculation of measures that are of interest in assessing the reliability of systems. We also show how the reliability of a system can be determined in terms of the reliability of its components.

### 4.8.1    The Failure Rate Function

Let $T$ be the lifetime of a component, a subsystem, or a system. The **reliability** at time $t$ is defined as the probability that the component, subsystem, or system is still functioning at time $t$:

$$R(t) = P[T > t]. \tag{4.90}$$

The relative frequency interpretation implies that, in a large number of components or systems, $R(t)$ is the fraction that fail after time $t$. The reliability can be expressed in terms of the cdf of $T$:

$$R(t) = 1 - P[T \le t] = 1 - F_T(t). \tag{4.91}$$

Note that the derivative of $R(t)$ gives the negative of the pdf of $T$:

$$R'(t) = -f_T(t). \tag{4.92}$$

The **mean time to failure (MTTF)** is given by the expected value of $T$:

$$E[T] = \int_0^\infty f_T(t)\,dt = \int_0^\infty R(t)\,dt,$$

where the second expression was obtained using Eqs. (4.28) and (4.91).

Suppose that we know a system is still functioning at time $t$; what is its future behavior? In Example 4.10, we found that the conditional cdf of $T$ given that $T > t$ is given by

$$F_T(x|T > t) = P[T \le x|T > t]$$

$$= \begin{cases} 0 & x < t \\ \dfrac{F_T(x) - F_T(t)}{1 - F_T(t)} & x \ge t. \end{cases} \tag{4.93}$$

The pdf associated with $F_T(x|T > t)$ is

$$f_T(x|T > t) = \frac{f_T(x)}{1 - F_T(t)} \quad x \ge t. \tag{4.94}$$

Note that the denominator of Eq. (4.94) is equal to $R(t)$.

The **failure rate function** $r(t)$ is defined as $f_T(x|T > t)$ evaluated at $x = t$:

$$r(t) = f_T(t|T > t)$$

$$= \frac{-R'(t)}{R(t)}, \tag{4.95}$$

since by Eq. (4.92), $R'(t) = -f_T(t)$. The failure rate function has the following meaning:

$$P[t < T \le t + dt|T > t] = f_T(t|T > t)\,dt = r(t)\,dt. \tag{4.96}$$

In words, $r(t)\,dt$ is the probability that a component that has functioned up to time $t$ will fail in the next $dt$ seconds.

---

### Example 4.47    Exponential Failure Law

Suppose a component has a constant failure rate function, say $r(t) = \lambda$. Find the pdf and the MTTF for its lifetime $T$.

Equation (4.95) implies that

$$\frac{R'(t)}{R(t)} = -\lambda. \tag{4.97}$$

Equation (4.97) is a first-order differential equation with initial condition $R(0) = 1$. If we integrate both sides of Eq. (4.97) from 0 to $t$, we obtain

$$-\int_0^t \lambda\,dt' + k = \int_0^t \frac{R'(t')}{R(t')}\,dt' = \ln R(t),$$

which implies that

$$R(t) = Ke^{-\lambda t}, \qquad \text{where } K = e^k.$$

The initial condition $R(0) = 1$ implies that $K = 1$. Thus

$$R(t) = e^{-\lambda t} \qquad t > 0 \tag{4.98}$$

and

$$f_T(t) = \lambda e^{-\lambda t} \qquad t > 0.$$

Thus if $T$ has a constant failure rate function, then $T$ is an exponential random variable. This is not surprising, since the exponential random variable satisfies the memoryless property. The MTTF $= E[T] = 1/\lambda$.

---

The derivation that was used in Example 4.47 can be used to show that, in general, the failure rate function and the reliability are related by

$$R(t) = \exp\left\{ -\int_0^t r(t')\, dt' \right\} \tag{4.99}$$

and from Eq. (4.92),

$$f_T(t) = r(t) \exp\left\{ -\int_0^t r(t')\, dt' \right\}. \tag{4.100}$$

Figure 4.16 shows the failure rate function for a typical system. Initially there may be a high failure rate due to defective parts or installation. After the "bugs" have been worked out, the system is stable and has a low failure rate. At some later point, ageing and wear effects set in, resulting in an increased failure rate. Equations (4.99) and (4.100) allow us to postulate reliability functions and the associated pdf's in terms of the failure rate function, as shown in the following example.

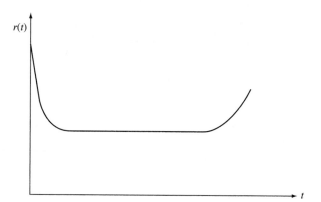

**FIGURE 4.16**
Failure rate function for a typical system.

---

### Example 4.48    Weibull Failure Law

The Weibull failure law has failure rate function given by

$$r(t) = \alpha \beta t^{\beta-1}, \tag{4.101}$$

where $\alpha$ and $\beta$ are positive constants. Equation (4.99) implies that the reliability is given by

$$R(t) = e^{-\alpha t^{\beta}}.$$

Equation (4.100) then implies that the pdf for $T$ is

$$f_T(t) = \alpha \beta t^{\beta-1} e^{-\alpha t^{\beta}} \quad t > 0. \tag{4.102}$$

Figure 4.17 shows $f_T(t)$ for $\alpha = 1$ and several values of $\beta$. Note that $\beta = 1$ yields the exponential failure law, which has a constant failure rate. For $\beta > 1$, Eq. (4.101) gives a failure rate function that increases with time. For $\beta < 1$, Eq. (4.101) gives a failure rate function that decreases with time. Further properties of the Weibull random variable are developed in the problems.

---

### 4.8.2    Reliability of Systems

Suppose that a system consists of several components or subsystems. We now show how the reliability of a system can be computed in terms of the reliability of its subsystems if the components are assumed to fail independently of each other.

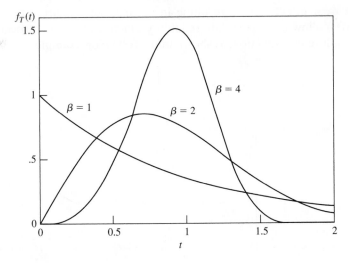

**FIGURE 4.17**
Probability density function of Weibull random variable, $\alpha = 1$ and $\beta = 1, 2, 4$.

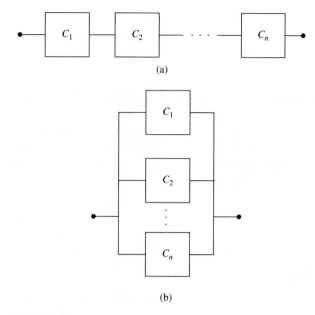

**FIGURE 4.18**
(a) System consisting of *n* components in series. (b) System consisting
of *n* components in parallel.

Consider first a system that consists of the series arrangement of $n$ components as shown in Fig. 4.18(a). This system is considered to be functioning only if all the components are functioning. Let $A_s$ be the event "system functioning at time $t$," and let $A_j$ be the event "$j$th component is functioning at time $t$," then the probability that the system is functioning at time $t$ is

$$R(t) = P[A_s]$$
$$= P[A_1 \cap A_2 \cap \cdots \cap A_n] = P[A_1]P[A_2]\ldots P[A_n]$$
$$= R_1(t)R_2(t)\ldots R_n(t), \tag{4.103}$$

since $P[A_j] = R_j(t)$, the reliability function of the $j$th component. Since probabilities are numbers that are less than or equal to one, we see that $R(t)$ can be no more reliable than the least reliable of the components, that is, $R(t) \leq \min_j R_j(t)$.

If we apply Eq. (4.99) to each of the $R_j(t)$ in Eq. (4.103), we then find that the failure rate function of a series system is given by the sum of the component failure rate functions:

$$R(t) = \exp\left\{-\int_0^t r_1(t')\,dt'\right\}\exp\left\{-\int_0^t r_2(t')\,dt'\right\}\ldots\exp\left\{-\int_0^t r_n(t')\,dt'\right\}$$
$$= \exp\left\{-\int_0^t [r_1(t') + r_2(t') + \cdots + r_n(t')]\,dt'\right\}.$$

---

**Example 4.49**

Suppose that a system consists of $n$ components in series and that the component lifetimes are exponential random variables with rates $\lambda_1, \lambda_2, \ldots, \lambda_n$. Find the system reliability.

From Eqs. (4.98) and (4.103), we have

$$R(t) = e^{-\lambda_1 t}e^{-\lambda_2 t}\dots e^{-\lambda_n t}$$

$$= e^{-(\lambda_1 + \dots + \lambda_n)t}.$$

Thus the system reliability is exponentially distributed with rate $\lambda_1 + \lambda_2 + \dots + \lambda_n$.

Now suppose that a system consists of $n$ components in parallel, as shown in Fig. 4.18(b). This system is considered to be functioning as long as at least one of the components is functioning. The system will *not* be functioning if and only if all the components have failed, that is,

$$P[A_s^c] = P[A_1^c]P[A_2^c]\dots P[A_n^c].$$

Thus

$$1 - R(t) = (1 - R_1(t))(1 - R_2(t))\dots(1 - R_n(t)),$$

and finally,

$$R(t) = 1 - (1 - R_1(t))(1 - R_2(t))\dots(1 - R_n(t)). \tag{4.104}$$

### Example 4.50

Compare the reliability of a single-unit system against that of a system that operates two units in parallel. Assume all units have exponentially distributed lifetimes with rate 1.

The reliability of the single-unit system is

$$R_s(t) = e^{-t}.$$

The reliability of the two-unit system is

$$R_p(t) = 1 - (1 - e^{-t})(1 - e^{-t})$$

$$= e^{-t}(2 - e^{-t}).$$

The parallel system is more reliable by a factor of

$$(2 - e^{-t}) > 1.$$

More complex configurations can be obtained by combining subsystems consisting of series and parallel components. The reliability of such systems can then be computed in terms of the subsystem reliabilities. See Example 2.35 for an example of such a calculation.

## 4.9    COMPUTER METHODS FOR GENERATING RANDOM VARIABLES

The computer simulation of any random phenomenon involves the generation of random variables with prescribed distributions. For example, the simulation of a queueing system involves generating the time between customer arrivals as well as the service times of each customer. Once the cdf's that model these random quantities have been selected, an algorithm for generating random variables with these cdf's must be found. MATLAB and Octave have built-in functions for generating random variables for all of the well known distributions. In this section we present the methods that are used for generating random variables. All of these methods are based on the availability of random numbers that are uniformly distributed between zero and one. Methods for generating these numbers were discussed in Section 2.7.

All of the methods for generating random variables require the evaluation of either the pdf, the cdf, or the inverse of the cdf of the random variable of interest. We can write programs to perform these evaluations, or we can use the functions available in programs such as MATLAB and Octave. The following example shows some typical evaluations for the Gaussian random variable.

---

### Example 4.51    Evaluation of pdf, cdf, and Inverse cdf

Let $X$ be a Gaussian random variable with mean 1 and variance 2. Find the pdf at $x = 7$. Find the cdf at $x = -2$. Find the value of $x$ at which the cdf = 0.25.

The following commands show how these results are obtained using Octave.

```
> normal_pdf (7, 1, 2)
ans = 3.4813e-05
> normal_cdf (-2, 1, 2)
ans = 0.016947
> normal_inv (0.25, 1, 2)
ans = 0.046127
```

---

### 4.9.1    The Transformation Method

Suppose that $U$ is uniformly distributed in the interval $[0, 1]$. Let $F_X(x)$ be the cdf of the random variable we are interested in generating. Define the random variable, $Z = F_X^{-1}(U)$; that is, first $U$ is selected and then $Z$ is found as indicated in Fig. 4.19. The cdf of $Z$ is

$$P[Z \le x] = P[F_X^{-1}(U) \le x] = P[U \le F_X(x)].$$

But if $U$ is uniformly distributed in $[0, 1]$ and $0 \le h \le 1$, then $P[U \le h] = h$ (see Example 4.6). Thus

$$P[Z \le x] = F_X(x),$$

and $Z = F_X^{-1}(U)$ has the desired cdf.

### Transformation Method for Generating $X$:

1. Generate $U$ uniformly distributed in $[0, 1]$.
2. Let $Z = F_X^{-1}(U)$.

---

### Example 4.52    Exponential Random Variable

To generate an exponentially distributed random variable $X$ with parameter $\lambda$, we need to invert the expression $u = F_X(x) = 1 - e^{-\lambda x}$. We obtain

$$X = -\frac{1}{\lambda}\ln(1 - U).$$

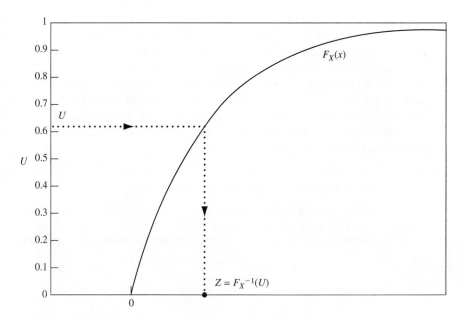

**FIGURE 4.19**
Transformation method for generating a random variable with cdf $F_X(x)$.

Note that we can use the simpler expression $X = -\ln(U)/\lambda$, since $1 - U$ is also uniformly distributed in $[0, 1]$. The first two lines of the Octave commands below show how to implement the transformation method to generate 1000 exponential random variables with $\lambda = 1$. Figure 4.20 shows the histogram of values obtained. In addition, the figure shows the probability that samples of the random variables fall in the corresponding histogram bins. Good correspondence between the histograms and these probabilities are observed. In Chapter 8 we introduce methods for assessing the goodness-of-fit of data to a given distribution. Both MATLAB and Octave use the transformation method in their function `exponential_rnd`.

```
> U=rand(1, 1000);          % Generate 1000 uniform random variables.
> X=-log(U);                % Compute 1000 exponential RVs.
> K=0.25:0.5:6;
> P(1)=1-exp(-0.5)
> for i=2:12,               % The remaining lines show how to generate
> P(i)=P(i-1)*exp(-0.5)     % the histogram bins.
> end;
> stem(K, P)
> hold on
> Hist(X, K, 1)
```

## 4.9.2    The Rejection Method

We first consider the simple version of this algorithm and explain why it works; then we present it in its general form. Suppose that we are interested in generating a random variable $Z$ with pdf $f_X(x)$ as shown in Fig. 4.21. In particular, we assume that: (1) the pdf is nonzero only in the interval $[0, a]$, and (2) the pdf takes on values in the range $[0, b]$. The **rejection method** in this case works as follows:

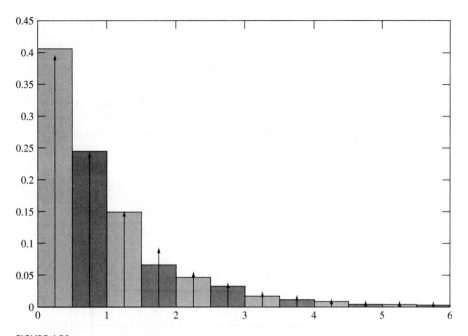

**FIGURE 4.20**
Histogram of 1000 exponential random variables using transformation method.

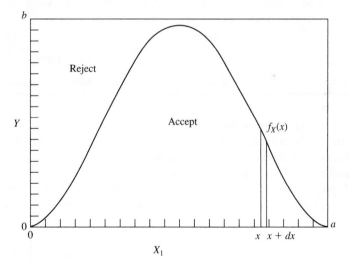

**FIGURE 4.21**
Rejection method for generating a random variable with pdf $f_X(x)$.

1. Generate $X_1$ uniform in the interval $[0, a]$.
2. Generate $Y$ uniform in the interval $[0, b]$.
3. If $Y \leq f_X(X_1)$, then output $Z = X_1$; else, reject $X_1$ and return to step 1.

Note that this algorithm will perform a random number of steps before it produces the output $Z$.

We now show that the output $Z$ has the desired pdf. Steps 1 and 2 select a point at random in a rectangle of width $a$ and height $b$. The probability of selecting a point in any region is simply the area of the region divided by the total area of the rectangle, $ab$. Thus the probability of accepting $X_1$ is the probability of the region below $f_X(x)$ divided by $ab$. But the area under any pdf is 1, so we conclude that the probability of success (i.e., acceptance) is $1/ab$. Consider now the following probability:

$$P[x < X_1 \le x + dx | X_1 \text{ is accepted}]$$

$$= \frac{P[\{x < X_1 \le x + dx\} \cap \{X_1 \text{ accepted}\}]}{P[X_1 \text{ accepted}]}$$

$$= \frac{\text{shaded area}/ab}{1/ab} = \frac{f_X(x) \, dx/ab}{1/ab}$$

$$= f_X(x) \, dx.$$

Therefore $X_1$ when accepted has the desired pdf. Thus $Z$ has the desired pdf.

---

**Example 4.53    Generating Beta Random Variables**

Show that the beta random variables with $a' = b' = 2$ can be generated using the rejection method.

The pdf of the beta random variable with $a' = b' = 2$ is similar to that shown in Fig. 4.21. This beta pdf is maximum at $x = 1/2$ and the maximum value is:

$$\frac{(1/2)^{2-1}(1/2)^{2-1}}{B(2, 2)} = \frac{1/4}{\Gamma(2)\Gamma(2)/\Gamma(4)} = \frac{1/4}{1!1!/3!} = \frac{3}{2}.$$

Therefore we can generate this beta random variable using the rejection method with $b = 1.5$.

---

The algorithm as stated above can have two problems. First, if the rectangle does not fit snugly around $f_X(x)$, the number of $X_1$'s that need to be generated before acceptance may be excessive. Second, the above method cannot be used if $f_X(x)$ is unbounded or if its range is not finite. The general version of this algorithm overcomes both problems. Suppose we want to generate $Z$ with pdf $f_X(x)$. Let $W$ be a random variable with pdf $f_W(x)$ that is *easy* to generate and such that for some constant $K > 1$,

$$K f_W(x) \ge f_X(x) \qquad \text{for all } x,$$

that is, the region under $K f_W(x)$ contains $f_X(x)$ as shown in Fig. 4.22.

**Rejection Method for Generating $X$:**

1. Generate $X_1$ with pdf $f_W(x)$. Define $B(X_1) = K f_W(X_1)$.
2. Generate $Y$ uniform in $[0, B(X_1)]$.
3. If $Y \le f_X(X_1)$, then output $Z = X_1$; else reject $X_1$ and return to step 1.

See Problem 4.143 for a proof that $Z$ has the desired pdf.

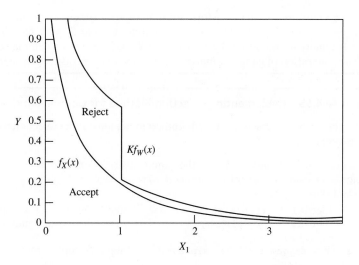

**FIGURE 4.22**
Rejection method for generating a random variable with gamma pdf and with $0 < \alpha < 1$.

## Example 4.54  Gamma Random Variable

We now show how the rejection method can be used to generate $X$ with gamma pdf and parameters $0 < \alpha < 1$ and $\lambda = 1$. A function $Kf_W(x)$ that "covers" $f_X(x)$ is easily obtained (see Fig. 4.22):

$$f_X(x) = \frac{x^{\alpha-1}e^{-x}}{\Gamma(\alpha)} \le Kf_W(x) = \begin{cases} \dfrac{x^{\alpha-1}}{\Gamma(\alpha)} & 0 \le x \le 1 \\ \dfrac{e^{-x}}{\Gamma(\alpha)} & x > 1. \end{cases}$$

The pdf $f_W(x)$ that corresponds to the function on the right-hand side is

$$f_W(x) = \begin{cases} \dfrac{\alpha e x^{\alpha-1}}{\alpha + e} & 0 \le x \le 1 \\ \alpha e \dfrac{e^{-x}}{\alpha + e} & x \ge 1. \end{cases}$$

The cdf of $W$ is

$$F_W(x) = \begin{cases} \dfrac{e x^{\alpha}}{\alpha + e} & 0 \le x \le 1 \\ 1 - \alpha e \dfrac{e^{-x}}{\alpha + e} & x > 1. \end{cases}$$

$W$ is easy to generate using the transformation method, with

$$F_W^{-1}(u) = \begin{cases} \left[ \dfrac{(\alpha + e)u}{e} \right]^{1/\alpha} & u \le e/(\alpha + e) \\ -\ln\left[ (\alpha + e)\dfrac{(1-u)}{\alpha e} \right] & u > e/(\alpha + e). \end{cases}$$

We can therefore use the transformation method to generate this $f_W(x)$, and then the rejection method to generate any gamma random variable $X$ with parameters $0 < \alpha < 1$ and $\lambda = 1$. Finally we note that if we let $W = \lambda X$, then $W$ will be gamma with parameters $\alpha$ and $\lambda$. The generation of gamma random variables with $\alpha > 1$ is discussed in Problem 4.142.

---

### Example 4.55 Implementing Rejection Method for Gamma Random Variables

Given below is an Octave function definition to implement the rejection method using the above transformation.

```
% Generate random numbers from the gamma distribution for 0 ≤ α ≤ 1.
function X = gamma_rejection_method_altone(alpha)
while (true),
    X = special_inverse(alpha);        % Step 1: Generate X with pdf f_X(x).
    B = special_pdf (X, alpha);         % Step 2: Generate Y uniform in [0, Kf_X(X)].
    Y = rand.* B;
    if (Y <= fx_gamma_pdf (X, alpha)),  % Step 3: Accept or reject . . .
        break;
    end
end
```

```
% Helper function to generate random variables according to Kf_Z(x).
function X = special_inverse (alpha)
u = rand;
if (u <= e./(alpha+e)),
    X = ((alpha+e).*u./e).^(1./alpha);
elseif (u > e./(alpha+e)),
    X = -log((alpha+e).*(1-u)./(alpha.*e));
end
```

```
% Return B in order to generate uniform variables in [0, Kf_Z(X)].
function B = special_pdf (X, alpha)
if (X >=0 && X <= 1),
    B = alpha.*e.*X.^(alpha-1)./(alpha + e);
elseif (X > 1),
    B = alpha.*e.*(e. ^(-X)./(alpha + e));
end
```

```
% pdf of the gamma distribution.
% Could also use the built in gamma_pdf (X, A, B) function supplied with Octave
setting B = 1
function Y = fx_gamma_pdf (x, alpha)
y = (x.^(alpha-1)).*(e.^(-x))./(gamma(alpha));
```

Figure 4.23 shows the histogram of 1000 samples obtained using this function. The figure also shows the probability that the samples fall in the bins of the histogram.

---

We have presented the most common methods that are used to generate random variables. These methods are incorporated in the functions provided by programs such as MATLAB and Octave, so in practice you do not need to write programs to

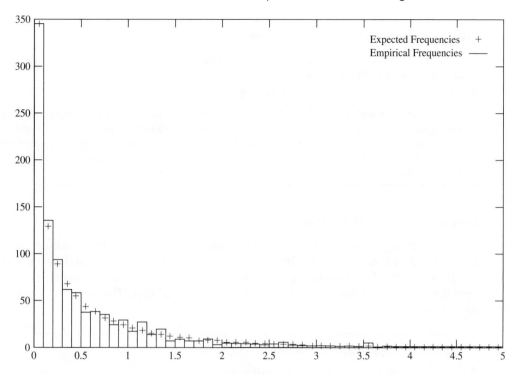

**FIGURE 4.23**
1000 samples of gamma random variable using rejection method.

generate the most common random variables. You simply need to invoke the appropriate functions.

---

### Example 4.56    Generating Gamma Random Variables

Use Octave to obtain eight Gamma random variables with $\alpha = 0.25$ and $\lambda = 1$.
    The Octave command and the corresponding answer are given below:

```
> gamma_rnd (0.25, 1, 1, 8)
ans =
 Columns 1 through 6:
   0.00021529   0.09331491   0.24606757   0.08665787
   0.00013400   0.23384718
 Columns 7 and 8:
   1.72940941   1.29599702
```

---

### 4.9.3    Generation of Functions of a Random Variable

Once we have a simple method of generating a random variable $X$, we can easily generate any random variable that is defined by $Y = g(X)$ or even $Z = h(X_1, X_2, \ldots, X_n)$, where $X_1, \ldots, X_n$ are $n$ outputs of the random variable generator.

### Example 4.57    *m*-Erlang Random Variable

Let $X_1, X_2, \ldots$ be independent, exponentially distributed random variables with parameter $\lambda$. In Chapter 7 we show that the random variable

$$Y = X_1 + X_2 + \cdots + X_m$$

has an $m$-Erlang pdf with parameter $\lambda$. We can therefore generate an $m$-Erlang random variable by first generating $m$ exponentially distributed random variables using the transformation method, and then taking the sum. Since the $m$-Erlang random variable is a special case of the gamma random variable, for large $m$ it may be preferable to use the rejection method described in Problem 4.142.

### 4.9.4    Generating Mixtures of Random Variables

We have seen in previous sections that sometimes a random variable consists of a mixture of several random variables. In other words, the generation of the random variable can be viewed as first selecting a random variable type according to some pmf, and then generating a random variable from the selected pdf type. This procedure can be simulated easily.

### Example 4.58    Hyperexponential Random Variable

A two-stage hyperexponential random variable has pdf

$$f_X(x) = pae^{-ax} + (1 - p)be^{-bx}.$$

It is clear from the above expression that $X$ consists of a mixture of two exponential random variables with parameters $a$ and $b$, respectively. $X$ can be generated by first performing a Bernoulli trial with probability of success $p$. If the outcome is a success, we then use the transformation method to generate an exponential random variable with parameter $a$. If the outcome is a failure, we generate an exponential random variable with parameter $b$ instead.

## *4.10    ENTROPY

Entropy is a measure of the uncertainty in a random experiment. In this section, we first introduce the notion of the entropy of a random variable and develop several of its fundamental properties. We then show that entropy quantifies uncertainty by the amount of information required to specify the outcome of a random experiment. Finally, we discuss the method of maximum entropy, which has found wide use in characterizing random variables when only some parameters, such as the mean or variance, are known.

### 4.10.1    The Entropy of a Random Variable

Let $X$ be a discrete random variable with $S_X = \{1, 2, \ldots, K\}$ and pmf $p_k = P[X = k]$. We are interested in quantifying the uncertainty of the event $A_k = \{X = k\}$. Clearly, the uncertainty of $A_k$ is low if the probability of $A_k$ is close to one, and it is high if the probability of $A_k$ is small. The following measure of uncertainty satisfies these two properties:

$$I(X = k) = \ln \frac{1}{P[X = k]} = -\ln P[X = k]. \tag{4.105}$$

Note from Fig. 4.24 that $I(X = k) = 0$ if $P[X = k] = 1$, and $I(X = k)$ increases with decreasing $P[X = k]$. The **entropy of a random variable** $X$ is defined as the expected value of the uncertainty of its outcomes:

$$\begin{aligned} H_X = E[I(X)] &= \sum_{k=1}^{K} P[X = k] \ln \frac{1}{P[X = k]} \\ &= -\sum_{k=1}^{K} P[X = k] \ln P[X = k]. \end{aligned} \tag{4.106}$$

Note that in the above definition we have used $I(X)$ as a function of a random variable. We say that entropy is in units of "bits" when the logarithm is base 2. In the above expression we are using the natural logarithm, so we say the units are in "nats." Changing the base of the logarithm is equivalent to multiplying entropy by a constant, since $\ln(x) = \ln 2 \log_2 x$.

---

### Example 4.59  Entropy of a Binary Random Variable

Suppose that $S_X = \{0, 1\}$ and $p = P[X = 0] = 1 - P[X = 1]$. Figure 4.25 shows $-p \ln(p)$, $-(1 - p)\ln(1 - p)$, and the entropy of the binary random variable $H_X = h(p) = -p \ln(p) - (1 - p)\ln(1 - p)$ as functions of $p$. Note that $h(p)$ is symmetric about $p = 1/2$ and that it achieves its maximum at $p = 1/2$. Note also how the uncertainties of the events $\{X = 0\}$ and $\{X = 1\}$ vary together in complementary fashion: When $P[X = 0]$ is very small (i.e., highly uncertain), then $P[X = 1]$ is close to one (i.e., highly certain), and vice versa. Thus the highest average uncertainty occurs when $P[X = 0] = P[X = 1] = 1/2$.

$H_X$ can be viewed as the average uncertainty that is resolved by observing $X$. This suggests that if we are designing a binary experiment (for example, a yes/no question), then the average uncertainty that is resolved will be maximized if the two outcomes are designed to be equiprobable.

---

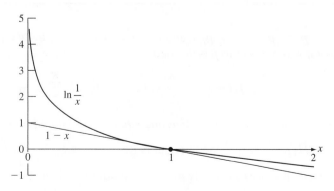

**FIGURE 4.24**
$\ln(1/x) \geq 1 - x$

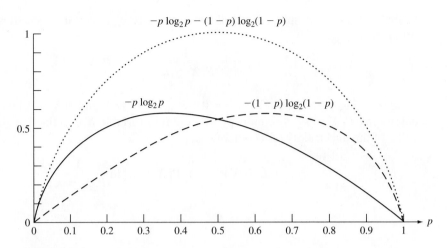

**FIGURE 4.25**
Entropy of binary random variable.

---

### Example 4.60 Reduction of Entropy Through Partial Information

The binary representation of the random variable $X$ takes on values from the set $\{000, 001, 010, \ldots, 111\}$ with equal probabilities. Find the reduction in the entropy of $X$ given the event $A = \{X \text{ begins with a } 1\}$.

The entropy of $X$ is

$$H_X = -\frac{1}{8}\log_2\frac{1}{8} - \frac{1}{8}\log_2\frac{1}{8} - \cdots - \frac{1}{8}\log_2\frac{1}{8} = 3 \text{ bits.}$$

The event $A$ implies that $X$ is in the set $\{100, 101, 110, 111\}$, so the entropy of $X$ given $A$ is

$$H_{X|A} = -\frac{1}{4}\log_2\frac{1}{4} - \cdots - \frac{1}{4}\log_2\frac{1}{4} = 2 \text{ bits.}$$

Thus the reduction in entropy is $H_X - H_{X|A} = 3 - 2 = 1$ bit.

---

Let $\boldsymbol{p} = (p_1, p_2, \ldots, p_K)$, and $\boldsymbol{q} = (q_1, q_2, \ldots, q_K)$ be two pmf's. The **relative entropy** of $\boldsymbol{q}$ with respect to $\boldsymbol{p}$ is defined by

$$H(p; q) = \sum_{k=1}^{K} p_k \ln\frac{1}{q_k} - H_X = \sum_{k=1}^{K} p_k \ln\frac{p_k}{q_k}. \tag{4.107}$$

*The relative entropy is nonnegative, and equal to zero if and only if $p_k = q_k$ for all $k$:*

$$H(p; q) \geq 0 \quad \text{with equality iff} \quad p_k = q_k \quad \text{for } k = 1, \ldots, K. \tag{4.108}$$

We will use this fact repeatedly in the remainder of this section.

To show that the relative entropy is nonnegative, we use the inequality $\ln(1/x) \geq 1 - x$ with equality iff $x = 1$, as shown in Fig. 4.24. Equation (4.107) then becomes

$$H(p; q) = \sum_{k=1}^{K} p_k \ln \frac{p_k}{q_k} \geq \sum_{k=1}^{K} p_k \left(1 - \frac{q_k}{p_k}\right) = \sum_{k=1}^{K} p_k - \sum_{k=1}^{K} q_k = 0. \quad (4.109)$$

In order for equality to hold in the above expression, we must have $p_k = q_k$ for $k = 1, \ldots, K$.

Let $X$ be any random variable with $S_X = \{1, 2, \ldots, K\}$ and pmf $p$. If we let $q_k = 1/K$ in Eq. (4.108), then

$$H(p; q) = \ln K - H_X = \sum_{k=1}^{K} p_k \ln \frac{p_k}{1/K} \geq 0,$$

which implies that for any random variable $X$ with $S_X = \{1, 2, \ldots, K\}$,

$$H_X \leq \ln K \quad \text{with equality iff} \quad p_k = \frac{1}{K} \quad k = 1, \ldots, K. \quad (4.110)$$

Thus *the maximum entropy attainable by the random variable $X$ is $\ln K$, and this maximum is attained when all the outcomes are equiprobable.*

Equation (4.110) shows that the entropy of random variables with finite $S_X$ is always finite. On the other hand, it also shows that as the size of $S_X$ is increased, the entropy can increase without bound. The following example shows that some countably infinite random variables have finite entropy.

---

**Example 4.61    Entropy of a Geometric Random Variable**

The entropy of the geometric random variable with $S_X = \{0, 1, 2, \ldots\}$ is:

$$H_X = -\sum_{k=0}^{\infty} p(1 - p)^k \ln(p(1 - p)^k)$$

$$= -\ln p - \ln(1 - p) \sum_{k=0}^{\infty} k p(1 - p)^k$$

$$= -\ln p - \frac{(1 - p) \ln(1 - p)}{p}$$

$$= \frac{-p \ln p - (1 - p) \ln(1 - p)}{p} = \frac{h(p)}{p}, \quad (4.111)$$

where $h(p)$ is the entropy of a binary random variable. Note that $H_X = 2$ bits when $p = 1/2$.

---

For continuous random variables we have that $P[X = x] = 0$ for all $x$. Therefore by Eq. (4.105) the uncertainty for every event $\{X = x\}$ is infinite, and it follows from

Eq. (4.106) that the *entropy of continuous random variables is infinite*. The next example takes a look at how the notion of entropy may be applied to continuous random variables.

---

### Example 4.62    Entropy of a Quantized Continuous Random Variable

Let $X$ be a continuous random variable that takes on values in the interval $[a, b]$. Suppose that the interval $[a, b]$ is divided into a large number $K$ of subintervals of length $\Delta$. Let $Q(X)$ be the midpoint of the subinterval that contains $X$. Find the entropy of $Q$.

Let $x_k$ be the midpoint of the $k$th subinterval, then $P[Q = x_k] = P[X \text{ is in } k\text{th subinterval}]$ $= P[x_k - \Delta/2 < X < x_k + \Delta/2] \simeq f_X(x_k)\Delta$, and thus

$$H_Q = \sum_{k=1}^{K} P[Q = x_k] \ln P[Q = x_k]$$

$$\simeq -\sum_{k=1}^{K} f_X(x_k)\Delta \ln(f_X(x_k)\Delta)$$

$$= -\ln(\Delta) - \sum_{k=1}^{K} f_X(x_k) \ln(f_X(x_k))\Delta. \tag{4.112}$$

The above equation shows that there is a tradeoff between the entropy of $Q$ and the quantization error $X - Q(X)$. As $\Delta$ is decreased the error decreases, but the entropy increases without bound, once again confirming the fact that the entropy of continuous random variables is infinite.

---

In the final expression for $H_X$ in Eq. (4.112), as $\Delta$ approaches zero, the first expression approaches infinity, but the second expression approaches an integral which may be finite in some cases. The **differential entropy** is defined by this integral:

$$H_X = -\int_{-\infty}^{\infty} f_X(x) \ln f_X(x)\, dx = -E[\ln f_X(X)]. \tag{4.113}$$

In the above expression, we reuse the term $H_X$ with the understanding that we deal with differential entropy when dealing with continuous random variables.

---

### Example 4.63    Differential Entropy of a Uniform Random Variable

The differential entropy for $X$ uniform in $[a, b]$ is

$$H_X = -E\left[\ln\left(\frac{1}{b-a}\right)\right] = \ln(b - a). \tag{4.114}$$

---

### Example 4.64    Differential Entropy of a Gaussian Random Variable

The differential entropy for $X$, a Gaussian random variable (see Eq. 4.47), is

$$H_X = -E[\ln f_X(X)]$$

$$= -E\left[\ln\frac{1}{\sqrt{2\pi\sigma^2}} - \frac{(X-m)^2}{2\sigma^2}\right]$$

$$= \frac{1}{2}\ln(2\pi\sigma^2) + \frac{1}{2}$$

$$= \frac{1}{2}\ln(2\pi e\sigma^2). \tag{4.115}$$

The entropy function and the differential entropy function differ in several fundamental ways. In the next section we will see that the entropy of a random variable has a very well defined operational interpretation as the average number of information bits required to specify the value of the random variable. Differential entropy does not possess this operational interpretation. In addition, the entropy function does not change when the random variable $X$ is mapped into $Y$ by an invertible transformation. Again, the differential entropy does not possess this property. (See Problems 4.153 and 4.160.) Nevertheless, the differential entropy does possess some useful properties. The differential entropy appears naturally in problems involving entropy reduction, as demonstrated in Problem 4.159. In addition, the relative entropy of continuous random variables, which is defined by

$$H(f_X; f_Y) = \int_{-\infty}^{\infty} f_X(x) \ln\frac{f_X(x)}{f_Y(x)} dx,$$

does not change under invertible transformations.

### 4.10.2    Entropy as a Measure of Information

Let $X$ be a discrete random variable with $S_X = \{1, 2, \ldots, K\}$ and pmf $p_k = P[X = k]$. Suppose that the experiment that produces $X$ is performed by John, and that he attempts to communicate the outcome to Mary by answering a series of yes/no questions. We are interested in characterizing the minimum average number of questions required to identify $X$.

### Example 4.65

An urn contains 16 balls: 4 balls are labeled "1", 4 are labeled "2", 2 are labeled "3", 2 are labeled "4", and the remaining balls are labeled "5", "6", "7", and "8." John picks a ball from the urn at random, and he notes the number. Discuss what strategies Mary can use to find out the number of the ball through a series of yes/no questions. Compare the average number of questions asked to the entropy of $X$.

If we let $X$ be the random variable denoting the number of the ball, then $S_X = \{1, 2, \ldots, 8\}$ and the pmf is $\boldsymbol{p} = (1/4, 1/4, 1/8, 1/8, 1/16, 1/16, 1/16, 1/16)$. We will compare the two strategies shown in Figs. 4.26(a) and (b).

The series of questions in Fig. 4.26(a) uses the fact that the probability of $\{X = k\}$ decreases with $k$. Thus it is reasonable to ask the question {"Was $X$ equal to 1?"}, {"Was $X$ equal to 2?"}, and so on, until the answer is yes. Let $L$ be the number of questions asked until the answer is yes, then the average number of questions asked is

$$E[L] = 1\left(\tfrac{1}{4}\right) + 2\left(\tfrac{1}{4}\right) + 3\left(\tfrac{1}{8}\right) + 4\left(\tfrac{1}{8}\right) + 5\left(\tfrac{1}{16}\right) + 6\left(\tfrac{1}{16}\right) + 7\left(\tfrac{1}{16}\right) + 7\left(\tfrac{1}{16}\right)$$

$$= 51/16.$$

The series of questions in Fig. 4.26(b) uses the observation made in Example 4.57 that yes/no questions should be designed so that the two answers are equiprobable. The questions in

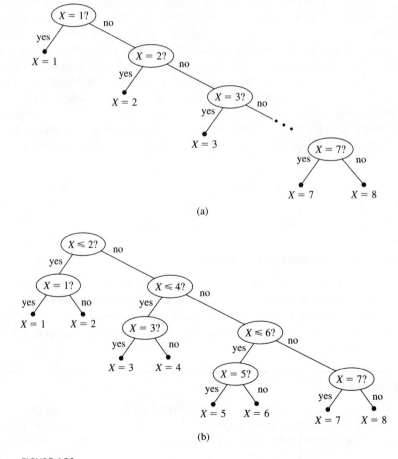

(a)

(b)

**FIGURE 4.26**
Two strategies for finding out the value of $X$ through a series of yes/no questions.

Fig. 4.26(b) meet this requirement. The average number of questions asked is

$$E[L] = 2\left(\tfrac{1}{4}\right) + 2\left(\tfrac{1}{4}\right) + 3\left(\tfrac{1}{8}\right) + 3\left(\tfrac{1}{8}\right) + 4\left(\tfrac{1}{16}\right) + 4\left(\tfrac{1}{16}\right) + 4\left(\tfrac{1}{16}\right) + 4\left(\tfrac{1}{16}\right)$$

$$= 44/16.$$

Thus the second series of questions has the better performance.

Finally, we find that the entropy of $X$ is

$$H_X = -\frac{1}{4}\log_2\frac{1}{4} - \frac{1}{4}\log_2\frac{1}{4} - \frac{1}{8}\log_2\frac{1}{8} - \cdots - \frac{1}{16}\log_2\frac{1}{16} = 44/16,$$

which is equal to the performance of the second series of questions.

---

The problem of designing the series of questions to identify the random variable $X$ is exactly the same as the problem of encoding the output of an information source. Each output of an information source is a random variable $X$, and the task of the encoder is to map each possible output into a unique string of binary digits. We can see this correspondence by taking the trees in Fig. 4.26 and identifying each yes/no answer with a 0/1. The sequence of 0's and 1's from the top node to each terminal node then defines the binary string ("codeword") for each outcome. It then follows that the problem of finding the best series of yes/no questions is the same as finding the binary tree code that minimizes the average codeword length.

In the remainder of this section we develop the following fundamental results from information theory. First, the average codeword length of *any* code cannot be less than the entropy. Second, if the pmf of $X$ consists of powers of 1/2, then there is a tree code that achieves the entropy. And finally, by encoding groups of outcomes of $X$ we can achieve average codeword length arbitrarily close to the entropy. Thus *the entropy of $X$ represents the minimum average number of bits required to establish the outcome of $X$.*

First, let's show that the average codeword length of *any* tree code cannot be less than the entropy. Note from Fig. 4.26 that the set of lengths $\{l_k\}$ of the codewords for every complete binary tree must satisfy

$$\sum_{k=1}^{K} 2^{-l_k} = 1. \tag{4.116}$$

To see this, extend the tree to the same depth as the longest codeword, as shown in Fig. 4.27. If we then "prune" the tree at a node of depth $l_k$, we remove a fraction $2^{-l_k}$ of the nodes at the bottom of the tree. Note that the converse result is also true: If a set of codeword lengths satisfies Eq. (4.116), then we can construct a tree code with these lengths.

Consider next the difference between the entropy and $E[L]$ for any binary tree code:

$$E[L] - H_X = \sum_{k=1}^{K} l_k P[X = k] + \sum_{k=1}^{K} P[X = k] \log_2 P[X = k]$$

$$= \sum_{k=1}^{K} P[X = k] \log_2 \frac{P[X = k]}{2^{-l_k}}, \tag{4.117}$$

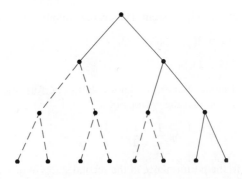

**FIGURE 4.27**
Extension of a binary tree code to a full tree.

where we have expressed the entropy in bits. Equation (4.17) is the relative entropy of Eq. (4.107) with $q_k = 2^{-l_k}$. Thus by Eq. (4.108)

$$E[L] \geq H_X \qquad \text{with equality iff} \qquad P[X = k] = 2^{-l_k}. \qquad (4.118)$$

Thus the average number of questions for *any* tree code (and in particular the *best* tree code) cannot be less than the entropy of $X$. Therefore we can use the entropy $H_X$ as a baseline against which to test any code.

Equation (4.118) also implies that if the outcomes of $X$ all have probabilities that are integer powers of 1/2 (as in Example 4.63), then we can find a tree code that achieves the entropy. If $P[X = k] = 2^{-l_k}$, then we assign the outcome $k$ a binary codeword of length $l_k$. We can show that we can always find a tree code with these lengths by using the fact that the probabilities add to one, and hence the codeword lengths satisfy Eq. (4.116). Equation (4.118) then implies that $E[L] = H$.

It is clear that Eq. (4.117) will be nonzero if the $p_k$'s are not integer powers of 1/2. Thus in general the best tree code does not always have $E[L] = H_X$. However, it is possible to show that the approach of grouping outcomes into sets that are approximately equiprobable leads to tree codes with lengths that are close to the entropy. Furthermore, by encoding vectors of outcomes of $X$, it is possible to obtain average codeword lengths that are arbitrarily close to the entropy. Problem 4.165 discusses how this is done.

We have now reached our objective of showing that the entropy of a random variable $X$ represents the minimum average number of bits required to identify its value. Before proceeding, let's reconsider continuous random variables. A continuous random variable can assume values from an uncountably infinite set, so in general an infinite number of bits is required to specify its value. Thus, the interpretation of entropy as the average number of bits required to specify a random variable immediately implies that continuous random variables have infinite entropy. This implies that any representation of a continuous random variable that uses a finite number of bits will inherently involve some approximation error.

### 4.10.3    The Method of Maximum Entropy

Let $X$ be a random variable with $S_X = \{x_1, x_2, \ldots, x_K\}$ and unknown pmf $p_k = P[X = x_k]$. Suppose that we are asked to estimate the pmf of $X$ given the expected value of some function $g(X)$ of $X$:

$$\sum_{k=1}^{K} g(x_k) P[X = x_k] = c. \tag{4.119}$$

For example, if $g(X) = X$ then $c = E[g(X)] = E[X]$, and if $g(X) = (X - E[X])^2$ then $c = \text{VAR}[X]$. Clearly, this problem is underdetermined since knowledge of these parameters is not sufficient to specify the pmf uniquely. The **method of maximum entropy** approaches this problem by seeking the pmf that maximizes the entropy subject to the constraint in Eq. (4.119).

Suppose we set up this maximization problem by using Lagrange multipliers:

$$H_X + \lambda\left(\sum_{k=1}^{K} P[X = x_k]g(x_k) - c\right) = -\sum_{k=1}^{K} P[X = x_k] \ln\frac{P[X = x_k]}{Ce^{-\lambda g(x_k)}}, \tag{4.120}$$

where $C = e^c$. Note that if $\{Ce^{-\lambda g(x_k)}\}$ forms a pmf, then the above expression is the negative value of the relative entropy of this pmf with respect to $\boldsymbol{p}$. Equation (4.108) then implies that the expression in Eq. (4.120) is always less than or equal to zero with equality iff $P[X = x_k] = Ce^{-\lambda g(x_k)}$. We now show that this does indeed lead to the maximum entropy solution.

Suppose that the random variable $X$ has pmf $p_k = Ce^{-\lambda g(x_k)}$, where $C$ and $\lambda$ are chosen so that Eq. (4.119) is satisfied and so that $\{p_k\}$ is a pmf. $X$ then has entropy

$$H_X = E[-\ln P[X]] = [-\ln Ce^{-\lambda g(x_k)}] = -\ln C + \lambda E[g(X)]$$

$$= -\ln C + \lambda c. \tag{4.121}$$

Now let's compare the entropy in Eq. (4.121) to that of some other pmf $q_k$ that also satisfies the constraint in Eq. (4.119). Consider the relative entropy of $\boldsymbol{p}$ with respect to $\boldsymbol{q}$:

$$0 \leq H(\boldsymbol{q}; \boldsymbol{p}) = \sum_{k=1}^{K} q_k \ln\frac{q_k}{p_k} = \sum_{k=1}^{K} q_k \ln q_k + \sum_{k=1}^{K} q_k(-\ln C + \lambda g(x_k))$$

$$= -\ln C + \lambda c - H(q) = H_X - H(q). \tag{4.122}$$

Thus $H_X \geq H(\boldsymbol{q})$, and $\boldsymbol{p}$ achieves the highest entropy.

---

### Example 4.66

Let $X$ be a random variable with $S_X = \{0, 1, \ldots\}$ and expected value $E[X] = m$. Find the pmf of $X$ that maximizes the entropy.

In this example $g(X) = X$, so

$$p_k = Ce^{-\lambda k} = C\alpha^k,$$

where $\alpha = e^{-\lambda}$. Clearly, $X$ is a geometric random variable with mean $m = \alpha/(1 - \alpha)$ and thus $\alpha = m/(m + 1)$. It then follows that $C = 1 - \alpha = 1/(m + 1)$.

When dealing with continuous random variables, the method of maximum entropy maximizes the differential entropy:

$$-\int_{-\infty}^{\infty} f_X(x) \ln f_X(x) \, dx. \tag{4.123}$$

The parameter information is in the form

$$c = E[g(X)] = \int_{-\infty}^{\infty} g(x) f_X(x) \, dx. \tag{4.124}$$

The relative entropy expression in Eq. (4.115) and the approach used for discrete random variables can be used to show that the pdf $f_X(x)$ that maximizes the differential entropy will have the form

$$f_X(x) = Ce^{-\lambda g(x)}, \tag{4.125}$$

where $C$ and $\lambda$ must be chosen so that Eq. (4.125) integrates to one and so that Eq. (4.124) is satisfied.

**Example 4.67**

Suppose that the continuous random variable $X$ has known variance $\sigma^2 = E[(X - m)^2]$, where the mean $m$ is not specified. Find the pdf that maximizes the entropy of $X$.

Equation (4.125) implies that the pdf has the form

$$f_X(x) = Ce^{-\lambda(x-m)^2}.$$

We can meet the constraint in Eq. (4.124) by picking

$$\lambda = \frac{1}{2\sigma^2} \qquad C = \frac{1}{\sqrt{2\pi\sigma^2}}.$$

We thus obtain a Gaussian pdf with variance $\sigma^2$. Note that the mean $m$ is arbitrary; that is, any choice of $m$ yields a pdf that maximizes the differential entropy.

The method of maximum entropy can be extended to the case where several parameters of the random variable $X$ are known. It can also be extended to the case of vectors and sequences of random variables.

**SUMMARY**

- The cumulative distribution function $F_X(x)$ is the probability that $X$ falls in the interval $(-\infty, x]$. The probability of any event consisting of the union of intervals can be expressed in terms of the cdf.

- A random variable is continuous if its cdf can be written as the integral of a nonnegative function. A random variable is mixed if it is a mixture of a discrete and a continuous random variable.

- The probability of events involving a continuous random variable $X$ can be expressed as integrals of the probability density function $f_X(x)$.

- If $X$ is a random variable, then $Y = g(X)$ is also a random variable. The notion of equivalent events allows us to derive expressions for the cdf and pdf of $Y$ in terms of the cdf and pdf of $X$.

- The cdf and pdf of the random variable $X$ are sufficient to compute all probabilities involving $X$ alone. The mean, variance, and moments of a random variable summarize some of the information about the random variable $X$. These parameters are useful in practice because they are easier to measure and estimate than the cdf and pdf.

- Conditional cdf's or pdf's incorporate partial knowledge about the outcome of an experiment in the calculation of probabilities of events.

- The Markov and Chebyshev inequalities allow us to bound probabilities involving $X$ in terms of its first two moments only.

- Transforms provide an alternative but equivalent representation of the pmf and pdf. In certain types of problems it is preferable to work with the transforms rather than the pmf or pdf. The moments of a random variable can be obtained from the corresponding transform.

- The reliability of a system is the probability that it is still functioning after $t$ hours of operation. The reliability of a system can be determined from the reliability of its subsystems.

- There are a number of methods for generating random variables with prescribed pmf's or pdf's in terms of a random variable that is uniformly distributed in the unit interval. These methods include the transformation and the rejection methods as well as methods that simulate random experiments (e.g., functions of random variables) and mixtures of random variables.

- The entropy of a random variable $X$ is a measure of the uncertainty of $X$ in terms of the average amount of information required to identify its value.

- The maximum entropy method is a procedure for estimating the pmf or pdf of a random variable when only partial information about $X$, in the form of expected values of functions of $X$, is available.

## CHECKLIST OF IMPORTANT TERMS

Characteristic function
Chebyshev inequality
Chernoff bound
Conditional cdf, pdf
Continuous random variable
Cumulative distribution function
Differential entropy
Discrete random variable
Entropy
Equivalent event
Expected value of $X$
Failure rate function
Function of a random variable
Laplace transform of the pdf
Markov inequality

Maximum entropy method
Mean time to failure (MTTF)
Moment theorem
$n$th moment of $X$
Probability density function
Probability generating function
Probability mass function
Random variable
Random variable of mixed type
Rejection method
Reliability
Standard deviation of $X$
Transformation method
Variance of $X$

## ANNOTATED REFERENCES

Reference [1] is the standard reference for electrical engineers for the material on random variables. Reference [2] is entirely devoted to continuous distributions. Reference [3] discusses some of the finer points regarding the concept of a random variable at a level accessible to students of this course. Reference [4] presents detailed discussions of the various methods for generating random numbers with specified distributions. Reference [5] also discusses the generation of random variables. Reference [9] is focused on signal processing. Reference [11] discusses entropy in the context of information theory.

1. A. Papoulis and S. Pillai, *Probability, Random Variables, and Stochastic Processes*, McGraw-Hill, New York, 2002.
2. N. Johnson et al., *Continuous Univariate Distributions*, vol. 2, Wiley, New York, 1995.
3. K. L. Chung, *Elementary Probability Theory*, Springer-Verlag, New York, 1974.
4. A. M. Law and W. D. Kelton, *Simulation Modeling and Analysis*, McGraw-Hill, New York, 2000.
5. S. M. Ross, *Introduction to Probability Models*, Academic Press, New York, 2003.
6. H. Cramer, *Mathematical Methods of Statistics*, Princeton University Press, Princeton, N.J., 1946.
7. M. Abramowitz and I. Stegun, *Handbook of Mathematical Functions*, National Bureau of Standards, Washington, D.C., 1964. Downloadable: *www.math.sfu.ca/~cbm/aands/*.
8. R. C. Cheng, "The Generation of Gamma Variables with Nonintegral Shape Parameter," *Appl. Statist.*, 26: 71–75, 1977.
9. R. Gray and L.D. Davisson, *An Introduction to Statistical Signal Processing*, Cambridge Univ. Press, Cambridge, UK, 2005.

10. P. O. Börjesson and C. E. W. Sundberg, "Simple Approximations of the Error Function $Q(x)$ for Communications Applications," *IEEE Trans. on Communications*, March 1979, 639–643.

11. R. G. Gallager, *Information Theory and Reliable Communication*, Wiley, New York, 1968.

## PROBLEMS

### Section 4.1: The Cumulative Distribution Function

**4.1.** An information source produces binary pairs that we designate as $S_X = \{1, 2, 3, 4\}$ with the following pmf's:

    **(i)** $p_k = p_1/k$ for all $k$ in $S_X$.

    **(ii)** $p_{k+1} = p_k/2$ for $k = 2, 3, 4$.

    **(iii)** $p_{k+1} = p_k/2^k$ for $k = 2, 3, 4$.

    **(a)** Plot the cdf of these three random variables.

    **(b)** Use the cdf to find the probability of the events: $\{X \le 1\}, \{X < 2.5\}, \{0.5 < X \le 2\}, \{1 < X < 4\}$.

**4.2.** A die is tossed. Let $X$ be the number of full pairs of dots in the face showing up, and $Y$ be the number of full or partial pairs of dots in the face showing up. Find and plot the cdf of $X$ and $Y$.

**4.3.** The loose minute hand of a clock is spun hard. The coordinates $(x, y)$ of the point where the tip of the hand comes to rest is noted. $Z$ is defined as the sgn function of the product of $x$ and $y$, where $\text{sgn}(t)$ is 1 if $t > 0$, 0 if $t = 0$, and $-1$ if $t < 0$.

    **(a)** Find and plot the cdf of the random variable $X$.

    **(b)** Does the cdf change if the clock hand has a propensity to stop at 3, 6, 9, and 12 o'clock?

**4.4.** An urn contains 8 \$1 bills and two \$5 bills. Let $X$ be the total amount that results when two bills are drawn from the urn without replacement, and let $Y$ be the total amount that results when two bills are drawn from the urn *with* replacement.

    **(a)** Plot and compare the cdf's of the random variables.

    **(b)** Use the cdf to compare the probabilities of the following events in the two problems: $\{X = \$2\}, \{X < \$7\}, \{X \ge 6\}$.

**4.5.** Let $Y$ be the difference between the number of heads and the number of tails in the 3 tosses of a fair coin.

    **(a)** Plot the cdf of the random variable $Y$.

    **(b)** Express $P[|Y| < y]$ in terms of the cdf of $Y$.

**4.6.** A dart is equally likely to land at any point inside a circular target of radius 2. Let $R$ be the distance of the landing point from the origin.

    **(a)** Find the sample space $S$ and the sample space of $R, S_R$.

    **(b)** Show the mapping from $S$ to $S_R$.

    **(c)** The "bull's eye" is the central disk in the target of radius 0.25. Find the event $A$ in $S_R$ corresponding to "dart hits the bull's eye." Find the equivalent event in $S$ and $P[A]$.

    **(d)** Find and plot the cdf of $R$.

**4.7.** A point is selected at random inside a square defined by $\{(x, y): 0 \le x \le b, 0 \le y \le b\}$. Assume the point is equally likely to fall anywhere in the square. Let the random variable $Z$ be given by the minimum of the two coordinates of the point where the dart lands.

    **(a)** Find the sample space $S$ and the sample space of $Z, S_Z$.

**(b)** Show the mapping from $S$ to $S_Z$.

**(c)** Find the region in the square corresponding to the event $\{Z \leq z\}$.

**(d)** Find and plot the cdf of $Z$.

**(e)** Use the cdf to find: $P[Z > 0], P[Z > b], P[Z \leq b/2], P[Z > b/4]$.

**4.8.** Let $\zeta$ be a point selected at random from the unit interval. Consider the random variable $X = (1 - \zeta)^{-1/2}$.

**(a)** Sketch $X$ as a function of $\zeta$.

**(b)** Find and plot the cdf of $X$.

**(c)** Find the probability of the events $\{X > 1\}, \{5 < X < 7\}, \{X \leq 20\}$.

**4.9.** The loose hand of a clock is spun hard and the outcome $\zeta$ is the angle in the range $[0, 2\pi)$ where the hand comes to rest. Consider the random variable $\zeta = 2 \sin(\zeta/4)$.

**(a)** Sketch $X$ as a function of $\zeta$.

**(b)** Find and plot the cdf of $X$.

**(c)** Find the probability of the events $\{X > 1\}, \{-1/2 < X < 1/2\}, \{X \leq 1/\sqrt{2}\}$.

**4.10.** Repeat Problem 4.9 if 80% of the time the hand comes to rest anywhere in the circle, but 20% of the time the hand comes to rest at 3, 6, 9, or 12 o'clock.

**4.11.** The random variable $X$ is uniformly distributed in the interval $[-1, 2]$.

**(a)** Find and plot the cdf of $X$.

**(b)** Use the cdf to find the probabilities of the following events: $\{X \leq 0\}$, $\{|X - 0.5| < 1\}$, and $C = \{X > -0.5\}$.

**4.12.** The cdf of the random variable $X$ is given by:

$$F_X(x) = \begin{cases} 0 & x < -1 \\ 0.5 & -1 \leq x \leq 0 \\ (1 + x)/2 & 0 \leq x \leq 1 \\ 1 & x \geq 1. \end{cases}$$

**(a)** Plot the cdf and identify the type of random variable.

**(b)** Find $P[X \leq -1], P[X = -1], P[X < 0.5], P[-0.5 < X < 0.5], P[X > -1]$, $P[X \leq 2], P[X > 3]$.

**4.13.** A random variable $X$ has cdf:

$$F_X(x) = \begin{cases} 0 & \text{for } x < 0 \\ 1 - \dfrac{1}{4}e^{-2x} & \text{for } x \geq 0. \end{cases}$$

**(a)** Plot the cdf and identify the type of random variable.

**(b)** Find $P[X \leq 2], P[X = 0], P[X < 0], P[2 < X < 6], P[X > 10]$.

**4.14.** The random variable $X$ has cdf shown in Fig. P4.1.

**(a)** What type of random variable is $X$?

**(b)** Find the following probabilities: $P[X < -1], P[X \leq -1], P[-1 < X < -0.75]$, $P[-0.5 \leq X < 0], P[-0.5 \leq X \leq 0.5], P[|X - 0.5| < 0.5]$.

**4.15.** For $\beta > 0$ and $\lambda > 0$, the Weibull random variable $Y$ has cdf:

$$F_X(x) = \begin{cases} 0 & \text{for } x < 0 \\ 1 - e^{-(x/\lambda)^\beta} & \text{for } x \geq 0. \end{cases}$$

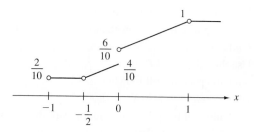

**FIGURE P4.1**

  **(a)**  Plot the cdf of $Y$ for $\beta = 0.5, 1$, and 2.
  **(b)**  Find the probability $P[j\lambda < X < (j + 1)\lambda]$ and $P[X > j\lambda]$.
  **(c)**  Plot $\log P[X > x]$ vs. $\log x$.
**4.16.**  The random variable $X$ has cdf:

$$F_X(x) = \begin{cases} 0 & x < 0 \\ 0.5 + c\,\sin^2(\pi x/2) & 0 \le x \le 1 \\ 1 & x > 1. \end{cases}$$

  **(a)**  What values can $c$ assume?
  **(b)**  Plot the cdf.
  **(c)**  Find $P[X > 0]$.

## Section 4.2:  The Probability Density Function

**4.17.**  A random variable $X$ has pdf:

$$f_X(x) = \begin{cases} c(1 - x^2) & -1 \le x \le 1 \\ 0 & \text{elsewhere.} \end{cases}$$

  **(a)**  Find $c$ and plot the pdf.
  **(b)**  Plot the cdf of $X$.
  **(c)**  Find $P[X = 0]$, $P[0 < X < 0.5]$, and $P[|X - 0.5| < 0.25]$.
**4.18.**  A random variable $X$ has pdf:

$$f_X(x) = \begin{cases} cx(1 - x^2) & 0 \le x \le 1 \\ 0 & \text{elsewhere.} \end{cases}$$

  **(a)**  Find $c$ and plot the pdf.
  **(b)**  Plot the cdf of $X$.
  **(c)**  Find $P[0 < X < 0.5]$, $P[X = 1]$, $P[.25 < X < 0.5]$.
**4.19. (a)**  In Problem 4.6, find and plot the pdf of the random variable $R$, the distance from the dart to the center of the target.
  **(b)**  Use the pdf to find the probability that the dart is outside the bull's eye.
**4.20. (a)**  Find and plot the pdf of the random variable $Z$ in Problem 4.7.
  **(b)**  Use the pdf to find the probability that the minimum is greater than $b/3$.

**4.21. (a)** Find and plot the pdf in Problem 4.8.

   **(b)** Use the pdf to find the probabilities of the events: $\{X > a\}$ and $\{X > 2a\}$.

**4.22. (a)** Find and plot the pdf in Problem 4.12.

   **(b)** Use the pdf to find $P[-1 \le X < 0.25]$.

**4.23. (a)** Find and plot the pdf in Problem 4.13.

   **(b)** Use the pdf to find $P[X = 0]$, $P[X > 8]$.

**4.24. (a)** Find and plot the pdf of the random variable in Problem 4.14.

   **(b)** Use the pdf to calculate the probabilities in Problem 4.14b.

**4.25.** Find and plot the pdf of the Weibull random variable in Problem 4.15a.

**4.26.** Find the cdf of the Cauchy random variable which has pdf:

$$f_X(x) = \frac{\alpha/\pi}{x^2 + \alpha^2} \quad -\infty < x < \infty.$$

**4.27.** A voltage $X$ is uniformly distributed in the set $\{-3, -2, \ldots, 3, 4\}$.

   **(a)** Find the pdf and cdf of the random variable $X$.

   **(b)** Find the pdf and cdf of the random variable $Y = -2X^2 + 3$.

   **(c)** Find the pdf and cdf of the random variable $W = \cos(\pi X/8)$.

   **(d)** Find the pdf and cdf of the random variable $Z = \cos^2(\pi X/8)$.

**4.28.** Find the pdf and cdf of the Zipf random variable in Problem 3.70.

**4.29.** Let $C$ be an event for which $P[C] > 0$. Show that $F_X(x|C)$ satisfies the eight properties of a cdf.

**4.30. (a)** In Problem 4.13, find $F_X(x|C)$ where $C = \{X > 0\}$.

   **(b)** Find $F_X(x|C)$ where $C = \{X = 0\}$.

**4.31. (a)** In Problem 4.10, find $F_X(x|B)$ where $B = \{$hand does not stop at $3, 6, 9,$ or $12$ o'clock$\}$.

   **(b)** Find $F_X(x|B^c)$.

**4.32.** In Problem 4.13, find $f_X(x|B)$ and $F_X(x|B)$ where $B = \{X > 0.25\}$.

**4.33.** Let $X$ be the exponential random variable.

   **(a)** Find and plot $F_X(x|X > t)$. How does $F_X(x|X > t)$ differ from $F_X(x)$?

   **(b)** Find and plot $f_X(x|X > t)$.

   **(c)** Show that $P[X > t + x|X > t] = P[X > x]$. Explain why this is called the memoryless property.

**4.34.** The Pareto random variable $X$ has cdf:

$$F_X(x) = \begin{cases} 0 & x < x_m \\ 1 - \dfrac{x_m^\alpha}{x^\alpha} & x \ge x_m. \end{cases}$$

   **(a)** Find and plot the pdf of $X$.

   **(b)** Repeat Problem 4.33 parts a and b for the Pareto random variable.

   **(c)** What happens to $P[X > t + x|X > t]$ as $t$ becomes large? Interpret this result.

**4.35. (a)** Find and plot $F_X(x|a \le X \le b)$. Compare $F_X(x|a \le X \le b)$ to $F_X(x)$.

   **(b)** Find and plot $f_X(x|a \le X \le b)$.

**4.36.** In Problem 4.6, find $F_R(r|R > 1)$ and $f_R(r|R > 1)$.

**4.37. (a)** In Problem 4.7, find $F_Z(z \mid b/4 \leq Z \leq b/2)$ and $f_Z(z \mid b/4 \leq Z \leq b/2)$.

**(b)** Find $F_Z(z \mid B)$ and $f_Z(z \mid B)$, where $B = \{x > b/2\}$.

**4.38.** A binary transmission system sends a "0" bit using a $-1$ voltage signal and a "1" bit by transmitting a $+1$. The received signal is corrupted by noise $N$ that has a Laplacian distribution with parameter $\alpha$. Assume that "0" bits and "1" bits are equiprobable.

**(a)** Find the pdf of the received signal $Y = X + N$, where $X$ is the transmitted signal, given that a "0" was transmitted; that a "1" was transmitted.

**(b)** Suppose that the receiver decides a "0" was sent if $Y < 0$, and a "1" was sent if $Y \geq 0$. What is the probability that the receiver makes an error given that a $+1$ was transmitted? a $-1$ was transmitted?

**(c)** What is the overall probability of error?

## Section 4.3: The Expected Value of $X$

**4.39.** Find the mean and variance of $X$ in Problem 4.17.

**4.40.** Find the mean and variance of $X$ in Problem 4.18.

**4.41.** Find the mean and variance of $Y$, the distance from the dart to the origin, in Problem 4.19.

**4.42.** Find the mean and variance of $Z$, the minimum of the coordinates in a square, in Problem 4.20.

**4.43.** Find the mean and variance of $X = (1 - \zeta)^{-1/2}$ in Problem 4.21. Find $E[X]$ using Eq. (4.28).

**4.44.** Find the mean and variance of $X$ in Problems 4.12 and 4.22.

**4.45.** Find the mean and variance of $X$ in Problems 4.13 and 4.23. Find $E[X]$ using Eq. (4.28).

**4.46.** Find the mean and variance of the Gaussian random variable by direct integration of Eqs. (4.27) and (4.34).

**4.47.** Prove Eqs. (4.28) and (4.29).

**4.48.** Find the variance of the exponential random variable.

**4.49. (a)** Show that the mean of the Weibull random variable in Problem 4.15 is $\Gamma(1 + 1/\beta)$ where $\Gamma(x)$ is the gamma function defined in Eq. (4.56).

**(b)** Find the second moment and the variance of the Weibull random variable.

**4.50.** Explain why the mean of the Cauchy random variable does not exist.

**4.51.** Show that $E[X]$ does not exist for the Pareto random variable with $\alpha = 1$ and $x_m = 1$.

**4.52.** Verify Eqs. (4.36), (4.37), and (4.38).

**4.53.** Let $Y = A \cos(\omega t) + c$ where $A$ has mean $m$ and variance $\sigma^2$ and $\omega$ and $c$ are constants. Find the mean and variance of $Y$. Compare the results to those obtained in Example 4.15.

**4.54.** A limiter is shown in Fig. P4.2.

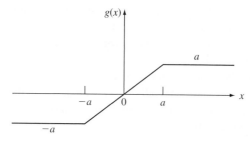

**FIGURE P4.2**

(a) Find an expression for the mean and variance of $Y = g(X)$ for an arbitrary continuous random variable $X$.

(b) Evaluate the mean and variance if $X$ is a Laplacian random variable with $\lambda = a = 1$.

(c) Repeat part (b) if $X$ is from Problem 4.17 with $a = 1/2$.

(d) Evaluate the mean and variance if $X = U^3$ where $U$ is a uniform random variable in the unit interval, $[-1, 1]$ and $a = 1/2$.

**4.55.** A limiter with center-level clipping is shown in Fig. P4.3.

(a) Find an expression for the mean and variance of $Y = g(X)$ for an arbitrary continuous random variable $X$.

(b) Evaluate the mean and variance if $X$ is Laplacian with $\lambda = a = 1$ and $b = 2$.

(c) Repeat part (b) if $X$ is from Problem 4.22, $a = 1/2, b = 3/2$.

(d) Evaluate the mean and variance if $X = b \cos(2\pi U)$ where $U$ is a uniform random variable in the unit interval $[-1, 1]$ and $a = 3/4, b = 1/2$.

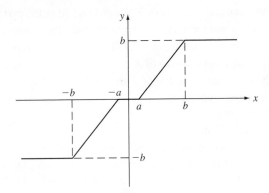

**FIGURE P4.3**

**4.56.** Let $Y = 3X + 2$.

(a) Find the mean and variance of $Y$ in terms of the mean and variance of $X$.

(b) Evaluate the mean and variance of $Y$ if $X$ is Laplacian.

(c) Evaluate the mean and variance of $Y$ if $X$ is an arbitrary Gaussian random variable.

(d) Evaluate the mean and variance of $Y$ if $X = b \cos(2\pi U)$ where $U$ is a uniform random variable in the unit interval.

**4.57.** Find the $n$th moment of $U$, the uniform random variable in the unit interval. Repeat for $X$ uniform in $[a, b]$.

**4.58.** Consider the quantizer in Example 4.20.

(a) Find the conditional pdf of $X$ given that $X$ is in the interval $(d, 2d)$.

(b) Find the conditional expected value and conditional variance of $X$ given that $X$ is in the interval $(d, 2d)$.

(c) Now suppose that when $X$ falls in $(d, 2d)$, it is mapped onto the point $c$ where $d < c < 2d$. Find an expression for the expected value of the mean square error: $E[(X - c)^2 | d < X < 2d]$.

(d) Find the value $c$ that minimizes the above mean square error. Is $c$ the midpoint of the interval? Explain why or why not by sketching possible conditional pdf shapes.

(e) Find an expression for the overall mean square error using the approach in parts c and d.

## Section 4.4: Important Continuous Random Variables

**4.59.** Let $X$ be a uniform random variable in the interval $[-2, 2]$. Find and plot $P[|X| > x]$.

**4.60.** In Example 4.20, let the input to the quantizer be a uniform random variable in the interval $[-4d, 4d]$. Show that $Z = X - Q(X)$ is uniformly distributed in $[-d/2, d/2]$.

**4.61.** Let $X$ be an exponential random variable with parameter $\lambda$.

(a) For $d > 0$ and $k$ a nonnegative integer, find $P[kd < X < (k + 1)d]$.

(b) Segment the positive real line into four equiprobable disjoint intervals.

**4.62.** The $r$th percentile, $\pi(r)$, of a random variable $X$ is defined by $P[X \leq \pi(r)] = r/100$.

(a) Find the 90%, 95%, and 99% percentiles of the exponential random variable with parameter $\lambda$.

(b) Repeat part a for the Gaussian random variable with parameters $m = 0$ and $\sigma^2$.

**4.63.** Let $X$ be a Gaussian random variable with $m = 5$ and $\sigma^2 = 16$.

(a) Find $P[X > 4]$, $P[X \geq 7]$, $P[6.72 < X < 10.16]$, $P[2 < X < 7]$, $P[6 \leq X \leq 8]$.

(b) $P[X < a] = 0.8869$, find $a$.

(c) $P[X > b] = 0.11131$, find $b$.

(d) $P[13 < X \leq c] = 0.0123$, find $c$.

**4.64.** Show that the $Q$-function for the Gaussian random variable satisfies $Q(-x) = 1 - Q(x)$.

**4.65.** Use Octave to generate Tables 4.2 and 4.3.

**4.66.** Let $X$ be a Gaussian random variable with mean $m$ and variance $\sigma^2$.

(a) Find $P[X \leq m]$.

(b) Find $P[|X - m| < k\sigma]$, for $k = 1, 2, 3, 4, 5, 6$.

(c) Find the value of $k$ for which $Q(k) = P[X > m + k\sigma] = 10^{-j}$ for $j = 1, 2, 3, 4, 5, 6$.

**4.67.** A binary transmission system transmits a signal $X$ ($-1$ to send a "0" bit; $+1$ to send a "1" bit). The received signal is $Y = X + N$ where noise $N$ has a zero-mean Gaussian distribution with variance $\sigma^2$. Assume that "0" bits are three times as likely as "1" bits.

(a) Find the conditional pdf of $Y$ given the input value: $f_Y(y | X = +1)$ and $f_Y(y | X = -1)$.

(b) The receiver decides a "0" was transmitted if the observed value of $y$ satisfies

$$f_Y(y | X = -1)P[X = -1] > f_Y(y | X = +1)P[X = +1]$$

and it decides a "1" was transmitted otherwise. Use the results from part a to show that this decision rule is equivalent to: If $y < T$ decide "0"; if $y \geq T$ decide "1".

(c) What is the probability that the receiver makes an error given that a $+1$ was transmitted? a $-1$ was transmitted? Assume $\sigma^2 = 1/16$.

(d) What is the overall probability of error?

**4.68.** Two chips are being considered for use in a certain system. The lifetime of chip 1 is modeled by a Gaussian random variable with mean 20,000 hours and standard deviation 5000 hours. (The probability of negative lifetime is negligible.) The lifetime of chip 2 is also a Gaussian random variable but with mean 22,000 hours and standard deviation 1000 hours. Which chip is preferred if the target lifetime of the system is 20,000 hours? 24,000 hours?

**4.69.** Passengers arrive at a taxi stand at an airport at a rate of one passenger per minute. The taxi driver will not leave until seven passengers arrive to fill his van. Suppose that passenger interarrival times are exponential random variable, and let $X$ be the time to fill a van. Find the probability that more than 10 minutes elapse until the van is full.

**4.70. (a)** Show that the gamma random variable has mean:

$$E[X] = \alpha/\lambda.$$

**(b)** Show that the gamma random variable has second moment, and variance given by:

$$E[X^2] = \alpha(\alpha + 1)/\lambda^2 \text{ and } \text{VAR}[X] = \alpha/\lambda^2.$$

**(c)** Use parts a and b to obtain the mean and variance of an $m$-Erlang random variable.

**(d)** Use parts a and b to obtain the mean and variance of a chi-square random variable.

**4.71.** The time $X$ to complete a transaction in a system is a gamma random variable with mean 4 and variance 8. Use Octave to plot $P[X > x]$ as a function of $x$. Note: Octave uses $\beta = 1/2$.

**4.72. (a)** Plot the pdf of an $m$-Erlang random variable for $m = 1, 2, 3$ and $\lambda = 1$.

**(b)** Plot the chi-square pdf for $k = 1, 2, 3$.

**4.73.** A repair person keeps four widgets in stock. What is the probability that the widgets in stock will last 15 days if the repair person needs to replace widgets at an average rate of one widget every three days, where the time between widget failures is an exponential random variable?

**4.74. (a)** Find the cdf of the $m$-Erlang random variable by integration of the pdf. *Hint:* Use integration by parts.

**(b)** Show that the derivative of the cdf given by Eq. (4.58) gives the pdf of an $m$-Erlang random variable.

**4.75.** Plot the pdf of a beta random variable with: $a = b = 1/4, 1, 4, 8$; $a = 5, b = 1$; $a = 1, b = 3$; $a = 2, b = 5$.

## Section 4.5: Functions of a Random Variable

**4.76.** Let $X$ be a Gaussian random variable with mean 2 and variance 4. The reward in a system is given by $Y = (X)^+$. Find the pdf of $Y$.

**4.77.** The amplitude of a radio signal $X$ is a Rayleigh random variable with pdf:

$$f_X(x) = \frac{x}{\alpha^2} e^{-x^2/2\alpha^2} \qquad x > 0, \quad \alpha > 0.$$

**(a)** Find the pdf of $Z = (X - r)^+$.

**(b)** Find the pdf of $Z = X^2$.

**4.78.** A wire has length $X$, an exponential random variable with mean $5\pi$ cm. The wire is cut to make rings of diameter 1 cm. Find the probability for the number of complete rings produced by each length of wire.

**4.79.** A signal that has amplitudes with a Gaussian pdf with zero mean and unit variance is applied to the quantizer in Example 4.27.

    **(a)** Pick $d$ so that the probability that $X$ falls outside the range of the quantizer is 1%.

    **(b)** Find the probability of the output levels of the quantizer.

**4.80.** The signal $X$ is amplified and shifted as follows: $Y = 2X + 3$, where $X$ is the random variable in Problem 4.12. Find the cdf and pdf of $Y$.

**4.81.** The net profit in a transaction is given by $Y = 2 - 4X$ where $X$ is the random variable in Problem 4.13. Find the cdf and pdf of $Y$.

**4.82.** Find the cdf and pdf of the output of the limiter in Problem 4.54 parts b, c, and d.

**4.83.** Find the cdf and pdf of the output of the limiter with center-level clipping in Problem 4.55 parts b, c, and d.

**4.84.** Find the cdf and pdf of $Y = 3X + 2$ in Problem 4.56 parts b, c, and d.

**4.85.** The exam grades in a certain class have a Gaussian pdf with mean $m$ and standard deviation $\sigma$. Find the constants $a$ and $b$ so that the random variable $y = aX + b$ has a Gaussian pdf with mean $m'$ and standard deviation $\sigma'$.

**4.86.** Let $X = U^n$ where $n$ is a positive integer and $U$ is a uniform random variable in the unit interval. Find the cdf and pdf of $X$.

**4.87.** Repeat Problem 4.86 if $U$ is uniform in the interval $[-1, 1]$.

**4.88.** Let $Y = |X|$ be the output of a full-wave rectifier with input voltage $X$.

    **(a)** Find the cdf of $Y$ by finding the equivalent event of $\{Y \le y\}$. Find the pdf of $Y$ by differentiation of the cdf.

    **(b)** Find the pdf of $Y$ by finding the equivalent event of $\{y < Y \le y + dy\}$. Does the answer agree with part a?

    **(c)** What is the pdf of $Y$ if the $f_X(x)$ is an even function of $x$?

**4.89.** Find and plot the cdf of $Y$ in Example 4.34.

**4.90.** A voltage $X$ is a Gaussian random variable with mean 1 and variance 2. Find the pdf of the power dissipated by an $R$-ohm resistor $P = RX^2$.

**4.91.** Let $Y = e^X$.

    **(a)** Find the cdf and pdf of $Y$ in terms of the cdf and pdf of $X$.

    **(b)** Find the pdf of $Y$ when $X$ is a Gaussian random variable. In this case $Y$ is said to be a lognormal random variable. Plot the pdf and cdf of $Y$ when $X$ is zero-mean with variance 1/8; repeat with variance 8.

**4.92.** Let a radius be given by the random variable $X$ in Problem 4.18.

    **(a)** Find the pdf of the area covered by a disc with radius $X$.

    **(b)** Find the pdf of the volume of a sphere with radius $X$.

    **(c)** Find the pdf of the volume of a sphere in $R^n$:

$$Y = \begin{cases} (2\pi)^{(n-1)/2} X^n/(2 \times 4 \times \cdots \times n) & \text{for } n \text{ even} \\ 2(2\pi)^{(n-1)/2} X^n/(1 \times 3 \times \cdots \times n) & \text{for } n \text{ odd.} \end{cases}$$

**4.93.** In the quantizer in Example 4.20, let $Z = X - q(X)$. Find the pdf of $Z$ if $X$ is a Laplacian random variable with parameter $\alpha = d/2$.

**4.94.** Let $Y = \alpha \tan \pi X$, where $X$ is uniformly distributed in the interval $(-1, 1)$.

    **(a)** Show that $Y$ is a Cauchy random variable.

    **(b)** Find the pdf of $Y = 1/X$.

**4.95.** Let $X$ be a Weibull random variable in Problem 4.15. Let $Y = (X/\lambda)^\beta$. Find the cdf and pdf of $Y$.

**4.96.** Find the pdf of $X = -\ln(1 - U)$, where $U$ is a uniform random variable in $(0, 1)$.

### Section 4.6: The Markov and Chebyshev Inequalities

**4.97.** Compare the Markov inequality and the exact probability for the event $\{X > c\}$ as a function of $c$ for:

    **(a)** $X$ is a uniform random variable in the interval $[0, b]$.

    **(b)** $X$ is an exponential random variable with parameter $\lambda$.

    **(c)** $X$ is a Pareto random variable with $\alpha > 1$.

    **(d)** $X$ is a Rayleigh random variable.

**4.98.** Compare the Markov inequality and the exact probability for the event $\{X > c\}$ as a function of $c$ for:

    **(a)** $X$ is a uniform random variable in $\{1, 2, \ldots, L\}$.

    **(b)** $X$ is a geometric random variable.

    **(c)** $X$ is a Zipf random variable with $L = 10$; $L = 100$.

    **(d)** $X$ is a binomial random variable with $n = 10$, $p = 0.5$; $n = 50$, $p = 0.5$.

**4.99.** Compare the Chebyshev inequality and the exact probability for the event $\{|X - m| > c\}$ as a function of $c$ for:

    **(a)** $X$ is a uniform random variable in the interval $[-b, b]$.

    **(b)** $X$ is a Laplacian random variable with parameter $\alpha$.

    **(c)** $X$ is a zero-mean Gaussian random variable.

    **(d)** $X$ is a binomial random variable with $n = 10$, $p = 0.5$; $n = 50$, $p = 0.5$.

**4.100.** Let $X$ be the number of successes in $n$ Bernoulli trials where the probability of success is $p$. Let $Y = X/n$ be the average number of successes per trial. Apply the Chebyshev inequality to the event $\{|Y - p| > a\}$. What happens as $n \to \infty$?

**4.101.** Suppose that light bulbs have exponentially distributed lifetimes with unknown mean $E[X]$. Suppose we measure the lifetime of $n$ light bulbs, and we estimate the mean $E[X]$ by the arithmetic average $Y$ of the measurements. Apply the Chebyshev inequality to the event $\{|Y - E[X]| > a\}$. What happens as $n \to \infty$? *Hint:* Use the $m$-Erlang random variable.

### Section 4.7: Transform Methods

**4.102. (a)** Find the characteristic function of the uniform random variable in $[-b, b]$.

    **(b)** Find the mean and variance of $X$ by applying the moment theorem.

**4.103. (a)** Find the characteristic function of the Laplacian random variable.

    **(b)** Find the mean and variance of $X$ by applying the moment theorem.

**4.104.** Let $\Phi_X(\omega)$ be the characteristic function of an exponential random variable. What random variable does $\Phi_X^n(\omega)$ correspond to?

**4.105.** Find the mean and variance of the Gaussian random variable by applying the moment theorem to the characteristic function given in Table 4.1.

**4.106.** Find the characteristic function of $Y = aX + b$ where $X$ is a Gaussian random variable. *Hint:* Use Eq. (4.79).

**4.107.** Show that the characteristic function for the Cauchy random variable is $e^{-|\omega|}$.

**4.108.** Find the Chernoff bound for the exponential random variable with $\lambda = 1$. Compare the bound to the exact value for $P[X > 5]$.

**4.109.** **(a)** Find the probability generating function of the geometric random variable.

**(b)** Find the mean and variance of the geometric random variable from its pgf.

**4.110.** **(a)** Find the pgf for the binomial random variable $X$ with parameters $n$ and $p$.

**(b)** Find the mean and variance of $X$ from the pgf.

**4.111.** Let $G_X(z)$ be the pgf for a binomial random variable with parameters $n$ and $p$, and let $G_Y(z)$ be the pgf for a binomial random variable with parameters $m$ and $p$. Consider the function $G_X(z)\,G_Y(z)$. Is this a valid pgf? If so, to what random variable does it correspond?

**4.112.** Let $G_N(z)$ be the pgf for a Poisson random variable with parameter $\alpha$, and let $G_M(z)$ be the pgf for a Poisson random variable with parameters $\beta$. Consider the function $G_N(z)\,G_M(z)$. Is this a valid pgf? If so, to what random variable does it correspond?

**4.113.** Let $N$ be a Poisson random variable with parameter $\alpha = 1$. Compare the Chernoff bound and the exact value for $P[X \geq 5]$.

**4.114.** **(a)** Find the pgf $G_U(z)$ for the discrete uniform random variable $U$.

**(b)** Find the mean and variance from the pgf.

**(c)** Consider $G_U(z)^2$. Does this function correspond to a pgf? If so, find the mean of the corresponding random variable.

**4.115.** **(a)** Find $P[X = r]$ for the negative binomial random variable from the pgf in Table 3.1.

**(b)** Find the mean of $X$.

**4.116.** Derive Eq. (4.89).

**4.117.** Obtain the $n$th moment of a gamma random variable from the Laplace transform of its pdf.

**4.118.** Let $X$ be the mixture of two exponential random variables (see Example 4.58). Find the Laplace transform of the pdf of $X$.

**4.119.** The Laplace transform of the pdf of a random variable $X$ is given by:

$$X^*(s) = \frac{a}{s+a}\frac{b}{s+b}.$$

Find the pdf of $X$. *Hint:* Use a partial fraction expansion of $X^*(s)$.

**4.120.** Find a relationship between the Laplace transform of a gamma random variable pdf with parameters $\alpha$ and $\lambda$ and the Laplace transform of a gamma random variable with parameters $\alpha - 1$ and $\lambda$. What does this imply if $X$ is an $m$-Erlang random variable?

**4.121.** **(a)** Find the Chernoff bound for $P[X > t]$ for the gamma random variable.

**(b)** Compare the bound to the exact value of $P[X \geq 9]$ for an $m = 3, \lambda = 1$ Erlang random variable.

### Section 4.8: Basic Reliability Calculations

**4.122.** The lifetime $T$ of a device has pdf

$$f_T(t) = \begin{cases} 1/10T_0 & 0 < t < T_0 \\ 0.9\lambda e^{-\lambda(t-T_0)} & t \geq T_0 \\ 0 & t < T_0. \end{cases}$$

   **(a)** Find the reliability and MTTF of the device.
   **(b)** Find the failure rate function.
   **(c)** How many hours of operation can be considered to achieve 99% reliability?

**4.123.** The lifetime $T$ of a device has pdf

$$f_T(t) = \begin{cases} 1/T_0 & a \leq t \leq a + T_0 \\ 0 & \text{elsewhere.} \end{cases}$$

   **(a)** Find the reliability and MTTF of the device.
   **(b)** Find the failure rate function.
   **(c)** How many hours of operation can be considered to achieve 99% reliability?

**4.124.** The lifetime $T$ of a device is a Rayleigh random variable.
   **(a)** Find the reliability of the device.
   **(b)** Find the failure rate function. Does $r(t)$ increase with time?
   **(c)** Find the reliability of two devices that are in series.
   **(d)** Find the reliability of two devices that are in parallel.

**4.125.** The lifetime $T$ of a device is a Weibull random variable.
   **(a)** Plot the failure rates for $\alpha = 1$ and $\beta = 0.5$; for $\alpha = 1$ and $\beta = 2$.
   **(b)** Plot the reliability functions in part a.
   **(c)** Plot the reliability of two devices that are in series.
   **(d)** Plot the reliability of two devices that are in parallel.

**4.126.** A system starts with $m$ devices, 1 active and $m - 1$ on standby. Each device has an exponential lifetime. When a device fails it is immediately replaced with another device (if one is still available).
   **(a)** Find the reliability of the system.
   **(b)** Find the failure rate function.

**4.127.** Find the failure rate function of the memory chips discussed in Example 2.28. Plot $\ln(r(t))$ versus $\alpha t$.

**4.128.** A device comes from two sources. Devices from source 1 have mean $m$ and exponentially distributed lifetimes. Devices from source 2 have mean $m$ and Pareto-distributed lifetimes with $\alpha > 1$. Assume a fraction $p$ is from source 1 and a fraction $1 - p$ from source 2.
   **(a)** Find the reliability of an arbitrarily selected device.
   **(b)** Find the failure rate function.

**4.129.** A device has the failure rate function:

$$r(t) = \begin{cases} 1 + 9(1 - t) & 0 \le t < 1 \\ 1 & 1 \le t < 10 \\ 1 + 10(t - 10) & t \ge 10. \end{cases}$$

Find the reliability function and the pdf of the device.

**4.130.** A system has three identical components and the system is functioning if two or more components are functioning.

   **(a)**  Find the reliability and MTTF of the system if the component lifetimes are exponential random variables with mean 1.

   **(b)**  Find the reliability of the system if one of the components has mean 2.

**4.131.** Repeat Problem 4.130 if the component lifetimes are Weibull distributed with $\beta = 3$.

**4.132.** A system consists of two processors and three peripheral units. The system is functioning as long as one processor and two peripherals are functioning.

   **(a)**  Find the system reliability and MTTF if the processor lifetimes are exponential random variables with mean 5 and the peripheral lifetimes are Rayleigh random variables with mean 10.

   **(b)**  Find the system reliability and MTTF if the processor lifetimes are exponential random variables with mean 10 and the peripheral lifetimes are exponential random variables with mean 5.

**4.133.** An operation is carried out by a subsystem consisting of three units that operate in a series configuration.

   **(a)**  The units have exponentially distributed lifetimes with mean 1. How many subsystems should be operated in parallel to achieve a reliability of 99% in $T$ hours of operation?

   **(b)**  Repeat part a with Rayleigh-distributed lifetimes.

   **(c)**  Repeat part a with Weibull-distributed lifetimes with $\beta = 3$.

### Section 4.9:  Computer Methods for Generating Random Variables

**4.134.** Octave provides function calls to evaluate the pdf and cdf of important continuous random variables. For example, the functions \normal_cdf(x, m, var) and normal_pdf(x, m, var) compute the cdf and pdf, respectively, at $x$ for a Gaussian random variable with mean m and variance var.

   **(a)**  Plot the conditional pdfs in Example 4.11 if $v = \pm 2$ and the noise is zero-mean and unit variance.

   **(b)**  Compare the cdf of the Gaussian random variable with the Chernoff bound obtained in Example 4.44.

**4.135.** Plot the pdf and cdf of the gamma random variable for the following cases.

   **(a)**  $\lambda = 1$ and $\alpha = 1, 2, 4$.

   **(b)**  $\lambda = 1/2$ and $\alpha = 1/2, 1, 3/2, 5/2$.

**4.136.** The random variable $X$ has the triangular pdf shown in Fig. P4.4.

    **(a)** Find the transformation needed to generate $X$.

    **(b)** Use Octave to generate 100 samples of $X$. Compare the empirical pdf of the samples with the desired pdf.

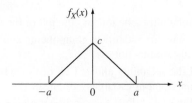

**FIGURE P4.4**

**4.137.** For each of the following random variables: Find the transformation needed to generate the random variable $X$; use Octave to generate 1000 samples of $X$; Plot the sequence of outcomes; compare the empirical pdf of the samples with the desired pdf.

    **(a)** Laplacian random variable with $\alpha = 1$.

    **(b)** Pareto random variable with $\alpha = 1.5, 2, 2.5$.

    **(c)** Weibull random variable with $\beta = 0.5, 2, 3$ and $\lambda = 1$.

**4.138.** *A* random variable $Y$ of mixed type has pdf

$$f_Y(x) = p\delta(x) + (1 - p)f_Y(x),$$

where $X$ is a Laplacian random variable and $p$ is a number between zero and one. Find the transformation required to generate $Y$.

**4.139.** Specify the transformation method needed to generate the geometric random variable with parameter $p = 1/2$. Find the average number of comparisons needed in the search to determine each outcome.

**4.140.** Specify the transformation method needed to generate the Poisson random variable with small parameter $\alpha$. Compute the average number of comparisons needed in the search.

**4.141.** The following rejection method can be used to generate Gaussian random variables:

    **1.** Generate $U_1$, a uniform random variable in the unit interval.

    **2.** Let $X_1 = -\ln(U_1)$.

    **3.** Generate $U_2$, a uniform random variable in the unit interval. If $U_2 \leq \exp\{-(X_1 - 1)^2/2\}$, accept $X_1$. Otherwise, reject $X_1$ and go to step 1.

    **4.** Generate a random sign ($+$ or $-$) with equal probability. Output $X$ equal to $X_1$ with the resulting sign.

    **(a)** Show that if $X_1$ is accepted, then its pdf corresponds to the pdf of the absolute value of a Gaussian random variable with mean 0 and variance 1.

    **(b)** Show that $X$ is a Gaussian random variable with mean 0 and variance 1.

**4.142.** Cheng (1977) has shown that the function $Kf_Z(x)$ bounds the pdf of a gamma random variable with $\alpha > 1$, where

$$f_Z(x) = \frac{\lambda\alpha^\lambda x^{\lambda-1}}{(\alpha^\lambda + x^\lambda)^2} \quad \text{and} \quad K = (2\alpha - 1)^{1/2}.$$

Find the cdf of $f_Z(x)$ and the corresponding transformation needed to generate $Z$.

**4.143.** (a) Show that in the modified rejection method, the probability of accepting $X_1$ is $1/K$. *Hint:* Use conditional probability.

(b) Show that $Z$ has the desired pdf.

**4.144.** Two methods for generating binomial random variables are: (1) Generate $n$ Bernoulli random variables and add the outcomes; (2) Divide the unit interval according to binomial probabilities. Compare the methods under the following conditions:

(a) $p = 1/2, n = 5, 25, 50$;

(b) $p = 0.1, n = 5, 25, 50$.

(c) Use Octave to implement the two methods by generating 1000 binomially distributed samples.

**4.145.** Let the number of event occurrences in a time interval be a Poisson random variable. In Section 3.4, it was found that the time between events for a Poisson random variable is an exponentially distributed random variable.

(a) Explain how one can generate Poisson random variables from a sequence of exponentially distributed random variables.

(b) How does this method compare with the one presented in Problem 4.140?

(c) Use Octave to implement the two methods when $\alpha = 3, \alpha = 25$, and $\alpha = 100$.

**4.146.** Write a program to generate the gamma pdf with $\alpha > 1$ using the rejection method discussed in Problem 4.142. Use this method to generate $m$-Erlang random variables with $m = 2, 10$ and $\lambda = 1$ and compare the method to the straightforward generation of $m$ exponential random variables as discussed in Example 4.57.

## *Section 4.10: Entropy

**4.147.** Let $X$ be the outcome of the toss of a fair die.

(a) Find the entropy of $X$.

(b) Suppose you are told that $X$ is even. What is the reduction in entropy?

**4.148.** A biased coin is tossed three times.

(a) Find the entropy of the outcome if the sequence of heads and tails is noted.

(b) Find the entropy of the outcome if the number of heads is noted.

(c) Explain the difference between the entropies in parts a and b.

**4.149.** Let $X$ be the number of tails until the first heads in a sequence of tosses of a biased coin.

(a) Find the entropy of $X$ given that $X \geq k$.

(b) Find the entropy of $X$ given that $X \leq k$.

**4.150.** One of two coins is selected at random: Coin A has $P[\text{heads}] = 1/10$ and coin B has $P[\text{heads}] = 9/10$.

(a) Suppose the coin is tossed once. Find the entropy of the outcome.

(b) Suppose the coin is tossed twice and the sequence of heads and tails is observed. Find the entropy of the outcome.

**4.151.** Suppose that the randomly selected coin in Problem 4.150 is tossed until the first occurrence of heads. Suppose that heads occurs in the $k$th toss. Find the entropy regarding the identity of the coin.

**4.152.** A communication channel accepts input $I$ from the set $\{0, 1, 2, 3, 4, 5, 6\}$. The channel output is $X = I + N \bmod 7$, where $N$ is equally likely to be $+1$ or $-1$.

(a) Find the entropy of $I$ if all inputs are equiprobable.

(b) Find the entropy of $I$ given that $X = 4$.

**4.153.** Let $X$ be a discrete random variable with entropy $H_X$.

   **(a)** Find the entropy of $Y = 2X$.

   **(b)** Find the entropy of any invertible transformation of $X$.

**4.154.** Let $(X, Y)$ be the pair of outcomes from two independent tosses of a die.

   **(a)** Find the entropy of $X$.

   **(b)** Find the entropy of the pair $(X, Y)$.

   **(c)** Find the entropy in $n$ independent tosses of a die. Explain why entropy is additive in this case.

**4.155.** Let $X$ be the outcome of the toss of a die, and let $Y$ be a randomly selected integer less than or equal to $X$.

   **(a)** Find the entropy of $Y$.

   **(b)** Find the entropy of the pair $(X, Y)$ and denote it by $H(X, Y)$.

   **(c)** Find the entropy of $Y$ given $X = k$ and denote it by $g(k) = H(Y \mid X = k)$. Find $E[g(X)] = E[H(Y \mid X)]$.

   **(d)** Show that $H(X, Y) = H_X + E[H(Y \mid X)]$. Explain the meaning of this equation.

**4.156.** Let $X$ take on values from $\{1, 2, \ldots, K\}$. Suppose that $P[X = K] = p$, and let $H_Y$ be the entropy of $X$ given that $X$ is not equal to $K$. Show that $H_X = -p \ln p - (1 - p) \ln(1 - p) + (1 - p)H_Y$.

**4.157.** Let $X$ be a uniform random variable in Example 4.62. Find and plot the entropy of $Q$ as a function of the variance of the error $X - Q(X)$. *Hint:* Express the variance of the error in terms of $d$ and substitute into the expression for the entropy of $Q$.

**4.158.** A communication channel accepts as input either 000 or 111. The channel transmits each binary input correctly with probability $1 - p$ and erroneously with probability $p$. Find the entropy of the input given that the output is 000; given that the output is 010.

**4.159.** Let $X$ be a uniform random variable in the interval $[-a, a]$. Suppose we are told that the $X$ is positive. Use the approach in Example 4.62 to find the reduction in entropy. Show that this is equal to the difference of the differential entropy of $X$ and the differential entropy of $X$ given $\{X > 0\}$.

**4.160.** Let $X$ be uniform in $[a, b]$, and let $Y = 2X$. Compare the differential entropies of $X$ and $Y$. How does this result differ from the result in Problem 4.153?

**4.161.** Find the pmf for the random variable $X$ for which the sequence of questions in Fig. 4.26(a) is optimum.

**4.162.** Let the random variable $X$ have $S_X = \{1, 2, 3, 4, 5, 6\}$ and pmf (3/8, 3/8, 1/8, 1/16, 1/32, 1/32). Find the entropy of $X$. What is the best code you can find for $X$?

**4.163.** Seven cards are drawn from a deck of 52 distinct cards. How many bits are required to represent all possible outcomes?

**4.164.** Find the optimum encoding for the geometric random variable with $p = 1/2$.

**4.165.** An urn experiment has 10 equiprobable distinct outcomes. Find the performance of the best tree code for encoding (a) a single outcome of the experiment; (b) a sequence of $n$ outcomes of the experiment.

**4.166.** A binary information source produces $n$ outputs. Suppose we are told that there are $k$ 1's in these $n$ outputs.

   **(a)** What is the best code to indicate which pattern of $k$ 1's and $n - k$ 0's occurred?

   **(b)** How many bits are required to specify the value of $k$ using a code with a fixed number of bits?

**4.167.** The random variable $X$ takes on values from the set $\{1, 2, 3, 4\}$. Find the maximum entropy pmf for $X$ given that $E[X] = 2$.

**4.168.** The random variable $X$ is nonnegative. Find the maximum entropy pdf for $X$ given that $E[X] = 10$.

**4.169.** Find the maximum entropy pdf of $X$ given that $E[X^2] = c$.

**4.170.** Suppose we are given two parameters of the random variable $X$, $E[g_1(X)] = c_1$ and $E[g_2(X)] = c_2$.

    **(a)** Show that the maximum entropy pdf for $X$ has the form

$$f_X(x) = Ce^{-\lambda_1 g_1(x) - \lambda_2 g_2(x)}.$$

    **(b)** Find the entropy of $X$.

**4.171.** Find the maximum entropy pdf of $X$ given that $E[X] = m$ and $\text{VAR}[X] = \sigma^2$.

## Problems Requiring Cumulative Knowledge

**4.172.** Three types of customers arrive at a service station. The time required to service type 1 customers is an exponential random variable with mean 2. Type 2 customers have a Pareto distribution with $\alpha = 3$ and $x_m = 1$. Type 3 customers require a constant service time of 2 seconds. Suppose that the proportion of type 1, 2, and 3 customers is 1/2, 1/8, and 3/8, respectively. Find the probability that an arbitrary customer requires more than 15 seconds of service time. Compare the above probability to the bound provided by the Markov inequality.

**4.173.** The lifetime $X$ of a light bulb is a random variable with

$$P[X > t] = 2/(2 + t) \text{ for } t > 0.$$

Suppose three new light bulbs are installed at time $t = 0$. At time $t = 1$ all three light bulbs are still working. Find the probability that at least one light bulb is still working at time $t = 9$.

**4.174.** The random variable $X$ is uniformly distributed in the interval $[0, a]$. Suppose $a$ is unknown, so we estimate $a$ by the maximum value observed in $n$ independent repetitions of the experiment; that is, we estimate $a$ by $Y = \max\{X_1, X_2, \ldots, X_n\}$.

    **(a)** Find $P[Y \leq y]$.

    **(b)** Find the mean and variance of $Y$, and explain why $Y$ is a good estimate for $a$ when $N$ is large.

**4.175.** The sample $X$ of a signal is a Gaussian random variable with $m = 0$ and $\sigma^2 = 1$. Suppose that $X$ is quantized by a nonuniform quantizer consisting of four intervals: $(-\infty, -a]$, $(-a, 0]$, $(0, a]$, and $(a, \infty)$.

    **(a)** Find the value of $a$ so that $X$ is equally likely to fall in each of the four intervals.

    **(b)** Find the representation point $x_i = q(X)$ for $X$ in $(0, a]$ that minimizes the mean-squared error, that is,

$$\int_0^a (x - x_1)^2 f_X(x) \, dx \text{ is minimized.}$$

    *Hint:* Differentiate the above expression with respect to $x_i$. Find the representation points for the other intervals.

    **(c)** Evaluate the mean-squared error of the quantizer $E[(X - q(X)^2]$.

**4.176.** The output $Y$ of a binary communication system is a unit-variance Gaussian random with mean zero when the input is "0" and mean one when the input is "one". Assume the input is 1 with probability $p$.

(a) Find $P[\text{input is } 1 \mid y < Y < y + h]$ and $P[\text{input is } 0 \mid y < Y < y + h]$.

(b) The receiver uses the following decision rule:

If $P[\text{input is } 1 \mid y < Y < y + h] > P[\text{input is } 0 \mid y < Y < y + h]$, decide input was 1; otherwise, decide input was 0.

Show that this decision rule leads to the following threshold rule:

If $Y > T$, decide input was 1; otherwise, decide input was 0.

(c) What is the probability of error for the above decision rule?

# CHAPTER 5

# Pairs of Random Variables

Many random experiments involve several random variables. In some experiments a number of different quantities are measured. For example, the voltage signals at several points in a circuit at some specific time may be of interest. Other experiments involve the repeated measurement of a certain quantity such as the repeated measurement ("sampling") of the amplitude of an audio or video signal that varies with time. In Chapter 4 we developed techniques for calculating the probabilities of events involving a single random variable *in isolation*. In this chapter, we extend the concepts already introduced to two random variables:

- We use the joint pmf, cdf, and pdf to calculate the probabilities of events that involve the *joint* behavior of two random variables;
- We use expected value to define joint moments that summarize the behavior of two random variables;
- We determine when two random variables are independent, and we quantify their degree of "correlation" when they are not independent;
- We obtain conditional probabilities involving a pair of random variables.

In a sense we have already covered all the fundamental concepts of probability and random variables, and we are "simply" elaborating on the case of two or more random variables. Nevertheless, there are significant analytical techniques that need to be learned, e.g., double summations of pmf's and double integration of pdf's, so we first discuss the case of two random variables in detail because we can draw on our geometric intuition. Chapter 6 considers the general case of vector random variables. Throughout these two chapters you should be mindful of the forest (fundamental concepts) and the trees (specific techniques)!

## 5.1 TWO RANDOM VARIABLES

The notion of a random variable as a mapping is easily generalized to the case where two quantities are of interest. Consider a random experiment with sample space $S$ and event class $\mathcal{F}$. We are interested in a function that assigns a pair of real numbers

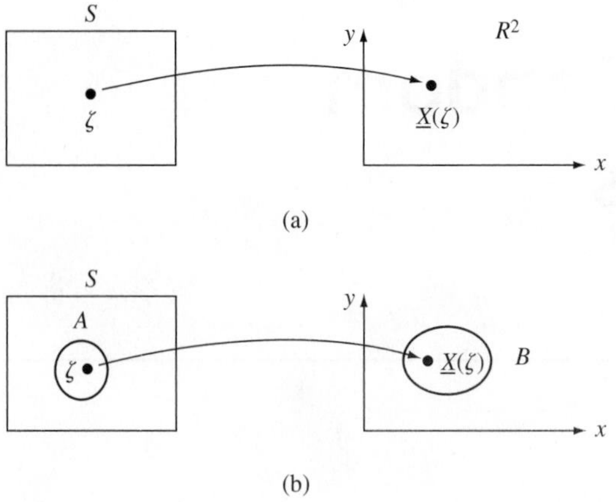

**FIGURE 5.1**
(a) A function assigns a pair of real numbers to each outcome in S. (b) Equivalent events for two random variables.

$\mathbf{X}(\zeta) = (X(\zeta), Y(\zeta))$ to each outcome $\zeta$ in $S$. Basically we are dealing with a vector function that maps $S$ into $R^2$, the real plane, as shown in Fig. 5.1(a). We are ultimately interested in events involving the pair $(X, Y)$.

---

## Example 5.1

Let a random experiment consist of selecting a student's name from an urn. Let $\zeta$ denote the outcome of this experiment, and define the following two functions:

$$H(\zeta) = \text{height of student } \zeta \text{ in centimeters}$$

$$W(\zeta) = \text{weight of student } \zeta \text{ in kilograms}$$

$(H(\zeta), W(\zeta))$ assigns a pair of numbers to each $\zeta$ in $S$.

We are interested in events involving the pair $(H, W)$. For example, the event $B = \{H \leq 183, W \leq 82\}$ represents students with height less that 183 cm (6 feet) and weight less than 82 kg (180 lb).

---

## Example 5.2

A Web page provides the user with a choice either to watch a brief ad or to move directly to the requested page. Let $\zeta$ be the patterns of user arrivals in $T$ seconds, e.g., number of arrivals, and listing of arrival times and types. Let $N_1(\zeta)$ be the number of times the Web page is directly requested and let $N_2(\zeta)$ be the number of times that the ad is chosen. $(N_1(\zeta), N_2(\zeta))$ assigns a pair of nonnegative integers to each $\zeta$ in $S$. Suppose that a type 1 request brings 0.001¢ in revenue and a type 2 request brings in 1¢. Find the event "revenue in $T$ seconds is less than \$100."

The total revenue in $T$ seconds is $0.001\, N_1 + 1 N_2$, and so the event of interest is $B = \{0.001\, N_1 + 1 N_2 < 10{,}000\}$.

---

## Example 5.3

Let the outcome $\zeta$ in a random experiment be the length of a randomly selected message. Suppose that messages are broken into packets of maximum length $M$ bytes. Let $Q$ be the number of full packets in a message and let $R$ be the number of bytes left over. $(Q(\zeta), R(\zeta))$ assigns a pair of numbers to each $\zeta$ in S. $Q$ takes on values in the range $0, 1, 2, \ldots$, and $R$ takes on values in the range $0, 1, \ldots, M - 1$. An event of interest may be $B = \{R < M/2\}$, "the last packet is less than half full."

## Example 5.4

Let the outcome of a random experiment result in a pair $\underline{\zeta} = (\zeta_1, \zeta_2)$ that results from two independent spins of a wheel. Each spin of the wheel results in a number in the interval $(0, 2\pi]$. Define the pair of numbers $(X, Y)$ in the plane as follows:

$$X(\underline{\zeta}) = \left(2 \ln \frac{2\pi}{\zeta_1}\right)^{1/2} \cos \zeta_2 \qquad Y(\underline{\zeta}) = \left(2 \ln \frac{2\pi}{\zeta_1}\right)^{1/2} \sin \zeta_2.$$

The vector function $(X(\underline{\zeta}), Y(\underline{\zeta}))$ assigns a pair of numbers in the plane to each $\underline{\zeta}$ in S. The square root term corresponds to a radius and to $\zeta_2$ an angle.

We will see that $(X, Y)$ models the noise voltages encountered in digital communication systems. An event of interest here may be $B = \{X^2 + Y^2 < r^2\}$, "total noise power is less than $r^2$."

The events involving a pair of random variables $(X, Y)$ are specified by conditions that we are interested in and can be represented by regions in the plane. Figure 5.2 shows three examples of events:

$$A = \{X + Y \leq 10\}$$
$$B = \{\min(X, Y) \leq 5\}$$
$$C = \{X^2 + Y^2 \leq 100\}.$$

Event $A$ divides the plane into two regions according to a straight line. Note that the event in Example 5.2 is of this type. Event $C$ identifies a disk centered at the origin and

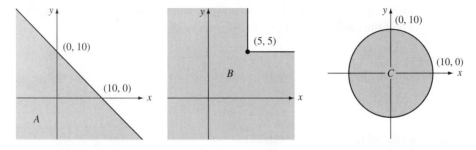

**FIGURE 5.2**
Examples of two-dimensional events.

it corresponds to the event in Example 5.4. Event $B$ is found by noting that $\{\min(X, Y) \leq 5\} = \{X \leq 5\} \cup \{Y \leq 5\}$, that is, the minimum of $X$ and $Y$ is less than or equal to 5 if either $X$ and/or $Y$ is less than or equal to 5.

To determine the probability that the pair $\mathbf{X} = (X, Y)$ is in some region $B$ in the plane, we proceed as in Chapter 3 to find the equivalent event for $B$ in the underlying sample space $S$:

$$A = \mathbf{X}^{-1}(B) = \{\zeta: (X(\zeta), Y(\zeta)) \text{ in } B\}. \tag{5.1a}$$

The relationship between $A = \mathbf{X}^{-1}(B)$ and $B$ is shown in Fig. 5.1(b). If $A$ is in $\mathcal{F}$, then it has a probability assigned to it, and we obtain:

$$P[X \text{ in } B] = P[A] = P[\{\zeta: (X(\zeta), Y(\zeta)) \text{ in } B\}]. \tag{5.1b}$$

The approach is identical to what we followed in the case of a single random variable. The only difference is that we are considering the *joint behavior of X and Y* that is induced by the underlying random experiment.

A scattergram can be used to deduce the joint behavior of two random variables. A scattergram plot simply places a dot at every observation pair $(x, y)$ that results from performing the experiment that generates $(X, Y)$. Figure 5.3 shows the scattergram for 200 observations of four different pairs of random variables. The pairs in Fig. 5.3(a) appear to be uniformly distributed in the unit square. The pairs in Fig. 5.3(b) are clearly confined to a disc of unit radius and appear to be more concentrated near the origin. The pairs in Fig. 5.3(c) are concentrated near the origin, and appear to have circular symmetry, but are not bounded to an enclosed region. The pairs in Fig. 5.3(d) again are concentrated near the origin and appear to have a clear linear relationship of some sort, that is, larger values of $x$ tend to have linearly proportional increasing values of $y$. We later introduce various functions and moments to characterize the behavior of pairs of random variables illustrated in these examples.

The joint probability mass function, joint cumulative distribution function, and joint probability density function provide approaches to specifying the probability law that governs the behavior of the pair $(X, Y)$. Our general approach is as follows. We first focus on events that correspond to rectangles in the plane:

$$B = \{X \text{ in } A_1\} \cap \{Y \text{ in } A_2\} \tag{5.2}$$

where $A_k$ is a one-dimensional event (i.e., subset of the real line). We say that these events are of **product form**. The event $B$ occurs when both $\{X \text{ in } A_1\}$ and $\{Y \text{ in } A_2\}$ occur jointly. Figure 5.4 shows some two-dimensional product-form events. We use Eq. (5.1b) to find the probability of product-form events:

$$P[B] = P[\{X \text{ in } A_1\} \cap \{Y \text{ in } A_2\}] \triangleq P[X \text{ in } A_1, Y \text{ in } A_n]. \tag{5.3}$$

By defining $A$ appropriately we then obtain the joint pmf, joint cdf, and joint pdf of $(X, Y)$.

## 5.2    PAIRS OF DISCRETE RANDOM VARIABLES

Let the vector random variable $\mathbf{X} = (X, Y)$ assume values from some countable set $S_{X,Y} = \{(x_j, y_k), j = 1, 2, \ldots, k = 1, 2, \ldots\}$. The **joint probability mass function** of $\mathbf{X}$ specifies the probabilities of the event $\{X = x\} \cap \{Y = y\}$:

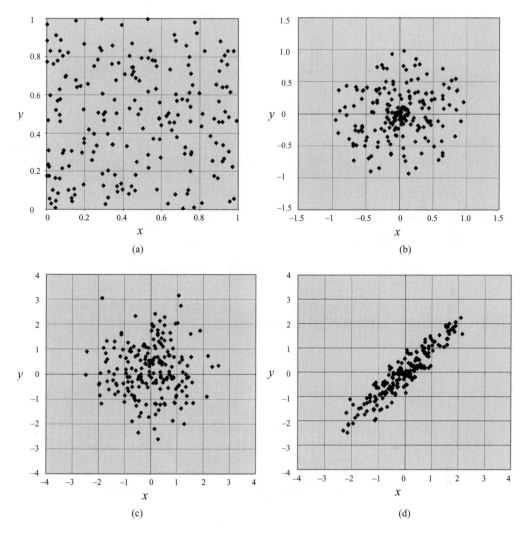

**FIGURE 5.3**
A scattergram for 200 observations of four different pairs of random variables.

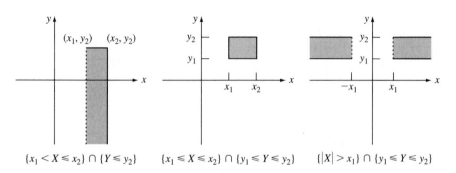

**FIGURE 5.4**
Some two-dimensional product-form events.

$$p_{X,Y}(x, y) = P[\{X = x\} \cap \{Y = y\}]$$
$$\triangleq P[X = x, Y = y] \quad \text{for } (x, y) \in R^2. \quad (5.4a)$$

The values of the pmf on the set $S_{X,Y}$ provide the essential information:

$$p_{X,Y}(x_j, y_k) = P[\{X = x_j\} \cap \{Y = y_k\}]$$
$$\triangleq P[X = x_j, Y = y_k] \quad (x_j, y_k) \in S_{X,Y}. \quad (5.4b)$$

There are several ways of showing the pmf graphically: (1) For small sample spaces we can present the pmf in the form of a table as shown in Fig. 5.5(a). (2) We can present the pmf using arrows of height $p_{X,Y}(x_j, y_k)$ placed at the points $\{(x_j, y_k)\}$ in the plane, as shown in Fig. 5.5(b), but this can be difficult to draw. (3) We can place dots at the points $\{(x_j, y_k)\}$ and label these with the corresponding pmf value as shown in Fig. 5.5(c).

The probability of any event $B$ is the sum of the pmf over the outcomes in $B$:

$$P[\mathbf{X} \text{ in } B] = \sum_{(x_j, y_k) \text{ in } B} \sum p_{X,Y}(x_j, y_k). \quad (5.5)$$

Frequently it is helpful to sketch the region that contains the points in $B$ as shown, for example, in Fig. 5.6. When the event $B$ is the entire sample space $S_{X,Y}$, we have:

$$\sum_{j=1}^{\infty} \sum_{k=1}^{\infty} p_{X,Y}(x_j, y_k) = 1. \quad (5.6)$$

---

### Example 5.5

A packet switch has two input ports and two output ports. At a given time slot a packet arrives at each input port with probability 1/2, and is equally likely to be destined to output port 1 or 2. Let $X$ and $Y$ be the number of packets destined for output ports 1 and 2, respectively. Find the pmf of $X$ and $Y$, and show the pmf graphically.

The outcome $I_j$ for an input port $j$ can take the following values: "n", no packet arrival (with probability 1/2); "a1", packet arrival destined for output port 1 (with probability 1/4); "a2", packet arrival destined for output port 2 (with probability 1/4). The underlying sample space $S$ consists of the pair of input outcomes $\zeta = (I_1, I_2)$. The mapping for $(X, Y)$ is shown in the table below:

| $\zeta$ | (n, n) | (n, a1) | (n, a2) | (a1, n) | (a1, a1) | (a1, a2) | (a2, n) | (a2, a1) | (a2, a2) |
|---|---|---|---|---|---|---|---|---|---|
| $X, Y$ | (0,0) | (1,0) | (0,1) | (1,0) | (2,0) | (1,1) | (0,1) | (1,1) | (0,2) |

The pmf of $(X, Y)$ is then:

$$p_{X,Y}(0, 0) = P[\zeta = (\text{n, n})] = \frac{1}{2}\frac{1}{2} = \frac{1}{4},$$

$$p_{X,Y}(0, 1) = P[\zeta \in \{(\text{n, a2}), (\text{a2, n})\}] = 2 * \frac{1}{8} = \frac{1}{4},$$

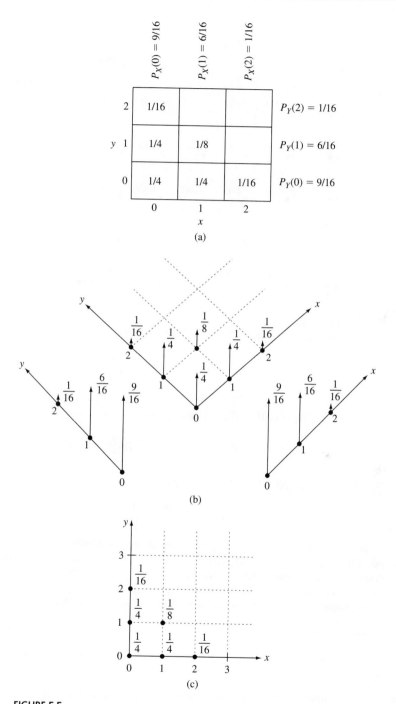

**FIGURE 5.5**
Graphical representations of pmf's: (a) in table format; (b) use of arrows to show height;
(c) labeled dots corresponding to pmf value.

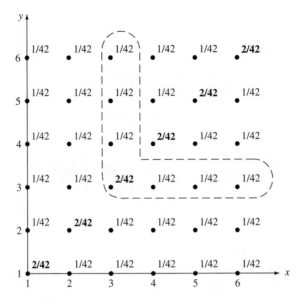

**FIGURE 5.6**
Showing the pmf via a sketch containing the points in B.

$$p_{X,Y}(1, 0) = P[\zeta \in \{(n, a1), (a1, n)\}] = \frac{1}{4},$$

$$p_{X,Y}(1, 1) = P[\zeta \in \{(a1, a2), (a2, a1)\}] = \frac{1}{8},$$

$$p_{X,Y}(0, 2) = P[\zeta = (a2, a2)] = \frac{1}{16},$$

$$p_{X,Y}(2, 0) = P[\zeta = (a1, a1)] = \frac{1}{16}.$$

Figure 5.5(a) shows the pmf in tabular form where the number of rows and columns accommodate the range of $X$ and $Y$ respectively. Each entry in the table gives the pmf value for the corresponding $x$ and $y$. Figure 5.5(b) shows the pmf using arrows in the plane. An arrow of height $p_{X,Y}(j, k)$ is placed at each of the points in $S_{X,Y} = \{(0, 0), (0, 1), (1, 0), (1, 1), (0, 2), (2, 0)\}$. Figure 5.5(c) shows the pmf using labeled dots in the plane. A dot with label $p_{X,Y}(j, k)$ is placed at each of the points in $S_{X,Y}$.

## Example 5.6

A random experiment consists of tossing two "loaded" dice and noting the pair of numbers $(X, Y)$ facing up. The joint pmf $p_{X,Y}(j, k)$ for $j = 1, \ldots, 6$ and $k = 1, \ldots, 6$ is given by the two-dimensional table shown in Fig. 5.6. The $(j, k)$ entry in the table contains the value $p_{X,Y}(j, k)$. Find the $P[\min(X, Y) = 3]$.

Figure 5.6 shows the region that corresponds to the set $\{\min(x, y) = 3\}$. The probability of this event is given by:

$$P[\min(X, Y) = 3] = p_{X,Y}(6, 3) + p_{X,Y}(5, 3) + p_{X,Y}(4, 3)$$
$$+ p_{X,Y}(3, 3) + p_{X,Y}(3, 4) + p_{X,Y}(3, 5) + p_{X,Y}(3, 6)$$
$$= 6\left(\frac{1}{42}\right) + \frac{2}{42} = \frac{8}{42}.$$

### 5.2.1 Marginal Probability Mass Function

The joint pmf of **X** provides the information about the joint behavior of $X$ and $Y$. We are also interested in the probabilities of events involving each of the random variables in isolation. These can be found in terms of the **marginal probability mass functions**:

$$p_X(x_j) = P[X = x_j]$$
$$= P[X = x_j, Y = \text{anything}]$$
$$= P[\{X = x_j \text{ and } Y = y_1\} \cup \{X = x_j \text{ and } Y = y_2\} \cup \ldots]$$
$$= \sum_{k=1}^{\infty} p_{X,Y}(x_j, y_k), \tag{5.7a}$$

and similarly,

$$p_Y(y_k) = P[Y = y_k]$$
$$= \sum_{j=1}^{\infty} p_{X,Y}(x_j, y_k). \tag{5.7b}$$

The marginal pmf's satisfy all the properties of one-dimensional pmf's, and they supply the information required to compute the probability of events involving the corresponding random variable.

The probability $p_{X,Y}(x_j, y_k)$ can be interpreted as the long-term relative frequency of the joint event $\{X = X_j\} \cap \{Y = Y_k\}$ in a sequence of repetitions of the random experiment. Equation (5.7a) corresponds to the fact that the relative frequency of the event $\{X = X_j\}$ is found by adding the relative frequencies of all outcome pairs in which $X_j$ appears. In general, it is impossible to deduce the relative frequencies of pairs of values $X$ and $Y$ from the relative frequencies of $X$ and $Y$ in isolation. The same is true for pmf's: In general, knowledge of the marginal pmf's is insufficient to specify the joint pmf.

### Example 5.7

Find the marginal pmf for the output ports $(X, Y)$ in Example 5.2.

Figure 5.5(a) shows that the marginal pmf is found by adding entries along a row or column in the table. For example, by adding along the $x = 1$ column we have:

$$p_X(1) = P[X = 1] = p_{X,Y}(1, 0) + p_{X,Y}(1, 1) = \frac{1}{4} + \frac{1}{8} = \frac{3}{8}.$$

Similarly, by adding along the $y = 0$ row:

$$p_Y(0) = P[Y = 0] = p_{X,Y}(0, 0) + p_{X,Y}(1, 0) + p_{X,Y}(2, 0) = \frac{1}{4} + \frac{1}{4} + \frac{1}{16} = \frac{9}{16}.$$

Figure 5.5(b) shows the marginal pmf using arrows on the real line.

**Example 5.8**

Find the marginal pmf's in the loaded dice experiment in Example 5.2.

The probability that $X = 1$ is found by summing over the first row:

$$P[X = 1] = \frac{2}{42} + \frac{1}{42} + \cdots + \frac{1}{42} = \frac{1}{6}.$$

Similarly, we find that $P[X = j] = 1/6$ for $j = 2, \ldots, 6$. The probability that $Y = k$ is found by summing over the $k$th column. We then find that $P[Y = k] = 1/6$ for $k = 1, 2, \ldots, 6$. Thus each die, in isolation, appears to be fair in the sense that each face is equiprobable. If we knew only these marginal pmf's we would have no idea that the dice are loaded.

**Example 5.9**

In Example 5.3, let the number of bytes $N$ in a message have a geometric distribution with parameter $1 - p$ and range $S_N = \{0, 1, 2, \ldots\}$. Find the joint pmf and the marginal pmf's of $Q$ and $R$.

If a message has $N$ bytes, then the number of full packets is the quotient $Q$ in the division of $N$ by $M$, and the number of remaining bytes is the remainder $R$. The probability of the pair $\{(q, r)\}$ is given by

$$P[Q = q, R = r] = P[N = qM + r] = (1 - p)p^{qM+r}.$$

The marginal pmf of $Q$ is

$$P[Q = q] = P[N \text{ in} \{qM, qM + 1, \ldots, qM + (M - 1)\}]$$

$$= \sum_{k=0}^{(M-1)} (1 - p)p^{qM+k}$$

$$= (1 - p)p^{qM}\frac{1 - p^M}{1 - p} = (1 - p^M)(p^M)^q \qquad q = 0, 1, 2, \ldots$$

The marginal pmf of $Q$ is geometric with parameter $p^M$. The marginal pmf of $R$ is:

$$P[R = r] = P[N \text{ in} \{r, M + r, 2M + r, \ldots\}]$$

$$= \sum_{q=0}^{\infty} (1 - p)p^{qM+r} = \frac{(1 - p)}{1 - p^M}p^r \quad r = 0, 1, \ldots, M - 1.$$

$R$ has a truncated geometric pmf. As an exercise, you should verify that all the above marginal pmf's add to 1.

## 5.3    THE JOINT CDF OF $X$ AND $Y$

In Chapter 3 we saw that semi-infinite intervals of the form $(-\infty, x]$ are a basic building block from which other one-dimensional events can be built. By defining the cdf $F_X(x)$ as the probability of $(-\infty, x]$, we were then able to express the probabilities of other events in terms of the cdf. In this section we repeat the above development for two-dimensional random variables.

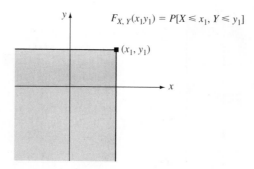

**FIGURE 5.7**
The joint cumulative distribution function is defined as
the probability of the semi-infinite rectangle defined by
the point $(x_1, y_1)$.

A basic building block for events involving two-dimensional random variables is the semi-infinite rectangle defined by $\{(x, y): x \leq x_1 \text{ and } y \leq y_1\}$, as shown in Fig. 5.7. We also use the more compact notation $\{x \leq x_1, y \leq y_1\}$ to refer to this region. The **joint cumulative distribution function of $X$ and $Y$** is defined as the probability of the event $\{X \leq x_1\} \cap \{Y \leq y_1\}$:

$$F_{X,Y}(x_1, y_1) = P[X \leq x_1, Y \leq y_1]. \tag{5.8}$$

In terms of relative frequency, $F_{X,Y}(x_1, y_1)$ represents the long-term proportion of time in which the outcome of the random experiment yields a point $X$ that falls in the rectangular region shown in Fig. 5.7. In terms of probability "mass," $F_{X,Y}(x_1, y_1)$ represents the amount of mass contained in the rectangular region.

The joint cdf satisfies the following properties.

**(i)** The joint cdf is a nondecreasing function of $x$ and $y$:

$$F_{X,Y}(x_1, y_1) \leq F_{X,Y}(x_2, y_2) \qquad \text{if } x_1 \leq x_2 \text{ and } y_1 \leq y_2, \tag{5.9a}$$

**(ii)** $F_{X,Y}(x_1, -\infty) = 0, \qquad F_{X,Y}(-\infty, y_1) = 0, \qquad F_{X,Y}(\infty, \infty) = 1.$ (5.9b)

**(iii)** We obtain the **marginal cumulative distribution functions** by removing the constraint on one of the variables. The marginal cdf's are the probabilities of the regions shown in Fig. 5.8:

$$F_X(x_1) = F_{X,Y}(x_1, \infty) \quad \text{and} \quad F_Y(y_1) = F_{X,Y}(\infty, y_1). \tag{5.9c}$$

**(iv)** The joint cdf is continuous from the "north" and from the "east," that is,

$$\lim_{x \to a^+} F_{X,Y}(x, y) = F_{X,Y}(a, y) \quad \text{and} \quad \lim_{y \to b^+} F_{X,Y}(x, y) = F_{X,Y}(x, b). \tag{5.9d}$$

**(v)** The probability of the rectangle $\{x_1 < x \leq x_2, y_1 < y \leq y_2\}$ is given by:

$$P[x_1 < X \leq x_2, y_1 < Y \leq y_2] =$$
$$F_{X,Y}(x_2, y_2) - F_{X,Y}(x_2, y_1) - F_{X,Y}(x_1, y_2) + F_{X,Y}(x_1, y_1). \tag{5.9e}$$

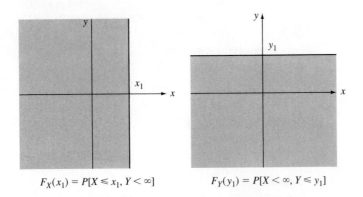

$$F_X(x_1) = P[X \le x_1, Y < \infty] \qquad F_Y(y_1) = P[X < \infty, Y \le y_1]$$

**FIGURE 5.8**
The marginal cdf's are the probabilities of these half-planes.

Property (i) follows by noting that the semi-infinite rectangle defined by $(x_1, y_1)$ is contained in that defined by $(x_2, y_2)$ and applying Corollary 7. Properties (ii) to (iv) are obtained by limiting arguments. For example, the sequence $\{x \le x_1 \text{ and } y \le -n\}$ is decreasing and approaches the empty set $\varnothing$, so

$$F_{X,Y}(x_1, -\infty) = \lim_{n \to \infty} F_{X,Y}(x_1, -n) = P[\varnothing] = 0.$$

For property (iii) we take the sequence $\{x \le x_1 \text{ and } y \le n\}$ which increases to $\{x \le x_1\}$, so

$$\lim_{n \to \infty} F_{X,Y}(x_1, n) = P[X \le x_1] = F_X(x_1).$$

For property (v) note in Fig. 5.9(a) that $B = \{x_1 < x \le x_2, y \le y_1\} = \{X \le x_2, Y \le y_1\} - \{X \le x_1, Y \le y_1\}$, so $P[B] = P[x_1 < X \le x_2, Y \le y_1] = F_{X,Y}(x_2, y_1) - F_{X,Y}(x_1, y_1)$. In Fig. 5.9(b), note that $F_{X,Y}(x_2, y_2) = P[A] + P[B] + F_{X,Y}(x_1, y_2)$. Property (v) follows by solving for $P[A]$ and substituting the expression for $P[B]$.

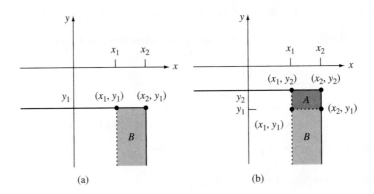

(a) (b)

**FIGURE 5.9**
The joint cdf can be used to determine the probability of various events.

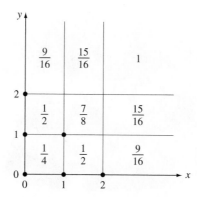

**FIGURE 5.10**
Joint cdf for packet switch example.

## Example 5.10

Plot the joint cdf of $X$ and $Y$ from Example 5.6. Find the marginal cdf of $X$.

To find the cdf of $\mathbf{X}$, we identify the regions in the plane according to which points in $S_{X,Y}$ are included in the rectangular region defined by $(x, y)$. For example,

- The regions outside the first quadrant do not include any of the points, so $F_{X,Y}(x, y) = 0$.
- The region $\{0 \le x < 1, 0 \le y < 1\}$ contains the point $(0, 0)$, so $F_{X,Y}(x, y) = 1/4$.

Figure 5.10 shows the cdf after all possible regions are examined.

We need to consider several cases to find $F_X(x)$. For $x < 0$, we have $F_X(x) = 0$. For $0 \le x < 1$, we have $F_X(x) = F_{X,Y}(x, \infty) = 9/16$. For $1 \le x < 2$, we have $F_X(x) = F_{X,Y}(x, \infty) = 15/16$. Finally, for $x \ge 1$, we have $F_X(x) = F_{X,Y}(x, \infty) = 1$. Therefore $F_X(x)$ is a staircase function and $X$ is a discrete random variable with $p_X(0) = 9/16$, $p_X(1) = 6/16$, and $p_X(2) = 1/16$.

## Example 5.11

The joint cdf for the pair of random variables $\mathbf{X} = (X, Y)$ is given by

$$
F_{X,Y}(x, y) = \begin{cases} 0 & x < 0 \text{ or } y < 0 \\ xy & 0 \le x \le 1, 0 \le y \le 1 \\ x & 0 \le x \le 1, y > 1 \\ y & 0 \le y \le 1, x > 1 \\ 1 & x \ge 1, y \ge 1. \end{cases} \tag{5.10}
$$

Plot the joint cdf and find the marginal cdf of $X$.

Figure 5.11 shows a plot of the joint cdf of $X$ and $Y$. $F_{X,Y}(x, y)$ is continuous for all points in the plane. $F_{X,Y}(x, y) = 1$ for all $x \ge 1$ and $y \ge 1$, which implies that $X$ and $Y$ each assume values less than or equal to one.

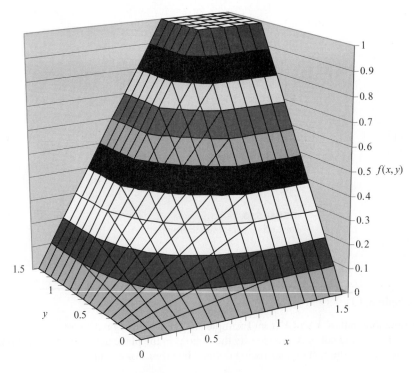

**FIGURE 5.11**
Joint cdf for two uniform random variables.

The marginal cdf of $X$ is:

$$F_X(x) = F_{X,Y}(x, \infty) = \begin{cases} 0 & x < 0 \\ x & 0 \leq x \leq 1 \\ 1 & x \geq 1. \end{cases}$$

$X$ is uniformly distributed in the unit interval.

---

**Example 5.12**

The joint cdf for the vector of random variable $\mathbf{X} = (X, Y)$ is given by

$$F_{X,Y}(x, y) = \begin{cases} (1 - e^{-\alpha x})(1 - e^{-\beta y}) & x \geq 0, y \geq 0 \\ 0 & \text{elsewhere.} \end{cases}$$

Find the marginal cdf's.

The marginal cdf's are obtained by letting one of the variables approach infinity:

$$F_X(x) = \lim_{y \to \infty} F_{X,Y}(x, y) = 1 - e^{-\alpha x} \quad x \geq 0$$

$$F_Y(y) = \lim_{x \to \infty} F_{X,Y}(x, y) = 1 - e^{-\beta y} \quad y \geq 0.$$

$X$ and $Y$ individually have exponential distributions with parameters $\alpha$ and $\beta$, respectively.

**Example 5.13**

Find the probability of the events $A = \{X \leq 1, Y \leq 1\}$, $B = \{X > x, Y > y\}$, where $x > 0$ and $y > 0$, and $D = \{1 < X \leq 2, 2 < Y \leq 5\}$ in Example 5.12.

The probability of $A$ is given directly by the cdf:

$$P[A] = P[X \leq 1, Y \leq 1] = F_{X,Y}(1, 1) = (1 - e^{-\alpha})(1 - e^{-\beta}).$$

The probability of $B$ requires more work. By DeMorgan's rule:

$$B^c = (\{X > x\} \cap \{Y > y\})^c = \{X \leq x\} \cup \{Y \leq y\}.$$

Corollary 5 in Section 2.2 gives the probability of the union of two events:

$$
\begin{aligned}
P[B^c] &= P[X \leq x] + P[Y \leq y] - P[X \leq x, Y \leq y] \\
&= (1 - e^{-\alpha x}) + (1 - e^{-\beta y}) - (1 - e^{-\alpha x})(1 - e^{-\beta y}) \\
&= 1 - e^{-\alpha x}e^{-\beta y}.
\end{aligned}
$$

Finally we obtain the probability of $B$:

$$P[B] = 1 - P[B^c] = e^{-\alpha x}e^{-\beta y}.$$

You should sketch the region $B$ on the plane and identify the events involved in the calculation of the probability of $B^c$.

The probability of event $D$ is found by applying property (vi) of the joint cdf:

$$
\begin{aligned}
P[1 < X &\leq 2, 2 < Y \leq 5] \\
&= F_{X,Y}(2, 5) - F_{X,Y}(2, 2) - F_{X,Y}(1, 5) + F_{X,Y}(1, 2) \\
&= (1 - e^{-2\alpha})(1 - e^{-5\beta}) - (1 - e^{-2\alpha})(1 - e^{-2\beta}) \\
&\quad -(1 - e^{-\alpha})(1 - e^{-5\beta}) + (1 - e^{-\alpha})(1 - e^{-2\beta}).
\end{aligned}
$$

## 5.3.1    Random Variables That Differ in Type

In some problems it is necessary to work with joint random variables that differ in type, that is, one is discrete and the other is continuous. Usually it is rather clumsy to work with the joint cdf, and so it is preferable to work with either $P[X = k, Y \leq y]$ or $P[X = k, y_1 < Y \leq y_2]$. These probabilities are sufficient to compute the joint cdf should we have to.

## Example 5.14    Communication Channel with Discrete Input and Continuous Output

The input $X$ to a communication channel is $+1$ volt or $-1$ volt with equal probability. The output $Y$ of the channel is the input plus a noise voltage $N$ that is uniformly distributed in the interval from $-2$ volts to $+2$ volts. Find $P[X = +1, Y \leq 0]$.

This problem lends itself to the use of conditional probability:

$$P[X = +1, Y \leq y] = P[Y \leq y \mid X = +1]P[X = +1],$$

where $P[X = +1] = 1/2$. When the input $X = 1$, the output $Y$ is uniformly distributed in the interval $[-1, 3]$; therefore

$$P[Y \leq y \mid X = +1] = \frac{y + 1}{4} \quad \text{for } -1 \leq y \leq 3.$$

Thus $P[X = +1, Y \leq 0] = P[Y \leq 0 \mid X = +1]P[X = +1] = (1/2)(1/4) = 1/8$.

## 5.4 THE JOINT PDF OF TWO CONTINUOUS RANDOM VARIABLES

The joint cdf allows us to compute the probability of events that correspond to "rectangular" shapes in the plane. To compute the probability of events corresponding to regions other than rectangles, we note that any reasonable shape (i.e., disk, polygon, or half-plane) can be approximated by the union of disjoint infinitesimal rectangles, $B_{j,k}$. For example, Fig. 5.12 shows how the events $A = \{X + Y \leq 1\}$ and $B = \{X^2 + X^2 \leq 1\}$ are approximated by rectangles of infinitesimal width. The probability of such events can therefore be approximated by the sum of the probabilities of infinitesimal rectangles, and if the cdf is sufficiently smooth, the probability of each rectangle can be expressed in terms of a density function:

$$P[B] \approx \sum_j \sum_k P[B_{j,k}] = \sum \sum_{(x_j,\, y_k) \in B} f_{X,Y}(x_j, y_k) \, \Delta x \Delta y.$$

As $\Delta x$ and $\Delta y$ approach zero, the above equation becomes an integral of a probability density function over the region $B$.

We say that the random variables **X and Y are jointly continuous** if the probabilities of events involving $(X, Y)$ can be expressed as an integral of a probability density function. In other words, there is a nonnegative function $f_{X,Y}(x, y)$, called the **joint**

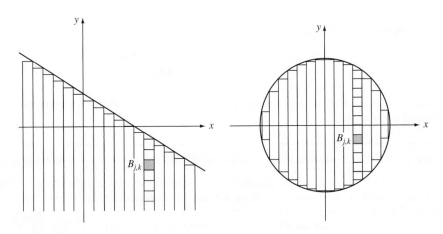

**FIGURE 5.12**
Some two-dimensional non-product form events.

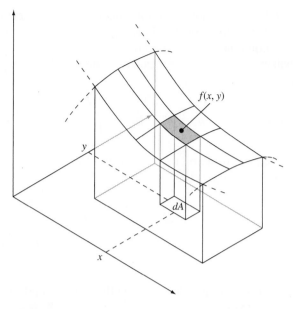

**FIGURE 5.13**
The probability of $A$ is the integral of $f_{X,Y}(x, y)$ over the region
defined by $A$.

**probability density function**, that is defined on the real plane such that for every event $B$, a subset of the plane,

$$P[\mathbf{X} \text{ in } B] = \int_B \int f_{X,Y}(x', y') \, dx' \, dy', \qquad (5.11)$$

as shown in Fig. 5.13. Note the similarity to Eq. (5.5) for discrete random variables. When $B$ is the entire plane, the integral must equal one:

$$1 = \int_{-\infty}^{\infty} \int_{-\infty}^{\infty} f_{X,Y}(x', y') \, dx' \, dy'. \qquad (5.12)$$

Equations (5.11) and (5.12) again suggest that the probability "mass" of an event is found by integrating the density of probability mass over the region corresponding to the event.

The joint cdf can be obtained in terms of the joint pdf of jointly continuous random variables by integrating over the semi-infinite rectangle defined by $(x, y)$:

$$F_{X,Y}(x, y) = \int_{-\infty}^{x} \int_{-\infty}^{y} f_{X,Y}(x', y') \, dx' \, dy'. \qquad (5.13)$$

It then follows that *if $X$ and $Y$ are jointly continuous random variables, then the pdf can be obtained from the cdf by differentiation*:

$$f_{X,Y}(x, y) = \frac{\partial^2 F_{X,Y}(x, y)}{\partial x \, \partial y}. \qquad (5.14)$$

Note that if $X$ and $Y$ are not jointly continuous, then it is possible that the above partial derivative does not exist. In particular, if the $F_{X,Y}(x, y)$ is discontinuous or if its partial derivatives are discontinuous, then the joint pdf as defined by Eq. (5.14) will not exist.

The probability of a rectangular region is obtained by letting $B = \{(x, y): a_1 < x \leq b_1$ and $a_2 < y \leq b_2\}$ in Eq. (5.11):

$$P[a_1 < X \leq b_1, a_2 < Y \leq b_2] = \int_{a_1}^{b_1} \int_{a_2}^{b_2} f_{X,Y}(x', y') \, dx' \, dy'. \qquad (5.15)$$

It then follows that the probability of an infinitesimal rectangle is the product of the pdf and the area of the rectangle:

$$P[x < X \leq x + dx, y < Y \leq y + dy] = \int_{x}^{x+dx} \int_{y}^{y+dy} f_{X,Y}(x', y') \, dx' \, dy'$$

$$\simeq f_{X,Y}(x, y) \, dx \, dy. \qquad (5.16)$$

Equation (5.16) can be interpreted as stating that the joint pdf specifies the probability of the product-form events

$$\{x < X \leq x + dx\} \cap \{y < Y \leq y + dy\}.$$

The **marginal pdf's** $f_X(x)$ and $f_Y(y)$ are obtained by taking the derivative of the corresponding marginal cdf's, $F_X(x) = F_{X,Y}(x, \infty)$ and $F_Y(y) = F_{X,Y}(\infty, y)$. Thus

$$f_X(x) = \frac{d}{dx} \int_{-\infty}^{x} \left\{ \int_{-\infty}^{\infty} f_{X,Y}(x', y') \, dy' \right\} dx'$$

$$= \int_{-\infty}^{\infty} f_{X,Y}(x, y') \, dy'. \qquad (5.17a)$$

Similarly,

$$f_Y(y) = \int_{-\infty}^{\infty} f_{X,Y}(x', y) \, dx'. \qquad (5.17b)$$

Thus the marginal pdf's are obtained by integrating out the variables that are not of interest.

Note that $f_X(x) \, dx \simeq P[x < X \leq x + dx, Y < \infty]$ is the probability of the infinitesimal strip shown in Fig. 5.14(a). This reminds us of the interpretation of the marginal pmf's as the probabilities of columns and rows in the case of discrete random variables. It is not surprising then that Eqs. (5.17a) and (5.17b) for the marginal pdf's and Eqs. (5.7a) and (5.7b) for the marginal pmf's are identical except for the fact that one contains an integral and the other a summation. As in the case of pmf's, we note that, in general, the joint pdf cannot be obtained from the marginal pdf's.

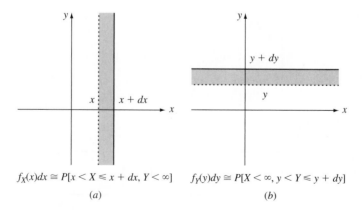

$$f_X(x)dx \cong P[x < X \leqslant x + dx, Y < \infty] \qquad f_Y(y)dy \cong P[X < \infty, y < Y \leqslant y + dy]$$

$$(a) \qquad\qquad\qquad (b)$$

**FIGURE 5.14**
Interpretation of marginal pdf's.

---

### Example 5.15    Jointly Uniform Random Variables

A randomly selected point $(X, Y)$ in the unit square has the uniform joint pdf given by

$$f_{X,Y}(x, y) = \begin{cases} 1 & 0 \leq x \leq 1 \text{ and } 0 \leq y \leq 1 \\ 0 & \text{elsewhere.} \end{cases}$$

The scattergram in Fig. 5.3(a) corresponds to this pair of random variables. Find the joint cdf of $X$ and $Y$.

The cdf is found by evaluating Eq. (5.13). You must be careful with the limits of the integral: The limits should define the region consisting of the intersection of the semi-infinite rectangle defined by $(x, y)$ and the region where the pdf is nonzero. There are five cases in this problem, corresponding to the five regions shown in Fig. 5.15.

**1.**    If $x < 0$ or $y < 0$, the pdf is zero and Eq. (5.14) implies

$$F_{X,Y}(x, y) = 0.$$

**2.**    If $(x, y)$ is inside the unit interval,

$$F_{X,Y}(x, y) = \int_0^x \int_0^y 1 \, dx' \, dy' = xy.$$

**3.**    If $0 \leq x \leq 1$ and $y > 1$,

$$F_{X,Y}(x, y) = \int_0^x \int_0^1 1 \, dx' \, dy' = x.$$

**4.**    Similarly, if $x > 1$ and $0 \leq y \leq 1$,

$$F_{X,Y}(x, y) = y.$$

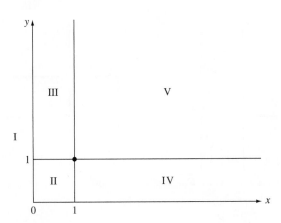

**FIGURE 5.15**
Regions that need to be considered separately in computing cdf
in Example 5.15.

5.   Finally, if $x > 1$ and $y > 1$,

$$F_{X,Y}(x, y) = \int_0^1 \int_0^1 1 \, dx' \, dy' = 1.$$

We see that this is the joint cdf of Example 5.11.

## Example 5.16

Find the normalization constant $c$ and the marginal pdf's for the following joint pdf:

$$f_{X,Y}(x, y) = \begin{cases} ce^{-x}e^{-y} & 0 \le y \le x < \infty \\ 0 & \text{elsewhere.} \end{cases}$$

The pdf is nonzero in the shaded region shown in Fig. 5.16(a). The constant $c$ is found from the normalization condition specified by Eq. (5.12):

$$1 = \int_0^\infty \int_0^x ce^{-x}e^{-y} \, dy \, dx = \int_0^\infty ce^{-x}(1 - e^{-x}) \, dx = \frac{c}{2}.$$

Therefore $c = 2$. The marginal pdf's are found by evaluating Eqs. (5.17a) and (5.17b):

$$f_X(x) = \int_0^\infty f_{X,Y}(x, y) \, dy = \int_0^x 2e^{-x}e^{-y} \, dy = 2e^{-x}(1 - e^{-x}) \qquad 0 \le x < \infty$$

and

$$f_Y(y) = \int_0^\infty f_{X,Y}(x, y) \, dx = \int_y^\infty 2e^{-x}e^{-y} \, dx = 2e^{-2y} \qquad 0 \le y < \infty.$$

You should fill in the steps in the evaluation of the integrals as well as verify that the marginal pdf's integrate to 1.

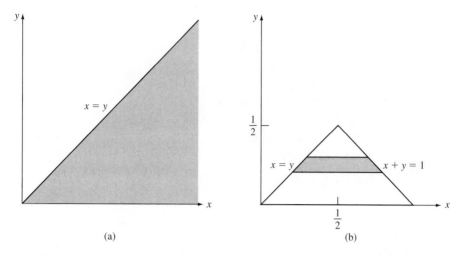

**FIGURE 5.16**
The random variables $X$ and $Y$ in Examples 5.16 and 5.17 have a pdf that is nonzero only in the shaded region shown in part (a).

---

### Example 5.17

Find $P[X + Y \leq 1]$ in Example 5.16.

Figure 5.16(b) shows the intersection of the event $\{X + Y \leq 1\}$ and the region where the pdf is nonzero. We obtain the probability of the event by "adding" (actually integrating) infinitesimal rectangles of width $dy$ as indicated in the figure:

$$P[X + Y \leq 1] = \int_0^{.5} \int_y^{1-y} 2e^{-x}e^{-y}\, dx\, dy = \int_0^{.5} 2e^{-y}[e^{-y} - e^{-(1-y)}]\, dy$$

$$= 1 - 2e^{-1}.$$

---

### Example 5.18   Jointly Gaussian Random Variables

The joint pdf of $X$ and $Y$, shown in Fig. 5.17, is

$$f_{X,Y}(x, y) = \frac{1}{2\pi\sqrt{1 - \rho^2}}e^{-(x^2 - 2\rho xy + y^2)/2(1 - \rho^2)} \qquad -\infty < x, y < \infty. \qquad (5.18)$$

We say that $X$ and $Y$ are jointly Gaussian.[1] Find the marginal pdf's.

The marginal pdf of $X$ is found by integrating $f_{X,Y}(x, y)$ over $y$:

$$f_X(x) = \frac{e^{-x^2/2(1 - \rho^2)}}{2\pi\sqrt{1 - \rho^2}}\int_{-\infty}^{\infty} e^{-(y^2 - 2\rho xy)/2(1 - \rho^2)}\, dy.$$

---

[1] This is an important special case of jointly Gaussian random variables. The general case is discussed in Section 5.9.

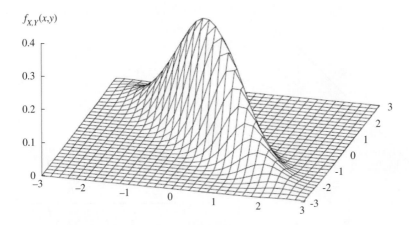

$f_{X,Y}(x,y)$

**FIGURE 5.17**
Joint pdf of two jointly Gaussian random variables.

We complete the square of the argument of the exponent by adding and subtracting $\rho^2 x^2$, that is, $y^2 - 2\rho xy + \rho^2 x^2 - \rho^2 x^2 = (y - \rho x)^2 - \rho^2 x^2$. Therefore

$$f_X(x) = \frac{e^{-x^2/2(1-\rho^2)}}{2\pi\sqrt{1 - \rho^2}} \int_{-\infty}^{\infty} e^{-[(y-\rho x)^2 - \rho^2 x^2]/2(1-\rho^2)} \, dy$$

$$= \frac{e^{-x^2/2}}{\sqrt{2\pi}} \int_{-\infty}^{\infty} \frac{e^{-(y-\rho x)^2/2(1-\rho^2)}}{\sqrt{2\pi(1 - \rho^2)}} \, dy$$

$$= \frac{e^{-x^2/2}}{\sqrt{2\pi}},$$

where we have noted that the last integral equals one since its integrand is a Gaussian pdf with mean $\rho x$ and variance $1 - \rho^2$. The marginal pdf of $X$ is therefore a one-dimensional Gaussian pdf with mean 0 and variance 1. From the symmetry of $f_{X,Y}(x, y)$ in $x$ and $y$, we conclude that the marginal pdf of $Y$ is also a one-dimensional Gaussian pdf with zero mean and unit variance.

## 5.5   INDEPENDENCE OF TWO RANDOM VARIABLES

**X and Y are independent random variables** if *any* event $A_1$ defined in terms of $X$ is independent of *any* event $A_2$ defined in terms of $Y$; that is,

$$P[X \text{ in } A_1, Y \text{ in } A_2] = P[X \text{ in } A_1]P[Y \text{ in } A_2]. \tag{5.19}$$

In this section we present a simple set of conditions for determining when $X$ and $Y$ are independent.

Suppose that $X$ and $Y$ are a pair of discrete random variables, and suppose we are interested in the probability of the event $A = A_1 \cap A_2$, where $A_1$ involves only $X$ and $A_2$ involves only $Y$. In particular, if $X$ and $Y$ are independent, then $A_1$ and $A_2$ are independent events. If we let $A_1 = \{X = x_j\}$ and $A_2 = \{Y = y_k\}$, then the independence of $X$ and $Y$ implies that

$$\begin{aligned}
p_{X,Y}(x_j, y_k) &= P[X = x_j, Y = y_k] \\
&= P[X = x_j]P[Y = y_k] \\
&= p_X(x_j)p_Y(y_k) \qquad \text{for all } x_j \text{ and } y_k.
\end{aligned} \tag{5.20}$$

Therefore, *if $X$ and $Y$ are independent discrete random variables, then the joint pmf is equal to the product of the marginal pmf's.*

Now suppose that we don't know if $X$ and $Y$ are independent, but we do know that the pmf satisfies Eq. (5.20). Let $A = A_1 \cap A_2$ be a product-form event as above, then

$$\begin{aligned}
P[A] &= \sum_{x_j \text{ in } A_1} \sum_{y_k \text{ in } A_2} p_{X,Y}(x_j, y_k) \\
&= \sum_{x_j \text{ in } A_1} \sum_{y_k \text{ in } A_2} p_X(x_j)p_Y(y_k) \\
&= \sum_{x_j \text{ in } A_1} p_X(x_j) \sum_{y_k \text{ in } A_2} p_Y(y_k) \\
&= P[A_1]P[A_2],
\end{aligned} \tag{5.21}$$

which implies that $A_1$ and $A_2$ are independent events. Therefore, *if the joint pmf of $X$ and $Y$ equals the product of the marginal pmf's, then $X$ and $Y$ are independent.* We have just proved that the statement "$X$ and $Y$ are independent" is equivalent to the statement "the joint pmf is equal to the product of the marginal pmf's." In mathematical language, we say, the "*discrete random variables $X$ and $Y$ are independent if and only if the joint pmf is equal to the product of the marginal pmf's for all $x_j$, $y_k$.*"

---

### Example 5.19

Is the pmf in Example 5.6 consistent with an experiment that consists of the independent tosses of two fair dice?

The probability of each face in a toss of a fair die is 1/6. If two fair dice are tossed and if the tosses are independent, then the probability of any pair of faces, say $j$ and $k$, is:

$$P[X = j, Y = k] = P[X = j]P[Y = k] = \frac{1}{36}.$$

Thus all possible pairs of outcomes should be equiprobable. This is not the case for the joint pmf given in Example 5.6. Therefore the tosses in Example 5.6 are not independent.

---

### Example 5.20

Are $Q$ and $R$ in Example 5.9 independent? From Example 5.9 we have

$$\begin{aligned}
P[Q = q]P[R = r] &= (1 - p^M)(p^M)^q \frac{(1 - p)}{1 - p^M} p^r \\
&= (1 - p)p^{Mq+r}
\end{aligned}$$

$$= P[Q = q, R = r] \qquad \text{for all } q = 0, 1, \ldots$$
$$r = 0, \ldots, M - 1.$$

Therefore $Q$ and $R$ are independent.

In general, it can be shown that the random variables *X and Y are independent if and only if their joint cdf is equal to the product of its marginal cdf's*:

$$F_{X,Y}(x, y) = F_X(x)F_Y(y) \qquad \text{for all } x \text{ and } y. \tag{5.22}$$

Similarly, if $X$ and $Y$ are jointly continuous, then *X and Y are independent if and only if their joint pdf is equal to the product of the marginal pdf's*:

$$f_{X,Y}(x, y) = f_X(x)f_Y(y) \qquad \text{for all } x \text{ and } y. \tag{5.23}$$

Equation (5.23) is obtained from Eq. (5.22) by differentiation. Conversely, Eq. (5.22) is obtained from Eq. (5.23) by integration.

### Example 5.21

Are the random variables $X$ and $Y$ in Example 5.16 independent?

Note that $f_X(x)$ and $f_Y(y)$ are nonzero for all $x > 0$ and all $y > 0$. Hence $f_X(x)f_Y(y)$ is nonzero in the entire positive quadrant. However $f_{X,Y}(x, y)$ is nonzero only in the region $y < x$ inside the positive quadrant. Hence Eq. (5.23) does not hold for all $x, y$ and the random variables are not independent. You should note that in this example the joint pdf appears to factor, but nevertheless it is not the product of the marginal pdf's.

### Example 5.22

Are the random variables $X$ and $Y$ in Example 5.18 independent? The product of the marginal pdf's of $X$ and $Y$ in Example 5.18 is

$$f_X(x)f_Y(y) = \frac{1}{2\pi}e^{-(x^2+y^2)/2} \qquad -\infty < x, y < \infty.$$

By comparing to Eq. (5.18) we see that the product of the marginals is equal to the joint pdf if and only if $\rho = 0$. Therefore the jointly Gaussian random variables $X$ and $Y$ are independent if and only if $\rho = 0$. We see in a later section that $\rho$ is the *correlation coefficient* between $X$ and $Y$.

### Example 5.23

Are the random variables $X$ and $Y$ independent in Example 5.12? If we multiply the marginal cdf's found in Example 5.12 we find

$$F_X(x)F_Y(y) = (1 - e^{-\alpha x})(1 - e^{-\beta y}) = F_{X,Y}(x, y) \qquad \text{for all } x \text{ and } y.$$

Therefore Eq. (5.22) is satisfied so $X$ and $Y$ are independent.

If $X$ and $Y$ are independent random variables, then the random variables defined by any pair of functions $g(X)$ and $h(Y)$ are also independent. To show this, consider the one-dimensional events $A$ and $B$. Let $A'$ be the set of all values of $x$ such that if $x$ is in $A'$ then $g(x)$ is in $A$, and let $B'$ be the set of all values of $y$ such that if $y$ is in $B'$ then $h(y)$ is in $B$. (In Chapter 3 we called $A'$ and $B'$ the equivalent events of $A$ and $B$.) Then

$$
\begin{aligned}
P[g(X) \text{ in } A, h(Y) \text{ in } B] &= P[X \text{ in } A', Y \text{ in } B'] \\
&= P[X \text{ in } A']P[Y \text{ in } B'] \\
&= P[g(X) \text{ in } A]P[h(Y) \text{ in } B].
\end{aligned}
\tag{5.24}
$$

The first and third equalities follow from the fact that $A$ and $A'$ and $B$ and $B'$ are equivalent events. The second equality follows from the independence of $X$ and $Y$. Thus $g(X)$ and $h(Y)$ are independent random variables.

## 5.6   JOINT MOMENTS AND EXPECTED VALUES OF A FUNCTION OF TWO RANDOM VARIABLES

The expected value of $X$ identifies the center of mass of the distribution of $X$. The variance, which is defined as the expected value of $(X - m)^2$, provides a measure of the spread of the distribution. In the case of two random variables we are interested in how $X$ and $Y$ vary together. In particular, we are interested in whether the variation of $X$ and $Y$ are correlated. For example, if $X$ increases does $Y$ tend to increase or to decrease? The joint moments of $X$ and $Y$, which are defined as expected values of functions of $X$ and $Y$, provide this information.

### 5.6.1   Expected Value of a Function of Two Random Variables

The problem of finding the expected value of a function of two or more random variables is similar to that of finding the expected value of a function of a single random variable. It can be shown that the expected value of $Z = g(X, Y)$ can be found using the following expressions:

$$
E[Z] =
\begin{cases}
\displaystyle\int_{-\infty}^{\infty}\int_{-\infty}^{\infty} g(x, y) f_{X,Y}(x, y)\, dx\, dy & X, Y \text{ jointly continuous} \\[2ex]
\displaystyle\sum_i \sum_n g(x_i, y_n) p_{X,Y}(x_i, y_n) & X, Y \text{ discrete.}
\end{cases}
\tag{5.25}
$$

---

**Example 5.24   Sum of Random Variables**

Let $Z = X + Y$. Find $E[Z]$.

$$
\begin{aligned}
E[Z] &= E[X + Y] \\
&= \int_{-\infty}^{\infty}\int_{-\infty}^{\infty} (x' + y') f_{X,Y}(x', y')\, dx'\, dy' \\
&= \int_{-\infty}^{\infty}\int_{-\infty}^{\infty} x' f_{X,Y}(x', y')\, dy'\, dx' + \int_{-\infty}^{\infty}\int_{-\infty}^{\infty} y' f_{X,Y}(x', y')\, dx'\, dy' \\
&= \int_{-\infty}^{\infty} x' f_X(x')\, dx' + \int_{-\infty}^{\infty} y' f_Y(y')\, dy' = E[X] + E[Y].
\end{aligned}
\tag{5.26}
$$

Thus the expected value of the sum of two random variables is equal to the sum of the individual expected values. Note that $X$ and $Y$ need not be independent.

The result in Example 5.24 and a simple induction argument show that *the expected value of a sum of n random variables is equal to the sum of the expected values:*

$$E[X_1 + X_2 + \cdots + X_n] = E[X_1] + \cdots + E[X_n]. \tag{5.27}$$

Note that the random variables do not have to be independent.

### Example 5.25    Product of Functions of Independent Random Variables

Suppose that $X$ and $Y$ are independent random variables, and let $g(X, Y) = g_1(X)g_2(Y)$. Find $E[g(X, Y)] = E[g_1(X)g_2(Y)]$.

$$
\begin{aligned}
E[g_1(X)g_2(Y)] &= \int_{-\infty}^{\infty} \int_{-\infty}^{\infty} g_1(x')g_2(y')f_X(x')f_Y(y') \, dx' \, dy' \\
&= \left\{ \int_{-\infty}^{\infty} g_1(x')f_X(x') \, dx' \right\} \left\{ \int_{-\infty}^{\infty} g_2(y')f_Y(y') \, dy' \right\} \\
&= E[g_1(X)]E[g_2(Y)].
\end{aligned}
$$

### 5.6.2    Joint Moments, Correlation, and Covariance

The joint moments of two random variables $X$ and $Y$ summarize information about their joint behavior. The $jk$th **joint moment of $X$ and $Y$** is defined by

$$
E[X^j Y^k] = \begin{cases} \displaystyle\int_{-\infty}^{\infty} \int_{-\infty}^{\infty} x^j y^k f_{X,Y}(x, y) \, dx \, dy & X, Y \text{ jointly continuous} \\[2ex] \displaystyle\sum_i \sum_n x_i^j y_n^k p_{X,Y}(x_i, y_n) & X, Y \text{ discrete.} \end{cases} \tag{5.28}
$$

If $j = 0$, we obtain the moments of $Y$, and if $k = 0$, we obtain the moments of $X$. In electrical engineering, it is customary to call the $j = 1\ k = 1$ moment, $E[XY]$, the **correlation of $X$ and $Y$**. If $E[XY] = 0$, then we say that **$X$ and $Y$ are orthogonal**.

The $jk$th **central moment of $X$ and $Y$** is defined as the joint moment of the centered random variables, $X - E[X]$ and $Y - E[Y]$:

$$E[(X - E[X])^j (Y - E[Y])^k].$$

Note that $j = 2\ k = 0$ gives VAR$(X)$ and $j = 0\ k = 2$ gives VAR$(Y)$.

The **covariance of $X$ and $Y$** is defined as the $j = k = 1$ central moment:

$$\mathrm{COV}(X, Y) = E[(X - E[X])(Y - E[Y])]. \tag{5.29}$$

The following form for $\mathrm{COV}(X, Y)$ is sometimes more convenient to work with:

$$\mathrm{COV}(X, Y) = E[XY - XE[Y] - YE[X] + E[X]E[Y]]$$

$$= E[XY] - 2E[X]E[Y] + E[X]E[Y]$$

$$= E[XY] - E[X]E[Y]. \tag{5.30}$$

Note that $\text{COV}(X, Y) = E[XY]$ if either of the random variables has mean zero.

---

**Example 5.26    Covariance of Independent Random Variables**

Let $X$ and $Y$ be independent random variables. Find their covariance.

$$\text{COV}(X, Y) = E[(X - E[X])(Y - E[Y])]$$

$$= E[X - E[X]]E[Y - E[Y]]$$

$$= 0,$$

where the second equality follows from the fact that $X$ and $Y$ are independent, and the third equality follows from $E[X - E[X]] = E[X] - E[X] = 0$. Therefore *pairs of independent random variables have covariance zero.*

---

Let's see how the covariance measures the correlation between $X$ and $Y$. The covariance measures the deviation from $m_X = E[X]$ and $m_Y = E[Y]$. If a positive value of $(X - m_X)$ tends to be accompanied by a positive values of $(Y - m_Y)$, and negative $(X - m_X)$ tend to be accompanied by negative $(Y - m_Y)$; then $(X - m_X)(Y - m_Y)$ will tend to be a positive value, and its expected value, $\text{COV}(X, Y)$, will be positive. This is the case for the scattergram in Fig. 5.3(d) where the observed points tend to cluster along a line of positive slope. On the other hand, if $(X - m_X)$ and $(Y - m_Y)$ tend to have opposite signs, then $\text{COV}(X, Y)$ will be negative. A scattergram for this case would have observation points cluster along a line of negative slope. Finally if $(X - m_X)$ and $(Y - m_Y)$ sometimes have the same sign and sometimes have opposite signs, then $\text{COV}(X, Y)$ will be close to zero. The three scattergrams in Figs. 5.3(a), (b), and (c) fall into this category.

Multiplying either $X$ or $Y$ by a large number will increase the covariance, so we need to normalize the covariance to measure the correlation in an absolute scale. The **correlation coefficient of $X$ and $Y$** is defined by

$$\rho_{X,Y} = \frac{\text{COV}(X, Y)}{\sigma_X \sigma_Y} = \frac{E[XY] - E[X]E[Y]}{\sigma_X \sigma_Y}, \tag{5.31}$$

where $\sigma_X = \sqrt{\text{VAR}(X)}$ and $\sigma_Y = \sqrt{\text{VAR}(Y)}$ are the standard deviations of $X$ and $Y$, respectively.

The correlation coefficient is a number that is at most 1 in magnitude:

$$-1 \le \rho_{X,Y} \le 1. \tag{5.32}$$

To show Eq. (5.32), we begin with an inequality that results from the fact that the expected value of the square of a random variable is nonnegative:

$$0 \le E\left\{ \left( \frac{X - E[X]}{\sigma_X} \pm \frac{Y - E[Y]}{\sigma_Y} \right)^2 \right\}$$

$$= 1 \pm 2\rho_{X,Y} + 1$$

$$= 2(1 \pm \rho_{X,Y}).$$

The last equation implies Eq. (5.32).

The extreme values of $\rho_{X,Y}$ are achieved when $X$ and $Y$ are related linearly, $Y = aX + b$; $\rho_{X,Y} = 1$ if $a > 0$ and $\rho_{X,Y} = -1$ if $a < 0$. In Section 6.5 we show that $\rho_{X,Y}$ can be viewed as a statistical measure of the extent to which $Y$ can be predicted by a linear function of $X$.

$X$ and $Y$ are said to be **uncorrelated** if $\rho_{X,Y} = 0$. If $X$ and $Y$ are independent, then COV$(X, Y) = 0$, so $\rho_{X,Y} = 0$. Thus *if $X$ and $Y$ are independent, then $X$ and $Y$ are uncorrelated.* In Example 5.22, we saw that if $X$ and $Y$ are jointly Gaussian and $\rho_{X,Y} = 0$, *then $X$ and $Y$ are independent random variables.* Example 5.27 shows that this is not always true for non-Gaussian random variables: It is possible for $X$ and $Y$ to be uncorrelated but not independent.

---

### Example 5.27 Uncorrelated but Dependent Random Variables

Let $\Theta$ be uniformly distributed in the interval $(0, 2\pi)$. Let

$$X = \cos \Theta \qquad \text{and} \qquad Y = \sin \Theta.$$

The point $(X, Y)$ then corresponds to the point on the unit circle specified by the angle $\Theta$, as shown in Fig. 5.18. In Example 4.36, we saw that the marginal pdf's of $X$ and $Y$ are arcsine pdf's, which are nonzero in the interval $(-1, 1)$. The product of the marginals is nonzero in the square defined by $-1 \le x \le 1$ and $-1 \le y \le 1$, so if $X$ and $Y$ were independent the point $(X, Y)$ would assume all values in this square. This is not the case, so $X$ and $Y$ are dependent.

We now show that $X$ and $Y$ are uncorrelated:

$$E[XY] = E[\sin \Theta \cos \Theta] = \frac{1}{2\pi} \int_0^{2\pi} \sin \phi \cos \phi \, d\phi$$

$$= \frac{1}{4\pi} \int_0^{2\pi} \sin 2\phi \, d\phi = 0.$$

Since $E[X] = E[Y] = 0$, Eq. (5.30) then implies that $X$ and $Y$ are uncorrelated.

---

### Example 5.28

Let $X$ and $Y$ be the random variables discussed in Example 5.16. Find $E[XY]$, COV$(X, Y)$, and $\rho_{X,Y}$.

Equations (5.30) and (5.31) require that we find the mean, variance, and correlation of $X$ and $Y$. From the marginal pdf's of $X$ and $Y$ obtained in Example 5.16, we find that $E[X] = 3/2$ and VAR$[X] = 5/4$, and that $E[Y] = 1/2$ and VAR$[Y] = 1/4$. The correlation of $X$ and $Y$ is

$$E[XY] = \int_0^\infty \int_0^x xy 2e^{-x} e^{-y} \, dy \, dx$$

$$= \int_0^\infty 2xe^{-x}(1 - e^{-x} - xe^{-x}) \, dx = 1.$$

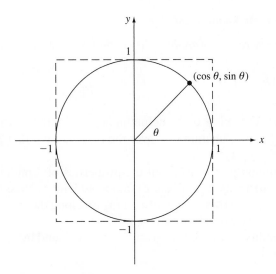

**FIGURE 5.18**
$(X, Y)$ is a point selected at random *on* the unit circle. $X$ and $Y$
are uncorrelated but not independent.

Thus the correlation coefficient is given by

$$\rho_{X,Y} = \frac{1 - \dfrac{3}{2}\dfrac{1}{2}}{\sqrt{\dfrac{5}{4}}\sqrt{\dfrac{1}{4}}} = \frac{1}{\sqrt{5}}.$$

## 5.7 CONDITIONAL PROBABILITY AND CONDITIONAL EXPECTATION

Many random variables of practical interest are not independent: The output $Y$ of a communication channel must depend on the input $X$ in order to convey information; consecutive samples of a waveform that varies slowly are likely to be close in value and hence are not independent. In this section we are interested in computing the probability of events concerning the random variable $Y$ given that we know $X = x$. We are also interested in the expected value of $Y$ given $X = x$. We show that the notions of conditional probability and conditional expectation are extremely useful tools in solving problems, even in situations where we are only concerned with one of the random variables.

### 5.7.1 Conditional Probability

The definition of conditional probability in Section 2.4 allows us to compute the probability that $Y$ is in $A$ given that we know that $X = x$:

$$P[Y \text{ in } A \mid X = x] = \frac{P[Y \text{ in } A, X = x]}{P[X = x]} \quad \text{for } P[X = x] > 0. \qquad (5.33)$$

### Case 1: *X* Is a Discrete Random Variable

*For X and Y discrete random variables,* the **conditional pmf of Y given** $X = x$ is defined by:

$$p_Y(y \mid x) = P[Y = y \mid X = x] = \frac{P[X = x, Y = y]}{P[X = x]} = \frac{p_{X,Y}(x, y)}{p_X(x)} \qquad (5.34)$$

for $x$ such that $P[X = x] > 0$. We define $p_Y(y \mid x) = 0$ for $x$ such that $P[X = x] = 0$. Note that $p_Y(y \mid x)$ is a function of $y$ over the real line, and that $p_Y(y \mid x) > 0$ only for $y$ in a discrete set $\{y_1, y_2, \dots\}$.

The conditional pmf satisfies all the properties of a pmf, that is, it assigns non-negative values to every $y$ and these values add to 1. Note from Eq. (5.34) that $p_Y(y \mid x_k)$ is simply the cross section of $p_{X,Y}(x_k, y)$ along the $X = x_k$ column in Fig. 5.6, but normalized by the probability $p_X(x_k)$.

The probability of an event $A$ given $X = x_k$ is found by adding the pmf values of the outcomes in $A$:

$$P[Y \text{ in } A \mid X = x_k] = \sum_{y_j \text{in } A} p_Y(y_j \mid x_k). \qquad (5.35)$$

If *X and Y are independent,* then using Eq (5.20)

$$p_Y(y_j \mid x_k) = \frac{P[X = x_k, Y = y_j]}{P[X = x_k]} = P[Y = y_j] = p_Y(y_j). \qquad (5.36)$$

In other words, knowledge that $X = x_k$ does not affect the probability of events $A$ involving $Y$.

Equation (5.34) implies that the joint pmf $p_{X,Y}(x, y)$ can be expressed as the product of a conditional pmf and a marginal pmf:

$$p_{X,Y}(x_k, y_j) = p_Y(y_j \mid x_k)p_X(x_k) \text{ and } p_{X,Y}(x_k, y_j) = p_X(x_k \mid y_j)p_Y(y_j). \qquad (5.37)$$

This expression is very useful when we can view the pair $(X, Y)$ as being generated sequentially, e.g., first $X$, and then $Y$ given $X = x$. We find the probability that $Y$ is in $A$ as follows:

$$P[Y \text{ in } A] = \sum_{\text{all } x_k} \sum_{y_j \text{ in } A} p_{X,Y}(x_k, y_j)$$

$$= \sum_{\text{all } x_k} \sum_{y_j \text{ in } A} p_Y(y_j \mid x_k)p_X(x_k)$$

$$= \sum_{\text{all } x_k} p_X(x_k) \sum_{y_j \text{ in } A} p_Y(y_j \mid x_k)$$

$$= \sum_{\text{all } x_k} P[Y \text{ in } A \mid X = x_k]p_X(x_k). \qquad (5.38)$$

Equation (5.38) is simply a restatement of the theorem on total probability discussed in Chapter 2. In other words, to compute $P[Y \text{ in } A]$ we can first compute $P[Y \text{ in } A \mid X = x_k]$ and then "average" over $X_k$.

### Example 5.29    Loaded Dice

Find $p_Y(y|5)$ in the loaded dice experiment considered in Examples 5.6 and 5.8.

In Example 5.8 we found that $p_X(5) = 1/6$. Therefore:

$$p_Y(y|5) = \frac{p_{X,Y}(5, y)}{p_X(5)} \text{ and so } p_Y(5|5) = 2/7 \text{ and}$$

$$p_Y(1|5) = p_Y(2|5) = p_Y(3|5) = p_Y(4|5) = p_Y(6|5) = 1/7.$$

Clearly this die is loaded.

### Example 5.30    Number of Defects in a Region; Random Splitting of Poisson Counts

The total number of defects $X$ on a chip is a Poisson random variable with mean $\alpha$. Each defect has a probability $p$ of falling in a specific region $R$ and the location of each defect is independent of the locations of other defects. Find the pmf of the number of defects $Y$ that fall in the region $R$.

We can imagine performing a Bernoulli trial each time a defect occurs with a "success" occurring when the defect falls in the region $R$. If the total number of defects is $X = k$, then $Y$ is a binomial random variable with parameters $k$ and $p$:

$$p_Y(j|k) = \begin{cases} 0 & j > k \\ \binom{k}{j} p^j (1 - p)^{k-j} & 0 \le j \le k. \end{cases}$$

From Eq. (5.38) and noting that $k \ge j$, we have

$$p_Y(j) = \sum_{k=0}^{\infty} p_Y(j|k) p_X(k) = \sum_{k=j}^{\infty} \frac{k!}{j!(k-j)!} p^j (1 - p)^{k-j} \frac{\alpha^k}{k!} e^{-\alpha}$$

$$= \frac{(\alpha p)^j e^{-\alpha}}{j!} \sum_{k=j}^{\infty} \frac{\{(1 - p)\alpha\}^{k-j}}{(k-j)!}$$

$$= \frac{(\alpha p)^j e^{-\alpha}}{j!} e^{(1-p)\alpha} = \frac{(\alpha p)^j}{j!} e^{-\alpha p}.$$

Thus $Y$ is a Poisson random variable with mean $\alpha p$.

Suppose $Y$ is a continuous random variable. Eq. (5.33) can be used to define the **conditional cdf of $Y$ given $X = x_k$:**

$$F_Y(y|x_k) = \frac{P[Y \le y, X = x_k]}{P[X = x_k]}, \quad \text{for } P[X = x_k] > 0. \quad (5.39)$$

It is easy to show that $F_Y(y|x_k)$ satisfies all the properties of a cdf. The **conditional pdf of $Y$ given $X = x_k$**, if the derivative exists, is given by

$$f_Y(y|x_k) = \frac{d}{dy} F_Y(y|x_k). \quad (5.40)$$

*If X and Y are independent, $P[Y \leq y, X = X_k] = P[Y \leq y]P[X = X_k]$ so $F_Y(y \mid x) =$ $F_Y(y)$ and $f_Y(y \mid x) = f_Y(y)$.* The probability of event $A$ given $X = x_k$ is obtained by integrating the conditional pdf:

$$P[Y \text{ in } A \mid X = x_k] = \int_{y \text{ in } A} f_Y(y \mid x_k) \, dy. \tag{5.41}$$

We obtain $P[Y \text{ in } A]$ using Eq. (5.38).

---

**Example 5.31   Binary Communications System**

The input $X$ to a communication channel assumes the values $+1$ or $-1$ with probabilities $1/3$ and $2/3$. The output $Y$ of the channel is given by $Y = X + N$, where $N$ is a zero-mean, unit variance Gaussian random variable. Find the conditional pdf of $Y$ given $X = +1$, and given $X = -1$. Find $P[X = +1 \mid Y > 0]$.

The conditional cdf of $Y$ given $X = +1$ is:

$$F_Y(y \mid +1) = P[Y \leq y \mid X = +1] = P[N + 1 \leq y]$$

$$= P[N \leq y - 1] = \int_{-\infty}^{y-1} \frac{1}{\sqrt{2\pi}} e^{-x^2/2} \, dx$$

where we noted that if $X = +1$, then $Y = N + 1$ and $Y$ depends only on $N$. Thus, if $X = +1$, then $Y$ is a Gaussian random variable with mean 1 and unit variance. Similarly, if $X = -1$, then $Y$ is Gaussian with mean $-1$ and unit variance.

The probabilities that $Y > 0$ given $X = +1$ and $X = -1$ is:

$$P[Y > 0 \mid X = +1] = \int_0^\infty \frac{1}{\sqrt{2\pi}} e^{-(x-1)^2/2} \, dx = \int_{-1}^\infty \frac{1}{\sqrt{2\pi}} e^{-t^2/2} \, dt = 1 - Q(1) = 0.841.$$

$$P[Y > 0 \mid X = -1] = \int_0^\infty \frac{1}{\sqrt{2\pi}} e^{-(x+1)^2/2} \, dx = \int_1^\infty \frac{1}{\sqrt{2\pi}} e^{-t^2/2} \, dt = Q(1) = 0.159.$$

Applying Eq. (5.38), we obtain:

$$P[Y > 0] = P[Y > 0 \mid X = +1]\frac{1}{3} + P[Y > 0 \mid X = -1]\frac{2}{3} = 0.386.$$

From Bayes' theorem we find:

$$P[X = +1 \mid Y > 0] = \frac{P[Y > 0 \mid X = +1]P[X = +1]}{P[Y > 0]} = \frac{(1 - Q(1))/3}{(1 + Q(1))/3} = 0.726.$$

We conclude that if $Y > 0$, then $X = +1$ is more likely than $X = -1$. Therefore the receiver should decide that the input is $X = +1$ when it observes $Y > 0$.

---

In the previous example, we made an interesting step that is worth elaborating on because it comes up quite frequently: $P[Y \leq y \mid X = +1] = P[N + 1 \leq y]$, where $Y = X + N$. Let's take a closer look:

$$P[Y \leq z \mid X = x] = \frac{P[\{X + N \leq z\} \cap \{X = x\}]}{P[X = x]} = \frac{P[\{x + N \leq z\} \cap \{X = x\}]}{P[X = x]}$$

$$= P[x + N \leq z \mid X = x] = P[N \leq z - x \mid X = x].$$

In the first line, the events $\{X + N \leq z\}$ and $\{x + N \leq z\}$ are quite different. The first involves the two random variables $X$ and $N$, whereas the second only involves $N$ and consequently is much simpler. We can then apply an expression such as Eq. (5.38) to obtain $P[Y \leq z]$. The step we made in the example, however, is even more interesting. Since $X$ and $N$ are independent random variables, we can take the expression one step further:

$$P[Y \leq z \mid X = x] = P[N \leq z - x \mid X = x] = P[N \leq z - x].$$

The independence of $X$ and $N$ allows us to dispense with the conditioning on $x$ altogether!

### Case 2: X Is a Continuous Random Variable

*If X is a continuous random variable*, then $P[X = x] = 0$ so Eq. (5.33) is undefined for all $x$. If $X$ and $Y$ have a joint pdf that is continuous and nonzero over some region of the plane, we define the **conditional cdf of $Y$ given $X = x$** by the following limiting procedure:

$$F_Y(y \mid x) = \lim_{h \to 0} F_Y(y \mid x < X \leq x + h). \tag{5.42}$$

The conditional cdf on the right side of Eq. (5.42) is:

$$F_Y(y \mid x < X \leq x + h) = \frac{P[Y \leq y, x < X \leq x + h]}{P[x < X \leq x + h]}$$

$$= \frac{\displaystyle\int_{-\infty}^{y} \int_{x}^{x+h} f_{X,Y}(x', y') \, dx' \, dy'}{\displaystyle\int_{x}^{x+h} f_X(x') \, dx'} = \frac{\displaystyle\int_{-\infty}^{y} f_{X,Y}(x, y') \, dy' h}{f_X(x) h}. \tag{5.43}$$

As we let $h$ approach zero, Eqs. (5.42) and (5.43) imply that

$$F_Y(y \mid x) = \frac{\displaystyle\int_{-\infty}^{y} f_{X,Y}(x, y') \, dy'}{f_X(x)}. \tag{5.44}$$

The **conditional pdf of $Y$ given $X = x$** is then:

$$f_Y(y \mid x) = \frac{d}{dy} F_Y(y \mid x) = \frac{f_{X,Y}(x, y)}{f_X(x)}. \tag{5.45}$$

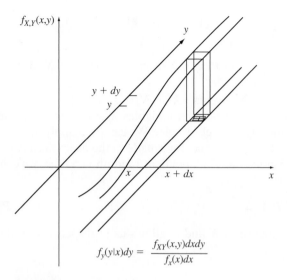

**FIGURE 5.19**
Interpretation of conditional pdf.

It is easy to show that $f_Y(y\,|\,x)$ satisfies the properties of a pdf. We can interpret $f_Y(y\,|\,x)\,dy$ as the probability that $Y$ is in the infinitesimal strip defined by $(y, y + dy)$ given that $X$ is in the infinitesimal strip defined by $(x, x + dx)$, as shown in Fig. 5.19.

The probability of event $A$ given $X = x$ is obtained as follows:

$$P[Y \text{ in } A\,|\,X = x] = \int_{y \text{ in } A} f_Y(y\,|\,x)\,dy. \qquad (5.46)$$

There is a strong resemblance between Eq. (5.34) for the discrete case and Eq. (5.45) for the continuous case. Indeed many of the same properties hold. For example, we obtain the multiplication rule from Eq. (5.45):

$$f_{X,Y}(x, y) = f_Y(y\,|\,x)f_X(x) \text{ and } f_{X,Y}(x, y) = f_X(x\,|\,y)f_Y(y). \qquad (5.47)$$

*If X and Y are independent*, then $f_{X,Y}(x, y) = f_X(x)f_Y(y)$ and $f_Y(y\,|\,x) = f_Y(y)$, $f_X(x\,|\,y) = f_X(x)$, $F_Y(y\,|\,x) = F_Y(y)$, and $F_X(x\,|\,y) = F_X(x)$.

By combining Eqs. (5.46) and (5.47), we can show that:

$$P[Y \text{ in } A] = \int_{-\infty}^{\infty} P[Y \text{ in } A\,|\,X = x]f_X(x)\,dx. \qquad (5.48)$$

You can think of Eq. (5.48) as the "continuous" version of the theorem on total probability. The following examples show the usefulness of the above results in calculating the probabilities of complicated events.

## Example 5.32

Let $X$ and $Y$ be the random variables in Example 5.8. Find $f_X(x\,|\,y)$ and $f_Y(y\,|\,x)$.
  Using the marginal pdf's obtained in Example 5.8, we have

$$f_X(y\,|\,x) = \frac{2e^{-x}e^{-y}}{2e^{-2y}} = e^{-(x-y)} \qquad\qquad \text{for } x \geq y$$

$$f_Y(y\,|\,x) = \frac{2e^{-x}e^{-y}}{2e^{-x}(1 - e^{-x})} = \frac{e^{-y}}{1 - e^{-x}} \qquad \text{for } 0 < y < x.$$

The conditional pdf of $X$ is an exponential pdf shifted by $y$ to the right. The conditional pdf of $Y$ is an exponential pdf that has been truncated to the interval $[0, x]$.

## Example 5.33   Number of Arrivals During a Customer's Service Time

The number $N$ of customers that arrive at a service station during a time $t$ is a Poisson random variable with parameter $\beta t$. The time $T$ required to service each customer is an exponential random variable with parameter $\alpha$. Find the pmf for the number $N$ that arrive during the service time $T$ of a specific customer. Assume that the customer arrivals are independent of the customer service time.
  Equation (5.48) holds even if $Y$ is a discrete random variable, thus

$$P[N = k] = \int_0^\infty P[N = k\,|\,T = t]f_T(t)\,dt$$

$$= \int_0^\infty \frac{(\beta t)^k}{k!}e^{-\beta t}\alpha e^{-\alpha t}\,dt$$

$$= \frac{\alpha\beta^k}{k!}\int_0^\infty t^k e^{-(\alpha+\beta)t}\,dt.$$

Let $r = (\alpha + \beta)t$, then

$$P[N = k] = \frac{\alpha\beta^k}{k!(\alpha + \beta)^{k+1}}\int_0^\infty r^k e^{-r}\,dr$$

$$= \frac{\alpha\beta^k}{(\alpha + \beta)^{k+1}} = \left(\frac{\alpha}{(\alpha + \beta)}\right)\left(\frac{\beta}{(\alpha + \beta)}\right)^k,$$

where we have used the fact that the last integral is a gamma function and is equal to $k!$. Thus $N$ is a geometric random variable with probability of "success" $\alpha/(\alpha + \beta)$. Each time a customer arrives we can imagine that a new Bernoulli trial begins where "success" occurs if the customer's service time is completed before the next arrival.

## Example 5.34

$X$ is selected at random from the unit interval; $Y$ is then selected at random from the interval$(0, X)$. Find the cdf of $Y$.

When $X = x$, $Y$ is uniformly distributed in $(0, x)$ so the conditional cdf given $X = x$ is

$$P[Y \le y \,|\, X = k] = \begin{cases} y/x & 0 \le y \le x \\ 1 & x < y. \end{cases}$$

Equation (5.48) and the above conditional cdf yield:

$$F_Y(y) = P[Y \le y] = \int_0^1 P[Y \le y \,|\, X = x] f_X(x) \, dx =$$

$$= \int_0^y 1 \, dx' + \int_y^1 \frac{y}{x'} \, dx' = y - y \ln y.$$

The corresponding pdf is obtained by taking the derivative of the cdf:

$$f_Y(y) = -\ln y \quad 0 \le y \le 1.$$

---

### Example 5.35    Maximum A Posteriori Receiver

For the communications system in Example 5.31, find the probability that the input was $X = +1$ given that the output of the channel is $Y = y$.

This is a tricky version of Bayes' rule. Condition on the event $\{y < Y \le y + \Delta\}$ instead of $\{Y = y\}$:

$$P[X = +1 \,|\, y < Y < y + \Delta] = \frac{P[y < Y < y + \Delta \,|\, X = +1]P[X = +1]}{P[y < Y < y + \Delta]}$$

$$= \frac{f_Y(y \,|\, +1)\Delta(1/3)}{f_Y(y \,|\, +1)\Delta(1/3) + f_Y(y \,|\, -1)\Delta(2/3)}$$

$$= \frac{\dfrac{1}{\sqrt{2\pi}} e^{-(y-1)^2/2}(1/3)}{\dfrac{1}{\sqrt{2\pi}} e^{-(y-1)^2/2}(1/3) + \dfrac{1}{\sqrt{2\pi}} e^{-(y+1)^2/2}(2/3)}$$

$$= \frac{e^{-(y-1)^2/2}}{e^{-(y-1)^2/2} + 2e^{-(y+1)^2/2}} = \frac{1}{1 + 2e^{-2y}}.$$

The above expression is equal to 1/2 when $y_T = 0.3466$. For $y > y_T$, $X = +1$ is more likely, and for $y < y_T$, $X = -1$ is more likely. A receiver that selects the input $X$ that is more likely given $Y = y$ is called a *maximum a posteriori receiver*.

---

### 5.7.2    Conditional Expectation

The **conditional expectation of $Y$ given $X = x$** is defined by

$$E[Y \,|\, x] = \int_{-\infty}^{\infty} y f_Y(y \,|\, x) \, dy. \tag{5.49a}$$

In the special case where $X$ and $Y$ are both discrete random variables we have:

$$E[Y \mid x_k] = \sum_{y_j} y_j p_Y(y_j \mid x_k). \tag{5.49b}$$

Clearly, $E[Y \mid x]$ is simply the center of mass associated with the conditional pdf or pmf.

The conditional expectation $E[Y \mid x]$ can be viewed as defining a function of $x$: $g(x) = E[Y \mid x]$. It therefore makes sense to talk about the random variable $g(X) = E[Y \mid X]$. We can imagine that a random experiment is performed and a value for $X$ is obtained, say $X = x_0$, and then the value $g(x_0) = E[Y \mid x_0]$ is produced. We are interested in $E[g(X)] = E[E[Y \mid X]]$. In particular, we now show that

$$E[Y] = E[E[Y \mid X]], \tag{5.50}$$

where the right-hand side is

$$E[E[Y \mid X]] = \int_{-\infty}^{\infty} E[Y \mid x] f_X(x)\, dx \qquad X \text{ continuous} \tag{5.51a}$$

$$E[E[Y \mid X]] = \sum_{x_k} E[Y \mid x_k] p_X(x_k) \qquad X \text{ discrete.} \tag{5.51b}$$

We prove Eq. (5.50) for the case where $X$ and $Y$ are jointly continuous random variables, then

$$\begin{aligned}
E[E[Y \mid X]] &= \int_{-\infty}^{\infty} E[Y \mid x] f_X(x)\, dx \\
&= \int_{-\infty}^{\infty} \int_{-\infty}^{\infty} y f_Y(y \mid x)\, dy\, f_X(x)\, dx \\
&= \int_{-\infty}^{\infty} y \int_{-\infty}^{\infty} f_{X,Y}(x, y)\, dx\, dy \\
&= \int_{-\infty}^{\infty} y f_Y(y)\, dy = E[Y].
\end{aligned}$$

The above result also holds for the expected value of a function of $Y$:

$$E[h(Y)] = E[E[h(Y) \mid X]].$$

In particular, the $k$th moment of $Y$ is given by

$$E[Y^k] = E[E[Y^k \mid X]].$$

---

## Example 5.36    Average Number of Defects in a Region

Find the mean of $Y$ in Example 5.30 using conditional expectation.

$$E[Y] = \sum_{k=0}^{\infty} E[Y \mid X = k] P[X = k] = \sum_{k=0}^{\infty} kp P[X = k] = pE[X] = p\alpha.$$

The second equality uses the fact that $E[Y \mid X = k] = kp$ since $Y$ is binomial with parameters $k$ and $p$. Note that the second to the last equality holds for *any* pmf of $X$. The fact that $X$ is Poisson with mean $\alpha$ is not used until the last equality.

---

### Example 5.37    Binary Communications Channel

Find the mean of the output $Y$ in the communications channel in Example 5.31.

Since $Y$ is a Gaussian random variable with mean $+1$ when $X = +1$, and $-1$ when $X = -1$, the conditional expected values of $Y$ given $X$ are:

$$E[Y \mid +1] = 1 \quad \text{and} \quad E[Y \mid -1] = -1.$$

Equation (5.38b) implies

$$E[Y] = \sum_{k=0}^{\infty} E[Y \mid X = k] P[X = k] = +1(1/3) - 1(2/3) = -1/3.$$

The mean is negative because the $X = -1$ inputs occur twice as often as $X = +1$.

---

### Example 5.38    Average Number of Arrivals in a Service Time

Find the mean and variance of the number of customer arrivals $N$ during the service time $T$ of a specific customer in Example (5.33).

$N$ is a Poisson random variable with parameter $\beta t$ when $T = t$ is given, so the first two conditional moments are:

$$E[N \mid T = t] = \beta t \qquad E[N^2 \mid T = t] = (\beta t) + (\beta t)^2.$$

The first two moments of $N$ are obtained from Eq. (5.50):

$$E[N] = \int_0^{\infty} E[N \mid T = t] f_T(t) \, dt = \int_0^{\infty} \beta t f_T(t) \, dt = \beta E[T]$$

$$E[N^2] = \int_0^{\infty} E[N^2 \mid T = t] f_T(t) \, dt = \int_0^{\infty} \{\beta t + \beta^2 t^2\} f_T(t) \, dt$$

$$= \beta E[T] + \beta^2 E[T^2].$$

The variance of $N$ is then

$$\begin{aligned}
\mathrm{VAR}[N] &= E[N^2] - (E[N])^2 \\
&= \beta^2 E[T^2] + \beta E[T] - \beta^2 (E[T])^2 \\
&= \beta^2 \, \mathrm{VAR}[T] + \beta E[T].
\end{aligned}$$

Note that if $T$ is not random (i.e., $E[T] = $ constant and $\mathrm{VAR}[T] = 0$) then the mean and variance of $N$ are those of a Poisson random variable with parameter $\beta E[T]$. When $T$ is random, the mean of $N$ remains the same but the variance of $N$ increases by the term $\beta^2 \, \mathrm{VAR}[T]$, that is, the variability of $T$ causes greater variability in $N$. Up to this point, we have intentionally avoided using the fact that $T$ has an exponential distribution to emphasize that the above results hold for *any* service time distribution $f_T(t)$. If *T is exponential with parameter* $\alpha$, then $E[T] = 1/\alpha$ and $\text{VAR}[T] = 1/\alpha^2$, so

$$E[N] = \frac{\beta}{\alpha} \quad \text{and} \quad \text{VAR}[N] = \frac{\beta^2}{\alpha^2} + \frac{\beta}{\alpha}.$$

## 5.8    FUNCTIONS OF TWO RANDOM VARIABLES

Quite often we are interested in one or more functions of the random variables associated with some experiment. For example, if we make repeated measurements of the same random quantity, we might be interested in the maximum and minimum value in the set, as well as the sample mean and sample variance. In this section we present methods of determining the probabilities of events involving functions of two random variables.

### 5.8.1    One Function of Two Random Variables

Let the random variable $Z$ be defined as a function of two random variables:

$$Z = g(X, Y). \tag{5.52}$$

The cdf of $Z$ is found by first finding the equivalent event of $\{Z \leq z\}$, that is, the set $R_z = \{\mathbf{x} = (x, y) \text{ such that } g(\mathbf{x}) \leq z\}$, then

$$F_z(z) = P[\mathbf{X} \text{ in } R_z] = \iint\limits_{(x,y)\in R_z} f_{X,Y}(x', y')\, dx'\, dy'. \tag{5.53}$$

The pdf of $Z$ is then found by taking the derivative of $F_z(z)$.

---

### Example 5.39    Sum of Two Random Variables

Let $Z = X + Y$. Find $F_Z(z)$ and $f_Z(z)$ in terms of the joint pdf of $X$ and $Y$.

  The cdf of $Z$ is found by integrating the joint pdf of $X$ and $Y$ over the region of the plane corresponding to the event $\{Z \leq z\}$, as shown in Fig. 5.20.

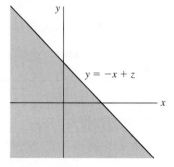

**FIGURE 5.20**
$P[Z \leq z] = P[X + Y \leq z]$.

$$F_Z(z) = \int_{-\infty}^{\infty} \int_{-\infty}^{z-x'} f_{X,Y}(x', y') \, dy' \, dx'.$$

The pdf of $Z$ is

$$f_Z(z) = \frac{d}{dz} F_Z(z) = \int_{-\infty}^{\infty} f_{X,Y}(x', z - x') \, dx'. \tag{5.54}$$

Thus the pdf for the sum of two random variables is given by a *superposition* integral.

If $X$ and $Y$ are independent random variables, then by Eq. (5.23) the pdf is given by the *convolution integral* of the marginal pdf's of $X$ and $Y$:

$$f_Z(z) = \int_{-\infty}^{\infty} f_X(x') f_Y(z - x') \, dx'. \tag{5.55}$$

In Chapter 7 we show how transform methods are used to evaluate convolution integrals such as Eq. (5.55).

---

## Example 5.40    Sum of Nonindependent Gaussian Random Variables

Find the pdf of the sum $Z = X + Y$ of two zero-mean, unit-variance Gaussian random variables with correlation coefficient $\rho = -1/2$.

The joint pdf for this pair of random variables was given in Example 5.18. The pdf of $Z$ is obtained by substituting the pdf for the joint Gaussian random variables into the superposition integral found in Example 5.39:

$$
\begin{aligned}
f_Z(z) &= \int_{-\infty}^{\infty} f_{X,Y}(x', z - x') \, dx' \\
&= \frac{1}{2\pi(1 - \rho^2)^{1/2}} \int_{-\infty}^{\infty} e^{-[x'^2 - 2\rho x'(z-x') + (z-x')^2]/2(1-\rho^2)} \, dx' \\
&= \frac{1}{2\pi(3/4)^{1/2}} \int_{-\infty}^{\infty} e^{-(x'^2 - x'z + z^2)/2(3/4)} \, dx'.
\end{aligned}
$$

After completing the square of the argument in the exponent we obtain

$$f_Z(z) = \frac{e^{-z^2/2}}{\sqrt{2\pi}}.$$

Thus the sum of these two nonindependent Gaussian random variables is also a zero-mean, unit-variance Gaussian random variable.

---

## Example 5.41    A System with Standby Redundancy

A system with standby redundancy has a single key component in operation and a duplicate of that component in standby mode. When the first component fails, the second component is put into operation. Find the pdf of the lifetime of the standby system if the components have independent exponentially distributed lifetimes with the same mean.

Let $T_1$ and $T_2$ be the lifetimes of the two components, then the system lifetime is $T = T_1 + T_2$, and the pdf of $T$ is given by Eq. (5.55). The terms in the integrand are

$$f_{T_1}(x) = \begin{cases} \lambda e^{-\lambda x} & x \geq 0 \\ 0 & x < 0 \end{cases}$$

$$f_{T_2}(z - x) = \begin{cases} \lambda e^{-\lambda(z-x)} & z - x \geq 0 \\ 0 & x > z. \end{cases}$$

Note that the first equation sets the lower limit of integration to 0 and the second equation sets the upper limit to $z$. Equation (5.55) becomes

$$f_T(z) = \int_0^z \lambda e^{-\lambda x} \lambda e^{-\lambda(z-x)} \, dx$$

$$= \lambda^2 e^{-\lambda z} \int_0^z dx = \lambda^2 z e^{-\lambda z}.$$

Thus $T$ is an Erlang random variable with parameter $m = 2$.

---

The conditional pdf can be used to find the pdf of a function of several random variables. Let $Z = g(X, Y)$, and suppose we are given that $Y = y$, then $Z = g(X, y)$ is a function of one random variable. Therefore we can use the methods developed in Section 4.5 for single random variables to find the pdf of $Z$ *given* $Y = y$: $f_Z(z | Y = y)$. The pdf of $Z$ is then found from

$$f_Z(z) = \int_{-\infty}^{\infty} f_Z(z | y') f_Y(y') \, dy'.$$

---

## Example 5.42

Let $Z = X/Y$. Find the pdf of $Z$ if $X$ and $Y$ are independent and both exponentially distributed with mean one.

Assume $Y = y$, then $Z = X/y$ is simply a scaled version of $X$. Therefore from Example 4.31

$$f_Z(z | y) = |y| f_X(yz | y).$$

The pdf of $Z$ is therefore

$$f_Z(z) = \int_{-\infty}^{\infty} |y'| f_X(y'z | y') f_Y(y') \, dy' = \int_{-\infty}^{\infty} |y'| f_{X,Y}(y'z, y') \, dy'.$$

We now use the fact that $X$ and $Y$ are independent and exponentially distributed with mean one:

$$f_Z(z) = \int_0^{\infty} y' f_X(y'z) f_Y(y') \, dy' \qquad z > 0$$

$$= \int_0^{\infty} y' e^{-y'z} e^{-y'} \, dy'$$

$$= \frac{1}{(1 + z)^2} \qquad z > 0.$$

### 5.8.2    Transformations of Two Random Variables

Let $X$ and $Y$ be random variables associated with some experiment, and let the random variables $Z_1$ and $Z_2$ be defined by two functions of $\mathbf{X} = (X, Y)$:

$$Z_1 = g_1(\mathbf{X}) \qquad \text{and} \qquad Z_2 = g_2(\mathbf{X}).$$

We now consider the problem of finding the joint cdf and pdf of $Z_1$ and $Z_2$.

The joint cdf of $Z_1$ and $Z_2$ at the point $\mathbf{z} = (z_1, z_2)$ is equal to the probability of the region of $\mathbf{x}$ where $g_k(\mathbf{x}) \le z_k$ for $k = 1, 2$:

$$F_{Z_1, Z_2}(z_1, z_2) = P[g_1(\mathbf{X}) \le z_1, g_2(\mathbf{X}) \le z_2]. \tag{5.56a}$$

If $X, Y$ have a joint pdf, then

$$F_{Z_1, Z_2}(z_1, z_2) = \iint\limits_{\mathbf{x'}:\, g_k(\mathbf{x'}) \le z_k} f_{X,Y}(x', y')\, dx'\, dy'. \tag{5.56b}$$

---

**Example 5.43**

Let the random variables $W$ and $Z$ be defined by

$$W = \min(X, Y) \qquad \text{and} \qquad Z = \max(X, Y).$$

Find the joint cdf of $W$ and $Z$ in terms of the joint cdf of $X$ and $Y$.

Equation (5.56a) implies that

$$F_{W, Z}(w\ z) = P[\{\min(X, Y) \le w\} \cap \{\max(X, Y) \le z\}].$$

The region corresponding to this event is shown in Fig. 5.21. From the figure it is clear that if $z > w$, the above probability is the probability of the semi-infinite rectangle defined by the

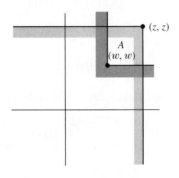

**FIGURE 5.21**
$\{\min(X, Y) \le w = \{X \le w\} \cup \{Y \le w\}$ and
$\{\max(X, Y) \le z = \{X \le z\} \cap \{Y \le z\}.$

point $(z, z)$ minus the square region denoted by $A$. Thus if $z > w$,

$$
\begin{aligned}
F_{W,Z}(w, z) &= F_{X,Y}(z, z) - P[A] \\
&= F_{X,Y}(z, z) \\
&\quad - \{F_{X,Y}(z, z) - F_{X,Y}(w, z) - F_{X,Y}(z, w) + F_{X,Y}(w, w)\} \\
&= F_{X,Y}(w, z) + F_{X,Y}(z, w) - F_{X,Y}(w, w).
\end{aligned}
$$

If $z < w$ then

$$
F_{W,Z}(w, z) = F_{X,Y}(z, z).
$$

---

### Example 5.44    Radius and Angle of Independent Gaussian Random Variables

Let $X$ and $Y$ be zero-mean, unit-variance independent Gaussian random variables. Find the joint cdf and pdf of $R$ and $\Theta$, the radius and angle of the point $(X, Y)$:

$$
R = (X^2 + Y^2)^{1/2} \qquad \Theta = \tan^{-1}(Y/X).
$$

The joint cdf of $R$ and $\Theta$ is:

$$
F_{R,\Theta}(r_0, \theta_0) = P[R \le r_0, \Theta \le \theta_0] = \iint\limits_{(x,y)\in R_{(r_0,\theta_0)}} \frac{e^{-(x^2+y^2)/2}}{2\pi}\, dx\, dy
$$

where

$$
R_{(r_0, \theta_0)} = \{(x, y): \sqrt{x^2 + y^2} \le r_0, 0 < \tan^{-1}(Y/X) \le \theta_0\}.
$$

The region $R_{r_0,\theta_0}$ is the pie-shaped region in Fig. 5.22. We change variables from Cartesian to polar coordinates to obtain:

$$
F_{R,\Theta}(r_0, \theta_0) = P[R \le r_0, \Theta \le \theta_0] = \int_0^{r_0}\int_0^{\theta_0} \frac{e^{-r^2/2}}{2\pi} r\, dr\, d\theta
$$

$$
= \frac{\theta_0}{2\pi}\left(1 - e^{-r_0^2/2}\right), \quad 0 < \theta_0 < 2\pi \quad 0 < r_0 < \infty. \tag{5.57}
$$

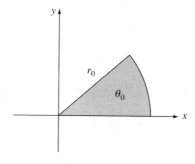

**FIGURE 5.22**
Region of integration $R_{r_0, \theta_0}$ in Example 5.44.

$R$ and $\Theta$ are independent random variables, where $R$ has a Rayleigh distribution and $\Theta$ is uniformly distributed in $(0, 2\pi)$. The joint pdf is obtained by taking partial derivatives with respect to $r$ and $\theta$:

$$f_{R,\Theta}(r, \theta) = \frac{\partial^2}{\partial r \partial \theta} \frac{\theta}{2\pi} (1 - e^{-r^2/2})$$

$$= \frac{1}{2\pi} \left( r e^{-r^2/2} \right), \quad 0 < \theta < 2\pi \quad 0 < r < \infty.$$

This transformation maps every point in the plane from Cartesian coordinates to polar coordinates. We can also go *backwards* from polar to Cartesian coordinates. First we generate independent Rayleigh $R$ and uniform $\Theta$ random variables. We then transform $R$ and $\Theta$ into Cartesian coordinates to obtain an independent pair of zero-mean, unit-variance Gaussians. Neat!

### 5.8.3    pdf of Linear Transformations

The joint pdf of $\mathbf{Z}$ can be found directly in terms of the joint pdf of $\mathbf{X}$ by finding the equivalent events of infinitesimal rectangles. We consider the **linear transformation** of two random variables:

$$\begin{aligned} V &= aX + bY \\ W &= cX + eY \end{aligned} \quad \text{or} \quad \begin{bmatrix} V \\ W \end{bmatrix} = \begin{bmatrix} a & b \\ c & e \end{bmatrix} \begin{bmatrix} X \\ Y \end{bmatrix}.$$

Denote the above matrix by $A$. We will assume that $A$ has an inverse, that is, it has determinant $|ae - bc| \neq 0$, so each point $(v, w)$ has a unique corresponding point $(x, y)$ obtained from

$$\begin{bmatrix} x \\ y \end{bmatrix} = A^{-1} \begin{bmatrix} v \\ w \end{bmatrix}. \tag{5.58}$$

Consider the infinitesimal rectangle shown in Fig. 5.23. The points in this rectangle are mapped into the parallelogram shown in the figure. The infinitesimal rectangle and the parallelogram are equivalent events, so their probabilities must be equal. Thus

$$f_{X,Y}(x, y) dx \, dy \simeq f_{V,W}(v, w) \, dP$$

where $dP$ is the area of the parallelogram. The joint pdf of $V$ and $W$ is thus given by

$$f_{V,W}(v, w) = \frac{f_{X,Y}(x, y)}{\left| \dfrac{dP}{dx \, dy} \right|}, \tag{5.59}$$

where $x$ and $y$ are related to $(v, w)$ by Eq. (5.58). Equation (5.59) states that the joint pdf of $V$ and $W$ at $(v, w)$ is the pdf of $X$ and $Y$ at the corresponding point $(x, y)$, but rescaled by the "stretch factor" $dP/dx \, dy$. It can be shown that $dP = (|ae - bc|) \, dx \, dy$, so the "stretch factor" is

$$\left| \frac{dP}{dx \, dy} \right| = \frac{|ae - bc|(dx \, dy)}{(dx \, dy)} = |ae - bc| = |A|,$$

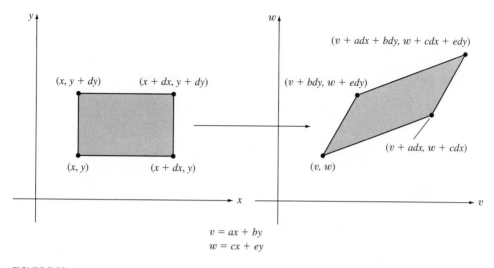

$$v = ax + by$$
$$w = cx + ey$$

**FIGURE 5.23**
Image of an infinitesimal rectangle under a linear transformation.

where $|A|$ is the determinant of $A$.

The above result can be written compactly using matrix notation. Let the vector $\mathbf{Z}$ be

$$\mathbf{Z} = A\mathbf{X},$$

where $A$ is an $n \times n$ invertible matrix. The joint pdf of $\mathbf{Z}$ is then

$$f_{\mathbf{z}}(\mathbf{z}) = \frac{f_{\mathbf{x}}(A^{-1}\mathbf{z})}{|A|} \tag{5.60}$$

---

### Example 5.45   Linear Transformation of Jointly Gaussian Random Variables

Let $X$ and $Y$ be the jointly Gaussian random variables introduced in Example 5.18. Let $V$ and $W$ be obtained from $(X, Y)$ by

$$\begin{bmatrix} V \\ W \end{bmatrix} = \frac{1}{\sqrt{2}} \begin{bmatrix} 1 & 1 \\ -1 & 1 \end{bmatrix} \begin{bmatrix} X \\ Y \end{bmatrix} = A \begin{bmatrix} X \\ Y \end{bmatrix}.$$

Find the joint pdf of $V$ and $W$.

The determinant of the matrix is $|A| = 1$, and the inverse mapping is given by

$$\begin{bmatrix} X \\ Y \end{bmatrix} = \frac{1}{\sqrt{2}} \begin{bmatrix} 1 & -1 \\ 1 & 1 \end{bmatrix} \begin{bmatrix} V \\ W \end{bmatrix},$$

so $X = (V - W)/\sqrt{2}$ and $Y = (V + W)/\sqrt{2}$. Therefore the pdf of $V$ and $W$ is

$$f_{V,W}(v, w) = f_{X,Y}\left( \frac{v - w}{\sqrt{2}}, \frac{v + w}{\sqrt{2}} \right),$$

where

$$f_{X,Y}(x, y) = \frac{1}{2\pi\sqrt{1 - \rho^2}} e^{-(x^2 - 2\rho xy + y^2)/2(1-\rho^2)}.$$

By substituting for $x$ and $y$, the argument of the exponent becomes

$$\frac{(v - w)^2/2 - 2\rho(v - w)(v + w)/2 + (v + w)^2/2}{2(1 - \rho^2)}$$

$$= \frac{v^2}{2(1 + \rho)} + \frac{w^2}{2(1 - \rho)}.$$

Thus

$$f_{V,W}(v, w) = \frac{1}{2\pi(1 - \rho^2)^{1/2}} e^{-\{[v^2/2(1+\rho)] + [w^2/2(1-\rho)]\}}.$$

It can be seen that the transformed variables $V$ and $W$ are independent, zero-mean Gaussian random variables with variance $1 + \rho$ and $1 - \rho$, respectively. Figure 5.24 shows contours of equal value of the joint pdf of $(X, Y)$. It can be seen that the pdf has elliptical symmetry about the origin with principal axes at $45°$ with respect to the axes of the plane. In Section 5.9 we show that the above linear transformation corresponds to a rotation of the coordinate system so that the axes of the plane are aligned with the axes of the ellipse.

## 5.9    PAIRS OF JOINTLY GAUSSIAN RANDOM VARIABLES

The jointly Gaussian random variables appear in numerous applications in electrical engineering. They are frequently used to model signals in signal processing applications, and they are the most important model used in communication systems that involve dealing with signals in the presence of noise. They also play a central role in many statistical methods.

The random variables $X$ and $Y$ are said to be **jointly Gaussian** if their joint pdf has the form

$$f_{X,Y}(x, y) = \frac{\exp\left\{\frac{-1}{2(1 - \rho_{X,Y}^2)}\left[\left(\frac{x - m_1}{\sigma_1}\right)^2 - 2\rho_{X,Y}\left(\frac{x - m_1}{\sigma_1}\right)\left(\frac{y - m_2}{\sigma_2}\right) + \left(\frac{y - m_2}{\sigma_2}\right)^2\right]\right\}}{2\pi\sigma_1\sigma_2\sqrt{1 - \rho_{X,Y}^2}}$$

(5.61a)

for $-\infty < x < \infty$ and $-\infty < y < \infty$.

The pdf is centered at the point $(m_1, m_2)$, and it has a bell shape that depends on the values of $\sigma_1, \sigma_2$, and $\rho_{X,Y}$ as shown in Fig. 5.25. As shown in the figure, the pdf is constant for values $x$ and $y$ for which the argument of the exponent is constant:

$$\left[\left(\frac{x - m_1}{\sigma_1}\right)^2 - 2\rho_{X,Y}\left(\frac{x - m_1}{\sigma_1}\right)\left(\frac{y - m_2}{\sigma_2}\right) + \left(\frac{y - m_2}{\sigma_2}\right)^2\right] = \text{constant.} \qquad (5.61b)$$

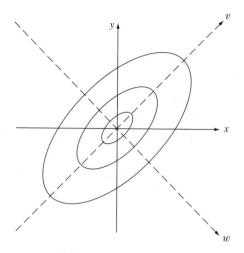

**FIGURE 5.24**
Contours of equal value of joint Gaussian pdf
discussed in Example 5.45.

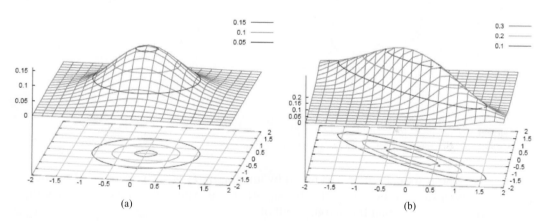

**FIGURE 5.25**
Jointly Gaussian pdf (a) $\rho = 0$ (b) $\rho = -0.9$.

Figure 5.26 shows the orientation of these elliptical contours for various values of $\sigma_1$, $\sigma_2$, and $\rho_{X,Y}$. When $\rho_{X,Y} = 0$, that is, when $X$ and $Y$ are independent, the equal-pdf contour is an ellipse with principal axes aligned with the $x$- and $y$-axes. When $\rho_{X,Y} \neq 0$, the major axis of the ellipse is oriented along the angle [Edwards and Penney, pp. 570–571]

$$\theta = \tfrac{1}{2} \arctan^{-1} \tan\!\left( \frac{2\rho_{X,Y}\sigma_1\sigma_2}{\sigma_1^2 - \sigma_2^2} \right). \tag{5.62}$$

Note that the angle is 45° when the variances are equal.

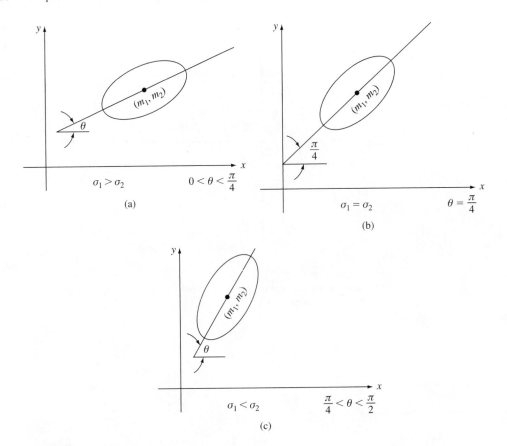

**FIGURE 5.26**
Orientation of contours of equal value of joint Gaussian pdf for $\rho_{X,Y} > 0$.

The marginal pdf of $X$ is found by integrating $f_{X,Y}(x, y)$ over all $y$. The integration is carried out by completing the square in the exponent as was done in Example 5.18. The result is that the marginal pdf of $X$ is

$$f_X(x) = \frac{e^{-(x-m_1)^2/2\sigma_1^2}}{\sqrt{2\pi}\sigma_1}, \tag{5.63}$$

that is, $X$ is a Gaussian random variable with mean $m_1$ and variance $\sigma_1^2$. Similarly, the marginal pdf for $Y$ is found to be Gaussian with pdf mean $m_2$ and variance $\sigma_2^2$.

The conditional pdf's $f_X(x\,|\,y)$ and $f_Y(y\,|\,x)$ give us information about the interrelation between $X$ and $Y$. The conditional pdf of $X$ given $Y = y$ is

$$f_X(x\,|\,y) = \frac{f_{X,Y}(x, y)}{f_Y(y)}$$

$$= \frac{\exp\left\{\dfrac{-1}{2(1 - \rho_{X,Y}^2)\sigma_1^2}\left[x - \rho_{X,Y}\dfrac{\sigma_1}{\sigma_2}(y - m_2) - m_1\right]^2\right\}}{\sqrt{2\pi}\sigma_1^2(1 - \rho_{X,Y}^2)}. \tag{5.64}$$

Equation (5.64) shows that the conditional pdf of $X$ given $Y = y$ is also Gaussian but with conditional mean $m_1 + \rho_{X,Y}(\sigma_1/\sigma_2)(y - m_2)$ and conditional variance $\sigma_1^2(1 - \rho_{X,Y}^2)$. Note that when $\rho_{X,Y} = 0$, the conditional pdf of $X$ given $Y = y$ equals the marginal pdf of $X$. This is consistent with the fact that $X$ and $Y$ are independent when $\rho_{X,Y} = 0$. On the other hand, as $|\rho_{X,Y}| \to 1$ the variance of $X$ about the conditional mean approaches zero, so the conditional pdf approaches a delta function at the conditional mean. Thus when $|\rho_{X,Y}| = 1$, the conditional variance is zero and $X$ is equal to the conditional mean with probability one. We note that similarly $f_Y(y \mid x)$ is Gaussian with conditional mean $m_2 + \rho_{X,Y}$ $(\sigma_2/\sigma_1)(x - m_1)$ and conditional variance $\sigma_2^2(1 - \rho_{X,Y}^2)$.

We now show that the $\rho_{X,Y}$ in Eq. (5.61a) is indeed the correlation coefficient between $X$ and $Y$. The covariance between $X$ and $Y$ is defined by

$$COV(X, Y) = E[(X - m_1)(Y - m_2)]$$
$$= E[E[(X - m_1)(Y - m_2) \mid Y]].$$

Now the conditional expectation of $(X - m_1)(Y - m_2)$ given $Y = y$ is

$$E[(X - m_1)(Y - m_2) \mid Y = y] = (y - m_2)E[X - m_1 \mid Y = y]$$
$$= (y - m_2)(E[X \mid Y = y] - m_1)$$
$$= (y - m_2)\left(\rho_{X,Y}\frac{\sigma_1}{\sigma_2}(y - m_2)\right),$$

where we have used the fact that the conditional mean of $X$ given $Y = y$ is $m_1 + \rho_{X,Y}(\sigma_1/\sigma_2)(y - m_2)$. Therefore

$$E[(X - m_1)(Y - m_2) \mid Y] = \rho_{X,Y}\frac{\sigma_1}{\sigma_2}(Y - m_2)^2$$

and

$$COV(X, Y) = E[E[(X - m_1)(Y - m_2) \mid Y]] = \rho_{X,Y}\frac{\sigma_1}{\sigma_2}E[(Y - m_2)^2]$$
$$= \rho_{X,Y}\sigma_1\sigma_2.$$

The above equation is consistent with the definition of the correlation coefficient, $\rho_{X,Y} = COV(X, Y)/\sigma_1\sigma_2$. Thus the $\rho_{X,Y}$ in Eq. (5.61a) is indeed the correlation coefficient between $X$ and $Y$.

---

**Example 5.46**

The amount of yearly rainfall in city 1 and in city 2 is modeled by a pair of jointly Gaussian random variables, $X$ and $Y$, with pdf given by Eq. (5.61a). Find the most likely value of $X$ given that we know $Y = y$.

The most likely value of $X$ given $Y = y$ is the value of $x$ for which $f_X(x \mid y)$ is maximum. The conditional pdf of $X$ given $Y = y$ is given by Eq. (5.64), which is maximum at the conditional mean

$$E[X \mid y] = m_1 + \rho_{X,Y}\frac{\sigma_1}{\sigma_2}(y - m_2).$$

Note that this "maximum likelihood" estimate is a linear function of the observation $y$.

---

## Example 5.47    Estimation of Signal in Noise

Let $Y = X + N$ where $X$ (the "signal") and $N$ (the "noise') are independent zero-mean Gaussian random variables with different variances. Find the correlation coefficient between the observed signal $Y$ and the desired signal $X$. Find the value of $x$ that maximizes $f_X(x \mid y)$.

The mean and variance of $Y$ and the covariance of $X$ and $Y$ are:

$$E[Y] = E[X] + E[N] = 0$$

$$\sigma_Y^2 = E[Y^2] = E[(X + N)^2] = E[X^2 + 2XN + N^2] = E[X^2] + E[N^2] = \sigma_X^2 + \sigma_N^2.$$

$$\text{COV}(X, Y) = E[(X - E[X])(E(Y - E[Y])] = E[XY] = E[X(X + N)] = \sigma_X^2.$$

Therefore, the correlation coefficient is:

$$\rho_{X,Y} = \frac{\text{COV}(X,Y)}{\sigma_X \sigma_Y} = \frac{\sigma_X}{\sigma_Y} = \frac{\sigma_X}{(\sigma_X^2 + \sigma_N^2)^{1/2}} = \frac{1}{\left(1 + \dfrac{\sigma_N^2}{\sigma_X^2}\right)^{1/2}}.$$

Note that $\rho_{X,Y}^2 = \sigma_X^2/\sigma_Y^2 = 1 - \sigma_N^2/\sigma_Y^2$.

To find the joint pdf of $X$ and $Y$ consider the following linear transformation:

$$X = X \qquad \text{which has inverse} \qquad X = X$$
$$Y = X + N \qquad\qquad\qquad\qquad N = -X + Y.$$

From Eq. (5.52) we have:

$$f_{X,Y}(x, y) = \frac{f_{X,N}(x, y)}{\det A}\bigg|_{x=x, n=y-x} = \frac{e^{-x^2/2\sigma_X^2}}{\sqrt{2\pi}\sigma_X} \frac{e^{-n^2/2\sigma_N^2}}{\sqrt{2\pi}\sigma_N}\bigg|_{x=x, n=y-x}$$

$$= \frac{e^{-x^2/2\sigma_X^2}}{\sqrt{2\pi}\sigma_X} \frac{e^{-(y-x)^2/2\sigma_N^2}}{\sqrt{2\pi}\sigma_N}.$$

The conditional pdf of the signal $X$ given the observation $Y$ is then:

$$f_X(x \mid y) = \frac{f_{X,Y}(x, y)}{f_Y(y)} = \frac{e^{-x^2/2\sigma_X^2}}{\sqrt{2\pi}\sigma_X} \frac{e^{-(y-x)^2/2\sigma_N^2}}{\sqrt{2\pi}\sigma_N} \frac{\sqrt{2\pi}\sigma_Y}{e^{-y^2/2\sigma_Y^2}}$$

$$= \frac{\exp\left\{-\frac{1}{2}\left(\left(\frac{x}{\sigma_X}\right)^2 + \left(\frac{y-x}{\sigma_N}\right)^2 - \left(\frac{y}{\sigma_Y}\right)^2\right)\right\}}{\sqrt{2\pi}\sigma_N \sigma_X/\sigma_Y} = \frac{\exp\left\{-\frac{1}{2}\frac{\sigma_Y^2}{\sigma_X^2\sigma_N^2}\left(x - \frac{\sigma_X^2}{\sigma_Y^2}y\right)^2\right\}}{\sqrt{2\pi}\sigma_N \sigma_X/\sigma_Y}$$

$$= \frac{\exp\left\{-\frac{1}{2(1 - \rho_{X,Y}^2)\sigma_X^2}\left(x - \left(\frac{\sigma_X^2}{\sigma_X^2 + \sigma_X^2}\right)y\right)^2\right\}}{\sqrt{1 - \rho_{X,Y}^2}\,\sigma_X}.$$

This pdf has its maximum value, when the argument of the exponent is zero, that is,

$$x = \left(\frac{\sigma_X^2}{\sigma_X^2 + \sigma_N^2}\right)y = \left(\frac{1}{1 + \dfrac{\sigma_N^2}{\sigma_X^2}}\right)y.$$

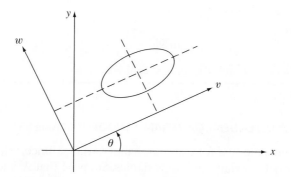

**FIGURE 5.27**
A rotation of the coordinate system transforms a pair of
dependent Gaussian random variables into a pair of independent
Gaussian random variables.

The signal-to-noise ratio (SNR) is defined as the ratio of the variance of $X$ and the variance of $N$. At high SNRs this estimator gives $x \approx y$, and at very low signal-to-noise ratios, it gives $x \approx 0$.

---

### Example 5.48    Rotation of Jointly Gaussian Random Variables

The ellipse corresponding to an arbitrary two-dimensional Gaussian vector forms an angle

$$\theta = \frac{1}{2}\arctan\left(\frac{2\rho\sigma_1\sigma_2}{\sigma_1^2 - \sigma_2^2}\right)$$

relative to the $x$-axis. Suppose we define a new coordinate system whose axes are aligned with those of the ellipse as shown in Fig. 5.27. This is accomplished by using the following rotation matrix:

$$\begin{bmatrix} V \\ W \end{bmatrix} = \begin{bmatrix} \cos\theta & \sin\theta \\ -\sin\theta & \cos\theta \end{bmatrix} \begin{bmatrix} X \\ Y \end{bmatrix}.$$

To show that the new random variables are independent it suffices to show that they have covariance zero:

$$\begin{aligned}
\mathrm{COV}(V, W) &= E[(V - E[V])(W - E[W])] \\
&= E[\{(X - m_1)\cos\theta + (Y - m_2)\sin\theta\} \\
&\quad \times \{-(X - m_1)\sin\theta + (Y - m_2)\cos\theta\}] \\
&= -\sigma_1^2 \sin\theta\cos\theta + \mathrm{COV}(X, Y)\cos^2\theta \\
&\quad -\mathrm{COV}(X, Y)\sin^2\theta + \sigma_2^2 \sin\theta\cos\theta \\
&= \frac{(\sigma_2^2 - \sigma_1^2)\sin 2\theta + 2\,\mathrm{COV}(X, Y)\cos 2\theta}{2} \\
&= \frac{\cos 2\theta[(\sigma_2^2 - \sigma_1^2)\tan 2\theta + 2\,\mathrm{COV}(X, Y)]}{2}.
\end{aligned}$$

If we let the angle of rotation $\theta$ be such that

$$\tan 2\theta = \frac{2\,\text{COV}(X, Y)}{\sigma_1^2 - \sigma_2^2},$$

then the covariance of $V$ and $W$ is zero as required.

---

## *5.10  GENERATING INDEPENDENT GAUSSIAN RANDOM VARIABLES

We now present a method for generating unit-variance, uncorrelated (and hence independent) jointly Gaussian random variables. Suppose that $X$ and $Y$ are two independent zero-mean, unit-variance jointly Gaussian random variables with pdf:

$$f_{X,Y}(x, y) = \frac{1}{2\pi} e^{-(x^2+y^2)/2}.$$

In Example 5.44 we saw that the transformation

$$R = \sqrt{X^2 + Y^2} \quad \text{and} \quad \Theta = \tan^{-1} Y/X$$

leads to the pair of independent random variables

$$f_{R,\Theta}(r, \theta) = \frac{1}{2\pi} r e^{-r^2/2} = f_R(r)f_\Theta(\theta),$$

where $R$ is a Rayleigh random variable and $\Theta$ is a uniform random variable. The above transformation is invertible. Therefore we can also start with independent Rayleigh and uniform random variables and produce zero-mean, unit-variance independent Gaussian random variables through the transformation:

$$X = R \cos \Theta \quad \text{and} \quad Y = R \sin \Theta. \tag{5.65}$$

Consider $W = R^2$ where $R$ is a Rayleigh random variable. From Example 5.41 we then have that: $W$ has pdf

$$f_W(w) = \frac{f_R(\sqrt{w})}{2\sqrt{w}} = \frac{\sqrt{w}e^{-\sqrt{w}^2/2}}{2\sqrt{w}} = \frac{1}{2}e^{-w/2}.$$

$W = R^2$ has an exponential distribution with $\lambda = 1/2$.

Therefore we can generate $R^2$ by generating an exponential random variable with parameter $1/2$, and we can generate $\Theta$ by generating a random variable that is uniformly distributed in the interval $(0, 2\pi)$. If we substitute these random variables into Eq. (5.65), we then obtain a pair of independent zero-mean, unit-variance Gaussian random variables. The above discussion thus leads to the following algorithm:

1. Generate $U_1$ and $U_2$, two independent random variables uniformly distributed in the unit interval.
2. Let $R^2 = -2 \log U_1$ and $\Theta = 2\pi U_2$.
3. Let $X = R \cos \Theta = (-2 \log U_1)^{1/2} \cos 2\pi U_2$ and $Y = R \sin \Theta = (-2 \log U_1)^{1/2} \sin 2\pi U_2$.

Then $X$ and $Y$ are independent, zero-mean, unit-variance Gaussian random variables. By repeating the above procedure we can generate any number of such random variables.

### Example 5.49

Use Octave or MATLAB to generate 1000 independent zero-mean, unit-variance Gaussian random variables. Compare a histogram of the observed values with the pdf of a zero-mean unit-variance random variable.

The Octave commands below show the steps for generating the Gaussian random variables. A set of histogram range values $K$ from $-4$ to $4$ is created and used to build a normalized histogram $Z$. The points in $Z$ are then plotted and compared to the value predicted to fall in each interval by the Gaussian pdf. These plots are shown in Fig. 5.28, which shows excellent agreement.

```
> U1=rand(1000,1);          % Create a 1000-element vector U₁ (step 1).
> U2=rand(1000,1);          % Create a 1000-element vector U₂ (step 1).
> R2=-2*log(U1);            % Find R² (step 2).
> TH=2*pi*U2;               % Find θ (step 2).
> X=sqrt(R2).*sin(TH);      % Generate X (step 3).
```

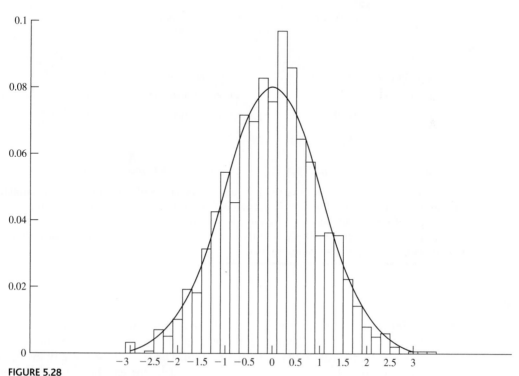

**FIGURE 5.28**

Histogram of 1000 observations of a Gaussian random variable.

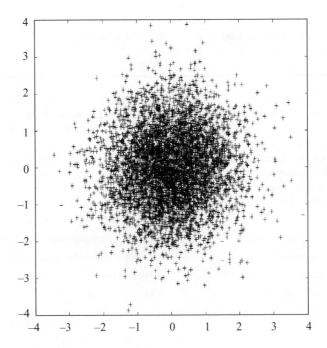

**FIGURE 5.29**
Scattergram of 5000 pairs of jointly Gaussian random variables.

```
> Y=sqrt(R2).*cos(TH);          % Generate Y (step 3).
> K=-4:.2:4;                    % Create histogram range values K.
> Z=hist(X,K)/1000             % Create normalized histogram Z based on K.
> bar(K,Z)                      % Plot Z.
> hold on
> stem(K,.2*normal_pdf(K,0,1))  % Compare to values predicted by pdf.
```

We also plotted the $X$ values vs. the $Y$ values for 5000 pairs of generated random variables in a scattergram as shown in Fig. 5.29. Good agreement with the circular symmetry of the jointly Gaussian pdf of zero-mean, unit-variance pairs is observed.

In the next chapter we will show how to generate a vector of jointly Gaussian random variables with an arbitrary covariance matrix.

## SUMMARY

- The joint statistical behavior of a pair of random variables $X$ and $Y$ is specified by the joint cumulative distribution function, the joint probability mass function, or the joint probability density function. The probability of any event involving the joint behavior of these random variables can be computed from these functions.

- The statistical behavior of individual random variables from **X** is specified by the marginal cdf, marginal pdf, or marginal pmf that can be obtained from the joint cdf, joint pdf, or joint pmf of **X**.

- Two random variables are independent if the probability of a product-form event is equal to the product of the probabilities of the component events. Equivalent conditions for the independence of a set of random variables are that the joint cdf, joint pdf, or joint pmf factors into the product of the corresponding marginal functions.

- The covariance and the correlation coefficient of two random variables are measures of the linear dependence between the random variables.

- If **X** and **Y** are independent, then **X** and **Y** are uncorrelated, but not vice versa. If **X** and **Y** are jointly Gaussian and uncorrelated, then they are independent.

- The statistical behavior of **X**, given the exact values of $X$ or $Y$, is specified by the conditional cdf, conditional pmf, or conditional pdf. Many problems lend themselves to a solution that involves conditioning on the value of one of the random variables. In these problems, the expected value of random variables can be obtained by conditional expectation.

- The joint pdf of a pair of jointly Gaussian random variables is determined by the means, variances, and covariance. All marginal pdf's and conditional pdf's are also Gaussian pdf's.

- Independent Gaussian random variables can be generated by a transformation of uniform random variables.

## CHECKLIST OF IMPORTANT TERMS

Central moments of $X$ and $Y$

Conditional cdf

Conditional expectation

Conditional pdf

Conditional pmf

Correlation of $X$ and $Y$

Covariance $X$ and $Y$

Independent random variables

Joint cdf

Joint moments of $X$ and $Y$

Joint pdf

Joint pmf

Jointly continuous random variables

Jointly Gaussian random variables

Linear transformation

Marginal cdf

Marginal pdf

Marginal pmf

Orthogonal random variables

Product-form event

Uncorrelated random variables

## ANNOTATED REFERENCES

Papoulis [1] is the standard reference for electrical engineers for the material on random variables. References [2] and [3] present many interesting examples involving multiple random variables. The book by Jayant and Noll [4] gives numerous applications of probability concepts to the digital coding of waveforms.

**1.** A. Papoulis and S. Pillai, *Probability, Random Variables, and Stochastic Processes*, McGraw-Hill, New York, 2002.

2. L. Breiman, *Probability and Stochastic Processes*, Houghton Mifflin, Boston, 1969.

3. H. J. Larson and B. O. Shubert, *Probabilistic Models in Engineering Sciences*, vol. 1, Wiley, New York, 1979.

4. N. S. Jayant and P. Noll, *Digital Coding of Waveforms*, Prentice Hall, Englewood Cliffs, N.J., 1984.

5. N. Johnson et al., *Continuous Multivariate Distributions*, Wiley, New York, 2000.

6. H. Stark and J. W. Woods, *Probability, Random Processes, and Estimation Theory for Engineers*, Prentice Hall, Englewood Cliffs, N.J., 1986.

7. H. Anton, *Elementary Linear Algebra*, 9th ed., Wiley, New York, 2005.

8. C. H. Edwards, Jr., and D. E. Penney, *Calculus and Analytic Geometry*, 4th ed., Prentice Hall, Englewood Cliffs, N.J., 1994.

## PROBLEMS

### Section 5.1: Two Random Variables

**5.1.** Let $X$ be the maximum and let $Y$ be the minimum of the number of heads obtained when Carlos and Michael each flip a fair coin twice.

    **(a)** Describe the underlying space $S$ of this random experiment and show the mapping from $S$ to $S_{XY}$, the range of the pair $(X, Y)$.

    **(b)** Find the probabilities for all values of $(X, Y)$.

    **(c)** Find $P[X = Y]$.

    **(d)** Repeat parts b and c if Carlos uses a biased coin with $P[\text{heads}] = 3/4$.

**5.2.** Let $X$ be the difference and let $Y$ be the sum of the number of heads obtained when Carlos and Michael each flip a fair coin twice.

    **(a)** Describe the underlying space $S$ of this random experiment and show the mapping from $S$ to $S_{XY}$, the range of the pair $(X, Y)$.

    **(b)** Find the probabilities for all values of $(X, Y)$.

    **(c)** Find $P[X + Y = 1]$, $P[X + Y = 2]$.

**5.3.** The input $X$ to a communication channel is "−1"or "1", with respective probabilities 1/4 and 3/4. The output of the channel $Y$ is equal to: the corresponding input $X$ with probability $1 - p - p_e$; $-X$ with probability $p$; 0 with probability $p_e$.

    **(a)** Describe the underlying space $S$ of this random experiment and show the mapping from $S$ to $S_{XY}$, the range of the pair $(X, Y)$.

    **(b)** Find the probabilities for all values of $(X, Y)$.

    **(c)** Find $P[X \neq Y]$, $P[Y = 0]$.

**5.4.** **(a)** Specify the range of the pair $(N_1, N_2)$ in Example 5.2.

    **(b)** Specify and sketch the event "more revenue comes from type 1 requests than type 2 requests."

**5.5.** **(a)** Specify the range of the pair $(Q, R)$ in Example 5.3.

    **(b)** Specify and sketch the event "last packet is more than half full."

**5.6.** Let the pair of random variables $H$ and $W$ be the height and weight in Example 5.1. The body mass index is a measure of body fat and is defined by $\text{BMI} = W/H^2$ where $W$ is in kilograms and $H$ is in meters. Determine and sketch on the plane the following events: $A = \{\text{"obese," BMI} \geq 30\}$; $B = \{\text{"overweight," } 25 \leq \text{BMI} < 30\}$; $C = \{\text{"normal," } 18.5 \leq \text{BMI} < 25\}$; and $D = \{\text{"underweight," BMI} < 18.5\}$.

**5.7.** Let $(X, Y)$ be the two-dimensional noise signal in Example 5.4. Specify and sketch the events:

    **(a)** "Maximum noise magnitude is greater than 5."

    **(b)** "The noise power $X^2 + Y^2$ is greater than 4."

    **(c)** "The noise power $X^2 + Y^2$ is greater than 4 and less than 9."

**5.8.** For the pair of random variables $(X, Y)$ sketch the region of the plane corresponding to the following events. Identify which events are of product form.

    **(a)** $\{X + Y > 3\}$.

    **(b)** $\{e^X > Ye^3\}$.

    **(c)** $\{\min(X, Y) > 0\} \cup \{\max\{X, Y\} < 0\}$.

    **(d)** $\{|X - Y| \geq 1\}$.

    **(e)** $\{|X/Y| > 2\}$.

    **(f)** $\{X/Y < 2\}$.

    **(g)** $\{X^3 > Y\}$.

    **(h)** $\{XY < 0\}$.

    **(i)** $\{\max(|X|, Y) < 3\}$.

## Section 5.2: Pairs of Discrete Random Variables

**5.9.**   **(a)** Find and sketch $p_{X,Y}(x, y)$ in Problem 5.1 when using a fair coin.

    **(b)** Find $p_X(x)$ and $p_Y(y)$.

    **(c)** Repeat parts a and b if Carlos uses a biased coin with $P[\text{heads}] = 3/4$.

**5.10.** **(a)** Find and sketch $p_{X,Y}(x, y)$ in Problem 5.2 when using a fair coin.

    **(b)** Find $p_X(x)$ and $p_Y(y)$.

    **(c)** Repeat parts a and b if Carlos uses a biased coin with $P[\text{heads}] = 3/4$.

**5.11.** **(a)** Find the marginal pmf's for the pairs of random variables with the indicated joint pmf.

|  | (i) |  |  |  | (ii) |  |  |  | (iii) |  |  |
|---|---|---|---|---|---|---|---|---|---|---|---|
| X/Y | −1 | 0 | 1 | X/Y | −1 | 0 | 1 | X/Y | −1 | 0 | 1 |
| −1 | 1/6 | 1/6 | 0 | −1 | 1/9 | 1/9 | 1/9 | −1 | 1/3 | 0 | 0 |
| 0 | 0 | 0 | 1/3 | 0 | 1/9 | 1/9 | 1/9 | 0 | 0 | 1/3 | 0 |
| 1 | 1/6 | 1/6 | 0 | 1 | 1/9 | 1/9 | 1/9 | 1 | 0 | 0 | 1/3 |

    **(b)** Find the probability of the events $A = \{X > 0\}, B = \{X \geq Y\}$, and $C = \{X = -Y\}$ for the above joint pmf's.

**5.12.** A modem transmits a two-dimensional signal $(X, Y)$ given by:

$$X = r \cos(2\pi\Theta/8) \quad \text{and} \quad Y = r \sin(2\pi\Theta/8)$$

where $\Theta$ is a discrete uniform random variable in the set $\{0, 1, 2, \ldots, 7\}$.

    **(a)** Show the mapping from $S$ to $S_{XY}$, the range of the pair $(X, Y)$.

    **(b)** Find the joint pmf of $X$ and $Y$.

    **(c)** Find the marginal pmf of $X$ and of $Y$.

    **(d)** Find the probability of the following events: $A = \{X = 0\}, B = \{Y \leq r/\sqrt{2}\}$, $C = \{X \geq r/\sqrt{2}, Y \geq r/\sqrt{2}\}, D = \{X < -r/\sqrt{2}\}$.

**5.13.** Let $N_1$ be the number of Web page requests arriving at a server in a 100-ms period and let $N_2$ be the number of Web page requests arriving at a server in the next 100-ms period. Assume that in a 1-ms interval either zero or one page request takes place with respective probabilities $1 - p = 0.95$ and $p = 0.05$, and that the requests in different 1-ms intervals are independent of each other.

    **(a)** Describe the underlying space $S$ of this random experiment and show the mapping from $S$ to $S_{XY}$, the range of the pair $(X, Y)$.

    **(b)** Find the joint pmf of $X$ and $Y$.

    **(c)** Find the marginal pmf for $X$ and for $Y$.

    **(d)** Find the probability of the events $A = \{X \geq Y\}$, $B = \{X = Y = 0\}$, $C = \{X > 5, Y > 3\}$.

    **(e)** Find the probability of the event $D = \{X + Y = 10\}$.

**5.14.** Let $N_1$ be the number of Web page requests arriving at a server in the period $(0, 100)$ ms and let $N_2$ be the *total* combined number of Web page requests arriving at a server in the period $(0, 200)$ ms. Assume arrivals occur as in Problem 5.13.

    **(a)** Describe the underlying space $S$ of this random experiment and show the mapping from $S$ to $S_{XY}$, the range of the pair $(X, Y)$.

    **(b)** Find the joint pmf of $N_1$ and $N_2$.

    **(c)** Find the marginal pmf for $N_1$ and $N_2$.

    **(d)** Find the probability of the events $A = \{N_1 < N_2\}$, $B = \{N_2 = 0\}$, $C = \{N_1 > 5, N_2 > 3\}$, $D = \{|N_2 - 2N_1| < 2\}$.

**5.15.** At even time instants, a robot moves either $+\Delta$ cm or $-\Delta$ cm in the $x$-direction according to the outcome of a coin flip; at odd time instants, a robot moves similarly according to another coin flip in the $y$-direction. Assuming that the robot begins at the origin, let $X$ and $Y$ be the coordinates of the location of the robot after $2n$ time instants.

    **(a)** Describe the underlying space $S$ of this random experiment and show the mapping from $S$ to $S_{XY}$, the range of the pair $(X, Y)$.

    **(b)** Find the marginal pmf of the coordinates $X$ and $Y$.

    **(c)** Find the probability that the robot is within distance $\sqrt{2}$ of the origin after $2n$ time instants.

## Section 5.3: The Joint cdf of x and y

**5.16.** **(a)** Sketch the joint cdf for the pair $(X, Y)$ in Problem 5.1 and verify that the properties of the joint cdf are satisfied. You may find it helpful to first divide the plane into regions where the cdf is constant.

    **(b)** Find the marginal cdf of $X$ and of $Y$.

**5.17.** A point $(X, Y)$ is selected at random inside a triangle defined by $\{(x, y): 0 \leq y \leq x \leq 1\}$. Assume the point is equally likely to fall anywhere in the triangle.

    **(a)** Find the joint cdf of $X$ and $Y$.

    **(b)** Find the marginal cdf of $X$ and of $Y$.

    **(c)** Find the probabilities of the following events in terms of the joint cdf: $A = \{X \leq 1/2, Y \leq 3/4\}$; $B = \{1/4 < X \leq 3/4, 1/4 < Y \leq 3/4\}$.

**5.18.** A dart is equally likely to land at any point $(X_1, X_2)$ inside a circular target of unit radius. Let $R$ and $\Theta$ be the radius and angle of the point $(X_1, X_2)$.

    **(a)** Find the joint cdf of $R$ and $\Theta$.

    **(b)** Find the marginal cdf of $R$ and of $\Theta$.

(c) Use the joint cdf to find the probability that the point is in the first quadrant of the real plane and that the radius is greater than 0.5.

**5.19.** Find an expression for the probability of the events in Problem 5.8 parts c, h, and i in terms of the joint cdf of $X$ and $Y$.

**5.20.** The pair $(X, Y)$ has joint cdf given by:

$$F_{X,Y}(x, y) = \begin{cases} (1 - 1/x^2)(1 - 1/y^2) & \text{for } x > 1, y > 1 \\ 0 & \text{elsewhere.} \end{cases}$$

(a) Sketch the joint cdf.

(b) Find the marginal cdf of $X$ and of $Y$.

(c) Find the probability of the following events: $\{X < 3, Y \le 5\}, \{X > 4, Y > 3\}$.

**5.21.** Is the following a valid cdf? Why?

$$F_{X,Y}(x, y) = \begin{cases} (1 - 1/x^2 y^2) & \text{for } x > 1, y > 1 \\ 0 & \text{elsewhere.} \end{cases}$$

**5.22.** Let $F_X(x)$ and $F_Y(y)$ be valid one-dimensional cdf's. Show that $F_{X,Y}(x, y) = F_X(x)F_Y(y)$ satisfies the properties of a two-dimensional cdf.

**5.23.** The number of users logged onto a system $N$ and the time $T$ until the next user logs off have joint probability given by:

$$P[N = n, X \le t] = (1 - \rho)\rho^{n-1}(1 - e^{-n\lambda t}) \qquad \text{for } n = 1, 2, \ldots \quad t > 0.$$

(a) Sketch the above joint probability.

(b) Find the marginal pmf of $N$.

(c) Find the marginal cdf of $X$.

(d) Find $P[N \le 3, X > 3/\lambda]$.

**5.24.** A factory has $n$ machines of a certain type. Let $p$ be the probability that a machine is working on any given day, and let $N$ be the total number of machines working on a certain day. The time $T$ required to manufacture an item is an exponentially distributed random variable with rate $k\alpha$ if $k$ machines are working. Find and $P[T \le t]$. Find $P[T \le t]$ as $t \to \infty$ and explain the result.

## Section 5.4: The Joint pdf of Two Continuous Random Variables

**5.25.** The amplitudes of two signals $X$ and $Y$ have joint pdf:

$$f_{X,Y}(x, y) = e^{-x/2}ye^{-y^2} \qquad \text{for } x > 0, y > 0.$$

(a) Find the joint cdf.

(b) Find $P[X^{1/2} > Y]$.

(c) Find the marginal pdfs.

**5.26.** Let $X$ and $Y$ have joint pdf:

$$f_{X,Y}(x, y) = k(x + y) \qquad \text{for } 0 \le x \le 1, 0 \le y \le 1.$$

(a) Find $k$.

(b) Find the joint cdf of $(X, Y)$.

(c) Find the marginal pdf of $X$ and of $Y$.

(d) Find $P[X < Y], P[Y < X^2], P[X + Y > 0.5]$.

**5.27.** Let $X$ and $Y$ have joint pdf:

$$f_{X,Y}(x, y) = kx(1 - x)y \qquad \text{for } 0 < x < 1, 0 < y < 1.$$

**(a)** Find $k$.

**(b)** Find the joint cdf of $(X, Y)$.

**(c)** Find the marginal pdf of $X$ and of $Y$.

**(d)** Find $P[Y < X^{1/2}], P[X < Y]$.

**5.28.** The random vector $(X, Y)$ is uniformly distributed (i.e., $f(x, y) = k$) in the regions shown in Fig. P5.1 and zero elsewhere.

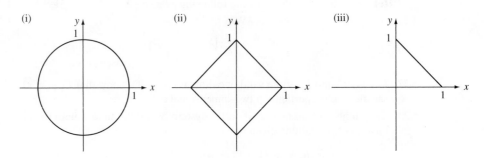

**FIGURE P5.1**

**(a)** Find the value of $k$ in each case.

**(b)** Find the marginal pdf for $X$ and for $Y$ in each case.

**(c)** Find $P[X > 0, Y > 0]$.

**5.29.** **(a)** Find the joint cdf for the vector random variable introduced in Example 5.16.

**(b)** Use the result of part a to find the marginal cdf of $X$ and of $Y$.

**5.30.** Let $X$ and $Y$ have the joint pdf:

$$f_{X,Y}(x, y) = ye^{-y(1+x)} \qquad \text{for } x > 0, y > 0.$$

Find the marginal pdf of $X$ and of $Y$.

**5.31.** Let $X$ and $Y$ be the pair of random variables in Problem 5.17.

**(a)** Find the joint pdf of $X$ and $Y$.

**(b)** Find the marginal pdf of $X$ and of $Y$.

**(c)** Find $P[Y < X^2]$.

**5.32.** Let $R$ and $\Theta$ be the pair of random variables in Problem 5.18.

**(a)** Find the joint pdf of $R$ and $\Theta$.

**(b)** Find the marginal pdf of $R$ and of $\Theta$.

**5.33.** Let $(X, Y)$ be the jointly Gaussian random variables discussed in Example 5.18. Find $P[X^2 + Y^2 > r^2]$ when $\rho = 0$. *Hint:* Use polar coordinates to compute the integral.

**5.34.** The general form of the joint pdf for two jointly Gaussian random variables is given by Eq. (5.61a). Show that $X$ and $Y$ have marginal pdfs that correspond to Gaussian random variables with means $m_1$ and $m_2$ and variances $\sigma_1^2$ and $\sigma_2^2$ respectively.

**5.35.** The input $X$ to a communication channel is $+1$ or $-1$ with probability $p$ and $1 - p$, respectively. The received signal $Y$ is the sum of $X$ and noise $N$ which has a Gaussian distribution with zero mean and variance $\sigma^2 = 0.25$.

    **(a)** Find the joint probability $P[X = j, Y \leq y]$.

    **(b)** Find the marginal pmf of $X$ and the marginal pdf of $Y$.

    **(c)** Suppose we are given that $Y > 0$. Which is more likely, $X = 1$ or $X = -1$?

**5.36.** A modem sends a two-dimensional signal $\mathbf{X}$ from the set $\{(1, 1), (1, -1), (-1, 1),$ $(-1, -1)\}$. The channel adds a noise signal $(N_1, N_2)$, so the received signal is $\mathbf{Y} = \mathbf{X} + \mathbf{N} = (X_1 + N_1, X_2 + N_2)$. Assume that $(N_1, N_2)$ have the jointly Gaussian pdf in Example 5.18 with $\rho = 0$. Let the distance between $\mathbf{X}$ and $\mathbf{Y}$ be $d(\mathbf{X}, \mathbf{Y}) = \{(X_1 - Y_1)^2 + (X_2 - Y_2)^2\}^{1/2}$.

    **(a)** Suppose that $\mathbf{X} = (1, 1)$. Find and sketch region for the event $\{\mathbf{Y}$ is closer to $(1, 1)$ than to the other possible values of $\mathbf{X}\}$. Evaluate the probability of this event.

    **(b)** Suppose that $\mathbf{X} = (1, 1)$. Find and sketch region for the event $\{\mathbf{Y}$ is closer to $(1, -1)$ than to the other possible values of $\mathbf{X}\}$. Evaluate the probability of this event.

    **(c)** Suppose that $\mathbf{X} = (1, 1)$. Find and sketch region for the event $\{d(\mathbf{X}, \mathbf{Y}) > 1\}$. Evaluate the probability of this event. Explain why this probability is an upper bound on the probability that $\mathbf{Y}$ is closer to a signal other than $\mathbf{X} = (1, 1)$.

## Section 5.5: Independence of Two Random Variables

**5.37.** Let $X$ be the number of full pairs and let $Y$ be the remainder of the number of dots observed in a toss of a fair die. Are $X$ and $Y$ independent random variables?

**5.38.** Let $X$ and $Y$ be the coordinates of the robot in Problem 5.15 after $2n$ time instants. Determine whether $X$ and $Y$ are independent random variables.

**5.39.** Let $X$ and $Y$ be the coordinates of the two-dimensional modem signal $(X, Y)$ in Problem 5.12.

    **(a)** Determine if $X$ and $Y$ are independent random variables.

    **(b)** Repeat part a if even values of $\Theta$ are twice as likely as odd values.

**5.40.** Determine which of the joint pmfs in Problem 5.11 correspond to independent pairs of random variables.

**5.41.** Michael takes the 7:30 bus every morning. The arrival time of the bus at the stop is uniformly distributed in the interval $[7{:}27, 7{:}37]$. Michael's arrival time at the stop is also uniformly distributed in the interval $[7{:}25, 7{:}40]$. Assume that Michael's and the bus's arrival times are independent random variables.

    **(a)** What is the probability that Michael arrives more than 5 minutes before the bus?

    **(b)** What is the probability that Michael misses the bus?

**5.42.** Are $R$ and $\Theta$ independent in Problem 5.18?

**5.43.** Are $X$ and $Y$ independent in Problem 5.20?

**5.44.** Are the signal amplitudes $X$ and $Y$ independent in Problem 5.25?

**5.45.** Are $X$ and $Y$ independent in Problem 5.26?

**5.46.** Are $X$ and $Y$ independent in Problem 5.27?

**5.47.** Let $X$ and $Y$ be independent random variables. Find an expression for the probability of the following events in terms of $F_X(x)$ and $F_Y(y)$.

(a) $\{a < X \le b\} \cap \{Y > d\}$.

(b) $\{a < X \le b\} \cap \{c \le Y < d\}$.

(c) $\{|X| < a\} \cap \{c \le Y \le d\}$.

**5.48.** Let $X$ and $Y$ be independent random variables that are uniformly distributed in $[-1, 1]$. Find the probability of the following events:

(a) $P[X^2 < 1/2, |Y| < 1/2]$.

(b) $P[4X < 1, Y < 0]$.

(c) $P[XY < 1/2]$.

(d) $P[\max(X, Y) < 1/3]$.

**5.49.** Let $X$ and $Y$ be random variables that take on values from the set $\{-1, 0, 1\}$.

(a) Find a joint pmf for which $X$ and $Y$ are independent.

(b) Are $X^2$ and $Y^2$ independent random variables for the pmf in part a?

(c) Find a joint pmf for which $X$ and $Y$ are not independent, but for which $X^2$ and $Y^2$ are independent.

**5.50.** Let $X$ and $Y$ be the jointly Gaussian random variables introduced in Problem 5.34.

(a) Show that $X$ and $Y$ are independent random variables if and only if $\rho = 0$.

(b) Suppose $\rho = 0$, find $P[XY < 0]$.

**5.51.** Two fair dice are tossed repeatedly until a pair occurs. Let $K$ be the number of tosses required and let $X$ be the number showing up in the pair. Find the joint pmf of $K$ and $X$ and determine whether $K$ and $X$ are independent.

**5.52.** The number of devices $L$ produced in a day is geometric distributed with probability of success $p$. Let $N$ be the number of working devices and let $M$ be the number of defective devices produced in a day.

(a) Are $N$ and $M$ independent random variables?

(b) Find the joint pmf of $N$ and $M$.

(c) Find the marginal pmfs of $N$ and $M$. (See hint in Problem 5.87b.)

(d) Are $L$ and $M$ independent random variables?

**5.53.** Let $N_1$ be the number of Web page requests arriving at a server in a 100-ms period and let $N_2$ be the number of Web page requests arriving at a server in the next 100-ms period. Use the result of Problem 5.13 parts a and b to develop a model where $N_1$ and $N_2$ are independent Poisson random variables.

**5.54.** (a) Show that Eq. (5.22) implies Eq. (5.21).

(b) Show that Eq. (5.21) implies Eq. (5.22).

**5.55.** Verify that Eqs. (5.22) and (5.23) can be obtained from each other.

## Section 5.6: Joint Moments and Expected Values of a Function of Two Random Variables

**5.56.** (a) Find $E[(X + Y)^2]$.

(b) Find the variance of $X + Y$.

(c) Under what condition is the variance of the sum equal to the sum of the individual variances?

**5.57.** Find $E[|X - Y|]$ if $X$ and $Y$ are independent exponential random variables with parameters $\lambda_1 = 1$ and $\lambda_2 = 2$, respectively.

**5.58.** Find $E[X^2 e^Y]$ where $X$ and $Y$ are independent random variables, $X$ is a zero-mean, unit-variance Gaussian random variable, and $Y$ is a uniform random variable in the interval $[0, 3]$.

**5.59.** For the discrete random variables $X$ and $Y$ in Problem 5.1, find the correlation and covariance, and indicate whether the random variables are independent, orthogonal, or uncorrelated.

**5.60.** For the discrete random variables $X$ and $Y$ in Problem 5.2, find the correlation and covariance, and indicate whether the random variables are independent, orthogonal, or uncorrelated.

**5.61.** For the three pairs of discrete random variables in Problem 5.11, find the correlation and covariance of $X$ and $Y$, and indicate whether the random variables are independent, orthogonal, or uncorrelated.

**5.62.** Let $N_1$ and $N_2$ be the number of Web page requests in Problem 5.13. Find the correlation and covariance of $N_1$ and $N_2$, and indicate whether the random variables are independent, orthogonal, or uncorrelated.

**5.63.** Repeat Problem 5.62 for $N_1$ and $N_2$, the number of Web page requests in Problem 5.14.

**5.64.** Let $N$ and $T$ be the number of users logged on and the time till the next logoff in Problem 5.23. Find the correlation and covariance of $N$ and $T$, and indicate whether the random variables are independent, orthogonal, or uncorrelated.

**5.65.** Find the correlation and covariance of $X$ and $Y$ in Problem 5.26. Determine whether $X$ and $Y$ are independent, orthogonal, or uncorrelated.

**5.66.** Repeat Problem 5.65 for $X$ and $Y$ in Problem 5.27.

**5.67.** For the three pairs of continuous random variables $X$ and $Y$ in Problem 5.29, find the correlation and covariance, and indicate whether the random variables are independent, orthogonal, or uncorrelated.

**5.68.** Find the correlation coefficient between $X$ and $Y = aX + b$. Does the answer depend on the sign of $a$?

**5.69.** Propose a method for estimating the covariance of two random variables.

**5.70.** **(a)** Complete the calculations for the correlation coefficient in Example 5.27.

   **(b)** Repeat the calculations if $X$ and $Y$ have the pdf:
   $$f_{X,Y}(x, y) = e^{-(x+|y|)} \qquad \text{for } x > 0, -x < y < x.$$

**5.71.** The output of a channel $Y = X + N$, where the input $X$ and the noise $N$ are independent, zero-mean random variables.

   **(a)** Find the correlation coefficient between the input $X$ and the output $Y$.

   **(b)** Suppose we estimate the input $X$ by a linear function $g(Y) = aY$. Find the value of $a$ that minimizes the mean squared error $E[(X - aY)^2]$.

   **(c)** Express the resulting mean-square error in terms of $\sigma_X/\sigma_N$.

**5.72.** In Example 5.27 let $X = \cos \Theta/4$ and $Y = \sin \Theta/4$. Are $X$ and $Y$ uncorrelated?

**5.73.** **(a)** Show that $\text{COV}(X, E[Y \mid X]) = \text{COV}(X, Y)$.

   **(b)** Show that $E[Y \mid X = x] = E[Y]$, for all $x$, implies that $X$ and $Y$ are uncorrelated.

**5.74.** Use the fact that $E[(tX + Y)^2] \geq 0$ for all $t$ to prove the Cauchy-Schwarz inequality:
$$(E[XY])^2 \leq E[X^2]E[Y^2].$$

*Hint:* Consider the discriminant of the quadratic equation in $t$ that results from the above inequality.

## Section 5.7: Conditional Probability and Conditional Expectation

**5.75.** (a)  Find $p_Y(y \mid x)$ and $p_X(x \mid y)$ in Problem 5.1 assuming fair coins are used.

    (b)  Find $p_Y(y \mid x)$ and $p_X(x \mid y)$ in Problem 5.1 assuming Carlos uses a coin with $p = 3/4$.

    (c)  What is the effect on $p_X(x \mid y)$ of Carlos using a biased coin?

    (d)  Find $E[Y \mid X = x]$ and $E[X \mid Y = y]$ in part a; then find $E[X]$ and $E[Y]$.

    (e)  Find $E[Y \mid X = x]$ and $E[X \mid Y = y]$ in part b; then find $E[X]$ and $E[Y]$.

**5.76.** (a)  Find $p_X(x \mid y)$ for the communication channel in Problem 5.3.

    (b)  For each value of $y$, find the value of $x$ that maximizes $p_X(x \mid y)$. State any assumptions about $p$ and $p_e$.

    (c)  Find the probability of error if a receiver uses the decision rule from part b.

**5.77.** (a)  In Problem 5.11(i), which conditional pmf given $X$ provides the most information about $Y$: $p_Y(y \mid -1)$, $p_Y(y \mid 0)$, or $p_Y(y \mid +1)$? Explain why.

    (b)  Compare the conditional pmfs in Problems 5.11(ii) and (iii) and explain which of these two cases is "more random."

    (c)  Find $E[Y \mid X = x]$ and $E[X \mid Y = y]$ in Problems 5.11(i), (ii), (iii); then find $E[X]$ and $E[Y]$.

    (d)  Find $E[Y^2 \mid X = x]$ and $E[X^2 \mid Y = y]$ in Problems 5.11(i), (ii), (iii); then find $\mathrm{VAR}[X]$ and $\mathrm{VAR}[Y]$.

**5.78.** (a)  Find the conditional pmf of $N_1$ given $N_2$ in Problem 5.14.

    (b)  Find $P[N_1 = k \mid N_2 = 2k]$ for $k = 5, 10, 20$. *Hint:* Use Stirling's fromula.

    (c)  Find $E[N_1 \mid N_2 = k]$, then find $E[N_1]$.

**5.79.**  In Example 5.30, let $Y$ be the number of defects inside the region $R$ and let $Z$ be the number of defects outside the region.

    (a)  Find the pmf of $Z$ given $Y$.

    (b)  Find the joint pmf of $Y$ and $Z$.

    (c)  Are $Y$ and $Z$ independent random variables? Is the result intuitive?

**5.80.** (a)  Find $f_Y(y \mid x)$ in Problem 5.26.

    (b)  Find $P[Y > X \mid x]$.

    (c)  Find $P[Y > X]$ using part b.

    (d)  Find $E[Y \mid X = x]$.

**5.81.** (a)  Find $f_Y(y \mid x)$ in Problem 5.28(i).

    (b)  Find $E[Y \mid X = x]$ and $E[Y]$.

    (c)  Repeat parts a and b of Problem 5.28(ii).

    (d)  Repeat parts a and b of Problem 5.28(iii).

**5.82.** (a)  Find $f_Y(y \mid x)$ in Example 5.27.

    (b)  Find $E[Y \mid X = x]$.

    (c)  Find $E[Y]$.

    (d)  Find $E[XY \mid X = x]$.

    (e)  Find $E[XY]$.

**5.83.**  Find $f_Y(y \mid x)$ and $f_X(x \mid y)$ for the jointly Gaussian pdf in Problem 5.34.

**5.84.** (a)  Find $f_X(t \mid N = n)$ in Problem 5.23.

    (b)  Find $E[X^t \mid N = n]$.

    (c)  Find the value of $n$ that maximizes $P[N = n \mid t < X < t + dt]$.

**5.85. (a)** Find $p_Y(y\,|\,x)$ and $p_X(x\,|\,y)$ in Problem 5.12.

    **(b)** Find $E[Y\,|\,X = x]$.

    **(c)** Find $E[XY\,|\,X = x]$ and $E[YX]$.

**5.86.** A customer enters a store and is equally likely to be served by one of three clerks. The time taken by clerk 1 is a constant random variable with mean two minutes; the time for clerk 2 is exponentially distributed with mean two minutes; and the time for clerk 3 is Pareto distributed with mean two minutes and $\alpha = 2.5$.

    **(a)** Find the pdf of $T$, the time taken to service a customer.

    **(b)** Find $E[T]$ and VAR$[T]$.

**5.87.** A message requires $N$ time units to be transmitted, where $N$ is a geometric random variable with pmf $p_i = (1 - a)a^{i-1}, i = 1, 2, \ldots$. A single new message arrives during a time unit with probability $p$, and no messages arrive with probability $1 - p$. Let $K$ be the number of new messages that arrive during the transmission of a single message.

    **(a)** Find $E[K]$ and VAR$[K]$ using conditional expectation.

    **(b)** Find the pmf of $K$. *Hint:* $(1 - \beta)^{-(k+1)} = \sum_{n=k}^{\infty} \binom{n}{k} \beta^{n-k}$.

    **(c)** Find the conditional pmf of $N$ given $K = k$.

    **(d)** Find the value of $n$ that maximizes $P[N = n\,|\,X = k]$.

**5.88.** The number of defects in a VLSI chip is a Poisson random variable with rate $r$. However, $r$ is itself a gamma random variable with parameters $\alpha$ and $\lambda$.

    **(a)** Use conditional expectation to find $E[N]$ and VAR$[N]$.

    **(b)** Find the pmf for $N$, the number of defects.

**5.89. (a)** In Problem 5.35, find the conditional pmf of the input $X$ of the communication channel given that the output is in the interval $y < Y \le y + dy$.

    **(b)** Find the value of $X$ that is more probable given $y < Y \le y + dy$.

    **(c)** Find an expression for the probability of error if we use the result of part b to decide what the input to the channel was.

## Section 5.8: Functions of Two Random Variables

**5.90.** Two toys are started at the same time each with a different battery. The first battery has a lifetime that is exponentially distributed with mean 100 minutes; the second battery has a Rayleigh-distributed lifetime with mean 100 minutes.

    **(a)** Find the cdf to the time $T$ until the battery in a toy first runs out.

    **(b)** Suppose that both toys are still operating after 100 minutes. Find the cdf of the time $T_2$ that subsequently elapses until the battery in a toy first runs out.

    **(c)** In part b, find the cdf of the total time that elapses until a battery first fails.

**5.91. (a)** Find the cdf of the time that elapses until both batteries run out in Problem 5.90a.

    **(b)** Find the cdf of the remaining time until both batteries run out in Problem 5.90b.

**5.92.** Let $K$ and $N$ be independent random variables with nonnegative integer values.

    **(a)** Find an expression for the pmf of $M = K + N$.

    **(b)** Find the pmf of $M$ if $K$ and $N$ are binomial random variables with parameters $(k, p)$ and $(n, p)$.

    **(c)** Find the pmf of $M$ if $K$ and $N$ are Poisson random variables with parameters $\alpha_1$ and $\alpha_2$, respectively.

**5.93.** The number $X$ of goals the Bulldogs score against the Flames has a geometric distribution with mean 2; the number of goals $Y$ that the Flames score against the Bulldogs is also geometrically distributed but with mean 4.

    **(a)** Find the pmf of the $Z = X - Y$. Assume $X$ and $Y$ are independent.

    **(b)** What is the probability that the Bulldogs beat the Flames? Tie the Flames?

    **(c)** Find $E[Z]$.

**5.94.** Passengers arrive at an airport taxi stand every minute according to a Bernoulli random variable. A taxi will not leave until it has two passengers.

    **(a)** Find the pmf until the time $T$ when the taxi has two passengers.

    **(b)** Find the pmf for the time that the first customer waits.

**5.95.** Let $X$ and $Y$ be independent random variables that are uniformly distributed in the interval $[0, 1]$. Find the pdf of $Z = XY$.

**5.96.** Let $X_1$, $X_2$, and $X_3$ be independent and uniformly distributed in $[-1, 1]$.

    **(a)** Find the cdf and pdf of $Y = X_1 + X_2$.

    **(b)** Find the cdf of $Z = Y + X_3$.

**5.97.** Let $X$ and $Y$ be independent random variables with gamma distributions and parameters $(\alpha_1, \lambda)$ and $(\alpha_2, \lambda)$, respectively. Show that $Z = X + Y$ is gamma-distributed with parameters $(\alpha_1 + \alpha_2, \lambda)$. *Hint:* See Eq. (4.59).

**5.98.** Signals $X$ and $Y$ are independent. $X$ is exponentially distributed with mean 1 and $Y$ is exponentially distributed with mean 1.

    **(a)** Find the cdf of $Z = |X - Y|$.

    **(b)** Use the result of part a to find $E[Z]$.

**5.99.** The random variables $X$ and $Y$ have the joint pdf

$$f_{X,Y}(x, y) = e^{-(x+y)} \qquad \text{for } 0 < y < x < 1.$$

Find the pdf of $Z = X + Y$.

**5.100.** Let $X$ and $Y$ be independent Rayleigh random variables with parameters $\alpha = \beta = 1$. Find the pdf of $Z = X/Y$.

**5.101.** Let $X$ and $Y$ be independent Gaussian random variables that are zero mean and unit variance. Show that $Z = X/Y$ is a Cauchy random variable.

**5.102.** Find the joint cdf of $W = \min(X, Y)$ and $Z = \max(X, Y)$ if $X$ and $Y$ are independent and $X$ is uniformly distributed in $[0, 1]$ and $Y$ is uniformly distributed in $[0, 1]$.

**5.103.** Find the joint cdf of $W = \min(X, Y)$ and $Z = \max(X, Y)$ if $X$ and $Y$ are independent exponential random variables with the same mean.

**5.104.** Find the joint cdf of $W = \min(X, Y)$ and $Z = \max(X, Y)$ if $X$ and $Y$ are the independent Pareto random variables with the same distribution.

**5.105.** Let $W = X + Y$ and $Z = X - Y$.

    **(a)** Find an expression for the joint pdf of $W$ and $Z$.

    **(b)** Find $f_{W,Z}(z, w)$ if $X$ and $Y$ are independent exponential random variables with parameter $\lambda = 1$.

    **(c)** Find $f_{W,Z}(z, w)$ if $X$ and $Y$ are independent Pareto random variables with the same distribution.

**5.106.** The pair $(X, Y)$ is uniformly distributed in a ring centered about the origin and inner and outer radii $r_1 < r_2$. Let $R$ and $\Theta$ be the radius and angle corresponding to $(X, Y)$. Find the joint pdf of $R$ and $\Theta$.

**5.107.** Let $X$ and $Y$ be independent, zero-mean, unit-variance Gaussian random variables. Let $V = aX + bY$ and $W = cX + eY$.

  **(a)** Find the joint pdf of $V$ and $W$, assuming the transformation matrix $A$ is invertible.

  **(b)** Suppose $A$ is not invertible. What is the joint pdf of $V$ and $W$?

**5.108.** Let $X$ and $Y$ be independent Gaussian random variables that are zero mean and unit variance. Let $W = X^2 + Y^2$ and let $\Theta = \tan^{-1}(Y/X)$. Find the joint pdf of $W$ and $\Theta$.

**5.109.** Let $X$ and $Y$ be the random variables introduced in Example 5.4. Let $R = (X^2 + Y^2)^{1/2}$ and let $\Theta = \tan^{-1}(Y/X)$.

  **(a)** Find the joint pdf of $R$ and $\Theta$.

  **(b)** What is the joint pdf of $X$ and $Y$?

## Section 5.9: Pairs of Jointly Gaussian Variables

**5.110.** Let $X$ and $Y$ be jointly Gaussian random variables with pdf

$$f_{X,Y}(x, y) = \frac{\exp\{-2x^2 - y^2/2\}}{2\pi c} \quad \text{for all } x, y.$$

Find VAR[$X$], VAR[$Y$], and COV($X, Y$).

**5.111.** Let $X$ and $Y$ be jointly Gaussian random variables with pdf

$$f_{X,Y}(x, y) = \frac{\exp\left\{\dfrac{-1}{2}[x^2 + 4y^2 - 3xy + 3y - 2x + 1]\right\}}{2\pi} \quad \text{for all } x, y.$$

Find $E[X], E[Y], $ VAR[$X$], VAR[$Y$], and COV($X, Y$).

**5.112.** Let $X$ and $Y$ be jointly Gaussian random variables with $E[Y] = 0, \sigma_1 = 1, \sigma_2 = 2$, and $E[X | Y] = Y/4 + 1$. Find the joint pdf of $X$ and $Y$.

**5.113.** Let $X$ and $Y$ be zero-mean, independent Gaussian random variables with $\sigma^2 = 1$.

  **(a)** Find the value of $r$ for which the probability that $(X, Y)$ falls inside a circle of radius $r$ is 1/2.

  **(b)** Find the conditional pdf of $(X, Y)$ given that $(X, Y)$ is not inside a ring with inner radius $r_1$ and outer radius $r_2$.

**5.114.** Use a plotting program (as provided by Octave or MATLAB) to show the pdf for jointly Gaussian zero-mean random variables with the following parameters:

  **(a)** $\sigma_1 = 1, \sigma_2 = 1, \rho = 0$.

  **(b)** $\sigma_1 = 1, \sigma_2 = 1, \rho = 0.8$.

  **(c)** $\sigma_1 = 1, \sigma_2 = 1, \rho = -0.8$.

  **(d)** $\sigma_1 = 1, \sigma_2 = 2, \rho = 0$.

  **(e)** $\sigma_1 = 1, \sigma_2 = 2, \rho = 0.8$.

  **(f)** $\sigma_1 = 1, \sigma_2 = 10, \rho = 0.8$.

**5.115.** Let $X$ and $Y$ be zero-mean, jointly Gaussian random variables with $\sigma_1 = 1, \sigma_2 = 2$, and correlation coefficient $\rho$.

  **(a)** Plot the principal axes of the constant-pdf ellipse of $(X, Y)$.

  **(b)** Plot the conditional expectation of $Y$ given $X = x$.

  **(c)** Are the plots in parts a and b the same or different? Why?

**5.116.** Let $X$ and $Y$ be zero-mean, unit-variance jointly Gaussian random variables for which $\rho = 1$. Sketch the joint cdf of $X$ and $Y$. Does a joint pdf exist?

**5.117.** Let $h(x, y)$ be a joint Gaussian pdf for zero-mean, unit-variance Gaussian random variables with correlation coefficient $\rho_1$. Let $g(x, y)$ be a joint Gaussian pdf for zero-mean, unit-variance Gaussian random variables with correlation coefficient $\rho_2 \neq \rho_1$. Suppose the random variables $X$ and $Y$ have joint pdf

$$f_{X,Y}(x, y) = \{h(x, y) + g(x, y)\}/2.$$

   **(a)** Find the marginal pdf for $X$ and for $Y$.

   **(b)** Explain why $X$ and $Y$ are not jointly Gaussian random variables.

**5.118.** Use conditional expectation to show that for $X$ and $Y$ zero-mean, jointly Gaussian random variables, $E[X^2Y^2] = E[X^2]E[Y^2] + 2E[XY]^2$.

**5.119.** Let $\mathbf{X} = (X, Y)$ be the zero-mean jointly Gaussian random variables in Problem 5.110. Find a transformation $A$ such that $\mathbf{Z} = A\mathbf{X}$ has components that are zero-mean, unit-variance Gaussian random variables.

**5.120.** In Example 5.47, suppose we estimate the value of the signal $X$ from the noisy observation $Y$ by:

$$\hat{X} = \frac{1}{1 + \sigma_N^2/\sigma_X^2} Y.$$

   **(a)** Evaluate the mean square estimation error: $E[(X - \hat{X})^2]$.

   **(b)** How does the estimation error in part a vary with signal-to-noise ratio $\sigma_X/\sigma_N$?

## Section 5.10: Generating Independent Gaussian Random Variables

**5.121.** Find the inverse of the cdf of the Rayleigh random variable to derive the transformation method for generating Rayleigh random variables. Show that this method leads to the same algorithm that was presented in Section 5.10.

**5.122.** Reproduce the results presented in Example 5.49.

**5.123.** Consider the two-dimensional modem in Problem 5.36.

   **(a)** Generate 10,000 discrete random variables uniformly distributed in the set $\{1, 2, 3, 4\}$. Assign each outcome in this set to one of the signals $\{(1, 1), (1, -1), (-1, 1), (-1, -1)\}$. The sequence of discrete random variables then produces a sequence of 10,000 signal points $\mathbf{X}$.

   **(b)** Generate 10,000 noise pairs $\mathbf{N}$ of independent zero-mean, unit-variance jointly Gaussian random variables.

   **(c)** Form the sequence of 10,000 received signals $\mathbf{Y} = (Y_1, Y_2) = \mathbf{X} + \mathbf{N}$.

   **(d)** Plot the scattergram of received signal vectors. Is the plot what you expected?

   **(e)** Estimate the transmitted signal by the quadrant that $\mathbf{Y}$ falls in: $\hat{X} = (\text{sgn}(Y_1), \text{sgn}(Y_2))$.

   **(f)** Compare the estimates with the actually transmitted signals to estimate the probability of error.

**5.124.** Generate a sequence of 1000 pairs of independent zero-mean Gaussian random variables, where $X$ has variance 2 and $N$ has variance 1. Let $Y = X + N$ be the noisy signal from Example 5.47.

   **(a)** Estimate $X$ using the estimator in Problem 5.120, and calculate the sequence of estimation errors.

   **(b)** What is the pdf of the estimation error?

   **(c)** Compare the mean, variance, and relative frequencies of the estimation error with the result from part b.

**5.125.** Let $X_1, X_2, \ldots, X_{1000}$ be a sequence of zero-mean, unit-variance independent Gaussian random variables. Suppose that the sequence is "smoothed" as follows:

$$Y_n = (X_n + X_{N-1})/2 \text{ where } X_0 = 0.$$

(a) Find the pdf of $(Y_n, Y_{n+1})$.

(b) Generate the sequence of $X_n$ and the corresponding sequence $Y_n$. Plot the scattergram of $(Y_n, Y_{n+1})$. Does it agree with the result from part a?

(c) Repeat parts a and b for $Z_n = (X_n - X_{N-1})/2$.

**5.126.** Let $X$ and $Y$ be independent, zero-mean, unit-variance Gaussian random variables. Find the linear transformation to generate jointly Gaussian random variables with means $m_1, m_2$, variances $\sigma_1^2, \sigma_2^2$, and correlation coefficient $\rho$. *Hint:* Use the conditional pdf in Eq. (5.64).

**5.127.** (a) Use the method developed in Problem 5.126 to generate 1000 pairs of jointly Gaussian random variables with $m_1 = 1$, $m_2 = -1$, variances $\sigma_1^2 = 1$, $\sigma_2^2 = 2$, and correlation coefficient $\rho = -1/2$.

(b) Plot a two-dimensional scattergram of the 1000 pairs and compare to equal-pdf contour lines for the theoretical pdf.

**5.128.** Let $H$ and $W$ be the height and weight of adult males. Studies have shown that $H$ (in cm) and $V = \ln W$ ($W$ in kg) are jointly Gaussian with parameters $m_H = 174$ cm, $m_V = 4.4$, $\sigma_H^2 = 42.36$, $\sigma_V^2 = 0.021$, and $\text{COV}(H, V) = 0.458$.

(a) Use the method in part a to generate 1000 pairs $(H, V)$. Plot a scattergram to check the joint pdf.

(b) Convert the $(H, V)$ pairs into $(H, W)$ pairs.

(c) Calculate the body mass index for each outcome, and estimate the proportion of the population that is underweight, normal, overweight, or obese. (See Problem 5.6.)

## Problems Requiring Cumulative Knowledge

**5.129.** The random variables $X$ and $Y$ have joint pdf:

$$f_{X,Y}(x, y) = c \sin (x + y) \qquad 0 \le x \le \pi/2, 0 \le y \le \pi/2.$$

(a) Find the value of the constant $c$.

(b) Find the joint cdf of $X$ and $Y$.

(c) Find the marginal pdf's of $X$ and of $Y$.

(d) Find the mean, variance, and covariance of $X$ and $Y$.

**5.130.** An inspector selects an item for inspection according to the outcome of a coin flip: The item is inspected if the outcome is heads. Suppose that the time between item arrivals is an exponential random variable with mean one. Assume the time to inspect an item is a constant value $t$.

(a) Find the pmf for the number of item arrivals between consecutive inspections.

(b) Find the pdf for the time $X$ between item inspections. *Hint:* Use conditional expectation.

(c) Find the value of $p$, so that with a probability of 90% an inspection is completed before the next item is selected for inspection.

**5.131.** The lifetime $X$ of a device is an exponential random variable with mean $= 1/R$. Suppose that due to irregularities in the production process, the parameter $R$ is random and has a gamma distribution.

(a) Find the joint pdf of $X$ and $R$.

(b) Find the pdf of $X$.

(c) Find the mean and variance of $X$.

**5.132.** Let $X$ and $Y$ be samples of a random signal at two time instants. Suppose that $X$ and $Y$ are independent zero-mean Gaussian random variables with the same variance. When signal "0" is present the variance is $\sigma_0^2$, and when signal "1" is present the variance is $\sigma_1^2 > \sigma_0^2$. Suppose signals 0 and 1 occur with probabilities $p$ and $1 - p$, respectively. Let $R^2 = X^2 + Y^2$ be the total energy of the two observations.

**(a)** Find the pdf of $R^2$ when signal 0 is present; when signal 1 is present. Find the pdf of $R^2$.

**(b)** Suppose we use the following "signal detection" rule: If $R^2 > T$, then we decide signal 1 is present; otherwise, we decide signal 0 is present. Find an expression for the probability of error in terms of $T$.

**(c)** Find the value of $T$ that minimizes the probability of error.

**5.133.** Let $U_0, U_1, \ldots$ be a sequence of independent zero-mean, unit-variance Gaussian random variables. A "low-pass filter" takes the sequence $U_i$ and produces the output sequence $X_n = (U_n + U_{n-1})/2$, and a "high-pass filter" produces the output sequence $Y_n = (U_n - U_{n-1})/2$.

**(a)** Find the joint pdf of $X_n$ and $X_{n-1}$; of $X_n$ and $X_{n+m}$, $m > 1$.

**(b)** Repeat part a for $Y_n$.

**(c)** Find the joint pdf of $X_n$ and $Y_m$.

# Vector Random Variables

**CHAPTER**

**6**

In the previous chapter we presented methods for dealing with two random variables. In this chapter we extend these methods to the case of $n$ random variables in the following ways:

- By representing $n$ random variables as a vector, we obtain a compact notation for the joint pmf, cdf, and pdf as well as marginal and conditional distributions.
- We present a general method for finding the pdf of transformations of vector random variables.
- Summary information of the distribution of a vector random variable is provided by an expected value vector and a covariance matrix.
- We use linear transformations and characteristic functions to find alternative representations of random vectors and their probabilities.
- We develop optimum estimators for estimating the value of a random variable based on observations of other random variables.
- We show how jointly Gaussian random vectors have a compact and easy-to-work-with pdf and characteristic function.

## 6.1 VECTOR RANDOM VARIABLES

The notion of a random variable is easily generalized to the case where several quantities are of interest. A **vector random variable X** is a function that assigns a vector of real numbers to each outcome $\zeta$ in $S$, the sample space of the random experiment. We use uppercase boldface notation for vector random variables. By convention **X** is a column vector ($n$ rows by 1 column), so the vector random variable with components $X_1, X_2, \ldots, X_n$ corresponds to

$$
\mathbf{X} = \begin{bmatrix} X_1 \\ X_2 \\ \vdots \\ X_n \end{bmatrix} = [X_1, X_2, \ldots, X_n]^{\mathrm{T}},
$$

where "$^\text{T}$" denotes the transpose of a matrix or vector. We will sometimes write $\mathbf{X} = (X_1, X_2, \ldots, X_n)$ to save space and omit the transpose unless dealing with matrices. Possible values of the vector random variable are denoted by $\mathbf{x} = (x_1, x_2, \ldots, x_n)$ where $x_i$ corresponds to the value of $X_i$.

---

### Example 6.1   Arrivals at a Packet Switch

Packets arrive at each of three input ports of a packet switch according to independent Bernoulli trials with $p = 1/2$. Each arriving packet is equally likely to be destined to any of three output ports. Let $\mathbf{X} = (X_1, X_2, X_3)$ where $X_i$ is the total number of packets arriving for output port $i$. $\mathbf{X}$ is a vector random variable whose values are determined by the pattern of arrivals at the input ports.

---

### Example 6.2   Joint Poisson Counts

A random experiment consists of finding the number of defects in a semiconductor chip and identifying their locations. The outcome of this experiment consists of the vector $\zeta = (n, \mathbf{y}_1, \mathbf{y}_2, \ldots, \mathbf{y}_n)$, where the first component specifies the total number of defects and the remaining components specify the coordinates of their location. Suppose that the chip consists of $M$ regions. Let $N_1(\zeta), N_2(\zeta), \ldots, N_M(\zeta)$ be the number of defects in each of these regions, that is, $N_k(\zeta)$ is the number of $\mathbf{y}$'s that fall in region $k$. The vector $\mathbf{N}(\zeta) = (N_1, N_2, \ldots, N_M)$ is then a vector random variable.

---

### Example 6.3   Samples of an Audio Signal

Let the outcome $\zeta$ of a random experiment be an audio signal $X(t)$. Let the random variable $X_k = X(kT)$ be the sample of the signal taken at time $kT$. An MP3 codec processes the audio in blocks of $n$ samples $\mathbf{X} = (X_1, X_2, \ldots, X_n)$. $\mathbf{X}$ is a vector random variable.

---

### 6.1.1   Events and Probabilities

Each event $A$ involving $\mathbf{X} = (X_1, X_2, \ldots, X_n)$ has a corresponding region in an $n$-dimensional real space $R^n$. As before, we use "rectangular" product-form sets in $R^n$ as building blocks. For the $n$-dimensional random variable $\mathbf{X} = (X_1, X_2, \ldots, X_n)$, we are interested in events that have the **product form**

$$A = \{X_1 \text{ in } A_1\} \cap \{X_2 \text{ in } A_2\} \cap \cdots \cap \{X_n \text{ in } A_n\}, \tag{6.1}$$

where each $A_k$ is a one-dimensional event (i.e., subset of the real line) that involves $X_k$ only. The event $A$ occurs when all of the events $\{X_k \text{ in } A_k\}$ occur jointly.

We are interested in obtaining the probabilities of these product-form events:

$$P[A] = P[\mathbf{X} \in A] = P[\{X_1 \text{ in } A_1\} \cap \{X_2 \text{ in } A_2\} \cap \cdots \cap \{X_n \text{ in } A_n\}]$$
$$\triangleq P[X_1 \text{ in } A_1, X_2 \text{ in } A_2, \ldots, X_n \text{ in } A_n]. \tag{6.2}$$

In principle, the probability in Eq. (6.2) is obtained by finding the probability of the equivalent event in the underlying sample space, that is,

$$P[A] = P[\{\zeta \text{ in } S : \mathbf{X}(\zeta) \text{ in } A\}]$$

$$= P[\{\zeta \text{ in } S : X_1(\zeta) \in A_1, X_2(\zeta) \in A_2, \ldots, X_n(\zeta) \in A_n\}]. \quad (6.3)$$

Equation (6.2) forms the basis for the definition of the $n$-dimensional joint probability mass function, cumulative distribution function, and probability density function. The probabilities of other events can be expressed in terms of these three functions.

### 6.1.2   Joint Distribution Functions

The **joint cumulative distribution function** of $X_1, X_2, \ldots, X_n$ is defined as the probability of an $n$-dimensional semi-infinite rectangle associated with the point $(x_1, \ldots, x_n)$:

$$F_{\mathbf{X}}(\mathbf{x}) \triangleq F_{X_1, X_2, \ldots, X_n}(x_1, x_2, \ldots, x_n) = P[X_1 \le x_1, X_2 \le x_2, \ldots, X_n \le x_n]. \quad (6.4)$$

The joint cdf is defined for discrete, continuous, and random variables of mixed type. The probability of product-form events can be expressed in terms of the joint cdf.

The joint cdf generates a family of **marginal cdf's** for subcollections of the random variables $X_1, \ldots, X_n$. These marginal cdf's are obtained by setting the appropriate entries to $+\infty$ in the joint cdf in Eq. (6.4). For example:

Joint cdf for $X_1, \ldots, X_{n-1}$ is given by $F_{X_1, X_2, \ldots, X_n}(x_1, x_2, \ldots, x_{n-1}, \infty)$ and
Joint cdf for $X_1$ and $X_2$ is given by $F_{X_1, X_2, \ldots, X_n}(x_1, x_2, \infty, \ldots, \infty)$.

---

### Example 6.4

A radio transmitter sends a signal to a receiver using three paths. Let $X_1$, $X_2$, and $X_3$ be the signals that arrive at the receiver along each path. Find $P[\max(X_1, X_2, X_3) \le 5]$.

The maximum of three numbers is less than 5 if and only if each of the three numbers is less than 5; therefore

$$P[A] = P[\{X_1 \le 5\} \cap \{X_2 \le 5\} \cap \{X_3 \le 5\}]$$

$$= F_{X_1, X_2, X_3}(5, 5, 5).$$

---

The **joint probability mass function** of $n$ discrete random variables is defined by

$$p_{\mathbf{X}}(\mathbf{x}) \triangleq p_{X_1, X_2, \ldots, X_n}(x_1, x_2, \ldots, x_n) = P[X_1 = x_1, X_2 = x_2, \ldots, X_n = x_n]. \quad (6.5)$$

The probability of any $n$-dimensional event $A$ is found by summing the pmf over the points in the event

$$P[\mathbf{X} \text{ in } A] = \sum_{\mathbf{x} \text{ in } A} \cdots \sum p_{X_1, X_2, \ldots, X_n}(x_1, x_2, \ldots, x_n). \quad (6.6)$$

The joint pmf generates a family of **marginal pmf's** that specifies the joint probabilities for subcollections of the $n$ random variables. For example, the one-dimensional pmf of $X_j$ is found by adding the joint pmf over all variables other than $x_j$:

$$p_{X_j}(x_j) = P[X_j = x_j] = \sum_{x_1} \cdots \sum_{x_{j-1}x_{j+1}} \sum \cdots \sum_{x_n} p_{X_1, X_2, \ldots, X_n}(x_1, x_2, \ldots, x_n). \quad (6.7)$$

The two-dimensional joint pmf of any pair $X_j$ and $X_k$ is found by adding the joint pmf over all $n - 2$ other variables, and so on. Thus, the marginal pmf for $X_1, \ldots, X_{n-1}$ is given by

$$p_{X_1, \ldots, X_{n-1}}(x_1, x_2, \ldots, x_{n-1}) = \sum_{x_n} p_{X_1, \ldots, X_n}(x_1, x_2, \ldots, x_n). \quad (6.8)$$

A family of **conditional pmf's** is obtained from the joint pmf by conditioning on different subcollections of the random variables. For example, if $p_{X_1, \ldots, X_{n-1}}(x_1, \ldots, x_{n-1}) > 0$:

$$p_{X_n}(x_n \mid x_1, \ldots, x_{n-1}) = \frac{p_{X_1, \ldots, X_n}(x_1, \ldots, x_n)}{p_{X_1, \ldots, X_{n-1}}(x_1, \ldots, x_{n-1})}. \quad (6.9a)$$

Repeated applications of Eq. (6.9a) yield the following very useful expression:

$$p_{X_1, \ldots, X_n}(x_1, \ldots, x_n) =$$

$$p_{X_n}(x_n \mid x_1, \ldots, x_{n-1}) p_{X_{n-1}}(x_{n-1} \mid x_1, \ldots, x_{n-2}) \cdots p_{X_2}(x_2 \mid x_1) p_{X_1}(x_1). \quad (6.9b)$$

---

### Example 6.5    Arrivals at a Packet Switch

Find the joint pmf of $\mathbf{X} = (X_1, X_2, X_3)$ in Example 6.1. Find $P[X_1 > X_3]$.

Let $N$ be the total number of packets arriving in the three input ports. Each input port has an arrival with probability $p = 1/2$, so $N$ is binomial with pmf:

$$p_N(n) = \binom{3}{n} \frac{1}{2^3} \quad \text{for} \quad 0 \le n \le 3.$$

Given $N = n$, the number of packets arriving for each output port has a multinomial distribution:

$$p_{X_1, X_2, X_3}(i, j, k \mid i + j + k = n) = \begin{cases} \dfrac{n!}{i!\, j!\, k!} \dfrac{1}{3^n} & \text{for} \quad i + j + k = n, i \ge 0, j \ge 0, k \ge 0 \\ 0 & \text{otherwise.} \end{cases}$$

The joint pmf of $\mathbf{X}$ is then:

$$p_{\mathbf{X}}(i, j, k) = p_{\mathbf{X}}(i, j, k \mid n) \binom{3}{n} \frac{1}{2^3} \quad \text{for} \quad i \ge 0, j \ge 0, k \ge 0, i + j + k = n \le 3.$$

The explicit values of the joint pmf are:

$$p_{\mathbf{X}}(0, 0, 0) = \frac{0!}{0!\, 0!\, 0!} \frac{1}{3^0} \binom{3}{0} \frac{1}{2^3} = \frac{1}{8}$$

$$p_{\mathbf{X}}(1, 0, 0) = p_{\mathbf{X}}(0, 1, 0) = p_{\mathbf{X}}(0, 0, 1) = \frac{1!}{0!\,0!\,1!} \frac{1}{3^1} \binom{3}{1} \frac{1}{2^3} = \frac{3}{24}$$

$$p_{\mathbf{X}}(1, 1, 0) = p_{\mathbf{X}}(1, 0, 1) = p_{\mathbf{X}}(0, 1, 1) = \frac{2!}{0!\,1!\,1!} \frac{1}{3^2} \binom{3}{2} \frac{1}{2^3} = \frac{6}{72}$$

$$p_{\mathbf{X}}(2, 0, 0) = p_{\mathbf{X}}(0, 2, 0) = p_{\mathbf{X}}(0, 0, 2) = 3/72$$

$$p_{\mathbf{X}}(1, 1, 1) = 6/216$$

$$p_{\mathbf{X}}(0, 1, 2) = p_{\mathbf{X}}(0, 2, 1) = p_{\mathbf{X}}(1, 0, 2) = p_{\mathbf{X}}(1, 2, 0) = p_{\mathbf{X}}(2, 0, 1) = p_{\mathbf{X}}(2, 1, 0) = 3/216$$

$$p_{\mathbf{X}}(3, 0, 0) = p_{\mathbf{X}}(0, 3, 0) = p_{\mathbf{X}}(0, 0, 3) = 1/216.$$

Finally:

$$P[X_1 > X_3] = p_{\mathbf{X}}(1, 0, 0) + p_{\mathbf{X}}(1, 1, 0) + p_{\mathbf{X}}(2, 0, 0) + p_{\mathbf{X}}(1, 2, 0)$$
$$+ p_{\mathbf{X}}(2, 0, 1) + p_{\mathbf{X}}(2, 1, 0) + p_{\mathbf{X}}(3, 0, 0)$$
$$= 8/27.$$

We say that the random variables $X_1, X_2, \ldots, X_n$ are **jointly continuous random variables** if the probability of any $n$-dimensional event $A$ is given by an $n$-dimensional integral of a probability density function:

$$P[\mathbf{X} \text{ in } A] = \int \cdots_{\mathbf{x} \text{ in } A} \int f_{X_1, \ldots, X_n}(x'_1, \ldots, x'_n)\, dx'_1 \ldots dx'_n, \qquad (6.10)$$

where $f_{X_1, \ldots, X_n}(x_1, \ldots, x_n)$ is the **joint probability density function**.

The joint cdf of $\mathbf{X}$ is obtained from the joint pdf by integration:

$$F_{\mathbf{X}}(\mathbf{x}) = F_{X_1, X_2, \ldots, X_n}(x_1, x_2, \ldots, x_n) = \int_{-\infty}^{x_1} \cdots \int_{-\infty}^{x_n} f_{X_1, \ldots, X_n}(x'_1, \ldots, x'_n)\, dx'_1 \ldots dx'_n. \qquad (6.11)$$

The joint pdf (if the derivative exists) is given by

$$f_{\mathbf{X}}(\mathbf{x}) \triangleq f_{X_1, X_2, \ldots, X_n}(x_1, x_2, \ldots, x_n) = \frac{\partial^n}{\partial x_1 \ldots \partial x_n} F_{X_1, \ldots, X_n}(x_1, \ldots, x_n). \qquad (6.12)$$

A family of **marginal pdf's** is associated with the joint pdf in Eq. (6.12). The marginal pdf for a subset of the random variables is obtained by integrating the other variables out. For example, the marginal pdf of $X_1$ is

$$f_{X_1}(x_1) = \int_{-\infty}^{\infty} \cdots \int_{-\infty}^{\infty} f_{X_1, X_2, \ldots, X_n}(x_1, x'_2, \ldots, x'_n)\, dx'_2 \ldots dx'_n. \qquad (6.13)$$

As another example, the marginal pdf for $X_1, \ldots, X_{n-1}$ is given by

$$f_{X_1, \ldots, X_{n-1}}(x_1, \ldots, x_{n-1}) = \int_{-\infty}^{\infty} f_{X_1, \ldots, X_n}(x_1, \ldots, x_{n-1}, x'_n)\, dx'_n. \qquad (6.14)$$

A family of **conditional pdf's** is also associated with the joint pdf. For example, the pdf of $X_n$ given the values of $X_1, \ldots, X_{n-1}$ is given by

$$f_{X_n}(x_n | x_1, \ldots, x_{n-1}) = \frac{f_{X_1, \ldots, X_n}(x_1, \ldots, x_n)}{f_{X_1, \ldots, X_{n-1}}(x_1, \ldots, x_{n-1})} \qquad (6.15a)$$

if $f_{X_1, \ldots, X_{n-1}}(x_1, \ldots, x_{n-1}) > 0$.

Repeated applications of Eq. (6.15a) yield an expression analogous to Eq. (6.9b):

$$f_{X_1, \ldots, X_n}(x_1, \ldots, x_n) = \\ f_{X_n}(x_n \mid x_1, \ldots, x_{n-1}) f_{X_{n-1}}(x_{n-1} \mid x_1, \ldots, x_{n-2}) \ldots f_{X_2}(x_2 \mid x_1) f_{X_1}(x_1). \tag{6.15b}$$

---

### Example 6.6

The random variables $X_1$, $X_2$, and $X_3$ have the joint Gaussian pdf

$$f_{X_1,X_2,X_3}(x_1, x_2, x_3) = \frac{e^{-(x_1^2 + x_2^2 - \sqrt{2}\, x_1 x_2 + 1/2 x_3^2)}}{2\pi\sqrt{\pi}}.$$

Find the marginal pdf of $X_1$ and $X_3$. Find the conditional pdf of $X_2$ given $X_1$ and $X_3$.

The marginal pdf for the pair $X_1$ and $X_3$ is found by integrating the joint pdf over $x_2$:

$$f_{X_1,X_3}(x_1, x_3) = \frac{e^{-x_3^2/2}}{\sqrt{2\pi}} \int_{-\infty}^{\infty} \frac{e^{-(x_1^2 + x_2^2 - \sqrt{2}x_1 x_2)}}{2\pi/\sqrt{2}} dx_2.$$

The above integral was carried out in Example 5.18 with $\rho = -1/\sqrt{2}$. By substituting the result of the integration above, we obtain

$$f_{X_1,X_3}(x_1, x_3) = \frac{e^{-x_3^2/2}}{\sqrt{2\pi}} \frac{e^{-x_1^2/2}}{\sqrt{2\pi}}.$$

Therefore $X_1$ and $X_3$ are independent zero-mean, unit-variance Gaussian random variables.

The conditional pdf of $X_2$ given $X_1$ and $X_3$ is:

$$f_{X_2}(x_2 \mid x_1, x_3) = \frac{e^{-(x_1^2 + x_2^2 - \sqrt{2}x_1 x_2 + 1/2 x_3^2)}}{2\pi\sqrt{\pi}} \frac{\sqrt{2\pi}\sqrt{2\pi}}{e^{-x_3^2/2}e^{-x_1^2/2}}$$

$$= \frac{e^{-(1/2 x_1^2 + x_2^2 - \sqrt{2}x_1 x_2)}}{\sqrt{\pi}} = \frac{e^{-(x_2 - x_1/\sqrt{2}x_1)^2}}{\sqrt{\pi}}.$$

We conclude that $X_2$ given $X_1$ and $X_3$ is a Gaussian random variable with mean $x_1/\sqrt{2}$ and variance $1/2$.

---

### Example 6.7    Multiplicative Sequence

Let $X_1$ be uniform in $[0, 1]$, $X_2$ be uniform in $[0, X_1]$, and $X_3$ be uniform in $[0, X_2]$. (Note that $X_3$ is also the product of three uniform random variables.) Find the joint pdf of **X** and the marginal pdf of $X_3$.

For $0 < z < y < x < 1$, the joint pdf is nonzero and given by:

$$f_{X_1,X_2,X_3}(x_1, x_2, x_3) = f_{X_3}(z \mid x, y) f_{X_2}(y \mid x) f_{X_1}(x) = \frac{1}{y}\frac{1}{x}1 = \frac{1}{xy}.$$

The joint pdf of $X_2$ and $X_3$ is nonzero for $0 < z < y < 1$ and is obtained by integrating $x$ between $y$ and 1:

$$f_{X_2, X_3}(x_2, x_3) = \int_y^1 \frac{1}{xy} dx = \frac{1}{y} \ln x \Big|_y^1 = \frac{1}{y} \ln \frac{1}{y}.$$

We obtain the pdf of $X_3$ by integrating $y$ between $z$ and 1:

$$f_{X_3}(x_3) = -\int_z^1 \frac{1}{y} \ln y \, dy = -\frac{1}{2} (\ln y)^2 \Big|_z^1 = \frac{1}{2} (\ln z)^2.$$

Note that the pdf of $X_3$ is concentrated at the values close to $x = 0$.

### 6.1.3    Independence

The collection of random variables $X_1, \ldots, X_n$ is **independent** if

$$P[X_1 \text{ in } A_1, X_2 \text{ in } A_2, \ldots, X_n \text{ in } A_n] = P[X_1 \text{ in } A_1]P[X_2 \text{ in } A_2]\ldots P[X_n \text{ in } A_n]$$

for *any* one-dimensional events $A_1, \ldots, A_n$. It can be shown that $X_1, \ldots, X_n$ are independent *if and only if*

$$F_{X_1, \ldots, X_n}(x_1, \ldots, x_n) = F_{X_1}(x_1) \ldots F_{X_n}(x_n) \tag{6.16}$$

for all $x_1, \ldots, x_n$. If the random variables are discrete, Eq. (6.16) is equivalent to

$$p_{X_1, \ldots, X_n}(x_1, \ldots, x_n) = p_{X_1}(x_1) \ldots p_{X_n}(x_n) \qquad \text{for all } x_1, \ldots, x_n.$$

If the random variables are jointly continuous, Eq. (6.16) is equivalent to

$$f_{X_1, \ldots, X_n}(x_1, \ldots, x_n) = f_{X_1}(x_1) \ldots f_{X_n}(x_n)$$

for all $x_1, \ldots, x_n$.

---

**Example 6.8**

The $n$ samples $X_1, X_2, \ldots, X_n$ of a noise signal have joint pdf given by

$$f_{X_1, \ldots, X_n}(x_1, \ldots, x_n) = \frac{e^{-(x_1^2 + \ldots + x_n^2)/2}}{(2\pi)^{n/2}} \qquad \text{for all } x_1, \ldots, x_n.$$

It is clear that the above is the product of $n$ one-dimensional Gaussian pdf's. Thus $X_1, \ldots, X_n$ are independent Gaussian random variables.

---

## 6.2    FUNCTIONS OF SEVERAL RANDOM VARIABLES

Functions of vector random variables arise naturally in random experiments. For example $\mathbf{X} = (X_1, X_2, \ldots, X_n)$ may correspond to observations from $n$ repetitions of an experiment that generates a given random variable. We are almost always interested in the sample mean and the sample variance of the observations. In another example

$\mathbf{X} = (X_1, X_2, \ldots, X_n)$ may correspond to samples of a speech waveform and we may be interested in extracting features that are defined as functions of $\mathbf{X}$ for use in a speech recognition system.

### 6.2.1    One Function of Several Random Variables

Let the random variable $Z$ be defined as a function of several random variables:

$$Z = g(X_1, X_2, \ldots, X_n). \tag{6.17}$$

The cdf of $Z$ is found by finding the equivalent event of $\{Z \leq z\}$, that is, the set $R_z = \{\mathbf{x}: g(\mathbf{x}) \leq z\}$, then

$$F_Z(z) = P[\mathbf{X} \text{ in } R_z] = \int \cdots_{\mathbf{x} \text{ in } R_z} \int f_{X_1, \ldots, X_n}(x_1', \ldots, x_n') \, dx_1' \ldots dx_n'. \tag{6.18}$$

The pdf of $Z$ is then found by taking the derivative of $F_Z(z)$.

---

### Example 6.9    Maximum and Minimum of $n$ Random Variables

Let $W = \max(X_1, X_2, \ldots, X_n)$ and $Z = \min(X_1, X_2, \ldots, X_n)$, where the $X_i$ are independent random variables with the same distribution. Find $F_W(w)$ and $F_Z(z)$.

The maximum of $X_1, X_2, \ldots, X_n$ is less than $x$ if and only if each $X_i$ is less than $x$, so:

$$F_W(w) = P[\max(X_1, X_2, \ldots, X_n) \leq w]$$
$$= P[X_1 \leq w]P[X_2 \leq w] \ldots P[X_n \leq w] = (F_X(w))^n.$$

The minimum of $X_1, X_2, \ldots, X_n$ is greater than $x$ if and only if each $X_i$ is greater than $x$, so:

$$1 - F_Z(z) = P[\min(X_1, X_2, \ldots, X_n) > z]$$
$$= P[X_1 > z]P[X_2 > z] \ldots P[X_n > z] = (1 - F_X(z))^n$$

and

$$F_Z(z) = 1 - (1 - F_X(z))^n.$$

---

### Example 6.10    Merging of Independent Poisson Arrivals

Web page requests arrive at a server from $n$ independent sources. Source $j$ generates packets with exponentially distributed interarrival times with rate $\lambda_j$. Find the distribution of the interarrival times between consecutive requests at the server.

Let the interarrival times for the different sources be given by $X_1, X_2, \ldots, X_n$. Each $X_j$ satisfies the memoryless property, so the time that has elapsed since the last arrival from each source is irrelevant. The time until the next arrival at the multiplexer is then:

$$Z = \min(X_1, X_2, \ldots, X_n).$$

Therefore the pdf of $Z$ is:

$$1 - F_Z(z) = P[\min(X_1, X_2, \ldots, X_n) > z]$$
$$= P[X_1 > z]P[X_2 > z] \ldots P[X_n > z]$$

$$= \left(1 - F_{X_1}(z)\right)\left(1 - F_{X_2}(z)\right)\ldots\left(1 - F_{X_n}(z)\right)$$

$$= e^{-\lambda_1 z} e^{-\lambda_2 z} \ldots e^{-\lambda_n z} = e^{-(\lambda_1 + \lambda_2 + \cdots + \lambda_n)z}.$$

The interarrival time is an exponential random variable with rate $\lambda_1 + \lambda_2 + \cdots + \lambda_n$.

---

**Example 6.11   Reliability of Redundant Systems**

A computing cluster has $n$ independent redundant subsystems. Each subsystem has an exponentially distributed lifetime with parameter $\lambda$. The cluster will operate as long as at least one subsystem is functioning. Find the cdf of the time until the system fails.

Let the lifetime of each subsystem be given by $X_1, X_2, \ldots, X_n$. The time until the last subsystem fails is:

$$W = \max(X_1, X_2, \ldots, X_n).$$

Therefore the cdf of $W$ is:

$$F_W(w) = \left(F_X(w)\right)^n = (1 - e^{-\lambda w})^n = 1 - \binom{n}{1} e^{-\lambda w} + \binom{n}{2} e^{-2\lambda w} + \cdots.$$

---

## 6.2.2   Transformations of Random Vectors

Let $X_1, \ldots, X_n$ be random variables in some experiment, and let the random variables $Z_1, \ldots, Z_n$ be defined by a transformation that consists of $n$ functions of $\mathbf{X} = (X_1, \ldots, X_n)$:

$$Z_1 = g_1(\mathbf{X}) \qquad Z_2 = g_2(\mathbf{X}) \qquad \ldots \qquad Z_n = g_n(\mathbf{X}).$$

The joint cdf of $\mathbf{Z} = (Z_1, \ldots, Z_n)$ at the point $\mathbf{z} = (z_1, \ldots, z_n)$ is equal to the probability of the region of $\mathbf{x}$ where $g_k(\mathbf{x}) \le z_k$ for $k = 1, \ldots, n$:

$$F_{Z_1, \ldots, Z_n}(z_1, \ldots, z_n) = P[g_1(\mathbf{X}) \le z_1, \ldots, g_n(\mathbf{X}) \le z_n]. \qquad (6.19a)$$

If $X_1, \ldots, X_n$ have a joint pdf, then

$$F_{Z_1, \ldots, Z_n}(z_1, \ldots, z_n) = \iint_{\mathbf{x}': g_k(\mathbf{x}') \le z_k} f_{X_1, \ldots, X_n}(x_1', \ldots, x_n') \, dx_1' \ldots dx' . \qquad (6.19b)$$

---

**Example 6.12**

Given a random vector $\mathbf{X}$, find the joint pdf of the following transformation:

$$Z_1 = g_1(X_1) = a_1 X_1 + b_1,$$

$$Z_2 = g_2(X_2) = a_2 X_2 + b_2,$$

$$\vdots$$

$$Z_n = g_n(X_n) = a_n X_n + b_n.$$

Note that $Z_k = a_k X_k + b_k, \leq z_k$, if and only if $X_k \leq (z_k - b_k)/a_k$, if $a_k > 0$, so

$$F_{Z_1, Z_2, \ldots, Z_n}(z_1, z_2, \ldots, z_n) = P\left[X_1 \leq \frac{z_1 - b_1}{a_1}, X_2 \leq \frac{z_2 - b_2}{a_2}, \ldots, X_n \leq \frac{z_n - b_n}{a_n}\right]$$

$$= F_{X_1, X_2, \ldots, X_n}\left(\frac{z_1 - b_1}{a_1}, \frac{z_2 - b_2}{a_2}, \ldots, \frac{z_n - b_n}{a_n}\right)$$

$$f_{Z_1, Z_2, \ldots, Z_n}(z_1, z_2, \ldots, z_n) = \frac{\partial^n}{\partial z_1 \ldots \partial z_n} F_{Z_1, Z_2, \ldots, Z_n}(z_1, z_2, \ldots, z_n)$$

$$= \frac{1}{a_1 \ldots a_n} f_{X_1, X_2, \ldots, X_n}\left(\frac{z_1 - b_1}{a_1}, \frac{z_2 - b_2}{a_2}, \ldots, \frac{z_n - b_n}{a_n}\right).$$

### *6.2.3 pdf of General Transformations

We now introduce a general method for finding the pdf of a transformation of $n$ jointly continuous random variables. We first develop the two-dimensional case. Let the random variables $V$ and $W$ be defined by two functions of $X$ and $Y$:

$$V = g_1(X, Y) \quad \text{and} \quad W = g_2(X, Y). \tag{6.20}$$

Assume that the functions $v(x, y)$ and $w(x, y)$ are invertible in the sense that the equations $v = g_1(x, y)$ and $w = g_2(x, y)$ can be solved for $x$ and $y$, that is,

$$x = h_1(v, w) \text{ and } y = h_2(v, w).$$

The joint pdf of $X$ and $Y$ is found by finding the equivalent event of infinitesimal rectangles. The image of the infinitesimal rectangle is shown in Fig. 6.1(a). The image can be approximated by the parallelogram shown in Fig. 6.1(b) by making the approximation

$$g_k(x + dx, y) \simeq g_k(x, y) + \frac{\partial}{\partial x} g_k(x, y) \, dx \quad k = 1, 2$$

and similarly for the $y$ variable. The probabilities of the infinitesimal rectangle and the parallelogram are approximately equal, therefore

$$f_{X,Y}(x, y) \, dx \, dy = f_{V,W}(v, w) \, dP$$

and

$$f_{V,W}(v, w) = \frac{f_{X,Y}(h_1(v, w), (h_2(v, w)))}{\left|\dfrac{dP}{dxdy}\right|}, \tag{6.21}$$

where $dP$ is the area of the parallelogram. By analogy with the case of a linear transformation (see Eq. 5.59), we can match the derivatives in the above approximations with the coefficients in the linear transformations and conclude that the

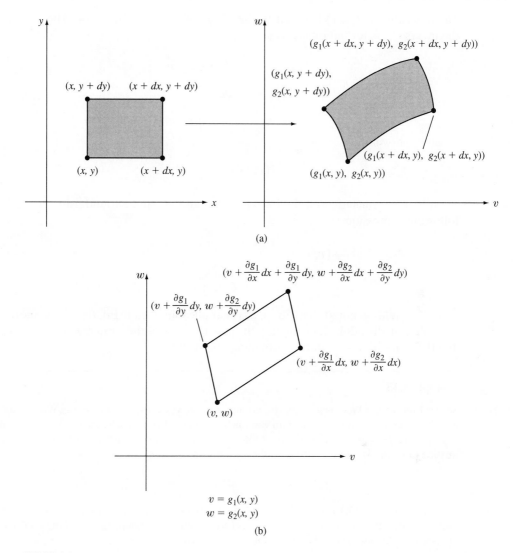

**FIGURE 6.1**

(a) Image of an infinitesimal rectangle under general transformation. (b) Approximation of image by a parallelogram.

"stretch factor" at the point $(v, w)$ is given by the determinant of a matrix of partial derivatives:

$$J(x, y) = \det \begin{bmatrix} \dfrac{\partial v}{\partial x} & \dfrac{\partial v}{\partial y} \\[2mm] \dfrac{\partial w}{\partial x} & \dfrac{\partial w}{\partial y} \end{bmatrix}.$$

The determinant $J(x, y)$ is called the **Jacobian** of the transformation. The Jacobian of the inverse transformation is given by

$$J(v, w) = \det \begin{bmatrix} \dfrac{\partial x}{\partial v} & \dfrac{\partial x}{\partial w} \\ \dfrac{\partial y}{\partial v} & \dfrac{\partial y}{\partial w} \end{bmatrix}.$$

It can be shown that

$$|J(v, w)| = \frac{1}{|J(x, y)|}.$$

We therefore conclude that the joint pdf of $V$ and $W$ can be found using either of the following expressions:

$$f_{V,W}(v, w) = \frac{f_{X,Y}(h_1(v, w), (h_2(v, w))}{|J(x, y)|} \tag{6.22a}$$

$$= f_{X,Y}(h_1(v, w), (h_2(v, w))|J(v, w)|. \tag{6.22b}$$

It should be noted that Eq. (6.21) is applicable even if Eq. (6.20) has more than one solution; the pdf is then equal to the sum of terms of the form given by Eqs. (6.22a) and (6.22b), with each solution providing one such term.

---

### Example 6.13

Server 1 receives $m$ Web page requests and server 2 receives $k$ Web page requests. Web page transmission times are exponential random variables with mean $1/\mu$. Let $X$ be the total time to transmit files from server 1 and let $Y$ be the total time for server 2. Find the joint pdf for $T$, the total transmission time, and $W$, the proportion of the total transmission time contributed by server 1:

$$T = X + Y \quad \text{and} \quad W = \frac{X}{X + Y}.$$

From Chapter 4, the sum of $j$ independent exponential random variables is an Erlang random variable with parameters $j$ and $\mu$. Therefore $X$ and $Y$ are independent Erlang random variables with parameters $m$ and $\mu$, and $k$ and $\mu$, respectively:

$$f_X(x) = \frac{\mu e^{-\mu x}(\mu x)^{m-1}}{(m - 1)!} \quad \text{and} \quad f_Y(y) = \frac{\mu e^{-\mu y}(\mu y)^{k-1}}{(k - 1)!}.$$

We solve for $X$ and $Y$ in terms of $T$ and $W$:

$$X = TW \quad \text{and} \quad Y = T(1 - W).$$

The Jacobian of the transformation is:

$$J(x, y) = \det \begin{bmatrix} 1 & 1 \\ \dfrac{y}{(x + y)^2} & \dfrac{-x}{(x + y)^2} \end{bmatrix}$$

$$= \frac{-x}{(x + y)^2} - \frac{y}{(x + y)^2} = \frac{-1}{x + y} = \frac{-1}{t}.$$

The joint pdf of $T$ and $W$ is then:

$$f_{T,W}(t, w) = \frac{1}{|J(x, y)|}\left[\frac{\mu e^{-\mu x}(\mu x)^{m-1}}{(m-1)!}\frac{\mu e^{-\mu y}(\mu y)^{k-1}}{(k-1)!}\right]_{\substack{x=tw \\ y=t(1-w)}}$$

$$= t\frac{\mu e^{-\mu tw}(\mu tw)^{m-1}}{(m-1)!}\frac{\mu e^{-\mu t(1-w)}(\mu t(1-w))^{k-1}}{(k-1)!}$$

$$= \frac{\mu e^{-\mu t}(\mu t)^{m+k-1}}{(m+k-1)!}\frac{(m+k-1)!}{(m-1)!(k-1)!}(w)^{m-1}(1-w)^{k-1}.$$

We see that $T$ and $W$ are independent random variables. As expected, $T$ is Erlang with parameters $m+k$ and $\mu$, since it is the sum of $m+k$ independent Erlang random variables. $W$ is the beta random variable introduced in Chapter 3.

---

The method developed above can be used even if we are interested in only one function of a random variable. By defining an "auxiliary" variable, we can use the transformation method to find the joint pdf of both random variables, and then we can find the marginal pdf involving the random variable of interest. The following example demonstrates the method.

---

### Example 6.14    Student's *t*-distribution

Let $X$ be a zero-mean, unit-variance Gaussian random variable and let $Y$ be a chi-square random variable with $n$ degrees of freedom. Assume that $X$ and $Y$ are independent. Find the pdf of $V = X/\sqrt{Y/n}$.

Define the auxiliary function of $W = Y$. The variables $X$ and $Y$ are then related to $V$ and $W$ by

$$X = V\sqrt{W/n} \quad \text{and} \quad Y = W.$$

The Jacobian of the inverse transformation is

$$|J(v, w)| = \begin{vmatrix} \sqrt{w/n} & (v/2)\sqrt{wn} \\ 0 & 1 \end{vmatrix} = \sqrt{w/n}.$$

Since $f_{X,Y}(x, y) = f_X(x)f_Y(y)$, the joint pdf of $V$ and $W$ is thus

$$f_{V,W}(v, w) = \frac{e^{-x^2/2}}{\sqrt{2\pi}}\frac{(y/2)^{n/2-1}e^{-y/2}}{2\Gamma(n/2)}|J(v, w)|\Bigg|_{\substack{x = v\sqrt{w/n} \\ y = w}}$$

$$= \frac{(w/2)^{(n-1)/2}e^{-[(w/2)(1+v^2/n)]}}{2\sqrt{n\pi}\Gamma(n/2)}.$$

The pdf of $V$ is found by integrating the joint pdf over $w$:

$$f_V(v) = \frac{1}{2\sqrt{n\pi}\Gamma(n/2)}\int_0^\infty (w/2)^{(n-1)/2}e^{-[(w/2)(1+v^2/n)]}\,dw.$$

If we let $w' = (w/2)(v^2/n + 1)$, the integral becomes

$$f_V(v) = \frac{(1+v^2/n)^{-(n+1)/2}}{\sqrt{n\pi}\Gamma(n/2)}\int_0^\infty (w')^{(n-1)/2}e^{-w'}\,dw'.$$

By noting that the above integral is the gamma function evaluated at $(n + 1)/2$, we finally obtain the *Student's t-distribution*:

$$f_V(v) = \frac{(1 + v^2/n)^{-(n+1)/2} \Gamma((n + 1)/2)}{\sqrt{n\pi} \Gamma(n/2)}.$$

This pdf is used extensively in statistical calculations. (See Chapter 8.)

---

Next consider the problem of finding the joint pdf for $n$ functions of $n$ random variables $\mathbf{X} = (X_1, \ldots, X_n)$:

$$Z_1 = g_1(\mathbf{X}), \quad Z_2 = g_2(\mathbf{X}), \ldots, \quad Z_n = g_n(\mathbf{X}).$$

We assume as before that the set of equations

$$z_1 = g_1(\mathbf{x}), \quad z_2 = g_2(\mathbf{x}), \ldots, \quad z_n = g_n(\mathbf{x}). \tag{6.23}$$

has a unique solution given by

$$x_1 = h_1(\mathbf{x}), \quad x_2 = h_2(\mathbf{x}), \ldots, \quad x_n = h_n(\mathbf{x}).$$

The joint pdf of $\mathbf{Z}$ is then given by

$$f_{Z_1,\ldots,Z_n}(z_1, \ldots, z_n) = \frac{f_{X_1,\ldots,X_n}(h_1(\mathbf{z}), h_2(\mathbf{z}), \ldots, h_n(\mathbf{z}))}{|J(x_1, x_2, \ldots, x_n)|} \tag{6.24a}$$

$$= f_{X_1,\ldots,X_n}(h_1(\mathbf{z}), h_2(\mathbf{z}), \ldots, h_n(\mathbf{z}))|J(z_1, z_2, \ldots, z_n)|, \tag{6.24b}$$

where $|J(x_1, \ldots, x_n)|$ and $|J(z_1, \ldots, z_n)|$ are the determinants of the transformation and the inverse transformation, respectively,

$$J(x_1, \ldots, x_n) = \det \begin{bmatrix} \dfrac{\partial g_1}{\partial x_1} & \cdots & \dfrac{\partial g_1}{\partial x_n} \\ \vdots & & \vdots \\ \dfrac{\partial g_n}{\partial x_1} & \cdots & \dfrac{\partial g_n}{\partial x_n} \end{bmatrix}$$

and

$$J(z_1, \ldots, z_n) = \det \begin{bmatrix} \dfrac{\partial h_1}{\partial z_1} & \cdots & \dfrac{\partial h_1}{\partial z_n} \\ \vdots & & \vdots \\ \dfrac{\partial h_n}{\partial z_1} & \cdots & \dfrac{\partial h_n}{\partial z_n} \end{bmatrix}.$$

In the special case of a linear transformation we have:

$$\mathbf{Z} = \mathbf{AX} = \begin{bmatrix} a_{11} & a_{12} & \cdots & a_{1n} \\ a_{21} & a_{22} & \cdots & a_{2n} \\ \cdot & \cdot & \cdots & \cdot \\ a_{n1} & a_{n2} & \cdots & a_{nn} \end{bmatrix} \begin{bmatrix} X_1 \\ X_2 \\ \cdots \\ X_n \end{bmatrix}.$$

The components of $\mathbf{Z}$ are:

$$Z_j = a_{j1}X_1 + a_{j2}X_2 + \ldots + a_{jn}X_n.$$

Since $dz_j/dx_i = a_{ji}$, the Jacobian is then simply:

$$J(x_1, x_2, \ldots, x_n) = \det \begin{bmatrix} a_{11} & a_{12} & \cdots & a_{1n} \\ a_{21} & a_{22} & \cdots & a_{2n} \\ \cdot & \cdot & \cdots & \cdot \\ a_{n1} & a_{n2} & \cdots & a_{nn} \end{bmatrix} = \det \mathbf{A}.$$

Assuming that $\mathbf{A}$ is invertible,[1] we then have that:

$$f_{\mathbf{Z}}(\mathbf{z}) = \frac{f_{\mathbf{X}}(\mathbf{x})}{|\det \mathbf{A}|} \bigg|_{\mathbf{x}=\mathbf{A}^{-1}\mathbf{z}} = \frac{f_{\mathbf{X}}(\mathbf{A}^{-1}\mathbf{z})}{|\det \mathbf{A}|}.$$

---

### Example 6.15    Sum of Random Variables

Given a random vector $\mathbf{X} = (X_1, X_2, X_3)$, find the joint pdf of the sum:

$$Z = X_1 + X_2 + X_3.$$

We will use the transformation by introducing auxiliary variables as follows:

$$Z_1 = X_1, Z_2 = X_1 + X_2, Z_3 = X_1 + X_2 + X_3.$$

The inverse transformation is given by:

$$X_1 = Z_1, X_2 = Z_2 - Z_1, X_3 = Z_3 - Z_2.$$

The Jacobian matrix is:

$$J(x_1, x_2, x_3) = \det \begin{bmatrix} 1 & 0 & 0 \\ 1 & 1 & 0 \\ 1 & 1 & 1 \end{bmatrix} = 1.$$

Therefore the joint pdf of $\mathbf{Z}$ is

$$f_{\mathbf{Z}}(z_1, z_2, z_3) = f_{\mathbf{X}}(z_1, z_2 - z_1, z_3 - z_2).$$

The pdf of $Z_3$ is obtained by integrating with respect to $z_1$ and $z_2$:

$$f_{Z_3}(z) = \int_{-\infty}^{\infty} \int_{-\infty}^{\infty} f_{\mathbf{X}}(z_1, z_2 - z_1, z - z_2) \, dz_1 dz_2.$$

This expression can be simplified further if $X_1$, $X_2$, and $X_3$ are independent random variables.

---

[1] Appendix C provides a summary of definitions and useful results from linear algebra.

## 6.3    EXPECTED VALUES OF VECTOR RANDOM VARIABLES

In this section we are interested in the characterization of a vector random variable through the expected values of its components and of functions of its components. We focus on the characterization of a vector random variable through its mean vector and its covariance matrix. We then introduce the joint characteristic function for a vector random variable.

The expected value of a function $g(\mathbf{X}) = g(X_1, \ldots, X_n)$ of a vector random variable $\mathbf{X} = (X_1, X_2, \ldots, X_n)$ is given by:

$$E[Z] = \begin{cases} \int_{-\infty}^{\infty} \cdots \int_{-\infty}^{\infty} g(x_1, x_2, \ldots, x_n) f_{\mathbf{X}}(x_1, x_2, \ldots, x_n) \, dx_1 \, dx_2 \ldots dx_n & \mathbf{X} \text{ jointly continuous} \\ \sum_{x_1} \cdots \sum_{x_n} g(x_1, x_2, \ldots, x_n) p_{\mathbf{X}}(x_1, x_2, \ldots, x_n) & \mathbf{X} \text{ discrete.} \end{cases}$$
(6.25)

An important example is $g(\mathbf{X})$ equal to the sum of functions of $\mathbf{X}$. The procedure leading to Eq. (5.26) and a simple induction argument show that:

$$E[g_1(\mathbf{X}) + g_2(\mathbf{X}) + \cdots + g_n(\mathbf{X})] = E[g_1(\mathbf{X})] + \cdots + E[g_n(\mathbf{X})]. \quad (6.26)$$

Another important example is $g(\mathbf{X})$ equal to the product of $n$ individual functions of the components. If $X_1, \ldots, X_n$ are *independent* random variables, then

$$E[g_1(X_1)g_2(X_2) \ldots g_n(X_n)] = E[g_1(X_1)]E[g_2(X_2)] \ldots E[g_n(X_n)]. \quad (6.27)$$

### 6.3.1    Mean Vector and Covariance Matrix

The mean, variance, and covariance provide useful information about the distribution of a random variable and are easy to estimate, so we are frequently interested in characterizing multiple random variables in terms of their first and second moments. We now introduce the mean vector and the covariance matrix. We then investigate the mean vector and the covariance matrix of a linear transformation of a random vector.

For $\mathbf{X} = (X_1, X_2, \ldots, X_n)$, the **mean vector** is defined as the column vector of expected values of the components $X_k$:

$$\mathbf{m_X} = E[\mathbf{X}] = E\begin{bmatrix} X_1 \\ X_2 \\ \vdots \\ X_n \end{bmatrix} \triangleq \begin{bmatrix} E[X_1] \\ E[X_2] \\ \vdots \\ E[X_n] \end{bmatrix}. \quad (6.28a)$$

Note that we define the vector of expected values as a column vector. In previous sections we have sometimes written $\mathbf{X}$ as a row vector, but in this section and wherever we deal with matrix transformations, we will represent $\mathbf{X}$ and its expected value as a column vector.

The **correlation matrix** has the second moments of **X** as its entries:

$$\mathbf{R_X} = \begin{bmatrix} E[X_1^2] & E[X_1X_2] & \cdots & E[X_1X_n] \\ E[X_2X_1] & E[X_2^2] & \cdots & E[X_2X_n] \\ \cdot & \cdot & \cdots & \cdot \\ E[X_nX_1] & E[X_nX_2] & \cdots & E[X_n^2] \end{bmatrix}. \tag{6.28b}$$

The **covariance matrix** has the second-order central moments as its entries:

$$\mathbf{K_X} = \begin{bmatrix} E[(X_1-m_1)^2] & E[(X_1-m_1)(X_2-m_2)] & \cdots & E[(X_1-m_1)(X_n-m_n)] \\ E[(X_2-m_2)(X_1-m_1)] & E[(X_2-m_2)^2] & \cdots & E[(X_2-m_2)(X_n-m_n)] \\ \cdot & \cdot & \cdots & \cdot \\ E[(X_n-m_n)(X_1-m_1)] & E[(X_n-m_n)(X_2-m_2)] & \cdots & E[(X_n-m_n)^2] \end{bmatrix}. \tag{6.28c}$$

Both $\mathbf{R_X}$ and $\mathbf{K_X}$ are $n \times n$ symmetric matrices. The diagonal elements of $\mathbf{K_X}$ are given by the variances $\mathrm{VAR}[X_k] = E[(X_k - m_k)^2]$ of the elements of **X**. If these elements are uncorrelated, then $\mathrm{COV}(X_j, X_k) = 0$ for $j \neq k$, and $\mathbf{K_X}$ is a diagonal matrix. If the random variables $X_1, \ldots, X_n$ are independent, then they are uncorrelated and $\mathbf{K_X}$ is diagonal. Finally, if the vector of expected values is $\mathbf{0}$, that is, $m_k = E[X_k] = 0$ for all $k$, then $\mathbf{R_X} = \mathbf{K_X}$.

---

### Example 6.16

Let $\mathbf{X} = (X_1, X_2, X_3)$ be the jointly Gaussian random vector from Example 6.6. Find $E[\mathbf{X}]$ and $\mathbf{K_X}$. We rewrite the joint pdf as follows:

$$f_{X_1,X_2,X_3}(x_1, x_2, x_3) = \frac{e^{-(x_1^2+x_2^2-2\frac{1}{\sqrt{2}}x_1x_2)}}{2\pi\sqrt{1 - \left(-\dfrac{1}{\sqrt{2}}\right)^2}} \frac{e^{-x_3^2/2}}{\sqrt{2\pi}}.$$

We see that $X_3$ is a Gaussian random variable with zero mean and unit variance, and that it is independent of $X_1$ and $X_2$. We also see that $X_1$ and $X_2$ are jointly Gaussian with zero mean and unit variance, and with correlation coefficient

$$\rho_{X_1X_2} = -\frac{1}{\sqrt{2}} = \frac{\mathrm{COV}(X_1, X_2)}{\sigma_{X_1}\sigma_{X_2}} = \mathrm{COV}(X_1, X_2).$$

Therefore the vector of expected values is: $\mathbf{m_X} = \mathbf{0}$, and

$$\mathbf{K_X} = \begin{bmatrix} 1 & -\dfrac{1}{\sqrt{2}} & 0 \\ -\dfrac{1}{\sqrt{2}} & 1 & 0 \\ 0 & 0 & 1 \end{bmatrix}.$$

We now develop compact expressions for $\mathbf{R_X}$ and $\mathbf{K_X}$. If we multiply $\mathbf{X}$, an $n \times 1$ matrix, and $\mathbf{X}^T$, a $1 \times n$ matrix, we obtain the following $n \times n$ matrix:

$$\mathbf{XX}^T = \begin{bmatrix} X_1 \\ X_2 \\ \vdots \\ X_n \end{bmatrix} [X_1, X_2, \ldots, X_n] = \begin{bmatrix} X_1^2 & X_1X_2 & \ldots & X_1X_n \\ X_2X_1 & X_2^2 & \ldots & X_2X_n \\ . & . & \ldots & . \\ X_nX_1 & X_nX_2 & \ldots & X_n^2 \end{bmatrix}.$$

If we define the expected value of a matrix to be the matrix of expected values of the matrix elements, then we can write the correlation matrix as:

$$\mathbf{R_X} = E[\mathbf{XX}^T]. \tag{6.29a}$$

The covariance matrix is then:

$$\begin{aligned} \mathbf{K_X} &= E[(\mathbf{X} - \mathbf{m_X})(\mathbf{X} - \mathbf{m_X})^T] \\ &= E[\mathbf{XX}^T] - \mathbf{m_X}E[\mathbf{X}^T] - E[\mathbf{X}]\mathbf{m_X}^T + \mathbf{m_X}\mathbf{m_X}^T \\ &= \mathbf{R_X} - \mathbf{m_X}\mathbf{m_X}^T. \end{aligned} \tag{6.29b}$$

### 6.3.2 Linear Transformations of Random Vectors

Many engineering systems are linear in the sense that will be elaborated on in Chapter 10. Frequently these systems can be reduced to a linear transformation of a vector of random variables where the "input" is $\mathbf{X}$ and the "output" is $\mathbf{Y}$:

$$\mathbf{Y} = \begin{bmatrix} a_{11} & a_{12} & \ldots & a_n \\ a_{21} & a_{22} & \ldots & a_{2n} \\ . & . & \ldots & . \\ a_{n1} & a_{n2} & \ldots & a_{nn} \end{bmatrix} \begin{bmatrix} X_1 \\ X_2 \\ \vdots \\ X_n \end{bmatrix} = \mathbf{AX}.$$

The expected value of the $k$th component of $\mathbf{Y}$ is the inner product (dot product) of the $k$th row of $\mathbf{A}$ and $\mathbf{X}$:

$$E[Y_k] = E\left[\sum_{j=1}^{n} a_{kj}X_j\right] = \sum_{j=1}^{n} a_{kj}E[X_j].$$

Each component of $E[\mathbf{Y}]$ is obtained in this manner, so:

$$\mathbf{m_Y} = E[\mathbf{Y}] = \begin{bmatrix} \sum_{j=1}^{n} a_{1j}E[X_j] \\ \sum_{j=1}^{n} a_{2j}E[X_j] \\ \vdots \\ \sum_{j=1}^{n} a_{nj}E[X_j] \end{bmatrix} = \begin{bmatrix} a_{11} & a_{12} & \ldots & a_n \\ a_{21} & a_{22} & \ldots & a_{2n} \\ . & . & \ldots & . \\ a_{n1} & a_{n2} & \ldots & a_{nn} \end{bmatrix} \begin{bmatrix} E[X_1] \\ E[X_2] \\ \vdots \\ E[X_n] \end{bmatrix}$$

$$= \mathbf{A}E[\mathbf{X}] = \mathbf{A}\mathbf{m_X}. \tag{6.30a}$$

The covariance matrix of **Y** is then:

$$
\begin{aligned}
\mathbf{K_Y} &= E[(\mathbf{Y} - \mathbf{m_Y})(\mathbf{Y} - \mathbf{m_Y})^\mathsf{T}] = E[(\mathbf{AX} - \mathbf{Am_X})(\mathbf{AX} - \mathbf{Am_X})^\mathsf{T}] \\
&= E[\mathbf{A}(\mathbf{X} - \mathbf{m_X})(\mathbf{X} - \mathbf{m_X})^\mathsf{T}\mathbf{A}^\mathsf{T}] = \mathbf{A}E[(\mathbf{X} - \mathbf{m_X})(\mathbf{X} - \mathbf{m_X})^\mathsf{T}]\mathbf{A}^\mathsf{T} \\
&= \mathbf{AK_XA}^\mathsf{T},
\end{aligned}
\tag{6.30b}
$$

where we used the fact that the transpose of a matrix multiplication is the product of the transposed matrices in reverse order: $\{\mathbf{A}(\mathbf{X} - \mathbf{m_X})\}^\mathsf{T} = (\mathbf{X} - \mathbf{m_X})^\mathsf{T}\mathbf{A}^\mathsf{T}$.

The **cross-covariance** matrix of two random vectors **X** and **Y** is defined as:

$$
\mathbf{K_{XY}} = E[(\mathbf{X} - \mathbf{m_X})(\mathbf{Y} - \mathbf{m_Y})^\mathsf{T}] = E[\mathbf{XY}^\mathsf{T}] - \mathbf{m_X}\mathbf{m_Y}^\mathsf{T} = \mathbf{R_{XY}} - \mathbf{m_X}\mathbf{m_Y}^\mathsf{T}.
$$

We are interested in the cross-covariance between **X** and **Y** = **AX**:

$$
\begin{aligned}
\mathbf{K_{XY}} &= E[\mathbf{X} - \mathbf{m_X})(\mathbf{Y} - \mathbf{m_Y})^\mathsf{T}] = E[(\mathbf{X} - \mathbf{m_X})(\mathbf{X} - \mathbf{m_X})^\mathsf{T}\mathbf{A}^\mathsf{T}] \\
&= \mathbf{K_X}\mathbf{A}^\mathsf{T}.
\end{aligned}
\tag{6.30c}
$$

---

### Example 6.17    Transformation of Uncorrelated Random Vector

Suppose that the components of **X** are uncorrelated and have unit variance, then $\mathbf{K_X} = \mathbf{I}$, the identity matrix. The covariance matrix for **Y** = **AX** is

$$
\mathbf{K_Y} = \mathbf{AK_XA}^\mathsf{T} = \mathbf{AIA}^\mathsf{T} = \mathbf{AA}^\mathsf{T}.
\tag{6.31}
$$

In general $\mathbf{K_Y} = \mathbf{AA}^\mathsf{T}$ is not a diagonal matrix and so the components of **Y** are correlated. In Section 6.6 we discuss how to find a matrix **A** so that Eq. (6.31) holds for a given $\mathbf{K_Y}$. We can then generate a random vector **Y** with any desired covariance matrix $\mathbf{K_Y}$.

---

Suppose that the components of **X** are correlated so $\mathbf{K_X}$ is not a diagonal matrix. In many situations we are interested in finding a transformation matrix **A** so that **Y** = **AX** has uncorrelated components. This requires finding **A** so that $\mathbf{K_Y} = \mathbf{AK_XA}^\mathsf{T}$ is a diagonal matrix. In the last part of this section we show how to find such a matrix **A**.

---

### Example 6.18    Transformation to Uncorrelated Random Vector

Suppose the random vector $X_1$, $X_2$, and $X_3$ in Example 6.16 is transformed using the matrix:

$$
\mathbf{A} = \begin{bmatrix} \dfrac{1}{\sqrt{2}} & \dfrac{1}{\sqrt{2}} & 0 \\[2mm] \dfrac{1}{\sqrt{2}} & -\dfrac{1}{\sqrt{2}} & 0 \\[2mm] 0 & 0 & 1 \end{bmatrix}.
$$

Find the $E[\mathbf{Y}]$ and $\mathbf{K_Y}$.

Since $\mathbf{m_X} = \mathbf{0}$, then $E[\mathbf{Y}] = \mathbf{Am_X} = \mathbf{0}$. The covariance matrix of $\mathbf{Y}$ is:

$$\mathbf{K_Y} = \mathbf{AK_XA^T} = \frac{1}{2}\begin{bmatrix} 1 & 1 & 0 \\ 1 & -1 & 0 \\ 0 & 0 & 1 \end{bmatrix}\begin{bmatrix} 1 & -\dfrac{1}{\sqrt{2}} & 0 \\ -\dfrac{1}{\sqrt{2}} & 1 & 0 \\ 0 & 0 & 1 \end{bmatrix}\begin{bmatrix} 1 & 1 & 0 \\ 1 & -1 & 0 \\ 0 & 0 & 1 \end{bmatrix}$$

$$= \frac{1}{2}\begin{bmatrix} 1 & 1 & 0 \\ 1 & -1 & 0 \\ 0 & 0 & 1 \end{bmatrix}\begin{bmatrix} 1 - \dfrac{1}{\sqrt{2}} & 1 + \dfrac{1}{\sqrt{2}} & 0 \\ 1 - \dfrac{1}{\sqrt{2}} & -\left(1 + \dfrac{1}{\sqrt{2}}\right) & 0 \\ 0 & 0 & 1 \end{bmatrix} = \begin{bmatrix} 1 - \dfrac{1}{\sqrt{2}} & 0 & 0 \\ 0 & 1 + \dfrac{1}{\sqrt{2}} & 0 \\ 0 & 0 & 1 \end{bmatrix}.$$

The linear transformation has produced a vector of random variables $\mathbf{Y} = (Y_1, Y_2, Y_3)$ with components that are uncorrelated.

---

## *6.3.3   Joint Characteristic Function

The **joint characteristic function** of $n$ random variables is defined as

$$\Phi_{X_1, X_2, \ldots, X_n}(\omega_1, \omega_2, \ldots, \omega_n) = E[e^{j(\omega_1 X_1 + \omega_2 X_2 + \cdots + \omega_n X_n)}]. \tag{6.32a}$$

In this section we develop the properties of the joint characteristic function of two random variables. These properties generalize in straightforward fashion to the case of $n$ random variables. Therefore consider

$$\Phi_{X,Y}(\omega_1, \omega_2) = E[e^{j(\omega_1 X + \omega_2 Y)}]. \tag{6.32b}$$

If $X$ and $Y$ are jointly continuous random variables, then

$$\Phi_{X,Y}(\omega_1, \omega_2) = \int_{-\infty}^{\infty}\int_{-\infty}^{\infty} f_{X,Y}(x, y)e^{j(\omega_1 x + \omega_2 y)}\, dx\, dy. \tag{6.32c}$$

Equation (6.32c) shows that the joint characteristic function is the two-dimensional Fourier transform of the joint pdf of $X$ and $Y$. The inversion formula for the Fourier transform implies that the joint pdf is given by

$$f_{X,Y}(x, y) = \frac{1}{4\pi^2} = \int_{-\infty}^{\infty}\int_{-\infty}^{\infty} \Phi_{X,Y}(\omega_1, \omega_2)e^{-j(\omega_1 x + \omega_2 y)}\, d\omega_1\, d\omega_2. \tag{6.33}$$

Note in Eq. (6.32b) that the marginal characteristic functions can be obtained from joint characteristic function:

$$\Phi_X(\omega) = \Phi_{X,Y}(\omega, 0) \quad \Phi_Y(\omega) = \Phi_{X,Y}(0, \omega). \tag{6.34}$$

If $X$ and $Y$ are independent random variables, then the joint characteristic function is the product of the marginal characteristic functions since

$$\Phi_{X,Y}(\omega_1, \omega_2) = E[e^{j(\omega_1 X + \omega_2 Y)}] = E[e^{j\omega_1 X}e^{j\omega_2 Y}]$$

$$= E[e^{j\omega_1 X}]E[e^{j\omega_2 Y}] = \Phi_X(\omega_1)\Phi_Y(\omega_2), \tag{6.35}$$

where the third equality follows from Eq. (6.27).

The characteristic function of the sum $Z = aX + bY$ can be obtained from the joint characteristic function of $X$ and $Y$ as follows:

$$\Phi_Z(\omega) = E[e^{j\omega(aX+bY)}] = E[e^{j(\omega aX+\omega bY)}] = \Phi_{X,Y}(a\omega, b\omega). \qquad (6.36a)$$

If $X$ and $Y$ are independent random variables, the characteristic function of $Z = aX + bY$ is then

$$\Phi_Z(\omega) = \Phi_{X,Y}(a\omega, b\omega) = \Phi_X(a\omega)\Phi_Y(b\omega). \qquad (6.36b)$$

In Section 8.1 we will use the above result in dealing with sums of random variables.

The joint moments of $X$ and $Y$ (if they exist) can be obtained by taking the derivatives of the joint characteristic function. To show this we rewrite Eq. (6.32b) as the expected value of a product of exponentials and we expand the exponentials in a power series:

$$\Phi_{X,Y}(\omega_1, \omega_2) = E[e^{j\omega_1 X}e^{j\omega_2 Y}]$$

$$= E\left[\sum_{i=0}^{\infty}\frac{(j\omega_1 X)^i}{i!}\sum_{k=0}^{\infty}\frac{(j\omega_2 Y)^k}{k!}\right]$$

$$= \sum_{i=0}^{\infty}\sum_{k=0}^{\infty}E[X^iY^k]\frac{(j\omega_1)^i}{i!}\frac{(j\omega_2)^k}{k!}.$$

It then follows that the moments can be obtained by taking an appropriate set of derivatives:

$$E[X^iY^k] = \frac{1}{j^{i+k}}\frac{\partial^i\partial^k}{\partial\omega_1^i\partial\omega_2^k}\Phi_{X,Y}(\omega_1, \omega_2)|_{\omega_1=0,\omega_2=0}. \qquad (6.37)$$

---

### Example 6.19

Suppose $U$ and $V$ are independent zero-mean, unit-variance Gaussian random variables, and let

$$X = U + V \qquad Y = 2U + V.$$

Find the joint characteristic function of $X$ and $Y$, and find $E[XY]$.

The joint characteristic function of $X$ and $Y$ is

$$\Phi_{X,Y}(\omega_1, \omega_2) = E[e^{j(\omega_1 X+\omega_2 Y)}] = E[e^{j\omega_1(U+V)}e^{j\omega_2(2U+V)}]$$

$$= E[e^{j((\omega_1+2\omega_2)U+(\omega_1+\omega_2)V)}].$$

Since $U$ and $V$ are independent random variables, the joint characteristic function of $U$ and $V$ is equal to the product of the marginal characteristic functions:

$$\Phi_{X,Y}(\omega_1, \omega_2) = E[e^{j((\omega_1+2\omega_2)U)}]E[e^{j((\omega_1+\omega_2)V)}]$$

$$= \Phi_U(\omega_1 + 2\omega_2)\Phi_V(\omega_1 + \omega_2)$$

$$= e^{-\frac{1}{2}(\omega_1+2\omega_2)^2}e^{-\frac{1}{2}(\omega_1+\omega_2)^2}$$

$$= e\{^{-\frac{1}{2}(2\omega_1^2 +6\omega_1\omega_2+5\omega_2^2)}\}.$$

where marginal characteristic functions were obtained from Table 4.1.

The correlation $E[XY]$ is found from Eq. (6.37) with $i = 1$ and $k = 1$:

$$E[XY] = \frac{1}{j^2} \frac{\partial^2}{\partial \omega_1 \partial \omega_2} \Phi_{X,Y}(\omega_1, \omega_2)|_{\omega_1 = 0, \omega_2 = 0}$$

$$= -e\{-\tfrac{1}{2}(2\omega_{12} + 6\omega_1\omega_2 + 5\omega_{22})\}[6\omega_1 + 10\omega_2]\left(\frac{1}{4}\right)[4\omega_1 + 6\omega_2]$$

$$+ \frac{1}{2} e\{-\tfrac{1}{2}(2\omega_1^2 + 6\omega_1\omega_2 + 5\omega_2^2)\}[6]|_{\omega_1 = 0, \omega_2 = 0} = 3$$

You should verify this answer by evaluating $E[XY] = E[(U + V)(2U + V)]$ directly.

---

### *6.3.4    Diagonalization of Covariance Matrix

Let $\mathbf{X}$ be a random vector with covariance $\mathbf{K_X}$. We are interested in finding an $n \times n$ matrix $\mathbf{A}$ such that $\mathbf{Y} = \mathbf{AX}$ has a covariance matrix that is diagonal. The components of $\mathbf{Y}$ are then uncorrelated.

We saw that $\mathbf{K_X}$ is a real-valued symmetric matrix. In Appendix C we state results from linear algebra that $\mathbf{K_X}$ is then a diagonalizable matrix, that is, there is a matrix $\mathbf{P}$ such that:

$$\mathbf{P}^T\mathbf{K_X}\mathbf{P} = \Lambda \quad \text{and} \quad \mathbf{P}^T\mathbf{P} = \mathbf{I} \tag{6.38a}$$

where $\Lambda$ is a diagonal matrix and $\mathbf{I}$ is the identity matrix. Therefore if we let $\mathbf{A} = \mathbf{P}^T$, then from Eq. (6.30b) we obtain a diagonal $\mathbf{K_Y}$.

We now show how $\mathbf{P}$ is obtained. First, we find the eigenvalues and eigenvectors of $\mathbf{K_X}$ from:

$$\mathbf{K_X}\mathbf{e}_i = \lambda_i\mathbf{e}_i \tag{6.38b}$$

where $\mathbf{e}_i$ are $n \times 1$ column vectors.[2] We can normalize each eigenvector $\mathbf{e}_i$ so that $\mathbf{e}_i{}^T\mathbf{e}_i$, the sum of the square of its components, is 1. The normalized eigenvectors are then orthonormal, that is,

$$\mathbf{e}_i{}^T\mathbf{e}_j = \delta_{i,j} = \begin{cases} 1 & \text{if } i = j \\ 0 & \text{if } i \neq j. \end{cases} \tag{6.38c}$$

Let $\mathbf{P}$ be the matrix whose columns are the eigenvectors of $\mathbf{K_X}$ and let $\Lambda$ be the diagonal matrix of eigenvalues:

$$\mathbf{P} = [\mathbf{e}_1, \mathbf{e}_2, \ldots, \mathbf{e}_n] \qquad \Lambda = \text{diag}[\lambda_1].$$

From Eq. (6.38b) we have:

$$\mathbf{K_X}\mathbf{P} = \mathbf{K_X}[\mathbf{e}_1, \mathbf{e}_2, \ldots, \mathbf{e}_n] = [\mathbf{K_X}\mathbf{e}_1, \mathbf{K_X}\mathbf{e}_2, \ldots, \mathbf{K_X}\mathbf{e}_n]$$

$$= [\lambda_1\mathbf{e}_1, \lambda_2\mathbf{e}_2, \ldots, \lambda_n\mathbf{e}_n] = \mathbf{P}\Lambda \tag{6.39a}$$

where the second equality follows from the fact that each column of $\mathbf{K_X}\mathbf{P}$ is obtained by multiplying a column of $\mathbf{P}$ by $\mathbf{K_X}$. By premultiplying both sides of the above equations by $\mathbf{P}^T$, we obtain:

$$\mathbf{P}^T\mathbf{K_X}\mathbf{P} = \mathbf{P}^T\mathbf{P}\Lambda = \Lambda. \tag{6.39b}$$

---

[2]See Appendix C.

We conclude that if we let $\mathbf{A} = \mathbf{P}^{\mathrm{T}}$, and

$$\mathbf{Y} = \mathbf{AX} = \mathbf{P}^{\mathrm{T}}\mathbf{X}, \tag{6.40a}$$

then the random variables in $\mathbf{Y}$ are uncorrelated since

$$\mathbf{K_Y} = \mathbf{P}^{\mathrm{T}}\mathbf{K_X}\mathbf{P} = \Lambda. \tag{6.40b}$$

*In summary, any covariance matrix $\mathbf{K_X}$. can be diagonalized by a linear transformation.* The matrix $\mathbf{A}$ in the transformation is obtained from the eigenvectors of $\mathbf{K_X}$.

Equation (6.40b) provides insight into the invertibility of $\mathbf{K_X}$ and $\mathbf{K_Y}$. From linear algebra we know that the determinant of a product of $n \times n$ matrices is the product of the determinants, so:

$$\det \mathbf{K_Y} = \det \mathbf{P}^{\mathrm{T}} \det \mathbf{K_X} \det \mathbf{P} = \det \Lambda = \lambda_1\lambda_2\ldots\lambda_n,$$

where we used the fact that $\det \mathbf{P}^{\mathrm{T}} \det \mathbf{P} = \det \mathbf{I} = 1$. Recall that a matrix is invertible if and only if its determinant is nonzero. Therefore $\mathbf{K_Y}$ is not invertible if and only if one or more of the eigenvalues of $\mathbf{K_X}$ is zero.

Now suppose that one of the eigenvalues is zero, say $\lambda_k = 0$. Since $\mathrm{VAR}[Y_k] = \lambda_k = 0$, then $Y_k = 0$. But $Y_k$ is defined as a linear combination, so

$$0 = Y_k = a_{k1}X_1 + a_{k2}X_2 + \cdots + a_{kn}X_n.$$

We conclude that the components of $\mathbf{X}$ are linearly dependent. Therefore, one or more of the components in $\mathbf{X}$ are redundant and can be expressed as a linear combination of the other components.

It is interesting to look at the vector $\mathbf{X}$ expressed in terms of $\mathbf{Y}$. Multiply both sides of Eq. (6.40a) by $\mathbf{P}$ and use the fact that $\mathbf{PP}^{\mathrm{T}} = \mathbf{I}$:

$$\mathbf{X} = \mathbf{PP}^{\mathrm{T}}\mathbf{X} = \mathbf{PY} = [\mathbf{e}_1, \mathbf{e}_2, \ldots, \mathbf{e}_n] \begin{bmatrix} Y_1 \\ Y_2 \\ \vdots \\ Y_n \end{bmatrix} = \sum_{k=1}^{n} Y_k \mathbf{e}_k. \tag{6.41}$$

This equation is called the **Karhunen-Loeve expansion**. The equation shows that a random vector $\mathbf{X}$ can be expressed as a weighted sum of the eigenvectors of $\mathbf{K_X}$, where the coefficients are *uncorrelated* random variables $Y_k$. Furthermore, the eigenvectors form an orthonormal set. Note that if any of the eigenvalues are zero, $\mathrm{VAR}[Y_k] = \lambda_k = 0$, then $Y_k = 0$, and the corresponding term can be dropped from the expansion in Eq. (6.41). In Chapter 10, we will see that this expansion is very useful in the processing of random signals.

## 6.4    JOINTLY GAUSSIAN RANDOM VECTORS

The random variables $X_1, X_2, \ldots, X_n$ are said to be jointly Gaussian if their joint pdf is given by

$$f_\mathbf{X}(\mathbf{x}) \triangleq f_{X_1, X_2, \ldots, X_n}(x_1, \ldots, x_n) = \frac{\exp\{-\frac{1}{2}(\mathbf{x} - \mathbf{m})^{\mathrm{T}}K^{-1}(\mathbf{x} - \mathbf{m})\}}{(2\pi)^{n/2}|K|^{1/2}}, \tag{6.42a}$$

where **x** and **m** are column vectors defined by

$$
\mathbf{x} = \begin{bmatrix} x_1 \\ x_2 \\ \vdots \\ x_n \end{bmatrix}, \qquad \mathbf{m} = \begin{bmatrix} m_1 \\ m_2 \\ \vdots \\ m_n \end{bmatrix} = \begin{bmatrix} E[X_1] \\ E[X_2] \\ \vdots \\ E[X_n] \end{bmatrix}
$$

and $K$ is the covariance matrix that is defined by

$$
K = \begin{bmatrix}
\text{VAR}(X_1) & \text{COV}(X_1, X_2) & \cdots & \text{COV}(X_1, X_n) \\
\text{COV}(X_2, X_1) & \text{VAR}(X_2) & \cdots & \text{COV}(X_2, X_n) \\
\vdots & \vdots & & \vdots \\
\text{COV}(X_n, X_1) & \cdots & & \text{VAR}(X_n)
\end{bmatrix}. \tag{6.42b}
$$

The $(.)^{\mathrm{T}}$ in Eq. (6.42a) denotes the transpose of a matrix or vector. Note that the co-variance matrix is a symmetric matrix since $\text{COV}(X_i, X_j) = \text{COV}(X_j, X_i)$.

Equation (6.42a) shows that *the pdf of jointly Gaussian random variables is completely specified by the individual means and variances and the pairwise covariances.* It can be shown using the joint characteristic function that all the marginal pdf's associated with Eq. (6.42a) are also Gaussian and that these too are completely specified by the same set of means, variances, and covariances.

---

**Example 6.20**

Verify that the two-dimensional Gaussian pdf given in Eq. (5.61a) has the form of Eq. (6.42a).
   The covariance matrix for the two-dimensional case is given by

$$
K = \begin{bmatrix} \sigma_1^2 & \rho_{X,Y}\sigma_1\sigma_2 \\ \rho_{X,Y}\sigma_1\sigma_2 & \sigma_2^2 \end{bmatrix},
$$

where we have used the fact the $\text{COV}(X_1, X_2) = \rho_{X,Y}\sigma_1\sigma_2$. The determinant of $K$ is $\sigma_1^2\sigma_2^2(1 - \rho_{X,Y}^2)$ so the denominator of the pdf has the correct form. The inverse of the covariance matrix is also a real symmetric matrix:

$$
K^{-1} = \frac{1}{\sigma_1^2\sigma_2^2(1 - \rho_{X,Y}^2)} \begin{bmatrix} \sigma_2^2 & -\rho_{X,Y}\sigma_1\sigma_2 \\ -\rho_{X,Y}\sigma_1\sigma_2 & \sigma_1^2 \end{bmatrix}.
$$

The term in the exponent is therefore

$$
\frac{1}{\sigma_1^2\sigma_2^2(1 - \rho_{X,Y}^2)}(x - m_1, y - m_2)\begin{bmatrix} \sigma_2^2 & -\rho_{X,Y}\sigma_1\sigma_2 \\ -\rho_{X,Y}\sigma_1\sigma_2 & \sigma_1^2 \end{bmatrix}\begin{bmatrix} x - m_1 \\ y - m_2 \end{bmatrix}
$$

$$
= \frac{1}{\sigma_1^2\sigma_2^2(1 - \rho_{X,Y}^2)}(x - m_1, y - m_2)\begin{bmatrix} \sigma_2^2(x - m_1) - \rho_{X,Y}\sigma_1\sigma_2(y - m_2) \\ -\rho_{X,Y}\sigma_1\sigma_2(x - m_1) + \sigma_1^2(y - m_2) \end{bmatrix}
$$

$$
= \frac{((x - m_1)/\sigma_1)^2 - 2\rho_{X,Y}((x - m_1)/\sigma_1)((y - m_2)/\sigma_2) + ((y - m_2)/\sigma_2)^2}{(1 - \rho_{X,Y}^2)}.
$$

Thus the two-dimensional pdf has the form of Eq. (6.42a).

---

## Example 6.21

The vector of random variables $(X, Y, Z)$ is jointly Gaussian with zero means and covariance matrix:

$$K = \begin{bmatrix} \text{VAR}(X) & \text{COV}(X,Y) & \text{COV}(X,Z) \\ \text{COV}(Y,X) & \text{VAR}(Y) & \text{COV}(Y,Z) \\ \text{COV}(Z,X) & \text{COV}(Z,Y) & \text{VAR}(Z) \end{bmatrix} = \begin{bmatrix} 1.0 & 0.2 & 0.3 \\ 0.2 & 1.0 & 0.4 \\ 0.3 & 0.4 & 1.0 \end{bmatrix}.$$

Find the marginal pdf of $X$ and $Z$.

We can solve this problem two ways. The first involves integrating the pdf directly to obtain the marginal pdf. The second involves using the fact that the marginal pdf for $X$ and $Z$ is also Gaussian and has the same set of means, variances, and covariances. We will use the second approach.

The pair $(X, Z)$ has zero-mean vector and covariance matrix:

$$K' = \begin{bmatrix} \text{VAR}(X) & \text{COV}(X,Z) \\ \text{COV}(Z,X) & \text{VAR}(Z) \end{bmatrix} = \begin{bmatrix} 1.0 & 0.3 \\ 0.3 & 1.0 \end{bmatrix}.$$

The joint pdf of $X$ and $Z$ is found by substituting a zero-mean vector and this covariance matrix into Eq. (6.42a).

## Example 6.22    Independence of Uncorrelated Jointly Gaussian Random Variables

Suppose $X_1, X_2, \ldots, X_n$ are jointly Gaussian random variables with $\text{COV}(X_i, X_j) = 0$ for $i \neq j$. Show that $X_1, X_2, \ldots, X_n$ are independent random variables.

From Eq. (6.42b) we see that the covariance matrix is a diagonal matrix:

$$K = \text{diag}[\text{VAR}(X_i)] = \text{diag}[\sigma_i^2]$$

Therefore

$$K^{-1} = \text{diag}\left[\frac{1}{\sigma_i^2}\right]$$

and

$$(\mathbf{x} - \mathbf{m})^{\text{T}} K^{-1} (\mathbf{x} - \mathbf{m}) = \sum_{i=1}^{n} \left(\frac{x_i - m_i}{\sigma_i}\right)^2.$$

Thus from Eq. (6.42a)

$$f_{\mathbf{X}}(\mathbf{x}) = \frac{\exp\left\{-\frac{1}{2}\sum_{i=1}^{n} [(x_i - m_i)/\sigma_i]^2\right\}}{(2\pi)^{n/2}} |K|^{1/2} = \prod_{i=1}^{n} \frac{\exp\left\{-\frac{1}{2}[(x_i - m_i)/\sigma_i]^2\right\}}{\sqrt{2\pi\sigma_i^2}} = \prod_{i=1}^{n} f_{X_i}(x_i).$$

Thus $X_1, X_2, \ldots, X_n$ are independent Gaussian random variables.

## Example 6.23    Conditional pdf of Gaussian Random Variable

Find the conditional pdf of $X_n$ given $X_1, X_2, \ldots, X_{n-1}$.

Let $\mathbf{K}_n$ be the covariance matrix for $\mathbf{X}_n = (X_1, X_2, \ldots, X_n)$ and $\mathbf{K}_{n-1}$ be the covariance matrix for $\mathbf{X}_{n-1} = (X_1, X_2, \ldots, X_{n-1})$. Let $\mathbf{Q}_n = \mathbf{K}_n^{-1}$ and $\mathbf{Q}_{n-1} = \mathbf{K}_{n-1}^{-1}$, then the latter matrices are submatrices of the former matrices as shown below:

$$
\mathbf{K}_n = \begin{bmatrix} & & & K_{1n} \\ & \mathbf{K}_{n-1} & & K_{2n} \\ & & & \vdots \\ K_{1n} & K_{2n} & \cdots & K_{nn} \end{bmatrix}
\qquad
\mathbf{Q}_n = \begin{bmatrix} & & & Q_{1n} \\ & \mathbf{Q}_{n-1} & & Q_{2n} \\ & & & \vdots \\ Q_{1n} & Q_{2n} & \cdots & Q_{nn} \end{bmatrix}
$$

Below we will use the subscript $n$ or $n - 1$ to distinguish between the two random vectors and their parameters. The marginal pdf of $X_n$ given $X_1, X_2, \ldots, X_{n-1}$ is given by:

$$
f_{X_n}(x_n \mid x_1, \ldots, x_{n-1}) = \frac{f_{\mathbf{X}_n}(\mathbf{x}_n)}{f_{\mathbf{X}_{n-1}}(\mathbf{x}_{n-1})}
$$

$$
= \frac{\exp\{-\frac{1}{2}(\mathbf{x}_n - \mathbf{m}_n)^{\mathrm{T}} \mathbf{Q}_n (\mathbf{x}_n - \mathbf{m}_n)\}}{(2\pi)^{n/2} |\mathbf{K}_n|^{1/2}} \cdot \frac{(2\pi)^{(n-1)1/2} |\mathbf{K}_{n-1}|^{1/2}}{\exp\{-\frac{1}{2}(\mathbf{x}_{n-1} - \mathbf{m}_{n-1})^{\mathrm{T}} \mathbf{Q}_{n-1}(\mathbf{x}_{n-1} - \mathbf{m}_{n-1})\}}
$$

$$
= \frac{\exp\{-\frac{1}{2}(\mathbf{x}_n - \mathbf{m}_n)^{\mathrm{T}} \mathbf{Q}_n(\mathbf{x}_n - \mathbf{m}_n) + \frac{1}{2}(\mathbf{x}_{n-1} - \mathbf{m}_{n-1})^{\mathrm{T}} \mathbf{Q}_{n-1}(\mathbf{x}_{n-1} - \mathbf{m}_{n-1})\}}{\sqrt{2\pi} |\mathbf{K}_n|^{1/2} / |\mathbf{K}_{n-1}|^{1/2}}.
$$

In Problem 6.60 we show that the terms in the above expression are given by:

$$
\tfrac{1}{2}(\mathbf{x}_n - \mathbf{m}_n)^{\mathrm{T}} \mathbf{Q}_n(\mathbf{x}_n - \mathbf{m}_n) - \tfrac{1}{2}(\mathbf{x}_{n-1} - \mathbf{m}_{n-1})^{\mathrm{T}} \mathbf{Q}_{n-1}(\mathbf{x}_{n-1} - \mathbf{m}_{n-1})
$$

$$
= Q_{nn}\{(x_n - m_n) + B\}^2 - Q_{nn}B^2 \tag{6.43}
$$

where $B = \dfrac{1}{Q_{nn}} \displaystyle\sum_{j=1}^{n-1} Q_{jk}(x_j - m_j)$   and   $|\mathbf{K}_n| / |\mathbf{K}_{n-1}| = Q_{nn}$.

This implies that $X_n$ has mean $m_n - B$, and variance $1/Q_{nn}$. The term $Q_{nn}B^2$ is part of the normalization constant. We therefore conclude that:

$$
f_{X_n}(x_n \mid x_1, \ldots, x_{n-1}) = \frac{\exp\left\{ -\dfrac{1}{2Q_{nn}} \left( x_n - m_n + \dfrac{1}{Q_{nn}} \displaystyle\sum_{j=1}^{n-1} Q_{jk}(x_j - m_j) \right)^2 \right\}}{\sqrt{2\pi Q_{nn}}}
$$

We see that the conditional mean of $X_n$ is a linear function of the "observations" $x_1, x_2, \ldots, x_{n-1}$.

## *6.4.1   Linear Transformation of Gaussian Random Variables

A very important property of jointly Gaussian random variables is that *the linear transformation of any n jointly Gaussian random variables results in n random variables that are also jointly Gaussian.* This is easy to show using the matrix notation in Eq. (6.42a). Let $\mathbf{X} = (X_1, \ldots, X_n)$ be jointly Gaussian with covariance matrix $K_X$ and mean vector $\mathbf{m_X}$ and define $\mathbf{Y} = (Y_1, \ldots, Y_n)$ by

$$
\mathbf{Y} = A\mathbf{X},
$$

where $A$ is an invertible $n \times n$ matrix. From Eq. (5.60) we know that the pdf of $\mathbf{Y}$ is given by

$$f_{\mathbf{Y}}(\mathbf{y}) = \frac{f_{\mathbf{X}}(A^{-1}\mathbf{y})}{|A|}$$

$$= \frac{\exp\{-\frac{1}{2}(A^{-1}\mathbf{y} - \mathbf{m_X})^{\mathrm{T}}K_X^{-1}(A^{-1}\mathbf{y} - \mathbf{m_X})\}}{(2\pi)^{n/2}|A||K_X|^{1/2}}. \tag{6.44}$$

From elementary properties of matrices we have that

$$(A^{-1}\mathbf{y} - \mathbf{m_X}) = A^{-1}(\mathbf{y} - A\mathbf{m_X})$$

and

$$(A^{-1}\mathbf{y} - \mathbf{m_X})^{\mathrm{T}} = (\mathbf{y} - A\mathbf{m_X})^{\mathrm{T}}A^{-1\mathrm{T}}.$$

The argument in the exponential is therefore equal to

$$(\mathbf{y} - A\mathbf{m_X})^{\mathrm{T}}A^{-1\mathrm{T}}K_X^{-1}A^{-1}(\mathbf{y} - A\mathbf{m_X}) = (\mathbf{y} - A\mathbf{m_X})^{\mathrm{T}}(AK_XA^{\mathrm{T}})^{-1}(\mathbf{y} - A\mathbf{m_X})$$

since $A^{-1\mathrm{T}}K_X^{-1} = (AK_XA^{\mathrm{T}})^{-1}$. Letting $K_Y = AK_XA^{\mathrm{T}}$ and $\mathbf{m_Y} = A\mathbf{m_X}$ and noting that $\det(K_Y) = \det(AK_XA^{\mathrm{T}}) = \det(A)\det(K_X)\det(A^{\mathrm{T}}) = \det(A)^2\det(K_X)$, we finally have that the pdf of $\mathbf{Y}$ is

$$f_{\mathbf{Y}}(\mathbf{y}) = \frac{e^{-(1/2)(\mathbf{y}-\mathbf{m_Y})^{\mathrm{T}}K_Y^{-1}(\mathbf{y}-\mathbf{m_Y})}}{(2\pi)^{n/2}|K_Y|^{1/2}}. \tag{6.45}$$

Thus the pdf of $\mathbf{Y}$ has the form of Eq. (6.42a) and therefore $Y_1, \ldots, Y_n$ are jointly Gaussian random variables with mean vector and covariance matrix:

$$\mathbf{m_Y} = A\mathbf{m_X} \quad \text{and} \quad K_Y = AK_XA^{\mathrm{T}}.$$

This result is consistent with the mean vector and covariance matrix we obtained before in Eqs. (6.30a) and (6.30b).

In many problems we wish to transform $\mathbf{X}$ to a vector $\mathbf{Y}$ of independent Gaussian random variables. Since $K_X$ is a symmetric matrix, it is always possible to find a matrix $A$ such that $AK_XA^{\mathrm{T}} = \Lambda$ is a diagonal matrix. (See Section 6.6.) For such a matrix $A$, the pdf of $\mathbf{Y}$ will be

$$f_{\mathbf{Y}}(\mathbf{y}) = \frac{e^{-(1/2)(\mathbf{y}-\mathbf{n})^{\mathrm{T}}\Lambda^{-1}(\mathbf{y}-\mathbf{n})}}{(2\pi)^{n/2}|\Lambda|^{1/2}}$$

$$= \frac{\exp\left\{-\frac{1}{2}\sum_{i=1}^{n}(y_i - n_i)^2/\lambda_i\right\}}{[(2\pi\lambda_1)(2\pi\lambda_2)\ldots(2\pi\lambda_n)]^{1/2}}, \tag{6.46}$$

where $\lambda_1, \ldots, \lambda_n$ are the diagonal components of $\Lambda$. We assume that these values are all nonzero. The above pdf implies that $Y_1, \ldots, Y_n$ are *independent* random variables with means $n_i$ and variance $\lambda_i$. In conclusion, *it is possible to linearly transform a vector of jointly Gaussian random variables into a vector of independent Gaussian random variables.*

It is always possible to select the matrix $A$ that diagonalizes $K$ so that $\det(A) = 1$. The transformation $A\mathbf{X}$ then corresponds to a rotation of the coordinate system so that the principal axes of the ellipsoid corresponding to the pdf are aligned to the axes of the system. Example 5.48 provides an $n = 2$ example of rotation.

In computer simulation models we frequently need to generate jointly Gaussian random vectors with specified covariance matrix and mean vector. Suppose that $\mathbf{X} = (X_1, X_2, \ldots, X_n)$ has components that are zero-mean, unit-variance Gaussian random variables, so its mean vector is $\mathbf{0}$ and its covariance matrix is the identity matrix $\mathbf{I}$. Let $\mathbf{K}$ denote the desired covariance matrix. Using the methods discussed in Section 6.3, it is possible to find a matrix $\mathbf{A}$ so that $\mathbf{A}^\mathsf{T}\mathbf{A} = \mathbf{K}$. Therefore $\mathbf{Y} = \mathbf{A}^\mathsf{T}\mathbf{U}$ has zero mean vector and covariance $\mathbf{K}$. From Eq. (6.46) we have that $\mathbf{Y}$ is also a jointly Gaussian random vector with zero mean vector and covariance $\mathbf{K}$. If we require a nonzero mean vector $\mathbf{m}$, we use $\mathbf{Y} + \mathbf{m}$.

---

### Example 6.24   Sum of Jointly Gaussian Random Variables

Let $X_1, X_2, \ldots, X_n$ be jointly Gaussian random variables with joint pdf given by Eq. (6.42a). Let

$$Z = a_1 X_1 + a_2 X_2 + \cdots + a_n X_n.$$

We will show that $Z$ is always a Gaussian random variable.

We find the pdf of $Z$ by introducing auxiliary random variables. Let

$$Z_2 = X_2, \quad Z_3 = X_3, \ldots, \quad Z_n = X_n.$$

If we define $\mathbf{Z} = (Z_1, Z_2, \ldots, Z_n)$, then

$$\mathbf{Z} = A\mathbf{X}$$

where

$$A = \begin{bmatrix} a_1 & a_2 & \ldots & \cdot & a_n \\ 0 & 1 & \ldots & \cdot & 0 \\ \cdot & \cdot & \ldots & \cdot & \cdot \\ 0 & \cdot & \ldots & 0 & 1 \end{bmatrix}.$$

From Eq. (6.45) we have that $\mathbf{Z}$ is jointly Gaussian with mean $\mathbf{n} = A\mathbf{m}$, and covariance matrix $C = AKA^\mathsf{T}$. Furthermore, it then follows that the marginal pdf of $Z$ is a Gaussian pdf with mean given by the first component of $\mathbf{n}$ and variance given by the 1-1 component of the covariance matrix $C$. By carrying out the above matrix multiplications, we find that

$$E[Z] = \sum_{i=1}^{n} a_i E[X_i] \tag{6.47a}$$

$$\mathrm{VAR}[Z] = \sum_{i=1}^{n} \sum_{j=1}^{n} a_i a_j \, \mathrm{COV}(X_i, X_j). \tag{6.47b}$$

---

## *6.4.2   Joint Characteristic Function of a Gaussian Random Variable

The joint characteristic function is very useful in developing the properties of jointly Gaussian random variables. We now show that **the joint characteristic function of $n$ jointly Gaussian random variables $X_1, X_2, \ldots, X_n$ is given by**

$$\Phi_{X_1, X_2, \ldots, X_n}(\omega_1, \omega_2, \ldots, \omega_n) = e^{j\sum_{i=1}^{n} \omega_i m_i - \frac{1}{2}\sum_{i=1}^{n}\sum_{k=1}^{n}\omega_i \omega_k \,\mathrm{COV}(X_i, X_k)}, \qquad (6.48a)$$

which can be written more compactly as follows:

$$\Phi_{\mathbf{X}}(\boldsymbol{\omega}) \triangleq \Phi_{X_1, X_2, \ldots, X_n}(\omega_1, \omega_2, \ldots, \omega_n) = e^{j\boldsymbol{\omega}^{\mathrm{T}}\mathbf{m} - \frac{1}{2}\boldsymbol{\omega}^{\mathrm{T}}K\boldsymbol{\omega}}, \qquad (6.48b)$$

where $\mathbf{m}$ is the vector of means and $K$ is the covariance matrix defined in Eq. (6.42b).

Equation (6.48) can be verified by direct integration (see Problem 6.65). We use the approach in [Papoulis] to develop Eq. (6.48) by using the result from Example 6.24 that a linear combination of jointly Gaussian random variables is always Gaussian. Consider the sum

$$Z = a_1 X_1 + a_2 X_2 + \cdots + a_n X_n.$$

The characteristic function of $Z$ is given by

$$\Phi_Z(\omega) = E[e^{j\omega Z}] = E[e^{j(\omega a_1 X_1 + \omega a_2 X_2 + \cdots + \omega a_n X_n)}]$$

$$= \Phi_{X_1, \ldots, X_n}(a_1 \omega, a_2 \omega, \ldots, a_n \omega).$$

On the other hand, since $Z$ is a Gaussian random variable with mean and variance given Eq. (6.47), we have

$$\Phi_Z(\omega) = e^{j\omega E[Z] - \frac{1}{2}\mathrm{VAR}[Z]\omega^2}$$

$$= e^{j\omega \sum_{i=1}^{n} a_i m_i - \frac{1}{2}\omega^2 \sum_{i=1}^{n}\sum_{k=1}^{n} a_i a_k \,\mathrm{COV}(X_i, X_k)}. \qquad (6.49)$$

By equating both expressions for $\Phi_Z(\omega)$ with $\omega = 1$, we finally obtain

$$\Phi_{X_1, X_2, \ldots, X_n}(a_1, a_2, \ldots, a_n) = e^{j\sum_{i=1}^{n} a_i m_i - \frac{1}{2}\sum_{i=1}^{n}\sum_{k=1}^{n} a_i a_k \,\mathrm{COV}(X_i, X_k)}$$

$$= e^{j\mathbf{a}^{\mathrm{T}}\mathbf{m} - \frac{1}{2}\mathbf{a}^{\mathrm{T}}K\mathbf{a}}. \qquad (6.50)$$

By replacing the $a_i$'s with $\omega_i$'s we obtain Eq. (6.48).

The marginal characteristic function of any subset of the random variables $X_1, X_2, \ldots, X_n$ can be obtained by setting appropriate $\omega_i$'s to zero. Thus, for example, the marginal characteristic function of $X_1, X_2, \ldots, X_m$ for $m < n$ is obtained by setting $\omega_{m+1} = \omega_{m+2} = \cdots = \omega_n = 0$. Note that the resulting characteristic function again corresponds to that of jointly Gaussian random variables with mean and covariance terms corresponding the reduced set $X_1, X_2, \ldots, X_m$.

The derivation leading to Eq. (6.50) suggests an alternative definition for jointly Gaussian random vectors:

**Definition:**  $\mathbf{X}$ is a jointly Gaussian random vector if and only every linear combination $Z = \mathbf{a}^{\mathrm{T}}\mathbf{X}$ is a Gaussian random variable.

In Example 6.24 we showed that if **X** is a jointly Gaussian random vector then the linear combination $Z = \boldsymbol{a}^{\mathrm{T}}\mathbf{X}$ is a Gaussian random variable. Suppose that we do not know the joint pdf of **X** but we are given that $Z = \boldsymbol{a}^{\mathrm{T}}\mathbf{X}$ is a Gaussian random variable for any choice of coefficients $\boldsymbol{a}^{\mathrm{T}} = (a_1, a_2, \ldots, a_n)$. This implies that Eqs. (6.48) and (6.49) hold, which together imply Eq. (6.50) which states that **X** has the characteristic function of a jointly Gaussian random vector.

The above definition is slightly broader than the definition using the pdf in Eq. (6.44). The definition based on the pdf requires that the covariance in the exponent be invertible. The above definition leads to the characteristic function of Eq. (6.50) which does not require that the covariance be invertible. Thus the above definition allows for cases where the covariance matrix is not invertible.

## 6.5    ESTIMATION OF RANDOM VARIABLES

In this book we will encounter two basic types of estimation problems. In the first type, we are interested in *estimating the parameters of one or more random variables,* e.g., probabilities, means, variances, or covariances. In Chapter 1, we stated that relative frequencies can be used to estimate the probabilities of events, and that sample averages can be used to estimate the mean and other moments of a random variable. In Chapters 7 and 8 we will consider this type of estimation further. In this section, we are concerned with the second type of estimation problem, where we are interested in *estimating the value of an inaccessible random variable X in terms of the observation of an accessible random variable Y.* For example, $X$ could be the input to a communication channel and $Y$ could be the observed output. In a prediction application, $X$ could be a future value of some quantity and $Y$ its present value.

### 6.5.1    MAP and ML Estimators

We have considered estimation problems informally earlier in the book. For example, in estimating the output of a discrete communications channel we are interested in finding the most probable input given the observation $Y = y$, that is, the value of input $x$ that maximizes $P[X = x \mid Y = y]$:

$$\max_{x} P[X = x \mid Y = y].$$

In general we refer to the above estimator for $X$ in terms of $Y$ as the **maximum a posteriori (MAP) estimator**. The a posteriori probability is given by:

$$P[X = x \mid Y = y] = \frac{P[Y = y \mid X = x]P[X = x]}{P[Y = y]}$$

and so the MAP estimator requires that we know the a priori probabilities $P[X = x]$. In some situations we know $P[Y = y \mid X = x]$ but we do not know the a priori probabilities, so we select the estimator value $x$ as the value that maximizes the likelihood of the observed value $Y = y$:

$$\max_{x} P[Y = y \mid X = x].$$

We refer to this estimator of $X$ in terms of $Y$ as the **maximum likelihood (ML) estimator**.

We can define MAP and ML estimators when $X$ and $Y$ are continuous random variables by replacing events of the form $\{Y = y\}$ by $\{y < Y < y + dy\}$. If $X$ and $Y$ are continuous, the **MAP estimator for $X$ given the observation $Y$** is given by:

$$\max_{x} f_X(X = x \,|\, Y = y),$$

and the **ML estimator for $X$ given the observation $Y$** is given by:

$$\max_{x} f_X(Y = y \,|\, X = x).$$

---

### Example 6.25    Comparison of ML and MAP Estimators

Let $X$ and $Y$ be the random pair in Example 5.16. Find the MAP and ML estimators for $X$ in terms of $Y$.

From Example 5.32, the conditional pdf of $X$ given $Y$ is given by:

$$f_X(x \,|\, y) = e^{-(x-y)} \quad \text{for} \quad y \le x$$

which decreases as $x$ increases beyond $y$. Therefore the MAP estimator is $\hat{X}_{\text{MAP}} = y$. On the other hand, the conditional pdf of $Y$ given $X$ is:

$$f_Y(y \,|\, x) = \frac{e^{-y}}{1 - e^{-x}} \quad \text{for} \quad 0 < y \le x.$$

As $x$ increases beyond $y$, the denominator becomes larger so the conditional pdf decreases. Therefore the ML estimator is $\hat{X}_{\text{ML}} = y$. In this example the ML and MAP estimators agree.

---

### Example 6.26    Jointly Gaussian Random Variables

Find the MAP and ML estimator of $X$ in terms of $Y$ when $X$ and $Y$ are jointly Gaussian random variables.

The conditional pdf of $X$ given $Y$ is given by:

$$f_X(x \,|\, y) = \frac{\exp\left\{ -\dfrac{1}{2(1 - \rho^2)\sigma_X^2} \left( x - \rho\dfrac{\sigma_X}{\sigma_Y}(y - m_Y) - m_X \right)^2 \right\}}{\sqrt{2\pi\sigma_X^2\,(1 - \rho^2)}}$$

which is maximized by the value of $x$ for which the exponent is zero. Therefore

$$\hat{X}_{\text{MAP}} = \rho\frac{\sigma_X}{\sigma_Y}(y - m_Y) + m_X.$$

The conditional pdf of $Y$ given $X$ is:

$$f_Y(y \,|\, x) = \frac{\exp\left\{ -\dfrac{1}{2(1 - \rho^2)\sigma_Y^2} \left( y - \rho\dfrac{\sigma_Y}{\sigma_X}(x - m_X) - m_Y \right)^2 \right\}}{\sqrt{2\pi\sigma_Y^2\,(1 - \rho^2)}}.$$

which is also maximized for the value of $x$ for which the exponent is zero:

$$0 = y - \rho\frac{\sigma_Y}{\sigma_X}(x - m_X) - m_Y.$$

The ML estimator for $X$ given $Y = y$ is then:

$$\hat{X}_{\mathrm{ML}} = \frac{\sigma_X}{\rho \sigma_Y}(y - m_Y) + m_X.$$

Therefore we conclude that $\hat{X}_{\mathrm{ML}} \neq \hat{X}_{\mathrm{MAP}}$. In other words, knowledge of the a priori probabilities of $X$ will affect the estimator.

---

### 6.5.2    Minimum MSE Linear Estimator

The estimate for $X$ is given by a function of the observation $\hat{X} = g(Y)$. In general, the *estimation error*, $X - \hat{X} = X - g(Y)$, is nonzero, and there is a *cost* associated with the error, $c(X - g(Y))$. We are usually interested in finding the function $g(Y)$ that minimizes the expected value of the cost, $E[c(X - g(Y))]$. For example, if $X$ and $Y$ are the discrete input and output of a communication channel, and $c$ is zero when $X = g(Y)$ and one otherwise, then the expected value of the cost corresponds to the probability of error, that is, that $X \neq g(Y)$. When $X$ and $Y$ are continuous random variables, we frequently use the **mean square error (MSE)** as the cost:

$$e = E[(X - g(Y))^2].$$

In the remainder of this section we focus on this particular cost function. We first consider the case where $g(Y)$ is constrained to be a linear function of $Y$, and then consider the case where $g(Y)$ can be any function, whether linear or nonlinear.

First, consider the problem of estimating a random variable $X$ by a *constant a* so that the mean square error is minimized:

$$\min_{a} E[(X - a)^2] = E[X^2] - 2aE[X] + a^2. \tag{6.51}$$

The best $a$ is found by taking the derivative with respect to $a$, setting the result to zero, and solving for $a$. The result is

$$a^* = E[X], \tag{6.52}$$

which makes sense since the expected value of $X$ is the center of mass of the pdf. The mean square error for this estimator is equal to $E[(X - a^*)^2] = \mathrm{VAR}(X)$.

Now consider estimating $X$ by a *linear* function $g(Y) = aY + b$:

$$\min_{a,b} E[(X - aY - b)^2]. \tag{6.53a}$$

Equation (6.53a) can be viewed as the approximation of $X - aY$ by the constant $b$. This is the minimization posed in Eq. (6.51) and the best $b$ is

$$b^* = E[X - aY] = E[X] - aE[Y]. \tag{6.53b}$$

Substitution into Eq. (6.53a) implies that the best $a$ is found by

$$\min_{a} E[\{(X - E[X]) - a(Y - E[Y])\}^2].$$

We once again differentiate with respect to $a$, set the result to zero, and solve for $a$:

$$0 = \frac{d}{da}E[(X - E[X]) - a(Y - E[Y])^2]$$

$$= -2E[\{(X - E[X]) - a(Y - E[Y])\}(Y - E[Y])]$$
$$= -2(\text{COV}(X, Y) - a\text{VAR}(Y)). \tag{6.54}$$

The best coefficient $a$ is found to be

$$a^* = \frac{\text{COV}(X, Y)}{\text{VAR}(Y)} = \rho_{X,Y}\frac{\sigma_X}{\sigma_Y},$$

where $\sigma_Y = \sqrt{\text{VAR}(Y)}$ and $\sigma_X = \sqrt{\text{VAR}(X)}$. Therefore, *the minimum mean square error (mmse) linear estimator* for $X$ in terms of $Y$ is

$$\hat{X} = a^*Y + b^*$$

$$= \rho_{X,Y}\sigma_X\frac{Y - E[Y]}{\sigma_Y} + E[X]. \tag{6.55}$$

The term $(Y - E[Y])/\sigma_Y$ is simply a zero-mean, unit-variance version of $Y$. Thus $\sigma_X(Y - E[Y])/\sigma_Y$ is a rescaled version of $Y$ that has the variance of the random variable that is being estimated, namely $\sigma_X^2$. The term $E[X]$ simply ensures that the estimator has the correct mean. The key term in the above estimator is the correlation coefficient: $\rho_{X,Y}$ *specifies the sign and extent of the estimate of Y relative to* $\sigma_X(Y - E[Y])/\sigma_Y$. If $X$ and $Y$ are uncorrelated (i.e., $\rho_{X,Y} = 0$) then the best estimate for $X$ is its mean, $E[X]$. On the other hand, if $\rho_{X,Y} = \pm 1$ then the best estimate is equal to $\pm\sigma_X(Y - E[Y])/\sigma_Y + E[X]$.

We draw our attention to the second equality in Eq. (6.54):

$$E[\{(X - E[X]) - a^*(Y - E[Y])\}(Y - E[Y])] = 0. \tag{6.56}$$

This equation is called the **orthogonality condition** because it states that the error of the best linear estimator, the quantity inside the braces, is orthogonal to the observation $Y - E[Y]$. The orthogonality condition is a fundamental result in mean square estimation.

The mean square error of the best *linear* estimator is

$$e_L^* = E[((X - E[X]) - a^*(Y - E[Y]))^2]$$
$$= E[((X - E[X]) - a^*(Y - E[Y]))(X - E[X])]$$
$$\quad - a^*E[((X - E[X]) - a^*(Y - E[Y]))(Y - E[Y])]$$
$$= E[((X - E[X]) - a^*(Y - E[Y]))(X - E[X])]$$
$$= \text{VAR}(X) - a^*\,\text{COV}(X, Y)$$
$$= \text{VAR}(X)(1 - \rho_{X,Y}^2) \tag{6.57}$$

where the second equality follows from the orthogonality condition. Note that when $|\rho_{X,Y}| = 1$, the mean square error is zero. This implies that $P[|X - a^*Y - b^*| = 0] = P[X = a^*Y + b^*] = 1$, so that $X$ is essentially a linear function of $Y$.

### 6.5.3    Minimum MSE Estimator

In general the estimator for $X$ that minimizes the mean square error is a *nonlinear* function of $Y$. The estimator $g(Y)$ that best approximates $X$ in the sense of minimizing mean square error must satisfy

$$\underset{g(.)}{\text{minimize}} \; E[(X - g(Y))^2].$$

The problem can be solved by using **conditional expectation**:

$$E[(X - g(Y))^2] = E[E[(X - g(Y))^2 | Y]]$$

$$= \int_{-\infty}^{\infty} E[(X - g(Y))^2 | Y = y]f_Y(y)dy.$$

The integrand above is positive for all $y$; therefore, the integral is minimized by minimizing $E[(X - g(Y))^2 | Y = y]$ for each $y$. But $g(y)$ is a constant as far as the conditional expectation is concerned, so the problem is equivalent to Eq. (6.51) and the "constant" that minimizes $E[(X - g(y))^2 | Y = y]$ is

$$g^*(y) = E[X | Y = y]. \tag{6.58}$$

The function $g^*(y) = E[X | Y = y]$ is called the **regression curve** which simply traces the conditional expected value of $X$ given the observation $Y = y$.

The mean square error of the best estimator is:

$$e^* = E[(X - g^*(Y))^2] = \int_R E[(X - E[X | y])^2 | Y = y]f_Y(y) \, dy$$

$$= \int_{R^n} \text{VAR}[X | Y = y]f_Y(y) \, dy.$$

Linear estimators in general are suboptimal and have larger mean square errors.

---

**Example 6.27    Comparison of Linear and Minimum MSE Estimators**

Let $X$ and $Y$ be the random pair in Example 5.16. Find the best linear and nonlinear estimators for $X$ in terms of $Y$, and of $Y$ in terms of $X$.

Example 5.28 provides the parameters needed for the linear estimator: $E[X] = 3/2$, $E[Y] = 1/2$, $\text{VAR}[X] = 5/4$, $\text{VAR}[Y] = 1/4$, and $\rho_{X,Y} = 1/\sqrt{5}$. Example 5.32 provides the conditional pdf's needed to find the nonlinear estimator. The best linear and nonlinear estimators for $X$ in terms of $Y$ are:

$$\hat{X} = \frac{1}{\sqrt{5}} \frac{\sqrt{5}}{2} \frac{Y - 1/2}{1/2} + \frac{3}{2} = Y + 1$$

$$E[X | y] = \int_y^{\infty} xe^{-(x-y)} \, dx = y + 1 \text{ and so } E[X | Y] = Y + 1.$$

Thus the optimum linear and nonlinear estimators are the same.

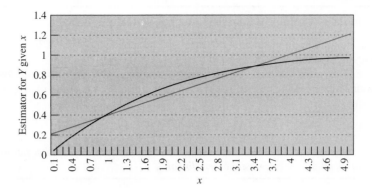

**FIGURE 6.2**
Comparison of linear and nonlinear estimators.

The best linear and nonlinear estimators for $Y$ in terms of $X$ are:

$$\hat{Y} = \frac{1}{\sqrt{5}}\frac{1}{2}\frac{X - 3/2}{\sqrt{5/2}} + \frac{1}{2} = (X + 1)/5.$$

$$E[Y \mid x] = \int_0^x y\frac{e^{-y}}{1 - e^{-x}}\,dy = \frac{1 - e^{-x} - xe^{-x}}{1 - e^{-x}} = 1 - \frac{xe^{-x}}{1 - e^{-x}}.$$

The optimum linear and nonlinear estimators are not the same in this case. Figure 6.2 compares the two estimators. It can be seen that the linear estimator is close to $E[Y \mid x]$ for lower values of $x$, where the joint pdf of $X$ and $Y$ are concentrated and that it diverges from $E[Y \mid x]$ for larger values of $x$.

---

**Example 6.28**

Let $X$ be uniformly distributed in the interval $(-1, 1)$ and let $Y = X^2$. Find the best linear estimator for $Y$ in terms of $X$. Compare its performance to the best estimator.
    The mean of $X$ is zero, and its correlation with $Y$ is

$$E[XY] = E[XX^2] = \int_{-\frac{1}{2}}^{1} x^3/2\,dx = 0.$$

Therefore $\mathrm{COV}(X, Y) = 0$ and the best linear estimator for $Y$ is $E[Y]$ by Eq. (6.55). The mean square error of this estimator is the $\mathrm{VAR}(Y)$ by Eq. (6.57).
    The best estimator is given by Eq. (6.58):

$$E[Y \mid X = x] = E[X^2 \mid X = x] = x^2.$$

The mean square error of this estimator is

$$E[(Y - g(X))^2] = E[(X^2 - X^2)^2] = 0.$$

Thus in this problem, the best linear estimator performs poorly while the nonlinear estimator gives the smallest possible mean square error, zero.

**Example 6.29    Jointly Gaussian Random Variables**

Find the minimum mean square error estimator of $X$ in terms of $Y$ when $X$ and $Y$ are jointly Gaussian random variables.

    The minimum mean square error estimator is given by the conditional expectation of $X$ given $Y$. From Eq. (5.63), we see that the conditional expectation of $X$ given $Y = y$ is given by

$$E[X \mid Y = y] = E[X] + \rho_{X,Y} \frac{\sigma_X}{\sigma_Y}(Y - E[Y]).$$

This is identical to the best linear estimator. Thus *for jointly Gaussian random variables the minimum mean square error estimator is linear.*

### 6.5.4    Estimation Using a Vector of Observations

The MAP, ML, and mean square estimators can be extended to where a vector of observations is available. Here we focus on mean square estimation. We wish to estimate $X$ by a function $g(\mathbf{Y})$ of a random vector of observations $\mathbf{Y} = (Y_1, Y_2, \ldots, Y_n)^{\mathrm{T}}$ so that the **mean square error** is minimized:

$$\underset{g(\cdot)}{\text{minimize}}\ E[(X - g(\mathbf{Y}))^2].$$

To simplify the discussion we will assume that $X$ and the $Y_i$ have zero means. The same derivation that led to Eq. (6.58) leads to the *optimum minimum mean square estimator*:

$$g^*(\mathbf{y}) = E[X \mid \mathbf{Y} = \mathbf{y}]. \tag{6.59}$$

The minimum mean square error is then:

$$E[(X - g^*(Y))^2] = \int_{R^n} E[(X - E[X \mid \mathbf{Y}])^2 \mid \mathbf{Y} = \mathbf{y}] f_{\mathbf{Y}}(\mathbf{y}) d\mathbf{y}$$

$$= \int_{R^n} \text{VAR}[X \mid \mathbf{Y} = \mathbf{y}] f_{\mathbf{Y}}(\mathbf{y}) d\mathbf{y}.$$

Now suppose the estimate is a linear function of the observations:

$$g(\mathbf{Y}) = \sum_{k=1}^{n} a_k Y_k = \mathbf{a}^{\mathrm{T}} \mathbf{Y}.$$

The mean square error is now:

$$E[(X - g(\mathbf{Y}))^2] = E\left[\left(X - \sum_{k=1}^{n} a_k Y_k\right)^2\right].$$

We take derivatives with respect to $a_k$ and again obtain the orthogonality conditions:

$$E\left[\left(X - \sum_{k=1}^{n} a_k Y_k\right) Y_j\right] = 0 \quad \text{for } j = 1, \ldots, n.$$

The orthogonality condition becomes:

$$E[XY_j] = E\left[\left(\sum_{k=1}^{n} a_k Y_k\right) Y_j\right] = \sum_{k=1}^{n} a_k E[Y_k Y_j] \quad \text{for } j = 1, \ldots, n.$$

We obtain a compact expression by introducing matrix notation:

$$E[XY] = \mathbf{R_Y} a \qquad \text{where } a = (a_1, a_2, \ldots, a_n)^{\text{T}}. \tag{6.60}$$

where $E[XY] = [E[XY_1], E[XY_2], \ldots, E[XY_n]]^{\text{T}}$ and $\mathbf{R_Y}$ is the correlation matrix. Assuming $\mathbf{R_Y}$ is invertible, the optimum coefficients are:

$$a = \mathbf{R}_Y^{-1} E[XY]. \tag{6.61a}$$

We can use the methods from Section 6.3 to invert $\mathbf{R_Y}$. The mean square error of the optimum linear estimator is:

$$\begin{aligned} E[(X - a^{\text{T}}\mathbf{Y})^2] &= E[(X - a^{\text{T}}\mathbf{Y})X] - E[(X - a^{\text{T}}\mathbf{Y})a^{\text{T}}\mathbf{Y}] \\ &= E[(X - a^{\text{T}}\mathbf{Y})X] = \text{VAR}(X) - a^{\text{T}}E[\mathbf{Y}X]. \end{aligned} \tag{6.61b}$$

Now suppose that $X$ has mean $m_X$ and $\mathbf{Y}$ has mean vector $\mathbf{m_Y}$, so our estimator now has the form:

$$\hat{X} = g(\mathbf{Y}) = \sum_{k=1}^{n} a_k Y_k + b = a^{\text{T}}\mathbf{Y} + b. \tag{6.62}$$

The same argument that led to Eq. (6.53b) implies that the optimum choice for $b$ is:

$$b = E[X] - a^{\text{T}}\mathbf{m_Y}.$$

*Therefore the optimum linear estimator has the form:*

$$\hat{X} = g(\mathbf{Y}) = a^{\text{T}}(\mathbf{Y} - \mathbf{m_Y}) + m_X = a^{\text{T}}\mathbf{Z} + m_X$$

where $\mathbf{Z} = \mathbf{Y} - \mathbf{m_Y}$ is a random vector with zero mean vector. The mean square error for this estimator is:

$$E[(X - g(\mathbf{Y}))^2] = E[(X - a^{\text{T}}\mathbf{Z} - m_X)^2] = E[(W - a^{\text{T}}\mathbf{Z})^2]$$

where $W = X - m_X$ has zero mean. We have reduced the general estimation problem to one with zero mean random variables, i.e., $W$ and $\mathbf{Z}$, which has solution given by Eq. (6.61a). Therefore the optimum set of linear predictors is given by:

$$a = \mathbf{R_z}^{-1} E[W\mathbf{Z}] = \mathbf{K_Y}^{-1} E[(X - m_X)(\mathbf{Y} - \mathbf{m_Y})]. \tag{6.63a}$$

The mean square error is:

$$\begin{aligned} E[(X - a^{\text{T}}\mathbf{Y} - b)^2] &= E[(W - a^{\text{T}}\mathbf{Z}\,W] = \text{VAR}(W) - a^{\text{T}}E[W\mathbf{Z}] \\ &= \text{VAR}(X) - a^{\text{T}}E[(X - \mathbf{m_X})(\mathbf{Y} - \mathbf{m_Y})]. \end{aligned} \tag{6.63b}$$

This result is of particular importance in the case where $X$ and $\mathbf{Y}$ are jointly Gaussian random variables. In Example 6.23 we saw that the conditional expected value of $X$ given $Y$ is a linear function of $Y$ of the form in Eq. (6.62). Therefore in this case the optimum minimum mean square estimator corresponds to the optimum linear estimator.

---

### Example 6.30    Diversity Receiver

A radio receiver has two antennas to receive noisy versions of a signal $X$. The desired signal $X$ is a Gaussian random variable with zero mean and variance 2. The signals received in the first and second antennas are $Y_1 = X + N_1$ and $Y_2 = X + N_2$ where $N_1$ and $N_2$ are zero-mean, unit-variance Gaussian random variables. In addition, $X$, $N_1$, and $N_2$ are independent random variables. Find the optimum mean square error linear estimator for $X$ based on a single antenna signal and the corresponding mean square error. Compare the results to the optimum mean square estimator for $X$ based on both antenna signals $\mathbf{Y} = (Y_1, Y_2)$.

Since all random variables have zero mean, we only need the correlation matrix and the cross-correlation vector in Eq. (6.61):

$$\mathbf{R}_Y = \begin{bmatrix} E[Y_1^2] & E[Y_1Y_2] \\ E[Y_1Y_2] & E[Y_2^2] \end{bmatrix}$$

$$= \begin{bmatrix} E[(X + N_1)^2] & E[(X + N_1)(X + N_2)] \\ E[(X + N_1)(X + N_2)] & E[(X + N_2)^2] \end{bmatrix}$$

$$= \begin{bmatrix} E[X^2] + E[N_1^2] & E[X^2] \\ E[X^2] & E[X^2] + E[N_2^2] \end{bmatrix} = \begin{bmatrix} 3 & 2 \\ 2 & 3 \end{bmatrix}$$

and

$$E[X\mathbf{Y}] = \begin{bmatrix} E[XY_1] \\ E[XY_2] \end{bmatrix} = \begin{bmatrix} E[X^2] \\ E[X^2] \end{bmatrix} = \begin{bmatrix} 2 \\ 2 \end{bmatrix}.$$

The optimum estimator using a single antenna received signal involves solving the $1 \times 1$ version of the above system:

$$\hat{X} = \frac{E[X^2]}{E[X^2] + E[N_1^2]} Y_1 = \frac{2}{3} Y_1$$

and the associated mean square error is:

$$\text{VAR}(X) - a^* \text{COV}(Y_1, X) = 2 - \frac{2}{3} 2 = \frac{2}{3}.$$

The coefficients of the optimum estimator using two antenna signals are:

$$a = \mathbf{R}_Y^{-1} E[X\mathbf{Y}] = \begin{bmatrix} 3 & 2 \\ 2 & 3 \end{bmatrix}^{-1} \begin{bmatrix} 2 \\ 2 \end{bmatrix} = \frac{1}{5} \begin{bmatrix} 3 & -2 \\ -2 & 3 \end{bmatrix} \begin{bmatrix} 2 \\ 2 \end{bmatrix} = \begin{bmatrix} 0.4 \\ 0.4 \end{bmatrix}$$

and the optimum estimator is:

$$\hat{X} = 0.4Y_1 + 0.4Y_2.$$

The mean square error for the two antenna estimator is:

$$E[(X - a^T\mathbf{Y})^2] = \text{VAR}(X) - a^T E[\mathbf{Y}X] = 2 - [0.4, 0.4] \begin{bmatrix} 2 \\ 2 \end{bmatrix} = 0.4.$$

As expected, the two antenna system has a smaller mean square error. Note that the receiver adds the two received signals and scales the result by 0.4. The sum of the signals is:

$$\hat{X} = 0.4Y_1 + 0.4Y_2 = 0.4(2X + N_1 + N_2) = 0.8\left(X + \frac{N_1 + N_2}{2}\right)$$

so combining the signals keeps the desired signal portion, $X$, constant while averaging the two noise signals $N_1$ and $N_2$. The problems at the end of the chapter explore this topic further.

---

### Example 6.31    Second-Order Prediction of Speech

Let $X_1, X_2, \ldots$ be a sequence of samples of a speech voltage waveform, and suppose that the samples are fed into the second-order predictor shown in Fig. 6.3. Find the set of predictor coefficients $a$ and $b$ that minimize the mean square value of the predictor error when $X_n$ is estimated by $aX_{n-2} + bX_{n-1}$.

We find the best predictor for $X_1$, $X_2$, and $X_3$ and assume that the situation is identical for $X_2$, $X_3$, and $X_4$ and so on. It is common practice to model speech samples as having zero mean and variance $\sigma^2$, and a covariance that does not depend on the specific index of the samples, but rather on the separation between them:

$$\mathrm{COV}(X_j, X_k) = \rho_{|j-k|}\sigma^2.$$

The equation for the optimum linear predictor coefficients becomes

$$\sigma^2\begin{bmatrix} 1 & \rho_1 \\ \rho_1 & 1 \end{bmatrix}\begin{bmatrix} a \\ b \end{bmatrix} = \sigma^2\begin{bmatrix} \rho_2 \\ \rho_1 \end{bmatrix}.$$

Equation (6.61a) gives

$$a = \frac{\rho_2 - \rho_1^2}{1 - \rho_1^2} \quad \text{and} \quad b = \frac{\rho_1(1 - \rho_1^2)}{1 - \rho_1^2}.$$

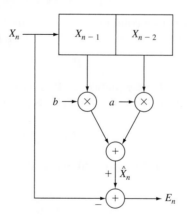

**FIGURE 6.3**
A two-tap linear predictor for processing speech.

In Problem 6.78, you are asked to show that the mean square error using the above values of $a$ and $b$ is

$$\sigma^2 \left\{ 1 - \rho_1^2 - \frac{(\rho_1^2 - \rho_2)^2}{1 - \rho_1^2} \right\}. \tag{6.64}$$

Typical values for speech signals are $\rho_1 = .825$ and $\rho_2 = .562$. The mean square value of the predictor output is then $.281\sigma^2$. The lower variance of the output ($.281\sigma^2$) relative to the input variance ($\sigma^2$) shows that the linear predictor is effective in anticipating the next sample in terms of the two previous samples. The order of the predictor can be increased by using more terms in the linear predictor. Thus a third-order predictor has three terms and involves inverting a $3 \times 3$ correlation matrix, and an $n$-th order predictor will involve an $n \times n$ matrix. Linear predictive techniques are used extensively in speech, audio, image and video compression systems. We discuss linear prediction methods in greater detail in Chapter 10.

---

## *6.6    GENERATING CORRELATED VECTOR RANDOM VARIABLES

Many applications involve vectors or sequences of correlated random variables. Computer simulation models of such applications therefore require methods for generating such random variables. In this section we present methods for generating vectors of random variables with specified covariance matrices. We also discuss the generation of jointly Gaussian vector random variables.

### 6.6.1    Generating Random Vectors with Specified Covariance Matrix

Suppose we wish to generate a random vector $\mathbf{Y}$ with an arbitrary valid covariance matrix $\mathbf{K_Y}$. Let $\mathbf{Y} = \mathbf{A}^T\mathbf{X}$ as in Example 6.17, where $\mathbf{X}$ is a vector random variable with components that are uncorrelated, zero mean, and unit variance. $\mathbf{X}$ has covariance matrix equal to the identity matrix $\mathbf{K_X} = \mathbf{I}$, $\mathbf{m_Y} = \mathbf{Am_X} = \mathbf{0}$, and

$$\mathbf{K_Y} = \mathbf{A}^T\mathbf{K_X}\mathbf{A} = \mathbf{A}^T\mathbf{A}.$$

Let $\mathbf{P}$ be the matrix whose columns are the eigenvectors of $\mathbf{K_Y}$ and let $\Lambda$ be the diagonal matrix of eigenvalues, then from Eq. (6.39b) we have:

$$\mathbf{P}^T\mathbf{K_Y}\mathbf{P} = \mathbf{P}^T\mathbf{P}\Lambda = \Lambda.$$

If we premultiply the above equation by $\mathbf{P}$ and then postmultiply by $\mathbf{P}^T$, we obtain expression for an arbitrary covariance matrix $\mathbf{K_Y}$ in terms of its eigenvalues and eigenvectors:

$$\mathbf{P}\Lambda\mathbf{P}^T = \mathbf{PP}^T\mathbf{K_Y}\mathbf{PP}^T = \mathbf{K_Y}. \tag{6.65}$$

Define the matrix $\Lambda^{1/2}$ as the diagonal matrix of square roots of the eigenvalues:

$$\Lambda^{1/2} \triangleq \begin{bmatrix} \sqrt{\lambda_1} & 0 & \cdots & 0 \\ 0 & \sqrt{\lambda_2} & \cdots & 0 \\ \cdot & \cdot & \cdots & \cdot \\ 0 & 0 & \cdots & \sqrt{\lambda_n} \end{bmatrix}.$$

In Problem 6.53 we show that any covariance matrix $\mathbf{K_Y}$ is positive semi-definite, which implies that it has nonnegative eigenvalues, and so taking the square root is always possible. If we now let

$$\mathbf{A} = (\mathbf{P\Lambda}^{1/2})^{\mathrm{T}} \tag{6.66}$$

then

$$\mathbf{A}^{\mathrm{T}}\mathbf{A} = \mathbf{P\Lambda}^{1/2}\mathbf{\Lambda}^{1/2}\mathbf{P}^{\mathrm{T}} = \mathbf{P\Lambda P}^{\mathrm{T}} = \mathbf{K_Y}.$$

Therefore $\mathbf{Y}$ has the desired covariance matrix $\mathbf{K_Y}$.

---

### Example 6.32

Let $\mathbf{X} = (X_1, X_2)$ consist of two zero-mean, unit-variance, uncorrelated random variables. Find the matrix $A$ such that $\mathbf{Y} = A\mathbf{X}$ has covariance matrix

$$K = \begin{bmatrix} 4 & 2 \\ 2 & 4 \end{bmatrix}.$$

First we need to find the eigenvalues of $K$ which are determined from the following equation:

$$\det(\mathbf{K} - \lambda\mathbf{I}) = 0 = \det\begin{bmatrix} 4 - \lambda & 2 \\ 2 & 4 - \lambda \end{bmatrix} = (4 - \lambda)^2 - 4 = \lambda^2 - 8\lambda + 12$$

$$= (\lambda - 6)(\lambda - 2).$$

We find the eigenvalues to be $\lambda_1 = 2$ and $\lambda_2 = 6$. Next we need to find the eigenvectors corresponding to each eigenvalue:

$$\begin{bmatrix} 4 & 2 \\ 2 & 4 \end{bmatrix}\begin{bmatrix} e_1 \\ e_2 \end{bmatrix} = \lambda_1\begin{bmatrix} e_1 \\ e_2 \end{bmatrix} = 2\begin{bmatrix} e_1 \\ e_2 \end{bmatrix}$$

which implies that $2e_1 + 2e_2 = 0$. Thus any vector of the form $[1, -1]^{\mathrm{T}}$ is an eigenvector. We choose the normalized eigenvector corresponding to $\lambda_1 = 2$ as $\mathbf{e}_1 = [1/\sqrt{2}, -1/\sqrt{2}]^{\mathrm{T}}$. We similarly find the eigenvector corresponding to $\lambda_2 = 6$ as $\mathbf{e}_2 = [1/\sqrt{2}, 1/\sqrt{2}]^{\mathrm{T}}$.

The method developed in Section 6.3 requires that we form the matrix $P$ whose columns consist of the eigenvectors of $K$:

$$P = \frac{1}{\sqrt{2}}\begin{bmatrix} 1 & 1 \\ -1 & 1 \end{bmatrix}.$$

Next it requires that we form the diagonal matrix with elements equal to the square root of the eigenvalues:

$$\Lambda^{1/2} = \begin{bmatrix} \sqrt{2} & 0 \\ 0 & \sqrt{6} \end{bmatrix}.$$

The desired matrix is then

$$\mathbf{A} = \mathbf{P\Lambda}^{1/2} = \begin{bmatrix} 1 & \sqrt{3} \\ -1 & \sqrt{3} \end{bmatrix}.$$

You should verify that $K = AA^{\mathrm{T}}$.

---

### Example 6.33

Use Octave to find the eigenvalues and eigenvectors calculated in the previous example.

After entering the matrix $K$, we use the eig($K$) function to find the matrix of eigenvectors $P$ and eigenvalues $\Lambda$. We then find $A$ and its transpose $A^{\mathrm{T}}$. Finally we confirm that $A^{\mathrm{T}}A$ gives the desired covariance matrix.

```
> K=[4, 2; 2, 4];
> [P,D] =eig (K)
P =
  -0.70711  0.70711
   0.70711  0.70711
D =
   2  0
   0  6
> A=(P*sqrt(D))'
A =
  -1.0000  1.0000
   1.7321  1.7321
> A'
ans =
  -1.0000  1.7321
   1.0000  1.7321
> A'*A
ans =
   4.0000  2.0000
   2.0000  4.0000
```

The above steps can be used to find the transformation $A^{\mathrm{T}}$ for any desired covariance matrix $K$. The only check required is to ascertain that $K$ is a valid covariance matrix: (1) $K$ is symmetric (trivial); (2) $K$ has positive eigenvalues (easy to check numerically).

### 6.6.2  Generating Vectors of Jointly Gaussian Random Variables

In Section 6.4 we found that if $\mathbf{X}$ is a vector of jointly Gaussian random variables with covariance $K_X$, then $\mathbf{Y} = A\mathbf{X}$ is also jointly Gaussian with covariance matrix $K_Y = AK_XA^{\mathrm{T}}$. If we assume that $\mathbf{X}$ consists of unit-variance, uncorrelated random variables, then $K_X = I$, the identity matrix, and therefore $K_Y = AA^{\mathrm{T}}$.

We can use the method from the first part of this section to find $A$ for any desired covariance matrix $K_Y$. We generate jointly Gaussian random vectors $\mathbf{Y}$ with arbitrary covariance matrix $K_Y$ and mean vector $\mathbf{m_Y}$ as follows:

1. Find a matrix $A$ such that $K_Y = AA^{\mathrm{T}}$.
2. Use the method from Section 5.10 to generate $\mathbf{X}$ consisting of $n$ independent, zero-mean, Gaussian random variables.
3. Let $\mathbf{Y} = A\mathbf{X} + \mathbf{m_Y}$.

**Example 6.34**

The Octave commands below show necessary steps for generating the Gaussian random variables with the covariance matrix from Example 6.30.

```
> U1=rand(1000, 1);          % Create a 1000-element vector U₁.

> U2=rand(1000, 1);          % Create a 1000-element vector U₂.

> R2=-2*log(U1);             % Find R².

> TH=2*pi*U2;                % Find Θ.

> X1=sqrt(R2).*sin(TH);      % Generate X1.

> X2=sqrt(R2).*cos(TH);      % Generate X2.

> Y1=X1+sqrt(3)*X2           % Generate Y1.

> Y2=-X1+sqrt(3)*X2          % Generate Y2.

> plot(Y1,Y2,'+')           % Plot scattergram.
```

We plotted the $Y_1$ values vs. the $Y_2$ values for 1000 pairs of generated random variables in a scattergram as shown in Fig. 6.4. Good agreement with the elliptical symmetry of the desired jointly Gaussian pdf is observed.

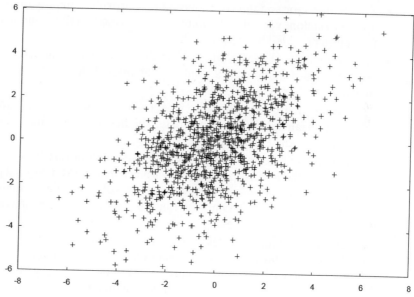

**FIGURE 6.4**
Scattergram of jointly Gaussian random variables.

## SUMMARY

- The joint statistical behavior of a vector of random variables $\mathbf{X}$ is specified by the joint cumulative distribution function, the joint probability mass function, or the joint probability density function. The probability of any event involving the joint behavior of these random variables can be computed from these functions.

- The statistical behavior of subsets of random variables from a vector $\mathbf{X}$ is specified by the marginal cdf, marginal pdf, or marginal pmf that can be obtained from the joint cdf, joint pdf, or joint pmf of $\mathbf{X}$.

- A set of random variables is independent if the probability of a product-form event is equal to the product of the probabilities of the component events. Equivalent conditions for the independence of a set of random variables are that the joint cdf, joint pdf, or joint pmf factors into the product of the corresponding marginal functions.

- The statistical behavior of a subset of random variables from a vector $\mathbf{X}$, given the exact values of the other random variables in the vector, is specified by the conditional cdf, conditional pmf, or conditional pdf. Many problems naturally lend themselves to a solution that involves conditioning on the values of some of the random variables. In these problems, the expected value of random variables can be obtained through the use of conditional expectation.

- The mean vector and the covariance matrix provide summary information about a vector random variable. The joint characteristic function contains all of the information provided by the joint pdf.

- Transformations of vector random variables generate other vector random variables. Standard methods are available for finding the joint distributions of the new random vectors.

- The orthogonality condition provides a set of linear equations for finding the minimum mean square linear estimate. The best mean square estimator is given by the conditional expected value.

- The joint pdf of a vector $\mathbf{X}$ of jointly Gaussian random variables is determined by the vector of the means and by the covariance matrix. All marginal pdf's and conditional pdf's of subsets of $\mathbf{X}$ have Gaussian pdf's. Any linear function or linear transformation of jointly Gaussian random variables will result in a set of jointly Gaussian random variables.

- A vector of random variables with an arbitrary covariance matrix can be generated by taking a linear transformation of a vector of unit-variance, uncorrelated random variables. A vector of Gaussian random variables with an arbitrary covariance matrix can be generated by taking a linear transformation of a vector of independent, unit-variance jointly Gaussian random variables.

## CHECKLIST OF IMPORTANT TERMS

Conditional cdf
Conditional expectation
Conditional pdf
Conditional pmf
Correlation matrix
Covariance matrix
Independent random variables
Jacobian of a transformation
Joint cdf
Joint characteristic function
Joint pdf
Joint pmf
Jointly continuous random variables
Jointly Gaussian random variables

Karhunen-Loeve expansion
MAP estimator
Marginal cdf
Marginal pdf
Marginal pmf
Maximum likelihood estimator
Mean square error
Mean vector
MMSE linear estimator
Orthogonality condition
Product-form event
Regression curve
Vector random variables

## ANNOTATED REFERENCES

Reference [3] provides excellent coverage on linear transformation and jointly Gaussian random variables. Reference [5] provides excellent coverage of vector random variables. The book by Anton [6] provides an accessible introduction to linear algebra.

1. A. Papoulis and S. Pillai, *Probability, Random Variables, and Stochastic Processes*, McGraw-Hill, New York, 2002.

2. N. Johnson et al., *Continuous Multivariate Distributions*, Wiley, New York, 2000.

3. H. Cramer, *Mathematical Methods of Statistics*, Princeton Press, 1999.

4. R. Gray and L.D. Davisson, *An Introduction to Statistical Signal Processing*, Cambridge Univ. Press, Cambridge, UK, 2005.

5. H. Stark and J. W. Woods, *Probability, Random Processes, and Estimation Theory for Engineers*, Prentice Hall, Englewood Cliffs, N.J., 1986.

6. H. Anton, *Elementary Linear Algebra*, 9th ed., Wiley, New York, 2005.

7. C. H. Edwards, Jr., and D. E. Penney, *Calculus and Analytic Geometry*, 4th ed., Prentice Hall, Englewood Cliffs, N.J., 1984.

## PROBLEMS

### Section 6.1: Vector Random Variables

**6.1.** The point $\mathbf{X} = (X, Y, Z)$ is uniformly distributed inside a sphere of radius 1 about the origin. Find the probability of the following events:

(a) $\mathbf{X}$ is inside a sphere of radius $r, r > 0$.

(b) $\mathbf{X}$ is inside a cube of length $2/\sqrt{3}$ centered about the origin.

(c) All components of $\mathbf{X}$ are positive.

(d) $Z$ is negative.

**6.2.** A random sinusoid signal is given by $X(t) = A \sin(t)$ where $A$ is a uniform random variable in the interval $[0, 1]$. Let $\mathbf{X} = (X(t_1), X(t_2), X(t_3))$ be samples of the signal taken at times $t_1, t_2$, and $t_3$.

(a) Find the joint cdf of $\mathbf{X}$ in terms of the cdf of $A$ if $t_1 = 0, t_2 = \pi/2$, and $t_3 = \pi$. Are $X(t_1), X(t_2), X(t_3)$ independent random variables?

(b) Find the joint cdf of $\mathbf{X}$ for $t_1, t_2 = t_1 + \pi/2$, and $t_3 = t_1 + \pi$ Let $t_1 = \pi/6$.

**6.3.** Let the random variables $X$, $Y$, and $Z$ be independent random variables. Find the following probabilities in terms of $F_X(x)$, $F_Y(y)$, and $F_Z(z)$.

(a) $P[|X| < 5, Y < 4, Z^3 > 8]$.

(b) $P[X = 5, Y < 0, Z > 1]$.

(c) $P[\min(X, Y, Z) < 2]$.

(d) $P[\max(X, Y, Z) > 6]$.

**6.4.** A radio transmitter sends a signal $s > 0$ to a receiver using three paths. The signals that arrive at the receiver along each path are:

$$X_1 = s + N_1, X_2 = s + N_2, \text{ and } X_3 = s + N_3,$$

where $N_1$, $N_2$, and $N_3$ are independent Gaussian random variables with zero mean and unit variance.

(a) Find the joint pdf of $\mathbf{X} = (X_1, X_2, X_3)$. Are $X_1$, $X_2$, and $X_3$ independent random variables?

(b) Find the probability that the minimum of all three signals are positive.

(c) Find the probability that a majority of the signals are positive.

**6.5.** An urn contains one black ball and two white balls. Three balls are drawn from the urn. Let $I_k = 1$ if the outcome of the $k$th draw is the black ball and let $I_k = 0$ otherwise. Define the following three random variables:

$$X = I_1 + I_2 + I_3,$$
$$Y = \min\{I_1, I_2, I_3\},$$
$$Z = \max\{I_1, I_2, I_3\}.$$

(a) Specify the range of values of the triplet $(X, Y, Z)$ if each ball is put back into the urn after each draw; find the joint pmf for $(X, Y, Z)$.

(b) In part a, are $X$, $Y$, and $Z$ independent? Are $X$ and $Y$ independent?

(c) Repeat part a if each ball is not put back into the urn after each draw.

**6.6.** Consider the packet switch in Example 6.1. Suppose that each input has one packet with probability $p$ and no packets with probability $1 - p$. Packets are equally likely to be destined to each of the outputs. Let $X_1, X_2$ and $X_3$ be the number of packet arrivals destined for output 1, 2, and 3, respectively.

(a) Find the joint pmf of $X_1$, $X_2$, and $X_3$ Hint: Imagine that every input has a packets go to a fictional port 4 with probality 1-p.

(b) Find the joint pmf of $X_1$ and $X_2$.

(c) Find the pmf of $X_2$.

(d) Are $X_1$, $X_2$, and $X_3$ independent random variables?

(e) Suppose that each output will accept at most one packet and discard all additional packets destined to it. Find the average number of packets discarded by the module in each $T$-second period.

**6.7.** Let $X, Y, Z$ have joint pdf

$$f_{X,Y,Z}(x, y, z) = k(x + y + z) \quad \text{for} \quad 0 \le x \le 1, 0 \le y \le 1, 0 \le z \le 1.$$

(a) Find $k$.

(b) Find $f_X(x \mid y, z)$ and $f_Z(z \mid x, y)$.

(c) Find $f_X(x)$, $f_Y(y)$, and $f_Z(z)$.

**6.8.** A point $\mathbf{X} = (X, Y, Z)$ is selected at random inside the unit sphere.

(a) Find the marginal joint pdf of $Y$ and $Z$.

(b) Find the marginal pdf of $Y$.

(c) Find the conditional joint pdf of $X$ and $Y$ given $Z$.

(d) Are $X, Y$, and $Z$ independent random variables?

(e) Find the joint pdf of $\mathbf{X}$ given that the distance from $\mathbf{X}$ to the origin is greater than 1/2 and all the components of $\mathbf{X}$ are positive.

**6.9.** Show that $p_{X_1,X_2,X_3}(x_1, x_2, x_3) = p_{X_3}(x_3 \mid x_1, x_2) p_{X_2}(x_2 \mid x_1) p_{X_1}(x_1)$.

**6.10.** Let $X_1, X_2, \ldots, X_n$ be binary random variables taking on values 0 or 1 to denote whether a speaker is silent (0) or active (1). A silent speaker remains idle at the next time slot with probability 3/4, and an active speaker remains active with probability 1/2. Find the joint pmf for $X_1, X_2, X_3$, and the marginal pmf of $X_3$. Assume that the speaker begins in the silent state.

**6.11.** Show that $f_{X,Y,Z}(x, y, z) = f_Z(z \mid x, y) f_Y(y \mid x) f_X(x)$.

**6.12.** Let $U_1, U_2$, and $U_3$ be independent random variables and let $X = U_1, Y = U_1 + U_2$, and $Z = U_1 + U_2 + U_3$.

(a) Use the result in Problem 6.11 to find the joint pdf of $X, Y$, and $Z$.

(b) Let the $U_i$ be independent uniform random variables in the interval $[0, 1]$. Find the marginal joint pdf of $Y$ and $Z$. Find the marginal pdf of $Z$.

(c) Let the $U_i$ be independent zero-mean, unit-variance Gaussian random variables. Find the marginal pdf of $Y$ and $Z$. Find the marginal pdf of $Z$.

**6.13.** Let $X_1, X_2$, and $X_3$ be the multiplicative sequence in Example 6.7.

(a) Find, plot, and compare the marginal pdfs of $X_1, X_2$, and $X_3$.

(b) Find the conditional pdf of $X_3$ given $X_1 = x$.

(c) Find the conditional pdf of $X_1$ given $X_3 = z$.

**6.14.** Requests at an online music site are categorized as follows: Requests for most popular title with $p_1 = 1/2$; second most popular title with $p_2 = 1/4$; third most popular title with $p_3 = 1/8$; and other $p_4 = 1 - p_1 - p_2 - p_3 = 1/8$. Suppose there are a total number of

$n$ requests in $T$ seconds. Let $X_k$ be the number of times category $k$ occurs.
   (a)   Find the joint pmf of $(X_1, X_2, X_3)$.
   (b)   Find the marginal pmf of $(X_1, X_2)$. *Hint:* Use the binomial theorem.
   (c)   Find the marginal pmf of $X_1$.
   (d)   Find the conditional joint pmf of $(X_2, X_3)$ given $X_1 = m$, where $0 \leq m \leq n$.

**6.15.** The number $N$ of requests at the online music site in Problem 6.14 is a Poisson random variable with mean $\alpha$ customers per second. Let $X_k$ be the number of type $k$ requests in $T$ seconds. Find the joint pmf of $(X_1, X_2, X_3, X_4)$.

**6.16.** A random experiment has four possible outcomes. Suppose that the experiment is repeated $n$ independent times and let $X_k$ be the number of times outcome $k$ occurs. The joint pmf of $(X_1, X_2, X_3)$ is given by

$$p(k_1, k_2, k_3) = \frac{n!\, 3!}{(n + 3)!} = \binom{n + 3}{3}^{-1} \quad \text{for} \quad 0 \leq k_i \text{ and } k_1 + k_2 + k_3 \leq n.$$

   (a)   Find the marginal pmf of $(X_1, X_2)$.
   (b)   Find the marginal pmf of $X_1$.
   (c)   Find the conditional joint pmf of $(X_2, X_3)$ given $X_1 = m$, where $0 \leq m \leq n$.

**6.17.** The number of requests of types 1, 2, and 3, respectively, arriving at a service station in $t$ seconds are independent Poisson random variables with means $\lambda_1 t$, $\lambda_2 t$, and $\lambda_3 t$. Let $N_1$, $N_2$, and $N_3$ be the number of requests that arrive during an exponentially distributed time $T$ with mean $\alpha t$.
   (a)   Find the joint pmf of $N_1$, $N_2$, and $N_3$.
   (b)   Find the marginal pmf of $N_1$.
   (c)   Find the conditional pmf of $N_1$ and $N_2$, given $N_3$.

## Section 6.2:  Functions of Several Random Variables

**6.18.** $N$ devices are installed at the same time. Let $Y$ be the time until the first device fails.
   (a)   Find the pdf of $Y$ if the lifetimes of the devices are independent and have the same Pareto distribution.
   (b)   Repeat part a if the device lifetimes have a Weibull distribution.

**6.19.** In Problem 6.18 let $I_k(t)$ be the indicator function for the event "$k$th device is still working at time $t$." Let $N(t)$ be the number of devices still working at time $t$: $N(t) = I_1(t) + I_2(t) + \cdots + I_N(t)$. Find the pmf of $N(t)$ as well as its mean and variance.

**6.20.** A diversity receiver receives $N$ independent versions of a signal. Each signal version has an amplitude $X_k$ that is Rayleigh distributed. The receiver selects that signal with the largest amplitude $\alpha x_k^2$. A signal is not useful if the squared amplitude falls below a threshold $\gamma$. Find the probability that all $N$ signals are below the threshold.

**6.21.** (Haykin) A receiver in a multiuser communication system accepts $K$ binary signals from $K$ independent transmitters: $\mathbf{Y} = (Y_1, Y_2, \ldots, Y_K)$, where $Y_k$ is the received signal from the $k$th transmitter. In an ideal system the received vector is given by:

$$\mathbf{Y} = \mathbf{Ab} + \mathbf{N}$$

where $\mathbf{A} = [\alpha_k]$ is a diagonal matrix of positive channel gains, $\mathbf{b} = (b_1, b_2, \ldots, b_K)$ is the vector of bits from each of the transmitters where $b_k = \pm 1$, and $\mathbf{N}$ is a vector of $K$

independent zero-mean, unit-variance Gaussian random variables.

    **(a)** Find the joint pdf of **Y**.

    **(b)** Suppose $\mathbf{b} = (1, 1, \ldots, 1)$, find the probability that all components of **Y** are positive.

**6.22. (a)** Find the joint pdf of $U = X_1, V = X_1 + X_2$, and $W = X_1 + X_2 + X_3$.

    **(b)** Evaluate the joint pdf of $(U, V, W)$ if the $X_i$ are independent zero-mean, unit variance Gaussian random variables.

    **(c)** Find the marginal pdf of $V$ and of $W$.

**6.23. (a)** Find the joint pdf of the sample mean and variance of two random variables:

$$M = \frac{X_1 + X_2}{2} \qquad V = \frac{(X_1 - M)^2 + (X_2 - M)^2}{2}$$

    in terms of the joint pdf of $X_1$ and $X_2$.

    **(b)** Evaluate the joint pdf if $X_1$ and $X_2$ are independent Gaussian random variables with the same mean 1 and variance 1.

    **(c)** Evaluate the joint pdf if $X_1$ and $X_2$ are independent exponential random variables with the same parameter 1.

**6.24. (a)** Use the auxiliary variable method to find the pdf of

$$Z = \frac{X}{X + Y}.$$

    **(b)** Find the pdf of $Z$ if $X$ and $Y$ are independent exponential random variables with the parameter 1.

    **(c)** Repeat part b if $X$ and $Y$ are independent Pareto random variables with parameters $k = 2$ and $x_m = 1$.

**6.25.** Repeat Problem 6.24 parts a and b for $Z = X/Y$.

**6.26.** Let $X$ and $Y$ be zero-mean, unit-variance Gaussian random variables with correlation coefficient 1/2. Find the joint pdf of $U = X^2$ and $V = Y^4$.

**6.27.** Use auxilliary variables to find the pdf of $Z = X_1 X_2 X_3$ where the $X_i$ are independent random variables that are uniformly distributed in $[0, 1]$.

**6.28.** Let $X, Y$, and $Z$ be independent zero-mean, unit-variance Gaussian random variables.

    **(a)** Find the pdf of $R = (X^2 + Y^2 + Z^2)^{1/2}$.

    **(b)** Find the pdf of $R^2 = X^2 + Y^2 + Z^2$.

**6.29.** Let $X_1, X_2, X_3, X_4$ be processed as follows:

$$Y_1 = X_1, Y_2 = X_1 + X_2, Y_3 = X_2 + X_3, Y_4 = X_3 + X_4.$$

    **(a)** Find an expression for the joint pdf of $\mathbf{Y} = (Y_1, Y_2, Y_3, Y_4)$ in terms of the joint pdf of $\mathbf{X} = (X_1, X_2, X_3, X_4)$.

    **(b)** Find the joint pdf of **Y** if $X_1, X_2, X_3, X_4$ are independent zero-mean, unit-variance Gaussian random variables.

## Section 6.3: Expected Values of Vector Random Variables

**6.30.** Find $E[M], E[V]$, and $E[MV]$ in Problem 6.23c.

**6.31.** Compute $E[Z]$ in Problem 6.27 in two ways:

    **(a)** by integrating over $f_Z(z)$;

    **(b)** by integrating over the joint pdf of $(X_1, X_2, X_3)$.

**6.32.** Find the mean vector and covariance matrix for three multipath signals $\mathbf{X} = (X_1, X_2, X_3)$ in Problem 6.4.

**6.33.** Find the mean vector and covariance matrix for the samples of the sinusoidal signals $\mathbf{X} = (X(t_1), X(t_2), X(t_3))$ in Problem 6.2.

**6.34.** **(a)** Find the mean vector and covariance matrix for $(X, Y, Z)$ in Problem 6.5a.

    **(b)** Repeat part a for Problem 6.5c.

**6.35.** Find the mean vector and covariance matrix for $(X, Y, Z)$ in Problem 6.7.

**6.36.** Find the mean vector and covariance matrix for the point $(X, Y, Z)$ inside the unit sphere in Problem 6.8.

**6.37.** **(a)** Use the results of Problem 6.6c to find the mean vector for the packet arrivals $X_1, X_2$, and $X_3$ in Example 6.5.

    **(b)** Use the results of Problem 6.6b to find the covariance matrix.

    **(c)** Explain why $X_1, X_2$, and $X_3$ are correlated.

**6.38.** Find the mean vector and covariance matrix for the joint number of packet arrivals in a random time $N_1, N_2$, and $N_3$ in Problem 6.17. *Hint:* Use conditional expectation.

**6.39.** **(a)** Find the mean vector and covariance matrix $(U, V, W)$ in terms of $(X_1, X_2, X_3)$ in Problem 6.22b.

    **(b)** Find the cross-covariance matrix between $(U, V, W)$ and $(X_1, X_2, X_3)$.

**6.40.** **(a)** Find the mean vector and covariance matrix of $\mathbf{Y} = (Y_1, Y_2, Y_3, Y_4)$ in terms of those of $\mathbf{X} = (X_1, X_2, X_3, X_4)$ in Problem 6.29.

    **(b)** Find the cross-covariance matrix between $\mathbf{Y}$ and $\mathbf{X}$.

    **(c)** Evaluate the mean vector, covariance, and cross-covariance matrices if $X_1, X_2, X_3, X_4$ are independent random variables.

    **(d)** Generalize the results in part c to $\mathbf{Y} = (Y_1, Y_2, \ldots, Y_{n-1}, Y_n)$.

**6.41.** Let $\mathbf{X} = (X_1, X_2, X_3, X_4)$ consist of equal mean, independent, unit-variance random variables. Find the mean vector, covariance, and cross-covariance matrices of $\mathbf{Y} = \mathbf{AX}$:

**(a)** $\mathbf{A} = \begin{bmatrix} 1 & 1/2 & 1/4 & 1/8 \\ 0 & 1 & 1/2 & 1/4 \\ 0 & 0 & 1 & 1/2 \\ 0 & 0 & 0 & 1 \end{bmatrix}$

**(b)** $\mathbf{A} = \begin{bmatrix} 1 & 1 & 1 & 1 \\ 1 & -1 & 1 & -1 \\ 1 & 1 & -1 & -1 \\ 1 & -1 & -1 & 1 \end{bmatrix}.$

**6.42.** Let $W = aX + bY + c$, where $X$ and $Y$ are random variables.

    **(a)** Find the characteristic function of $W$ in terms of the joint characteristic function of $X$ and $Y$.

    **(b)** Find the characteristic function of $W$ if $X$ and $Y$ are the random variables discussed in Example 6.19. Find the pdf of $W$.

**6.43. (a)** Find the joint characteristic function of the jointly Gaussian random variables $X$ and $Y$ introduced in Example 5.45. *Hint*: Consider $X$ and $Y$ as a transformation of the independent Gaussian random variables $V$ and $W$.

**(b)** Find $E[X^2Y]$.

**(c)** Find the joint characteristic function of $X' = X + a$ and $Y' = Y + b$.

**6.44.** Let $X = aU + bV$ and $y = cU + dV$, where $|ad - bc| \neq 0$.

**(a)** Find the joint characteristic function of $X$ and $Y$ in terms of the joint characteristic function of $U$ and $V$.

**(b)** Find an expression for $E[XY]$ in terms of joint moments of $U$ and $V$.

**6.45.** Let $X$ and $Y$ be nonnegative, integer-valued random variables. The joint probability generating function is defined by

$$G_{X,Y}(z_1, z_2) = E[z_1^X z_2^Y] = \sum_{j=0}^{\infty}\sum_{k=0}^{\infty} z_1^j z_2^k P[X = j, Y = k].$$

**(a)** Find the joint pgf for two independent Poisson random variables with parameters $\alpha_1$ and $\alpha_2$.

**(b)** Find the joint pgf for two independent binomial random variables with parameters $(n, p)$ and $(m, p)$.

**6.46.** Suppose that $X$ and $Y$ have joint pgf

$$G_{X,Y}(z_1, z_2) = e^{\alpha_1(z_1-1)+\alpha_2(z_2-1)+\beta(z_1z_2-1)}.$$

**(a)** Use the marginal pgf's to show that $X$ and $Y$ are Poisson random variables.

**(b)** Find the pgf of $Z = X + Y$. Is $Z$ a Poisson random variable?

**6.47.** Let $X$ and $Y$ be trinomial random variables with joint pmf

$$P[X = j, Y = k] = \frac{n!\, p_1^j p_2^k (1 - p_1 - p_2)^{n-j-k}}{j!\, k!(n - j - k)!} \quad \text{for} \quad 0 \le j, k \text{ and } j + k \le n.$$

**(a)** Find the joint pgf of $X$ and $Y$.

**(b)** Find the correlation and covariance of $X$ and $Y$.

**6.48.** Find the mean vector and covariance matrix for $(X, Y)$ in Problem 6.46.

**6.49.** Find the mean vector and covariance matrix for $(X, Y)$ in Problem 6.47.

**6.50.** Let $\mathbf{X} = (X_1, X_2)$ have covariance matrix:

$$\mathbf{K_X} = \begin{bmatrix} 1 & 1/4 \\ 1/4 & 1 \end{bmatrix}.$$

**(a)** Find the eigenvalues and eigenvectors of $\mathbf{K_X}$.

**(b)** Find the orthogonal matrix $\mathbf{P}$ that diagonalizes $\mathbf{K_X}$. Verify that $\mathbf{P}$ is orthogonal and that $\mathbf{P^T K_X P} = \Lambda$.

**(c)** Express $\mathbf{X}$ in terms of the eigenvectors of $\mathbf{K_X}$ using the Karhunen-Loeve expansion.

**6.51.** Repeat Problem 6.50 for $\mathbf{X} = (X_1, X_2, X_3)$ with covariance matrix:

$$\mathbf{K_X} = \begin{bmatrix} 1 & -1/2 & -1/2 \\ -1/2 & 1 & -1/2 \\ -1/2 & -1/2 & 1 \end{bmatrix}.$$

**6.52.** A square matrix $\mathbf{A}$ is said to be nonnegative definite if for any vector $\boldsymbol{a} = (a_1, a_2, \ldots, a_n)^{\mathrm{T}}$: $\boldsymbol{a}^{\mathrm{T}}\mathbf{A}\,\boldsymbol{a} \geq 0$. Show that the covariance matrix is nonnegative definite. *Hint:* Use the fact that $E[(\boldsymbol{a}^{\mathrm{T}}(\mathbf{X} - \mathbf{m_X}))^2] \geq 0$.

**6.53.** $\mathbf{A}$ is positive definite if for any nonzero vector $\boldsymbol{a} = (a_1, a_2, \ldots, a_n)^{\mathrm{T}}$: $\boldsymbol{a}^{\mathrm{T}}\mathbf{A}\,\boldsymbol{a} > 0$.

    **(a)** Show that if all the eigenvalues are positive, then $\mathbf{K_X}$ is positive definite. *Hint:* Let $\mathbf{b} = \mathbf{P}^{\mathrm{T}}a$.

    **(b)** Show that if $\mathbf{K_X}$ is positive definite, then all the eigenvalues are positive. *Hint:* Let $\boldsymbol{a}$ be an eigenvector of $\mathbf{K_X}$.

## Section 6.4:  Jointly Gaussian Random Vectors

**6.54.** Let $\mathbf{X} = (X_1, X_2)$ be the jointly Gaussian random variables with mean vector and covariance matrix given by:

$$\mathbf{m_X} = \begin{bmatrix} 1 \\ 0 \end{bmatrix} \qquad \mathbf{K_X} = \begin{bmatrix} 3/2 & -1/2 \\ -1/2 & 3/2 \end{bmatrix}.$$

    **(a)** Find the pdf of $\mathbf{X}$ in matrix notation.

    **(b)** Find the pdf of $\mathbf{X}$ using the quadratic expression in the exponent.

    **(c)** Find the marginal pdfs of $X_1$ and $X_2$.

    **(d)** Find a transformation $A$ such that the vector $\mathbf{Y} = A\mathbf{X}$ consists of independent Gaussian random variables.

    **(e)** Find the joint pdf of $\mathbf{Y}$.

**6.55.** Let $\mathbf{X} = (X_1, X_2, X_3)$ be the jointly Gaussian random variables with mean vector and covariance matrix given by:

$$\mathbf{m_X} = \begin{bmatrix} 1 \\ 0 \\ 2 \end{bmatrix} \qquad \mathbf{K_X} = \begin{bmatrix} 3/2 & 0 & 1/2 \\ 0 & 1 & 0 \\ 1/2 & 0 & 3/2 \end{bmatrix}.$$

    **(a)** Find the pdf of $\mathbf{X}$ in matrix notation.

    **(b)** Find the pdf of $\mathbf{X}$ using the quadratic expression in the exponent.

    **(c)** Find the marginal pdfs of $X_1$, $X_2$, and $X_3$.

    **(d)** Find a transformation $A$ such that the vector $\mathbf{Y} = A\mathbf{X}$ consists of independent Gaussian random variables.

    **(e)** Find the joint pdf of $\mathbf{Y}$.

**6.56.** Let $U_1, U_2$, and $U_3$ be independent zero-mean, unit-variance Gaussian random variables and let $X = U_1, Y = U_1 + U_2$, and $Z = U_1 + U_2 + U_3$.

    **(a)** Find the covariance matrix of $(X, Y, Z)$.

    **(b)** Find the joint pdf of $(X, Y, Z)$.

    **(c)** Find the conditional pdf of $Y$ and $Z$ given $X$.

    **(d)** Find the conditional pdf of $Z$ given $X$ and $Y$.

**6.57.** Let $X_1, X_2, X_3, X_4$ be independent zero-mean, unit-variance Gaussian random variables that are processed as follows:

$$Y_1 = X_1 + X_2, Y_2 = X_2 + X_3, Y_3 = X_3 + X_4.$$

    **(a)** Find the covariance matrix of $\mathbf{Y} = (Y_1, Y_2, Y_3)$.

    **(b)** Find the joint pdf of $\mathbf{Y}$.

    **(c)** Find the joint pdf of $Y_1$ and $Y_2$; $Y_1$ and $Y_3$.

    **(d)** Find a transformation $A$ such that the vector $\mathbf{Z} = A\mathbf{Y}$ consists of independent Gaussian random variables.

**6.58.** A more realistic model of the receiver in the multiuser communication system in Problem 6.21 has the $K$ received signals $\mathbf{Y} = (Y_1, Y_2, \ldots, Y_K)$ given by:

$$\mathbf{Y} = \mathbf{ARb} + \mathbf{N}$$

where $\mathbf{A} = [\alpha_k]$ is a diagonal matrix of positive channel gains, $\mathbf{R}$ is a symmetric matrix that accounts for the interference between users, and $\mathbf{b} = (b_1, b_2, \ldots, b_K)$ is the vector of bits from each of the transmitters. $\mathbf{N}$ is the vector of $K$ independent zero-mean, unit-variance Gaussian noise random variables.

(a) Find the joint pdf of $\mathbf{Y}$.

(b) Suppose that in order to recover $\mathbf{b}$, the receiver computes $\mathbf{Z} = (\mathbf{AR})^{-1}\mathbf{Y}$. Find the joint pdf of $\mathbf{Z}$.

**6.59.** (a) Let $\mathbf{K_3}$ be the covariance matrix in Problem 6.55. Find the corresponding $\mathbf{Q_2}$ and $\mathbf{Q_3}$ in Example 6.23.

(b) Find the conditional pdf of $X_3$ given $X_1$ and $X_2$.

**6.60.** In Example 6.23, show that:

$$\tfrac{1}{2}(\mathbf{x}_n - \mathbf{m}_n)^\mathrm{T}\mathbf{Q}_n(\mathbf{x}_n - \mathbf{m}_n) - \tfrac{1}{2}(\mathbf{x}_{n-1} - \mathbf{m}_{n-1})^\mathrm{T}\mathbf{Q}_{n-1}(\mathbf{x}_{n-1} - \mathbf{m}_{n-1})$$
$$= Q_{nn}\{(x_n - m_n) + B\}^2 - Q_{nn}B^2$$
$$\text{where } B = \frac{1}{Q_{nn}}\sum_{j=1}^{n-1}Q_{jk}(x_j - m_j) \quad \text{and} \quad |\mathbf{K}_n|/|\mathbf{K}_{n-1}| = Q_{nn}.$$

**6.61.** Find the pdf of the sum of Gaussian random variables in the following cases:

(a) $Z = X_1 + X_2 + X_3$ in Problem 6.55.

(b) $Z = X + Y + Z$ in Problem 6.56.

(c) $Z = Y_1 + Y_2 + Y_3$ in Problem 6.57.

**6.62.** Find the joint characteristic function of the jointly Gaussian random vector $\mathbf{X}$ in Problem 6.54.

**6.63.** Suppose that a jointly Gaussian random vector $\mathbf{X}$ has zero mean vector and the covariance matrix given in Problem 6.51.

(a) Find the joint characteristic function.

(b) Can you obtain an expression for the joint pdf? Explain your answer.

**6.64.** Let $X$ and $Y$ be jointly Gaussian random variables. Derive the joint characteristic function for $X$ and $Y$ using conditional expectation.

**6.65.** Let $\mathbf{X} = (X_1, X_2, \ldots, X_n)$ be jointly Gaussian random variables. Derive the characteristic function for $\mathbf{X}$ by carrying out the integral in Eq. (6.32). *Hint*: You will need to complete the square as follows:

$$(\mathbf{x} - j\mathbf{K}\boldsymbol{\omega})^\mathrm{T}\mathbf{K}^{-1}(\mathbf{x} - j\mathbf{K}\boldsymbol{\omega}) = \mathbf{x}^\mathrm{T}\mathbf{K}^{-1}\mathbf{x} - 2j\mathbf{x}^\mathrm{T}\boldsymbol{\omega} + j^2\boldsymbol{\omega}^\mathrm{T}\mathbf{K}\boldsymbol{\omega}.$$

**6.66.** Find $E[X^2Y^2]$ for jointly Gaussian random variables from the characteristic function.

**6.67.** Let $\mathbf{X} = (X_1, X_2, X_3, X_4)$ be zero-mean jointly Gaussian random variables. Show that $E[X_1X_2X_3X_4] = E[X_1X_2]E[X_3X_4] + E[X_1X_3]E[X_2X_4] + E[X_1X_4]E[X_2X_3]$.

## Section 6.5: Mean Square Estimation

**6.68.** Let $X$ and $Y$ be discrete random variables with three possible joint pmf's:

| (i) | | | | (ii) | | | | (iii) | | | |
|---|---|---|---|---|---|---|---|---|---|---|---|
| $X/Y$ | −1 | 0 | 1 | $X/Y$ | −1 | 0 | 1 | $X/Y$ | −1 | 0 | 1 |
| −1 | 1/6 | 1/6 | 0 | −1 | 1/9 | 1/9 | 1/9 | −1 | 1/3 | 0 | 0 |
| 0 | 0 | 0 | 1/3 | 0 | 1/9 | 1/9 | 1/9 | 0 | 0 | 1/3 | 0 |
| 1 | 1/6 | 1/6 | 0 | 1 | 1/9 | 1/9 | 1/9 | 1 | 0 | 0 | 1/3 |

   **(a)** Find the minimum mean square error linear estimator for $Y$ given $X$.
   **(b)** Find the minimum mean square error estimator for $Y$ given $X$.
   **(c)** Find the MAP and ML estimators for $Y$ given $X$.
   **(d)** Compare the mean square error of the estimators in parts a, b, and c.

**6.69.** Repeat Problem 6.68 for the continuous random variables $X$ and $Y$ in Problem 5.26.

**6.70.** Find the ML estimator for the signal $s$ in Problem 6.4.

**6.71.** Let $N_1$ be the number of Web page requests arriving at a server in the period $(0, 100)$ ms and let $N_2$ be the *total* combined number of Web page requests arriving at a server in the period $(0, 200)$ ms. Assume page requests occur every 1-ms interval according to independent Bernoulli trials with probability of success $p$.

   **(a)** Find the minimum linear mean square estimator for $N_2$ given $N_1$ and the associated mean square error.
   **(b)** Find the minimum mean square error estimator for $N_2$ given $N_1$ and the associated mean square error.
   **(c)** Find the maximum a posteriori estimator for $N_2$ given $N_1$.
   **(d)** Repeat parts a, b, and c for the estimation of $N_1$ given $N_2$.

**6.72.** Let $Y = X + N$ where $X$ and $N$ are independent Gaussian random variables with different variances and $N$ is zero mean.

   **(a)** Plot the correlation coefficient between the "observed signal" $Y$ and the "desired signal" $X$ as a function of the signal-to-noise ratio $\sigma_X/\sigma_N$.
   **(b)** Find the minimum mean square error estimator for $X$ given $Y$.
   **(c)** Find the MAP and ML estimators for $X$ given $Y$.
   **(d)** Compare the mean square error of the estimators in parts a, b and c.

**6.73.** Let $X, Y, Z$ be the random variables in Problem 6.7.

   **(a)** Find the minimum mean square error linear estimator for $Y$ given $X$ and $Z$.
   **(b)** Find the minimum mean square error estimator for $Y$ given $X$ and $Z$.
   **(c)** Find the MAP and ML estimators for $Y$ given $X$ and $Z$.
   **(d)** Compare the mean square error of the estimators in parts b and c.

**6.74.** **(a)** Repeat Problem 6.73 for the estimator of $X_2$, given $X_1$ and $X_3$ in Problem 6.13.
   **(b)** Repeat Problem 6.73 for the estimator of $X_3$ given $X_1$ and $X_2$.

**6.75.** Consider the ideal multiuser communication system in Problem 6.21. Assume the transmitted bits $b_k$ are independent and equally likely to be $+1$ or $-1$.

   **(a)** Find the ML and MAP estimators for **b** given the observation **Y**.
   **(b)** Find the minimum mean square linear estimator for **b** given the observation **Y**. How can this estimator be used in deciding what were the transmitted bits?

**6.76.** Repeat Problem 6.75 for the multiuser system in Problem 6.58.

**6.77.** A second-order predictor for samples of an image predicts the sample $E$ as a linear function of sample $D$ to its left and sample $B$ in the previous line, as shown below:

$$\begin{array}{lccccc} \text{line } j & \ldots & A & B & C \ldots \\ \text{line } j+1 & \ldots & D & E & \ldots \end{array}$$

$$\text{Estimate for } E = aD + bB.$$

   **(a)** Find $a$ and $b$ if all samples have variance $\sigma^2$ and if the correlation coefficient between $D$ and $E$ is $\rho$, between $B$ and $E$ is $\rho$, and between $D$ and $B$ is $\rho^2$.
   **(b)** Find the mean square error of the predictor found in part a, and determine the reduction in the variance of the signal in going from the input to the output of the predictor.

**6.78.** Show that the mean square error of the two-tap linear predictor is given by Eq. (6.64).

**6.79.** In "hexagonal sampling" of an image, the samples in consecutive lines are offset relative to each other as shown below:

$$
\begin{array}{ccccc}
\text{line } j & \cdots & & A & B \\
\text{line } j + 1 & \cdots & C & D
\end{array}
$$

The covariance between two samples $a$ and $b$ is given by $\rho^{d(a,b)}$ where $d(a, b)$ is the Euclidean distance between the points. In the above samples, the distance between $A$ and $B$, $A$ and $C$, $A$ and $D$, $C$ and $D$, and $B$ and $D$ is 1. Suppose we wish to use a two-tap linear predictor to predict the sample $D$. Which two samples from the set $\{A, B, C\}$ should we use in the predictor? What is the resulting mean square error?

## *Section 6.6:  Generating Correlated Vector Random Variables

**6.80.** Find a linear transformation that diagonalizes **K**.

(a) $\mathbf{K} = \begin{bmatrix} 2 & 1 \\ 1 & 4 \end{bmatrix}.$

(b) $\mathbf{K} = \begin{bmatrix} 4 & 1 \\ 1 & 4 \end{bmatrix}.$

**6.81.** Generate and plot the scattergram of 1000 pairs of random variables **Y** with the covariance matrices in Problem 6.80 if:

(a) $X_1$ and $X_2$ are independent random variables that are each uniform in the unit interval;

(b) $X_1$ and $X_2$ are independent zero-mean, unit-variance Gaussian random variables.

**6.82.** Let $\mathbf{X} = (X_1, X_2, X_3)$ be the jointly Gaussian random variables in Problem 6.55.

(a) Find a linear transformation that diagonalizes the covariance matrix.

(b) Generate 1000 triplets of $\mathbf{Y} = \mathbf{AX}$ and plot the scattergrams for $Y_1$ and $Y_2$, $Y_1$ and $Y_3$, and $Y_2$ and $Y_3$. Confirm that the scattergrams are what is expected.

**6.83.** Let **X** be a jointly Gaussian random vector with mean $\mathbf{m_X}$ and covariance matrix $\mathbf{K_X}$ and let **A** be a matrix that diagonalizes $\mathbf{K_X}$. What is the joint pdf of $\mathbf{A}^{-1}(\mathbf{X} - \mathbf{m_X})$?

**6.84.** Let $X_1, X_2, \ldots, X_n$ be independent zero-mean, unit-variance Gaussian random variables. Let $Y_k = (X_k + X_{k-1})/2$, that is, $Y_k$ is the moving average of pairs of values of $X$. Assume $X_{-1} = 0 = X_{n+1}$.

(a) Find the covariance matrix of the $Y_k$'s.

(b) Use Octave to generate a sequence of 1000 samples $Y_1, \ldots, Y_n$. How would you check whether the $Y_k$'s have the correct covariances?

**6.85.** Repeat Problem 6.84 with $Y_k = X_k - X_{k-1}$.

**6.86.** Let **U** be an orthogonal matrix. Show that if **A** diagonalizes the covariance matrix **K**, then $\mathbf{B} = \mathbf{UA}$ also diagonalizes **K**.

**6.87.** The transformation in Problem 6.56 is said to be "causal" because each output depends only on "past" inputs.

(a) Find the covariance matrix of $X, Y, Z$ in Problem 6.56.

(b) Find a noncausal transformation that diagonalizes the covariance matrix in part a.

**6.88.** (a) Find a causal transformation that diagonalizes the covariance matrix in Problem 6.54.

(b) Repeat for the covariance matrix in Problem 6.55.

## Problems Requiring Cumulative Knowledge

**6.89.** Let $U_0, U_1, \ldots$ be a sequence of independent zero-mean, unit-variance Gaussian random variables. A "low-pass filter" takes the sequence $U_i$ and produces the output sequence $X_n = (U_n + U_{n-1})/2$, and a "high-pass filter" produces the output sequence $Y_n = (U_n - U_{n-1})/2$.

(a) Find the joint pdf of $X_{n+1}$, $X_n$, and $X_{n-1}$; of $X_n$, $X_{n+m}$, and $X_{n+2m}$, $m > 1$.

(b) Repeat part a for $Y_n$.

(c) Find the joint pdf of $X_n$, $X_m$, $Y_n$, and $Y_m$.

(d) Find the corresponding joint characteristic functions in parts a, b, and c.

**6.90.** Let $X_1, X_2, \ldots, X_n$ be the samples of a speech waveform in Example 6.31. Suppose we want to interpolate for the value of a sample in terms of the previous and the next samples, that is, we wish to find the best linear estimate for $X_2$ in terms of $X_1$ and $X_3$.

(a) Find the coefficients of the best linear estimator (interpolator).

(b) Find the mean square error of the best linear interpolator and compare it to the mean square error of the two-tap predictor in Example 6.31.

(c) Suppose that the samples are jointly Gaussian. Find the pdf of the interpolation error.

**6.91.** Let $X_1, X_2, \ldots, X_n$ be samples from some signal. Suppose that the samples are jointly Gaussian random variables with covariance

$$\text{COV}(X_i, X_j) = \begin{cases} \sigma^2 & \text{for } i = j \\ \rho\sigma^2 & \text{for } |i - j| = 1 \\ 0 & \text{otherwise.} \end{cases}$$

Suppose we take blocks of two consecutive samples to form a vector $\mathbf{X}$, which is then linearly transformed to form $\mathbf{Y} = \mathbf{AX}$.

(a) Find the matrix $\mathbf{A}$ so that the components of $\mathbf{Y}$ are independent random variables.

(b) Let $\mathbf{X}_i$ and $\mathbf{X}_{i+1}$ be two consecutive blocks and let $\mathbf{Y}_i$ and $\mathbf{Y}_{i+1}$ be the corresponding transformed variables. Are the components of $\mathbf{Y}_i$ and $\mathbf{Y}_{i+1}$ independent?

**6.92.** A multiplexer combines $N$ digital television signals into a common communications line. TV signal $n$ generates $X_n$ bits every 33 milliseconds, where $X_n$ is a Gaussian random variable with mean $m$ and variance $\sigma^2$. Suppose that the multiplexer accepts a maximum total of $T$ bits from the combined sources every 33 ms, and that any bits in excess of $T$ are discarded. Assume that the $N$ signals are independent.

(a) Find the probability that bits are discarded in a given 33-ms period, if we let $T = m_a + t\sigma$, where $m_a$ is the mean total bits generated by the combined sources, and $\sigma$ is the standard deviation of the total number of bits produced by the combined sources.

(b) Find the average number of bits discarded per period.

(c) Find the long-term fraction of bits lost by the multiplexer.

(d) Find the average number of bits per source allocated in part a, and find the average number of bits lost per source. What happens as $N$ becomes large?

(e) Suppose we require that $t$ be adjusted with $N$ so that the fraction of bits lost per source is kept constant. Find an equation whose solution yields the desired value of $t$.

(f) Do the above results change if the signals have pairwise covariance $\rho$?

**6.93.** Consider the estimation of $T$ given $N_1$ and arrivals in Problem 6.17.

(a) Find the ML and MAP estimators for $T$.

(b) Find the linear mean square estimator for $T$.

(c) Repeat parts a and b if $N_1$ and $N_2$ are given.

# Sums of Random Variables and Long-Term Averages

Many problems involve the counting of the number of occurrences of events, the measurement of cumulative effects, or the computation of arithmetic averages in a series of measurements. Usually these problems can be reduced to the problem of finding, exactly or approximately, the distribution of a random variable that consists of the sum of $n$ independent, identically distributed random variables. In this chapter, we investigate sums of random variables and their properties as $n$ becomes large.

In Section 7.1, we show how the characteristic function is used to compute the pdf of the sum of independent random variables. In Section 7.2, we discuss the sample mean estimator for the expected value of a random variable and the relative frequency estimator for the probability of an event. We introduce measures for assessing the goodness of these estimators. We then discuss the laws of large numbers, which are theorems that state that the sample mean and relative frequency estimators converge to the corresponding expected values and probabilities as the number of samples is increased. These theoretical results demonstrate the remarkable consistency between probability theory and observed behavior, and they reinforce the relative frequency interpretation of probability.

In Section 7.3, we present the central limit theorem, which states that, under very general conditions, the cdf of a sum of random variables approaches that of a Gaussian random variable even though the cdf of the individual random variables may be far from Gaussian. This result enables us to approximate the pdf of sums of random variables by the pdf of a Gaussian random variable. The result also explains why the Gaussian random variable appears in so many diverse applications.

In Section 7.4 we consider sequences of random variables and their convergence properties. In Section 7.5 we discuss random experiments in which events occur at random times. In these experiments we are interested in the average rate at which events occur as well as the rate at which quantities associated with the events grow. Finally, Section 7.6 introduces computer methods based on the discrete Fourier transform that prove very useful in the numerical calculation of pmf's and pdf's from their transforms.

## 7.1    SUMS OF RANDOM VARIABLES

Let $X_1, X_2, \ldots, X_n$ be a sequence of random variables, and let $S_n$ be their sum:

$$S_n = X_1 + X_2 + \cdots + X_n. \tag{7.1}$$

In this section, we find the mean and variance of $S_n$, as well as the pdf of $S_n$ in the important special case where the $X_j$'s are independent random variables.

### 7.1.1    Mean and Variance of Sums of Random Variables

In Section 6.3, it was shown that *regardless of statistical dependence, the expected value of a sum of n random variables is equal to the sum of the expected values:*

$$E[X_1 + X_2 + \cdots + X_n] = E[X_1] + \cdots + E[X_n]. \tag{7.2}$$

Thus knowledge of the means of the $X_j$'s suffices to find the mean of $S_n$.

The following example shows that in order to compute the variance of a sum of random variables, we need to know the variances and covariances of the $X_j$'s.

---

### Example 7.1

Find the variance of $Z = X + Y$.

From Eq. (7.2), $E[Z] = E[X + Y] = E[X] + E[Y]$. The variance of $Z$ is therefore

$$\begin{aligned}
\text{VAR}(Z) &= E[(Z - E[Z])^2] = E[(X + Y - E[X] - E[Y])^2] \\
&= E[\{(X - E[X]) + (Y - E[Y])\}^2] \\
&= E[(X - E[X])^2 + (Y - E[Y])^2 + (X - E[X])(Y - E[Y]) \\
&\quad + (Y - E[Y])(X - E[X])] \\
&= \text{VAR}[X] + \text{VAR}[Y] + \text{COV}(X, Y) + \text{COV}(Y, X) \\
&= \text{VAR}[X] + \text{VAR}[Y] + 2\,\text{COV}(X, Y).
\end{aligned}$$

In general, the covariance $\text{COV}(X, Y)$ is not equal to zero, so the variance of a sum is not necessarily equal to the sum of the individual variances.

---

The result in Example 7.1 can be generalized to the case of $n$ random variables:

$$\begin{aligned}
\text{VAR}(X_1 + X_2 + \cdots + X_n) &= E\left\{\sum_{j=1}^{n}(X_j - E[X_j])\sum_{k=1}^{n}(X_k - E[X_k])\right\} \\
&= \sum_{j=1}^{n}\sum_{k=1}^{n}E[(X_j - E[X_j])(X_k - E[X_k])] \\
&= \sum_{k=1}^{n}\text{VAR}(X_k) + \sum_{\substack{j=1\,k=1 \\ j \neq k}}^{n}\sum \text{COV}(X_j, X_k). \tag{7.3}
\end{aligned}$$

Thus *in general, the variance of a sum of random variables is not equal to the sum of the individual variances.*

An important special case is when the $X_j$'s are independent random variables. *If $X_1, X_2, \ldots, X_n$ are independent random variables*, then $\text{COV}(X_j, X_k) = 0$ for $j \neq k$ and

$$\text{VAR}(X_1 + X_2 + \cdots + X_n) = \text{VAR}(X_1) + \cdots + \text{VAR}(X_n). \qquad (7.4)$$

---

**Example 7.2    Sum of iid Random Variables**

Find the mean and variance of the sum of $n$ **independent, identically distributed** (iid) random variables, each with mean $\mu$ and variance $\sigma^2$.

The mean of $S_n$ is obtained from Eq. (7.2):

$$E[S_n] = E[X_1] + \cdots + E[X_n] = n\mu.$$

The covariance of pairs of independent random variables is zero, so by Eq. (7.4),

$$\text{VAR}[S_n] = n \, \text{VAR}[X_j] = n\sigma^2,$$

since $\text{VAR}[X_j] = \sigma^2$ for $j = 1, \ldots, n$.

---

### 7.1.2    pdf of Sums of Independent Random Variables

Let $X_1, X_2, \ldots, X_n$ be $n$ *independent* random variables. In this section we show how transform methods can be used to find the pdf of $S_n = X_1 + X_2 + \cdots + X_n$.

First, consider the $n = 2$ case, $Z = X + Y$, where $X$ and $Y$ are independent random variables. The characteristic function of $Z$ is given by

$$
\begin{aligned}
\Phi_Z(\omega) &= E[e^{j\omega Z}] \\
&= E[e^{j\omega(X+Y)}] \\
&= E[e^{j\omega X} e^{j\omega Y}] \\
&= E[e^{j\omega X}] E[e^{j\omega Y}] \\
&= \Phi_X(\omega) \Phi_Y(\omega), \qquad (7.5)
\end{aligned}
$$

where the fourth equality follows from the fact that functions of independent random variables (i.e., $e^{j\omega X}$ and $e^{j\omega Y}$) are also independent random variables, as discussed in Example 5.25. Thus the characteristic function of $Z$ is the product of the individual characteristic functions of $X$ and $Y$.

In Example 5.39, we saw that the pdf of $Z = X + Y$ is given by the convolution of the pdf's of $X$ and $Y$:

$$f_Z(z) = f_X(x) * f_Y(y). \qquad (7.6)$$

Recall that $\Phi_Z(\omega)$ can also be viewed as the Fourier transform of the pdf of $Z$:

$$\Phi_Z(\omega) = \mathscr{F}\{f_Z(z)\}.$$

By equating the transform of Eq. (7.6) to Eq. (7.5) we obtain

$$\Phi_Z(\omega) = \mathscr{F}\{f_Z(z)\} = \mathscr{F}\{f_X(x) * f_Y(y)\} = \Phi_X(\omega) \Phi_Y(\omega). \qquad (7.7)$$

Equation (7.7) states the well-known result that the Fourier transform of a convolution of two functions is equal to the product of the individual Fourier transforms.

Now consider the sum of $n$ independent random variables:

$$S_n = X_1 + X_2 + \cdots + X_n.$$

The characteristic function of $S_n$ is

$$
\begin{aligned}
\Phi_{S_n}(\omega) &= E[e^{j\omega S_n}] = E[e^{j\omega(X_1+X_2+\cdots+X_n)}] \\
&= E[e^{j\omega X_1}] \ldots E[e^{j\omega X_n}] \\
&= \Phi_{X_1}(\omega) \ldots \Phi_{X_n}(\omega).
\end{aligned}
\tag{7.8}
$$

Thus the pdf of $S_n$ can then be found by finding the inverse Fourier transform of the product of the individual characteristic functions of the $X_j$'s.

$$f_{S_n}(X) = \mathscr{F}^{-1}\{\Phi_{X_1}(\omega) \ldots \Phi_{X_n}(\omega)\}. \tag{7.9}$$

---

**Example 7.3    Sum of Independent Gaussian Random Variables**

Let $S_n$ be the sum of $n$ independent Gaussian random variables with respective means and variances, $m_1, \ldots, m_n$ and $\sigma_1^2, \ldots, \sigma_n^2$. Find the pdf of $S_n$.

The characteristic function of $X_k$ is

$$\Phi_{X_k}(\omega) = e^{+j\omega m_k - \omega^2 \sigma_k^2/2}$$

so by Eq. (7.8),

$$
\begin{aligned}
\Phi_{S_n}(\omega) &= \prod_{k=1}^{n} e^{+j\omega m_k - \omega^2 \sigma_k^2/2} \\
&= \exp\{+j\omega(m_1 + \cdots + m_n) - \omega^2(\sigma_1^2 + \cdots + \sigma_n^2)/2\}
\end{aligned}
$$

This is the characteristic function of a Gaussian random variable. Thus $S_n$ is a Gaussian random variable with mean $m_1 + \cdots + m_n$ and variance $\sigma_1^2 + \cdots + \sigma_n^2$.

---

**Example 7.4    Sum of iid Random Variables**

Find the pdf of a sum of $n$ independent, identically distributed random variables with characteristic functions

$$\Phi_{X_k}(\omega) = \Phi_X(\omega) \qquad \text{for } k = 1, \ldots, n.$$

Equation (7.8) immediately implies that the characteristic function of $S_n$ is

$$\Phi_{S_n}(\omega) = \{\Phi_X(\omega)\}^n. \tag{7.10}$$

The pdf of $S_n$ is found by taking the inverse transform of this expression.

---

**Example 7.5    Sum of iid Exponential Random Variables**

Find the pdf of a sum of $n$ independent exponentially distributed random variables, all with parameter $\alpha$.

The characteristic function of a single exponential random variable is

$$\Phi_X(\omega) = \frac{\alpha}{\alpha - j\omega}.$$

From the previous example we then have that

$$\Phi_{S_n}(\omega) = \left\{ \frac{\alpha}{\alpha - j\omega} \right\}^n.$$

From Table 4.1, we see that $S_n$ is an $m$-Erlang random variable.

When dealing with integer-valued random variables it is usually preferable to work with the probability generating function

$$G_N(z) = E[z^N].$$

The generating function for a sum of independent discrete random variables, $N = X_1 + \cdots + X_n$, is

$$G_N(z) = E[z^{X_1 + \cdots + X_n}] = E[z^{X_1}] \ldots E[z^{X_n}]$$
$$= G_{X_1}(z) \ldots G_{X_n}(z). \tag{7.11}$$

**Example 7.6**

Find the generating function for a sum of $n$ independent, identically geometrically distributed random variables.

The generating function for a single geometric random variable is given by

$$G_X(z) = \frac{pz}{1 - qz}.$$

Therefore the generating function for a sum of $n$ such independent random variables is

$$G_N(z) = \left\{ \frac{pz}{1 - qz} \right\}^n.$$

From Table 3.1, we see that this is the generating function of a negative binomial random variable with parameters $p$ and $n$.

## *7.1.3    Sum of a Random Number of Random Variables

In some problems we are interested in the sum of a random number $N$ of iid random variables:

$$S_N = \sum_{k=1}^{N} X_k, \tag{7.12}$$

where $N$ is assumed to be a random variable that is independent of the $X_k$'s. For example, $N$ might be the number of computer jobs submitted in an hour and $X_k$ might be the time required to execute the $k$th job.

The mean of $S_N$ is found readily by using conditional expectation:

$$E[S_N] = E[E[S_N|N]].$$
$$= E[NE[X]]$$
$$= E[N]E[X]. \tag{7.13}$$

The second equality follows from the fact that

$$E[S_N|N = n] = E\left[\sum_{k=1}^{n} X_k\right] = nE[X],$$

so $E[S_N|N] = NE[X]$.

The characteristic function of $S_n$ can also be found by using conditional expectation. From Eq. (7.10), we have that

$$E[e^{j\omega S_N}|N = n] = E[e^{j\omega(X_1 + \cdots + X_n)}] = \Phi_X(\omega)^n,$$

so

$$E[e^{j\omega S_N}|N] = \Phi_X(\omega)^N.$$

Therefore

$$\Phi_{S_N}(\omega) = E[E[e^{j\omega S_N}|N]]$$
$$= E[\Phi_X(\omega)^N]$$
$$= E[z^N]|_{z=\Phi_X(\omega)}$$
$$= G_N(\Phi_X(\omega)). \tag{7.14}$$

That is, the characteristic function of $S_N$ is found by evaluating the generating function of $N$ at $z = \Phi_X(\omega)$.

---

### Example 7.7

The number of jobs $N$ submitted to a computer in an hour is a geometric random variable with parameter $p$, and the job execution times are independent exponentially distributed random variables with mean $1/\alpha$. Find the pdf for the sum of the execution times of the jobs submitted in an hour.

The generating function for $N$ is

$$G_N(z) = \frac{p}{1 - qz},$$

and the characteristic function for an exponentially distributed random variable is

$$\Phi_X(\omega) = \frac{\alpha}{\alpha - j\omega}.$$

From Eq. (7.14), the characteristic function of $S_N$ is

$$\Phi_{S_N}(\omega) = \frac{p}{1 - q[\alpha/(\alpha - j\omega)]}$$

$$= p(\alpha - j\omega)/(p\alpha - j\omega)$$

$$= p + (1 - p)\frac{p\alpha}{p\alpha - j\omega}.$$

The pdf of $S_N$ is found by taking the inverse transform of the above expression:

$$f_{S_N}(x) = p\,\delta(x) + (1 - p)p\alpha e^{-p\alpha x} \qquad x \geq 0.$$

The pdf has a direct interpretation: With probability $p$ there are no job arrivals and hence the total execution time is zero; with probability $(1 - p)$ there are one or more arrivals, and the total execution time is an exponential random variable with mean $1/p\alpha$.

## 7.2    THE SAMPLE MEAN AND THE LAWS OF LARGE NUMBERS

Let $X$ be a random variable for which the mean, $E[X] = \mu$, is unknown. Let $X_1, \ldots, X_n$ denote $n$ independent, repeated measurements of $X$; that is, the $X_j$'s are **independent, identically distributed** (iid) random variables with the same pdf as $X$. The **sample mean** of the sequence is used to estimate $E[X]$:

$$M_n = \frac{1}{n}\sum_{j=1}^{n} X_j. \tag{7.15}$$

In this section, we compute the expected value and variance of $M_n$ in order to assess the effectiveness of $M_n$ as an estimator for $E[X]$. We also investigate the behavior of $M_n$ as $n$ becomes large.

The following example shows that the relative frequency estimator for the probability of an event is a special case of a sample mean. Thus the results derived below for the sample mean are also applicable to the relative frequency estimator.

## Example 7.8    Relative Frequency

Consider a sequence of independent repetitions of some random experiment, and let the random variable $I_j$ be the indicator function for the occurrence of event $A$ in the $j$th trial. The total number of occurrences of $A$ in the first $n$ trials is then

$$N_n = I_1 + I_2 + \cdots + I_n.$$

The **relative frequency** of event $A$ in the first $n$ repetitions of the experiment is then

$$f_A(n) = \frac{1}{n}\sum_{j=1}^{n} I_j. \tag{7.16}$$

Thus the relative frequency $f_A(n)$ is simply the sample mean of the random variables $I_j$.

---

The sample mean is itself a random variable, so it will exhibit random variation. A good estimator should have the following two properties: (1) On the average, it should give the correct value of the parameter being estimated, that is, $E[M_n] = \mu$; and (2) It should not vary too much about the correct value of this parameter, that is, $E[(M_n - \mu)^2]$ is small.

The expected value of the sample mean is given by

$$E[M_n] = E\left[\frac{1}{n}\sum_{j=1}^{n} X_j\right] = \frac{1}{n}\sum_{j=1}^{n} E[X_j] = \mu, \tag{7.17}$$

since $E[X_j] = E[X] = \mu$ for all $j$. Thus the sample mean is equal to $E[X] = \mu$, on the average. For this reason, we say that the sample mean is an **unbiased estimator** for $\mu$.

Equation (7.17) implies that the mean square error of the sample mean about $\mu$ is equal to the variance of $M_n$, that is,

$$E[(M_n - \mu)^2] = E[(M_n - E[M_n])^2].$$

Note that $M_n = S_n/n$, where $S_n = X_1 + X_2 + \cdots + X_n$. From Eq. (7.4), $\text{VAR}[S_n] = n\,\text{VAR}[X_j] = n\sigma^2$, since the $X_j$'s are iid random variables. Thus

$$\text{VAR}[M_n] = \frac{1}{n^2}\text{VAR}[S_n] = \frac{n\sigma^2}{n^2} = \frac{\sigma^2}{n}. \tag{7.18}$$

Equation (7.18) states that the variance of the sample mean approaches zero as the number of samples is increased. This implies that the probability that the sample mean is close to the true mean approaches one as $n$ becomes very large. We can formalize this statement by using the Chebyshev inequality, Eq. (4.76):

$$P[|M_n - E[M_n]| \geq \varepsilon] \leq \frac{\text{VAR}[M_n]}{\varepsilon^2}.$$

Substituting for $E[M_n]$ and $\text{VAR}[M_n]$, we obtain

$$P[|M_n - \mu| \geq \varepsilon] \leq \frac{\sigma^2}{n\varepsilon^2}. \tag{7.19}$$

If we consider the complement of the event considered in Eq. (7.19), we obtain

$$P[|M_n - \mu| < \varepsilon] \geq 1 - \frac{\sigma^2}{n\varepsilon^2}. \tag{7.20}$$

Thus for any choice of error $\varepsilon$ and probability $1 - \delta$, we can select the number of samples $n$ so that $M_n$ is within $\varepsilon$ of the true mean with probability $1 - \delta$ or greater. The following example illustrates this.

## Example 7.9

A voltage of constant, but unknown, value is to be measured. Each measurement $X_j$ is actually the sum of the desired voltage $v$ and a noise voltage $N_j$ of zero mean and standard deviation of 1 microvolt ($\mu V$):

$$X_j = v + N_j.$$

Assume that the noise voltages are independent random variables. How many measurements are required so that the probability that $M_n$ is within $\varepsilon = 1\ \mu V$ of the true mean is at least .99?

Each measurement $X_j$ has mean $v$ and variance 1, so from Eq. (7.20) we require that $n$ satisfy

$$1 - \frac{\sigma^2}{n\varepsilon^2} = 1 - \frac{1}{n} = .99.$$

This implies that $n = 100$.

Thus if we were to repeat the measurement 100 times and compute the sample mean, on the average, at least 99 times out of 100, the resulting sample mean will be within $1\ \mu V$ of the true mean.

---

Note that if we let $n$ approach infinity in Eq. (5.20) we obtain

$$\lim_{n \to \infty} P[|M_n - \mu| < \varepsilon] = 1.$$

Equation (7.20) requires that the $X_j$'s have finite variance. It can be shown that this limit holds even if the variance of the $X_j$'s does not exist [Gnedenko, p. 203]. We state this more general result:

> **Weak Law of Large Numbers**    Let $X_1, X_2, \ldots$ be a sequence of iid random variables with finite mean $E[X] = \mu$, then for $\varepsilon > 0$,
>
> $$\lim_{n \to \infty} P[|M_n - \mu| < \varepsilon] = 1. \tag{7.21}$$

The weak law of large numbers states that for a large enough *fixed* value of $n$, the sample mean using $n$ samples will be close to the true mean with high probability. The weak law of large numbers does not address the question about what happens to the sample mean as a function of $n$ as we make additional measurements. This question is taken up by the strong law of large numbers, which we discuss next.

Suppose we make a series of independent measurements of the same random variable. Let $X_1, X_2, \ldots$ be the resulting sequence of iid random variables with mean $\mu$. Now consider the *sequence of sample means* that results from the above measurements: $M_1, M_2, \ldots$, where $M_j$ is the sample mean computed using $X_1$ through $X_j$. The notion of statistical regularity discussed in Chapter 1 leads us to expect that this sequence of sample means converges to $\mu$, that is, we expect that with high probability, *each particular sequence of sample means approaches $\mu$ and stays there*, as shown in

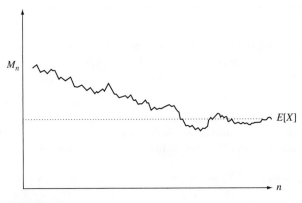

**FIGURE 7.1**
Convergence of sequence of sample means to $E[X]$.

Fig. 7.1. In terms of probabilities, we expect the following:

$$P[\lim_{n \to \infty} M_n = \mu] = 1;$$

that is, with virtual certainty, every sequence of sample mean calculations converges to the true mean of the quantity. The proof of this result is well beyond the level of this course (see [Gnedenko, p. 216]), but we will have the opportunity in later sections to apply the result in various situations.

> **Strong Law of Large Numbers**    Let $X_1, X_2, \ldots$ be a sequence of iid random variables with finite mean $E[X] = \mu$ and finite variance, then
>
> $$P[\lim_{n \to \infty} M_n = \mu] = 1. \tag{7.22}$$

Equation (7.22) appears similar to Eq. (7.21), but in fact it makes a dramatically different statement. It states that *with probability 1, every sequence of sample mean calculations will eventually approach and stay close to $E[X] = \mu$.* This is the type of convergence we expect in physical situations where statistical regularity holds.

With the strong law of large numbers we come full circle in the modeling process. We began in Chapter 1 by noting that statistical regularity is observed in many physical phenomena, and from this we deduced a number of properties of relative frequency. These properties were used to formulate a set of axioms from which we developed a mathematical theory of probability. We have now come full circle and shown that, under certain conditions, the *theory* predicts the convergence of sample means to expected values. There are still gaps between the mathematical theory and the real world (i.e., we can never actually carry out an infinite number of measurements and compute an infinite number of sample means). Nevertheless, the strong law of large numbers demonstrates the remarkable consistency between the theory and the observed physical behavior.

We already indicated that relative frequencies are special cases of sample averages. If we apply the weak law of large numbers to the relative frequency of an event $A$, $f_A(n)$, in a sequence of independent repetitions of a random experiment, we obtain

$$\lim_{n \to \infty} P[|f_A(n) - P[A]| < \varepsilon] = 1. \tag{7.23}$$

If we apply the strong law of large numbers, we obtain

$$P[\lim_{n \to \infty} f_A(n) = P[A]] = 1. \tag{7.24}$$

---

**Example 7.10**

In order to estimate the probability of an event $A$, a sequence of Bernoulli trials is carried out and the relative frequency of $A$ is observed. How large should $n$ be in order to have a .95 probability that the relative frequency is within 0.01 of $p = P[A]$?

Let $X = I_A$ be the indicator function of $A$. From Table 3.1 we have that the mean of $I_A$ is $\mu = p$ and the variance is $\sigma^2 = p(1 - p)$. Since $p$ is unknown, $\sigma^2$ is also unknown. However, it is easy to show that $p(1 - p)$ is at most 1/4 for $0 \le p \le 1$. Therefore, by Eq. (7.19),

$$P[|f_A(n) - p| \ge \varepsilon] \le \frac{\sigma^2}{n\varepsilon^2} \le \frac{1}{4n\varepsilon^2}.$$

The desired accuracy is $\varepsilon = 0.01$ and the desired probability is

$$1 - .95 = \frac{1}{4n\varepsilon^2}.$$

We then solve for $n$ and obtain $n = 50,000$. It has already been pointed out that the Chebyshev inequality gives very loose bounds, so we expect that this value for $n$ is probably overly conservative. In the next section, we present a better estimate for the required value of $n$.

---

**7.3    THE CENTRAL LIMIT THEOREM**

Let $X_1, X_2, \ldots$ be a sequence of iid random variables with finite mean $\mu$ and finite variance $\sigma^2$, and let $S_n$ be the sum of the first $n$ random variables in the sequence:

$$S_n = X_1 + X_2 + \cdots + X_n. \tag{7.25}$$

In Section 7.1, we developed methods for determining the exact pdf of $S_n$. We now present the central limit theorem, which states that, as $n$ becomes large, the cdf of a properly normalized $S_n$ approaches that of a Gaussian random variable. This enables us to approximate the cdf of $S_n$ with that of a Gaussian random variable.

The central limit theorem explains why the Gaussian random variable appears in so many diverse applications. In nature, many macroscopic phenomena result from the addition of numerous independent, microscopic processes; this gives rise to the Gaussian random variable. In many man-made problems, we are interested in averages that often consist of the sum of independent random variables. This again gives rise to the Gaussian random variable.

From Example 7.2, we know that if the $X_j$'s are iid, then $S_n$ has mean $n\mu$ and variance $n\sigma^2$. The central limit theorem states that the cdf of a suitably normalized version of $S_n$ approaches that of a Gaussian random variable.

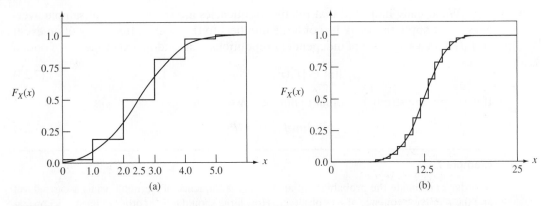

**FIGURE 7.2**
(a) The cdf of the sum of five independent Bernoulli random variables with $p = 1/2$ and the cdf of a Gaussian random variable of the same mean and variance. (b) The cdf of the sum of 25 independent Bernoulli random variables with $p = 1/2$ and the cdf of a Gaussian random variable of the same mean and variance.

**Central Limit Theorem** Let $S_n$ be the sum of $n$ iid random variables with finite mean $E[X] = \mu$ and finite variance $\sigma^2$, and let $Z_n$ be the zero-mean, unit-variance random variable defined by

$$Z_n = \frac{S_n - n\mu}{\sigma\sqrt{n}}, \tag{7.26a}$$

then

$$\lim_{n \to \infty} P[Z_n \leq z] = \frac{1}{\sqrt{2\pi}} \int_{-\infty}^{z} e^{-x^2/2} \, dx. \tag{7.26b}$$

Note that $Z_n$ is sometimes written in terms of the sample mean:

$$Z_n = \sqrt{n} \frac{M_n - \mu}{\sigma}. \tag{7.27}$$

The amazing part about the central limit theorem is that the summands $X_j$ can have *any* distribution as long as they have a finite mean and finite variance. This gives the result its wide applicability.

Figures 7.2 through 7.4 compare the exact cdf and the Gaussian approximation for the sums of Bernoulli, uniform, and exponential random variables, respectively. In all three cases, it can be seen that the approximation improves as the number of terms in the sum increases. The proof of the central limit theorem is discussed in the last part of this section.

---

**Example 7.11**

Suppose that orders at a restaurant are iid random variables with mean $\mu = \$8$ and standard deviation $\sigma = \$2$. Estimate the probability that the first 100 customers spend a total of more than \$840. Estimate the probability that the first 100 customers spend a total of between \$780 and \$820.

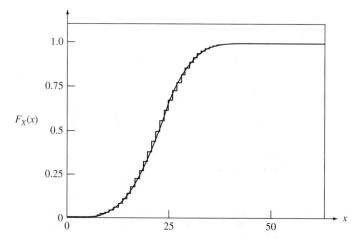

**FIGURE 7.3**
The cdf of the sum of five independent discrete, uniform random variables from the set $\{0, 1, \ldots, 9\}$ and the cdf of a Gaussian random variable of the same mean and variance .

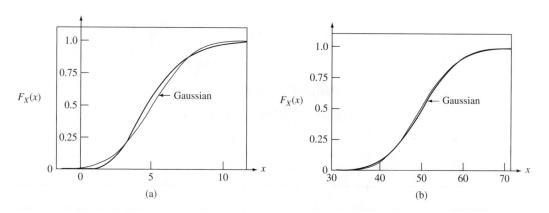

**FIGURE 7.4**
(a) The cdf of the sum of five independent exponential random variables of mean 1 and the cdf of a Gaussian random variable of the same mean and variance. (b) The cdf of the sum of 50 independent exponential random variables of mean 1 and the cdf of a Gaussian random variable of the same mean and variance.

Let $X_k$ denote the expenditure of the $k$th customer, then the total spent by the first 100 customers is

$$S_{100} = X_1 + X_2 + \cdots + X_{100}.$$

The mean of $S_{100}$ is $n\mu = 800$ and the variance is $n\sigma^2 = 400$. Figure 7.5 shows the pdf of $S_{100}$ where it can be seen that the pdf is highly concentrated about the mean. The normalized form of $S_{100}$ is

$$Z_{100} = \frac{S_{100} - 800}{20}.$$

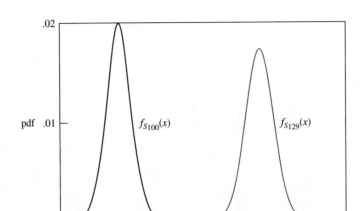

**FIGURE 7.5**
Gaussian pdf approximations $S_{100}$ and $S_{129}$ in Examples 7.11 and 7.12.

Thus

$$P[S_{100} > 840] = P\left[Z_{100} > \frac{840 - 800}{20}\right]$$
$$\simeq Q(2) = 2.28(10^{-2}),$$

where we used Table 4.2 to evaluate $Q(2)$. Similarly,

$$P[780 \le S_{100} \le 820] = P[-1 \le Z_{100} \le 1]$$
$$\simeq 1 - 2Q(1)$$
$$= .682.$$

**Example 7.12**

In Example 7.11, after how many orders can we be 90% sure that the total spent by all customers is more than $1000?

The problem here is to find the value of $n$ for which

$$P[S_n > 1000] = .90.$$

$S_n$ has mean $8n$ and variance $4n$. Proceeding as in the previous example, we have

$$P[S_n > 1000] = P\left[Z_n > \frac{1000 - 8n}{2\sqrt{n}}\right] = .90.$$

Using the fact that $Q(-x) = 1 - Q(x)$, Table 4.3 implies that $n$ must satisfy

$$\frac{1000 - 8n}{2\sqrt{n}} = -1.2815,$$

which yields the following quadratic equation for $\sqrt{n}$:

$$8n - 1.2815(2)\sqrt{n} - 1000 = 0.$$

The positive root of the equation yields $\sqrt{n} = 11.34$, or $n = 128.6$. Figure 7.5 shows the pdf for $S_{129}$.

---

### Example 7.13

The time between events in a certain random experiment is iid exponential random variables with mean $m$ seconds. Find the probability that the 1000th event occurs in the time interval $(1000 \pm 50)m$.

Let $X_j$ be the time between events and let $S_n$ be the time of the $n$th event, then $S_n$ is given by Eq. (7.25). From Table 4.1, the mean and variance of $X_j$ is given by $E[X_j] = m$ and $\mathrm{VAR}[X_j] = m^2$. The mean and variance of $S_n$ are then $E[S_n] = nE[X_j] = nm$ and $\mathrm{VAR}[S_n] = n\,\mathrm{VAR}[X_j] = nm^2$. The central limit theorem then gives

$$P[950m \leq S_{1000} \leq 1050m] = P\left[\frac{950m - 1000m}{m\sqrt{1000}} \leq Z_n \leq \frac{1050m - 1000m}{m\sqrt{1000}}\right]$$

$$\simeq Q(1.58) - Q(-1.58)$$

$$= 1 - 2Q(1.58)$$

$$= 1 - 2(0.0567) = .8866.$$

Thus as $n$ becomes large, $S_n$ is very likely to be close to its mean $nm$. We can therefore conjecture that the long-term average rate at which events occur is

$$\frac{n\text{ events}}{S_n\text{ seconds}} = \frac{n}{nm} = \frac{1}{m}\text{ events/second.} \tag{7.28}$$

The calculation of event occurrence rates and related averages is discussed in Section 7.5.

---

### 7.3.1    Gaussian Approximation for Binomial Probabilities

We found in Chapter 2 that the binomial random variable becomes difficult to compute directly for large $n$ because of the need to calculate factorial terms. A particularly important application of the central limit theorem is in the approximation of binomial probabilities. Since the binomial random variable is a sum of iid Bernoulli random variables (which have finite mean and variance), its cdf approaches that of a Gaussian random variable. Let $X$ be a binomial random variable with mean $np$ and variance $np(1 - p)$, and let $Y$ be a Gaussian random variable with the same mean and variance, then by the central limit theorem for $n$ large the probability that $X = k$ is approximately equal to the integral of the Gaussian pdf in an interval of unit length about $k$, as shown in Fig. 7.6:

$$P[X = k] \simeq P\left[k - \frac{1}{2} < Y < k + \frac{1}{2}\right]$$

$$= \frac{1}{\sqrt{2\pi np(1 - p)}} \int_{k-1/2}^{k+1/2} e^{-(x-np)^2/2np(1-p)}\, dx. \tag{7.29}$$

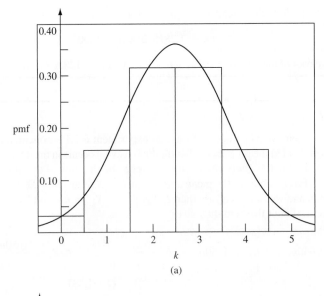

(a)

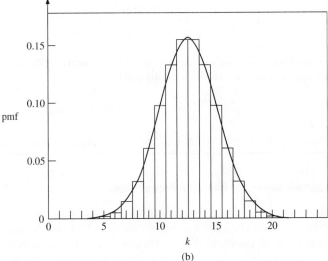

(b)

**FIGURE 7.6**
(a) Gaussian approximation for binomial probabilities with $n = 5$ and $p = 1/2$.
(b) Gaussian approximation for binomial with $n = 25$ and $p = 1/2$.

The above approximation can be simplified by approximating the integral by the product of the integrand at the center of the interval of integration (that is, $x = k$) and the length of the interval of integration (one):

$$P[X = k] \simeq \frac{1}{\sqrt{2\pi np(1 - p)}} e^{-(k-np)^2/2np(1-p)}. \tag{7.30}$$

Figures 7.6(a) and 7.6(b) compare the binomial probabilities and the Gaussian approximation using Eq. (7.30).

---

**Example 7.14**

In Example 7.10 in Section 7.2, we used the Chebyshev inequality to estimate the number of samples required for there to be a .95 probability that the relative frequency estimate for the probability of an event $A$ would be within 0.01 of $P[A]$. We now estimate the required number of samples using the Gaussian approximation for the binomial distribution.

Let $f_A(n)$ be the relative frequency of $A$ in $n$ Bernoulli trials. Since $f_A(n)$ has mean $p$ and variance $p(1 - p)/n$, then

$$Z_n = \frac{f_A(n) - p}{\sqrt{p(1 - p)/n}}$$

has zero mean and unit variance, and is approximately Gaussian for $n$ sufficiently large. The probability of interest is

$$P[|f_A(n) - p| < \varepsilon] \simeq P\left[|Z_n| < \frac{\varepsilon\sqrt{n}}{\sqrt{p(1 - p)}}\right] = 1 - 2Q\left(\frac{\varepsilon\sqrt{n}}{\sqrt{p(1 - p)}}\right).$$

The above probability cannot be computed because $p$ is unknown. However, it can be easily shown that $p(1 - p) \leq 1/4$ for $p$ in the unit interval. It then follows that for such $p$, $\sqrt{p(1 - p)} \leq 1/2$, and since $Q(x)$ decreases with increasing argument

$$P[|f_A(n) - p| < \varepsilon] > 1 - 2Q(2\varepsilon\sqrt{n}).$$

We want the above probability to equal .95. This implies that $Q(2\varepsilon\sqrt{n}) = (1 - .95)/2 = .025$. From Table 4.2, we see that the argument of $Q(x)$ should be approximately 1.95, thus

$$2\varepsilon\sqrt{n} = 1.95.$$

Solving for $n$, we obtain

$$n = (.98)^2/\varepsilon^2 = 9506.$$

---

**7.3.2    Chernoff Bound for Binomial Random Variable**

The Gaussian pdf extends over the entire real line. When taking the sum of random variables that have a finite range, such as the binomial random variable, the central limit theorem can be inaccurate at the extreme values of the sum. The Chernoff bound introduced in Chapter 3 gives better estimates.

The Chernoff bound for the binomial is given by:

$$P[X \geq a] \leq e^{-sa}E[e^{sX}] = e^{-sa}E[(e^s)^X] = e^{-sa}G_N(e^s) = e^{-sa}(q + pe^s)^n$$

where $s > 0$, and $G_N(z)$ is the pgf for the binomial random variable. To minimize the bound we take the derivative with respect to $s$ and set it to zero:

$$0 = \frac{d}{ds}e^{-sa}G_N(e^s) = -ae^{-sa}(q + pe^s)^n + e^{-sa}e^s np(q + pe^s)^{n-1}$$

$$a(q + pe^s) = e^s np$$

where the second line results after canceling common terms. The optimum $s$ and the associated bound are:

$$e^s = \frac{aq}{p(n-a)}$$

$$P[X \geq a] \leq \left(\frac{p(n-a)}{aq}\right)^a \left(q + p\frac{aq}{p(n-a)}\right)^n = \left(\frac{p(n-a)}{aq}\right)^a \left(\frac{qn}{(n-a)}\right)^n$$

$$= \left(\frac{p(1-a/n)}{(a/n)q}\right)^a \left(\frac{q}{1-a/n}\right)^n = \left(\frac{p^{a/n}q^{1-a/n}}{(a/n)^{\frac{a}{n}}(1-a/n)^{1-a/n}}\right)^n.$$

---

### Example 7.15

Compare the central limit estimate for $P[X > x]$ with the Chernoff bound for the binomial random variable with $n = 100$ and $p = 0.5$.

The central limit gives the estimate:

$$P[X \geq a] \approx Q\left(\frac{x-np}{\sqrt{npq}}\right) = Q\left(\frac{x-50}{5}\right).$$

The Chernoff bound is:

$$P[X \geq a] \leq \left(\frac{1/2}{(x/100)^{\frac{x}{100}}(1-x/100)^{1-x/100}}\right)^{100}.$$

Figure 7.7 shows a comparison of the exact values of the tail distribution with the Chernoff bound and the estimate from the central limit theorem. The central limit theorem estimate is

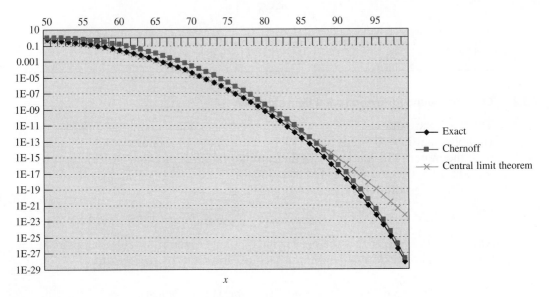

**FIGURE 7.7**
Comparison of Chernoff bound and central limit theorem.

more accurate than the Chernoff bounds up to about $x = 86$. At the extreme values of $x$, the Chernoff bound remains accurate while the central limit estimate loses its accuracy.

### *7.3.3    Proof of the Central Limit Theorem

We now sketch a proof of the central limit theorem. First note that

$$Z_n = \frac{S_n - n\mu}{\sigma\sqrt{n}} = \frac{1}{\sigma\sqrt{n}}\sum_{k=1}^{n}(X_k - \mu).$$

The characteristic function of $Z_n$ is given by

$$\begin{aligned}
\Phi_{Z_n}(\omega) &= E[e^{j\omega Z_n}] \\
&= E\left[\exp\left\{\frac{j\omega}{\sigma\sqrt{n}}\sum_{k=1}^{n}(X_k - \mu)\right\}\right] \\
&= E\left[\prod_{k=1}^{n}e^{j\omega(X_k-\mu)/\sigma\sqrt{n}}\right] \\
&= \prod_{k=1}^{n}E[e^{j\omega(X_k-\mu)/\sigma\sqrt{n}}] \\
&= \{E[e^{j\omega(X-\mu)/\sigma\sqrt{n}}]\}^n.
\end{aligned} \tag{7.31}$$

The third equality follows from the independence of the $X_k$'s and the last equality follows from the fact that the $X_k$'s are identically distributed.

By expanding the exponential in the expression, we obtain an expression in terms of $n$ and the central moments of $X$:

$$\begin{aligned}
E\left[e^{j\omega(X-\mu)/\sigma\sqrt{n}}\right] &= E\left[1 + \frac{j\omega}{\sigma\sqrt{n}}(X - \mu) + \frac{(j\omega)^2}{2!\,n\sigma^2}(X - \mu)^2 + R(\omega)\right] \\
&= 1 + \frac{j\omega}{\sigma\sqrt{n}}E[(X - \mu)] + \frac{(j\omega)^2}{2!\,n\sigma^2}E[(X - \mu)^2] + E[R(\omega)].
\end{aligned}$$

Noting that $E[(X - \mu)] = 0$ and $E[(X - \mu)^2] = \sigma^2$, we have

$$E\left[e^{j\omega(X-\mu)/\sigma\sqrt{n}}\right] = 1 - \frac{\omega^2}{2n} + E[R(\omega)]. \tag{7.32}$$

The term $E[R(\omega)]$ can be neglected relative to $\omega^2/2n$ as $n$ becomes large. If we substitute Eq. (7.32) into Eq. (7.31), we obtain

$$\Phi_{Z_n}(\omega) = \left\{1 - \frac{\omega^2}{2n}\right\}^n$$

$$\rightarrow e^{-\omega^2/2} \quad \text{as } n \rightarrow \infty.$$

The latter expression is the characteristic function of a zero-mean, unit-variance Gaussian random variable. Thus the cdf of $Z_n$ approaches the cdf of a zero-mean, unit-variance Gaussian random variable.

## *7.4    CONVERGENCE OF SEQUENCES OF RANDOM VARIABLES

In Section 7.2 we discussed the convergence of the sequence of arithmetic averages $M_n$ of iid random variables to the expected value $\mu$:

$$M_n \to \mu \quad \text{as } n \to \infty. \tag{7.33}$$

The weak law and strong law of large numbers describe two ways in which the *sequence of random variables $M_n$ converges to the constant value given by $\mu$*. In this section we consider the more general situation where a sequence of random variables (usually not iid) $X_1, X_2, \dots$ converges to some random variable $X$:

$$X_n \to X \quad \text{as } n \to \infty. \tag{7.34}$$

We will describe several ways in which this convergence can take place. Note that Eq. (7.33) is a special case of Eq. (7.34) where the limiting random variable $X$ is given by the constant $\mu$.

To understand the meaning of Eq. (7.34), we first need to revisit the definition of a vector random variable $\mathbf{X} = (X_1, X_2, \dots, X_n)$. $\mathbf{X}$ was defined as a function that assigns a vector of real values to each outcome $\zeta$ from some sample space $S$:

$$\mathbf{X}(\zeta) = (X_1(\zeta), X_2(\zeta), \dots, X_n(\zeta)).$$

The randomness in the vector random variable was induced by the randomness in the underlying probability law governing the selection of $\zeta$. We obtain a sequence of random variables by letting $n$ increase without bound, that is, *a **sequence of random variables X** is a function that assigns a countably infinite number of real values to each outcome $\zeta$ from some sample space $S$:*[1]

$$\mathbf{X}(\zeta) = (X_1(\zeta), X_2(\zeta), \dots, X_n(\zeta), \dots). \tag{7.35}$$

From now on, we will use the notation $\{X_n(\zeta)\}$ or $\{X_n\}$ instead of $\mathbf{X}(\zeta)$ to denote the sequence of random variables.

Equation (7.35) shows that a sequence of random variables can be viewed as a sequence of functions of $\zeta$. On the other hand, it is more natural to instead imagine that *each point in S, say $\zeta$, produces a particular sequence of real numbers,*

$$x_1, x_2, x_3, \dots, \tag{7.36}$$

where $x_1 = X_1(\zeta)$, $x_2 = X_2(\zeta)$, and so on. The sequence in Eq. (7.36) is called the *sample sequence* for the point $\zeta$.

---

[1]In Chapter 8, we will see that this is also the definition of a discrete-time stochastic process.

## Example 7.16

Let $\zeta$ be selected at random from the interval $S = [0, 1]$, where we assume that the probability that $\zeta$ is in a subinterval of $S$ is equal to the length of the subinterval. For $n = 1, 2, \ldots$ we define the sequence of random variables

$$V_n(\zeta) = \zeta\left(1 - \frac{1}{n}\right).$$

The two ways of looking at sequences of random variables is evident here. First, we can view $V_n(\zeta)$ as a sequence of functions of $\zeta$, as shown in Fig. 7.8(a). Alternatively, we can imagine that we first perform the random experiment that yields $\zeta$, and that we then observe the corresponding sequence of real numbers $V_n(\zeta)$, as shown in Fig. 7.8(b).

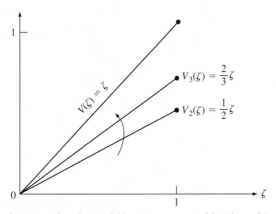

Sequence of random variables as a sequence of functions of $\zeta$

(a)

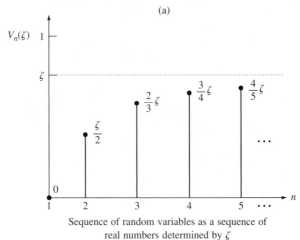

Sequence of random variables as a sequence of
real numbers determined by $\zeta$

(b)

**FIGURE 7.8**
Two ways of looking at sequences of random variables.

The standard methods from calculus can be used to determine the convergence of the sample sequence for each point $\zeta$. Intuitively, we say that the sequence of real numbers $x_n$ converges to the real number $x$ if the difference $|x_n - x|$ approaches zero as $n$ approaches infinity. More formally, we say that:

> The sequence $x_n$ converges to $x$ if, given any $\varepsilon > 0$, we can specify an integer $N$ such that for all values of $n$ beyond $N$ we can guarantee that $|x_n - x| < \varepsilon$.

Thus if a sequence converges, then for any $\varepsilon$ we can find an $N$ so that the sequence remains inside a $2\varepsilon$ corridor about $x$, as shown in Fig. 7.9(a).

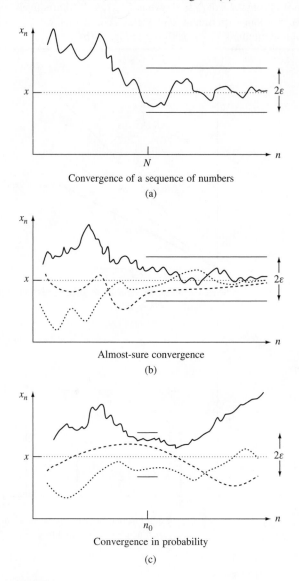

Convergence of a sequence of numbers

(a)

Almost-sure convergence

(b)

Convergence in probability

(c)

**FIGURE 7.9**
Sample sequences and convergence types.

If we make $\varepsilon$ smaller, $N$ becomes larger. Hence we arrive at our intuitive view that $x_n$ becomes closer and closer to $x$. If the limiting value $x$ is not known, we can still determine whether a sequence converges by applying the *Cauchy criterion*:

> The sequence $x_n$ converges if and only if, given $\varepsilon > 0$, we can specify integer $N'$ such that for $m$ and $n$ greater than $N'$, $|x_n - x_m| < \varepsilon$.

The Cauchy criterion states that the maximum variation in the sequence for points beyond $N'$ is less than $\varepsilon$.

---

**Example 7.17**

Let $V_n(\zeta)$ be the sequence of random variables from Example 7.16. Does the sequence of real numbers corresponding to a fixed $\zeta$ converge?

From Fig. 7.8(a), we expect that for a fixed value $\zeta$, $V_n(\zeta)$ will converge to the limit $\zeta$. Therefore, we consider the difference between the $n$th number in the sequence and the limit:

$$|V_n(\zeta) - \zeta| = \left| \zeta \left( 1 - \frac{1}{n} \right) - \zeta \right| = \left| \frac{\zeta}{n} \right| < \frac{1}{n},$$

where the last inequality follows from the fact that $\zeta$ is always less than one. In order to keep the above difference less than $\varepsilon$, we choose $n$ so that

$$|V_n(\zeta) - \zeta| < \frac{1}{n} < \varepsilon;$$

that is, we select $n > N = 1/\varepsilon$. Thus the sequence of real numbers $V_n(\zeta)$ converges to $\zeta$.

---

When we talk about the convergence of sequences of random variables, we are concerned with questions such as: Do all (or almost all) sample sequences converge, and if so, do they all converge to the same values or to different values? The first two definitions of convergence address these questions.

**Sure Convergence:**   The sequence of random variables $\{X_n(\zeta)\}$ converges surely to the random variable $X(\zeta)$ if the sequence of functions $X_n(\zeta)$ converges to the function $X(\zeta)$ as $n \to \infty$ *for all $\zeta$ in S*:

$$X_n(\zeta) \to X(\zeta) \qquad \text{as } n \to \infty \qquad \text{for all } \zeta \in S.$$

Sure convergence requires that the sample sequence corresponding to every $\zeta$ converges. Note that it does not require that all the sample sequences converge to the same values; that is, the sample sequences for different points $\zeta$ and $\zeta'$ can converge to different values.

**Almost-Sure Convergence:**   The sequence of random variables $\{X_n(\zeta)\}$ converges almost surely to the random variable $X(\zeta)$ if the sequence of functions $X_n(\zeta)$ converges to the function $X(\zeta)$ as $n \to \infty$ for all $\zeta$ in S, except possibly on a set of probability zero; that is,

$$P[\zeta : X_n(\zeta) \to X(\zeta) \text{ as } n \to \infty] = 1. \tag{7.37}$$

In Fig. 7.9(b) we illustrate almost-sure convergence for the case where sample sequences converge to the same value $x$; we see that almost all sequences must eventually enter and remain inside a $2\varepsilon$ corridor. In almost-sure convergence some of the sample sequences may not converge, but these must all belong to $\zeta$'s that are in a set that has probability zero.

The strong law of large numbers is an example of almost-sure convergence. Note that sure convergence implies almost-sure convergence.

---

**Example 7.18**

Let $\zeta$ be selected at random from the interval $S = [0, 1]$, where we assume that the probability that $\zeta$ is in a subinterval of $S$ is equal to the length of the subinterval. For $n = 1, 2, \ldots$ we define the following five sequences of random variables:

$$U_n(\zeta) = \frac{\zeta}{n}$$

$$V_n(\zeta) = \zeta\left(1 - \frac{1}{n}\right)$$

$$W_n(\zeta) = \zeta e^n$$

$$Y_n(\zeta) = \cos 2\pi n\zeta$$

$$Z_n(\zeta) = e^{-n(n\zeta-1)}.$$

Which of these sequences converge surely? almost surely? Identify the limiting random variable.

The sequence $U_n(\zeta)$ converges to 0 for all $\zeta$, and hence surely:

$$U_n(\zeta) \to U(\zeta) = 0 \quad \text{as } n \to \infty \quad \text{for all } \zeta \in S.$$

Note that in this case all sample sequences converge to the same value, namely zero.

The sequence $V_n(\zeta)$ converges to $\zeta$ for all $\zeta$, and hence surely:

$$V_n(\zeta) \to V(\zeta) = \zeta \quad \text{as } n \to \infty \quad \text{for all } \zeta \in S.$$

In this case all sample sequences converge to different values, and the limiting random variable $V(\zeta)$ is a uniform random variable on the unit interval.

The sequence $W_n(\zeta)$ converges to 0 for $\zeta = 0$, but diverges to infinity for all other values of $\zeta$. Thus this sequence of random variables does not converge.

The sequence $Y_n(\zeta)$ converges to 1 for $\zeta = 0$ and $\zeta = 1$, but oscillates between $-1$ and 1 for all other values of $\zeta$. Thus this sequence of random variables does not converge.

The sequence $Z_n(\zeta)$ is an interesting case. For $\zeta = 0$, we have

$$Z(0) = e^n \to \infty \quad \text{as } n \to \infty.$$

On the other hand, for $\zeta > 0$ and for values of $n > 1/\zeta$, the sequence $Z_n(\zeta)$ decreases exponentially to zero, thus:

$$Z_n(\zeta) \to 0 \quad \text{for all } \zeta > 0.$$

But $P[\zeta > 0] = 1$, thus $Z_n(\zeta)$ converges to zero almost surely. However, $Z_n(\zeta)$ does not converge surely to zero.

---

The dependence of the sequence of random variables on $\zeta$ is not always evident, as shown by the following examples.

---

**Example 7.19    iid Bernoulli Random Variables**

Let the sequence of random variables $X_n(\zeta)$ consist of independent equiprobable Bernoulli random variables, that is,

$$P[X_n(\zeta) = 0] = \frac{1}{2} = P[X_n(\zeta) = 1].$$

Does this sequence of random variables converge?

This sequence of random variables will generate sample sequences consisting of all possible sequences of 0's and 1's. In order for a sample sequence to converge, it must eventually stay equal to zero (or one) for all remaining values of $n$. However, the probability of obtaining all zeros (or all ones) in an infinite number of Bernoulli trials is zero. Hence the sample sequences that converge have zero probability, and therefore this sequence of random variables does not converge.

---

**Example 7.20**

An urn contains 2 black balls and 2 white balls. At time $n$ a ball is selected at random from the urn, and the color is noted. If the number of balls of this color is greater than the number of balls of the other color, then the ball is put back in the urn; otherwise, the ball is left out. Let $X_n(\zeta)$ be the number of black balls in the urn after the $n$th draw. Does this sequence of random variables converge?

The first draw is the critical draw. Suppose the first draw is black, then the black ball that is selected will be left out. Thereafter, each time a white ball is selected it will be put back in, and when the remaining black ball is selected it will be left out. Thus with probability one, the black ball will eventually be selected, and $X_n(\zeta)$ will converge to zero. On the other hand, if a white ball is selected in the first draw, then eventually the remaining white ball will be removed, and hence with probability one $X_n(\zeta)$ will converge to 2. Thus $X_n(\zeta)$ is equally likely to eventually converge to 0 or 2, that is,

$$X_n(\zeta) \rightarrow X(\zeta) \qquad \text{as } n \rightarrow \infty \qquad \text{almost surely,}$$

where

$$P[X(\zeta) = 0] = \frac{1}{2} = P[X(\zeta) = 2].$$

---

In order to determine whether a sequence of random variables converges almost surely, we need to know the probability law that governs the selection of $\zeta$ and the relation between $\zeta$ and the sequence (as in Example 7.16), or the sequence must be sufficiently simple that we can determine the convergence directly (as in Examples 7.19 and 7.20). In general it is easier to deal with other, "weaker" types of convergence that are much easier to verify. For example, we may require that *at particular time* $n_0$, most sample sequences $X_{n_0}$ be close to $X$ in the sense that $E[(X_{n_0} - X)^2]$ is small.

This requirement focuses on a particular time instant and, unlike almost-sure convergence, it does not address the behavior of entire sample sequences. It leads to the following type of convergence:

> **Mean Square Convergence:**  The sequence of random variables $\{X_n(\zeta)\}$ converges in the mean square sense to the random variable $X(\zeta)$ if

$$E[(X_n(\zeta) - X(\zeta))^2] \rightarrow 0 \qquad \text{as } n \rightarrow \infty. \tag{7.38a}$$

We denote mean square convergence by (l̲imit i̲n the m̲ean)

$$\text{l.i.m. } X_n(\zeta) = X(\zeta) \qquad \text{as } n \rightarrow \infty. \tag{7.38b}$$

Mean square convergence is of great practical interest in electrical engineering applications because of its analytical simplicity and because of the interpretation of $E[(X_n - X)^2]$ as the "power" in an error signal.

The Cauchy criterion can be used to ascertain convergence in the mean square sense when the limiting random variable $X$ is not known:

> **Cauchy Criterion:**   The sequence of random variables $\{X_n(\zeta)\}$ converges in the mean square sense if and only if

$$E[(X_n(\zeta) - X_m(\zeta))^2] \rightarrow 0 \qquad \text{as } n \rightarrow \infty \text{ and } m \rightarrow \infty. \tag{7.39}$$

---

**Example 7.21**

Does the sequence $V_n(\zeta)$ in Example 7.18 converge in the mean square sense?
  In Example 7.18, we found that $V_n(\zeta)$ converges surely to $\zeta$. We therefore consider

$$E[(V_n(\zeta) - \zeta)^2] = E\left[\left(\frac{\zeta}{n}\right)^2\right] = \int_0^1 \left(\frac{\zeta}{n}\right)^2 d\zeta = \frac{1}{3n^2},$$

where we have used the fact that $\zeta$ is uniformly distributed in the interval $[0, 1]$. As $n$ approaches infinity, the mean square error approaches zero, and so we have convergence in the mean square sense.

---

Mean square convergence occurs if the second moment of the error $X_n - X$ approaches zero as $n$ approaches infinity. This implies that as $n$ increases, an increasing proportion of sample sequences are close to $X$; however, it does not imply that all such sequences *remain* close to $X$ as in the case of almost-sure convergence. This difference will become apparent with the next type of convergence:

> **Convergence in Probability:**   The sequence of random variables $\{X_n(\zeta)\}$ converges in probability to the random variable $X(\zeta)$ if, for any $\varepsilon > 0$,

$$P[|X_n(\zeta) - X(\zeta)| > \varepsilon] \rightarrow 0 \qquad \text{as } n \rightarrow \infty. \tag{7.40}$$

In Fig. 7.9(c) we illustrate convergence in probability for the case where the limiting random variable is a constant $x$; we see that at the specified time $n_0$ most sample sequences

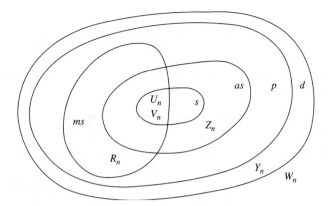

**FIGURE 7.10**
Relations between different types of convergence and classification of
sequences introduced in the examples.

must be within $\varepsilon$ of $x$. However, *the sequences are not required to remain inside a $2\varepsilon$ corridor.*
The weak law of large numbers is an example of convergence in probability. Thus we see
that the fundamental difference between almost-sure convergence and convergence in
probability is the same as that between the strong law and the weak law of large numbers.
    We now show that mean square convergence implies convergence in probability.
The Markov inequality (Eq. (4.75)) applied to $(X_n - X)^2$ implies

$$P[|X_n - X| > \varepsilon] = P[(X_n - X)^2 > \varepsilon^2] \le \frac{E[(X_n - X)^2]}{\varepsilon^2}.$$

If the sequence converges in the mean square sense, then the right-hand side
approaches zero as $n$ approaches infinity. It then follows that the sequence also converges in probability. Figure 7.10 shows a Venn diagram that indicates that mean square
convergence implies convergence in probability. The diagram shows that all sequences
that converge in the mean square sense (designated by the set *ms*) are contained inside
the set $p$ of all sequences that converge in probability. The diagram also shows some of
the sequences introduced in the examples.
    It can be shown that almost-sure convergence implies convergence in probability.
However, almost-sure convergence does not always imply mean square convergence,
as demonstrated by the following example.

---

**Example 7.22**

Does the sequence $Z_n(\zeta)$ in Example 7.18 converge in the mean square sense?
    In Example 7.18, we found that $Z_n(\zeta)$ converges to 0 almost surely, so we consider

$$E[(Z_n(\zeta) - 0)^2] = E[e^{-2n(n\zeta - 1)}]$$

$$= e^{2n} \int_0^1 e^{-2n^2\zeta} \, d\zeta = \frac{e^{2n}}{2n^2}(1 - e^{-2n^2}).$$

As $n$ approaches infinity, the rightmost term approaches infinity. Therefore this sequence does not converge in the mean square sense even though it converges almost surely.

The following example shows that mean square convergence does not imply almost-sure convergence.

### Example 7.23

Let $R_n(\zeta)$ be the error introduced by a communication channel in the $n$th transmission. Suppose that the channel introduces errors in the following way: In the first transmission the channel introduces an error; in the next two transmissions the channel randomly selects one transmission to introduce an error, and it allows the other transmission to be error-free; in the next three transmissions, the channel randomly selects one transmission to introduce an error, and it allows the other transmissions to be error-free; and so on. Suppose that when errors are introduced, they are uniformly distributed in the interval $[1, 2]$. Does the sequence of transmission errors converge, and if so, in what sense?

Figure 7.11 shows the manner in which the channel introduces errors. The errors become sparser as time progresses, so we expect that the sequence is approaching zero in the mean square sense. The probability of error $p_n$ in the $n$th transmission is $1/m$ for $n$ in the interval from $1 + 2 + \cdots + (m - 1) = (m - 1)m/2$ to $1 + 2 + \cdots + m = m(m + 1)/2$. If we let $Y$ be a uniform random variable in the interval $[1, 2]$, then the mean square error at time $n$ is

$$E[(X_n(\zeta) - 0)^2] = E[X_n^2] = E[Y^2]p_n + 0(1 - p_n) = \left(\frac{7}{3}\right)\frac{1}{m}$$

$$\text{for } \frac{(m - 1)m}{2} < n \le \frac{m(m + 1)}{2}.$$

Thus as $n$ (and $m$) increases, the mean square error approaches zero and the sequence $R_n$ converges to zero in the mean square sense.

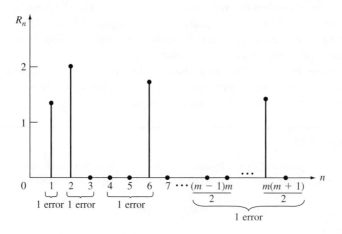

**FIGURE 7.11**
$R_n$ converges in mean square sense but not almost surely.

In order for the sequence $R_n$ to converge to 0 almost surely, almost all sample sequences must eventually become and remain close to zero. However, the manner in which errors are introduced guarantees that regardless of how large $n$ becomes, a value in the range $[1, 2]$ is certain to occur some time later. Thus none of the sample sequences converges to zero, and the sequence of random variables does not converge almost surely.

---

The last type of convergence we will discuss addresses the convergence of the cumulative distribution functions of a sequence of random variables, rather than the random variables themselves.

> **Convergence in Distribution:**  The sequence of random variables $\{X_n\}$ with cumulative distribution functions $\{F_n(x)\}$ converges in distribution to the random variable $X$ with cumulative distribution $F(x)$ if
>
> $$F_n(x) \rightarrow F(x) \qquad \text{as } n \rightarrow \infty \tag{7.41}$$
>
> for all $x$ at which $F(x)$ is continuous.

The central limit theorem is an example of convergence in distribution. To see that convergence in distribution does not make any statement regarding the convergence of the random variables in a sequence, consider the Bernoulli iid sequence in Example 7.19. These random variables do not converge in any of the previous convergence modes. However, they trivially converge in distribution since they have the same distribution for all $n$. All of the previous forms of convergence imply convergence in distribution as indicated in Fig. 7.10.

## *7.5    LONG-TERM ARRIVAL RATES AND ASSOCIATED AVERAGES

In many problems events of interest occur at random times, and we are interested in the long-term average rate at which the events occur. For example, suppose that a new electronic component is installed at time $t = 0$ and that it fails at time $X_1$; an identical new component is installed immediately, and it fails after $X_2$ seconds, and so on. Let $N(t)$ be the number of components that have failed by time $t$. $N(t)$ is called a **renewal counting process**. In this section, we are interested in the behavior of $N(t)/t$ as $t$ becomes very large.

Let $X_j$ denote the lifetime of the $j$th component, then the time when the $n$th component fails is given by

$$S_n = X_1 + X_2 + \cdots + X_n, \tag{7.42}$$

where we assume that the $X_j$ are iid nonnegative random variables with $0 < E[X] = E[X_j] < \infty$. We say that $S_n$ is the time of the $n$th arrival or renewal, and we call the $X_j$'s the *interarrival or cycle times*. Figure 7.12 shows a realization of $N(t)$ and the associated sequence of interarrival times. The lines in the time axis indicate the arrival times. Note that $N(t)$ is a nondecreasing, integer-valued staircase function of time that increases without bound as $t$ approaches infinity.

Since the mean interarrival time is $E[X]$ seconds per event, we expect intuitively that $N(t)$ grows at a rate of $1/E[X]$ events per second. We will now use the strong law of

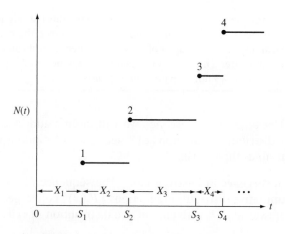

**FIGURE 7.12**
A counting process and its interarrival times.

large numbers to show this is the case. The average arrival rate in the first $t$ seconds is given by $N(t)/t$. We will show that with probability one, $N(t)/t \to 1/E[X]$ as $t \to \infty$.

Since $N(t)$ is the number of arrivals up to time $t$, then $S_{N(t)}$ is the time of the last arrival prior to time $t$, and $S_{N(t)+1}$ is the time of the first arrival after time $t$ (see Fig. 7.13). Therefore

$$S_{N(t)} \leq t < S_{N(t)+1}.$$

If we divide the above equation by $N(t)$, we obtain

$$\frac{S_{N(t)}}{N(t)} \leq \frac{t}{N(t)} < \frac{S_{N(t)+1}}{N(t)}. \tag{7.43}$$

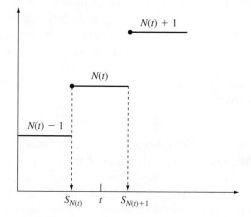

**FIGURE 7.13**
Time of first arrival after time $t$ and first arrival before time $t$.

The term on the left-hand side is the sample average interarrival time for the first $N(t)$ arrivals:

$$\frac{S_{N(t)}}{N(t)} = \frac{1}{N(t)} \sum_{j=1}^{N(t)} X_j.$$

As $t \to \infty$, $N(t)$ approaches infinity so the above sample average converges to $E[X]$, with probability one, by the strong law of large numbers. We now show that the term on the right-hand side also approaches $E[X]$:

$$\frac{S_{N(t)+1}}{N(t)} = \left( \frac{S_{N(t)+1}}{N(t) + 1} \right) \left( \frac{N(t) + 1}{N(t)} \right).$$

As $t \to \infty$, the first term on the right-hand side approaches $E[X]$ and the second term approaches 1 with probability one. Thus the lower and upper terms in Eq. (7.34) both approach $E[X]$ with probability one as $t$ approaches infinity. We have proved the following theorem:

***

**Theorem 1   Arrival Rate for iid Interarrivals**

Let $N(t)$ be the counting process associated with the iid interarrival sequence $X_j$, with $0 < E[X_j] = E[X] < \infty$. Then with probability one,

$$\lim_{t \to \infty} \frac{N(t)}{t} \to \frac{1}{E[X]}. \tag{7.44}$$

***

**Example 7.24   Exponential Interarrivals**

Customers arrive at a service station with iid exponential interarrival times with mean $E[X_j] = 1/\alpha$. Find the long-term average arrival rate.

From Theorem 1, it immediately follows that with probability one,

$$\lim_{t \to \infty} \frac{N(t)}{t} = \frac{1}{\alpha^{-1}} = \alpha.$$

Thus $\alpha$ represents the long-term average arrival rate.

***

**Example 7.25   Repair Cycles**

Let $U_j$ be the "up" time during which a system is continuously functioning, and let $D_j$ be the "down" time required to repair the system when it breaks down. Find the long-term average rate at which repairs need to be done.

Define a repair cycle to consist of an "up" time followed by a "down" time, $X_j = U_j + D_j$, then the average cycle time is $E[U] + E[D]$. The number of repairs required by time $t$ is $N(t)$, and by Theorem 1, the rate at which repairs need to be done is

$$\lim_{t \to \infty} \frac{N(t)}{t} = \frac{1}{E[U] + E[D]}.$$

### 7.5.1    Long-Term Time Averages

Suppose that events occur at random with iid interevent times $X_j$, and that a cost $C_j$ is associated with each occurrence of an event. Let $C(t)$ be the cost incurred up to time $t$. We now determine the long-term behavior of $C(t)/t$, that is, the long-term average rate at which costs are incurred.

We assume that the pairs $(X_j, C_j)$ form a sequence of iid random vectors, but that $X_j$ and $C_j$ need not be independent; that is, the cost associated with an event may depend on the associated interevent time. The total cost $C(t)$ incurred up to time $t$ is then the sum of costs associated with the $N(t)$ events that have occurred up to time $t$:

$$C(t) = \sum_{j=1}^{N(t)} C_j. \tag{7.45}$$

The time average of the cost up to time $t$ is $C(t)/t$, thus

$$\frac{C(t)}{t} = \frac{1}{t} \sum_{j=1}^{N(t)} C_j$$

$$= \frac{N(t)}{t} \left\{ \frac{1}{N(t)} \sum_{j=1}^{N(t)} C_j \right\}. \tag{7.46}$$

By Theorem 1, as $t \to \infty$, the first term on the right-hand side approaches $1/E[X]$ with probability one. The expression inside the brackets is simply the sample mean of the first $N(t)$ costs. As $t \to \infty$, $N(t)$ approaches infinity, so the second term approaches $E[C]$ with probability one, by the strong law of large numbers. Thus we have the following theorem:

---

**Theorem 2    Cost Accumulation Rate**

Let $(X_j, C_j)$ be a sequence of iid interevent times and associated costs, with $0 < E[X_j] < \infty$ and $E[C_j] < \infty$, and let $C(t)$ be the cost incurred up to time $t$. Then, with probability one,

$$\lim_{t \to \infty} \frac{C(t)}{t} = \frac{E[C]}{E[X]}. \tag{7.47}$$

---

The following series of examples demonstrate how Theorem 2 can be used to calculate long-term time averages.

---

### Example 7.26    Long-Term Proportion of "Up" Time

Find the long-term proportion of time that the system is "up" in Example 7.25.

Let $I_U(t)$ be equal to one if the system is up at time $t$ and zero otherwise, then the long-term proportion of time in which the system is up is

$$\lim_{t \to \infty} \frac{1}{t} \int_0^t I_U(t') \, dt',$$

where the integral is the total time the system is up in the time interval $[0, t]$.

Now define a cycle to consist of a system "up" time followed by a "down" time, then $X_j = U_j + D_j$, and $E[X] = E[U] + E[D]$. If we let the cost associated with each cycle be the "up" time $U_j$, then if $t$ is an instant when a cycle ends,

$$\int_0^t I_U(t')\, dt' = \sum_{j=1}^{N(t)} U_j = C(t).$$

Thus $C(t)/t$ is the proportion of time that the system is "up" in the time interval $(0, t)$. By Theorem 2, the long-term proportion of time that the system is "up" is

$$\lim_{t \to \infty} \frac{C(t)}{t} = \frac{E[U]}{E[U] + E[D]}.$$

## Example 7.27

In the previous example, suppose that a cost $C_j$ is associated with each repair. Find the long-term average rate at which repair costs are incurred.

The mean interevent time is $E[U] + E[D]$, and the mean cost per repair is $E[C]$. Thus by Theorem 2, the long-term average repair cost rate is

$$\lim_{t \to \infty} \frac{C(t)}{t} = \frac{E[C]}{E[U] + E[D]}.$$

## Example 7.28    A Packet Voice Transmission System

A packet voice multiplexer can transmit up to $M$ packets every 10-millisecond period. Let $N$ be the number of packets input into the multiplexer every 10 ms. If $N \le M$ the multiplexer transmits all $N$ packets, and if $N > M$ the multiplexer transmits $M$ packets and discards $(N - M)$ packets. Find the long-term proportion of packets discarded by the multiplexer.

Define a "cycle" by $X_j = N_j$, that is, the length of the "cycle" is equal to the number of packets produced in the $j$th interval. Define the cost in the $j$th cycle by $C_j = (N_j - M)^+ = \max (N_j - M, 0)$, that is, the number of packets that are discarded in the $j$th cycle. With these definitions, $t$ represents the first $t$ packets input into the multiplexer and $C(t)$ represents the number that had to be discarded. The long-term proportion of packets discarded is then

$$\lim_{t \to \infty} \frac{C(t)}{t} = \frac{E[(N - M)^+]}{E[N]}$$

where

$$E[(N - M)^+] = \sum_{k=m}^{\infty} (k - M) p_k,$$

where $p_k$ is the pmf of $N$.

## Example 7.29    The Residual Lifetime

Let $X_1, X_2, \ldots$ be a sequence of interarrival times, and let the residual lifetime $r(t)$ be defined as the time from an arbitrary time instant $t$ until the next arrival as shown in Fig. 7.14. Find the long-term proportion of time that $r(t)$ exceeds $c$ seconds.

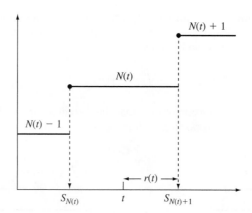

**FIGURE 7.14**
Residual lifetime in a cycle.

The amount of time that the residual lifetime exceeds $c$ in a cycle of length $X$ is $(X - c)^+$, that is, $X - c$ when the cycle is longer than $c$ seconds, and 0 when it is shorter than $c$ seconds. The long-term proportion of time that $r(t)$ exceeds $c$ seconds is obtained from Theorem 2 by defining the cost per cycle by $C_j = (X_j - c)^+$:

$$\text{proportion of time } r(t) \text{ exceeds } c = \frac{E[(X - c)^+]}{E[X]}$$

$$= \frac{1}{E[X]} \int_0^\infty P[(X - c)^+ > x] \, dx$$

$$= \frac{1}{E[X]} \int_0^\infty P[X > x + c] \, dx$$

$$= \frac{1}{E[X]} \int_0^\infty \{1 - F_X(x + c)\} \, dx$$

$$= \frac{1}{E[X]} \int_c^\infty \{1 - F_X(y)\} \, dy, \tag{7.48}$$

where Eq. (4.28) was used for $E[(X - c)^+]$ in the second equality. This result is used extensively in reliability theory and in queueing theory.

---

## *7.6 CALCULATING DISTRIBUTIONS USING THE DISCRETE FOURIER TRANSFORM

In many situations we are forced to obtain the pmf or pdf of a random variable from its characteristic function using numerical methods because the inverse transform cannot be expressed in closed form. In the most common case, we are interested in finding the pmf/pdf corresponding to $\Phi_X(\omega)^n$, which corresponds to the characteristic function of the sum of $n$ iid random variables. In this section we introduce the discrete Fourier transform, which enables us to perform this numerical calculation in an efficient manner.

### 7.6.1    Discrete Random Variables

First, suppose that $X$ is an integer-valued random variable that takes on values in the set $\{0, 1, \ldots, N - 1\}$. The pmf of the sum of $n$ such independent random variables is given by the $n$-fold convolution of the pmf of $X$, or equivalently by the $n$th power of the characteristic function of $X$. Therefore we can deal with the sum of $n$ random variables through the convolution of pmf's or through the product of characteristic functions and inverse transforms. Let us first consider the convolution approach.

---

**Example 7.30**

Use Octave to calculate the pmf of $Z = U_1 + U_2 + U_3 + U_4$ where the $U_i$ are iid uniform discrete random variables in the set $\{0, 1, \ldots, 9\}$.

Octave and MATLAB provide a function for convolving the elements of two vectors. The sequence of commands below produces a 4-fold convolution of the above discrete uniform pdf. The first convolution of the pmf with itself yields a pdf with triangular shape. Figure 7.15 shows that the 4-fold convolution is beginning to have a bell-shaped form.

```
> P= [1,1,1,1,1,1,1,1,1,1] /10;
> P2=conv (P, P);
> stem (conv (P2,"@11"))
> hold on
> stem (conv (P2,P2),"@22")
```

---

If a large number of sample values is involved in the calculations, then the characteristic function approach is more efficient. The characteristic function for this integer-valued random variable is

$$\Phi_X(\omega) = \sum_{k=0}^{N-1} e^{j\omega k} p_k, \tag{7.49}$$

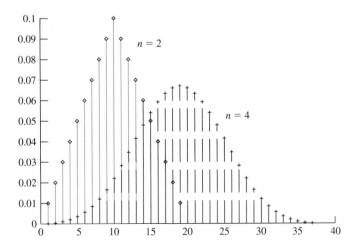

**FIGURE 7.15**
pmf of sum of random variables using convolution method.

where $p_k = P[X = k]$ is the pmf. $\Phi_X(\omega)$ is a periodic function of $\omega$ with period $2\pi$ since $e^{(j(\omega + 2\pi)k)} = e^{j\omega k}e^{jk2\pi} = e^{j\omega k}.^2$

Consider the characteristic function at $N$ equally spaced values in the interval $[0, 2\pi)$:

$$c_m = \Phi_X\left(\frac{2\pi m}{N}\right) = \sum_{k=0}^{N-1} p_k e^{j2\pi km/N} \qquad m = 0, 1, \ldots, N - 1. \qquad (7.50)$$

Equation (7.50) defines the **discrete Fourier transform** (DFT) of the sequence $p_0, \ldots, p_{N-1}$. (The sign in the exponent in Eq. (7.50) is the opposite of that used in the usual definition of the DFT.) In general, the $c_m$'s are complex numbers. Note that if we extend the range of $m$ outside the range $\{0, N - 1\}$ we obtain a periodic sequence consisting of a repetition of the basic sequence $c_0, \ldots, c_{N-1}$.

The sequence of $p_k$'s can be obtained from the sequence of $c_m$'s using the inverse DFT formula:

$$p_k = \frac{1}{N}\sum_{m=0}^{N-1} c_m e^{-j2\pi km/N} \qquad k = 0, 1, \ldots, N - 1. \qquad (7.51)$$

---

**Example 7.31**

A discrete random variable $X$ has pmf

$$p_0 = \frac{1}{2}, \qquad p_1 = \frac{3}{8}, \qquad \text{and} \qquad p_2 = \frac{1}{8}.$$

Find the characteristic function of $X$, the DFT for $N = 3$, and verify the inverse transform formula. The characteristic function of $X$ is given by Eq. (7.49):

$$\Phi_X(\omega) = \frac{1}{2} + \frac{3}{8}e^{j\omega} + \frac{1}{8}e^{j2\omega}.$$

The DFT for $N = 3$ is given by the values of the characteristic function at $\omega = 2\pi m/3$, for $m = 0, 1, 2$:

$$c_0 = \Phi_X(0) = 1$$

$$c_1 = \Phi_X\left(\frac{2\pi}{3}\right) = \frac{1}{2} + \frac{3}{8}e^{j2\pi/3} + \frac{1}{8}e^{j4\pi/3}$$

$$= \frac{1}{2} + \frac{3}{8}(-.5 + j(.75)^{1/2}) + \frac{1}{8}(-.5 - j(.75)^{1/2})$$

$$= \frac{1}{4} + \frac{j(.75)^{1/2}}{4}$$

$$c_2 = \Phi_X\left(\frac{4\pi}{3}\right) = \frac{1}{2} + \frac{3}{8}e^{j4\pi/3} + \frac{1}{8}e^{j8\pi/3},$$

$$= \frac{1}{4} - \frac{j(.75)^{1/2}}{4}$$

---

[2]This follows from Euler's formula $e^{j\theta} = \cos\theta + \sin\theta$.

where we have used Euler's formula to evaluate the complex exponentials.
We substitute the $c_j$'s into Eq. (7.51) to recover the pmf:

$$p_0 = \frac{1}{3}(c_0 + c_1 + c_2)$$

$$= \frac{1}{3}\left(1 + \frac{1}{4} + \frac{j(.75)^{1/2}}{4} + \frac{1}{4} - \frac{j(.75)^{1/2}}{4}\right)$$

$$= \frac{1}{2}$$

$$p_1 = \frac{1}{3}(c_0 + c_1 e^{-j2\pi/3} + c_2 e^{-j2\pi 2/3}) = \frac{3}{8}$$

$$p_2 = \frac{1}{3}(c_0 + c_1 e^{-j4\pi/3} + c_2 e^{-j4\pi 2/3}) = \frac{1}{8}.$$

---

The range of the integer-valued random variable $X$ can be extended to the larger
set $\{0, 1, \ldots, N - 1, N, \ldots, L - 1\}$ by defining a new pmf $p_j'$ given by

$$p_j' = \begin{cases} p_i & 0 \le j \le N - 1 \\ 0 & N \le j \le L - 1. \end{cases} \tag{7.52}$$

The characteristic function of the random variable, $\Phi_X(\omega)$, remains unchanged, but
the associated DFT now involves evaluating $\Phi_X(\omega)$ at a different set of points:

$$c_m = \Phi_X\left(\frac{2\pi m}{L}\right) \qquad \text{for} \quad m = 0, \ldots, L - 1. \tag{7.53}$$

The inverse transform of the sequence in Eq. (7.53) then yields Eq. (7.52). Thus the
pmf can be recovered using the DFT on $L \ge N$ samples of $\Phi_X(\omega)$ as specified by
Eq. (7.53). In essence, we have only padded the pmf with $L - N$ zeros in Eq. (7.52).

The zero-padding method discussed above is required to evaluate the pmf of a
sum of iid random variables. Suppose that

$$Z = X_1 + X_2 + \cdots + X_n,$$

where the $X_i$ are integer-valued iid random variables with characteristic function
$\Phi_X(\omega)$. If the $X_i$ assume values from $\{0, 1, \ldots, N - 1\}$, then $Z$ will assume values
from $\{0, \ldots, n(N - 1)\}$. The pmf of $Z$ is found using the DFT evaluated at the
$L = n(N - 1) + 1$ points:

$$d_m = \Phi_Z\left(\frac{2\pi m}{L}\right) = \Phi_X\left(\frac{2\pi m}{L}\right)^n \qquad m = 0, \ldots, L - 1,$$

since $\Phi_Z(\omega) = \Phi_X(\omega)^n$. Note that this requires evaluating the characteristic function
of $X$ at $L > N$ points. The pmf of $Z$ is then found from

$$P[Z = k] = \frac{1}{L}\sum_{m=0}^{L-1} d_m e^{-j2\pi km/L} \qquad k = 0, 1, \ldots, L - 1. \tag{7.54}$$

## Example 7.32

Let $Z = X_1 + X_2$, where the $X_j$ are iid random variables with characteristic function:

$$\Phi_X(w) = \frac{1}{3} + \frac{2}{3}e^{jw}.$$

Find $P[Z = 1]$ using the DFT method.

$X$ assumes values from $\{0, 1\}$ and $Z$ from $\{0, 1, 2\}$, so $\Phi_Z(\omega) = \Phi_X(\omega)^2$ needs to be evaluated at three points:

$$d_m = \left\{\frac{1}{3} + \frac{2}{3}e^{j2\pi m/3}\right\}^2 \qquad m = 0, 1, 2.$$

These values are found to be

$$d_0 = 1, \qquad d_1 = -\frac{1}{3}, \qquad \text{and} \qquad d_2 = -\frac{1}{3}.$$

Substituting these values into Eq. (7.54) with $k = 1$ gives

$$P[Z = 1] = \frac{1}{3}\{d_0 + d_1 e^{-j2\pi/3} + d_2 e^{-j4\pi/3}\}$$

$$= \frac{1}{3}\left\{1 - \frac{1}{3}(e^{-j2\pi/3} + e^{-j4\pi/3})\right\}$$

$$= \frac{4}{9}.$$

We can verify this answer by noting that

$$P[Z = 1] = P[\{X_1 = 0\} \cap \{X_2 = 1\}] + P[\{X_1 = 1\} \cap \{X_2 = 0\}]$$

$$= \frac{1}{3}\frac{2}{3} + \frac{2}{3}\frac{1}{3} = \frac{4}{9}.$$

In practice we are interested in using the DFT when the number of points in the pmf is large. An examination of Eq. (7.51) shows that the calculation of all $N$ points requires approximately $N^2$ multiplications of complex numbers. Thus if $N = 2^{10} = 1024$, approximately $10^6$ multiplications will be required. The popularity of the DFT method stems from the fact that algorithms, called **fast Fourier transform (FFT) algorithms**, have been developed that can carry out the above calculations in $N \log_2 N$ multiplications. For $N = 2^{10}$, $10^4$ multiplications will be required, a reduction by a factor of 100.

## Example 7.33

Use Octave to calculate the pmf of $Z = U_1 + U_2 + \cdots + U_{10}$ where the $U_i$ are iid uniform discrete random variables in the set $\{0, 1, \ldots, 9\}$.

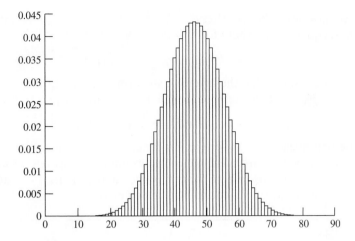

**FIGURE 7.16**
FFT calculation of 10-fold convolution of discrete uniform random variable
$\{0,1,\ldots,9\}$.

The commands below show the definition of the discrete uniform pmf and the calculation of the FFT. This result is raised to the 10th power and the inverse transform is calculated. Figure 7.16 shows that the resulting pmf is starting to look very Gaussian in shape.

```
> P= [1,1,1,1,1,1,1,1,1,1]/10;
> bar (ifft (fft (P, 128).^;10))
```

So far, we have restricted $X$ to be an integer-valued random variable that takes on only a finite set of values $S_X = \{0, 1, \ldots, N - 1\}$. We now consider the case where $S_X = \{0, 1, 2, \ldots\}$. Suppose that we know $\Phi_X(\omega)$, and that we obtain a pmf $p'_k$ from Eq. (7.51) using a finite set of sample points from $\Phi_X(\omega)$, $c_m = \Phi_X(2\pi m/N)$ for $m = 0, 1, \ldots, N - 1$,

$$p'_k = \frac{1}{N} \sum_{m=0}^{N-1} c_m e^{-j2\pi km/N} \qquad k = 0, 1, \ldots, N - 1. \qquad (7.55)$$

To see what this calculation yields consider the points $c_m$:

$$\Phi_X\left(\frac{2\pi m}{N}\right) = \sum_{n=0}^{\infty} p_n e^{j2\pi mn/N}$$

$$= (p_0 + p_N + \cdots)e^{j0}$$

$$+ (p_1 + p_{N+1} + \cdots)e^{j2\pi m/N}$$

$$+ \cdots$$

$$+ (p_{N-1} + p_{2N-1} + \cdots)e^{j2\pi m(N-1)/N}$$

$$= \sum_{k=0}^{N-1} p'_k e^{j2\pi km/N}, \qquad (7.56)$$

where we have used the fact that $e^{j2\pi mn/N} = e^{j2\pi m(n+hN)/N}$, for $h$ an integer, to obtain the second equality and where for $k = 0, \ldots, N - 1$,

$$p'_k = p_k + p_{N+k} + p_{2N+k} + \cdots. \tag{7.57}$$

Equation (7.55) states that the inverse transform of the points $c_m = \Phi_X(2\pi m/N)$ will yield $p'_0, \ldots, p'_{N-1}$, which are equal to the desired value $p_k$ plus the error

$$e_k = p_{N+k} + p_{2N+k} + \cdots.$$

Since the pmf must decay to zero as $k$ increases, the error term can be made small by making $N$ sufficiently large. The following example carries out an evaluation of the above error term in a case where the pmf is known. In practice, the pmf is not known so the appropriate value of $N$ is found by trial and error.

---

**Example 7.34**

Suppose that $X$ is a geometric random variable. How large should $N$ be so that the percent error is 1%?

The error term for $p_k$ is given by

$$e_k = \sum_{h=1}^{\infty} p_{k+hN} = \sum_{h=1}^{\infty} (1-p)p^{k+hN} = (1-p)p^k \frac{p^N}{1-p^N}.$$

The percent error term for $p_k$ is

$$\frac{e_k}{p_k} = \frac{p^N}{1-p^N} = a \times 100\%.$$

By solving for $N$, we find that the error is less than $a = 0.01$ if

$$N > \frac{\log(a/1-a)}{\log p} \simeq \frac{-2.0}{\log_{10} p}.$$

Thus for example if $p = .1, .5, .9$, then the required $N$ is 2, 7, and 44, respectively. These numbers show how the required $N$ depends strongly on the rate of decay of the pmf.

---

### 7.6.2    Continuous Random Variables

Let $X$ be a continuous random variable, and suppose that we are interested in finding the pdf of $X$ from $\Phi_X(\omega)$ using a numerical method. We can take the inverse Fourier transform formula and approximate it by a sum over intervals of width $\omega_0$:

$$f_X(x) = \frac{1}{2\pi} \int_{-\infty}^{\infty} \Phi_X(\omega) e^{-j\omega x} \, d\omega$$

$$\simeq \frac{1}{2\pi} \sum_{m=-M}^{M-1} \Phi_X(m\omega_0) e^{-jm\omega_0 x} \omega_0, \tag{7.58}$$

where the sum neglects the integral outside the range $[-M\omega_0, M\omega_0)$. The above sum takes on the form of a DFT if we consider the pdf in the range $[-2\pi/\omega_0, 2\pi/\omega_0)$ with

$x = nd$, $d = 2\pi/N\omega_0$, and $N = 2M$:

$$f_X(nd) \simeq \frac{\omega_0}{2\pi} \sum_{m=-M}^{M-1} \Phi_X(m\omega_0)e^{-j2\pi nm/N} \qquad -M \leq n \leq M - 1. \qquad (7.59)$$

Equation (7.59) is a $2M$-point DFT of the sequence

$$c_m = \frac{\omega_0}{2\pi} \Phi_X(m\omega_0).$$

The FFT algorithm requires that $n$ range from 0 to $2M - 1$. Equation (7.59) can be cast into this form by recalling that the sequence $c_m$ is periodic with period $N$. An FFT algorithm will then calculate Eq. (7.59) if we input the sequence

$$c'_m = \begin{cases} c_m & 0 \leq m \leq M - 1 \\ c_{m-2M-1} & M < m \leq 2M - 1. \end{cases}$$

Three types of errors are introduced in approximating the pdf using Eq. (7.59). The first error involves approximating the integral by a sum. The second error results from neglecting the integral for frequencies outside the range $[-M\omega_0, M\omega_0)$. The third error results from neglecting the pdf outside the range $[-2\pi/\omega_0, 2\pi/\omega_0)$. The first and third errors are reduced by reducing $\omega_0$. The second error can be decreased by increasing $M$ while keeping $\omega_0$ fixed.

---

**Example 7.35**

The Laplacian random variable with parameter $\alpha = 1$ has characteristic function

$$\Phi_X(\omega) = \frac{1}{1 + \omega^2} \qquad -\infty < \omega < \infty.$$

Figures 7.17(a) and 7.17(b) compare the pdf with the approximation obtained using Eq. (7.59) with $N = 512$ points and two values of $\omega_0$. It can be seen that decreasing $\omega_0$ increases the accuracy of the approximation.

The Octave code for obtaining the figure is shown below. The first part shows the commands to generate the characteristic function and call the FFT function `fft_pxs`, which calculates the pdf. The function `fft_pxs` accepts a vector of values of the characteristic function from $-M$ (negative frequencies) to $M-1$ (positive frequencies). The function forms a new vector where the negative frequency terms are placed in the last $M$ entries. It performs the FFT and then shifts the results back.

    **(a)**  Interactive commands

```
>N=512
>M=N/2;
>w0=1;
>n=[-M:(M-1)];
>phix=1./1.+(w0^2*(n.*n));        % Evaluate the characteristic function.
>fx=zeros(size(n));
>[n1,x1,afx1]=fft_pxs(phix,w0,N);  % Find inverse of characteristic function.
>fx1=laplace_pdf(x1);              % Calculate exact pdf.
>plot(n1,afx1)
>hold on;
>plot (n1,fx1)
```

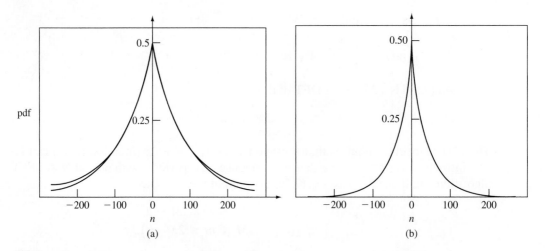

**FIGURE 7.17**
(a) Comparison of exact pdf and pdf obtained by numerically inverting the characteristic function of a Laplacian random variable. Approximation using $\omega_0 = 1$ and $N = 512$. (b) Comparison of exact pdf and pdf obtained by numerically inverting the characteristic function of a Laplacian random variable. Approximation using $\omega_0 = 1/2$ and $N = 512$.

**(b)** Function definition

```
function [n,t,rx]=fft_pxs(sx,w0,N)
% Accepts N=2M samples of frequency spectrum from
% frequency range −M w0 to (M−1) w0;
% Performs periodic extension before 2M-point FFT;
% Performs FFT shift and returns time function
% in time range −M d to (M−1)d, where d=2pi/Nw0
M=N/2;
n=[−M:(M−1)];
d=2*pi/(N*w0);
t=n.*d;
sxc=zeros(size(n));
for j=1:M
sxc(j)=sx(j+M);        % Positive frequency terms occupy first M entries.
sxc(j+M)=sx(j);        % Move negative frequency terms to last M entries.
end
rx=zeros(size(n));
rx=fft(sxc);           % Calculate the FFT.
rx=rx.*w0./(2.*pi);
rx=fftshift(rx);       % Rearrange vector values so negative amplitude
endfunction            % terms occupy first M entries.
```

## SUMMARY

- The expected value of a sum of random variables is always equal to the sum of the expected values of the random variables. In general, the variance of such a sum is not equal to the sum of the individual variances.
- The characteristic function of the sum of independent random variables is equal to the product of the characteristic functions of the individual random variables.

- The sample mean and the relative frequency estimators are used to estimate the expected value of random variables and the probabilities of events. The laws of large numbers state conditions under which these estimators approach the true values of the parameters they estimate as the number of samples becomes large.
- The central limit theorem states that the cdf of a sum of iid finite-mean, finite-variance random variables approaches that of a Gaussian random variable. This result allows us to approximate the pdf of sums of random variables by that of a Gaussian random variable.
- The Chernoff bound provides estimates of the probability of the tails of a distribution.
- A sequence of random variables can be viewed as a sequence of functions of $\zeta$, or as a family of sample sequences, one sample sequence for each $\zeta$ in $S$. Sure and almost-sure convergence address the question of whether all or almost all sample sequences converge. Mean square convergence and convergence in probability do not address the behavior of entire sample sequences but instead address the question of whether the sample sequences are "close" to some $X$ at some particular time instant.
- A counting process counts the number of occurrences of an event in a certain time interval. When the times between occurrences of events are iid random variables, the strong law of large numbers enables us to obtain results concerning the rate at which events occur, and results concerning various long-term time averages.
- The discrete Fourier transform and the FFT algorithm allow us to compute numerically the pmf and pdf of random variables from their characteristic functions.

## CHECKLIST OF IMPORTANT TERMS

Almost-sure convergence
Arrival rate
Central limit theorem
Chernoff bound
Convergence in distribution
Convergence in probability
Discrete Fourier transform
Fast Fourier transform
iid random variables

Relative frequency
Renewal counting process
Sample mean
Sample variance
Sequence of random variables
Strong law of large numbers
Sure convergence
Weak law of large numbers

## ANNOTATED REFERENCES

See Chung [1, pp. 220–233] for an insightful discussion of the laws of large numbers and the central limit theorem. Chapter 6 in Gnedenko [2] gives a detailed discussion of the laws of large numbers. Chapter 7 in Ross [3] focuses on counting processes and their properties. Cadzow [4] gives a good introduction to the FFT algorithm. Larson and Shubert [ref 8] and Stark and Woods [ref 9] contain excellent discussions on sequences of random variables.

1. K. L. Chung, *Elementary Probability Theory with Stochastic Processes*, Springer-Verlag, New York, 1975.
2. B. V. Gnedenko, *The Theory of Probability*, MIR Publishers, Moscow, 1976.

3. S. M. Ross, *Introduction to Probability Models*, Academic Press, New York, 2003.
4. J. A. Cadzow, *Foundations of Digital Signal Processing and Data Analysis*, Macmillan, New York, 1987.
5. P. L. Meyer, *Introductory Probability and Statistical Applications*, 2nd ed., Addison-Wesley, Reading, Mass., 1970.
6. J. W. Cooley, P. Lewis, and P. D. Welch, "The Fast Fourier Transform and Its Applications," *IEEE Transactions on Education*, vol. 12, pp. 27–34, March 1969.
7. H. J. Larson and B. O. Shubert, *Probability Models in Engineering Sciences*, vol. 1, Wiley, New York, 1979.
8. H. Stark and J. W. Woods, *Probability and Random Processes with Applications to Signal Processing*, 3d ed., Prentice Hall, Upper Saddle River, N.J., 2002.

## PROBLEMS

### Section 7.1: Sums of Random Variables

**7.1.** Let $Z = X + Y + Z$, where $X, Y$, and $Z$ are zero-mean, unit-variance random variables with $\text{COV}(X, Y) = 1/2$, and $\text{COV}(Y, Z) = -1/4$ and $\text{COV}(X, Z) = 1/2$.

   **(a)** Find the mean and variance of $Z$.

   **(b)** Repeat part a assuming $X, Y$, and $Z$ are uncorrelated random variables.

**7.2.** Let $X_1, \ldots, X_n$ be random variables with the same mean and with covariance function:

$$\text{COV}(X_i, X_j) = \begin{cases} \sigma^2 & \text{if } i = j \\ \rho\sigma^2 & \text{if } |i - j| = 1, \\ 0 & \text{otherwise,} \end{cases}$$

where $|\rho| < 1$. Find the mean and variance of $S_n = X_1 + \cdots + X_n$.

**7.3.** Let $X_1, \ldots, X_n$ be random variables with the same mean and with covariance function

$$\text{COV}(X_i, X_j) = \sigma^2 \rho^{|i-j|},$$

where $|\rho| < 1$. Find the mean and variance of $S_n = X_1 + \cdots + X_n$.

**7.4.** Let $X$ and $Y$ be independent Cauchy random variables with parameters 1 and 4, respectively. Let $Z = X + Y$.

   **(a)** Find the characteristic function of $Z$.

   **(b)** Find the pdf of $Z$ from the characteristic function found in part a.

**7.5.** Let $S_k = X_1 + \cdots + X_k$, where the $X_i$'s are independent random variables, with $X_i$ a chi-square random variable with $n_i$ degrees of freedom. Show that $S_k$ is a chi-square random variable with $n = n_1 + \cdots + n_k$ degrees of freedom.

**7.6.** Let $S_n = X_1^2 + \cdots + X_n^2$, where the $X_i$'s are iid zero-mean, unit-variance Gaussian random variables.

   **(a)** Show that $S_n$ is a chi-square random variable with $n$ degrees of freedom. *Hint:* See Example 4.34.

   **(b)** Use the methods of Section 4.5 to find the pdf of

$$T_n = \sqrt{X_1^2 + \cdots + X_n^2}.$$

(c)  Show that $T_2$ is a Rayleigh random variable.

(d)  Find the pdf for $T_3$. The random variable $T_3$ is used to model the speed of molecules in a gas. $T_3$ is said to have the Maxwell distribution.

**7.7.** Let $X$ and $Y$ be independent exponential random variables with parameters 2 and 10, respectively. Let $Z = X + Y$.

(a)  Find the characteristic function of $Z$.

(b)  Find the pdf of $Z$ from the characteristic function found in part a.

**7.8.** Let $Z = 3X - 7Y$, where $X$ and $Y$ are independent random variables.

(a)  Find the characteristic function of $Z$.

(b)  Find the mean and variance of $Z$ by taking derivatives of the characteristic function found in part a.

**7.9.** Let $M_n$ be the sample mean of $n$ iid random variables $X_j$. Find the characteristic function of $M_n$ in terms of the characteristic function of the $X_i$'s.

**7.10.** The number $X_j$ of raffle winners in classroom $j$ is a binomial random variable with parameter $n_j$ and $p$. Suppose that the school has $K$ classrooms. Find the pmf of the total number of raffle winners in the school, assuming the $X_i$'s are independent random variables.

**7.11.** The number of packet arrivals $X_i$ at port $i$ in a router is a Poisson random variable with mean $\alpha_i$. Given that the router has $k$ ports, find the pmf for the total number of packet arrivals at the router. Assume that the $X_i$'s are independent random variables.

**7.12.** Let $X_1, X_2, \ldots$ be a sequence of independent integer-valued random variables, let $N$ be an integer-valued random variable independent of the $X_j$, and let

$$S = \sum_{k=1}^{N} X_k.$$

(a)  Find the mean and variance of $S$.

(b)  Show that

$$G_S(z) = E(z^S) = G_N(G_X(z)),$$

where $G_X(z)$ is the generating function of each of the $X_k$'s.

**7.13.** Let the number of smashed-up cars arriving at a body shop in a week be a Poisson random variable with mean $L$. Each job repair costs $X_j$ dollars, the $X_j$'s are iid random variables that are equally likely to be \$500 or \$1000.

(a)  Find the mean and variance of the total revenue $R$ arriving in a week.

(b)  Find the $G_R(z) = E[z^R]$.

**7.14.** Let the number of widgets tested in an assembly line in 1 hour be a binomial random variable with parameters $n = 600$ and $p$. Suppose that the probability that a widget is faulty is $a$. Let $S$ be the number of widgets that are found faulty in a 1-hour period.

(a)  Find the mean and variance of $S$.

(b)  Find $G_S(z) = E[z^S]$.

## Section 7.2: The Sample Mean and the Laws of Large Numbers

**7.15.** Suppose that the number of particle emissions by a radioactive mass in $t$ seconds is a Poisson random variable with mean $\lambda t$. Use the Chebyshev inequality to obtain a bound for the probability that $|N(t)/t - \lambda|$ exceeds $\varepsilon$.

**7.16.** Suppose that 20% of voters are in favor of certain legislation. A large number $n$ of voters are polled and a relative frequency estimate $f_A(n)$ for the above proportion is obtained.

Use Eq. (7.20) to determine how many voters should be polled in order that the probability is at least .95 that $f_A(n)$ differs from 0.20 by less than 0.02.

**7.17.** A fair die is tossed 20 times. Use Eq. (7.20) to bound the probability that the total number of dots is between 60 and 80.

**7.18.** Let $X_i$ be a sequence of independent zero-mean, unit-variance Gaussian random variables. Compare the bound given by Eq. (7.20) with the exact value obtained from the $Q$ function for $n = 16$ and $n = 81$.

**7.19.** Does the weak law of large numbers hold for the sample mean if the $X_i$'s have the covariance functions given in Problem 7.2? Assume the $X_i$ have the same mean.

**7.20.** Repeat Problem 7.19 if the $X_i$'s have the covariance functions given in Problem 7.3.

**7.21.** (The **sample variance**) Let $X_1, \ldots, X_n$ be an iid sequence of random variables for which the mean and variance are unknown. The sample variance is defined as follows:

$$V_n^2 = \frac{1}{n-1} \sum_{j=1}^{n} (X_j - M_n)^2,$$

where $M_n$ is the sample mean.

**(a)**  Show that

$$\sum_{j=1}^{n} (X_j - \mu)^2 = \sum_{j=1}^{n} (X_j - M_n)^2 + n(M_n - \mu)^2.$$

**(b)**  Use the result in part a to show that

$$E\left[ k \sum_{j=1}^{n} (X_j - M_n)^2 \right] = k(n-1)\sigma^2.$$

**(c)**  Use part b to show that $E[V_n^2] = \sigma^2$. Thus $V_n^2$ is an unbiased estimator for the variance.

**(d)**  Find the expected value of the sample variance if $n - 1$ is replaced by $n$. Note that this is a biased estimator for the variance.

## Section 7.3: The Central Limit Theroem

**7.22. (a)**  A fair coin is tossed 100 times. Estimate the probability that the number of heads is between 40 and 60. Estimate the probability that the number is between 50 and 55.

**(b)**  Repeat part a for $n = 1000$ and the intervals $[400, 600]$ and $[500, 550]$.

**7.23.** Repeat Problem 7.16 using the central limit theorem.

**7.24.** Use the central limit theorem to estimate the probability in Problem 7.17.

**7.25.** The lifetime of a cheap light bulb is an exponential random variable with mean 36 hours. Suppose that 16 light bulbs are tested and their lifetimes measured. Use the central limit theorem to estimate the probability that the sum of the lifetimes is less than 600 hours.

**7.26.** A student uses pens whose lifetime is an exponential random variable with mean 1 week. Use the central limit theorem to determine the minimum number of pens he should buy at the beginning of a 15-week semester, so that with probability .99 he does not run out of pens during the semester.

**7.27.** Let $S$ be the sum of 80 iid Poisson random variables with mean 0.25. Compare the exact value of $P[S = k]$ to an approximation given by the central limit theorem as in Eq. (7.30).

**7.28.** The number of messages arriving at a multiplexer is a Poisson random variable with mean 15 messages/second. Use the central limit theorem to estimate the probability that more than 950 messages arrive in one minute.

**7.29.** A binary transmission channel introduces bit errors with probability .15. Estimate the probability that there are 20 or fewer errors in 100 bit transmissions.

**7.30.** The sum of a list of 100 real numbers is to be computed. Suppose that numbers are rounded off to the nearest integer so that each number has an error that is uniformly distributed in the interval $(-0.5, 0.5)$. Use the central limit theorem to estimate the probability that the total error in the sum of the 64 numbers exceeds 4.

**7.31.** **(a)** A fair coin is tossed 100 times. Use the Chernoff bound to estimate the probability that the number of heads is greater than 90. Compare to an estimate using the central limit theorem.

**(b)** Repeat part a for $n = 1000$ and the probability that the number of heads is greater than 650.

**7.32.** A binary transmission channel introduces bit errors with probability .01. Use the Chernoff bound to estimate the probability that there are more than 3 errors in 100 bit transmissions. Compare to an estimate using the central limit theorem.

**7.33.** **(a)** When you play the rock/paper/scissors game against your sister you lose with probability 3/5. Use the Chernoff bound to estimate the probability that you win more than half of 20 games played.

**(b)** Repeat for 100 games.

**(c)** Use trial and error to find the number of games $n$ that need to be played so that the probability that your sister wins more than 1/2 the games is 90%.

**7.34.** Show that the Chernoff bound for $X$, a Poisson random variable with mean $\alpha$, is $P[X \geq a] \leq e^{-a \ln(a/\alpha) + a - \alpha}$ for $a > \alpha$. *Hint:* Use $E[e^{sX}] = e^{\alpha(e^s - 1)}$.

**7.35.** Redo Problem 7.26 using the Chernoff bound.

**7.36.** Show that the Chernoff bound for $X$, a Gaussian random variable with mean $\mu$ and variance $\sigma^2$, is $P[X \geq a] \leq e^{-(a-\mu)^2/2\sigma^2}$, $a > \mu$. *Hint:* Use $E[e^{sX}] = e^{s\mu + s^2\sigma^2/2}$.

**7.37.** Compare the Chernoff bound for the Gaussian random variable with the estimates provided by Eq. (4.54).

**7.38.** **(a)** Find the Chernoff bound for the exponential random variable with rate $\lambda$.

**(b)** Compare the exact probability of $P[X \geq k/\lambda]$ with the Chernoff bound.

**7.39.** **(a)** Generalize the approach in Problem 7.38 to find the Chernoff bound for a gamma random variable with parameters $\lambda$ and $\alpha$.

**(b)** Use the result of part a to obtain the Chernoff bound for a chi-square random variable with $k$ degrees of freedom.

**\*Section 7.4: Convergence of Sequences of Random Variables**

**7.40.** Let $U_n(\zeta), W_n(\zeta), Y_n(\zeta)$, and $Z_n(\zeta)$ be the sequences of random variables defined in Example 7.18.

**(a)** Plot the sequence of functions of $\zeta$ associated with each sequence of random variables.

**(b)** For $\zeta = 1/4$, plot the associated sample sequence.

**7.41.** Let $\zeta$ be selected at random from the interval $S = [0, 1]$, and let the probability that $\zeta$ is in a subinterval of $S$ be given by the length of the subinterval. Define the following sequences of random variables for $n \geq 1$:

$$X_n(\zeta) = \zeta^n, Y_n(\zeta) = \cos^2 2\pi\zeta, Z_n(\zeta) = \cos^n 2\pi\zeta.$$

Do the sequences converge, and if so, in what sense and to what limiting random variable?

**7.42.** Let $b_i, i \geq 1$, be a sequence of iid, equiprobable Bernoulli random variables, and let $\zeta$ be the number between $[0, 1]$ determined by the binary expansion

$$\zeta = \sum_{i=1}^{\infty} b_i 2^{-i}.$$

**(a)** Explain why $\zeta$ is uniformly distributed in $[0, 1]$.

**(b)** How would you use this definition of $\zeta$ to generate the sample sequences that occur in the urn problem of Example 7.20?

**7.43.** Let $X_n$ be a sequence of iid, equiprobable Bernoulli random variables, and let

$$Y_n = 2^n X_1 X_2 \ldots X_n.$$

**(a)** Plot a sample sequence. Does this sequence converge almost surely, and if so, to what limit?

**(b)** Does this sequence converge in the mean square sense?

**7.44.** Let $X_n$ be a sequence of iid random variables with mean $m$ and variance $\sigma^2 < \infty$. Let $M_n$ be the associated sequence of arithmetic averages,

$$M_n = \frac{1}{n} \sum_{i=0}^{n} X_i.$$

Show that $M_n$ converges to $m$ in the mean square sense.

**7.45.** Let $X_n$ and $Y_n$ be two (possibly dependent) sequences of random variables that converge in the mean square sense to $X$ and $Y$, respectively. Does the sequence $X_n + Y_n$ converge in the mean square sense, and if so, to what limit?

**7.46.** Let $U_n$ be a sequence of iid zero-mean, unit-variance Gaussian random variables. A "low-pass filter" takes the sequence $U_n$ and produces the sequence

$$X_n = \frac{1}{2}(U_n + U_{n-1}).$$

**(a)** Does this sequence converge in the mean square sense?

**(b)** Does it converge in distribution?

**7.47.** Does the sequence of random variables introduced in Example 7.20 converge in the mean square sense?

**7.48.** Customers arrive at an automated teller machine at discrete instants of time, $n = 1, 2, \ldots$. The number of customer arrivals in a time instant is a Bernoulli random variable with parameter $p$, and the sequence of arrivals is iid. Assume the machine services a customer in less than one time unit. Let $X_n$ be the total number of customers served by the machine up to time $n$. Suppose that the machine fails at time $N$, where $N$ is a geometric random variable with mean 100, so that the customer count remains at $X_N$ thereafter.

**(a)** Sketch a sample sequence for $X_n$.

**(b)** Do the sample sequences converge almost surely, and if so, to what limit?

**(c)** Do the sample sequences converge in the mean square sense?

**7.49.** Show that the sequence $Y_n(\zeta)$ defined in Example 7.18 converges in distribution.

**7.50.** Let $X_n$ be a sequence of Laplacian random variables with parameter $\alpha = n$. Does this sequence converge in distribution?

## *Section 7.5: Long-Term Arrival Rates and Associated Averages

**7.51.** The customer arrival times at a bus depot are iid exponential random variables with mean 1 minute. Suppose that buses leave as soon as 30 seats are full. At what rate do buses leave the depot?

**7.52.** A faulty clock ticks forward every minute with probability $p = 0.1$ and it does not tick forward with probability $1 - p$. What is the rate at which this clock moves forward?

**7.53.** **(a)** Show that $\{N(t) \geq n\}$ and $\{S_n \leq t\}$ are equivalent events.

  **(b)** Use part a to find $P[N(t) \leq n]$ when the $X_i$ are iid exponential random variables with mean $1/\alpha$.

**7.54.** Explain why the following are not equivalent events:

  **(a)** $\{N(t) \leq n\}$ and $\{S_n \geq t\}$.

  **(b)** $\{N(t) > n\}$ and $\{S_n < t\}$.

**7.55.** A communication channel alternates between periods when it is error free and periods during which it introduces errors. Assuming that these periods are independent random variables of means $m_1 = 100$ hours and $m_2 = 1$ minute, respectively, find the long-term proportion of time during which the channel is error free.

**7.56.** A worker works at a rate $r_1$ when the boss is around and at a rate $r_2$ when the boss is not present. Suppose that the sequence of durations of the time periods when the boss is present and absent are independent random variables with means $m_1$ and $m_2$, respectively. Find the long-term average rate at which the worker works.

**7.57.** A computer (repairman) continuously cycles through three tasks (machines). Suppose that each time the computer services task $i$, it spends time $X_i$ doing so.

  **(a)** What is the long-term rate at which the computer cycles through the three tasks?

  **(b)** What is the long-term proportion of time spent by the computer servicing task $i$?

  **(c)** Repeat parts a and b if a random time $W$ is required for the computer (repairman) to switch (walk) from one task (machine) to another.

**7.58.** Customers arrive at a phone booth and use the phone for a random time $Y$, with mean 3 minutes, if the phone is free. If the phone is not free, the customers leave immediately. Suppose that the time between customer arrivals is an exponential random variable with mean 10 minutes.

  **(a)** Find the long-term rate at which customers use the phone.

  **(b)** Find the long-term proportion of customers that leave without using the phone.

**7.59.** The lifetime of a certain system component is an exponential random variable with mean $T = 2$ months. Suppose that the component is replaced when it fails or when it reaches the age of $3T$ months.

  **(a)** Find the long-term rate at which components are replaced.

  **(b)** Find the long-term rate at which working components are replaced.

**7.60.** A data compression encoder segments a stream of information bits into patterns as shown below. Each pattern is then encoded into the codeword shown below.

| Pattern | Codeword | Probability |
|---------|----------|-------------|
| 1       | 100      | .1          |
| 01      | 101      | .09         |
| 001     | 110      | .081        |
| 0001    | 111      | .0729       |
| 0000    | 0        | .6521       |

(a) If the information source produces a bit every millisecond, find the rate at which codewords are produced.

(b) Find the long-term ratio of encoded bits to information bits.

**7.61.** In Example 7.29 evaluate the proportion of time that the residual lifetime $r(t)$ exceeds $c$ seconds for the following cases:

(a) $X_j$ iid uniform random variables in the interval $[0, 2]$.

(b) $X_j$ iid exponential random variables with mean 1.

(c) $X_j$ iid Rayleigh random variables with mean 1.

(d) Calculate and compare the mean residual time in each of the above three cases.

**7.62.** Let the age $a(t)$ of a cycle be defined as the time that has elapsed from the last arrival up to an arbitrary time instant $t$. Show that the long-term proportion of time that $a(t)$ exceeds $c$ seconds is given by Eq. (7.48).

**7.63.** Suppose that the cost in each cycle grows at a rate proportional to the age $a(t)$ of the cycle, that is,

$$C_j = \int_0^{X_j} a(t')\, dt'.$$

(a) Show that $C_j = X_j^2/2$.

(b) Show that the long-term rate at which the cost grows is $E[X^2]/2E[X]$.

(c) Show that the result in part b is also the long-term time average of $a(t)$, that is,

$$\lim_{t \to \infty} \frac{1}{t} \int_0^t a(t')\, dt' = \frac{E[X^2]}{2E[X]}.$$

(d) Explain why the average residual life is also given by the above expression.

**7.64.** Calculate the mean age and mean residual life in Problem 7.63 in the following cases:

(a) $X_j$ iid uniform random variables in the interval $[0, 2]$.

(b) $X_j$ iid exponential random variables with mean 1.

(c) $X_j$ iid Rayleigh random variables with mean 1.

**7.65.** (The Regenerative Method) Suppose that a queueing system has the property that when a customer arrives and finds an empty system, the future behavior of the system is completely independent of the past. Define a cycle to consist of the time period between two consecutive customer arrivals to an empty system. Let $N_j$ be the number of customers served during the $j$th cycle and let $T_j$ be the total delay of all customers served during the $j$th cycle.

(a) Use Theorem 2 to show that the average customer delay is given by $E[T]/E[N]$, that is,

$$\lim_{n \to \infty} \frac{1}{n} \sum_{k=1}^n D_k = \frac{E[T]}{E[N]},$$

where $D_k$ is the delay of the $k$th customer.

(b) How would you use this result to estimate the average delay in a computer simulation of a queueing system?

## *Section 7.6: Calculating Distributions Using the Discrete Fourier Transform

**7.66.** Let the discrete random variable $X$ be uniformly distributed in the set $\{0, 1, 2\}$.

(a) Find the $N = 3$ DFT for $X$.

(b) Use the inverse DFT to recover $P[X = 1]$.

**7.67.** Let $S = X + Y$, where $X$ and $Y$ are iid random variables uniformly distributed in the set $\{0, 1, 2\}$.

    **(a)** Find the $N = 5$ DFT for $S$.

    **(b)** Use the inverse DFT to find $P[S = 2]$.

**7.68.** Let $X$ be a binomial random variable with parameter $n = 8$ and $p = 1/2$.

    **(a)** Use the FFT to obtain the pmf of $X$ from $\Phi_X(\omega)$.

    **(b)** Use the FFT to obtain the pmf of $Z = X + Y$ where $X$ and $Y$ are iid binomial random variables with $n = 8$ and $p = 1/2$.

**7.69.** Let $X_i$ be a discrete random variable that is uniformly distributed in the set $\{0, 1, \ldots, 9\}$. Use the FFT to find the pmf of $S_n = X_1 + \cdots + X_n$ for $n = 5$ and $n = 10$. Plot your results and compare them to Fig. 7.16.

**7.70.** Let $X$ be the geometric random variable with parameter $p = 1/2$. Use the FFT to evaluate Eq. (7.55) to compute $p_k'$ for $N = 8$ and $N = 16$. Compare the results to those given by Eq. (7.57).

**7.71.** Let $X$ be a Poisson random variable with mean $L = 5$.

    **(a)** Use the FFT to obtain the pmf from $\Phi_X(\omega)$. Find the value of $N$ for which the error in Eq. (7.55) is less than 1%.

    **(b)** Let $S = X_1 + X_2 + \cdots + X_5$, where the $X_i$ are iid Poisson random variables with mean $L = 5$. Use the FFT to compute the pmf of $S$ from $\Phi_X(\omega)$.

**7.72.** The probability generating function for the number $N$ of customers in a certain queueing system (the so-called M/D/1 system discussed in Chapter 12) is

$$G_N(z) = \frac{(1 - \rho)(1 - z)}{1 - z e^{\rho(1-z)}},$$

where $0 \le \rho \le 1$. Use the FFT to obtain the pmf of $N$ for $\rho = 1/2$.

**7.73.** Use the FFT to obtain approximately the pdf of a Laplacian random variable from its characteristic function. Use the same parameters as in Example 7.33 and compare your results to those shown in Fig. 7.17.

**7.74.** Use the FFT to obtain approximately the pdf of $Z = X + Y$, where $X$ and $Y$ are independent Laplacian random variables with parameters $\alpha = 1$ and $\alpha = 2$, respectively.

**7.75.** Use the FFT to obtain approximately the pdf of a zero-mean, unit-variance Gaussian random variable from its characteristic function. Experiment with the values of $N$ and $\omega_0$ and compare the results given by the FFT with the exact values.

**7.76.** Figures 7.2 through 7.4 for the cdf of the sum of iid Bernoulli, uniform, and exponential random variables were obtained using the FFT. Reproduce the results shown in these figures.

## Problems Requiring Cumulative Knowledge

**7.77.** The number $X$ of type 1 defects in a system is a binomial random variable with parameters $n$ and $p$, and the number $Y$ of type 2 defects is binomial with parameters $m$ and $r$.

    **(a)** Find the probability generating function for the total number of defects in the system.

    **(b)** Find an expression for the probability that the total number of defects is $k$.

    **(c)** Let $n = 32$, $p = 1/10$, and $m = 16$, $r = 1/8$. Use the FFT to evaluate the pmf for the total number of defects in the system.

**7.78.** Let $U_n$ be a sequence of iid zero-mean, unit-variance Gaussian random variables. A "low-pass filter" takes the sequence $U_n$ and produces the sequence

$$X_n = \frac{1}{2}U_n + \left(\frac{1}{2}\right)^2 U_{n-1} + \cdots + \left(\frac{1}{2}\right)^n U_1.$$

(a) Find the mean and variance of $X_n$.

(b) Find the characteristic function of $X_n$. What happens as $n$ approaches infinity?

(c) Does this sequence of random variables converge? In what sense?

**7.79.** Let $S_n$ be the sum of a sequence of $X_i$'s that are jointly Gaussian random variables with mean $\mu$ and with the covariance function given in Problem 7.2.

(a) Find the characteristic function of $S_n$.

(b) Find the mean and variance of $S_n - S_m$.

(c) Find the joint characteristic function of $S_n$ and $S_m$. *Hint:* Assuming $n > m$, condition on the value of $S_m$.

(d) Does $S_n$ converge in the mean square sense?

**7.80.** Repeat Problem 7.79 with the sequence of $X_i$'s given as jointly Gaussian random variables with mean and covariance functions given in Problem 7.3.

**7.81.** Let $Z_n$ be the sequence of random variables defined in the formulation of the central limit theorem, Eq. (7.26a). Does $Z_n$ converge in the mean square sense?

**7.82.** Let $X_n$ be the sequence of independent, identically distributed outputs of an information source. At time $n$, the source produces symbols according to the following probabilities:

| Symbol | Probability | Codeword |
|--------|-------------|----------|
| A | 1/2 | 0 |
| B | 1/4 | 10 |
| C | 1/8 | 110 |
| D | 1/16 | 1110 |
| E | 1/16 | 1111 |

(a) The self-information of the output at time $n$ is defined by the random variable $Y_n = -\log_2 P[X_n]$. Thus, for example, if the output is $C$, the self-information is $-\log_2 1/8 = 3$. Find the mean and variance of $Y_n$. Note that the expected value of the self-information is equal to the entropy of $X$ (cf. Section 4.10).

(b) Consider the sequence of arithmetic averages of the self-information:

$$S_n = \frac{1}{n}\sum_{k=1}^{n} Y_k.$$

Do the weak law and strong law of large numbers apply to $S_n$?

(c) Now suppose that the outputs of the information source are encoded using the variable-length binary codewords indicated above. Note that the length of the codewords corresponds to the self-information of the corresponding symbol. Interpret the result of part b in terms of the rate at which bits are produced when the above code is applied to the information source outputs.

# Statistics

Probability theory allows us to model situations that exhibit randomness in terms of random experiments involving sample spaces, events, and probability distributions. The axioms of probability allow us to develop an extensive set of tools for calculating probabilities and averages for a wide array of random experiments. The field of statistics plays the key role of bridging probability models to the real world. In applying probability models to real situations, we must perform experiments and gather data to answer questions such as:

- What are the values of parameters, e.g., mean and variance, of a random variable of interest?
- Are the observed data consistent with an assumed distribution?
- Are the observed data consistent with a given parameter value of a random variable?

Statistics is concerned with the gathering and analysis of data and with the drawing of conclusions or inferences from the data. The methods from statistics provide us with the means to answer the above questions.

In this chapter we first consider the estimation of parameters of random variables. We develop methods for obtaining point estimates as well as confidence intervals for parameters of interest. We then consider hypothesis testing and develop methods that allow us to accept or reject statements about a random variable based on observed data. We will apply these methods to determine the goodness of fit of distributions to observed data.

The Gaussian random variable plays a crucial role in statistics. We note that the Gaussian random variable is referred to as the **normal random variable** in the statistics literature.

## 8.1 SAMPLES AND SAMPLING DISTRIBUTIONS

The origin of the term "statistics" is in the gathering of data about the *population* in a state or locality in order to draw conclusions about properties of the population, e.g., potential tax revenue or size of pool of potential army recruits. Typically the

size of a population was too large to make an exhaustive analysis, so *statistical inferences* about the entire population were drawn based on observations from a *sample*
of individuals.

The term **population** is still used in statistics, but it now refers to the collection
of all objects or elements under study in a given situation. We suppose that the property of interest is observable and measurable, and that it can be modeled by a random
variable $X$. We gather observation data by taking samples from the population. In
order for inferences about the population to be valid, it is important that the individuals in the sample be representative of the entire population. In essence, we
require that the $n$ observations be made from random experiments conducted
under the same conditions. For this reason we define a **random sample $\mathbf{X}_n =$**
$(X_1, X_2, \ldots, X_n)$ as consisting of $n$ independent random variables with the same
distribution as $X$.

Statistical methods invariably involve performing calculations on the observed
data. For example, we might be interested in inferring the values of a certain parameter
$\theta$ of the population, that is, of the random variable $X$, such as the mean, variance, or
probability of a certain event. We may also be interested in drawing conclusions about
$\theta$ based on $\mathbf{X}_n$. Typically we calculate a **statistic** based on the random sample
$\mathbf{X}_n = (X_1, X_2, \ldots, X_n)$:

$$\hat{\Theta}(\mathbf{X}_n) = g(X_1, X_2, \ldots, X_n). \tag{8.1}$$

In other words, *a statistic is simply a function of the random vector $\mathbf{X}_n$.* Clearly the
statistic $\hat{\Theta}$ is itself a random variable, and so is subject to random variability. Therefore
estimates, inferences and conclusions based on the statistic must be stated in probabilistic terms.

We have already encountered statistics to estimate important parameters of a
random variable. The *sample mean* is used to estimate the expected value of a random
variable $X$:

$$\overline{X}_n = \frac{1}{n} \sum_{j=1}^{n} X_j. \tag{8.2}$$

The *relative frequency* of an event $A$ is a special case of a sample mean and is used to
estimate the probability of $A$:

$$f_A(n) = \frac{1}{n} \sum_{j=1}^{n} I_j(A). \tag{8.3}$$

Other statistics involve estimation of the variance of $X$, the minimum and maximum of
$X$, and the correlation between random variables $X$ and $Y$.

The **sampling distribution** of a statistic $\hat{\Theta}$ is given by its probability distribution (cdf, pdf, or pmf). The sampling distribution allows us to calculate parameters
of $\hat{\Theta}$, e.g., mean, variance, and moments, as well as probabilities involving $\hat{\Theta}$,
$P[a < \hat{\Theta} < b]$. We will see that the sampling distribution and its parameters allow us to
determine the accuracy and quality of the statistic $\hat{\Theta}$.

### Example 8.1    Mean and Variance of the Sample Mean

Suppose that $X$ has expected value $E[X] = \mu$ and variance $\text{VAR}[X] = \sigma_X^2$. Find the mean and variance of $\hat{\Theta}(\mathbf{X}_n) = \overline{X}_n$, the sample mean.

The expected value of $\overline{X}_n$ is given by:

$$E[\overline{X}_n] = \frac{1}{n} E\left[ \sum_{j=1}^{n} X_j \right] = \mu. \tag{8.4}$$

The variance of $\overline{X}_n$ is given by:

$$\text{VAR}[\overline{X}_n] = \frac{1}{n^2} \text{VAR}\left[ \sum_{j=1}^{n} X_j \right] = \frac{\sigma_X^2}{n}, \tag{8.5}$$

since the $X_i$ are iid random variables. Equation (8.4) asserts that the sample mean is centered about the true mean $m$, and Eq. (8.5) states that the sample-mean estimates become clustered about $m$ as $n$ is increased. The Chebyshev inequality then leads to the weak law of large numbers which then asserts that $\hat{\Theta}(\mathbf{X}_n) = \overline{X}_n$ converges to $m$ in probability.

### Example 8.2    Sampling Distribution for the Sample Mean of Gaussian Random Variables

Let $X$ be a Gaussian random variable with expected value $E[X] = \mu$ and variance $\text{VAR}[X] = \sigma_X^2$. Find the distribution of the sample mean based on iid observations $X_1, X_2, \ldots, X_n$.

If the samples $X_i$ are iid Gaussian random variables, then from Example 6.24 $\overline{X}_n$ is also a Gaussian random variable with mean and variance given by Eqs. (8.4) and (8.5). We will see that many important statistical methods involve the following "one-tail" probability for the sample mean of Gaussian random variables:

$$\alpha = P\left[\overline{X}_n - \mu > c\right] = P\left[ \frac{\overline{X}_n - \mu}{\sigma_X/\sqrt{n}} > \frac{c}{\sigma_X/\sqrt{n}} \right]$$

$$= Q\left( \frac{c}{\sigma_X/\sqrt{n}} \right). \tag{8.6}$$

Let $z_\alpha$ be the **critical value** for the standard (zero-mean, unit-variance) Gaussian random variable as shown in Fig. 8.1, so that

$$\alpha = Q(z_\alpha) = Q\left( \frac{c}{\sigma_X/\sqrt{n}} \right).$$

The desired value for the constant $c$ in the one-tail probability is:

$$c = \frac{\sigma_X}{\sqrt{n}} z_\alpha. \tag{8.7}$$

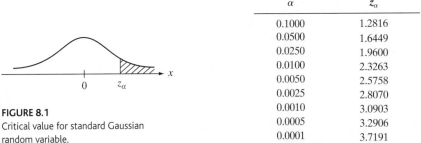

**FIGURE 8.1**
Critical value for standard Gaussian random variable.

**TABLE 8.1**  Critical values for standard Gaussian random variable.

| $\alpha$ | $z_\alpha$ |
|---|---|
| 0.1000 | 1.2816 |
| 0.0500 | 1.6449 |
| 0.0250 | 1.9600 |
| 0.0100 | 2.3263 |
| 0.0050 | 2.5758 |
| 0.0025 | 2.8070 |
| 0.0010 | 3.0903 |
| 0.0005 | 3.2906 |
| 0.0001 | 3.7191 |

Table 8.1 shows common critical values for the Gaussian random variable. Thus for the one-tail probability with $\alpha = 0.05$, $z_\alpha = 1.6449$ and $c = 1.6449\sigma_X/\sqrt{n}$.

In the "two-tail" case we are interested in:

$$1 - \alpha = P\left[-c \leq \overline{X}_n - \mu \leq c\right] = P\left[\frac{-c}{\sigma_X/\sqrt{n}} \leq \frac{\overline{X}_n - \mu}{\sigma_X/\sqrt{n}} \leq \frac{c}{\sigma_X/\sqrt{n}}\right]$$

$$= 1 - 2Q\left(\frac{c}{\sigma_X/\sqrt{n}}\right).$$

Let $\alpha/2 = Q(z_{\alpha/2})$, then the desired value of constant $c$ is:

$$c = \frac{\sigma_X}{\sqrt{n}}z_{\alpha/2}. \tag{8.8}$$

For the two-tail probability with $\alpha = 0.010$ then $z_{\alpha/2} = 2.5758$ and $c = 2.5758\sigma_X/\sqrt{n}$.

---

### Example 8.3    Sampling Distribution for the Sample Mean, Large $n$

When $X$ is not Gaussian but has finite mean and variance, then by the central limit theorem we have that for large $n$,

$$\frac{\overline{X}_n - \mu}{\sigma_X/\sqrt{n}} = \sqrt{n}\frac{\overline{X}_n - \mu}{\sigma_X} \tag{8.9}$$

has approximately a zero-mean, unit-variance Gaussian distribution. Therefore when the number of samples is large, the sample mean is approximately Gaussian. This allows us to compute probabilities involving $\overline{X}_n$ even though we do not know the distribution of $X$. This result finds numerous applications in statistics when the number of samples $n$ is large.

---

### Example 8.4    Sampling Distribution of Binomial Random Variable

We wish to estimate the probability of error $p$ in a binary communication channel. We transmit a predetermined sequence of bits and observe the corresponding received sequence to determine the sequence of transmission errors, $I_1, I_2, \ldots, I_n$, where $I_j$ is the indicator function for the occurrence of the event $A$ that corresponds to an error in the $j$th transmission. Let $N_A(n)$ be the total number of errors. The relative frequency of errors is used to estimate the probability of error $p$:

$$f_A(n) = \frac{1}{n}\sum_{j=1}^{n} I_j(A) = \frac{N_A(n)}{n}.$$

Assuming that the outcomes of different transmissions are independent, then the number of errors in the $n$ transmissions, $N_A(n)$, is a binomial random variable with parameters $n$ and $p$. The mean and variance of $f_A(n)$ are then:

$$E[f_A(n)] = \frac{np}{n} = p \quad \text{and} \quad \mathrm{VAR}[f_A(n)] = \frac{np(1-p)}{n^2}.$$

Using the approach from Example 7.10, we can bound the variance of $f_A(n)$ by $1/4n$, and use the Chebyshev inequality to estimate the number of samples required so that there is some probability, say $1 - \alpha$, that $f_A(n)$ is within $\varepsilon$ of $p$.

$$P\big[|f_A(n) - p| < \varepsilon\big] > 1 - \frac{1}{4n\varepsilon^2} = 1 - \alpha.$$

For $n$ large, we can apply the central limit theorem where

$$Z_n = \frac{f_A(n) - p}{\sqrt{1/4n}}$$

is approximately Gaussian with mean zero and unit variance. We then obtain:

$$P[|f_A(n) - p| < \varepsilon] = P[|Z_n| < \varepsilon\sqrt{4n}] \approx 1 - 2Q(\varepsilon\sqrt{4n}) = 1 - \alpha.$$

For example, if $\alpha = 0.05$, then $\varepsilon\sqrt{4n} = z_{\alpha/2} = 1.96$ and $n = 1.96^2/4\varepsilon^2$.

## 8.2    PARAMETER ESTIMATION

In this section, we consider the problem of estimating a parameter $\theta$ of a random variable $X$. We suppose that we have obtained a **random sample** $\mathbf{X}_n = (X_1, X_2, \ldots, X_n)$ consisting of independent, identically distributed versions of $X$. Our estimator is given by a function of $\mathbf{X}_n$:

$$\hat{\Theta}(\mathbf{X}_n) = g(X_1, X_2, \ldots, X_n). \tag{8.10}$$

After making our $n$ observations, we have the values $(x_1, x_2, \ldots, x_n)$ and evaluate the estimate for $\theta$ by a *single value* $g(x_1, x_2, \ldots, x_n)$. For this reason $\hat{\Theta}(\mathbf{X}_n)$ is called a **point estimator** for the parameter $\theta$.

We consider the following three questions:

1. What properties characterize a good estimator?
2. How do we determine that an estimator is better than another?
3. How do we find good estimators?

In addressing the above questions, we also introduce a variety of useful estimators.

### 8.2.1    Properties of Estimators

Ideally, a good estimator should be equal to the parameter $\theta$, on the average. We say that the estimator $\hat{\Theta}$ is an **unbiased estimator** for $\theta$ if

$$E[\hat{\Theta}] = \theta. \tag{8.11}$$

The **bias** of any estimator $\hat{\Theta}$ is defined by

$$B[\hat{\Theta}] = E[\hat{\Theta}] - \theta. \tag{8.12}$$

From Eq. (8.4) in Example 8.1, we see that *the sample mean is an unbiased estimator for the mean $\mu$*. However, biased estimators are not unusual as illustrated by the following example.

---

### Example 8.5    The Sample Variance

The sample mean gives us an estimate of the center of mass of observations of a random variable. We are also interested in the spread of these observations about this center of mass. An obvious estimator for the variance $\sigma_X^2$ of $X$ is the arithmetic average of the square variation about the sample mean:

$$\hat{S}^2 = \frac{1}{n}\sum_{j=1}^{n}(X_j - \overline{X}_n)^2 \tag{8.13}$$

where the sample mean is given by:

$$\overline{X}_n = \frac{1}{n}\sum_{j=1}^{n}X_j. \tag{8.14}$$

Let's check whether $\hat{S}^2$ is an unbiased estimator. First, we rewrite Eq. (8.13):

$$\hat{S}^2 = \frac{1}{n}\sum_{j=1}^{n}(X_j - \overline{X}_n)^2 = \frac{1}{n}\sum_{j=1}^{n}(X_j - \mu + \mu - \overline{X}_n)^2$$

$$= \frac{1}{n}\sum_{j=1}^{n}\left\{(X_j - \mu)^2 + 2(X_j - \mu)(\mu - \overline{X}_n) + (\mu - \overline{X}_n)^2\right\}$$

$$= \frac{1}{n}\sum_{j=1}^{n}(X_j - \mu)^2 + \frac{2}{n}(\mu - \overline{X}_n)\sum_{j=1}^{n}(X_j - \mu) + \frac{1}{n}\sum_{j=1}^{n}(\mu - \overline{X}_n)^2$$

$$= \frac{1}{n}\sum_{j=1}^{n}(X_j - \mu)^2 + \frac{2}{n}(\mu - \overline{X}_n)(n\overline{X}_n - n\mu) + \frac{n(\mu - \overline{X}_n)^2}{n}$$

$$= \frac{1}{n}\sum_{j=1}^{n}(X_j - \mu)^2 - 2(\overline{X}_n - \mu)^2 + (\overline{X}_n - \mu)^2$$

$$= \frac{1}{n}\sum_{j=1}^{n}(X_j - \mu)^2 - (\overline{X}_n - \mu)^2. \tag{8.15}$$

The expected value of $\hat{S}^2$ is then:

$$E[\hat{S}^2] = E\left[\frac{1}{n}\sum_{j=1}^{n}(X_j - \mu)^2 - (\overline{X}_n - \mu)^2\right]$$

$$= \frac{1}{n}\sum_{j=1}^{n}[E[(X_j - \mu)^2] - E[(\overline{X}_n - \mu)^2]]$$

$$= \sigma_X^2 - \frac{\sigma_X^2}{n} = \frac{n-1}{n}\sigma_X^2 \qquad (8.16)$$

where we used Eq. (8.2) for the variance of the sample mean. Equation (8.16) shows that the simple estimator given by Eq. (8.13) is a *biased* estimator for the variance. We can obtain an **unbiased estimator for** $\sigma_X^2$ by dividing the sum in Eq. (8.15) by $n - 1$ instead of by $n$:

$$\hat{\sigma}_n^2 = \frac{1}{n-1}\sum_{j=1}^{n}(X_j - \overline{X}_n)^2. \qquad (8.17)$$

Equation (8.17) is used as the standard estimator for the variance of a random variable.

---

A second measure of the quality of an estimator is the **mean square estimation error**:

$$E[(\hat{\Theta} - \theta)^2] = E[(\hat{\Theta} - E[\hat{\Theta}] + E[\hat{\Theta}] - \theta)^2]$$

$$= \text{VAR}[\hat{\Theta}] + B(\hat{\Theta})^2. \qquad (8.18)$$

Obviously a good estimator should have a small mean square estimation error because this implies that the estimator values are clustered close to $\theta$. If $\hat{\Theta}$ is an unbiased estimator of $\theta$, then $B[\hat{\Theta}] = 0$ and the mean square error is simply the variance of the estimator $\hat{\Theta}$. In comparing two unbiased estimators, we clearly prefer the one with the smallest estimator variance. The comparison of biased estimators with unbiased estimators can be tricky. It is possible for a biased estimator to have a smaller mean square error than any unbiased estimator [Hardy]. In such situations the biased estimator may be preferable.

The observant student will have noted that we already considered the problem of finding minimum mean square estimators in Chapter 6. In that discussion we were estimating the value of one random variable $Y$ by a function of one or more observed random variables $X_1, X_2, \ldots, X_n$. In this section we are estimating a parameter $\theta$ that is unknown but not random.

---

### Example 8.6    Estimators for the Exponential Random Variable

The message interarrival times at a message center are exponential random variables with rate $\lambda$ messages per second. Compare the following two estimators for $\theta = 1/\lambda$ the mean interarrival time:

$$\hat{\Theta}_1 = \frac{1}{n}\sum_{j=1}^{n} X_j \quad \text{and} \quad \hat{\Theta}_2 = n^* \min(X_1, X_2, \ldots, X_n). \tag{8.19}$$

The first estimator is simply the sample mean of the observed interarrival times. The second estimator uses the fact from Example 6.10 that the minimum of $n$ iid exponential random variables is itself an exponential random variable with mean interarrival time $1/n\lambda$.

$\hat{\Theta}_1$ is the sample mean so we know that it is an unbiased estimator and that its mean square error is:

$$E\left[\left(\hat{\Theta}_1 - \frac{1}{\lambda}\right)^2\right] = \text{VAR}[\hat{\Theta}_1] = \frac{\sigma_X^2}{n} = \frac{1}{n\lambda^2}.$$

On the other hand, $\min(X_1, X_2, \ldots, X_n)$ is an exponential random variable with mean interarrival time $1/n\lambda$, so

$$E[\hat{\Theta}_2] = E[n^* \min(X_1, \ldots, X_n)] = \frac{n}{n\lambda} = \frac{1}{\lambda}.$$

Therefore $\hat{\Theta}_2$ is also an unbiased estimator for $\theta = 1/\lambda$. The mean square error is:

$$E\left[\left(\hat{\Theta}_2 - \frac{1}{\lambda}\right)^2\right] = \text{VAR}[\hat{\Theta}_2] = n^2\,\text{VAR}[\min(X_1, \ldots, X_n)] = \frac{n^2}{n^2\lambda^2} = \frac{1}{\lambda^2}.$$

Clearly, $\hat{\Theta}_1$ is the preferred estimator because it has the smaller mean square estimation error.

---

A third measure of quality of an estimator pertains to its behavior as the sample size $n$ is increased. We say that $\hat{\Theta}$ is a **consistent estimator** if $\hat{\Theta}$ converges to $\theta$ in probability, that is, as per Eq. (7.21), for every $\varepsilon > 0$,

$$\lim_{n \to \infty} P[|\hat{\Theta} - \theta| > \varepsilon] = 0. \tag{8.20}$$

The estimator $\hat{\Theta}$ is said to be a **strongly consistent estimator** if $\hat{\Theta}$ converges to $\theta$ almost surely, that is, with probability 1, cf. Eqs. (7.22) and (7.37). Consistent estimators, whether biased or unbiased, tend towards the correct value of $\theta$ as $n$ is increased.

---

### Example 8.7    Consistency of Sample Mean Estimator

The weak law of large numbers states that the sample mean $\overline{X}_n$ converges to $\mu = E[X]$ in probability. Therefore *the sample mean is a consistent estimator*. Furthermore, the strong law of large numbers states the sample mean converges to $\mu$ with probability 1. Therefore *the sample mean is a strongly consistent estimator*.

---

### Example 8.8    Consistency of Sample Variance Estimator

Consider the unbiased sample variance estimator in Eq. (8.17). It can be shown (see Problem 8. 21) that the variance of $\hat{\sigma}_n^2$ is:

$$\text{VAR}[\hat{\sigma}_n^2] = \frac{1}{n}\left\{\mu_4 - \frac{n-3}{n-1}\sigma^4\right\} \quad \text{where} \quad \mu_4 = E[(X - m)^4].$$

If the fourth central moment $\mu_4$ is finite, then the above variance term approaches zero as $n$ increases. By Chebyshev's inequality we have that:

$$P[|\hat{\sigma}_n^2 - \sigma^2| > \varepsilon] \leq \frac{\text{VAR}[\hat{\sigma}_n^2]}{\varepsilon^2} \to 0 \quad \text{as} \quad n \to \infty.$$

Therefore the sample variance estimator is consistent if $\mu_4$ is finite.

## 8.2.2    Finding Good Estimators

Ideally we would like to have estimators that are unbiased, have minimum mean square error, and are consistent. Unfortunately, there is no guarantee that unbiased estimators or consistent estimators exist for all parameters of interest. There is also no straightforward method for finding the minimum mean square estimator for arbitrary parameters. Fortunately we do have the class of maximum likelihood estimators which are relatively easy to work with, have a number of desirable properties for $n$ large, and often provide estimators that can be modified to be unbiased and minimum variance. The next section deals with maximum likelihood estimation.

## 8.3    MAXIMUM LIKELIHOOD ESTIMATION

We now consider the maximum likelihood method for finding a point estimator $\hat{\Theta}(\mathbf{X}_n)$ for an unknown parameter $\theta$. In this section we first show how the method works. We then present several properties that make maximum likelihood estimators very useful in practice.

The maximum likelihood method selects as its estimate the parameter value that maximizes the probability of the observed data $\mathbf{X}_n = (X_1, X_2, \ldots, X_n)$. Before introducing the formal method we use an example to demonstrate the basic approach.

### Example 8.9    Poisson Distributed Typos

Papers submitted by Bob have been found to have a Poisson distributed number of typos with mean 1 typo per page, whereas papers prepared by John have a Poisson distributed number of typos with mean 5 typos per page. Suppose that a page that was submitted by either Bob or John has 2 typos. Who is the likely author?

In the maximum likelihood approach we first calculate the probability of obtaining the given observation for each possible parameter value, thus:

$$P[X = 2 \,|\, \theta = 1] = \frac{1^2}{2!}e^{-1} = \frac{1}{2e} = 0.18394$$

$$P[X = 2 \,|\, \theta = 5] = \frac{5^2}{2!}e^{-5} = \frac{25}{2e^5} = 0.084224.$$

We then select the parameter value that gives the higher probability for the observation. In this case $\hat{\Theta}(2) = 1$ gives the higher probability, so the estimator selects Bob as the more likely author of the page.

Let $\mathbf{x}_n = (x_1, x_2, \ldots, x_n)$ be the observed values of a random sample for the random variable $X$ and let $\theta$ be the parameter of interest. The **likelihood function** of the sample is a function of $\theta$ defined as follows:

$$l(\mathbf{x}_n; \theta) = l(x_1, x_2, \ldots, x_n; \theta)$$
$$= \begin{cases} p_X(x_1, x_2, \ldots, x_n | \theta) & X \text{ discrete random variable} \\ f_X(x_1, x_2, \ldots, x_n | \theta) & X \text{ continuous random variable} \end{cases} \quad (8.21)$$

where $p_X(x_1, x_2, \ldots, x_n | \theta)$ and $f_X(x_1, x_2, \ldots, x_n | \theta)$ are the joint pmf and joint pdf evaluated at the observation values if the parameter value is $\theta$. Since the samples $X_1, X_2, \ldots, X_n$ are iid, we have a simple expression for the likelihood function:

$$p_X(x_1, x_2, \ldots, x_n | \theta) = p_X(x_1 | \theta) p_X(x_2 | \theta) \ldots p_X(x_n | \theta) = \prod_{j=1}^{n} p_X(x_j | \theta) \quad (8.22)$$

and

$$f_X(x_1, x_2, \ldots, x_n | \theta) = f_X(x_1 | \theta) f_X(x_2 | \theta) \ldots f_X(x_n | \theta) = \prod_{j=1}^{n} f_X(x_j | \theta). \quad (8.23)$$

The **maximum likelihood method** selects the estimator value $\hat{\Theta} = \theta^*$ where $\theta^*$ is the parameter value that maximizes the likelihood function, that is,

$$l(x_1, x_2, \ldots, x_n; \theta^*) = \max_{\theta} l(x_1, x_2, \ldots, x_n; \theta) \quad (8.24)$$

where the maximum is taken over all allowable values of $\theta$. Usually $\theta$ assumes a continuous set of values, so we find the maximum of the likelihood function over $\theta$ using standard methods from calculus.

It is usually more convenient to work with the **log likelihood function** because we then work with the sum of terms instead of the product of terms in Eqs. (8.22) and (8.23):

$$L(\mathbf{x}_n | \theta) = \ln l(\mathbf{x}_n; \theta)$$
$$= \begin{cases} \displaystyle\sum_{j=1}^{n} \ln p_X(x_j | \theta) = \sum_{j=1}^{n} L(x_j | \theta) & X \text{ discrete random variable} \\ \displaystyle\sum_{j=1}^{n} \ln f_X(x_j | \theta) = \sum_{j=1}^{n} L(x_j | \theta) & X \text{ continuous random variable.} \end{cases}$$

$$(8.25)$$

Maximizing the log likelihood function is equivalent to maximizing the likelihood function since $\ln(x)$ is an increasing function of $x$. We obtain the maximum likelihood estimate by finding the value $\theta^*$ for which:

$$\frac{\partial}{\partial \theta} L(\mathbf{x}_n | \theta) = \frac{\partial}{\partial \theta} \ln l(\mathbf{x}_n | \theta) = 0. \quad (8.26)$$

### Example 8.10    Estimation of $p$ for a Bernoulli random variable

Suppose we perform $n$ independent observations of a Bernoulli random variable with probability of success $p$. Find the maximum likelihood estimate for $p$.

Let $\mathbf{i}_n = (i_1, i_2, \ldots, i_n)$ be the observed outcomes of the $n$ Bernoulli trials. The pmf for an individual outcome can be written as follows:

$$p_X(i_j | p) = p^{i_j}(1 - p)^{1-i_j} = \begin{cases} p & \text{if } i_j = 1 \\ 1 - p & \text{if } i_j = 0. \end{cases}$$

The log likelihood function is:

$$\ln l(i_1, i_2, \ldots, i_n; p) = \sum_{j=1}^{n} \ln p_X(i_j | p) = \sum_{j=1}^{n}(i_j \ln p + (1 - i_j) \ln(1 - p)). \quad (8.27)$$

We take the first derivative with respect to $p$ and set the result equal to zero:

$$0 = \frac{d}{dp} \ln l(i_1, i_2, \ldots, i_n; p) = \frac{1}{p}\sum_{j=1}^{n} i_j - \frac{1}{1-p}\sum_{j=1}^{n}(1 - i_j)$$

$$= -\frac{n}{1-p} + \left(\frac{1}{p} + \frac{1}{1-p}\right)\sum_{j=1}^{n} i_j = -\frac{n}{1-p} + \frac{1}{p(1-p)}\sum_{j=1}^{n} i_j. \quad (8.28)$$

Solving for $p$, we obtain:

$$p^* = \frac{1}{n}\sum_{j=1}^{n} i_j.$$

Therefore the maximum likelihood estimator for $p$ is the relative frequency of successes, which is a special case of the sample mean. From the previous section we know that the sample mean estimator is unbiased and consistent.

### Example 8.11    Estimation of $\alpha$ for Poisson random variable

Suppose we perform $n$ independent observations of a Poisson random variable with mean $\alpha$. Find the maximum likelihood estimate for $\alpha$.

Let the counts in the $n$ independent trials be given by $k_1, k_2, \ldots, k_n$. The probability of observing $k_j$ events in the $j$th trial is:

$$p_X(k_j | \alpha) = \frac{\alpha^{k_j}}{k_j!}e^{-\alpha}.$$

The log likelihood function is then

$$\ln l(k_1, k_2, \ldots, k_n; \alpha) = \sum_{j=1}^{n} \ln p_X(x_j | \alpha) = \sum_{j=1}^{n}(k_j \ln \alpha - \alpha - \ln k_j!)$$

$$= \ln \alpha \sum_{j=1}^{n} k_j - n\alpha - \sum_{j=1}^{n} \ln k_j!.$$

To find the maximum, we take the first derivative with respect to $\alpha$ and set it equal to zero:

$$0 = \frac{d}{d\alpha} \ln l(k_1, k_2, \ldots, k_n; \alpha) = \frac{1}{\alpha} \sum_{j=1}^{n} k_j - n. \tag{8.29}$$

Solving for $\alpha$, we obtain:

$$\alpha^* = \frac{1}{n} \sum_{j=1}^{n} k_j.$$

The maximum likelihood estimator for $\alpha$ is the sample mean of the event counts.

---

**Example 8.12    Estimation of Mean and Variance for Gaussian Random Variable**

Let $\mathbf{x}_n = (x_1, x_2, \ldots, x_n)$ be the observed values of a random sample for a Gaussian random variable $X$ for which we wish to estimate two parameters: the mean $\theta_1 = \mu$ and variance $\theta_2 = \sigma_X^2$. The likelihood function is a function of two parameters $\theta_1$ and $\theta_2$, and we must simultaneously maximize the likelihood with respect to these two parameters.

The pdf for the $j$th observation is given by:

$$f_X(x_j \mid \theta_1, \theta_2) = \frac{1}{\sqrt{2\pi\theta_2}} e^{-(x_j - \theta_1)^2/2\theta_2}$$

where we have replaced the mean and variance by $\theta_1$ and $\theta_2$, respectively. The log likelihood function is given by:

$$\ln l(x_1, x_2, \ldots, x_n; \theta_1, \theta_2) = \sum_{j=1}^{n} \ln f_X(x_j \mid \theta_1, \theta_2)$$

$$= -\frac{n}{2} \ln 2\pi\theta_2 - \sum_{j=1}^{n} \frac{(x_j - \theta_1)^2}{2\theta_2}.$$

We take derivatives with respect to $\theta_1$ and $\theta_2$ and set the results equal to zero:

$$0 = \frac{\partial}{\partial \theta_1} \sum_{j=1}^{n} \ln f_X(x_j \mid \theta_1, \theta_2) = -2 \sum_{j=1}^{n} \frac{(x_j - \theta_1)}{2\theta_2}$$

$$= -\frac{1}{\theta_2} \left[ \sum_{j=1}^{n} x_j - n\theta_1 \right] \tag{8.30}$$

and

$$0 = \frac{\partial}{\partial \theta_2} \sum_{j=1}^{n} \ln f_X(x_j \mid \theta_1, \theta_2) = -\frac{n}{2\theta_2} + \frac{1}{2\theta_2^2} \sum_{j=1}^{n} (x_j - \theta_1)^2$$

$$= -\frac{1}{2\theta_2} \left[ n - \frac{1}{\theta_2} \sum_{j=1}^{n} (x_j - \theta_1)^2 \right]. \tag{8.31}$$

Equations (8.30) and (8.31) can be solved for $\theta_1^*$ and $\theta_2^*$, respectively, to obtain:

$$\theta_1^* = \frac{1}{n} \sum_{j=1}^{n} x_j \tag{8.32}$$

and

$$\theta_2^* = \frac{1}{n}\sum_{j=1}^{n}(x_j - \theta_1^*)^2. \tag{8.33}$$

Thus, $\theta_1^*$ is given by the sample mean and $\theta_2^*$ is given by the biased sample variance discussed in Example 8.5. It is easy to show that as $n$ becomes large, $\theta_2^*$ approaches the unbiased $\hat{\sigma}_n^2$.

---

The maximum likelihood estimator possesses an important **invariance property** that, in general, is not satisfied by other estimators. Suppose that instead of the parameter $\theta$, we are interested in estimating a function of $\theta$, say $h(\theta)$, which we assume is invertible. It can be shown then that if $\theta^*$ is the maximum likelihood estimate of $\theta$, then $h(\theta^*)$ is the maximum likelihood estimate for $h(\theta)$. (See Problem 8.34.) As an example, consider the exponential random variable. Suppose that $\lambda^*$ is the maximum likelihood estimate for the rate $\lambda$ of an exponential random variable. Suppose we are instead interested in $h(\lambda) = 1/\lambda$, the mean interarrival time of the exponential random variable. The invariance result of the maximum likelihood estimate implies that the maximum likelihood estimate is then $h(\lambda^*) = 1/\lambda^*$.

### *8.3.1   Cramer-Rao Inequality[1]

In general, we would like to find the unbiased estimator $\hat{\Theta}$ with the smallest possible variance. This estimator would produce the most accurate estimates in the sense of being tightly clustered around the true value $\theta$. The Cramer-Rao inequality addresses this question in two steps. First, it provides a lower bound to the minimum possible variance achievable by *any unbiased* estimator. This bound provides a benchmark for assessing all unbiased estimators of $\theta$. Second, if an unbiased estimator achieves the lower bound then it has the smallest possible variance and mean square error. Furthermore, this unbiased estimator can be found using the maximum likelihood method.

Since the random sample $\mathbf{X}_n$ is a vector random variable, we expect that the estimator $\hat{\Theta}(\mathbf{X}_n)$ will exhibit some unavoidable random variation and hence will have nonzero variance. Is there a lower limit to how small this variance can be? The answer is yes and the lower bound is given by the reciprocal of the **Fisher information** which is defined as follows:

$$I_n(\theta) = E\left[\left\{\frac{\partial L(\mathbf{X}_n|\theta)}{\partial\theta}\right\}^2\right] = E\left[\left\{\frac{\partial\ln f_{\mathbf{X}}(X_1, X_2,\ldots,X_n|\theta)}{\partial\theta}\right\}^2\right]. \tag{8.34}$$

The pdf in Eq. (8.34) is replaced by a pmf if $X$ is a discrete random variable. The term inside the braces is called the **score function**, which is defined as the partial derivative of the log likelihood function with respect to the parameter $\theta$. Note that the score function is a

---

[1]As a reminder, we note that this section (and other starred sections) presents advanced material and can be skipped without loss of continuity.

function of the vector random variable $\mathbf{X}_n$. We have already seen this function when finding maximum likelihood estimators. The expected value of the score function is zero since:

$$E\left[\frac{\partial L(\mathbf{X}_n \,|\, \theta)}{\partial \theta}\right] = E\left[\frac{\partial \ln f_{\mathbf{X}}(\mathbf{X}_n \,|\, \theta)}{\partial \theta}\right]$$

$$= \int_{\mathbf{x}_n} \frac{1}{f_{\mathbf{X}}(\mathbf{x}_n \,|\, \theta)} \frac{\partial f_{\mathbf{X}}(\mathbf{x}_n \,|\, \theta)}{\partial \theta} f_{\mathbf{X}}(\mathbf{x}_n \,|\, \theta)\, d\mathbf{x}_n$$

$$= \int_{\mathbf{x}_n} \frac{\partial f_{\mathbf{X}}(\mathbf{x}_n \,|\, \theta)}{\partial \theta}\, d\mathbf{x}_n = \frac{\partial}{\partial \theta} \int_{\mathbf{x}_n} f_{\mathbf{X}}(\mathbf{x}_n \,|\, \theta)\, d\mathbf{x}_n = \frac{\partial}{\partial \theta} 1 = 0, \quad (8.35)$$

where we assume that order of the partial derivative and integration can be exchanged. Therefore $I_n(\theta)$ *is equal to the variance of the score function.*

The score function measures the rate at which the log likelihood function changes as $\theta$ varies. If $L(\mathbf{X}_n \,|\, \theta)$ tends to change quickly about the value $\theta_0$ for most observations of $\mathbf{X}_n$, we can expect that: (1) The Fisher information will tend to be large since the argument inside the expected value in Eq. (8.34) will be large; (2) small departures from the value $\theta_0$ will be readily discernable in the observed statistics because the underlying pdf is changing quickly. On the other hand, if the likelihood function changes slowly about $\theta_0$, then the Fisher information will be small. In addition, significantly different values of $\theta_0$ may have quite similar likelihood functions making it difficult to distinguish among parameter values from the observed data. In summary, larger values of $I_n(\theta)$ should allow for better performing estimators that will have smaller variances.

The Fisher information has the following equivalent but more useful form when the pdf $f_{\mathbf{X}}(x_1, x_2, \ldots, x_n \,|\, \theta)$ satisfies certain additional conditions (see Problem 8.35):

$$I_n(\theta) = -E\left[\frac{\partial^2 \ln f_{\mathbf{X}}(X_1, X_2, \ldots, X_n \,|\, \theta)}{\partial^2 \theta}\right] = -E\left[\frac{\partial^2 L(\mathbf{X}_n \,|\, \theta)}{\partial^2 \theta}\right]. \quad (8.36)$$

---

### Example 8.13    Fisher Information for Bernoulli Random Variable

From Eqs. (8.27) and (8.28), the score and its derivative for the Bernoulli random variable are given by:

$$\frac{\partial}{\partial p} \ln l(i_1, i_2, \ldots, i_n; p) = \frac{1}{p}\sum_{j=1}^{n} i_j - \frac{1}{1-p}\sum_{j=1}^{n}(1 - i_j)$$

and

$$\frac{\partial^2}{\partial p^2} \ln l(i_1, i_2, \ldots, i_n; p) = -\frac{1}{p^2}\sum_{j=1}^{n} i_j - \frac{1}{(1-p)^2}\sum_{j=1}^{n}(1 - i_j).$$

The Fisher information, as given by Eq. (8.36), is then:

$$I_n(p) = E\left[\frac{1}{p^2}\sum_{j=1}^{n} I_j + \frac{1}{(1-p)^2}\sum_{j=1}^{n}(1 - I_j)\right]$$

$$= \frac{1}{p^2} E\left[\sum_{j=1}^n I_j\right] + \frac{1}{(1-p)^2} E\left[\sum_{j=1}^n (1 - I_j)\right]$$

$$= \frac{np}{p^2} + \frac{n - np}{(1-p)^2} = \frac{n}{p(1-p)}.$$

Note that $I_n(p)$ is smallest near $p = 1/2$, and that it increases as $p$ approaches 0 or 1, so $p$ is easier to estimate accurately at the extreme values of $p$. Note as well that the Fisher information is proportional to the number of samples, that is, more samples make it easier to estimate $p$.

---

### Example 8.14    Fisher Information for an Exponential Random Variable

The log likelihood function for the $n$ samples of an exponential random variable is:

$$\ln l(x_1, x_2, \ldots, x_n; \lambda) = \sum_{j=1}^n \ln \lambda e^{-\lambda x_j} = \sum_{j=1}^n (\ln \lambda - \lambda x_j).$$

The score for $n$ observations of an exponential random variable and its derivatives are given by:

$$\frac{\partial}{\partial \lambda} \ln l(x_1, x_2, \ldots, x_n; \lambda) = \frac{n}{\lambda} - \sum_{j=1}^n x_j$$

and

$$\frac{\partial^2}{\partial \lambda^2} \ln l(x_1, x_2, \ldots, x_n; \lambda) = -\frac{n}{\lambda^2}.$$

The Fisher information is then:

$$I_n(\lambda) = E\left[\frac{n}{\lambda^2}\right] = \frac{n}{\lambda^2}.$$

Note that $I_n(\lambda)$ decreases with increasing $\lambda$.

---

We are now ready to state the Cramer-Rao inequality.

---

### Theorem    Cramer-Rao Inequality

Let $\hat{\Theta}(\mathbf{X}_n)$ be any unbiased estimator for the parameter $\theta$ of $X$, then under certain regularity conditions[2] on the pdf $f_{\mathbf{X}}(x_1, x_2, \ldots, x_n | \theta)$,

**(a)** $\text{VAR}[\hat{\Theta}(\mathbf{X}_n)] \geq \dfrac{1}{I_n(\theta)}$,    (8.37)

**(b)** with equality being achieved if and only if

$$\frac{\partial}{\partial \theta} \ln f_{\mathbf{X}}(x_1, x_2, \ldots, x_n; \theta) = \{\hat{\Theta}(\mathbf{x}) - \theta\} k(\theta).$$    (8.38)

---

[2]See [Bickel, p. 179].

The Cramer-Rao lower bound confirms our conjecture that the variance of unbiased estimators must be bounded below by a nonzero value. If the Fisher information is high, then the lower bound is small, suggesting that low variance, and hence accurate, estimators are possible. The term $1/I_n(\theta)$ serves as a reference point for the variance of all unbiased estimators, and the ratio $(1/I_n(\theta))/\mathrm{VAR}[\hat{\Theta}]$ provides a measure of efficiency of an unbiased estimator. We say that an unbiased estimator is **efficient** if it achieves the lower bound.

Assume that Eq. (8.38) is satisfied. The maximum likelihood estimator must then satisfy Eq. (8.26), and therefore

$$0 = \frac{\partial}{\partial\theta}\ln f_{\mathbf{X}}(x_1, x_2, \ldots, x_n; \theta) = \left\{\hat{\Theta}(\mathbf{x}) - \theta^*\right\}k(\theta^*). \tag{8.39}$$

We discard the case $k(\theta^*) = 0$, and conclude that, in general, we must have $\theta^* = \hat{\Theta}(\mathbf{x})$. Therefore, *if an efficient estimator exists then it can be found using the maximum likelihood method*. If an efficient estimator does not exist, then the lower bound in Eq. (8.37) is not achieved by any unbiased estimator.

In Examples 8.10 and 8.11 we derived unbiased maximum likelihood estimators for Bernoulli and for Poisson random variables. We note that in these examples the score function in the maximum likelihood equations (Eqs. 8.28 and 8.29) can be rearranged to have the form given in Eq. (8.39). Therefore we conclude that these estimators are efficient.

---

**Example 8.15   Cramer-Rao Lower Bound for Bernoulli Random Variable**

From Example 8.13, the Fisher information for the Bernoulli random variable is

$$I_n(p) = \frac{n}{p(1 - p)}.$$

Therefore the Cramer-Rao lower bound for the variance of the sample mean estimator for $p$ is:

$$\mathrm{VAR}[\hat{\Theta}] \geq \frac{1}{I_n(p)} = \frac{p(1 - p)}{n}.$$

The relative frequency estimator for $p$ achieves this lower bound.

---

### 8.3.2    Proof of Cramer-Rao Inequality

The proof of the Cramer-Rao inequality involves an application of the Schwarz inequality. We assume that the score function exists and is finite. Consider the covariance of $\hat{\Theta}(\mathbf{X}_n)$ and the score function:

$$\mathrm{COV}\left(\hat{\Theta}(\mathbf{X}_n), \frac{\partial}{\partial\theta}L(\mathbf{X}_n; \theta)\right) = E\left[\hat{\Theta}(\mathbf{X}_n)\frac{\partial}{\partial\theta}L(\mathbf{X}_n; \theta)\right]$$

$$- E[\hat{\Theta}(\mathbf{X}_n)]E\left[\frac{\partial}{\partial\theta}L(\mathbf{X}_n; \theta)\right]$$

$$= E\left[\hat{\Theta}(\mathbf{X}_n)\frac{\partial}{\partial\theta}L(\mathbf{X}_n; \theta)\right],$$

where we used Eq. (5.30) and the fact that the expected value of the score is zero (Eq. 8.35). Next we evaluate the above expected value:

$$\text{COV}(\hat{\Theta}(\mathbf{X}_n), \frac{\partial}{\partial\theta}\ln f_{\mathbf{X}}(\mathbf{X}_n; \theta)) = E\left[\hat{\Theta}(\mathbf{X}_n)\frac{\partial}{\partial\theta}\ln f_{\mathbf{X}}(\mathbf{X}_n; \theta)\right]$$

$$= E\left[\hat{\Theta}(\mathbf{X}_n)\frac{1}{f_{\mathbf{X}}(\mathbf{X}_n; \theta)}\frac{\partial}{\partial\theta}f_{\mathbf{X}}(\mathbf{X}_n; \theta)\right]$$

$$= \int_{\mathbf{x}_n}\left\{\hat{\Theta}(\mathbf{x}_n)\frac{1}{f_{\mathbf{X}}(\mathbf{x}_n; \theta)}\frac{\partial}{\partial\theta}f_{\mathbf{X}}(\mathbf{x}_n; \theta)\right\}f_{\mathbf{X}}(\mathbf{x}_n; \theta)\, d\mathbf{x}_n$$

$$= \int_{\mathbf{x}_n}\left\{\hat{\Theta}(\mathbf{x}_n)\frac{\partial}{\partial\theta}f_{\mathbf{X}}(\mathbf{x}_n; \theta)\right\} d\mathbf{x}_n$$

$$= \frac{\partial}{\partial\theta}\int_{\mathbf{x}_n}\left\{\hat{\Theta}(\mathbf{x}_n)f_{\mathbf{X}}(\mathbf{x}_n; \theta)\right\} d\mathbf{x}_n.$$

In the last step we assume that the integration and the partial derivative with respect to $\theta$ can be interchanged. (The regularity conditions required by the theorem are needed to ensure that this step is valid.) Note that the integral in the last expression is $E[\hat{\Theta}(\mathbf{X}_n)] = \theta$, so

$$\text{COV}(\hat{\Theta}(\mathbf{X}_n), \frac{\partial}{\partial\theta}\ln f_{\mathbf{X}}(\mathbf{X}_n; \theta)) = \frac{\partial}{\partial\theta}\theta = 1.$$

Next we apply the Schwarz inequality to the covariance:

$$1 = \text{COV}(\hat{\Theta}(\mathbf{X}_n), \frac{\partial}{\partial\theta}\ln f_{\mathbf{X}}(\mathbf{X}_n; \theta)) \leq \sqrt{\text{VAR}[\hat{\Theta}(\mathbf{X}_n)]\text{VAR}\left[\frac{\partial}{\partial\theta}\ln f_{\mathbf{X}}(\mathbf{X}_n; \theta)\right]}.$$

Taking the square of both sides we conclude that:

$$1 \leq \text{VAR}[\hat{\Theta}(\mathbf{X}_n)]\text{VAR}\left[\frac{\partial}{\partial\theta}\ln f_{\mathbf{X}}(\mathbf{X}_n; \theta)\right]$$

and finally

$$\text{VAR}[\hat{\Theta}(\mathbf{X}_n)] \geq 1/\text{VAR}\left[\frac{\partial}{\partial\theta}\ln f_{\mathbf{X}}(\mathbf{X}_n; \theta)\right] = 1/I_n(\theta).$$

The last step uses the fact that the Fisher information is the variance of the score function. This completes the proof of part a.

Equality holds in the Schwarz inequality when the random variables in the variances are proportional to each other, that is:

$$k(\theta)[\hat{\Theta}(\mathbf{X}_n) - E[\hat{\Theta}(\mathbf{X}_n)]] = k(\theta)[\hat{\Theta}(\mathbf{X}_n) - \theta]$$

$$= \frac{\partial}{\partial\theta}\ln f_{\mathbf{X}}(\mathbf{X}_n; \theta) - E\left[\frac{\partial}{\partial\theta}\ln f_{\mathbf{X}}(\mathbf{X}_n; \theta)\right]$$

$$= \frac{\partial}{\partial\theta}\ln f_{\mathbf{X}}(\mathbf{X}_n; \theta),$$

where we noted that the expected value of the score function is 0 and that the estimator $\hat{\Theta}(\mathbf{X}_n)$ is unbiased. This completes the proof of part b.

### *8.3.3 Asymptotic Properties of Maximum Likelihood Estimators

Maximum likelihood estimators satisfy the following asymptotic properties that make them very useful when the number of samples is large.

1. Maximum likelihood estimates are consistent:

$$\lim_{n\to\infty} \theta_n^* = \theta_0 \quad \text{where } \theta_0 \text{ is the true parameter value.}$$

2. For $n$ large, the maximum likelihood estimate $\theta_n^*$ is asymptotically Gaussian distributed, that is, $\sqrt{n}(\theta_n^* - \theta_0)$ has a Gaussian distribution with zero mean and variance $1/I_n(\theta)$.

3. Maximum likelihood estimates are asymptotically efficient:

$$\lim_{n\to\infty} \frac{\text{VAR}[\theta_n^*]}{1/I_n(\theta_0)} = 1. \tag{8.40}$$

The consistency property (1) implies that maximum likelihood estimates will be close to the true value for large $n$, and asymptotic efficiency (3) implies that the variance becomes as small as possible. The asymptotic Gaussian distributed property (2) is very useful because it allows us to evaluate the probabilities involving the maximum likelihood estimator.

---

### Example 8.16 Bernoulli Random Variable

Find the distribution of the sample mean estimator for $p$ for $n$ large.

If $p_0$ is the true value of the Bernoulli random variable, then $I(p_0) = (p_0(1 - p_0))^{-1}$. Therefore, the estimation error $p^* - p_0$ has a Gaussian pdf with mean zero and variance $p_0(1 - p_0)$. This is in agreement with Example 7.14 where we discussed the application of the central limit theorem to the sample mean of Bernoulli random variables.

---

The asymptotic properties of the maximum likelihood estimator result from the law of large numbers and the central limit theorem. In the remainder of this section we indicate how these results come about. See [Cramer] for a proof of these results. Consider the arithmetic average of the log likelihood function for $n$ samples of the random variable $X$:

$$\frac{1}{n}L(\mathbf{X}_n|\theta) = \frac{1}{n}\sum_{j=1}^{n} L(X_j|\theta) = \frac{1}{n}\sum_{j=1}^{n} \ln f_X(X_j|\theta). \tag{8.41}$$

We have intentionally written the log likelihood as a *function* of the random variables $X_1, X_2, \ldots, X_n$. Clearly this arithmetic average is the sample mean of $n$ independent observations of the following random variable:

$$Y = g(X) = L(X|\theta) = \ln f_X(X|\theta).$$

The random variable $Y$ has mean given by:

$$E[Y] = E[g(X)] = E[L(X|\theta)] = E[\ln f_X(X|\theta)] \triangleq L(\theta). \qquad (8.42)$$

Assuming that $Y$ satisfies the conditions for the law of large numbers, we then have:

$$\frac{1}{n}L(\mathbf{X}_n|\theta) = \frac{1}{n}\sum_{j=1}^{n}\ln f_X(X_j|\theta) = \frac{1}{n}\sum_{j=1}^{n}Y_j \rightarrow E[Y] = L(\theta). \qquad (8.43)$$

The function $L(\theta)$ can be viewed as a limiting form of the log likelihood function. In particular, using the steps that led to Eq. (4.109), we can show that the maximum of $L(\theta)$ occurs at the true value of $\theta$; that is, if $\theta_0$ is the true value of the parameter, then:

$$L(\theta) \leq L(\theta_0) \qquad \text{for all } \theta. \qquad (8.44)$$

First consider the consistency property. Let $\theta_n^*$ be the maximum likelihood obtained from maximizing $L(\mathbf{X}_n|\theta)$, or equivalently, $L(\mathbf{X}_n|\theta)/n$. According to Eq. (8.43), $L(\mathbf{X}_n|\theta)/n$ is a sequence of functions of $\theta$ that converges to $L(\theta)$. It then follows that the sequence of maxima of $L(\mathbf{X}_n|\theta)/n$, namely $\theta_n^*$, converge to the maximum of $L(\theta)$, which from Eq. (8.43) is the true value $\theta_0$. Therefore the maximum likelihood estimator is consistent.

Next we consider the asymptotic Gaussian property. To characterize the estimation error, $\theta_n^* - \theta_0$, we apply the mean value theorem[3] to the score function in the interval $[\theta_n^*, \theta_0]$:

$$\frac{\partial}{\partial\theta}L(\mathbf{X}_n;\theta)\bigg|_{\theta_0} - \frac{\partial}{\partial\theta}L(\mathbf{X}_n;\theta)\bigg|_{\theta_n^*}$$

$$= \frac{\partial^2}{\partial\theta^2}L(\mathbf{X}_n;\theta)\bigg|_{\bar{\theta}}(\theta_0 - \theta_n^*) \text{ for some } \bar{\theta}, \theta_n^* < \bar{\theta} < \theta_0.$$

Note that the second term in the left-hand side is zero since $\theta_n^*$ is the maximum likelihood estimator for $L(\mathbf{X}_n|\theta)$. The estimation error is then:

$$(\theta_n^* - \theta_0) = -\frac{\dfrac{\partial}{\partial\theta}L(\mathbf{X}_n;\theta)\bigg|_{\theta_0}}{\dfrac{\partial^2}{\partial\theta^2}L(\mathbf{X}_n;\theta)\bigg|_{\bar{\theta}}} = -\frac{\dfrac{1}{n}\dfrac{\partial}{\partial\theta}L(\mathbf{X}_n;\theta)\bigg|_{\theta_0}}{\dfrac{1}{n}\dfrac{\partial^2}{\partial\theta^2}L(\mathbf{X}_n;\theta)\bigg|_{\bar{\theta}}}. \qquad (8.45)$$

Consider the arithmetic average of the denominator:

$$\frac{1}{n}\frac{\partial^2}{\partial\theta^2}L(\mathbf{X}_n;\theta)\bigg|_{\bar{\theta}} = \frac{1}{n}\sum_{j=1}^{n}\frac{\partial^2}{\partial\theta^2}\ln f_X(X_j|\theta)$$

$$\rightarrow E\left[\frac{\partial^2}{\partial\theta^2}\ln f_X(X_j|\theta)\right]_{\bar{\theta}} = -I_1(\bar{\theta})$$

---

[3] $f(b) - f(a) = f'(c)(b - a)$ for some $c, a < c < b$, see, for example, [Edwards and Penney].

where we used the alternative expression for the Fisher information of a single observation. From the consistency property we have that $\theta_n^* \to \theta_0$, and consequently, $\bar{\theta} \to \theta_0$, since $\theta_n^* < \bar{\theta} < \theta_0$. Therefore the denominator approaches $-I_1(\theta_0)$ and Eq. (8.45) becomes

$$(\theta_n^* - \theta_0) = -\frac{\left.\dfrac{1}{n}\dfrac{\partial}{\partial \theta}L(\mathbf{X}_n;\theta)\right|_{\theta_0}}{-I_1(\theta)} \tag{8.46}$$

The numerator in Eq. (8.46) is an average of score functions, so

$$(\theta_n^* - \theta_0) = -\frac{\left.\dfrac{1}{n}\dfrac{\partial}{\partial \theta}L(\mathbf{X}_n;\theta)\right|_{\theta_0}}{-I_1(\theta)} = \frac{\dfrac{1}{n}\displaystyle\sum_{j=1}^{n}\dfrac{\partial}{\partial \theta}\ln f_X(X_j|\theta)}{I_1(\theta)} = \frac{\dfrac{1}{n}\displaystyle\sum_{j=1}^{n}Y_j}{I_1(\theta)}. \tag{8.47}$$

We know that the score function $Y_j$ for a single observation has zero mean and variance $I_1(\theta_0)$. The denominator in Eq. (8.47) scales each $Y_j$ by the factor $-1/I_1(\theta_0)$, so Eq. (8.47) becomes the sample mean of zero-mean random variables with variance $I_1(\theta_0)/I_1^2(\theta_0) = 1/I_1(\theta_0)$. The central limit theorem implies that

$$\sqrt{n}\,\frac{\theta_n^* - \theta_0}{\sqrt{1/I_1(\theta)}}$$

approaches a zero-mean, unit-variance Gaussian random variable. Therefore $\sqrt{n}(\theta_n^* - \theta_0)$ approaches a zero-mean Gaussian random variable with variance $1/I_1(\theta_0)$. The asymptotic efficiency property also follows from this result.

## 8.4    CONFIDENCE INTERVALS

The sample mean estimator $\overline{X}_n$ provides us with a single numerical value for the estimate of $E[X] = \mu$, namely,

$$\overline{X}_n = \frac{1}{n}\sum_{j=1}^{n}X_j. \tag{8.48}$$

This single number gives no indication of the accuracy of the estimate or the confidence that we can place on it. We can obtain an indication of accuracy by computing the sample variance, which is the average dispersion about $\overline{X}_n$:

$$\hat{\sigma}_n^2 = \frac{1}{n-1}\sum_{j=1}^{n}(X_j - \overline{X}_n)^2. \tag{8.49}$$

If $\hat{\sigma}_n^2$ is small, then the observations are tightly clustered about $\overline{X}_n$, and we can be confident that $\overline{X}_n$ is close to $E[X]$. On the other hand, if $\hat{\sigma}_n^2$ is large, the samples are widely dispersed about $\overline{X}_n$ and we cannot be confident that $\overline{X}_n$ is close to $E[X]$. In this section we introduce the notion of confidence intervals, which approach the question in a different way.

Instead of seeking a single value that we designate to be the "estimate" of the parameter of interest (i.e., $E[X] = \mu$), we attempt to specify an *interval or set of values* that is highly likely to contain the true value of the parameter. In particular, we can specify some high probability, say $1 - \alpha$, and pose the following problem: Find an interval $[l(\mathbf{X}), u(\mathbf{X})]$ such that

$$P[l(\mathbf{X}) \le \mu \le u(\mathbf{X})] = 1 - \alpha. \qquad (8.50)$$

In other words, we use the observed data to determine an interval that by design contains the true value of the parameter $\mu$ with probability $1 - \alpha$. We say that such an interval is a $(1 - \alpha) \times 100\%$ **confidence interval**.

This approach simultaneously handles the question of the accuracy and confidence of an estimate. The probability $1 - \alpha$ is a measure of the consistency, and hence degree of confidence, with which the interval contains the desired parameter: If we were to compute confidence intervals a large number of times, we would find that approximately $(1 - \alpha) \times 100\%$ of the time, the computed intervals would contain the true value of the parameter. For this reason, $1 - \alpha$ is called the **confidence level**. The width of a confidence interval is a measure of the accuracy with which we can pinpoint the estimate of a parameter. The narrower the confidence interval, the more accurately we can specify the estimate for a parameter.

The probability in Eq. (8.50) clearly depends on the pdf of the $X_j$'s. In the remainder of this section, we obtain confidence intervals in the cases where the $X_j$'s are Gaussian random variables or can be approximated by Gaussian random variables. We will use the equivalence between the following events:

$$\left\{ -a \le \frac{\overline{X}_n - \mu}{\sigma_X/\sqrt{n}} \le a \right\} = \left\{ \frac{-a\sigma_X}{\sqrt{n}} \le \overline{X}_n - \mu \le \frac{a\sigma_X}{\sqrt{n}} \right\}$$

$$= \left\{ -\overline{X}_n - \frac{a\sigma_X}{\sqrt{n}} \le -\mu \le -\overline{X}_n + \frac{a\sigma_X}{\sqrt{n}} \right\}$$

$$= \left\{ \overline{X}_n - \frac{a\sigma_X}{\sqrt{n}} \le \mu \le \overline{X}_n + \frac{a\sigma_X}{\sqrt{n}} \right\}.$$

The last event describes a confidence interval in terms of the observed data, and the first event will allow us to calculate probabilities from the sampling distributions.

### 8.4.1   Case 1: $X_j$'s Gaussian; Unknown Mean and Known Variance

Suppose that the $X_j$'s are iid Gaussian random variables with unknown mean $\mu$ and known variance $\sigma_X^2$. From Example 7.3 and Eqs. (7.17) and (7.18), $\overline{X}_n$ is then a Gaussian random variable with mean $\mu$ and variance $\sigma_X^2/n$, thus

$$1 - 2Q(z) = P\left[ -z \le \frac{\overline{X}_n - \mu}{\sigma/\sqrt{n}} \le z \right]$$

$$= P\left[ \overline{X}_n - \frac{z\sigma}{\sqrt{n}} \le \mu \le \overline{X}_n + \frac{z\sigma}{\sqrt{n}} \right]. \qquad (8.51)$$

Equation (8.51) states that the interval $\left[\overline{X}_n - z\sigma/\sqrt{n}, \overline{X}_n + z\sigma/\sqrt{n}\right]$ contains $\mu$ with probability $1 - 2Q(z)$. If we let $z_{\alpha/2}$ be the critical value such that $\alpha = 2Q(z_{\alpha/2})$, then *the* $(1 - \alpha)$ *confidence interval for the mean* $\mu$ is given by

$$\left[\overline{X}_n - z_{\alpha/2}\sigma/\sqrt{n}, \overline{X}_n + z_{\alpha/2}\sigma/\sqrt{n}\ \right]. \tag{8.52}$$

The confidence interval in Eq. (8.52) depends on the sample mean $\overline{X}_n$, the known variance $\sigma_X^2$ of the $X_j$'s, the number of measurements $n$, and the confidence level $1 - \alpha$. Table 8.1 shows the values of $z_\alpha$ corresponding to typical values of $\alpha$. We can use the Octave function `normal_inv`$(1 - \alpha/2, 0, 1)$ to find $z_{\alpha/2}$. This function was introduced in Example 4.51.

When $X$ is not Gaussian but the number of samples $n$ is large, the sample mean $\overline{X}_n$ will be approximately Gaussian if the central limit theorem applies. *Therefore if n is large, then Eq. (8.52) provides a good approximate confidence interval.*

---

### Example 8.17    Estimating Signal in Noise

A voltage $X$ is given by

$$X = v + N,$$

where $v$ is an unknown constant voltage and $N$ is a random noise voltage that has a Gaussian pdf with zero mean, and variance $1\mu V$. Find the 95% confidence interval for $v$ if the voltage $X$ is measured 100 independent times and the sample mean is found to be 5.25 $\mu V$.

From Example 4.17, we know that the voltage $X$ is a Gaussian random variable with mean $v$ and variance 1. Thus the 100 measurements $X_1, X_2, \ldots, X_{100}$ are iid Gaussian random variables with mean $v$ and variance 1. The confidence interval is given by Eq. (8.52) with $z_{\alpha/2} = 1.96$:

$$\left[5.25 - \frac{1.96(1)}{10}, 5.25 + \frac{1.96(1)}{10}\right] = [5.05, 5.45].$$

---

### 8.4.2    Case 2: $X_j$'s Gaussian; Mean and Variance Unknown

Suppose that the $X_j$'s are iid Gaussian random variables with unknown mean $\mu$ and unknown variance $\sigma_X^2$, and that we are interested in finding a confidence interval for the mean $\mu$. Suppose we do the obvious thing in the confidence interval given by Eq. (8.52) by replacing the variance $\sigma^2$ with its estimate, the sample variance $\hat{\sigma}_n^2$ as given by Eq. (8.17):

$$\left[\overline{X}_n - \frac{t\hat{\sigma}_n}{\sqrt{n}}, \overline{X}_n + \frac{t\hat{\sigma}_n}{\sqrt{n}}\right]. \tag{8.53}$$

The probability for the interval in Eq. (8.53) is

$$P\left[-t \le \frac{\overline{X}_n - \mu}{\hat{\sigma}_n/\sqrt{n}} \le t\right] = P\left[\overline{X}_n - \frac{t\hat{\sigma}_n}{\sqrt{n}} \le \mu \le \overline{X}_n + \frac{t\hat{\sigma}_n}{\sqrt{n}}\right]. \tag{8.54}$$

The random variable involved in Eq. (8.54) is

$$T = \frac{\overline{X}_n - \mu}{\hat{\sigma}_n/\sqrt{n}}. \tag{8.55}$$

In the end of this section we show that $T$ has a Student's $t$-distribution[4] with $n - 1$ degrees of freedom:

$$f_{n-1}(y) = \frac{\Gamma(n/2)}{\Gamma((n-1)/2)\sqrt{\pi(n-1)}} \left( 1 + \frac{y^2}{n-1} \right)^{-n/2}. \tag{8.56}$$

Let $F_{n-1}(y)$ be the cdf corresponding to $f_{n-1}(y)$, then the probability in Eq. (8.54) is given by

$$P\left[ \overline{X}_n - \frac{t\hat{\sigma}_n}{\sqrt{n}} \le \mu \le \overline{X}_n + \frac{t\hat{\sigma}_n}{\sqrt{n}} \right] = \int_{-t}^{t} f_{n-1}(y)\, dy = F_{n-1}(t) - F_{n-1}(-t)$$

$$= F_{n-1}(t) - (1 - F_{n-1}(t))$$

$$= 2F_{n-1}(t) - 1$$

$$= 1 - \alpha \tag{8.57}$$

where we used the fact that $f_{n-1}(y)$ is symmetric about $y = 0$. To obtain a confidence interval with confidence level $1 - \alpha$, we need to find the critical value $t_{\alpha/2, n-1}$ for which $1 - \alpha = 2F_{n-1}(t_{\alpha/2, n-1}) - 1$ or equivalently, $F_{n-1}(t_{\alpha/2, n-1}) = 1 - \alpha/2$. *The* $(1 - \alpha) \times 100\%$ *confidence interval for the mean* $\mu$ is then given by

$$\left[ \overline{X}_n - t_{\alpha/2, n-1}\hat{\sigma}_n/\sqrt{n}, \overline{X}_n + t_{\alpha/2, n-1}\hat{\sigma}_n/\sqrt{n} \right]. \tag{8.58}$$

The confidence interval in Eq. (8.58) depends on the sample mean $\overline{X}_n$ and the sample variance $\hat{\sigma}_n^2$, the number of measurements $n$, and $\alpha$. Table 8.2 shows values of $t_{\alpha, n}$ for typical values of $\alpha$ and $n$. The Octave function t_inv $(1 - \alpha/2, n - 1)$ can be used to find the value $t_{\alpha/2, n-1}$.

For a given $1 - \alpha$, the confidence intervals given by Eq. (8.58) should be wider than those given by Eq. (8.52), since the former assumes that the variance is unknown. Figure 8.2 compares the Gaussian pdf and the Student's $t$ pdf. It can be seen that the Student's $t$ pdf's are more dispersed than the Gaussian pdf and so they indeed lead to wider confidence intervals. On the other hand, since the accuracy of the sample variance increases with $n$, we can expect that the confidence interval given by Eq. (8.58) should approach that given by Eq. (8.52). It can be seen from Fig. 8.2 that the Student's $t$ pdf's do approach the pdf of a zero-mean, unit-variance Gaussian random variable

---

[4]The distribution is named after W. S. Gosset, who published under the pseudonym, "A. Student."

**TABLE 8.2**   Critical values for Student's $t$-distribution: $F_n(t_{\alpha, n}) = 1 - \alpha$.

| $n$ | $\alpha$ | | | | |
|---|---|---|---|---|---|
| | 0.1 | 0.05 | 0.025 | 0.01 | 0.005 |
| 1 | 3.0777 | 6.3137 | 12.7062 | 31.8210 | 63.6559 |
| 2 | 1.8856 | 2.9200 | 4.3027 | 6.9645 | 9.9250 |
| 3 | 1.6377 | 2.3534 | 3.1824 | 4.5407 | 5.8408 |
| 4 | 1.5332 | 2.1318 | 2.7765 | 3.7469 | 4.6041 |
| 5 | 1.4759 | 2.0150 | 2.5706 | 3.3649 | 4.0321 |
| 6 | 1.4398 | 1.9432 | 2.4469 | 3.1427 | 3.7074 |
| 7 | 1.4149 | 1.8946 | 2.3646 | 2.9979 | 3.4995 |
| 8 | 1.3968 | 1.8595 | 2.3060 | 2.8965 | 3.3554 |
| 9 | 1.3830 | 1.8331 | 2.2622 | 2.8214 | 3.2498 |
| 10 | 1.3722 | 1.8125 | 2.2281 | 2.7638 | 3.1693 |
| 15 | 1.3406 | 1.7531 | 2.1315 | 2.6025 | 2.9467 |
| 20 | 1.3253 | 1.7247 | 2.0860 | 2.5280 | 2.8453 |
| 30 | 1.3104 | 1.6973 | 2.0423 | 2.4573 | 2.7500 |
| 40 | 1.3031 | 1.6839 | 2.0211 | 2.4233 | 2.7045 |
| 60 | 1.2958 | 1.6706 | 2.0003 | 2.3901 | 2.6603 |
| 1000 | 1.2824 | 1.6464 | 1.9623 | 2.3301 | 2.5807 |

with increasing $n$. This confirms that Eqs. (8.52) and (8.58) give the same confidence intervals for large $n$. Thus the bottom row ($n = 1000$) of Table 8.2 yields the same confidence intervals as Table 8.1.

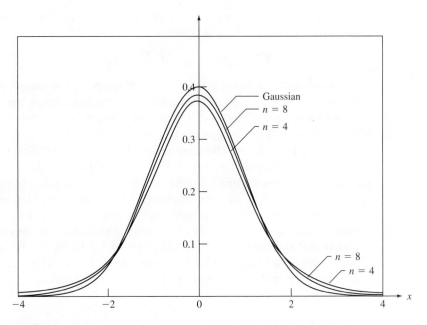

**FIGURE 8.2**
Gaussian pdf and Student's $t$ pdf for $n = 4$ and $n = 8$.

### Example 8.18   Device Lifetimes

The lifetime of a certain device is known to have a Gaussian distribution. Eight devices are tested and the sample mean and sample variance for the lifetime obtained are 10 days and 4 days². Find the 99% confidence interval for the mean lifetime of the device.

For a 99% confidence interval and $n - 1 = 7$, Table 8.2 gives $t_{\alpha/2,7} = 3.499$. Thus the confidence interval is given by

$$\left[ 10 - \frac{(3.499)(2)}{\sqrt{8}}, 10 + \frac{(3.499)(2)}{\sqrt{8}} \right] = [7.53, 12.47].$$

### 8.4.3   Case 3: $X_j$'s Non-Gaussian; Mean and Variance Unknown

Equation (8.58) can be misused to compute confidence intervals in experimental measurements and in computer simulation studies. The use of the method is justified only if the samples $X_j$ are iid and approximately Gaussian.

If the random variables $X_j$ are not Gaussian, the above method for computing confidence intervals can be modified using the **method of batch means**. This method involves performing a series of independent experiments in which the sample mean $\overline{X}$ of the random variable is computed. If we assume that in each experiment each sample mean is calculated from a large number $n$ of iid observations, then the central limit theorem implies that the sample mean in each experiment is approximately Gaussian. We can therefore compute a confidence interval from Eq. (8.58) using the set of $\overline{X}$ sample means as the $X_j$'s.

### Example 8.19   Method of Batch Means

A computer simulation program generates exponentially distributed random variables of unknown mean. Two hundred samples of these random variables are generated and grouped into 10 batches of 20 samples each. The sample means of the 10 batches are given below:

| | | | | |
|---|---|---|---|---|
| 1.04190 | 0.64064 | 0.80967 | 0.75852 | 1.12439 |
| 1.30220 | 0.98478 | 0.64574 | 1.39064 | 1.26890 |

Find the 90% confidence interval for the mean of the random variable.

The sample mean and the sample variance of the batch sample means are calculated from the above data and found to be

$$\overline{X}_{10} = 0.99674 \qquad \hat{\sigma}_{10}^2 = 0.07586.$$

The 90% confidence interval is given by Eq. (8.58) with $t_{\alpha/2,9} = 1.833$ from Table 8.2:

$$[0.83709, 1.15639].$$

This confidence interval suggests that $E[X] = 1$. Indeed the simulation program used to generate the above data was set to produce exponential random variables with mean one.

### 8.4.4    Confidence Intervals for the Variance of a Gaussian Random Variable

In principle, confidence intervals can be computed for any parameter $\theta$ as long as the sampling distribution of an estimator for the parameter is known. Suppose we wish to find a confidence interval for the variance of a Gaussian random variable. Assume the mean is not known. Consider the unbiased sample variance estimator:

$$\hat{\sigma}_n^2 = \frac{1}{n-1}\sum_{j=1}^{n}(X_j - \overline{X}_n)^2.$$

Later in this section we show that

$$\chi^2 = \frac{(n-1)\hat{\sigma}_n^2}{\sigma_X^2} = \frac{1}{\sigma_X^2}\sum \sum_{j=1}^{n}(X_j - \overline{X}_n)^2$$

has a chi-square distribution with $n-1$ degrees of freedom. We use this to develop confidence intervals for the variance of a Gaussian random variable.

The chi-square random variable was introduced in Example 4.34. It is easy to show (see Problem 8.6a) that the sum of the squares of $n$ iid zero-mean, unit-variance Gaussian random variables results in a chi-square random variable of degree $n$. Figure 8.3 shows the pdf of a chi-square random variable with 10 degrees of freedom. We need to find an interval that contains $\sigma_X^2$ with probability $1 - \alpha$. We select two intervals, one for small values of $\chi^2$ and one for large values of a chi-square random variable $Y$, each of which have probability $\alpha/2$, as shown in Fig. 8.3:

$$1 - \alpha = P\left[\chi_{1-\alpha/2,n-1}^2 < \frac{(n-1)}{\sigma_X^2}\hat{\sigma}_n^2 < \chi_{\alpha/2,n-1}^2\right]$$

$$= 1 - P[\chi_n^2 \le \chi_{1-\alpha/2,n-1}^2] - P[\chi_n^2 > \chi_{\alpha/2,n-1}^2].$$

The above probability is equivalent to:

$$1 - \alpha = P\left[\frac{(n-1)\hat{\sigma}_n^2}{\chi_{\alpha/2,n-1}^2} \le \sigma_X^2 \le \frac{(n-1)\hat{\sigma}_n^2}{\chi_{1-\alpha/2,n-1}^2}\right]$$

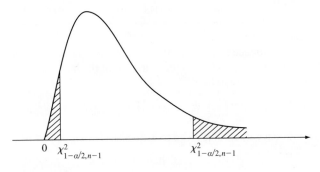

0    $\chi_{1-\alpha/2,n-1}^2$        $\chi_{1-\alpha/2,n-1}^2$

**FIGURE 8.3**
Critical values of chi-square random variables

and so we obtain the $(1 - \alpha)$ *confidence interval for the variance* $\sigma_X^2$:

$$\left[ \frac{(n-1)\hat{\sigma}_n^2}{\chi_{\alpha/2,n-1}^2}, \frac{(n-1)\hat{\sigma}_n^2}{\chi_{1-\alpha/2,n-1}^2} \right]. \tag{8.59}$$

Tables for the critical values $\chi_{\alpha/2,n-1}^2$ for which

$$P[\chi_n^2 > \chi_{\alpha/2,n-1}^2] = \alpha/2$$

can be found in statistics handbooks such as [Kokoska]. Table 8.3 provides a small set of critical values for the chi-square distribution. These values can also be found using the Octave function `chisquare_inv`$(1 - \alpha/2, n)$.

---

### Example 8.20    The Sample Variance

The sample variance in 10 measurements of a noise voltage is 5.67 millivolts. Find a 90% confidence interval for the variance. We need to find the critical values for $\alpha/2 = 0.05$ and $1 - \alpha/2 = 0.95$. From either Table 8.3 or Octave we find:

$\qquad$ `chisquare_inv`$(.95, 9) = 16.92$ $\qquad\qquad$ `chisquare_inv`$(.05, 9) = 3.33.$

The confidence interval for the variance is then:

$$\left[ \frac{(n-1)\hat{\sigma}_n^2}{\chi_{\alpha/2,n-1}^2} \le \sigma_X^2 \le \frac{(n-1)\hat{\sigma}_n^2}{\chi_{1-\alpha/2,n-1}^2} \right] = \left[ \frac{9(5.67)}{16.92} \le \sigma_X^2 \le \frac{9(5.67)}{3.33} \right] = [3.02, 15.32].$$

---

### 8.4.5    Summary of Confidence Intervals for Gaussian Random Variables

In this section we have developed confidence intervals for the mean and variance of Gaussian random variables. The choice of confidence interval method depends on which parameters are known and on whether the number of samples is small or large. The central limit theorem makes the confidence intervals presented here applicable in a broad range of situations. Table 8.4 summarizes the confidence intervals developed in this section. The assumptions for each case and the corresponding confidence intervals are listed.

### *8.4.6    Sampling Distributions for the Gaussian Random Variable

In this section we derive the joint sampling distribution for the sample mean and the sample variance of the Gaussian random variables. Let $\mathbf{X}_n = (X_1, X_2, \ldots, X_n)$ consist of independent, identically distributed versions of a Gaussian random variable with mean $\mu$ and variance $\sigma_X^2$. We will develop the following results:

**1.** The sample mean $\overline{X}_n$ and the sample variance $\hat{\sigma}_n^2$ are independent random variables:

$$\overline{X}_n = \frac{1}{n}\sum_{j=1}^{n} X_j \quad \text{and} \quad \hat{\sigma}_n^2 = \frac{1}{n-1}\sum_{j=1}^{n}(X_j - \overline{X}_n)^2.$$

**TABLE 8.3**    Critical values for chi-square distribution, $P[\chi^2 > \chi^2_{\alpha,\,n-1}] = \alpha$.

| $n\backslash\alpha$ | 0.995 | 0.975 | 0.95 | 0.05 | 0.025 | 0.01 | 0.005 |
|---|---|---|---|---|---|---|---|
| 1 | 3.9271E-05 | 0.0010 | 0.0039 | 3.8415 | 5.0239 | 6.6349 | 7.8794 |
| 2 | 0.0100 | 0.0506 | 0.1026 | 5.9915 | 7.3778 | 9.2104 | 10.5965 |
| 3 | 0.0717 | 0.2158 | 0.3518 | 7.8147 | 9.3484 | 11.3449 | 12.8381 |
| 4 | 0.2070 | 0.4844 | 0.7107 | 9.4877 | 11.1433 | 13.2767 | 14.8602 |
| 5 | 0.4118 | 0.8312 | 1.1455 | 11.0705 | 12.8325 | 15.0863 | 16.7496 |
| 6 | 0.6757 | 1.2373 | 1.6354 | 12.5916 | 14.4494 | 16.8119 | 18.5475 |
| 7 | 0.9893 | 1.6899 | 2.1673 | 14.0671 | 16.0128 | 18.4753 | 20.2777 |
| 8 | 1.3444 | 2.1797 | 2.7326 | 15.5073 | 17.5345 | 20.0902 | 21.9549 |
| 9 | 1.7349 | 2.7004 | 3.3251 | 16.9190 | 19.0228 | 21.6660 | 23.5893 |
| 10 | 2.1558 | 3.2470 | 3.9403 | 18.3070 | 20.4832 | 23.2093 | 25.1881 |
| 11 | 2.6032 | 3.8157 | 4.5748 | 19.6752 | 21.9200 | 24.7250 | 26.7569 |
| 12 | 3.0738 | 4.4038 | 5.2260 | 21.0261 | 23.3367 | 26.2170 | 28.2997 |
| 13 | 3.5650 | 5.0087 | 5.8919 | 22.3620 | 24.7356 | 27.6882 | 29.8193 |
| 14 | 4.0747 | 5.6287 | 6.5706 | 23.6848 | 26.1189 | 29.1412 | 31.3194 |
| 15 | 4.6009 | 6.2621 | 7.2609 | 24.9958 | 27.4884 | 30.5780 | 32.8015 |
| 16 | 5.1422 | 6.9077 | 7.9616 | 26.2962 | 28.8453 | 31.9999 | 34.2671 |
| 17 | 5.6973 | 7.5642 | 8.6718 | 27.5871 | 30.1910 | 33.4087 | 35.7184 |
| 18 | 6.2648 | 8.2307 | 9.3904 | 28.8693 | 31.5264 | 34.8052 | 37.1564 |
| 19 | 6.8439 | 8.9065 | 10.1170 | 30.1435 | 32.8523 | 36.1908 | 38.5821 |
| 20 | 7.4338 | 9.5908 | 10.8508 | 31.4104 | 34.1696 | 37.5663 | 39.9969 |
| 21 | 8.0336 | 10.2829 | 11.5913 | 32.6706 | 35.4789 | 38.9322 | 41.4009 |
| 22 | 8.6427 | 10.9823 | 12.3380 | 33.9245 | 36.7807 | 40.2894 | 42.7957 |
| 23 | 9.2604 | 11.6885 | 13.0905 | 35.1725 | 38.0756 | 41.6383 | 44.1814 |
| 24 | 9.8862 | 12.4011 | 13.8484 | 36.4150 | 39.3641 | 42.9798 | 45.5584 |
| 25 | 10.5196 | 13.1197 | 14.6114 | 37.6525 | 40.6465 | 44.3140 | 46.9280 |
| 26 | 11.1602 | 13.8439 | 15.3792 | 38.8851 | 41.9231 | 45.6416 | 48.2898 |
| 27 | 11.8077 | 14.5734 | 16.1514 | 40.1133 | 43.1945 | 46.9628 | 49.6450 |
| 28 | 12.4613 | 15.3079 | 16.9279 | 41.3372 | 44.4608 | 48.2782 | 50.9936 |
| 29 | 13.1211 | 16.0471 | 17.7084 | 42.5569 | 45.7223 | 49.5878 | 52.3355 |
| 30 | 13.7867 | 16.7908 | 18.4927 | 43.7730 | 46.9792 | 50.8922 | 53.6719 |
| 40 | 20.7066 | 24.4331 | 26.5093 | 55.7585 | 59.3417 | 63.6908 | 66.7660 |
| 50 | 27.9908 | 32.3574 | 34.7642 | 67.5048 | 71.4202 | 76.1538 | 79.4898 |
| 60 | 35.5344 | 40.4817 | 43.1880 | 79.0820 | 83.2977 | 88.3794 | 91.9518 |
| 70 | 43.2753 | 48.7575 | 51.7393 | 90.5313 | 95.0231 | 100.4251 | 104.2148 |
| 80 | 51.1719 | 57.1532 | 60.3915 | 101.8795 | 106.6285 | 112.3288 | 116.3209 |
| 90 | 59.1963 | 65.6466 | 69.1260 | 113.1452 | 118.1359 | 124.1162 | 128.2987 |
| 100 | 67.3275 | 74.2219 | 77.9294 | 124.3421 | 129.5613 | 135.8069 | 140.1697 |

**2.** The random variable $(n - 1)\hat{\sigma}_n^2/\sigma_X^2$ has a chi-square distribution with $n - 1$ degrees of freedom.

**3.** The statistic

$$W = \frac{\overline{X}_n - \mu}{\hat{\sigma}_n/\sqrt{n}} \tag{8.60}$$

has a Student's $t$-distribution.

**TABLE 8.4**   Summary of confidence intervals for Gaussian and non-Gaussian random variables.

| Parameter | Case | Confidence Interval |
|---|---|---|
| $\mu$ | Gaussian random variable, $\sigma^2$ known | $\left[\overline{X}_n - z_{\alpha/2}\sigma/\sqrt{n}, \overline{X}_n + z_{\alpha/2}\sigma/\sqrt{n}\right]$ |
| $\mu$ | Non-Gaussian random variable, $n$ large, $\sigma^2$ known | $\left[\overline{X}_n - z_{\alpha/2}\sigma/\sqrt{n}, \overline{X}_n + z_{\alpha/2}\sigma/\sqrt{n}\right]$ |
| $\mu$ | Gaussian random variable, $\sigma^2$ unknown | $\left[\overline{X}_n - t_{\alpha/2,n-1}\hat{\sigma}_n/\sqrt{n}, \overline{X}_n + t_{\alpha/2,n-1}\hat{\sigma}_n/\sqrt{n}\right]$ |
| $\mu$ | Non-Gaussian random variable, $\sigma^2$ unknown, batch means | $\left[\overline{X}_n - t_{\alpha/2,n-1}\hat{\sigma}_n/\sqrt{n}, \overline{X}_n + t_{\alpha/2,n-1}\hat{\sigma}_n/\sqrt{n}\right]$ |
| $\sigma^2$ | Gaussian random variable, $\mu$ unknown | $\left[\dfrac{(n-1)\hat{\sigma}_n^2}{\chi^2_{\alpha/2,n-1}}, \dfrac{(n-1)\hat{\sigma}_n^2}{\chi^2_{1-\alpha/2,n-1}}\right]$ |

These three results are needed to develop confidence intervals for the mean and variance of Gaussian distributed observations.

First we show that the sample mean $\overline{X}_n$ and the sample variance $\hat{\sigma}_n^2$ are independent random variables. For the sample mean we have

$$n\overline{X}_n = \sum_{j=1}^{n} X_j = \sum_{j=1}^{n-1} X_j + X_n,$$

which implies that

$$X_n - \overline{X}_n = (n-1)\overline{X}_n - \sum_{j=1}^{n-1} X_j = -\sum_{j=1}^{n-1}(X_j - \overline{X}_n).$$

By replacing the last term in the sum that defines $\hat{\sigma}_n^2$, we obtain

$$(n-1)\hat{\sigma}_n^2 = \sum_{j=1}^{n}(X_j - \overline{X}_n)^2 = \sum_{j=1}^{n-1}(X_j - \overline{X}_n)^2 + \left\{\sum_{j=1}^{n-1}(X_j - \overline{X}_n)\right\}^2. \quad (8.61)$$

Therefore $\hat{\sigma}_n^2$ is determined by $Y_i = X_i - \overline{X}_n$ for $i = 1, \ldots, n-1$.

Next we show that $\overline{X}_n$ and $Y_i = X_i - \overline{X}_n$ are uncorrelated:

$$E[\overline{X}_n(X_i - \overline{X}_n)] = E[\overline{X}_n X_i] - E[\overline{X}_n^2]$$

$$= E\left[\frac{1}{n}\sum_{j=1}^{n} E[X_j X_i]\right] - \frac{1}{n^2}\sum_{j=1}^{n}\sum_{i=1}^{n} E[X_j X_i]$$

$$= \frac{1}{n}\left[(n-1)\mu^2 + E[X^2] - \frac{1}{n}\left\{n(n-1)\mu^2 + nE[X^2]\right\}\right]$$

$$= 0. \quad (8.62)$$

Define the $n-1$ dimensional vector $\mathbf{Y} = (X_1 - \overline{X}_n, X_2 - \overline{X}_n, \ldots, X_{n-1} - \overline{X}_n)$, then $\mathbf{Y}$ and $\overline{X}_n$ are uncorrelated. Furthermore, $\mathbf{Y}$ and $\overline{X}_n$ are defined by the following linear transformation:

$$
\begin{aligned}
Y_1 &= X_1 - \overline{X}_n = (1 - 1/n)X_1 \quad - X_2 - \cdots \qquad\qquad\qquad - X_n \\
Y_2 &= X_2 - \overline{X}_n = \quad - X_1 + (1 - 1/n)X_2 - \cdots \qquad\qquad\qquad - X_n \\
&\ \ \vdots \\
Y_{n-1} &= X_{n-1} - \overline{X}_n = \quad - X_1 \quad - X_2 - \cdots + (1 - 1/n)X_{n-1} - X_n \\
Y_n &= \overline{X}_n \qquad = X_1/n \qquad\quad + X_2/n + \cdots \quad + X_n/n.
\end{aligned}
\tag{8.63}
$$

The first $n - 1$ equations correspond to the terms in $\mathbf{Y}$ and the last term corresponds to $\overline{X}_n$. We have shown that $\mathbf{Y}$ and $\overline{X}_n$ are defined by a linear transformation of jointly Gaussian random variables $\mathbf{X}_n = (X_1, X_2, \ldots, X_n)$. It follows that $\mathbf{Y}$ and $\overline{X}_n$ are jointly Gaussian. The fact that the components of $\mathbf{Y}$ and $\overline{X}_n$ are uncorrelated implies that the components of $\mathbf{Y}$ are independent of $\overline{X}_n$. Recalling from Eq. (8.61) that $\hat{\sigma}_n^2$ is completely determined by the components of $\mathbf{Y}$, we conclude that $\hat{\sigma}_n^2$ and $\overline{X}_n$ are independent random variables.

We now show that $(n - 1)\hat{\sigma}_n^2/\sigma_X^2$ has a chi-square distribution with $n - 1$ degrees of freedom. Using Eq. (8.15), we can express $(n - 1)\hat{\sigma}_n^2$ as:

$$
(n - 1)\hat{\sigma}_n^2 = \sum_{j=1}^{n}(X_j - \overline{X}_n)^2 = \sum_{j=1}^{n}(X_j - \mu)^2 - n(\overline{X}_n - \mu)^2,
$$

which can be rearranged as follows after dividing both sides by $\sigma_X^2$:

$$
\sum_{j=1}^{n}\left(\frac{X_j - \mu}{\sigma_X}\right)^2 = \frac{(n - 1)\hat{\sigma}_n^2}{\sigma_X^2} + \left(\frac{\overline{X}_n - \mu}{\sigma_X/\sqrt{n}}\right)^2.
$$

The left-hand side of the above equation is the sum of the squares of $n$ zero-mean, unit-variance independent Gaussian random variables. From Problem 7.6 we know that this sum is a chi-square random variable with $n$ degrees of freedom. The rightmost term in the above equation is the square of a zero-mean, unit-variance Gaussian random variable and hence it is chi square with one degree of freedom. Finally, the two terms on the right-hand side of the equation are independent random variables since one depends on the sample variance and the other on the sample mean. Let $\Phi(\omega)$ denote the characteristic function of the sample variance term. Using characteristic functions, the above equation becomes:

$$
\left(\frac{1}{1 - 2j\varpi}\right)^{n/2} = \Phi_n(\omega) = \Phi(\omega)\Phi_1(\omega) = \Phi(\omega)\left(\frac{1}{1 - 2j\varpi}\right)^{1/2},
$$

where we have inserted the expression for the chi-square random variables of degree $n$ and degree 1. We can finally solve for the characteristic function of $(n - 1)\hat{\sigma}_n^2/\sigma_X^2$:

$$
\Phi(\omega) = \left(\frac{1}{1 - 2j\varpi}\right)^{(n-1)/2}.
$$

We conclude that $(n - 1)\hat{\sigma}_n^2/\sigma_X^2$ is a chi-square random variable with $n - 1$ degrees of freedom.

Finally we consider the statistic:

$$T = \frac{\overline{X}_n - \mu}{\hat{\sigma}_n/\sqrt{n}} = \frac{\sqrt{n}(\overline{X}_n - \mu)/\sigma_X}{\sqrt{\hat{\sigma}_n^2/\sigma_X^2}} = \frac{(\overline{X}_n - \mu)/(\sigma_X/\sqrt{n})}{\sqrt{\{(n-1)\hat{\sigma}_n^2/\sigma_X^2\}/(n-1)}}. \quad (8.64)$$

The numerator in Eq. (8.64) is a zero-mean, unit-variance Gaussian random variable. We have just shown that $\{(n-1)\hat{\sigma}_n^2/\sigma_X^2\}$ is chi square with $n-1$ degrees of freedom. The numerator and denominator in the above expression are independent random variables since one depends on the sample mean and the other on the sample variance. In Example 6.14, we showed that given these conditions, $T$ then has a Student's $t$-distribution with $n-1$ degrees of freedom.

## 8.5    HYPOTHESIS TESTING

In some situations we are interested in testing an assertion about a population based on a random sample $\mathbf{X}_n$. This assertion is stated in the form of a hypothesis about the underlying distribution of $X$, and the objective of the test is to accept or reject the hypothesis based on the observed data $\mathbf{X}_n$. Examples of such assertions are:

- A given coin is fair.
- A new manufacturing process produces "new and improved" batteries that last longer.
- Two random noise signals have the same mean.

We first consider significance testing where the objective is to accept or reject a given "null" hypothesis $H_0$. Next we consider the testing of $H_0$ against an alternative hypothesis $H_1$. We develop decision rules for determining the outcome of each test and introduce metrics for assessing the goodness or quality of these rules.

In this section we use the traditional approach to hypothesis testing where we assume that the parameters of a distribution are unknown but not random. In the next section we use Bayesian models where the parameters of a distribution are random variables with known a priori probabilities.

### 8.5.1    Significance Testing

Suppose we want to test the hypothesis that a given coin is fair. We perform 100 flips of the coin and observe the number of heads $N$. Based on the value of $N$ we must decide whether to accept or reject the hypothesis. Essentially, we need to divide the set of possible outcomes of the coin flips $\{0, 1, \ldots, 100\}$ into a set of values for which we accept the hypothesis and another set of values for which we reject it. If the coin is fair we expect the value of $N$ to be close to 50, so we include the numbers close to 50 in the set that accept the hypothesis. But exactly at what values do we start rejecting the hypothesis? There are many ways of partitioning the observation space into two regions, and clearly we need some criterion to guide us in making this choice.

In the general case we wish to test a hypothesis $H_0$ about a parameter $\theta$ of the random variable $X$. We call $H_0$ the **null hypothesis**. The objective of a **significance test** is to accept or reject the null hypothesis based on a random sample $\mathbf{X}_n = (X_1, X_2, \ldots, X_n)$. In particular we are interested in whether the observed data $\mathbf{X}_n$ is *significantly* different from what would be expected if the null hypothesis is true. To specify a decision rule we partition the observation space into a **rejection or critical region** $\tilde{R}$ where we reject the hypothesis and an *acceptance region* $\tilde{R}^c$ where we accept the hypothesis. The **decision rule** is then:

$$
\begin{aligned}
&\text{Accept } H_0 \quad \text{if} \quad \mathbf{X}_n \in \tilde{R}^c \\
&\text{Reject } H_0 \quad \text{if} \quad \mathbf{X}_n \in \tilde{R}.
\end{aligned}
\tag{8.65}
$$

Two kinds of errors can occur when executing this decision rule:

$$
\begin{aligned}
&\textbf{Type I error:} \quad \text{Reject } H_0 \text{ when } H_0 \text{ is true.} \\
&\textbf{Type II error:} \quad \text{Accept } H_0 \text{ when } H_0 \text{ is false.}
\end{aligned}
\tag{8.66}
$$

If the hypothesis is true, then we can evaluate the probability of a Type I error:

$$
\alpha \triangleq P[\text{Type I error}] = \int_{\mathbf{x}_n \in \tilde{R}} f_{\mathbf{X}}(\mathbf{x}_n \mid H_0) \, d\mathbf{x}_n.
\tag{8.67}
$$

If the null hypothesis is false, we have no information about the true distribution of the observations $\mathbf{X}_n$ and hence we cannot evaluate the probability of Type II errors.

We call $\alpha$ the **significance level** of a test, and this value represents our tolerance for Type I errors, that is, of rejecting $H_0$ when in fact it is true. The level of significance of a test provides an important design criterion for testing. Specifically, the rejection region is chosen so that the probability of Type I error is no greater than a specified level $\alpha$. Typical values of $\alpha$ are 1% and 5%.

---

### Example 8.21    Testing a Fair Coin

Consider the significance test for $H_0$: coin is fair, that is, $p = 1/2$. Find a test at a significance level of 5%.

We count the number of heads $N$ in 100 flips of the coin. To find the rejection region $\tilde{R}$, we need to identify a subset of $S = \{0, 1, \ldots, n\}$ that has probability $\alpha$, when the coin is fair. For example, we can let $\tilde{R}$ be the set of integers outside the range $50 \pm c$:

$$
\alpha = 0.05 = 1 - P[50 - c \leq N \leq 50 + c \mid H_0]
$$

$$
= 1 - \sum_{j=50-c}^{50+c} \binom{100}{j} \left(\frac{1}{2}\right)^{100} \approx P\left[ \left| \frac{N - 50}{\sqrt{100(1/2)(1/2)}} \right| > c \right] = 2Q\left(\frac{c}{5}\right)
$$

where we have used the Gaussian approximation to the binomial cdf. The two-sided critical value is $z_{0.025} = 1.96$ where $Q(z_{0.025}) = 0.05/2 = 0.025$. The desired value of $c$ is then $c/5 = 1.96$, which gives $c = 10$ and the acceptance region $\tilde{R}^c = \{40, 41, \ldots, 60\}$ and rejection region $\tilde{R} = \{k : |k - 50| > 10\}$.

Note, however, that the choice of $\tilde{R}$ is not unique. As long as we meet the desired significance level, we could let $\tilde{R}$ be integers greater than $50 + c$.

$$
0.05 = P[N \geq 50 + c \mid H_0] \approx P\left[\frac{N - 50}{5} \geq \frac{c}{5}\right] = Q\left(\frac{c}{5}\right).
$$

The value $z_{0.05} = 1.64$ gives $Q(z_{0.05}) = 0.05$, which implies $c = 5 \times 1.64 \approx 8$ and the corresponding acceptance region is $\tilde{R}^c = \{0, 1, \dots, 58\}$ and rejection region $\tilde{R} = \{k > 58\}$.

Either of the above two choices of rejection region satisfies the significance level requirement. Intuitively, we have reason to believe that the two-sided choice of rejection region is more appropriate since deviations on the high or low side are significant insofar as judging the fairness of the coin is concerned. However, we need additional criteria to justify this choice.

---

The previous example shows rejection regions that are defined in terms of either two tails or one tail of the distribution. We say that a test is two-tailed or two-sided if it involves two tails, that is, the rejection region consists of two intervals. Similarly, we refer to one-tailed or one-sided regions where the rejection region consists of a single interval.

---

### Example 8.22    Testing an Improved Battery

A manufacturer claims that its new improved batteries have a longer lifetime. The old batteries are known to have a lifetime that is Gaussian distributed with mean 150 hours and variance 16. We measure the lifetime of nine batteries and obtain a sample mean of 155 hours. We assume that the variance of the lifetime is unchanged. Find a test at a 1% significance level.

Let $H_0$ be "battery lifetime is unchanged." If $H_0$ is true, then the sample mean $\overline{X}_9$ is Gaussian with mean 150 and variance 16/9. We reject the null hypothesis if the sample mean is significantly greater than 150. This leads to a one-sided test of the form $\tilde{R} = \{\overline{X}_9 > 150 + c\}$. We select the constant $c$ to achieve the desired significance level:

$$\alpha = 0.01 = P[\hat{X}_9 > 150 + c \mid H_0] = P\left[\frac{\overline{X}_9 - 150}{\sqrt{16/9}} > \frac{c}{\sqrt{16/9}}\right] = Q\left(\frac{c}{4/3}\right).$$

The critical value $z_{0.01} = 2.326$ corresponds to $Q(z_{0.01}) = 0.01 = \alpha$. Thus $3c/4 = 2.326$, or $c = 3.10$. The rejection region is then $\hat{X}_9 \geq 150 + 3.10 = 153.10$. The observed sample mean 155 is in the rejection region and so we reject the null hypothesis. The data suggest that the lifetime has improved.

---

An alternative approach to hypothesis testing is to not set the level $\alpha$ ahead of time and thus not decide on a rejection region. Instead, based on the observation, e.g., $\overline{X}_n$, we ask the question, "Assuming $H_0$ is true, what is the probability that the statistic would assume a value as extreme or more extreme than $\overline{X}_n$?" We call this probability the ***p*-value of the test statistic**. If $p(\overline{X}_n)$ is close to one, then there is no reason to reject the null hypothesis, but if $p(\overline{X}_n)$ is small, then there is reason to reject the null hypothesis.

For example, in Example 8.22, the sample mean of 155 hours for $n = 9$ batteries has a *p*-value:

$$P[\hat{X}_9 > 155 \mid H_0] = P\left[\frac{\hat{X}_9 - 150}{\sqrt{16/9}} > \frac{5}{\sqrt{16/9}}\right] = Q\left(\frac{5}{4/3}\right) = 8.84 \times 10^{-5}.$$

Note that an observation value of 153.10 would yield a *p*-value of 0.01. The *p*-value for 155 is much smaller, so clearly this observation calls for the null hypothesis to be rejected at 1% and even lower levels.

## 8.5.2    Testing Simple Hypotheses

A hypothesis test involves the testing of two or more hypotheses based on observed data. We will focus on the binary hypothesis case where we test a null hypothesis $H_0$ against an **alternative hypothesis** $H_1$. The outcome of the test is: accept $H_0$; or reject $H_0$ and accept $H_1$. A **simple hypothesis** specifies the associated distribution completely. If the distribution is not specified completely (e.g., a Gaussian pdf with mean zero and unknown variance), then we say that we have a **composite hypothesis**. We consider the testing of two simple hypotheses first. This case appears frequently in electrical engineering in the context of communications systems.

When the alternative hypothesis is simple, we can evaluate the probability of Type II errors, that is, of accepting $H_0$ when $H_1$ is true.

$$\beta \triangleq P[\text{Type II error}] = \int_{\mathbf{x}_n \in \tilde{R}^c} f_{\mathbf{X}}(\mathbf{X}_n \mid H_1) \, d\mathbf{X}_n. \tag{8.68}$$

The probability of Type II error provides us with a second criterion in the design of a hypothesis test.

---

### Example 8.23    The Radar Detection Problem

A radar system needs to distinguish between the presence or absence of a target. We pose the following simple binary hypothesis test based on the received signal $X$:

$H_0$:  no target present,   $X$ is Gaussian with $\mu = 0$ and $\sigma_X^2 = 1$

$H_1$:  target present,     $X$ is Gaussian with $\mu = 1$ and $\sigma_X^2 = 1$.

Unlike the case of significance testing, the pdf for the observation is given for both hypotheses:

$$f_X(x \mid H_0) = \frac{1}{\sqrt{2\pi}} e^{-x^2/2}$$

$$f_X(x \mid H_1) = \frac{1}{\sqrt{2\pi}} e^{-(x-1)^2/2}.$$

Figure 8.4 shows the pdf of the observation under each of the hypotheses. The rejection region should be clearly of the form $\{X > \gamma\}$ for some suitable constant $\gamma$. The decision rule

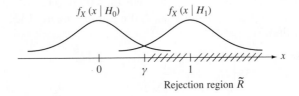

**FIGURE 8.4**
Rejection region.

is then:

$$\text{Accept } H_0 \text{ if } X \leq \gamma$$

$$\text{Accept } H_1 \text{ if } X > \gamma. \tag{8.69}$$

The Type I error corresponds to a **false alarm** and is given by:

$$\alpha = P[X > \gamma \,|\, H_0] = \int_\gamma^\infty \frac{1}{\sqrt{2\pi}} e^{-x^2/2} \, dx = Q(\gamma) = P_{FA}. \tag{8.70}$$

The Type II error corresponds to a *miss* and is given by:

$$\beta = P[X \leq \gamma \,|\, H_1] = \int_{-\infty}^\gamma \frac{1}{\sqrt{2\pi}} e^{-(x-1)^2/2} \, dx = 1 - Q(\gamma - 1) = 1 - P_D, \tag{8.71}$$

where $P_D$ is the probability of detection when the target is present. Note the tradeoff between the two types of errors: As $\gamma$ increases, the Type I error probability $\alpha$ decreases from 1 to 0, while the Type II error probability $\beta$ increases from 0 to 1. The choice $\gamma$ strikes a balance between the two types of errors.

---

The following example shows that the number of observation samples $n$ provides an additional degree of freedom in designing a hypothesis test.

---

### Example 8.24    Using Sample Size to Select Type I and Type II Error Probabilities

Select the number of samples $n$ in the radar detection problem so that the probability of false alarm is $\alpha = P_{FA} = 0.05$ and the probability of detection is $P_D = 1 - \beta = 0.99$.

If $H_0$ is true, then the sample mean of $n$ independent observations $\overline{X}_n$ is Gaussian with mean zero and variance $1/n$. If $H_1$ is true, then $\overline{X}_n$ is Gaussian with mean 1 and variance $1/n$. The false alarm probability is:

$$\alpha = P[\overline{X}_n > \gamma \,|\, H_0] = \int_\gamma^\infty \frac{\sqrt{n}}{\sqrt{2\pi}} e^{-\sqrt{n}x^2/2} \, dx = Q(\sqrt{n}\gamma) = P_{FA}, \tag{8.72}$$

and the detection probability is:

$$P_D = P[\overline{X}_n > \gamma] = \int_\gamma^\infty \frac{\sqrt{n}}{\sqrt{2\pi}} e^{-\sqrt{n}(x-1)^2/2} \, dx = Q(\sqrt{n}(\gamma - 1)). \tag{8.73}$$

We pick $\sqrt{n}\gamma = Q^{-1}(\alpha) = Q^{-1}(0.05) = 1.64$ to meet the significance level requirement and we pick $\sqrt{n}(\gamma - 1) = Q^{-1}(0.99) = -2.33$ to meet the detection probability requirement. We then obtain $\gamma = 0.41$ and $n = 16$.

---

Different criteria can be used to select the rejection region for rejecting the null hypothesis. A common approach is to select $\gamma$ so the Type I error is $\alpha$. This approach, however, does not completely specify the rejection region, for example, we may have a choice between one-sided and two-sided tests. The **Neyman-Pearson** criterion identifies the rejection region in a simple binary hypothesis test in which the Type I error is equal to $\alpha$ and where the Type II error $\beta$ is *minimized*. The following result shows how to obtain the Neyman-Pearson test.

---

**Theorem    Neyman-Pearson Hypothesis Test**

Assume that $X$ is a continuous random variable. The decision rule that minimizes the Type II error probability $\beta$ subject to the constraint that the Type I error probability is equal to $\alpha$ is given by:

$$\text{Accept } H_0 \text{ if } \mathbf{x} \in \tilde{R}^c = \left\{ \mathbf{x} : \Lambda(\mathbf{x}) = \frac{f_{\mathbf{X}}(\mathbf{x} \mid H_1)}{f_{\mathbf{X}}(\mathbf{x} \mid H_0)} < \kappa \right\}$$

$$\text{Accept } H_1 \text{ if } \mathbf{x} \in \tilde{R} = \left\{ \mathbf{x} : \Lambda(\mathbf{x}) = \frac{f_{\mathbf{X}}(\mathbf{x} \mid H_1)}{f_{\mathbf{X}}(\mathbf{x} \mid H_0)} \geq \kappa \right\} \tag{8.74}$$

where $\kappa$ is chosen so that:

$$\alpha = \int_{\Lambda(\mathbf{x}_n) \geq \kappa} f_{\mathbf{X}}(\mathbf{x}_n \mid H_0) \, d\mathbf{x}_n. \tag{8.75}$$

---

Note that terms where $\Lambda(\mathbf{x}) = \kappa$ can be assigned to either $\tilde{R}$ or $\tilde{R}^c$. We prove the theorem at the end of the section. $\Lambda(\mathbf{x})$ is called the **likelihood ratio function** and is given by the ratio of the likelihood of the observation $\mathbf{x}$ given $H_1$ to the likelihood given $H_0$. The Neyman-Pearson test rejects the null hypothesis whenever the likelihood ratio is equal or exceeds the threshold $\kappa$. A more compact form of writing the test is:

$$\Lambda(\mathbf{x}) \underset{H_0}{\overset{H_1}{\underset{<}{\gtrless}}} \kappa. \tag{8.76}$$

Since the log function is an increasing function, we can equivalently work with the log likelihood ratio:

$$\ln \Lambda(\mathbf{x}) \underset{H_0}{\overset{H_1}{\underset{<}{\gtrless}}} \ln \kappa. \tag{8.77}$$

---

**Example 8.25    Testing the Means of Two Gaussian Random Variables**

Let $\mathbf{X}_n = (X_1, X_2, \ldots, X_n)$ be iid samples of Gaussian random variables with known variance $\sigma_X^2$. For $m_1 > m_0$, find the Neyman-Pearson test for:

$$H_0: \quad X \text{ is Gaussian with } \mu = m_0 \text{ and } \sigma_X^2 \text{ known}$$

$$H_1: \quad X \text{ is Gaussian with } \mu = m_1 \text{ and } \sigma_X^2 \text{ known}.$$

The likelihood functions for the observation vector **x** are:

$$f_{\mathbf{X}}(\mathbf{x} \mid H_0) = \frac{1}{\sigma_X^n \sqrt{2\pi}^n} e^{-((x_1 - m_0)^2 + (x_2 - m_0)^2 + \cdots + (x_n - m_0)^2)/2\sigma_X^2}$$

$$f_{\mathbf{X}}(\mathbf{x} \mid H_1) = \frac{1}{\sigma_X^n \sqrt{2\pi}^n} e^{-((x_1 - m_1)^2 + (x_2 - m_1)^2 + \cdots + (x_n - m_1)^2)/2\sigma_X^2}$$

and so the likelihood ratio is:

$$\Lambda(\mathbf{x}) = \frac{f_{\mathbf{X}}(\mathbf{x} \mid H_1)}{f_{\mathbf{X}}(\mathbf{x} \mid H_0)} = \exp\left( -\frac{1}{2\sigma^2} \sum_{j=1}^{n} (x_j - m_1)^2 - (x_j - m_0)^2 \right)$$

$$= \exp\left( -\frac{1}{2\sigma_X^2} \sum_{j=1}^{n} (-2x_j(m_0 - m_1) + m_1^2 - m_0^2) \right)$$

$$= \exp\left( -\frac{1}{2\sigma_X^2} \left[ -2(m_0 - m_1)n\overline{X}_n - n(m_1^2 - m_0^2) \right] \right).$$

The log likelihood ratio test is then:

$$\ln \Lambda(\mathbf{x}) = -\frac{1}{2\sigma_X^2} \left[ -2(m_0 - m_1)n\overline{X}_n - n(m_1^2 - m_0^2) \right] \underset{H_0}{\overset{H_1}{\underset{<}{\gtrless}}} \ln \kappa$$

$$\left[ 2(m_1 - m_0)n\overline{X}_n - n(m_1^2 - m_0^2) \right] \underset{H_0}{\overset{H_1}{\underset{>}{\lessgtr}}} -2\sigma_X^2 \ln \kappa.$$

$$\overline{X}_n \underset{H_0}{\overset{H_1}{\underset{>}{\lessgtr}}} \frac{-2\sigma_X^2 \ln \kappa + n(m_1^2 - m_0^2)}{2(m_1 - m_0)n} \triangleq \gamma. \tag{8.78}$$

Note the change in the direction of the inequality when we divided both sides by the negative number $-2\sigma_X^2$. The threshold value $\gamma$ is selected so that the significance level is $\alpha$.

$$\alpha = P[\overline{X}_n > \gamma \mid H_0] = \int_{\gamma}^{\infty} \frac{1}{\sqrt{2\pi\sigma_X^2/n}} e^{-((x - m_0)^2)/((2\sigma_X^2))/n)} \, dx = Q\left( \sqrt{n}\frac{\gamma - m_0}{\sigma_X} \right)$$

and thus $\sqrt{n}(\gamma - m_0) = z_\alpha \sigma_X$, and $\gamma = m_0 + z_\alpha \sigma_X/\sqrt{n}$.

The radar detection problem is a special case of this problem, and after substituting for the appropriate variables, we see that the Neyman-Pearson test leads to the same choice of rejection region. Therefore we know that the test in Example 8.24 also minimizes the Type II error probability, and maximizes the detection probability $P_D = 1 - \beta$.

The Neyman-Pearson test also applies when $X$ is a discrete random variable, with the likelihood function defined as follows:

$$\Lambda(\mathbf{x}) = \frac{p_{\mathbf{X}}(\mathbf{x} \mid H_1)}{p_{\mathbf{X}}(\mathbf{x} \mid H_0)} \underset{H_0}{\overset{H_1}{\underset{<}{>}}} \kappa \qquad (8.79)$$

where the threshold $\kappa$ is the largest value for which

$$\sum_{\Lambda(\mathbf{x}_n) \geq \kappa} p_{\mathbf{X}}(\mathbf{x}_n \mid H_0) \leq \alpha. \qquad (8.80)$$

Note that equality cannot always be achieved in the above equation when dealing with discrete random variables.

The **maximum likelihood test** for a simple binary hypothesis can be obtained as the special case where $\kappa = 1$ in Eq. (8.76). In this case, we have:

$$\Lambda(\mathbf{x}) = \frac{f_{\mathbf{X}}(\mathbf{x} \mid H_1)}{f_{\mathbf{X}}(\mathbf{x} \mid H_0)} \underset{H_0}{\overset{H_1}{\underset{<}{>}}} 1,$$

which is equivalent to

$$f_{\mathbf{X}}(\mathbf{x} \mid H_1) \underset{H_0}{\overset{H_1}{\underset{<}{>}}} f_{\mathbf{X}}(\mathbf{x} \mid H_0). \qquad (8.81)$$

The test simply selects the hypothesis with the higher likelihood. Note that this decision rule can be readily generalized to the case of testing multiple simple hypotheses.

We conclude this subsection by proving the Neyman-Pearson result. We wish to minimize $\beta$ given by Eq. (8.68), subject to the constraint that the Type I error probability is $\alpha$, Eq. (8.75). We use Lagrange multipliers to perform this constrained minimization:

$$G = \int_{\tilde{R}^c} f_{\mathbf{X}}(\mathbf{x}_n \mid H_1) \, d\mathbf{x}_n + \lambda \left[ \int_{\tilde{R}} f_{\mathbf{X}}(\mathbf{x}_n \mid H_0) \, d\mathbf{x}_n - \alpha \right]$$

$$= \int_{\tilde{R}^c} f_{\mathbf{X}}(\mathbf{x}_n \mid H_1) \, d\mathbf{x}_n + \lambda \left[ 1 - \int_{\tilde{R}^c} f_{\mathbf{X}}(\mathbf{x}_n \mid H_0) \, d\mathbf{x}_n - \alpha \right]$$

$$= \lambda(1 - \alpha) + \int_{\tilde{R}^c} \{ f_{\mathbf{X}}(\mathbf{x}_n \mid H_1) - \lambda f_{\mathbf{X}}(\mathbf{x}_n \mid H_0) \} \, d\mathbf{x}.$$

For any $\lambda > 0$, we minimize $G$ by including in $\tilde{R}^c$ all points $\mathbf{x}_n$ for which the term in braces is negative, that is,

$$\tilde{R}^c = \{\mathbf{x}_n : f_{\mathbf{X}}(\mathbf{x}_n \mid H_1) - \lambda f_{\mathbf{X}}(\mathbf{x}_n \mid H_0) < 0\} = \left\{\mathbf{x}_n : \frac{f_{\mathbf{X}}(\mathbf{x}_n \mid H_1)}{f_{\mathbf{X}}(\mathbf{x}_n \mid H_0)} < \lambda\right\}.$$

We choose $\lambda$ to meet the constraint:

$$\alpha = \int_{\left\{\mathbf{x}_n : \frac{f_{\mathbf{X}}(\mathbf{x}_n \mid H_1)}{f_{\mathbf{X}}(\mathbf{x}_n \mid H_0)} > \lambda\right\}} f_{\mathbf{X}}(\mathbf{x}_n \mid H_0) \, d\mathbf{x}_n = \int_{\{\mathbf{x}_n : \Lambda(\mathbf{x}_n) > \lambda\}} f_{\mathbf{X}}(\mathbf{x}_n \mid H_0) \, d\mathbf{x}_n = \int_\lambda^\infty f_\Lambda(y \mid H_0) \, dy$$

where $f_\Lambda(y \mid H_0)$ is the pdf of the likelihood function $\Lambda(\mathbf{x})$. The likelihood function is the ratio of two pdfs, so it is always positive. Therefore the integral on the right-hand side will range over positive values of $y$, and the final choice of $\lambda$ will be positive as required above.

### 8.5.3  Testing Composite Hypotheses

Many situations in practice lead to the testing of a simple null hypothesis against a composite alternative hypothesis. This happens because frequently one hypothesis is very well specified and the other is not. Examples are not hard to find. In the testing of a "new longer lasting" battery, the natural null hypothesis is that the mean of the life-time is unchanged, that is $\mu = \theta_0$, and the alternative hypothesis is that the mean has increased, that is $\mu > \theta_0$. In another example, we may wish to test whether a certain voltage signal has a dc component. In this case, the null hypothesis is $\mu = 0$ and the alternative hypothesis is $\mu \neq 0$. In a third example, we may wish to determine whether response times in a certain system have become more variable. The null hypothesis is now $\sigma_X^2 = \theta_0$ and the alternative hypothesis is $\sigma_X^2 > \theta_0$.

All the above examples test a simple null hypothesis, $\theta = \theta_0$, against a composite alternative hypothesis such as $\theta \neq \theta_0$, $\theta > \theta_0$, or $\theta < \theta_0$. We now consider the design of tests for these scenarios. As before, we require that the rejection region $\tilde{R}$ be selected so that the Type I error probability is $\alpha$. We are now interested in the **power** $1 - \beta(\theta)$ of the test. $\beta(\theta)$ is the probability that a test accepts the null hypothesis when the true parameter is $\theta$. The power $1 - \beta(\theta)$ is then the probability of rejecting the null hypothesis when the true parameter is $\theta$. Therefore, we want $1 - \beta(\theta)$ to be near 1 when $\theta \neq \theta_0$ and small when $\theta = \theta_0$.

---

### Example 8.26    One-Sided Test for Mean of a Gaussian Random Variable (Known Variance)

Revisit Example 8.22 where we developed a test to decide whether a new design yields longer-lasting batteries. Plot the power of the test as a function of the true mean $\mu$. Assume a significance level of $\alpha = 0.01$ and consider the cases where the test uses $n = 4, 9, 25$, and $100$ observations.

This test involves a simple hypothesis with a Gaussian random variable with known mean and variance, and a composite alternative hypothesis with a Gaussian random variable with known variance but unknown mean:

$$H_0: \quad X \text{ is Gaussian with } \mu = 150 \text{ and } \sigma_X^2 = 16$$

$$H_1: \quad X \text{ is Gaussian with } \mu > 150 \text{ and } \sigma_X^2 = 16.$$

The rejection region has the form $\tilde{R} = \{\mathbf{x}: \overline{\mathbf{x}}_n - 150 > c\}$ where $c$ is chosen so:

$$\alpha = P[\hat{X}_n - 150 > c \,|\, H_0] = P\left[\frac{\hat{X}_n - 150}{\sqrt{16/n}} > \frac{c}{\sqrt{16/n}}\right] = 1 - Q\left(\frac{c\sqrt{n}}{4}\right).$$

Letting $z_\alpha$ be the critical value for $\alpha$, then $c = 4z_\alpha/\sqrt{n}$, and:

$$\tilde{R} = \{\mathbf{x}: \overline{\mathbf{x}}_n - 150 > 4z_\alpha/\sqrt{n}\}.$$

The Type II error probability depends on the true mean $\mu$ and is given by:

$$\beta(\mu) = P[\overline{X}_n - 150 \leq 4z_\alpha/\sqrt{n} \,|\, \mu] = P\left[\frac{\overline{X}_n - 150}{\sqrt{16/n}} \leq z_\alpha \,\Big|\, \mu\right].$$

If the true pdf of $X$ has mean $\mu$ and variance 16, then the sample mean $\overline{X}_n$ is Gaussian with mean $\mu$ and variance $16/n$. We need to rearrange the expression in the probability in terms of the standard Gaussian random variable $(\overline{X}_n - \mu)/\sqrt{16/n}$:

$$\beta(\mu) = P\left[\frac{\overline{X}_n - 150}{\sqrt{16/n}} \leq z_\alpha \,\Big|\, \mu\right] = P\left[\frac{\overline{X}_n - 150 - \mu}{\sqrt{16/n}} \leq z_\alpha - \frac{\mu}{\sqrt{16/n}} \,\Big|\, \mu\right]$$

$$= P\left[\frac{\overline{X}_n - \mu}{\sqrt{16/n}} \leq z_\alpha - \frac{\mu - 150}{\sqrt{16/n}} \,\Big|\, \mu\right] = 1 - Q\left(z_\alpha - \frac{\mu - 150}{\sqrt{16/n}}\right).$$

For $\alpha = 0.01$, $z_\alpha = 2.326$. The power function is then:

$$1 - \beta(\mu) = Q\left(z_\alpha - \frac{\mu - 150}{\sqrt{16/n}}\right) = Q\left(2.326 - \frac{\mu - 150}{\sqrt{16/n}}\right).$$

The ideal curve for the power function in this case is equal to $\alpha$ when $\mu = 150$, which is when null hypothesis is true, and then increases quickly as the true mean $\mu$ increases beyond 150. Figure 8.5 shows that the power curve for the test under consideration does drop near $\mu = 150$, and that the curve approaches the ideal shape as the number of observations $n$ is increased.

---

If we have two tests for a simple binary hypothesis that achieve a significance level $\alpha$, choosing between two tests is simple. We choose the test with the smaller Type II error probability $\beta$, which is equivalent to picking the test with higher power. Selecting between two tests is not quite as simple when we test a simple null hypothesis against a composite alternative hypothesis. The power $1 - \beta$ of a test will now vary with the true value of the alternative $\theta_a$. The perfect hypothesis test would be one that achieves the significance level $\alpha$, and that gives the highest power for each value of the alternative

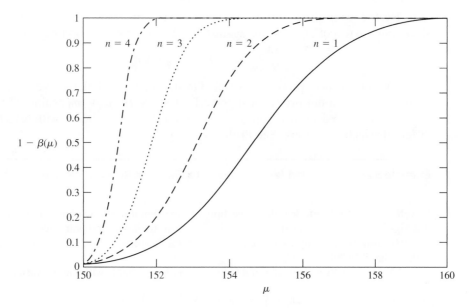

**FIGURE 8.5**
Power curve for one-sided test of Gaussian means.

hypothesis. We call such a test the *uniformly most powerful (UMP) test*. The following example shows that the one-sided test developed in Example 8.25 is uniformly most powerful.

---

### Example 8.27    One-Sided Test for Gaussian Means is UMP

In Example 8.25 we developed a test for two simple hypotheses:

$$H_0: \quad X \text{ is Gaussian with } \mu = m_0 \text{ and } \sigma_X^2 \text{ known}$$

$$H_1: \quad X \text{ is Gaussian with } \mu = m_1 \text{ and } \sigma_X^2 \text{ known.}$$

We used the Neyman-Pearson result to obtain the most powerful test for comparing $H_0: \mu = m_0$ and $H_1: \mu = m_1$. The rejection region of the test is:

$$\overline{X}_n > m_0 + z_\alpha \sigma/\sqrt{n}. \tag{8.82}$$

Note that in this test, the rejection region does not depend on the value of the alternative $m_1$. Therefore the Neyman-Pearson test for $H_0: \mu = m_0$ against $H_1: \mu = m_1$ for *any* $m_1 > m_0$, will lead to the same test specified by Eq. (8.82). It then follows that Eq. (8.82) is the uniformly most powerful test for

$$H_0: \quad X \text{ is Gaussian with } \mu = m_0 \text{ and } \sigma_X^2 \text{ known}$$

$$H_1: \quad X \text{ is Gaussian with } \mu > m_0 \text{ and } \sigma_X^2 \text{ known.}$$

By following the same development of the previous example, we can readily show that the test of $H_0: \mu = m_0$ against $H_1: \mu < m_0$ has rejection region

$$\overline{X}_n < m_0 - z_\alpha \sigma/\sqrt{n} \tag{8.83}$$

and is uniformly most powerful as well. On the other hand, the above results are not useful in finding a uniformly most powerful test for $H_0: \mu = m_0$ against $H_1: \mu \neq m_0$, where we need to deal with both $\mu < m_0$ and $\mu > m_0$, and hence with tests that have different rejection regions. (See Problem 8.62.)

---

**Example 8.28    Two-Sided Test for Mean of a Gaussian Random Variable (Known Variance)**

Develop a test to decide whether a certain voltage signal has a dc component. Assume that the signal is Gaussian distributed and is known to have unit variance. Assuming that $\alpha = 0.01$, how many samples are required so that a dc voltage of 0.25 volts would be rejected with probability 0.90?

This test involves the mean of a Gaussian random variable with known variance:

$$H_0: \quad X \text{ is Gaussian with } \mu = 0 \text{ and } \sigma_X^2 = 1$$

$$H_1: \quad X \text{ is Gaussian with } \mu \neq 0 \text{ and } \sigma_X^2 = 1.$$

When $H_0$ is true, the sample mean $\overline{X}_n$ is Gaussian with mean 0 and variance $1/n$. The rejection region involves two tails and has form $\tilde{R} = \{\mathbf{x}: |\overline{\mathbf{x}}_n| > c\}$ where $c$ is chosen so:

$$\alpha = P[|\overline{X}_n| > c | H_0] = 2P\left[\left|\frac{\overline{X}_n}{1/\sqrt{n}}\right| > \frac{c}{1/\sqrt{n}}\right] = 2Q(c\sqrt{n}). \tag{8.84}$$

Letting $z_{\alpha/2}$ be the rejection value for $\alpha/2$, then $c = z_{\alpha/2}/\sqrt{n}$, and the rejection region is:

$$\tilde{R} = \left\{\mathbf{x}: |\overline{\mathbf{x}}_n| > z_{\alpha/2}/\sqrt{n}\right\}.$$

When the true mean is $\mu$, the sample mean has mean $\mu$, and variance $1/n$, so the Type II error probability is given by:

$$\beta(\mu) = P\left[|\overline{X}_n| \leq \frac{z_{\alpha/2}}{\sqrt{n}} \Big| \mu\right] = P\left[-\frac{z_{\alpha/2}}{\sqrt{n}} - \mu \leq \overline{X}_n - \mu \leq \frac{z_{\alpha/2}}{\sqrt{n}} - \mu \Big| \mu\right]$$

$$= P\left[-z_{\alpha/2} - \sqrt{n}\mu \leq \frac{\overline{X}_n - \mu}{1/\sqrt{n}} \leq z_{\alpha/2} - \sqrt{n}\mu \Big| \mu\right]$$

$$= Q\left(-z_{\alpha/2} - \sqrt{n}\mu\right) - Q\left(z_{\alpha/2} - \sqrt{n}\mu\right).$$

For $\alpha = 0.01$, $z_{\alpha/2} = 2.576$. The Type II error probability for $\mu = 0.25$ is then:

$$\beta(0.25) = Q(-2.576 - 0.25\sqrt{n}) - Q(+2.576 - 0.25\sqrt{n}).$$

The above equation can be solved for $n$ by trial and error. Since $Q(x)$ is a decreasing function, and since the arguments of the two $Q$ functions differ by more than 5, we can neglect the second term so that

$$\beta(0.25) \approx Q(-2.576 - 0.25\sqrt{n}).$$

Letting $z_\beta$ be the critical value for $\beta$, then $z_\beta = -2.576 - 0.25\sqrt{n}$, and

$$n = \left(\frac{2.576 + z_\beta}{0.25}\right)^2.$$

If $\beta = 1 - 0.90 = 0.10$, then $z_\beta = 1.282$, and the required number of samples is $n = 238$.

In Examples 8.27 and 8.28 we have developed hypothesis tests involving the means of Gaussian random variables where the variances are known. The definition of the rejection regions in these tests depends on the fact that the sample mean $\overline{X}_n$ is a Gaussian random variable. *Therefore, these hypothesis tests can also be used in situations where the individual observations are not Gaussian, but where the number of samples n is sufficiently large to apply the central limit theorem and approximate $\overline{X}_n$ by a Gaussian random variable.*

### Example 8.29   Two-Sided Test for Mean of a Gaussian Random Variable (Unknown Variance)

Develop a test to decide whether a certain voltage signal has a dc component equal to $m_0 = 1.5$ volts. Assume that the signal samples are Gaussian but the variance is unknown. Apply the test at a 5% level in an experiment where a set of 9 measurements has resulted in a sample mean of 1.75 volts and a sample variance of 2.25 volts.

We now are considering two composite hypotheses:

$$H_0\text{: } X \text{ is Gaussian with } \mu = m_0 \text{ and } \sigma_X^2 \text{ unknown}$$

$$H_1\text{: } X \text{ is Gaussian with } \mu \neq m_0 \text{ and } \sigma_X^2 \text{ unknown.}$$

We proceed by emulating the solution in the case where the variance is known. We approximate the statistic $(\overline{X}_n - m_0)/(\sigma_X/\sqrt{n})$ by one that uses the sample variance given by Eq. (8.17):

$$T = \frac{(\overline{X}_n - m_0)}{\hat{\sigma}_n/\sqrt{n}}. \tag{8.85}$$

From the previous section (Eq. 8.64), we know that $T$ has a Student's $t$-distribution. For the rejection region we use:

$$\tilde{R} = \left\{ \mathbf{x}\text{: } \left| \frac{(\mathbf{x} - m_0)}{\hat{\sigma}_n/\sqrt{n}} \right| > c \right\}.$$

The threshold $c$ is chosen to provide the desired significance level:

$$\alpha = 1 - P\left[ -c \leq \frac{\overline{X}_n - m_0}{\hat{\sigma}_n/\sqrt{n}} \leq c \right] = 1 - (F_{n-1}(c) - F_{n-1}(-c)) = 2F_{n-1}(-c)$$

where $F_{n-1}(t)$ is the cdf of the Student's $t$ random variable with $n - 1$ degrees of freedom. Let $t_{\alpha/2,n-1}$ be the value for which $\alpha/2 = 1 - F_{n-1}(t_{\alpha/2,n-1}) = F_{n-1}(-t_{\alpha/2,n-1})$, then $c = t_{\alpha/2,n-1}$. The decision rule is then:

$$\text{Accept } H_0 \text{ if } \left| \frac{(\mathbf{x} - m_0)}{\hat{\sigma}_n/\sqrt{n}} \right| \leq t_{\alpha/2,n-1}$$

$$\text{Accept } H_1 \text{ if } \left| \frac{(\mathbf{x} - m_0)}{\hat{\sigma}_n/\sqrt{n}} \right| > t_{\alpha/2,n-1}. \tag{8.86}$$

The threshold for $\alpha/2 = 0.025$ and $n = 9 - 1 = 8$, is $t_{0.025,8} = 2.306$. The test statistic is $(1.75 - 1.5)/(2.25/9)1/2 = 0.5$, which is less than 2.306. Therefore the null hypothesis is accepted; the data support the assertion that the dc voltage is 1.5 volts.

One-sided tests for testing the mean of Gaussian random variables when the variance is unknown can be developed using the approach in the previous example. Recall from Table 8.2 that the critical values of the Student's $t$-distribution approach those of a Gaussian random variable as the number of samples is increased. Thus the Student's $t$ hypothesis tests are only necessary when dealing with a small number of Gaussian observations.

### Example 8.30    Testing the Variance of a Gaussian Random Variable

We wish to determine whether the variability of the response times in a certain system has changed from the past value of $\sigma_X^2 = 35 \text{ sec}^2$. We measure a sample variance of 37 $\text{sec}^2$ for $n = 30$ measurements of the response time. Determine whether the null hypothesis, $\sigma_X^2 = 35$, should be rejected against the alternative hypothesis, $\sigma_X^2 \neq 35$, at a 5% significance level.

We now have:

$$H_0: X \text{ is Gaussian with } \sigma_X^2 = \sigma_0^2 \text{ and } m \text{ unknown}$$

$$H_1: X \text{ is Gaussian with } \sigma_X^2 \neq \sigma_0^2 \text{ and } m \text{ unknown.}$$

In the previous section we showed that the statistic $(n - 1)\hat{\sigma}_n^2/\sigma_0^2$ is a chi-square random variable with $n - 1$ degrees of freedom if $X$ has variance $\sigma_0^2$. We consider a rejection region in which $H_0$ is rejected if the ratio of the statistic relative to $\sigma_0^2$ is too large:

$$\tilde{R}^c = \left\{ \mathbf{x} : a \leq \frac{(n - 1)\hat{\sigma}_n^2}{\sigma_0^2} \leq b \right\}.$$

We choose the threshold values $a$ and $b$ as we did in Eq. (8.59) to provide the desired significance level:

$$1 - \alpha = P\left[ a \leq \frac{(n - 1)\hat{\sigma}_n^2}{\sigma_0^2} \leq b \right] = P\left[ \chi_{1-\alpha/2,n-1}^2 < \frac{(n - 1)\hat{\sigma}_n^2}{\sigma_0^2} < \chi_{\alpha/2,n-1}^2 \right]$$

where $\chi_{\alpha/2,n-1}^2$ and $\chi_{1-\alpha/2,n-1}^2$ are critical values of the chi-square distribution. The decision rule is then:

$$\text{Accept } H_0 \quad \text{if} \quad \chi_{1-\alpha/2,n-1}^2 < \frac{(n - 1)\hat{\sigma}_n^2}{\sigma_0^2} < \chi_{\alpha/2,n-1}^2$$

$$\text{Accept } H_1 \quad \text{otherwise.} \tag{8.87}$$

Table 8.3 gives the required critical values $\chi^2_{0.025,29} = 45.72$ and $\chi^2_{0.975,29} = 16.04$, so the acceptance region is:

$$16.04 < \frac{(n-1)\hat{\sigma}^2_n}{\sigma^2} < 45.72.$$

The sample variance is 37 sec$^2$ and the statistic is $(n-1)\hat{\sigma}^2_n/\sigma^2_0 = 29(37)/35 = 30.66$. This statistic is inside the acceptance region so we accept the null hypothesis. The data do not suggest an increase in the variability of response times.

### 8.5.4   Confidence Intervals and Hypothesis Testing

Before concluding this section, we discuss the relationship between confidence intervals and hypothesis testing. Consider the acceptance region for a two-sided test involving the mean of a Gaussian random variable with known variance (Example 8.29): $H_0: \mu = m_0$ vs. $H_1: \mu \neq m_0$. In Section 8.4 we found the equivalence of the following events:

$$\left\{ -z_{\alpha/2} \leq \frac{\overline{X}_n - \mu}{\sigma_X/\sqrt{n}} \leq z_{\alpha/2} \right\} = \left\{ \overline{X}_n - \frac{z_{\alpha/2}\sigma_X}{\sqrt{n}} \leq \mu \leq \overline{X}_n + \frac{z_{\alpha/2}\sigma_X}{\sqrt{n}} \right\}.$$

The null hypothesis is accepted when the sample mean is inside the interval in the event on the left-hand side. The endpoints of the event have been selected so that the probability of the event is $1 - \alpha$ when $H_0$ is true. Now, when $H_0$ is true we have $\mu = m_0$, so the event on the right-hand side states that we accept $H_0$ when $m_0$ is inside the interval $[\overline{X}_n - z_{\alpha/2}\sigma_X/\sqrt{n}, \overline{X}_n + z_{\alpha/2}\sigma_X/\sqrt{n}]$. Thus we conclude that the hypothesis test will not reject $H_0$ in favor of $H_1$ if $m_0$ is in the $1 - \alpha$ confidence interval for $\mu$. Similar relationships exist between one-sided hypothesis tests and confidence intervals that attempt to find lower or upper bounds for parameters of interest.

### 8.5.5   Summary of Hypothesis Tests

This section has developed many of the most common hypothesis tests used in practice. We developed the tests in the context of specific examples. Table 8.5 summarizes the basic hypothesis tests that were developed in this section. The table presents the tests with the general test statistics and parameters.

## 8.6   BAYESIAN DECISION METHODS

In the previous sections we developed methods for estimating and for drawing inferences about a parameter $\theta$ assuming that $\theta$ is unknown but not random. In this section, we explore methods that assume that $\theta$ is a random variable and that we have a priori knowledge of its distribution. This new assumption leads to new methods for addressing estimation and hypothesis testing problems.

### 8.6.1   Bayes Hypothesis Testing

Consider a simple binary hypothesis problem where we are to decide between two hypotheses based on a random sample $\mathbf{X}_n = (X_1, X_2, \ldots, X_n)$:

**TABLE 8.5** Summary of basic hypothesis tests for Gaussian and non-Gaussian random variables.

| Hypothesis Test | Case | Statistic | Rejection Region |
|---|---|---|---|
| $H_0: \mu = m_0$ vs. $H_1: \mu \neq m_0$ <br> $H_0: \mu = m_0$ vs. $H_1: \mu > m_0$ <br> $H_0: \mu = m_0$ vs. $H_1: \mu < m_0$ | Gaussian random variable, $\sigma^2$ known; or non-Gaussian random variable, $n$ large, $\sigma^2$ known | $Z = \dfrac{\overline{X}_n - m_0}{\sigma/\sqrt{n}}$ | $\|Z\| \geq z_{\alpha/2}$ <br> $Z \geq z_\alpha$ <br> $Z \leq -z_\alpha$ |
| $H_0: \mu = m_0$ vs. $H_1: \mu \neq m_0$ <br> $H_0: \mu = m_0$ vs. $H_1: \mu > m_0$ <br> $H_0: \mu = m_0$ vs. $H_1: \mu < m_0$ | Gaussian random variable $\sigma^2$ unknown | $T = \dfrac{\overline{X}_n - m_0}{\hat{\sigma}_n/\sqrt{n}}$ | $\|T\| \geq t_{\alpha/2,n-1}$ <br> $T \geq t_{\alpha,n-1}$ <br> $T \leq -t_{\alpha,n-1}$ |
| $H_0: \sigma^2 = \sigma_0^2$ vs. $H_1: \sigma^2 \neq \sigma_0^2$ | Gaussian random variable $\mu$ unknown | $\chi^2 = \dfrac{(n-1)\hat{\sigma}_n^2}{\sigma_0^2}$ | $\chi^2 \leq \chi^2_{1-\alpha/2,n-1}$ <br> or <br> $\chi^2 \geq \chi^2_{\alpha/2,n-1}$ |
| $H_0: \sigma^2 = \sigma_0^2$ vs. $H_1: \sigma^2 > \sigma_0^2$ | | | $\chi^2 \geq \chi^2_{\alpha,n-1}$ |
| $H_0: \sigma^2 = \sigma_0^2$ vs. $H_1: \sigma^2 < \sigma_0^2$ | | | $\chi^2 \leq \chi^2_{1-\alpha,n-1}$ |

$$H_0: f_{\mathbf{X}}(\mathbf{x} \mid H_0)$$
$$H_1: f_{\mathbf{X}}(\mathbf{x} \mid H_1)$$

and we assume that we know that $H_0$ occurs with probability $p_0$ and $H_1$ with probability $p_1 = 1 - p_0$. There are four possible outcomes of the hypothesis test, and we assign a **cost** to each outcome as a measure of its relative importance:

1. $H_0$ true and decide $H_0$                                Cost $= C_{00}$
2. $H_0$ true and decide $H_1$ (Type I error)                 Cost $= C_{01}$
3. $H_1$ true and decide $H_0$ (Type II error)                Cost $= C_{10}$
4. $H_1$ true and decide $H_1$                                Cost $= C_{11}$

It is reasonable to assume that the cost of a correct decision is less than that of an erroneous decision, that is $C_{00} < C_{01}$ and $C_{11} < C_{10}$. Our objective is to find the decision rule that minimizes the average cost $C$:

$$C = C_{00}P[\text{decide } H_0 \mid H_0]p_0 + C_{01}P[\text{decide } H_1 \mid H_0]p_0$$
$$+ C_{10}P[\text{decide } H_0 \mid H_1]p_1 + C_{11}P[\text{decide } H_1 \mid H_1]p_1. \quad (8.88)$$

Each time we carry out this hypothesis test we can imagine that the following random experiment is performed. The parameter $\Theta$ is selected at random from the set $\{0, 1\}$ with probabilities $p_0$ and $p_1 = 1 - p_0$. The value of $\Theta$ determines which hypothesis is true. We cannot observe $\Theta$ directly, but we can collect the random sample $\mathbf{X}_n = (X_1, X_2, \ldots, X_n)$ in which the observations are distributed as per the true hypothesis. Let $\tilde{R}$ correspond to the subset of the observation space that is mapped into the value 1 (decide $H_1$). $\tilde{R}$ corresponds to the rejection region in the previous section. Similarly, let $\tilde{R}^c$ correspond to the subset that is mapped into the value 0 (decide $H_0$). The following theorem identifies the decision rule that minimizes the average cost.

**Theorem    Minimum Cost Hypothesis Test**

The decision rule that minimizes the average cost is given by:

$$\text{Accept } H_0 \text{ if } \mathbf{x} \in \tilde{R}^c = \left\{ \mathbf{x} : \Lambda(\mathbf{x}) = \frac{f_{\mathbf{X}}(\mathbf{x} \mid H_1)}{f_{\mathbf{X}}(\mathbf{x} \mid H_0)} < \frac{p_0(C_{01} - C_{00})}{p_1(C_{10} - C_{11})} \right\}$$

$$\text{Accept } H_1 \text{ if } \mathbf{x} \in \tilde{R} = \left\{ \mathbf{x} : \Lambda(\mathbf{x}) = \frac{f_{\mathbf{X}}(\mathbf{x} \mid H_1)}{f_{\mathbf{X}}(\mathbf{x} \mid H_0)} \geq \frac{p_0(C_{01} - C_{00})}{p_1(C_{10} - C_{11})} \right\} \quad (8.89)$$

if $X$ is a continuous random variable, and by

$$\text{Accept } H_0 \text{ if } \mathbf{x} \in \tilde{R}^c = \left\{ \mathbf{x} : \Lambda(\mathbf{x}) = \frac{p_{\mathbf{X}}(\mathbf{x} \mid H_1)}{p_{\mathbf{X}}(\mathbf{x} \mid H_0)} < \frac{p_0(C_{01} - C_{00})}{p_1(C_{10} - C_{11})} \right\}$$

$$\text{Accept } H_1 \text{ if } \mathbf{x} \in \tilde{R} = \left\{ \mathbf{x} : \Lambda(\mathbf{x}) = \frac{p_{\mathbf{X}}(\mathbf{x} \mid H_1)}{p_{\mathbf{X}}(\mathbf{x} \mid H_0)} \geq \frac{p_0(C_{01} - C_{00})}{p_1(C_{10} - C_{11})} \right\} \quad (8.90)$$

if $X$ is a discrete random variable.
      We will prove the theorem at the end of the section.

We already encountered $\Lambda(\mathbf{x})$, the *likelihood ratio function*, in our discussion of the Neyman-Pearson rule. The above decision rules are of threshold type and can involve the likelihood ratio function or the log likelihood ratio function:

$$\Lambda(\mathbf{x}) = \frac{f_{\mathbf{X}}(\mathbf{x} \mid H_1)}{f_{\mathbf{X}}(\mathbf{x} \mid H_0)} \overset{H_1}{\underset{H_0}{\gtrless}} \kappa \quad \text{or} \quad \ln \Lambda(\mathbf{x}) = \ln \frac{f_{\mathbf{X}}(\mathbf{x} \mid H_1)}{f_{\mathbf{X}}(\mathbf{x} \mid H_0)} \overset{H_1}{\underset{H_0}{\gtrless}} \ln \kappa.$$

**Example 8.31    Binary Communications**

A binary transmission system accepts a binary input $\Theta$ from an information source. The transmitter sends a $-1$ or $+1$ signal according to whether $\Theta = 0$ or $\Theta = 1$. The received signal is equal to the transmitted signal plus a Gaussian noise voltage that has zero mean and unit variance. Suppose that each information bit is transmitted $n$ times. Find a decision rule for the receiver that minimizes the probability of error.
      An error occurs if $\Theta = 0$ and we decide 1, or if $\Theta = 1$ and we decide 0. If we let $C_{00} = C_{11} = 0$ and $C_{01} = C_{10} = 1$, then the average cost is the probability of error:

$$C = P[\text{decide } H_1 \mid H_0] p_0 + P[\text{decide } H_0 \mid H_1] p_1 = P[\text{error}].$$

Each channel output is a Gaussian random variable with mean given by the input signal and unit variance. Each input signal is transmitted $n$ times and we assume that the noise values are independent. The pdf's of the $n$ observations are given by:

$$f_{\mathbf{X}}(\mathbf{x}\,|\,H_0) = \frac{1}{\sqrt{2\pi}^{\,n}}e^{-((x_1+1)^2+(x_2+1)^2+\cdots+(x_n+1)^2)/2}$$

$$f_{\mathbf{X}}(\mathbf{x}\,|\,H_1) = \frac{1}{\sqrt{2\pi}^{\,n}}e^{-((x_1-1)^2+(x_2-1)^2+\cdots+(x_n-1)^2)/2}.$$

The likelihood ratio is:

$$\Lambda(\mathbf{x}) = \frac{f_{\mathbf{X}}(\mathbf{x}\,|\,H_1)}{f_{\mathbf{X}}(\mathbf{x}\,|\,H_0)} = \exp\left(-\frac{1}{2}\sum_{j=1}^{n}(x_j-1)^2-(x_j+1)^2\right) = \exp\left(-\frac{1}{2}\sum_{j=1}^{n}-4x_j\right).$$

The log likelihood ratio test is then:

$$\ln \Lambda(\mathbf{x}) = 2n\overline{X}_n \mathop{\underset{H_0}{\overset{H_1}{\gtrless}}} \ln\frac{p_0(C_{01}-C_{00})}{p_1(C_{10}-C_{11})} = \ln\frac{p_0}{p_1},$$

which reduces to:

$$\overline{X}_n \mathop{\underset{H_0}{\overset{H_1}{\gtrless}}} \frac{1}{2n}\ln\frac{p_0}{p_1} = \gamma.$$

It is interesting to see how the decision threshold $\gamma$ varies with the a priori probabilities and the number of transmissions. If the inputs are equiprobable, then $p_0 = p_1$ and the threshold is always zero. However, if we know 1's are much more frequent, i.e., $p_1 \gg p_0$, then the threshold $\gamma$ decreases, thereby expanding the rejection region $\tilde{R} = \{\overline{X}_n > \gamma\}$. Thus this a priori knowledge biases the decision mechanism in favor of $H_1$. As we increase the number of transmissions $n$, the information from the observations becomes more important than the a priori knowledge. This effect is evident in the decrease of $\gamma$ to zero as $n$ is increased.

---

### Example 8.32    MAP Receiver for Binary Communications

The Maximum A Posteriori (MAP) receiver selects the input that has the larger a posteriori probability given the observed output. The MAP receiver uses the following decision rule:

Accept $H_0$ if $f_{\mathbf{X}}(\mathbf{x}\,|\,H_1)p_1 < f_{\mathbf{X}}(\mathbf{x}\,|\,H_0)p_0$

Accept $H_1$ otherwise.                                                            (8.91)

The receiver in the previous example is the MAP receiver. To see this, note that the likelihood function and threshold are:

$$\Lambda(\mathbf{x}) = \frac{f_{\mathbf{X}}(\mathbf{x}\,|\,H_1)}{f_{\mathbf{X}}(\mathbf{x}\,|\,H_0)} \mathop{\underset{H_0}{\overset{H_1}{\gtrless}}} \frac{p_0(C_{01}-C_{00})}{p_1(C_{10}-C_{11})} = \frac{p_0}{p_1},$$

which is equivalent to

$$f_{\mathbf{X}}(\mathbf{x} \mid H_1)p_1 \underset{H_0}{\overset{H_1}{\underset{<}{>}}} f_{\mathbf{X}}(\mathbf{x} \mid H_0)p_0.$$

The decision rule in the previous example minimizes the probability of error. Therefore we conclude that the MAP receiver minimizes the probability of error.

---

### Example 8.33    Server Allocation

Jobs arrive at a service station at rate $\alpha_0$ jobs per minute or rate $\alpha_1 = 2\alpha_0$ jobs per minute. A supervisor counts the number of arrivals in the first minute to decide which arrival rate is present, and based on that count decides whether to allocate one processor or two processors to the service station. Find a minimum cost rule for this problem.

We assume that the number of arrivals is a Poisson random variable with one of the two means, so we are testing the following hypotheses:

$$H_0 : p_{\mathbf{X}}(k \mid H_0) = \frac{\alpha_0^k}{k!} e^{-\alpha_0}$$

$$H_1 : p_{\mathbf{X}}(k \mid H_0) = \frac{\alpha_1^k}{k!} e^{-\alpha_1}.$$

Let the costs be given as follows:

$$C_{00} = S - r \quad C_{01} = 2S - r \quad C_{10} = S \quad \text{and} \quad C_{11} = 2S - 2r,$$

where $S$ is the cost of each server and $r$ is a unit of revenue. The term $C_{10}$ indicates that no revenue is earned when the arrival rate is $\alpha_1$ and there is only one server.

The minimum cost test is obtained from the likelihood ratio:

$$\Lambda(\mathbf{x}) = \frac{p_{\mathbf{X}}(k \mid H_1)}{p_{\mathbf{X}}(k \mid H_0)} = \frac{\alpha_1^k e^{-\alpha_1}/k!}{\alpha_0^k e^{-\alpha_0}/k!} = \left(\frac{\alpha_1}{\alpha_0}\right)^k e^{-(\alpha_1 - \alpha_0)}.$$

The log likelihood ratio is then:

$$\ln \Lambda(\mathbf{x}) = k \ln \frac{\alpha_1}{\alpha_0} - (\alpha_1 - \alpha_0) \underset{H_0}{\overset{H_1}{\underset{<}{>}}} \ln \frac{p_0 S}{p_1(2r - S)}$$

$$k \underset{H_0}{\overset{H_1}{\underset{<}{>}}} \frac{(\alpha_1 - \alpha_0) + \ln \dfrac{p_0 S}{p_1(2r - S)}}{\ln 2} = \frac{\alpha_0}{\ln 2} + \frac{1}{\ln 2} \ln \frac{p_0 S}{p_1(2r - S)} = \gamma.$$

It is interesting to examine how the parameter values affect the threshold. The term $p_0 S$ is the average cost when the lower rate is present and contains an extra cost of $S$ due to false alarms. The term $p_1(2r - S)$ is the average cost when the higher rate is present and it contains a loss in revenue due to not detecting the presence of the higher arrival rate. If the false alarm cost is higher than the miss cost, then the threshold $\gamma$ increases, thus expanding the acceptance region. This makes sense since we are motivated to have fewer false alarms. Conversely, the rejection region expands when the miss cost is higher.

---

### 8.6.2    Proof of Minimum Cost Theorem

To prove the minimum cost theorem we evaluate the probabilities in Eq. (8.88) by noting, for example, that $P[\text{decide } H_1 \,|\, H_0]$ is the probability that $\mathbf{X}_n$ is in $\tilde{R}$ when $H_0$ is true. Proceeding in such fashion, we obtain:

$$C = C_{00} \int_{\tilde{R}^c} f_{\mathbf{X}}(\mathbf{x} \,|\, H_0) p_0 \, d\mathbf{x} + C_{01} \int_{\tilde{R}} f_{\mathbf{X}}(\mathbf{x} \,|\, H_0) p_0 \, d\mathbf{x}$$

$$+ C_{10} \int_{\tilde{R}^c} f_{\mathbf{X}}(\mathbf{x} \,|\, H_1) p_1 \, d\mathbf{x} + C_{11} \int_{\tilde{R}} f_{\mathbf{X}}(\mathbf{x} \,|\, H_1) p_1. \tag{8.92}$$

Since $\tilde{R}$ and $\tilde{R}^c$ cover the entire observation space, we have

$$\int_{\tilde{R}^c} f_{\mathbf{X}}(\mathbf{x} \,|\, H_i) d\mathbf{x} = 1 - \int_{\tilde{R}} f_{\mathbf{X}}(\mathbf{x} \,|\, H_i) \, d\mathbf{x}.$$

Therefore

$$C = C_{00} p_0 \left\{ 1 - \int_{\tilde{R}} f_{\mathbf{X}}(\mathbf{x} \,|\, H_0) \, d\mathbf{x} \right\} + C_{01} \int_{\tilde{R}} f_{\mathbf{X}}(\mathbf{x} \,|\, H_0) p_0 \, d\mathbf{x}$$

$$+ C_{10} p_1 \left\{ 1 - \int_{\tilde{R}} f_{\mathbf{X}}(\mathbf{x} \,|\, H_1) \, d\mathbf{x} \right\} + C_{11} \int_{\tilde{R}} f_{\mathbf{X}}(\mathbf{x} \,|\, H_1) p_1 \, d\mathbf{x}$$

$$= C_{00} p_0 + C_{10} p_1 + \int_{\tilde{R}} \{(C_{01} - C_{00}) f_{\mathbf{X}}(\mathbf{x} \,|\, H_0) p_0 - (C_{10} - C_{11}) f_{\mathbf{X}}(\mathbf{x} \,|\, H_1) p_1\} \, d\mathbf{x}.$$

$$\tag{8.93}$$

We can deduce the minimum cost function from Eq. (8.93). The first two terms are fixed-cost components. The term inside the brace is the difference of two positive terms:

$$(C_{01} - C_{00}) f_{\mathbf{X}}(\mathbf{x} \,|\, H_0) p_0 - (C_{10} - C_{11}) f_{\mathbf{X}}(\mathbf{x} \,|\, H_1) p_1. \tag{8.94}$$

We claim that the minimum cost decision rule *always* selects an observation point $\mathbf{x}$ to be in $\tilde{R}$ if the above term is negative. By doing so, it minimizes the overall cost. Including in $\tilde{R}$ points $\mathbf{x}$ for which the above term is positive would only increase the overall cost and contradict the claim that the cost is minimum. Therefore, the minimum cost decision functions selects $H_1$ if

$$(C_{01} - C_{00})f_{\mathbf{X}}(\mathbf{x}\,|\,H_0)p_0 < (C_{10} - C_{11})f_{\mathbf{X}}(\mathbf{x}\,|\,H_1)p_1$$

and $H_0$ otherwise. This is equivalent to the decision rule in the theorem.

### 8.6.3    Bayes Estimation

The framework for hypothesis testing that we described above can also be applied to parameter estimation. To estimate a parameter we assume the following situation. We suppose that the parameter is a random variable $\Theta$ with a known a priori distribution. A random experiment is performed by "nature" to determine the value of $\Theta = \theta$ that is present. We cannot observe $\theta$ directly, but we can observe the random sample $\mathbf{X}_n = (X_1, X_2, \ldots, X_n)$, which is distributed according to the active value of $\theta$. Our objective is to obtain an estimator $g(\mathbf{X}_n)$ which minimizes a cost function that depends on $g(\mathbf{X}_n)$ and $\theta$:

$$C = E[C(g(\mathbf{X}_n), \Theta)] = \int_\theta \int_\mathbf{x} C(g(\mathbf{x}), \Theta)f_{\mathbf{X}}(\mathbf{x}\,|\,\theta)f_\Theta(\theta)\,d\mathbf{x}\,d\theta. \qquad (8.95)$$

If the cost function is the squared error, $C(g(\mathbf{X}), \Theta) = (g(\mathbf{X}) - \Theta)^2$, we have the mean square estimation problem. In Chapter 6 we showed that the optimum estimator is the conditional expected value of $\Theta$ given $\mathbf{X}_n$: $E(\Theta\,|\,\mathbf{X}_n)$.

Another cost function of interest is $C(g(\mathbf{X}),\Theta) = |g(\mathbf{X}) - \Theta|$, for which it can be shown that the optimum estimator is the median of the a posteriori pdf $f_\Theta(\theta\,|\,\mathbf{X})$. A third cost function of interest is:

$$C(g(\mathbf{X}), \Theta) = \begin{cases} 1 & \text{if } |g(\mathbf{X}) - \Theta| > \delta \\ 0 & \text{if } |g(\mathbf{X}) - \Theta| \leq \delta. \end{cases} \qquad (8.96)$$

This cost function is analogous to the cost function in Example 8.31 in that the cost is always equal to 1 except when the estimate is within $\delta$ of the true parameter value $\theta$. It can be shown that the best estimator for this cost function is the MAP estimator which maximizes the a posteriori probability $f_\Theta(\theta\,|\,\mathbf{X})$. We examine these estimators in the Problems.

We conclude with an estimator discovered by Bayes and which gave birth to the approach developed in this section. The approach was quite controversial because the use of an a priori distribution leads to two different interpretations of the meaning of probability. See [Bulmer, p. 169] for an interesting discussion on this controversy. In practice, we do encounter many situations where we have a priori knowledge of the parameters of interest. In such cases, Bayes' methods have proved to be very useful.

---

### Example 8.34    Estimating $p$ in $n$ Bernoulli Trials

Let $\mathbf{I}_n = (I_1, I_2, \ldots, I_n)$ be the outcomes of $n$ Bernoulli trials. Find the Bayes estimator for the probability of success $p$, assuming that $p$ is a random variable that is uniformly distributed in the unit interval. Use the squared error cost function.

The probability for the sequence of outcomes $i_1, i_2, \ldots, i_n$ is:

$$P[\mathbf{I}_n = (i_1, i_2, \ldots, i_n) \mid p] = p^{i_1}(1 - p)^{1-i_1} p^{i_2}(1 - p)^{1-i_2} \ldots p^{i_n}(1 - p)^{1-i_n}$$

$$= p^{\sum_{j=1}^{n} i_j}(1 - p)^{n - \sum_{j=1}^{n} i_j} = p^k(1 - p)^{n-k}$$

where $k$ is the number of successes in the $n$ trials. The probability of the sequence $i_1, i_2, \ldots, i_n$ over all possible values of $p$ is:

$$P[\mathbf{I}_n = (i_1, i_2, \ldots, i_n)] = \int_0^1 P[\mathbf{I}_n = (i_1, i_2, \ldots, i_n) \mid p] f_P(p) \, dp = \int_0^1 p^k(1 - p)^{n-k} \, dp,$$

where $f_P(p) = 1$ is the a priori pdf of $p$. In Problem 8.92, we show that:

$$\int_0^1 t^k(1 - t)^{n-k} \, dt = \frac{k!(n - k)!}{(n + 1)!}. \tag{8.97}$$

The a posteriori pdf of $p$, given the observation $i_1, i_2, \ldots, i_n$, is then:

$$f_P(p \mid i_1, i_2, \ldots, i_n) = \frac{p^k(1 - p)^{n-k} f_P(p)}{\int_0^1 t^k(1 - t)^{n-k} f_P(t) dt} = \frac{(n + 1)!}{k!(n - k)!} p^k(1 - p)^{n-k}.$$

The a posteriori pdf for the parameter $p$ depends on the observations only through the total number of heads $k$. The best estimator for $p$ in the mean square sense is given by the conditional expected value of $p$ given $i_1, i_2, \ldots, i_n$:

$$\hat{g}(p) = \int_0^1 p f_P(p \mid i_1, i_2, \ldots, i_n) \, dp = \int_0^1 p \frac{(n + 1)!}{k!(n - k)!} p^k(1 - p)^{n-k} \, dp$$

$$= \frac{(n + 1)!}{k!(n - k)!} \int_0^1 p^{k+1}(1 - p)^{n-k} \, dp = \frac{(n + 1)!}{k!(n - k)!} \frac{(k + 1)!(n - k)!}{(n + 2)!}$$

$$= \frac{k + 1}{n + 2}. \tag{8.98}$$

This estimator differs from the maximum likelihood estimator which we found to be given by the relative frequency in Example 8.10. For large $n$, the two estimators are in agreement if $k$ is also large. Problem 8.92 considers the more general case where $p$ has a beta a priori distribution.

---

## 8.7    TESTING THE FIT OF A DISTRIBUTION TO DATA

How well does the model fit the data? Suppose you have postulated a probability model for some random experiment, and you are now interested in determining how well the model fits your experimental data. How do you test this hypothesis? In this

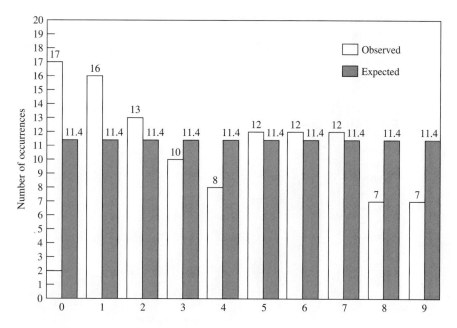

**FIGURE 8.6**
Histogram of last digit in telephone numbers.

section we present the chi-square test, which is widely used to determine the goodness of fit of a distribution to a set of experimental data.

The natural first test to carry out is an "eyeball" comparison of the postulated pmf, pdf, or cdf and an experimentally determined counterpart. If the outcome of the experiment, $X$, is discrete, then we can compare the relative frequency of outcomes with the probability specified by the pmf, as shown in Fig 8.6. If $X$ is continuous, then we can partition the real axis into $K$ mutually exclusive intervals and determine the relative frequency with which outcomes fall into each interval. These numbers would be compared to the probability of $X$ falling in the interval, as shown in Fig 8.7. If the relative frequencies and corresponding probabilities are in good agreement, then we have established that a good fit exists.

We now show that the approach outlined above leads to a test involving the multinomial distribution. Suppose that there are $K$ intervals. Let $p_i$ be the probability that $X$ falls in the $i$th interval. Since the intervals are selected to be a partition of the range of $X$, we have that $p_1 + p_2 + \cdots + p_K = 1$. Suppose we perform the experiment $n$ independent times and let $N_i$ be the number of times the outcome is in the $i$th interval. Let $(N_1, N_2, \ldots, N_K)$ be the vector of interval counts, then $(N_1, N_2, \ldots, N_K)$ has a multinomial pmf:

$$P[(N_1, N_2, \ldots, N_K) = (n_1, n_2, \ldots, n_K)] = \frac{n!}{n_1! \, n_2! \ldots n_K!} p_1^{n_1} p_2^{n_2} \cdots p_K^{n_K}$$

where   $n_j \geq 0$ and $n_1 + n_2 + \cdots + n_K = n$.

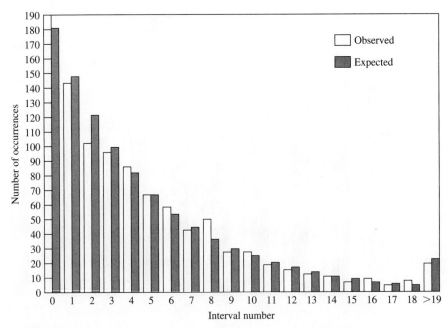

**FIGURE 8.7**
Histogram of computer simulation of exponential random variables.

First we show that the relative frequencies of the interval counts are a maximum likelihood estimator for the $K - 1$ independent parameters $p_1, p_2, \ldots, p_{K-1}$. Note that $p_K$ is determined by the other $K - 1$ probabilities. Suppose we perform the experiment $n$ times and observe a sequence of outcomes with counts $(n_1, n_2, \ldots, n_K)$. The likelihood of this sequence is:

$$P[\mathbf{N} = (n_1, n_2, \ldots, n_K) \mid p_1, p_2, \ldots, p_{K-1}] = p_1^{n_1} p_2^{n_2} \cdots p_K^{n_K}$$

and the log likelihood is:

$$\ln P[\mathbf{N} = (n_1, n_2, \ldots, n_K) \mid p_1, p_2, \ldots, p_{K-1}] = \sum_{j=1}^{K} n_j \ln p_j.$$

We take derivatives with respect to $p_j$ and set the result equal to zero:

For $i = 1, \ldots, K - 1$:

$$0 = \frac{\partial}{\partial p_i} \sum_{j=1}^{K} n_j \ln p_j = \frac{\partial}{\partial p_i} \left[ \sum_{j=1}^{K} n_j \ln p_j \right] = \left[ \sum_{j=1}^{K} \frac{n_j}{p_j} \frac{\partial p_j}{\partial p_i} \right]$$

$$= \left[ \frac{n_i}{p_i} \frac{\partial p_i}{\partial p_i} + \frac{n_K}{p_K} \frac{\partial p_K}{\partial p_i} \right] = \left[ \frac{n_i}{p_i} + \frac{n_K}{p_K} \frac{\partial}{\partial p_i} \left\{ 1 - \sum_{j=1}^{K-1} p_j \right\} \right] = \frac{n_i}{p_i} - \frac{n_K}{p_K},$$

where we have noted that $p_K$ depends on $p_i$. The above equation implies that $p_i = p_K n_i / n_K$, which in turn implies that the maximum likelihood estimates must satisfy

$$\hat{p}_K = 1 - \sum_{i=1}^{K-1} \hat{p}_i = 1 - \hat{p}_K \sum_{i=1}^{K-1} n_i/n_K = 1 - \hat{p}_K \frac{n - n_K}{n_K}.$$

This last equation implies that $\hat{p}_K = n_K/n$, and $\hat{p}_i = n_i/n$ for $i = 1, 2, \ldots, K - 1$. Therefore the relative frequencies of the counts provide maximum likelihood estimates for the interval probabilities. As $n$ increases we expect that the relative frequency estimates will approach the true probabilities.

We next consider a test statistic that measures the deviation from the expected count for each interval, that is, $m_i = np_i$.

$$D^2 = \sum_{i=1}^{K-1} c_i (N_i - np_i)^2.$$

The purpose of the term $c_i$ is to ensure that the terms in the sum have good asymptotic properties as $n$ becomes large. The choice of $c_i = 1/np_i$ results in the above sum approaching a chi-square distribution with $K - 1$ degrees of freedom as $n$ becomes large. We will not present the proof of this result, which can be found in [Cramer, p. 417]. The chi-square goodness-of-fit test involves calculating the $D^2$ and using an associated significance test. A threshold is selected to provide the desired significance level. The chi-square test is performed as follows:

1. Partition the sample space $S_X$, into the union of $K$ disjoint intervals.
2. Compute the probability $p_k$ that an outcome falls in the $k$th interval under the assumption that $X$ has the postulated distribution. Then $m_k = np_k$ is the expected number of outcomes that fall in the $k$th interval in $n$ repetitions of the experiment. (To see this, imagine performing Bernoulli trials in which a "success" corresponds to an outcome in the $k$th interval.)
3. The chi-square statistic is defined as the weighted difference between the observed number of outcomes, $n_k$, that fall in the $k$th interval, and the expected number $m_k$:

$$D^2 = \sum_{k=1}^{K} \frac{(n_k - m_k)^2}{m_k}. \tag{8.99}$$

4. If the fit is good, then $D^2$ will be small. Therefore the hypothesis is rejected if $D^2$ is too large, that is, if $D^2 \geq t_\alpha$, where $t_\alpha$ is a threshold determined by the significance level of the test.

The chi-square test is based on the fact that for large $n$, the random variable $D^2$ has a pdf that is approximately a chi-square pdf with $K - 1$ degrees of freedom. Thus the threshold $t_\alpha$ can be computed by finding the point at which

$$P[D^2 > \chi^2_{\alpha, K-1}] = \alpha,$$

where $D^2$ is a chi-square random variable with $K - 1$ degrees of freedom (see Fig. 8.8). The thresholds for 1% and 5% significance levels and various degrees of freedom are given in Table 8.3.

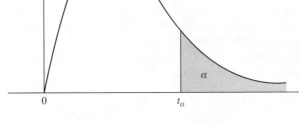

**FIGURE 8.8**
Threshold in chi-square test is selected so that $P[D^2 > \chi_{\alpha K-1}^2] = \alpha$.

## Example 8.35

The histogram over the set $\{0, 1, 2, \ldots, 9\}$ in Fig. 8.6 was obtained by taking the last digit of 114 telephone numbers in one column in a telephone directory. Are these observations consistent with the assumption that they have a discrete uniform pmf?

If the outcomes are uniformly distributed, then each has probability 1/10. The expected number of occurrences of each outcome in 114 trials is $114/10 = 11.4$. The chi-square statistic is then

$$D^2 = \frac{(17 - 11.4)^2}{11.4} + \frac{(16 - 11.4)^2}{11.4} + \cdots + \frac{(7 - 11.4)^2}{11.4}$$
$$= 9.51.$$

The number of degrees of freedom is $K - 1 = 10 - 1 = 9$, so from Table 8.3 the threshold for a 1% significance level is 21.7. $D^2$ does not exceed the threshold, so we conclude that the data are consistent with that of a uniformly distributed random variable.

## Example 8.36

The histogram in Fig. 8.7 was obtained by generating 1000 samples from a program designed to generate exponentially distributed random variables with parameter 1. The histogram was obtained by dividing the positive real line into 20 intervals of equal length 0.2. The exact numbers are given in Table 8.6. A second histogram was also taken using 20 intervals of equal probability. The numbers for this histogram are given in Table 8.7.

From Table 8.3 we find that the threshold for a 5% significance level is 30.1. The chi-square values for the two histograms are 14.2 and 11.6, respectively. Both histograms pass the goodness-of-fit test in this case, but it is apparent that the method of selecting the intervals can significantly affect the value of the chi-square measure.

Example 8.36 shows that there are many ways of selecting the intervals in the partition, and that these can yield different results. The following rules of thumb are

**TABLE 8.6**    Chi-square test for exponential random variable, equal-length intervals.

| Interval | Observed | Expected | $(O - E)^2/E$ |
|:--------:|:--------:|:--------:|:-------------:|
| 0 | 190 | 181.3 | 0.417484 |
| 1 | 144 | 148.4 | 0.130458 |
| 2 | 102 | 121.5 | 3.129629 |
| 3 | 96 | 99.5 | 0.123115 |
| 4 | 86 | 81.44 | 0.255324 |
| 5 | 67 | 66.7 | 0.001349 |
| 6 | 59 | 54.6 | 0.354578 |
| 7 | 43 | 44.7 | 0.064653 |
| 8 | 51 | 36.6 | 5.665573 |
| 9 | 28 | 30 | 0.133333 |
| 10 | 28 | 24.5 | 0.5 |
| 11 | 19 | 20.1 | 0.060199 |
| 12 | 15 | 16.4 | 0.119512 |
| 13 | 12 | 13.5 | 0.166666 |
| 14 | 11 | 11 | 0 |
| 15 | 7 | 9 | 0.444444 |
| 16 | 9 | 7.4 | 0.345945 |
| 17 | 5 | 6 | 0.166666 |
| 18 | 8 | 5 | 1.8 |
| >19 | 20 | 22.4 | 0.257142 |

Chi-square value = 14.13607

recommended. First, to the extent possible the intervals should be selected so that they are equiprobable. Second, the intervals should be selected so that the expected number of outcomes in each interval is five or more. This improves the accuracy of approximating the cdf of $D^2$ by a chi-square cdf.

The discussion so far has assumed that the postulated distribution is completely specified. In the typical case, however, one or two parameters of the distribution, namely the mean and variance, are estimated from the data. It is often recommended that if $r$ of the parameters of a cdf are estimated from the data, then $D^2$ is better approximated by a chi-square distribution with $K - r - 1$ degrees of freedom. See [Allen, p. 308]. In effect, each estimated parameter decreases the degrees of freedom by 1.

---

**Example 8.37**

The histogram in Table 8.8 was reported by Rutherford, Chadwick, and Ellis in a famous paper published in 1920. The number of particles emitted by a radioactive mass in a time period of 7.5 seconds was counted. A total number of 2608 periods were observed. It is postulated that the number of particles emitted in a time period is a random variable with a Poisson distribution. Perform the chi-square goodness-of-fit test.

In this case, the mean of the Poisson distribution is unknown, so it is estimated from the data to be 3.870. $D^2$ for $12 - 1 - 1 = 10$ degrees of freedom is then 12.94. The threshold at a 1% significance level is 23.2. $D^2$ does not exceed this, so we conclude that the data are in good agreement with the Poisson distribution.

---

**TABLE 8.7** Chi-square test for exponential random variable, equiprobable intervals.

| Interval | Observed | Expected | $(O - E)^2/E$ |
|---|---|---|---|
| 0 | 49 | 50 | 0.02 |
| 1 | 61 | 50 | 2.42 |
| 2 | 50 | 50 | 0 |
| 3 | 50 | 50 | 0 |
| 4 | 40 | 50 | 2 |
| 5 | 52 | 50 | 0.08 |
| 6 | 48 | 50 | 0.08 |
| 7 | 40 | 50 | 2 |
| 8 | 45 | 50 | 0.5 |
| 9 | 46 | 50 | 0.32 |
| 10 | 50 | 50 | 0 |
| 11 | 51 | 50 | 0.02 |
| 12 | 55 | 50 | 0.5 |
| 13 | 49 | 50 | 0.02 |
| 14 | 54 | 50 | 0.32 |
| 15 | 52 | 50 | 0.08 |
| 16 | 62 | 50 | 2.88 |
| 17 | 46 | 50 | 0.32 |
| 18 | 49 | 50 | 0.02 |
| 19 | 51 | 50 | 0.02 |

Chi-square value $= 11.6$

**TABLE 8.8** Chi-square test for Poisson random variable.

| Count | Observed | Expected | $(O - E)^2/E$ |
|---|---|---|---|
| 0 | 7,6757.00 | 54.40 | 0.12 |
| 1 | 203.00 | 210.50 | 0.27 |
| 2 | 383.00 | 407.40 | 1.46 |
| 3 | 525.00 | 525.50 | .00 |
| 4 | 532.00 | 508.40 | 1.10 |
| 5 | 408.00 | 393.50 | .053 |
| 6 | 273.00 | 253.80 | 1.45 |
| 7 | 139.00 | 140.30 | 0.01 |
| 8 | 45.00 | 67.80 | 7.67 |
| 9 | 27.00 | 29.20 | 0.17 |
| 10 | 10.00 | 11.30 | 0.15 |
| >11 | 6.00 | 5.80 | 0.01 |
| | | | 12.94 |

Based on [Cramer, p. 436].

## SUMMARY

- A statistic is a function of a random sample that consists of $n$ iid observations of a random variable of interest. The sampling distribution is the pdf or pmf of the statistic. The critical values of a given statistic are the interval endpoints at which the complementary cdf achieves certain probabilities.

- A point estimator is unbiased if its expected value equals the true value of the parameter of interest, and it is consistent if it is asymptotically unbiased. The mean square error of an estimator is a measure of its accuracy. The sample mean and the sample variance are consistent estimators.

- Maximum likelihood estimators are obtained by working with the likelihood and log likelihood functions. Maximum likelihood estimators are consistent and their estimation error is asymptotically Gaussian and efficient.

- The Cramer-Rao inequality provides a way of determining whether an unbiased estimator achieves the minimum mean square error. An estimator that achieves the lower bound is said to be efficient.

- Confidence intervals provide an interval that is determined from observed data and that by design contains a parameter interest with a specified probability level. We developed confidence intervals for binomial, Gaussian, Student's $t$, and chi-square sampling distributions.

- When the number of samples $n$ is large, the central limit theorem allows us to use estimators and confidence intervals for Gaussian random variables even if the random variable of interest is not Gaussian.

- The sample mean and sample variance for independent Gaussian random variables are independent random variables. The chi-square and Student's $t$-distribution are derived from statistics involving Gaussian random variables.

- A significance test is used to determine whether observed data are consistent with a hypothesized distribution. The level of significance of a test is the probability that the hypothesis is rejected when it is actually true.

- A binary hypothesis tests decides between a null hypothesis and an alternative hypothesis based on observed data. A hypothesis is simple if the associated distribution is specified completely. A hypothesis is composite if the associated distribution is not specified completely.

- Simple binary hypothesis tests are assessed in terms of their significance level and their Type II error probability or, equivalently, their power. The Neyman-Pearson test leads to a likelihood ratio test that meets a target Type I error probability while maximizing the power of the test.

- Bayesian models are based on the assumption of an a priori distribution for the parameters of interest, and they provide an alternative approach to assessing and deriving estimators and hypothesis tests.

- The chi-square distribution provides a significance test for the fit of observed data to a hypothetical distribution.

## CHECKLIST OF IMPORTANT TERMS

| | |
|---|---|
| Acceptance region | Mean square estimation error |
| Alternative hypothesis | Method of batch means |
| Bayes decision rule | Neyman-Pearson test |
| Bayes estimator | Normal random variable |
| Chi-square goodness-of-fit test | Null hypothesis |
| Composite hypothesis | Point estimator |
| Confidence interval | Population |
| Confidence level | Power |
| Consistent estimator | Probability of detection |
| Cramer-Rao inequality | Random sample |
| Critical region | Rejection region |
| Critical value | Sampling distribution |
| Decision rule | Score function |
| Efficiency | Significance level |
| False alarm probability | Significance test |
| Fisher information | Simple hypothesis |
| Invariance property | Statistic |
| Likelihood function | Strongly consistent estimator |
| Likelihood ratio function | Type I error |
| Log likelihood function | Type II error |
| Maximum likelihood method | Unbiased estimator |
| Maximum likelihood test | |

## ANNOTATED REFERENCES

Bulmer [1] is a classic introductory textbook on statistics. Ross [2] and Wackerly [3] provide excellent and up to-date introductions to statistics. Bickel [4] provides a more advanced treatment. Cramer [5] is a classic text that provides careful development of many traditional statistical methods. Van Trees [6] has influenced the application of statistical methods in modern communications. [10] provides a very useful online resource for learning probability and statistics.

1. M.G. Bulmer, *Principles of Statistics*, Dover Publications, New York, 1979.
2. S. M. Ross, *Introduction to Probability and Statistics for Engineers and Scientists*, Elsevier Academic Press, Burlington, Mass., 2004.
3. D. M. Wackerly, W. Mendenhall, and R. L. Scheaffer, *Mathematical Statistics with Applications*, Duxbury, Pacific Grove, Calif., 2002.
4. P. J. Bickel and K. A. Doksum, *Mathematical Statistics*, Prentice Hall, Upper Saddle River, N.J., 2007.
5. H. Cramer, *Mathematical Methods of Statistics*, Princeton University Press, Princeton, N.J., 1999.
6. H. L. Van Trees, *Detection, Estimation, and Modulation Theory*, John Wiley & Sons, New York, 1968.
7. A. O. Allen, *Probability, Statistics, and Queueing Theory*, Academic Press, New York, 1978.
8. S. Kokoska and D. Zwillinger, *Standard Probability and Statistics Tables and Formulae*, Chapman & Hall, Boca Raton, Fl., 2000.

**9.** M. Hardy, "An Illuminating Counter-example," *American Mathematical Monthly*, March 2003, pp.234–238.

**10.** *Virtual Laboratory in Probability and Statistics*, www.math.uah.edu/stat.

**11.** C. H. Edwards, Jr., and D. E. Penney, *Calculus and Analytic Geometry*, 4th ed. Prentice Hall, Englewood Cliffs, N.J., 1984.

## PROBLEMS

Note: Statistics involves working with data. For this reason the problems in this section incorporate exercises that involve the generation of random samples of random variables using the methods introduced in Chapters 3, 4, 5, and 6. These exercises can be skipped without loss of continuity.

### Section 8.1: Samples and Sampling Distributions

**8.1.** Let $X$ be a Gaussian random variable with mean 10 and variance 4. A sample of size 9 is obtained and the sample mean, minimum, and maximum of the sample are calculated.

(a) Find the probability that the sample mean is less than 9.

(b) Find the probability that the minimum is greater than 8.

(c) Find the probability that the maximum is less than 12.

(d) Find $n$ so the sample mean is within 1 of the true mean with probability 0.95.

(e) Generate 100 random samples of size 9. Compare the probabilities obtained in parts a, b, and c to the observed relative frequencies.

**8.2.** The lifetime of a device is an exponential random variable with mean 50 months. A sample of size 25 is obtained and the sample mean, maximum, and minimum of the sample are calculated.

(a) Estimate the probability that the sample mean differs from the true mean by more than 1 month.

(b) Find the probability that the longest-lived sample is greater than 100 months.

(c) Find the probability that the shortest-lived sample is less than 25 months.

(d) Find $n$ so the sample mean is within 5 months of the true mean with probability 0.9.

(e) Generate 100 random samples of size 25. Compare the probabilities obtained in parts a, b, and c to the observed relative frequencies.

**8.3.** Let the signal $X$ be a uniform random variable in the interval $[-3, 3]$, and suppose that a sample of size 50 is obtained.

(a) Estimate the probability that the sample mean is outside the interval $[-0.5, 0.5]$.

(b) Estimate the probability that the maximum of the sample is less than 2.5.

(c) Estimate the probability that the sample mean of the squares of the samples is greater than 3.

(d) Generate 100 random samples of size 50. Compare the probabilities obtained in parts a, b, and c to the observed relative frequencies.

**8.4.** Let $X$ be a Poisson random variable with mean $\alpha = 2$, and suppose that a sample of size 16 is obtained.

(a) Estimate the probability that the sample mean is greater than 2.5.

(b) Estimate the probability that the sample mean differs from the true mean by more than 0.5.

    **(c)** Find $n$ so the sample mean differs from the true mean by more than 0.5 with probability 0.95.

    **(d)** Generate 100 random samples of size 16. Compare the probabilities obtained in parts a and b to the observed relative frequencies.

**8.5.** The interarrival time of queries at a call center are exponential random variables with mean interarrival time 1/4. Suppose that a sample of size 9 is obtained.

    **(a)** The estimator $\hat{\lambda}_1 = 1/\overline{X}_9$ is used to estimate the arrival rate. Find the probability that the estimator differs from the true arrival rate by more than 1.

    **(b)** Suppose the estimator $\hat{\lambda}_2 = 1/9 \min(X_1, \ldots, X_9)$ is used to estimate the arrival rate. Find the probability that the estimator differs from the true arrival rate by more than 1.

    **(c)** Generate 100 random samples of size 9. Compare the probabilities obtained in parts a and b to the observed relative frequencies.

**8.6.** Let the sample $X_1, X_2, \ldots, X_n$ consist of iid versions of the random variable $X$. The method of moments involves estimating the moments of $X$ as follows:

$$\hat{m}_k = \frac{1}{n}\sum_{j=1}^{n} X_j^k.$$

    **(a)** Suppose that $X$ is a uniform random variable in the interval $[0, \theta]$. Use $\hat{m}_1$ to find an estimator for $\theta$.

    **(b)** Find the mean and variance of the estimator in part a.

**8.7.** Let $X$ be a gamma random variable with parameters $\alpha$ and $\beta = 1/\lambda$.

    **(a)** Use the first two moment estimators $\hat{m}_1$ and $\hat{m}_2$ of $X$ (defined in Problem 8.6) to estimate the parameters $\alpha$ and $\beta$.

    **(b)** Describe the behavior of the estimators in part a as $n$ becomes large.

**8.8.** Let $\mathbf{X} = (X, Y)$ be a pair of random variables with known means, $\mu_1$ and $\mu_2$. Consider the following estimator for the covariance of $X$ and $Y$:

$$\hat{C}_{X,Y} = \frac{1}{n}\sum_{j=1}^{n}(X_j - \mu_1)(Y_j - \mu_2).$$

    **(a)** Find the expected value and variance of this estimator.

    **(b)** Explain the behavior of the estimator as $n$ becomes large.

**8.9.** Let $\mathbf{X} = (X, Y)$ be a pair of random variables with unknown means and covariances. Consider the following estimator for the covariance of $X$ and $Y$:

$$\hat{K}_{X,Y} = \frac{1}{n-1}\sum_{j=1}^{n}(X_j - \overline{X}_n)(Y_j - \overline{Y}_n).$$

    **(a)** Find the expected value of this estimator.

    **(b)** Explain why the estimator approaches the estimator in Problem 8.8 for $n$ large. *Hint:* See Eq. (8.15).

**8.10.** Let the sample $X_1, X_2, \ldots, X_n$ consist of iid versions of the random variable $X$. Consider the maximum and minimum statistics for the sample:

$$W = \min(X_1, \ldots, X_n) \quad \text{and} \quad Z = \max(X_1, \ldots, X_n).$$

    **(a)** Show that the pdf of $Z$ is $f_Z(x) = n[F_X(x)]^{n-1} f_X(x)$.

    **(b)** Show that the pdf of $W$ is $f_W(x) = n[1 - F_X(x)]^{n-1} f_X(x)$.

## Section 8.2: Parameter Estimation

**8.11.** Show that the mean square estimation error satisfies $E[(\hat{\Theta} - \theta)^2] = \text{VAR}[\hat{\Theta}] + B(\hat{\Theta})^2$.

**8.12.** Let the sample $X_1$, $X_2$, $X_3$, $X_4$ consist of iid versions of a Poisson random variable $X$ with mean $\alpha = 4$. Find the mean and variance of the following estimators for $\alpha$ and determine whether they are biased or unbiased.

(a) $\hat{\alpha}_1 = (X_1 + X_2)/2$.

(b) $\hat{\alpha}_2 = (X_3 + X_4)/2$.

(c) $\hat{\alpha}_3 = (X_1 + 2X_2)/3$.

(d) $\hat{\alpha}_4 = (X_1 + X_2 + X_3 + X_4)/4$.

**8.13.** (a) Let $\hat{\Theta}_1$ and $\hat{\Theta}_2$ be unbiased estimators for the parameter $\theta$. Show that the estimator $\hat{\Theta} = p\hat{\Theta}_1 + (1 - p)\hat{\Theta}_2$ is also an unbiased estimator for $\theta$, where $0 \le p \le 1$.

(b) Find the value of $p$ in part a that minimizes the mean square error.

(c) Find the value of $p$ that minimizes the mean square error if $\hat{\Theta}_1$ and $\hat{\Theta}_2$ are the estimators in Problems 8.12a and 8.12b.

(d) Repeat part c for the estimators in Problems 8.12a and 8.12d.

(e) Let $\hat{\Theta}_1$ and $\hat{\Theta}_2$ be unbiased estimators for the first and second moments of $X$. Find an estimator for the variance of $X$. Is it biased?

**8.14.** The output of a communication system is $Y = \theta + N$, where $\theta$ is an input signal and $N$ is a noise signal that is uniformly distributed in the interval $[0, 2]$. Suppose the signal is transmitted $n$ times and that the noise terms are iid random variables.

(a) Show that the sample mean of the outputs is a biased estimator for $\theta$.

(b) Find the mean square error of the estimator.

**8.15.** The number of requests at a Web server is a Poisson random variable $X$ with mean $\alpha = 2$ requests per minute. Suppose that $n$ 1-minute intervals are observed and that the number $N_0$ of intervals with zero arrivals is counted. The probability of zero arrivals is then estimated by $\hat{p}_0 = N_0/n$. To estimate the arrival rate $\alpha$, $\hat{p}$ is set equal to the probability of zero arrivals in one minute:

$$\hat{p}_0 = N_0/n = P[X = 0] = \frac{\alpha^0}{0!}e^{-\alpha} = e^{-\alpha}.$$

(a) Solve the above equation for $\hat{\alpha}$ to obtain an estimator for the arrival rate.

(b) Show that $\hat{\alpha}$ is biased.

(c) Find the mean square error of $\hat{\alpha}$.

(d) Is $\hat{\alpha}$ a consistent estimator?

**8.16.** Generate 100 samples size 20 of the Poisson random variables in Problem 8.15.

(a) Estimate the arrival rate $\alpha$ using the sample mean estimator and the estimator from Problem 8.15.

(b) Compare the bias and mean square error of the two estimators.

**8.17.** To estimate the variance of a Bernoulli random variable $X$, we perform $n$ iid trials and count the number of successes $k$ and obtain the estimate $\hat{p} = k/n$. We then estimate the variance of $X$ by

$$\hat{\sigma}^2 = \hat{p}(1 - \hat{p}) = \frac{k}{n}\left(1 - \frac{k}{n}\right).$$

(a) Show that $\hat{\sigma}^2$ is a biased estimator for the variance of $X$.

(b) Is $\hat{\sigma}^2$ a consistent estimator for the variance of $X$?

(c) Find a constant $c$, so that $c\hat{\sigma}^2$ is an unbiased estimator for the variance of $X$.

(d) Find the mean square errors of the estimators in parts b and c.

**8.18.** Let $X_1, X_2, \ldots, X_n$ be a random sample of a uniform random variable that is uniformly distributed in the interval $[0, \theta]$. Consider the following estimator for $\theta$:

$$\hat{\Theta} = \max\{X_1, X_2, \ldots, X_n\}.$$

(a) Find the pdf of $\hat{\Theta}$ using the results of Problem 8.10.

(b) Show that $\hat{\Theta}$ is a biased estimator.

(c) Find the variance of $\hat{\Theta}$ and determine whether it is a consistent estimator.

(d) Find a constant $c$ so that $c\hat{\Theta}$ is an unbiased estimator.

(e) Generate a random sample of 20 uniform random variables with $\theta = 5$. Compare the values provided by the two estimators in 100 separate trials.

(f) Generate 1000 samples of the uniform random variable, updating the estimator value every 50 samples. Can you discern the bias of the estimator?

**8.19.** Let $X_1, X_2, \ldots, X_n$ be a random sample of a Pareto random variable:

$$f_X(x) = k \frac{\theta^k}{x^{k+1}} \quad \text{for } \theta \le x$$

with $k = 2.5$. Consider the estimator for $\theta$:

$$\hat{\Theta} = \min\{X_1, X_2, \ldots X_n\}.$$

(a) Show that $\hat{\Theta}$ is a biased estimator and find the bias.

(b) Find the mean squared error of $\hat{\Theta}$.

(c) Determine whether $\hat{\Theta}$ is a consistent estimator.

(d) Use Octave to generate 1000 samples of the Pareto random variable. Update the estimator value every 50 samples. Can you discern the bias of the estimator?

(e) Repeat part d with $k = 1.5$. What changes?

**8.20.** Generate 100 samples of sizes 5, 10, 20 of exponential random variables with mean 1. Compare the histograms of the estimates given by the biased and unbiased estimators for the sample variance.

**8.21.** Find the variance of the sample variance estimator in Example 8.8. *Hint:* Assume $m = 0$.

**8.22.** Generate 100 samples of size 20 of pairs of zero-mean, unit-variance jointly Gaussian random variables with correlation coefficient $\rho = 0.50$. Compare the histograms of the estimates given by the estimators for the sample covariance in Problems 8.8 and 8.9.

**8.23.** Repeat the scenario in Problem 8.22 for the following estimator for the correlation coefficient between two random variables $X$ and $Y$:

$$\hat{\rho}_{X,Y} = \frac{\sum_{j=1}^{n} (X_j - \overline{X}_n)(Y_j - \overline{Y}_n)}{\sqrt{\sum_{j=1}^{n} (X_j - \overline{X}_n)^2 \sum_{j=1}^{n} (Y_j - \overline{Y}_n)^2}}.$$

## Section 8.3: Maximum Likelihood Estimation

**8.24.** Let $X$ be an exponential random variable with mean $1/\lambda$.

(a) Find the maximum likelihood estimator $\hat{\Theta}_{ML}$ for $\theta = 1/\lambda$.

(b) Find the maximum likelihood estimator $\hat{\Theta}_{ML}$ for $\theta = \lambda$.

(c)  Find the pdfs of the estimators in part a.

(d)  Is the estimator in part a unbiased and consistent?

(e)  Repeat 20 trials of the following experiment: Generate a sample of 16 observations of the exponential random variable with $\lambda = 1/2$ and find the values given by the estimators in parts a and b. Show a histogram of the values produced by the estimators.

**8.25.**  Let $X = \theta + N$ be the output of a noisy channel where the input is the parameter $\theta$ and $N$ is a zero-mean, unit-variance Gaussian random variable. Suppose that the output is measured $n$ times to obtain the random sample $X_i = \theta + N_i$ for $i = 1, \ldots, n$.

(a)  Find the maximum likelihood estimator $\hat{\Theta}_{ML}$ for $\theta$.

(b)  Find the pdf of $\hat{\Theta}_{ML}$.

(c)  Determine whether $\hat{\Theta}_{ML}$ is unbiased and consistent.

**8.26.**  Show that the maximum likelihood estimator for a uniform random variable that is distributed in the interval $[0, \theta]$ is $\hat{\Theta} = \max\{X_1, X_2, \ldots, X_n\}$. *Hint:* You will need to show that the maximum occurs at an endpoint of the interval of parameter values.

**8.27.**  Let $X$ be a Pareto random variable with parameters $\alpha$ and $x_m$.

(a)  Find the maximum likelihood estimator for $\alpha$ assuming $x_m$ is known.

(b)  Show that the maximum likelihood estimators for $\alpha$ and $x_m$ are:

$$\hat{\alpha}_{ML} = n \left[ \sum_{j=1}^{n} \log \left( \frac{X_j}{\hat{x}_{m,ML}} \right) \right]^{-1} \quad \text{and} \quad \hat{x}_{m,ML} = \min(X_1, X_2, \ldots, X_n).$$

(c)  Discuss the behavior of the estimators in parts a and b as $n$ becomes large and determine whether they are consistent.

(d)  Repeat five trials of the following experiment: Generate a sample of 100 observations of the Pareto random variable with $\alpha = 2.5$ and $x_m = 1$ and obtain the values given by the estimators in part b. Repeat for $\alpha = 1.5$ and $x_m = 1$, and $\alpha = 0.5$ and $x_m = 1$.

**8.28.**  **(a)**  Show that the maximum likelihood estimator for the parameter $\theta = \alpha^2$ of the Rayleigh random variable is

$$\hat{\alpha}_{ML}^2 = \frac{1}{2n} \sum_{j=1}^{n} X_j^2.$$

(b)  Is the estimator is unbiased?

(c)  Repeat 50 trials of the following experiment: Generate a sample of 16 observations of the Rayleigh random variable with $\alpha = 2$ and find the values given by the estimator in part a. Show a histogram of the values produced by the estimator.

**8.29.**  **(a)**  Show that the maximum likelihood estimator for $\theta = a$ of the beta random variable with $b = 1$ is

$$\hat{a}_{ML} = \left[ \frac{1}{n} \sum_{j=1}^{n} \log X_j \right]^{-1}.$$

(b)  Generate a sample of 100 observations of the beta random variable with $b = 1$ and $a = 0.5$ to obtain the estimate for $a$. Repeat for $a = 1$, $a = 2$, and $a = 3$.

**8.30.**  Let $X$ be a Weibull random variable with parameters $\alpha$ and $\beta$ (see Eq. 4.102).

(a)  Assuming that $\beta$ is known, show that the maximum likelihood estimator for $\theta = \alpha$ is:

$$\hat{\alpha}_{ML} = \left[ \frac{1}{n} \sum_{j=1}^{n} X_j^{\beta} \right]^{-1}.$$

(b)    Generate a sample of 100 observations of the Weibull random variable with $\alpha = 1$ and $\beta = 1$ to obtain the estimate for $\alpha$. Repeat for $\beta = 2$ and $\beta = 4$.

**8.31.**    A certain device is known to have an exponential lifetime.

(a)    Suppose that $n$ devices are tested for $T$ seconds, and the number of devices that fail within the testing period is counted. Find the maximum likelihood estimator for the mean lifetime of the device. *Hint:* Use the invariance property.

(b)    Repeat ten trials of the following experiment: Generate a sample of 16 observations of the exponential random variable with $\lambda = 1/10$ and testing period $T = 15$. Find the estimates for the mean lifetime using the method in part a and compare these with the estimates provided by Problem 8.24a.

**8.32.**    Let $X$ be a gamma random variable with parameters $\alpha$ and $\lambda$.

(a)    Find the maximum likelihood estimator $\hat{\lambda}_{ML}$ for $\lambda$ assuming $\alpha$ is known.

(b)    Find the maximum likelihood estimators $\hat{\alpha}_{ML}$ and $\hat{\lambda}_{ML}$ for $\alpha$ and $\lambda$. Assume that the function $\Gamma'(\alpha)/\Gamma(\alpha)$ is known.

**8.33.**    Let $\mathbf{X} = (X, Y)$ be a jointly Gaussian random vector with zero means, unit variances, and unknown correlation coefficient $\rho$. Consider a random sample of $n$ such vectors.

(a)    Show that the ML estimator for $\rho$ involves solving a cubic eqation.

(b)    Show that Problem 8.23 gives the ML estimator if the mean and variances are unknown.

(c)    Repeat 5 trials of the following: Generate a sample of 100 observations of the pairs of zero-mean, unit-variance Gaussian random variables and estimate $\rho$. using parts a and b for the cases: $\rho = 0.5$, $\rho = 0.9$, and $\rho = 0$.

**8.34.**    (Invariance Property.) Let $\hat{\Theta}_{ML}$ be the maximum likelihood estimator for the parameter $\theta$ of $X$. Suppose that we are interested instead in finding the maximum likelihood estimator for $h(\theta)$, which is an invertible function of $\theta$. Explain why this maximum likelihood estimator is given by $h(\hat{\Theta}_{ML})$.

**8.35.**    Show that the Fisher information is also given by Eq. (8.36). Assume that the first two partial derivatives of the likelihood function exist and that they are absolutely integrable so that differentiation and integration with respect to $\theta$ can be interchanged.

**8.36.**    Show that the following random variables have the given Cramer-Rao lower bound and determine whether the associated maximum likelihood estimator is efficient:

(a)    Binomial with parameters $n$ and unknown $p$: $p(1 - p)/n^2$.

(b)    Gaussian with known variance $\sigma^2$ and unknown mean: $\sigma^2/n$.

(c)    Gaussian with unknown variance: $2\sigma^4/n$. Consider two cases: mean known; mean unknown. Does the standard unbiased estimator for the variance achieve the Cramer-Rao lower bound? Note that $E[(X - \mu)^4] = 3\sigma^4$.

(d)    Gamma with parameters known $\alpha$ and unknown $\beta = 1/\lambda$: $\beta^2/n\alpha$.

(e)    Poisson with parameter unknown $\alpha$: $\alpha/n$.

**8.37.**    Let $\hat{\Theta}_{ML}$ be the maximum likelihood estimator for the mean of an exponential random variable. Suppose we estimate the variance of this exponential random variable using the estimator $\hat{\Theta}_{ML}^2$. What is the probability that $\hat{\Theta}_{ML}^2$ is within 5% of the true value of the variance? Assume that the number of samples is large.

**8.38.**    Let $\hat{\Theta}_{ML}$ be the maximum likelihood estimator for the mean $\alpha$ of a Poisson random variable. Suppose we estimate the probability of no arrivals $P[X = 0] = e^{-\alpha}$ with the estimator $e^{-\hat{\Theta}_{ML}}$. Find the probability that this estimator is within 10% of the true value of $P[X = 0]$. Assume that the number of samples is large.

### Section 8.4: Confidence Intervals

**8.39.** A voltage measurement consists of the sum of a constant unknown voltage and a Gaussian-distributed noise voltage of zero mean and variance $10 \ \mu V^2$. Thirty independent measurements are made and a sample mean of $100 \ \mu V$ is obtained. Find the corresponding 95% confidence interval.

**8.40.** Let $X_j$ be a Gaussian random variable with unknown mean $E[X] = \mu$ and variance 1.

   **(a)** Find the width of the 95% confidence intervals for $\mu$ for $n = 4, 16, 100$.

   **(b)** Repeat for 99% confidence intervals.

**8.41.** The lifetime of 225 light bulbs is measured and the sample mean and sample variance are found to be 223 hr and 100 hr, respectively.

   **(a)** Find a 95% confidence interval for the mean lifetime.

   **(b)** Find a 95% confidence interval for the variance of the lifetime.

**8.42.** Let $X$ be a Gaussian random variable with unknown mean and unknown variance. A set of 10 independent measurements of $X$ yields

$$\sum_{j=1}^{10} X_j = 350 \quad \text{and} \quad \sum_{j=1}^{10} X_j^2 = 12{,}645.$$

   **(a)** Find a 90% confidence interval for the mean of $X$.

   **(b)** Find a 90% confidence interval for the variance of $X$.

**8.43.** Let $X$ be a Gaussian random variable with unknown mean and unknown variance. A set of 10 independent measurements of $X$ yields a sample mean of 57.3 and a sample variance of 23.2.

   **(a)** Find the 90%, 95%, and 99% confidence intervals for the mean.

   **(b)** Repeat part a if a set of 20 measurements had yielded the above sample mean and sample variance.

   **(c)** Find the 90%, 95%, and 99% confidence intervals for the variance in parts a and b.

**8.44.** A computer simulation program is used to produce 150 samples of a random variable. The samples are grouped into 15 batches of ten samples each. The batch sample means are listed below:

| | | | | |
|---|---|---|---|---|
| 0.228 | −1.941 | 0.141 | 1.979 | −0.224 |
| 0.501 | −5.907 | −1.367 | −1.615 | −1.013 |
| −0.397 | −3.360 | −3.330 | −0.033 | −0.976 |

   **(a)** Find the 90% confidence interval for the sample mean.

   **(b)** Repeat this experiment by generating beta random variables with parameters $\alpha = 2$ and $\beta = 3$.

   **(c)** Repeat part b using gamma random variables with $\lambda = 1$ and $\alpha = 2$.

   **(d)** Repeat part b using Pareto random variables with $x_m = 1$ and $\alpha = 3$; $x_m = 1$ and $\alpha = 1.5$.

**8.45.** A coin is flipped a total of 500 times, in 10 batches of 50 flips each. The number of heads in each of the batches is as follows:

$$24, 27, 22, 24, 25, 24, 28, 26, 23, 26.$$

**(a)** Find the 95% confidence interval for the probability of heads $p$ using the method of batch means.

**(b)** Simulate this experiment by generating Bernoulli random variables with $p = 0.25$; $p = 0.01$.

**8.46.** This exercise is intended to check the statement: "If we were to compute confidence intervals a large number of times, we would find that approximately $(1 - \alpha) \times 100\%$ of the time, the computed intervals would contain the true value of the parameter."

**(a)** Assuming that the mean is unknown and that the variance is known, find the 90% confidence interval for the mean of a Gaussian random variable with $n = 10$.

**(b)** Generate 500 batches of 10 zero-mean, unit-variance Gaussian random variables, and determine the associated confidence intervals. Find the proportion of confidence intervals that include the true mean (which by design is zero). Is this in agreement with the confidence level $1 - \alpha = .90$?

**(c)** Repeat part b using exponential random variables with mean one. Should the proportion of intervals including the true mean be given by $1 - \alpha$? Explain.

**8.47.** Generate 160 $X_i$ that are uniformly distributed in the interval $[-1, 1]$.

**(a)** Suppose that 90% confidence intervals for the mean are to be produced. Find the confidence intervals for the mean using the following combinations:

> 4 batches of 40 samples each,
>
> 8 batches of 20 samples each,
>
> 16 batches of 10 samples each, and
>
> 32 batches of 5 samples each.

**(b)** Redo the experiment in part a 500 times. In each repetition of the experiment, compute the four confidence intervals defined in part a. Calculate the proportion of time in which the above four confidence intervals include the true mean. Which of the above combinations of the batch size and number of batches are in better agreement with the results predicted by the confidence level? Explain why.

**8.48.** This exercise explores the behavior of confidence intervals as the number of samples is increased. Generate 1000 samples of independent Gaussian random variables with mean 25 and variance 36. Update and plot the confidence intervals for the mean and variance every 50 samples.

### Section 8.5: Hypothesis Testing

**8.49.** A new Web page design is intended to increase the rate at which customers place orders. Prior to the new design, the number of orders in an hour was a Poisson random variable with mean 30. Eight one-hour measurements with the new design find an average of 32 orders completed per hour.

**(a)** At a 5% significance level, do the data support the claim that the order placement rate has increased?

**(b)** Repeat part a at a 1% significance level.

**8.50.** Carlos and Michael play a game where each flips a coin once: If the outcomes of the tosses are the same, then no one wins; but if the outcome is different the player with "heads" wins. Michael uses a fair coin but he suspects that Carlos is using a biased coin.

**(a)** Find a 10% significance level test for an experiment that counts how many times Carlos wins in 6 games to test whether Carlos is cheating. Repeat for $n = 12$ games.

**(b)** Now design a 10% significance level test based on the number of times Carlos, tosses come up heads. Which test is more effective?

**(c)** Find the probability of detection if Carlos uses a coin with $p = 0.75$; $p = 0.55$.

**8.51.** The output of a receiver is the sum of the input voltage and a Gaussian random variable with zero mean and variance 4 volt$^2$. A scientist suspects that the receiver input is not properly calibrated and has a nonzero input voltage in the absence of a true input signal.

   **(a)** Find a 1% significance level test involving $n$ independent measurements of the output to test the scientist's hunch.

   **(b)** What is the outcome of the test if 10 measurements yield a sample mean of $-0.75$ volts?

   **(c)** Find the probability of a Type II error if there is indeed an input voltage of 1 volt; of 10 millivolts.

**8.52. (a)** Explain the relationship between the $p$-value and the level $\alpha$ of a test.

   **(b)** Explain why the $p$-value provides more information about the test statistic than simply stating the outcome of the hypothesis test.

   **(c)** How should the $p$-value be calculated in a one-sided test?

   **(d)** How should the $p$-value be calculated in a two-sided test?

**8.53.** The number of photons counted by an optical detector is a Poisson random variable with known mean $\alpha$ in the absence of a target and known mean $\beta = 6 > \alpha = 2$ when a target is present. Let the null hypothesis correspond to "no target present."

   **(a)** Use the Neyman-Pearson method to find a hypothesis test where the false alarm probability is set to 5%.

   **(b)** What is the probability of detection?

   **(c)** Suppose that $n$ independent measurements of the input are taken. Use trial and error to find the value of $n$ required to achieve a false alarm probability of 5% and a probability of detection of 90%.

**8.54.** The breaking strength of plastic bags is a Gaussian random variable. Bags from company 1 have a mean strength of 8 kilograms and a variance of 1 kg$^2$; bags from company 2 have a mean strength of 9 kilograms and a variance of 1 kg$^2$. We are interested in determining whether a batch of bags comes from company 1 (null hypothesis). Find a hypothesis test and determine the number of bags that needs to be tested so that $\alpha$ is 1% and the probability of detection is 99%.

**8.55.** Light Internet users have session times that are exponentially distributed with mean 2 hours, and heavy Internet users have session times that are exponentially distributed with mean 4 hours.

   **(a)** Use the Neyman-Pearson method to find a hypothesis test to determine whether a given user is a light user. Design the test for $\alpha = 5\%$.

   **(b)** What is the probability of detecting heavy users?

**8.56.** Normal Internet users have session times that are Pareto distributed with mean 3 hours and $a = 3$, and heavy peer-to-peer users have session times that are Pareto distributed with $a = 8/7$ and mean 16 hours.

   **(a)** Use the Neyman-Pearson method to find a hypothesis test to determine whether a given user is a normal user. Design the test for $\alpha = 1\%$

   **(b)** What is the probability of detecting heavy peer-to-peer users?

**8.57.** Coin factories A and B produce coins for which the probability of heads $p$ is a beta-distributed random variable. Factory A has parameters $a = b = 10$, and factory B has $a = b = 5$.

   **(a)** Design a hypothesis test for $\alpha = 5\%$ to determine whether a batch is from factory A.

   **(b)** What is the probability of detecting factory B coins? *Hint:* Use the Octave function beta_inv. Assume that the probability of heads in the batch can be determined accurately.

**8.58.** When operating correctly (null hypothesis), wires from a production line have a mean diameter of 2 mm, but under a certain fault condition the wires have a mean diameter of 1.75 mm. The diameters are Gaussian distributed with variance .04 mm$^2$. A batch of 10 sample wires is selected and the sample mean is found to be 1.82 mm.

  **(a)** Design a test to determine whether the line is operating correctly. Assume a false alarm probability of 5%.

  **(b)** What is the probability of detecting the fault condition?

  **(c)** What is the $p$-value for the above observation?

**8.59.** Coin 1 is fair and coin 2 has probability of heads 3/4. A test involves flipping a coin repeatedly until the first occurrence of heads. The number of tosses is observed.

  **(a)** Can you design a test to determine whether the fair coin is in use? Assume $\alpha = 5\%$. What is the probability of detecting the biased coin?

  **(b)** Repeat part a if the biased coin has probability 1/4.

**8.60.** The output of a radio signal detection system is the sum of an input voltage and a zero-mean, unit-variance Gaussian random variable.

  **(a)** Design a hypothesis test, at a level $\alpha = 10\%$, to determine whether there is a nonzero input assuming $n$ independent measurements of the receiver output (so the additive noise terms are iid random variables).

  **(b)** Find expressions for the Type II error probability and the power of the test in part a.

  **(c)** Plot the power of the test in part a as the input voltage varies from $-\infty$ to $+\infty$ for $n = 4, 16, 64, 256$.

**8.61. (a)** In Problem 8.60, design a hypothesis test, at a level $\alpha$, to determine whether there is a positive input assuming $n$ independent measurements.

  **(b)** Find expressions for the Type II error probability and the power of the test in part a.

  **(c)** Plot the power of the test in part a as the input voltage varies from $-\infty$ to $+\infty$ for $n = 4, 16, 64, 256$.

**8.62.** Compare the power curves obtained in Problems 8.60 and 8.61. Explain why the test in Problem 8.61 is uniformly most powerful, while the test in Problem 8.60 is not.

**8.63.** Consider Example 8.27 where we considered

$$H_0: X \text{ is Gaussian with } \mu = 0 \text{ and } \sigma_X^2 = 1$$
$$H_1: X \text{ is Gaussian with } \mu > 0 \text{ and } \sigma_X^2 = 1.$$

Let $n = 25$, $\alpha = 5\%$. For $\mu = k/2, k = 0, 1, 2, \ldots, 5$ perform the following experiment: Generate 500 batches of size 25 of the Gaussian random variable with mean $\mu$ and unit variance. For each batch determine whether the hypothesis test accepts or rejects the null hypothesis. Count the number of Type I errors and Type II errors. Plot the empirically obtained power function as a function of $\mu$.

**8.64.** Repeat Problem 8.63 for the following hypothesis test:

$$H_0: X \text{ is Gaussian with } \mu = 0 \text{ and } \sigma_X^2 = 1$$
$$H_1: X \text{ is Gaussian with } \mu \neq 0 \text{ and } \sigma_X^2 = 1.$$

Let $n = 25$, $\alpha = 5\%$, and run the experiments for $\mu = \pm k/2, k = 0, 1, 2, \ldots, 5$.

**8.65.** Consider the following three tests for a fair coin:

  **(i)** $H_0: p = 0.5$ vs. $H_1: p \neq 0.5$

**(ii)** $H_0: p = 0.5$ vs. $H_1: p > 0.5$

**(iii)** $H_0: p = 0.5$ vs. $H_1: p < 0.5$.

Assume $n = 100$ coin tosses in each test and that the rejection regions for the above tests are selected for $\alpha = 1\%$.

**(a)** Find the power curves for the three tests as a function of $p$.

**(b)** Explain the power curve of the two-sided test in comparison to those of the one-sided tests.

**8.66.** **(a)** Consider hypothesis test (i) of Problem 8.65 with $\alpha = 5\%$. For $p = k/10$, $k = 1$, $2, \ldots, 9$ perform the following experiment: Generate 500 batches of 100 tosses of a coin with probability of heads $p$. For each batch determine whether the hypothesis test accepts or rejects the null hypothesis. Count the number of Type I errors and Type II errors. Plot the empirically obtained power function as a function of $\mu$.

**(b)** Repeat part a for hypothesis test (ii) of Problem 8.65.

**8.67.** Consider the hypothesis test developed in Example 8.26 to test $H_0: m = \mu$ vs. $H_1: m > \mu$. Suppose we use this test, that is, the associated rejection and acceptance region, for the following hypothesis testing problem:

$$H_0: X \text{ is Gaussian with mean } m \le \mu \text{ and known variance } \sigma^2$$

$$H_1: X \text{ is Gaussian with mean } m > \mu \text{ and known variance } \sigma^2.$$

Show that the test achieves level $\alpha$ or better. *Hint:* Consider the power function of the test in Example 8.26.

**8.68.** A machine produces disks with mean thickness 2 mm. To test the machine after undergoing routine maintenance, 10 sample disks are selected and the sample mean of the thickness is found to be 2.2 mm and the sample variance is found to be 0.04 mm$^2$.

**(a)** Find a test to determine if the machine is working properly for $\alpha = 1\%$; $\alpha = 5\%$.

**(b)** Find the $p$-value of the observation.

**8.69.** A manufacturer claims that its new improved tire design increases tire lifetime from 50,000 km to 55,000 km. A test of 8 tires gives a sample mean lifetime of 52,500 km and a sample standard deviation of 3000 km.

**(a)** Find a test to determine if the claim can be supported at a level of $\alpha = 1\%$; $\alpha = 5\%$.

**(b)** Find the $p$-value of the observation.

**8.70.** A class of 100 engineering freshmen is provided with new laptop computers. The manufacturer claims the charge in the batteries will last four hours. The frosh run a test and find a sample mean of 3.3 hours and a sample standard deviation of 0.5 hours.

**(a)** Find a test to determine if the manufacturer's claim can be supported at a level of $\alpha = 1\%$; $\alpha = 5\%$.

**(b)** Find the $p$-value of the observation.

**8.71.** Consider the hypothesis test considered in Example 8.29:

$$H_0: X \text{ is Gaussian with } \mu = 0 \text{ and } \sigma_X^2 \text{ unknown}$$

$$H_1: X \text{ is Gaussian with } \mu \ne 0 \text{ and } \sigma_X^2 \text{ unknown}.$$

Let $n = 9$, $\alpha = 5\%$, $\sigma_X = 1$. For $\mu = \pm k/2$, $k = 0, 1, 2, \ldots, 5$ perform the following experiment: Generate 500 batches of size 9 of the Gaussian random variable with mean $\mu$ and unit variance. For each batch determine whether the hypothesis test accepts or rejects the null hypothesis. Count the number of Type I errors and Type II errors. Plot the empirically obtained power function as a function of $\mu$. Compare to the expected results.

**8.72.** Repeat Problem 8.71 for the following hypothesis test:

$$H_0: X \text{ is Gaussian with } \mu = 0 \text{ and } \sigma_X^2 \text{ unknown}$$

$$H_1: X \text{ is Gaussian with } \mu > 0 \text{ and } \sigma_X^2 \text{ unknown.}$$

Let $n = 9$, $\alpha = 5\%$, $\sigma_X = 1$, and $\mu = k/2$, $k = 0, 1, 2, \ldots, 5$.

**8.73.** Consider using the hypothesis test in Example 8.29 when the random variable is *not* Gaussian. Design tests for $\alpha = 5\%$, $n = 9$ and for $n = 25$. For $\mu = \pm k/2$, $k = 0, 1, 2, \ldots, 5$ perform the following experiment: Let $X$ be a uniform random variable in the interval $[-1/2, 1/2]$. Generate 500 batches of size $n$ of the uniform random variable with mean $\mu$. For each batch determine whether the hypothesis test accepts or rejects the null hypothesis. Count the number of Type I errors and Type II errors. Plot the empirically obtained power function as a function of $\mu$. Compare the empirical data to the values expected for the Gaussian random variable.

**8.74.** Consider using the hypothesis test in Problem 8.73 when the random variable is an exponential random variable. Design tests for $\alpha = 5\%$, $\mu = 1$, $n = 9$ and for $n = 25$. Repeat the experiment for $\mu = k/2$, $k = 1, 2, \ldots, 5$. Compare the empirical data to the values expected for the Gaussian random variable.

**8.75.** A stealth alarm system works by sending noise signals: A "situation normal" signal is sent by transmitting voltages that are Gaussian iid random variables with mean zero and variance 4; an "alarm" signal is sent by transmitting iid Gaussian voltages with mean zero and variance less than 4.

   **(a)** Find a 1% level hypothesis test to determine whether the situation is normal (null hypothesis) based on the calculation of the sample variance from $n$ voltage samples.

   **(b)** Find the power of the hypothesis test for $n = 8, 64, 256$ as the variance of the alarm signal is varied.

**8.76.** Repeat Problem 8.75 if the alarm signal uses iid Gaussian voltages that have variance greater than 4.

**8.77.** A stealth system summons Agent 00111 by sending a sequence of 71 Gaussian iid random variables with mean zero and variance $\mu_0 = 7$. Find a hypothesis test (to be implemented in Agent's 00111 wristwatch) to determine, at a 1% level, that she is being summoned. Plot the probability of Type II error.

**8.78.** Consider the hypothesis test in Example 8.30 for testing the variance:

$$H_0: X \text{ is Gaussian with } \sigma_X^2 = 1 \text{ and } m \text{ unknown}$$

$$H_1: X \text{ is Gaussian with } \sigma_X^2 \neq 1 \text{ and } m \text{ unknown.}$$

Let $n = 16$, $\alpha = 5\%$, $\mu = 0$. For $\sigma_X^2 = k/3$, $k = 1, 2, \ldots, 6$ perform the following experiment: Generate 500 batches of size 16 of the Gaussian random variable with zero mean and variance $\sigma_X^2$. For each batch determine whether the hypothesis test accepts or rejects the null hypothesis. Count the number of Type I errors and Type II errors. Plot the power function as a function of $\mu$. Compare to the expected results.

**8.79.** Consider using the hypothesis test in Problem 8.78 when the random variable is a uniform random variable. Repeat the experiment where $X$ is now a uniform random variable in the interval $[-1/2, 1/2]$. Compare the empirical data to the values expected for the Gaussian random variable. Repeat the experiment for $n = 9$ and $n = 36$.

**8.80.** In this exercise we explore the relation between confidence intervals and hypothesis testing. Consider the hypothesis test in Example 8.28 but with a level of $\alpha = 5\%$.

(a)  Run 200 trials of the following experiment: Generate 10 samples of $X$ given that $H_0$ is true; determine the confidence interval; determine if the interval includes 0; determine if the null hypothesis is accepted.

(b)  Is the relative frequency of Type I error as expected?

## Section 8.6: Bayesian Decision Methods

**8.81.**  The Premium Pen Factory tests one pen in each batch of 100 pens. The ink-filling machine is bipolar, so pens can write continuously for an exponential duration of mean either 1/2 hour or 5 hours. The machine is in the short-life production mode 10% of the time. A batch of short-life pens sold as long-life pens results in a loss of $5, while a batch of long-life pens mistakenly sold as short-life results in a loss of $3. Find the Bayes decision rule to decide whether a batch is long-life or short-life based on the measured lifetime of the test pen.

**8.82.**  Suppose we send binary information over an erasure channel. If the input to the channel is "0", then the output is equally likely to be "0" or "e" for "erased"; and if the input is "1" then the outputs are equally likely to be "1" or "e." Assume that $P[\Theta = 1] = 1/4 = 1 - P[\Theta = 0]$, and that the cost functions are: $C_{00} = C_{11} = 0$ and $C_{01} = bC_{10}$.

(a)  For $b = 1/6$, 1, and 6, find the maximum likelihood decision rule, which picks the input that maximizes the likelihood probability for the observed output. Find the average cost for each case.

(b)  For the three cases in part a, find the Bayes decision rule that minimizes the average cost. Find the average cost for each case.

**8.83.**  For the channel in Problem 8.82, suppose we transmit each input twice. The receiver makes its decision based on the observed pair of outputs. Find and compare the maximum likelihood and the Bayes' decision rules.

**8.84.**  When Bob throws a dart the coordinates of the landing point are a Gaussian pair of independent random variables $(X, Y)$ with zero mean and variance 1. When Rick throws the dart the coordinates are also a Gaussian independent pair but with zero mean and variance 4. Bob and Rick are asked to draw a circle centered about the origin with the inner disk assigned to Bob and the outer ring assigned to Rick.

(a)  Whenever either player lands on the other player's area, he must pay a $1 to the house. Find the disk radius that minimizes the players' average cost.

(b)  Repeat part a if Bob must pay $2 when he lands in Rick's area.

**8.85.**  A binary communications system accepts $\Theta$, which is "0" or "1", as input and outputs $X$, "0" or "1", with probability of error $P[\Theta \neq X] = p = 10^{-3}$. Suppose the sender uses a repetition code whereby each "0" or "1" is transmitted $n$ independent times, and the receiver makes its decision based on the $n = 8$ corresponding outputs. Assume that $1/5 = P[\Theta = 1] = \alpha = 1 - P[\Theta = 0]$.

(a)  Find the maximum likelihood decision rule that selects the input which is more likely for the given $n$ outputs. Find the probability of Type I and Type II errors, as well as the overall probability of error $P_e$.

(b)  Find the Bayes decision rule that minimizes the probability of error. Find the probability of Type I and Type II errors, as well as $P_e$.

(c)  For the decision rules in parts a and b find $n$ so that $P_e = 10^{-9}$.

**8.86.**  A binary communications system accepts $\Theta$, which is "+1" or "−1", as input and outputs $X = \Theta + N$, where $N$ is a zero-mean Gaussian random variable with variance $\sigma^2$. The sender uses a repetition code where each "+1" or "−1" is transmitted $n$ times, and the receiver makes its decision based on the $n$ outputs. Assume $P[\Theta = 1] = \alpha = 1 - P[\Theta = 0]$.

(a) Find the maximum likelihood decision rule and evaluate its Type I and Type II error probabilities as well as its overall probability of error.

(b) Find the Bayes decision rule and compare its error probabilities to part a.

(c) Suppose $\sigma$ is such that $P[N > 1] = 10^{-3}$. Find the value of $n$ in part b, so that $P_e = 10^{-9}$.

**8.87.** A widely used digital radio system transmits pairs of bits at a time. The input to the system is a pair $(\Theta_1, \Theta_2)$ where $\Theta_i$ can be $+1$ or $-1$ and where the output of the channel is a pair of independent Gaussian random variables $(X, Y)$ with variance $\sigma^2$ and means $\Theta_1$ and $\Theta_2$, respectively. Assume $P[\Theta_i = 1] = \alpha = 1 - P[\Theta_i = 0]$ and that the input bits are independent of each other. The receiver observes the pair $(X, Y)$ and based on their values decides on the input pair $(\Theta_1, \Theta_2)$.

(a) Plot $f_{X,Y}(x, y \,|\, \Theta_1, \Theta_2)$ for the four possible input pairs.

(b) Let the cost be zero if the receiver correctly identifies the input pair, and let the cost be one otherwise. Show that the Bayes' decision rule selects the input pair $(\theta_1, \theta_2)$ that maximizes:

$$f_{X,Y}(x, y \,|\, \theta_1, \theta_2) P[\Theta_1, = \theta_1, \Theta_2 = \theta_2].$$

(c) Find the four decision regions in the plane when the inputs are equally likely. Show that this corresponds to the maximum likelihood decision rule.

**8.88.** Show that the Bayes estimator for the cost function $C(g(\mathbf{X}), \Theta) = |g(\mathbf{X}) - \Theta|$, is given by the median of the a posteriori pdf $f_\Theta(\theta \,|\, \mathbf{X})$. *Hint:* Write the integral for the average cost as the sum of two integrals over the regions $g(\mathbf{X}) > \theta$ and $g(\mathbf{X}) < \theta$, and then differentiate with respect to $g(\mathbf{X})$.

**8.89.** Show that the Bayes' estimator for the cost function in Eq. (8.96) is given by the MAP estimator for $\theta$.

**8.90.** Let the observations $X_1, X_2, \ldots, X_n$ be iid Gaussian random variables with unit variance and unknown mean $\Theta$. Suppose that $\Theta$ is itself a Gaussian random variable with mean 0 and variance $\sigma^2$. Find the following estimators:

(a) The minimum mean square estimator for $\Theta$.

(b) The minimum mean absolute error estimator for $\Theta$.

(c) The MAP estimator for $\Theta$.

**8.91.** Let $X$ be a uniform random variable in the interval $(0, \Theta)$, where $\Theta$ has a gamma distribution $f_\Theta(\theta) = \theta e^{-\theta}$ for $\theta > 0$.

(a) Find the estimator that minimizes the mean absolute error.

(b) Find the estimator that minimizes the mean square error.

**8.92.** Let $X$ be a binomial random variable with parameters $n$ and $\Theta$. Suppose that $\Theta$ has a beta distribution with parameters $\alpha$ and $\beta$.

(a) Show that $f_\Theta(\theta \,|\, X = k)$ is a beta pdf with parameters $a + k$ and $\beta + n - k$.

(b) Show that the minimum mean square estimator is then $(\alpha + k)/(\alpha + \beta + n)$.

**8.93.** Let $X$ be a binomial random variable with parameters $n$ and $\Theta$. Suppose that $\Theta$ is uniform in the interval $[0, 1]$. Consider the following cost function which emphasizes the errors at the extreme values of $\theta$:

$$C(g(X), \theta) = \frac{(\theta - g(X))^2}{\theta(1 - \theta)}.$$

Show that the Bayes estimator is given by

$$g(k) = \frac{\Gamma(n)}{\Gamma(k)\Gamma(n-k)} \frac{k}{n}.$$

## Section 8.7: Testing the Fit of a Distribution to Data

**8.94.** The following histogram was obtained by counting the occurrence of the first digits in telephone numbers in one column of a telephone directory:

| digit | 0 | 1 | 2 | 3 | 4 | 5 | 6 | 7 | 8 | 9 |
|---|---|---|---|---|---|---|---|---|---|---|
| observed | 0 | 0 | 24 | 2 | 25 | 3 | 32 | 15 | 2 | 2 |

Test the goodness of fit of this data to a random variable that is uniformly distributed in the set $\{0, 1, \ldots, 9\}$ at a 1% significance level. Repeat for the set $\{2, 3, \ldots, 9\}$.

**8.95.** A die is tossed 96 times and the number of times each face occurs is counted:

| $k$ | 1 | 2 | 3 | 4 | 5 | 6 |
|---|---|---|---|---|---|---|
| $n_k$ | 25 | 8 | 17 | 20 | 13 | 13 |

**(a)** Test the goodness of fit of the data to the pmf of a fair die at a 5% significance level.

**(b)** Run the following experiment 100 times: Generate 50 iid random variables from the discrete pmf $\{1/6, 1/6, 1/6, 1/6, 3/24, 5/24\}$. Test the goodness of fit of this data to tosses from a fair die. What is the relative frequency with which the null hypothesis is rejected?

**(c)** Repeat part b using a sample size of 100 iid random variables.

**8.96. (a)** Show that the $D^2$ statistic when $K = 2$ is:

$$D^2 = \frac{(n_1 - np_1)^2}{np_1(1 - p_1)} = \left[ \frac{(n_1 - np_1)}{\sqrt{np_1(1 - p_1)}} \right]^2$$

**(b)** Explain why $D^2$ approaches a chi-square random variable with 1 degree of freedom as $n$ becomes large.

**8.97. (a)** Repeat the following experiment 500 times: Generate 100 samples of the sum of $X$ of 10 iid uniform random variables from the unit interval. Perform a goodness-of-fit test of the random samples of $X$ to the Gaussian random variable with the same mean and variance. What is the relative frequency with which the null hypothesis is rejected at a 5% level?

**(b)** Repeat part a for sums of 20 iid uniform random variables.

**8.98.** Repeat Problem 8.97 for the sum of exponential random variables with mean 1.

**8.99.** A computer simulation program gives pairs of numbers $(X, Y)$ that are supposed to be uniformly distributed in the unit square. Use the chi-square test to assess the goodness of fit of the computer output.

**8.100.** Use the approach in Problem 8.99 to develop a test for the independence between two random variables $X$ and $Y$.

## Problems Requiring Cumulative Knowledge

**8.101.** You are asked to characterize the behavior of a new binary communications system in which the inputs are $\{0, 1\}$ and the outputs are $\{0, 1\}$. Design a series of tests to characterize the errors introduced in transmissions using the system. How would you estimate the probability of error $p$? How would you determine whether the $p$ is fixed or whether it varies? How would you determine whether errors introduced by the system are independent of each other? How would you determine whether the errors introduced by the system are dependent on the input?

**8.102.** You are asked to characterize the behavior of a new binary communications system in which the inputs are $\{0, 1\}$ and the outputs assume a continuum of real values. What tests would you change and what tests would you keep from Problem 8.101?

**8.103.** Your summer job with the local bus company entails sitting at a busy intersection and recording the bus arrival times for several routes in a table next to their scheduled times. How would you characterize the arrival time behavior of the buses?

**8.104.** Your friend Khash has a summer job with an Internet access provider that involves characterizing the packet transit times to various key sites on the Internet. Your friend has access to some nifty hardware for generating test packets, including GPS systems, to provide accurate timestamps. How would your friend go about characterizing these transit times?

**8.105.** Leigh's summer job is with a startup testing a new optical device. Leigh runs a standard test on these devices to determine their failure rates and failure root causes. He looks at the dependence of failures on the supplier, on impurities in the devices, and on different approaches to preparing the devices. How should Leigh go about characterizing failure rate behavior? How should he identify root causes for failures?

# Random Processes

In certain random experiments, the outcome is a function of time or space. For example, in speech recognition systems, decisions are made on the basis of a voltage waveform corresponding to a speech utterance. In an image processing system, the intensity and color of the image varies over a rectangular region. In a peer-to-peer network, the number of peers in the system varies with time. In some situations, two or more functions of time may be of interest. For example, the temperature in a certain city and the demand placed on the local electric power utility vary together in time.

The random time functions in the above examples can be viewed as numerical quantities that evolve randomly in time or space. Thus what we really have is a family of random variables indexed by the time or space variable. In this chapter we begin the study of random processes. We will proceed as follows:

- In Section 9.1 we introduce the notion of a *random process* (or *stochastic process*), which is defined as an *indexed family of random variables*.
- We are interested in specifying the joint behavior of the random variables within a family (i.e., the temperature at two time instants). In Section 9.2 we see that this is done by specifying joint distribution functions, as well as mean and covariance functions.
- In Sections 9.3 to 9.5 we present examples of stochastic processes and show how models of complex processes can be developed from a few simple models.
- In Section 9.6 we introduce the class of stationary random processes that can be viewed as random processes in "steady state."
- In Section 9.7 we investigate the continuity properties of random processes and define their derivatives and integrals.
- In Section 9.8 we examine the properties of time averages of random processes and the problem of estimating the parameters of a random process.
- In Section 9.9 we describe methods for representing random processes by Fourier series and by the Karhunen-Loeve expansion.
- Finally, in Section 9.10 we present methods for generating random processes.

## 9.1   DEFINITION OF A RANDOM PROCESS

Consider a random experiment specified by the outcomes $\zeta$ from some sample space $S$, by the events defined on $S$, and by the probabilities on these events. Suppose that to every outcome $\zeta \in S$, we assign a function of time according to some rule:

$$X(t, \zeta) \qquad t \in I.$$

The graph of the function $X(t, \zeta)$ versus $t$, for $\zeta$ fixed, is called a **realization, sample path**, or **sample function** of the random process. Thus we can view the outcome of the random experiment as producing an entire function of time as shown in Fig. 9.1. On the other hand, if we fix a time $t_k$ from the index set $I$, then $X(t_k, \zeta)$ is a random variable (see Fig. 9.1) since we are mapping $\zeta$ onto a real number. Thus we have created a family (or ensemble) of random variables indexed by the parameter $t$, $\{X(t, \zeta), t \in I\}$. This family is called a **random process**. We also refer to random processes as **stochastic processes**. We usually suppress the $\zeta$ and use $X(t)$ to denote a random process.

A stochastic process is said to be **discrete-time** if the index set $I$ is a countable set (i.e., the set of integers or the set of nonnegative integers). When dealing with discrete-time processes, we usually use $n$ to denote the time index and $X_n$ to denote the random process. A **continuous-time** stochastic process is one in which $I$ is continuous (i.e., the real line or the nonnegative real line).

The following example shows how we can imagine a stochastic process as resulting from nature selecting $\zeta$ at the beginning of time and gradually revealing it in time through $X(t, \zeta)$.

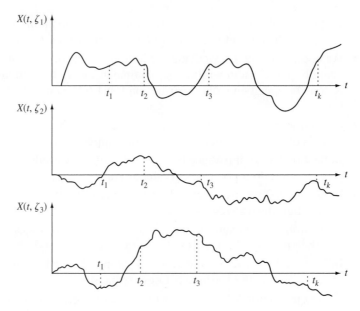

**FIGURE 9.1**
Several realizations of a random process.

### Example 9.1    Random Binary Sequence

Let $\zeta$ be a number selected at random from the interval $S = [0, 1]$, and let $b_1 b_2 \dots$ be the binary expansion of $\zeta$:

$$\zeta = \sum_{i=1}^{\infty} b_i 2^{-i} \qquad \text{where } b_i \in \{0, 1\}.$$

Define the discrete-time random process $X(n, \zeta)$ by

$$X(n, \zeta) = b_n \qquad n = 1, 2, \dots .$$

The resulting process is sequence of binary numbers, with $X(n, \zeta)$ equal to the $n$th number in the binary expansion of $\zeta$.

### Example 9.2    Random Sinusoids

Let $\zeta$ be selected at random from the interval $[-1, 1]$. Define the continuous-time random process $X(t, \zeta)$ by

$$X(t, \zeta) = \zeta \cos(2\pi t) \qquad -\infty < t < \infty.$$

The realizations of this random process are sinusoids with amplitude $\zeta$, as shown in Fig. 9.2(a).

Let $\zeta$ be selected at random from the interval $(-\pi, \pi)$ and let $Y(t, \zeta) = \cos(2\pi t + \zeta)$. The realizations of $Y(t, \zeta)$ are phase-shifted versions of $\cos 2\pi t$ as shown in Fig 9.2(b).

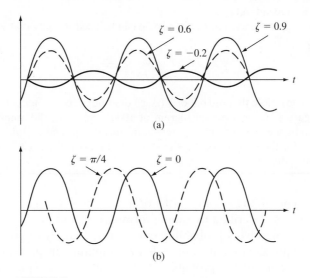

FIGURE 9.2
(a) Sinusoid with random amplitude, (b) Sinusoid with random phase.

The randomness in $\zeta$ induces randomness in the observed function $X(t, \zeta)$. In principle, one can deduce the probability of events involving a stochastic process at various instants of time from probabilities involving $\zeta$ by using the equivalent-event method introduced in Chapter 4.

---

**Example 9.3**

Find the following probabilities for the random process introduced in Example 9.1: $P[X(1, \zeta) = 0]$ and $P[X(1, \zeta) = 0 \text{ and } X(2, \zeta) = 1]$.

The probabilities are obtained by finding the equivalent events in terms of $\zeta$:

$$P[X(1, \zeta) = 0] = P\left[0 \leq \zeta < \frac{1}{2}\right] = \frac{1}{2}$$

$$P[X(1, \zeta) = 0 \text{ and } X(2, \zeta) = 1] = P\left[\frac{1}{4} \leq \zeta < \frac{1}{2}\right] = \frac{1}{4},$$

since all points in the interval $[0 \leq \zeta \leq 1]$ begin with $b_1 = 0$ and all points in $[1/4, 1/2)$ begin with $b_1 = 0$ and $b_2 = 1$. Clearly, any sequence of $k$ bits has a corresponding subinterval of length (and hence probability) $2^{-k}$.

---

**Example 9.4**

Find the pdf of $X_0 = X(t_0, \zeta)$ and $Y(t_0, \zeta)$ in Example 9.2.

If $t_0$ is such that $\cos(2\pi t_0) = 0$, then $X(t_0, \zeta) = 0$ for all $\zeta$ and the pdf of $X(t_0)$ is a delta function of unit weight at $x = 0$. Otherwise, $X(t_0, \zeta)$ is uniformly distributed in the interval $(-\cos 2\pi t_0, \cos 2\pi t_0)$ since $\zeta$ is uniformly distributed in $[-1, 1]$ (see Fig. 9.3a). Note that the pdf of $X(t_0, \zeta)$ depends on $t_0$.

The approach used in Example 4.36 can be used to show that $Y(t_0, \zeta)$ has an arcsine distribution:

$$f_Y(y) = \frac{1}{\pi\sqrt{1 - y^2}}, \qquad |y| < 1.$$

(see Fig. 9.3b). Note that the pdf of $Y(t_0, \zeta)$ does not depend on $t_0$.

Figure 9.3(c) shows a histogram of 1000 samples of the amplitudes $X(t_0, \zeta)$ at $t_0 = 0$, which can be seen to be approximately uniformly distributed in $[-1, 1]$. Figure 9.3(d) shows the histogram for the samples of the sinusoid with random phase. Clearly there is agreement with the arcsine pdf.

---

In general, the sample paths of a stochastic process can be quite complicated and cannot be described by simple formulas. In addition, it is usually not possible to identify an underlying probability space for the family of observed functions of time. Thus the equivalent-event approach for computing the probability of events involving $X(t, \zeta)$ in terms of the probabilities of events involving $\zeta$ does not prove useful in

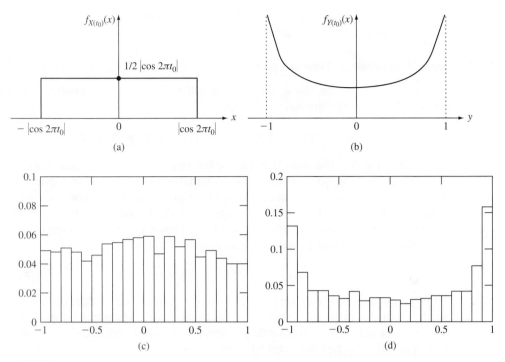

**FIGURE 9.3**
(a) pdf of sinusoid with random amplitude. (b) pdf of sinusoid with random phase. (c) Histogram of samples from uniform amplitude sinusoid at $t = 0$. (d) Histogram of samples from random phase sinusoid at $t = 0$.

practice. In the next section we show an alternative method for specifying the probabilities of events involving a stochastic process.

## 9.2    SPECIFYING A RANDOM PROCESS

There are many questions regarding random processes that cannot be answered with just knowledge of the distribution at a single time instant. For example, we may be interested in the temperature at a given locale at two different times. This requires the following information:

$$P[x_1 < X(t_1) \le x_1, x_2 < X(t_2) \le x_2].$$

In another example, the speech compression system in a cellular phone predicts the value of the speech signal at the next sampling time based on the previous $k$ samples. Thus we may be interested in the following probability:

$$P[a < X(t_{k+1}) \le b \mid X(t_1) = x_1, X(t_2) = x_2, \ldots, X(t_k) = x_k].$$

It is clear that a general description of a random process should provide probabilities for *vectors* of samples of the process.

### 9.2.1    Joint Distributions of Time Samples

Let $X_1, X_2, \ldots, X_k$ be the $k$ random variables obtained by sampling the random process $X(t, \zeta)$ at the times $t_1, t_2, \ldots, t_k$:

$$X_1 = X(t_1, \zeta), X_2 = X(t_2, \zeta,), \ldots, X_k = X(t_k, \zeta),$$

as shown in Fig. 9.1. The joint behavior of the random process at these $k$ time instants is specified by the joint cumulative distribution of the *vector* random variable $X_1, X_2, \ldots, X_k$. The probabilities of any event involving the random process at all or some of these time instants can be computed from this cdf using the methods developed for vector random variables in Chapter 6. Thus, *a stochastic process is specified by the collection of kth-order joint cumulative distribution functions*:

$$F_{X_1, \ldots, X_k}(x_1, x_2, \ldots, x_k) = P[X(t_1) \leq x_1, X(t_2) \leq x_2, \ldots, X(t_k) \leq x_k], \quad (9.1)$$

*for any k and any choice of sampling instants* $t_1, \ldots, t_k$. Note that the collection of cdf's must be consistent in the sense that lower-order cdf's are obtained as marginals of higher-order cdf's. If the stochastic process is *continuous-valued*, then a collection of probability density functions can be used instead:

$$f_{X_1, \ldots, X_k}(x_1, x_2, \ldots, x_k)\, dx_1 \ldots dx_n$$
$$= P\{x_1 < X(t_1) \leq x_1 + dx_1, \ldots, x_k < X(t_k) \leq x_k + dx_k\}. \quad (9.2)$$

If the stochastic process is *discrete-valued*, then a collection of probability mass functions can be used to specify the stochastic process:

$$p_{X_1, \ldots, X_k}(x_1, x_2, \ldots, x_k) = P[X(t_1) = x_1, X(t_2) = x_2, \ldots, X(t_k) = x_k] \quad (9.3)$$

*for any k and any choice of sampling instants* $n_1, \ldots, n_k$.

At first glance it does not appear that we have made much progress in specifying random processes because we are now confronted with the task of specifying a vast collection of joint cdf's! However, this approach works because most useful models of stochastic processes are obtained by elaborating on a few simple models, so the methods developed in Chapters 5 and 6 of this book can be used to derive the required cdf's. The following examples give a preview of how we construct complex models from simple models. We develop these important examples more fully in Sections 9.3 to 9.5.

---

### Example 9.5    iid Bernoulli Random Variables

Let $X_n$ be a sequence of independent, identically distributed Bernoulli random variables with $p = 1/2$. The joint pmf for any $k$ time samples is then

$$P[X_1 = x_1, X_2 = x_2, \ldots, X_k = x_k] = P[X_1 = x_1] \ldots P[X_k = x_k] = \left(\frac{1}{2}\right)^k$$

where $x_i \in \{0, 1\}$ for all $i$. This binary random process is equivalent to the one discussed in Example 9.1.

---

### Example 9.6    iid Gaussian Random Variables

Let $X_n$ be a sequence of independent, identically distributed Gaussian random variables with zero mean and variance $\sigma_X^2$. The joint pdf for any $k$ time samples is then

$$f_{X_1, X_2, \ldots, X_k}(x_1, x_2, \ldots, x_k) = \frac{1}{(2\pi\sigma^2)^{k/2}} e^{-(x_1^2 + x_2^2 + \cdots + x_k^2)/2\sigma^2}.$$

---

The following two examples show how more complex and interesting processes can be built from iid sequences.

---

### Example 9.7    Binomial Counting Process

Let $X_n$ be a sequence of independent, identically distributed Bernoulli random variables with $p = 1/2$. Let $S_n$ be the number of 1's in the first $n$ trials:

$$S_n = X_1 + X_2 + \cdots + X_n \quad \text{for} \quad n = 0, 1, \ldots.$$

$S_n$ is an integer-valued nondecreasing function of $n$ that grows by unit steps after a random number of time instants. From previous chapters we know that $S_n$ is a binomial random variable with parameters $n$ and $p = 1/2$. In the next section we show how to find the joint pmf's of $S_n$ using conditional probabilities.

---

### Example 9.8    Filtered Noisy Signal

Let $X_j$ be a sequence of independent, identically distributed observations of a signal voltage $\mu$ corrupted by zero-mean Gaussian noise $N_j$ with variance $\sigma^2$:

$$X_j = \mu + N_j \quad \text{for} \quad j = 0, 1, \ldots.$$

Consider the signal that results from averaging the sequence of observations:

$$S_n = (X_1 + X_2 + \cdots + X_n)/n \quad \text{for} \quad n = 0, 1, \ldots.$$

From previous chapters we know that $S_n$ is the sample mean of an iid sequence of Gaussian random variables. We know that $S_n$ itself is a Gaussian random variable with mean $\mu$ and variance $\sigma^2/n$, and so it tends towards the value $\mu$ as $n$ increases. In a later section, we show that $S_n$ is an example from the class of Gaussian random processes.

---

## 9.2.2    The Mean, Autocorrelation, and Autocovariance Functions

The moments of time samples of a random process can be used to partially specify the random process because they summarize the information contained in the joint cdf's.

The **mean function $m_X(t)$** and the **variance function VAR[$X(t)$]** of a continuous-time random process $X(t)$ are defined by

$$m_X(t) = E[X(t)] = \int_{-\infty}^{\infty} x f_{X(t)}(x)\, dx, \qquad (9.4)$$

and

$$\text{VAR}[X(t)] = \int_{-\infty}^{\infty} (x - m_X(t))^2 f_{X(t)}(x)\, dx, \qquad (9.5)$$

where $f_{X(t)}(x)$ is the pdf of $X(t)$. Note that $m_X(t)$ and VAR[$X(t)$] are *deterministic* functions of time. Trends in the behavior of $X(t)$ are reflected in the variation of $m_X(t)$ with time. The variance gives an indication of the spread in the values taken on by $X(t)$ at different time instants.

The **autocorrelation $R_X(t_1, t_2)$** of a random process $X(t)$ is defined as the joint moment of $X(t_1)$ and $X(t_2)$:

$$R_X(t_1, t_2) = E[X(t_1)X(t_2)] = \int_{-\infty}^{\infty} \int_{-\infty}^{\infty} xy f_{X(t_1),X(t_2)}(x, y)\, dx\, dy, \qquad (9.6)$$

where $f_{X(t_1),X(t_2)}(x, y)$ is the second-order pdf of $X(t)$. In general, the autocorrelation is a function of $t_1$ and $t_2$. Note that $R_X(t, t) = E[X^2(t)]$.

The **autocovariance $C_X(t_1, t_2)$** of a random process $X(t)$ is defined as the covariance of $X(t_1)$ and $X(t_2)$:

$$C_X(t_1, t_2) = E[\{X(t_1) - m_X(t_1)\}\{X(t_2) - m_X(t_2)\}]. \qquad (9.7)$$

From Eq. (5.30), the autocovariance can be expressed in terms of the autocorrelation and the means:

$$C_X(t_1, t_2) = R_X(t_1, t_2) - m_X(t_1)m_X(t_2). \qquad (9.8)$$

Note that the variance of $X(t)$ can be obtained from $C_X(t_1, t_2)$:

$$\text{VAR}[X(t)] = E[(X(t) - m_X(t))^2] = C_X(t, t). \qquad (9.9)$$

The *correlation coefficient* of $X(t)$ is defined as the correlation coefficient of $X(t_1)$ and $X(t_2)$ (see Eq. 5.31):

$$\rho_X(t_1, t_2) = \frac{C_X(t_1, t_2)}{\sqrt{C_X(t_1, t_1)}\sqrt{C_X(t_2, t_2)}}. \qquad (9.10)$$

From Eq. (5.32) we have that $|\rho_X(t_1, t_2)| \leq 1$. Recall that the correlation coefficient is a measure of the extent to which a random variable can be predicted as a linear function of another. In Chapter 10, we will see that the autocovariance function and the autocorrelation function play a critical role in the design of linear methods for analyzing and processing random signals.

The mean, variance, autocorrelation, and autocovariance functions for discrete-time random processes are defined in the same manner as above. We use a slightly different notation for the time index. The **mean and variance** of a *discrete-time* random process $X_n$ are defined as:

$$m_X(n) = E[X_n] \quad \text{and} \quad \text{VAR}[X_n] = E[(X_n - m_X(n))^2]. \tag{9.11}$$

The **autocorrelation and autocovariance functions** of a discrete-time random process $X_n$ are defined as follows:

$$R_X(n_1, n_2) = E[X(n_1)X(n_2)] \tag{9.12}$$

and

$$\begin{aligned} C_X(n_1, n_2) &= E[\{X(n_1) - m_X(n_1)\}\{X(n_2) - m_X(n_2)\}] \\ &= R_X(n_1, n_2) - m_X(n_1)m_X(n_2). \end{aligned} \tag{9.13}$$

Before proceeding to examples, we reiterate that the mean, autocorrelation, and autocovariance functions are only partial descriptions of a random process. Thus we will see later in the chapter that it is possible for two quite different random processes to have the same mean, autocorrelation, and autocovariance functions.

---

**Example 9.9    Sinusoid with Random Amplitude**

Let $X(t) = A \cos 2\pi t$, where $A$ is some random variable (see Fig. 9.2a). The mean of $X(t)$ is found using Eq. (4.30):

$$m_X(t) = E[A \cos 2\pi t] = E[A] \cos 2\pi t.$$

Note that the mean varies with $t$. In particular, note that the process is always zero for values of $t$ where $\cos 2\pi t = 0$.

The autocorrelation is

$$\begin{aligned} R_X(t_1, t_2) &= E[A \cos 2\pi t_1 \, A \cos 2\pi t_2] \\ &= E[A^2] \cos 2\pi t_1 \cos 2\pi t_2, \end{aligned}$$

and the autocovariance is then

$$\begin{aligned} C_X(t_1, t_2) &= R_X(t_1, t_2) - m_X(t_1)m_X(t_2) \\ &= \{E[A^2] - E[A]^2\} \cos 2\pi t_1 \cos 2\pi t_2 \\ &= \text{VAR}[A] \cos 2\pi t_1 \cos 2\pi t_2. \end{aligned}$$

---

**Example 9.10    Sinusoid with Random Phase**

Let $X(t) = \cos(\omega t + \Theta)$, where $\Theta$ is uniformly distributed in the interval $(-\pi, \pi)$ (see Fig. 9.2b). The mean of $X(t)$ is found using Eq. (4.30):

$$m_X(t) = E[\cos(\omega t + \Theta)] = \frac{1}{2\pi} \int_{-\pi}^{\pi} \cos(\omega t + \theta) \, d\theta = 0.$$

The autocorrelation and autocovariance are then

$$C_X(t_1, t_2) = R_X(t_1, t_2) = E[\cos(\omega t_1 + \Theta) \cos(\omega t_2 + \Theta)]$$

$$= \frac{1}{2\pi} \int_{-\pi}^{\pi} \frac{1}{2} \{\cos(\omega(t_1 - t_2)) + \cos(\omega(t_1 + t_2) + 2\theta)\} \, d\theta$$

$$= \frac{1}{2} \cos(\omega(t_1 - t_2)),$$

where we used the identity $\cos(a) \cos(b) = 1/2 \cos(a + b) + 1/2 \cos(a - b)$. Note that $m_X(t)$ is a constant and that $C_X(t_1, t_2)$ depends only on $|t_1 - t_2|$. Note as well that the samples at time $t_1$ and $t_2$ are uncorrelated if $\omega(t_1 - t_2) = k\pi$ where $k$ is any integer.

---

### 9.2.3    Multiple Random Processes

In most situations we deal with more than one random process at a time. For example, we may be interested in the temperatures at city a, $X(t)$, and city b, $Y(t)$. Another very common example involves a random process $X(t)$ that is the "input" to a system and another random process $Y(t)$ that is the "output" of the system. Naturally, we are interested in the interplay between $X(t)$ and $Y(t)$.

The joint behavior of two or more random processes is specified by the collection of joint distributions for all possible choices of time samples of the processes. Thus for a pair of continuous-valued random processes $X(t)$ and $Y(t)$ we must specify all possible joint density functions of $X(t_1), \ldots, X(t_k)$ and $Y(t_1'), \ldots, Y(t_j')$ for all $k, j$, and all choices of $t_1, \ldots, t_k$ and $t_1', \ldots, t_j'$. For example, the simplest joint pdf would be:

$$f_{X(t_1), Y(t_2)}(x, y) \, dx \, dy = P\{x < X(t_1) \le x + dx, y < Y(t_2) \le y + dy\}.$$

Note that the time indices of $X(t)$ and $Y(t)$ need not be the same. For example, we may be interested in the input at time $t_1$ and the output at a later time $t_2$.

The random processes $X(t)$ and $Y(t)$ are said to be **independent random processes** if the vector random variables $\mathbf{X} = (X(t_1), \ldots, X(t_k))$ and $\mathbf{Y} = (Y(t_1'), \ldots, Y(t_j'))$ are independent for *all* $k, j$, and *all* choices of $t_1, \ldots, t_k$ and $t_1', \ldots, t_j'$:

$$F^{\mathbf{X}, \mathbf{Y}}(x_1, \ldots, x_k, y_1, \ldots, y_j) = F^{\mathbf{X}}(X_1, \ldots, X_k) \, F^{\mathbf{Y}}(y_1, \ldots, y_j).$$

The **cross-correlation $R_{X,Y}(t_1, t_2)$** of $X(t)$ and $Y(t)$ is defined by

$$R_{X,Y}(t_1, t_2) = E[X(t_1)Y(t_2)]. \tag{9.14}$$

The processes $X(t)$ and $Y(t)$ are said to be **orthogonal random processes** if

$$R_{X,Y}(t_1, t_2) = 0 \quad \text{for all } t_1 \text{ and } t_2. \tag{9.15}$$

The **cross-covariance** $C_{X,Y}(t_1, t_2)$ of $X(t)$ and $Y(t)$ is defined by

$$C_{X,Y}(t_1, t_2) = E[\{X(t_1) - m_X(t_1)\}\{Y(t_2) - m_X(t_2)\}]$$
$$= R_{X,Y}(t_1, t_2) - m_X(t_1)m_X(t_2). \tag{9.16}$$

The processes $X(t)$ and $Y(t)$ are said to be **uncorrelated random processes** if

$$C_{X,Y}(t_1, t_2) = 0 \quad \text{for all } t_1 \text{ and } t_2. \tag{9.17}$$

---

### Example 9.11

Let $X(t) = \cos(\omega t + \Theta)$ and $Y(t) = \sin(\omega t + \Theta)$, where $\Theta$ is a random variable uniformly distributed in $[-\pi, \pi]$. Find the cross-covariance of $X(t)$ and $Y(t)$.

From Example 9.10 we know that $X(t)$ and $Y(t)$ are zero mean. From Eq. (9.16), the cross-covariance is then equal to the cross-correlation:

$$C_{X,Y}(t_1, t_2) = R_{X,Y}(t_1, t_2) = E[\cos(\omega t_1 + \Theta)\sin(\omega t_2 + \Theta)]$$
$$= E\left[-\frac{1}{2}\sin(\omega(t_1 - t_2)) + \frac{1}{2}\sin(\omega(t_1 + t_2) + 2\Theta)\right]$$
$$= -\frac{1}{2}\sin(\omega(t_1 - t_2)),$$

since $E[\sin(\omega(t_1 + t_2) + 2\Theta)] = 0$. $X(t)$ and $Y(t)$ are not uncorrelated random processes because the cross-covariance is not equal to zero for all choices of time samples. Note, however, that $X(t_1)$ and $Y(t_2)$ are *uncorrelated random variables* for $t_1$ and $t_2$ such that $\omega(t_1 - t_2) = k\pi$ where $k$ is any integer.

---

### Example 9.12    Signal Plus Noise

Suppose process $Y(t)$ consists of a desired signal $X(t)$ plus noise $N(t)$:

$$Y(t) = X(t) + N(t).$$

Find the cross-correlation between the observed signal and the desired signal assuming that $X(t)$ and $N(t)$ are independent random processes.

From Eq. (8.14), we have

$$R_{XY}(t_1, t_2) = E[X(t_1)Y(t_2)]$$
$$= E[X(t_1)\{X(t_2) + N(t_2)\}]$$
$$= R_X(t_1, t_2) + E[X(t_1)]E[N(t_2)]$$
$$= R_X(t_1, t_2) + m_X(t_1)m_N(t_2),$$

where the third equality followed from the fact that $X(t)$ and $N(t)$ are independent.

---

**9.3    DISCRETE-TIME PROCESSES: SUM PROCESS, BINOMIAL COUNTING PROCESS, AND RANDOM WALK**

In this section we introduce several important discrete-time random processes. We begin with the simplest class of random processes—independent, identically distributed sequences—and then consider the sum process that results from adding an iid sequence. We show that the sum process satisfies the independent increments property as well as the Markov property. Both of these properties greatly facilitate the calculation of joint probabilities. We also introduce the binomial counting process and the random walk process as special cases of sum processes.

### 9.3.1    iid Random Process

Let $X_n$ be a discrete-time random process consisting of a sequence of independent, identically distributed (iid) random variables with common cdf $F_X(x)$, mean $m$, and variance $\sigma^2$. The sequence $X_n$ is called the **iid random process**.

The joint cdf for any time instants $n_1, \dots, n_k$ is given by

$$F_{X_1,\dots,X_k}(x_1, x_2, \dots, x_k) = P[X_1 \le x_1, X_2 \le x_2, \dots, X_k \le x_k]$$
$$= F_X(x_1)F_X(x_2)\dots F_X(x_k), \qquad (9.18)$$

where, for simplicity, $X_k$ denotes $X_{n_k}$. Equation (9.18) implies that if $X_n$ is discrete-valued, the joint pmf factors into the product of individual pmf's, and if $X_n$ is continuous-valued, the joint pdf factors into the product of the individual pdf's.

The *mean of an iid process* is obtained from Eq. (9.4):

$$m_X(n) = E[X_n] = m \qquad \text{for all } n. \qquad (9.19)$$

Thus, the mean is constant.

The autocovariance function is obtained from Eq. (9.6) as follows. If $n_1 \ne n_2$, then

$$C_X(n_1, n_2) = E[(X_{n_1} - m)(X_{n_2} - m)]$$
$$= E[(X_{n_1} - m)]E[(X_{n_2} - m)] = 0,$$

since $X_{n_1}$ and $X_{n_2}$ are independent random variables. If $n_1 = n_2 = n$, then

$$C_X(n_1, n_2) = E[(X_n - m)^2] = \sigma^2.$$

We can express the *autocovariance of the iid process* in compact form as follows:

$$C_X(n_1, n_2) = \sigma^2 \delta_{n_1 n_2}, \qquad (9.20)$$

where $\delta_{n_1 n_2} = 1$ if $n_1 = n_2$, and 0 otherwise. Therefore the autocovariance function is zero everywhere except for $n_1 = n_2$. The *autocorrelation function of the iid process* is found from Eq. (9.7):

$$R_X(n_1, n_2) = C_X(n_1, n_2) + m^2. \qquad (9.21)$$

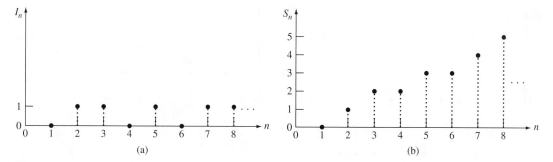

**FIGURE 9.4**

(a) Realization of a Bernoulli process. $I_n = 1$ indicates that a light bulb fails and is replaced on day $n$. (b) Realization of a binomial process. $S_n$ denotes the number of light bulbs that have failed up to time $n$.

---

## Example 9.13   Bernoulli Random Process

Let $I_n$ be a sequence of independent Bernoulli random variables. $I_n$ is then an iid random process taking on values from the set $\{0, 1\}$. A realization of such a process is shown in Fig. 9.4(a). For example, $I_n$ could be an indicator function for the event "a light bulb fails and is replaced on day $n$."

Since $I_n$ is a Bernoulli random variable, it has mean and variance

$$m_I(n) = p \qquad \text{VAR}[I_n] = p(1 - p).$$

The independence of the $I_n$'s makes probabilities easy to compute. For example, the probability that the first four bits in the sequence are 1001 is

$$P[I_1 = 1, I_2 = 0, I_3 = 0, I_4 = 1]$$
$$= P[I_1 = 1]P[I_2 = 0]P[I_3 = 0]P[I_4 = 1]$$
$$= p^2(1 - p)^2.$$

Similarly, the probability that the second bit is 0 and the seventh is 1 is

$$P[I_2 = 0, I_7 = 1] = P[I_2 = 0]P[I_7 = 1] = p(1 - p).$$

---

## Example 9.14   Random Step Process

An up-down counter is driven by $+1$ or $-1$ pulses. Let the input to the counter be given by $D_n = 2I_n - 1$, where $I_n$ is the Bernoulli random process, then

$$D_n = \begin{cases} +1 & \text{if } I_n = 1 \\ -1 & \text{if } I_n = 0. \end{cases}$$

For example, $D_n$ might represent the change in position of a particle that moves along a straight line in jumps of $\pm 1$ every time unit. A realization of $D_n$ is shown in Fig. 9.5(a).

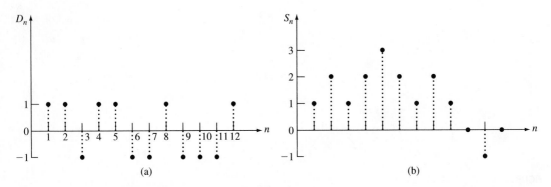

**FIGURE 9.5**
(a) Realization of a random step process. $D_n = 1$ implies that the particle moves one step to the right at time $n$. (b) Realization of a random walk process. $S_n$ denotes the position of a particle at time $n$.

The mean of $D_n$ is

$$m_D(n) = E[D_n] = E[2I_n - 1] = 2E[I_n] - 1 = 2p - 1.$$

The variance of $D_n$ is found from Eqs. (4.37) and (4.38):

$$\text{VAR}[D_n] = \text{VAR}[2I_n - 1] = 2^2\,\text{VAR}[I_n] = 4p(1 - p).$$

The probabilities of events involving $D_n$ are computed as in Example 9.13.

### 9.3.2    Independent Increments and Markov Properties of Random Processes

Before proceeding to build random processes from iid processes, we present two very useful properties of random processes. Let $X(t)$ be a random process and consider two time instants, $t_1 < t_2$. The increment of the random process in the interval $t_1 < t \leq t_2$ is defined as $X(t_2) - X(t_1)$. *A random process $X(t)$ is said to have **independent increments** if the increments in disjoint intervals are independent random variables,* that is, for any $k$ and any choice of sampling instants $t_1 < t_2 < \cdots < t_k$, the associated increments

$$X(t_2) - X(t_1),\ X(t_3) - X(t_2),\ldots, X(t_k) - X(t_{k-1})$$

are independent random variables. In the next subsection, we show that the joint pdf (pmf) of $X(t_1), X(t_2),\ldots, X(t_k)$ is given by the product of the pdf (pmf) of $X(t_1)$ and the marginal pdf's (pmf's) of the individual increments.

Another useful property of random processes that allows us to readily obtain the joint probabilities is the Markov property. *A random process $X(t)$ is said to be **Markov** if the future of the process given the present is independent of the past;* that is, for any $k$ and any choice of sampling instants $t_1 < t_2 < \cdots < t_k$ and for any $x_1, x_2,\ldots,x_k$,

$$f_{X(t_k)}(x_k \,|\, X(t_{k-1}) = x_{k-1},\ldots, X(t_1) = x_1)$$

$$= f_{X(t_k)}(x_k \,|\, X(t_{k-1}) = x_{k-1}) \qquad (9.22)$$

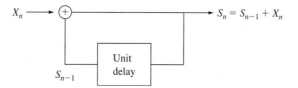

**FIGURE 9.6**
The sum process $S_n = X_1 + \cdots + X_n$, $S_0 = 0$, can be generated in this way.

if $X(t)$ is continuous-valued, and

$$P[X(t_k) = x_k \,|\, X(t_{k-1}) = x_{k-1}, \ldots, X(t_1) = x_1]$$
$$= P[X(t_k) = x_k \,|\, X(t_{k-1}) = x_{k-1}] \tag{9.23}$$

if $X(t)$ is discrete-valued. The expressions on the right-hand side of the above two equations are called the transition pdf and transition pmf, respectively. In the next sections we encounter several processes that satisfy the Markov property. Chapter 11 is entirely devoted to random processes that satisfy this property.

It is easy to show that a random process that has independent increments is also a Markov process. The converse is not true; that is, the Markov property does not imply independent increments.

### 9.3.3   Sum Processes: The Binomial Counting and Random Walk Processes

Many interesting random processes are obtained as the sum of a sequence of iid random variables, $X_1, X_2, \ldots$:

$$S_n = X_1 + X_2 + \cdots + X_n \qquad n = 1, 2, \ldots$$
$$= S_{n-1} + X_n, \tag{9.24}$$

where $S_0 = 0$. We call $S_n$ the **sum process**. The pdf or pmf of $S_n$ is found using the convolution or characteristic-equation methods presented in Section 7.1. Note that $S_n$ depends on the "past," $S_1, \ldots, S_{n-1}$, only through $S_{n-1}$, that is, $S_n$ is independent of the past when $S_{n-1}$ is known. This can be seen clearly from Fig. 9.6, which shows a recursive procedure for computing $S_n$ in terms of $S_{n-1}$ and the increment $X_n$. Thus $S_n$ *is a Markov process*.

---

### Example 9.15   Binomial Counting Process

Let the $I_i$ be the sequence of independent Bernoulli random variables in Example 9.13, and let $S_n$ be the corresponding sum process. $S_n$ is then the *counting process* that gives the number of successes in the first $n$ Bernoulli trials. The sample function for $S_n$ corresponding to a particular sequence of $I_i$'s is shown in Fig. 9.4(b). Note that the counting process can only increase over time. Note as well that the binomial process can increase by at most one unit at a time. If $I_n$ indicates that a light bulb fails and is replaced on day $n$, then $S_n$ denotes the number of light bulbs that have failed up to day $n$.

Since $S_n$ is the sum of $n$ independent Bernoulli random variables, $S_n$ is a binomial random variable with parameters $n$ and $p = P[I = 1]$:

$$P[S_n = j] = \binom{n}{j} p^j (1 - p)^{n-j} \qquad \text{for } 0 \leq j \leq n,$$

and zero otherwise. Thus $S_n$ has mean $np$ and variance $np(1 - p)$. Note that the mean and variance of this process grow linearly with time. This reflects the fact that as time progresses, that is, as $n$ grows, the range of values that can be assumed by the process increases. If $p > 0$ then we also know that $S_n$ has a tendency to grow steadily without bound over time.

The Markov property of the binomial counting process is easy to deduce. Given that the current value of the process at time $n - 1$ is $S_{n-1} = k$, the process at the next time instant will be $k$ with probability $1 - p$ or $k + 1$ with probability $p$. Once we know the value of the process at time $n - 1$, the values of the random process prior to time $n - 1$ are irrelevant.

---

### Example 9.16    One-Dimensional Random Walk

Let $D_n$ be the iid process of $\pm 1$ random variables in Example 9.14, and let $S_n$ be the corresponding sum process. $S_n$ can represent the position of a particle at time $n$. The random process $S_n$ is an example of a **one-dimensional random walk**. A sample function of $S_n$ is shown in Fig. 9.5(b). Unlike the binomial process, the random walk can increase or decrease over time. The random walk process changes by one unit at a time.

The pmf of $S_n$ is found as follows. If there are $k$ "+1"s in the first $n$ trials, then there are $n - k$ "−1"s, and $S_n = k - (n - k) = 2k - n$. Conversely, $S_n = j$ if the number of +1's is $k = (j + n)/2$. If $(j + n)/2$ is not an integer, then $S_n$ cannot equal $j$. Thus

$$P[S_n = 2k - n] = \binom{n}{k} p^k (1 - p)^{n-k} \qquad \text{for } k \in \{0, 1, \ldots, n\}.$$

Since $k$ is the number of successes in $n$ Bernoulli trials, the mean of the random walk is:

$$E[S_n] = 2np - n = n(2p - 1).$$

As time progresses, the random walk can fluctuate over an increasingly broader range of positive and negative values. $S_n$ has a tendency to either grow if $p > 1/2$, or to decrease if $p < 1/2$. The case $p = 1/2$ provides a precarious balance, and we will see later, in Chapter 12, very interesting dynamics. Figure 9.7(a) shows the first 100 steps from a sample function of the random walk with $p = 1/2$. Figure 9.7(b) shows four sample functions of the random walk process with $p = 1/2$ for 1000 steps. Figure 9.7(c) shows four sample functions in the asymmetric case where $p = 3/4$. Note the strong linear growth trend in the process.

---

The sum process $S_n$ has **independent increments** in nonoverlapping time intervals. To see this consider two time intervals: $n_0 < n \leq n_1$ and $n_2 < n \leq n_3$, where $n_1 \leq n_2$. The increments of $S_n$ in these disjoint time intervals are given by

$$S_{n_1} - S_{n_0} = X_{n_0+1} + \cdots + X_{n_1}$$
$$S_{n_3} - S_{n_2} = X_{n_2+1} + \cdots + X_{n_3}. \qquad (9.25)$$

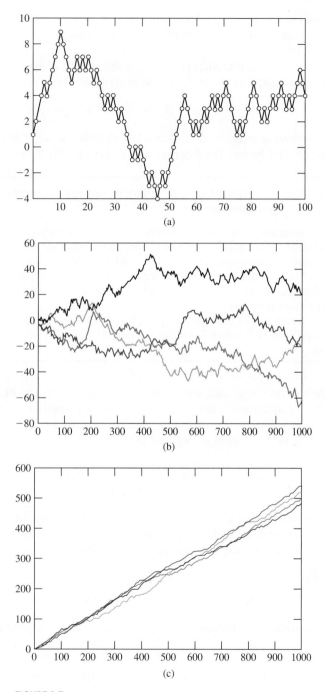

**FIGURE 9.7**

(a) Random walk process with $p = 1/2$. (b) Four sample functions of symmetric random walk process with $p = 1/2$. (c) Four sample functions of asymmetric random walk with $p = 3/4$.

The above increments do not have any of the $X_n$'s in common, so the independence of the $X_n$'s implies that the increments $(S_{n_1} - S_{n_0})$ and $(S_{n_3} - S_{n_2})$ are independent random variables.

For $n' > n$, the increment $S_{n'} - S_n$ is the sum of $n' - n$ iid random variables, so it has the same distribution as $S_{n'-n}$, the sum of the first $n' - n$ $X$'s, that is,

$$P[S_{n'} - S_n = y] = P[S_{n'-n} = y]. \tag{9.26}$$

Thus increments in intervals of the same length have the same distribution regardless of when the interval begins. For this reason, we also say that $S_n$ has **stationary increments**.

---

**Example 9.17    Independent and Stationary Increments of Binomial Process and Random Walk**

The independent and stationary increments property is particularly easy to see for the binomial process since the increments in an interval are the number of successes in the corresponding Bernoulli trials. The independent increment property follows from the fact that the numbers of successes in disjoint time intervals are independent. The stationary increments property follows from the fact that the pmf for the increment in a time interval is the binomial pmf with the corresponding number of trials.

The increment in a random walk process is determined by the same number of successes as a binomial process. It then follows that the random walk also has independent and stationary increments.

---

The independent and stationary increments property of the sum process $S_n$ makes it easy to compute the joint pmf/pdf for any number of time instants. For simplicity, suppose that the $X_n$ are integer-valued, so $S_n$ is also integer-valued. We compute the joint pmf of $S_n$ at times $n_1, n_2$, and $n_3$:

$$P[S_{n_1} = y_1, S_{n_2} = y_2, S_{n_3} = y_3]$$
$$= P[S_{n_1} = y_1, S_{n_2} - S_{n_1} = y_2 - y_1, S_{n_3} - S_{n_2} = y_3 - y_2], \tag{9.27}$$

since the process is equal to $y_1, y_2$, and $y_3$ at times $n_1, n_2$, and $n_3$, if and only if it is equal to $y_1$ at time $n_1$, and the subsequent increments are $y_2 - y_1$, and $y_3 - y_2$. The independent increments property then implies that

$$P[S_{n_1} = y_1, S_{n_2} = y_2, S_{n_3} = y_3]$$
$$= P[S_{n_1} = y_1]P[S_{n_2} - S_{n_1} = y_2 - y_1]P[S_{n_3} - S_{n_2} = y_3 - y_2]. \tag{9.28}$$

Finally, the stationary increments property implies that the *joint pmf of $S_n$ is given by*:

$$P[S_{n_1} = y_1, S_{n_2} = y_2, S_{n_3} = y_3]$$
$$= P[S_{n_1} = y_1]P[S_{n_2-n_1} = y_2 - y_1]P[S_{n_3-n_2} = y_3 - y_2].$$

Clearly, we can use this procedure to write the joint pmf of $S_n$ at any time instants $n_1 < n_2 < \cdots < n_k$ in terms of the pmf at the initial time instant and the pmf's of the subsequent increments:

$$P[S_{n_1} = y_1, S_{n_2} = y_2, \ldots, S_{n_k} = y_k]$$
$$= P[S_{n_1} = y_1] P[S_{n_2 - n_1} = y_2 - y_1] \ldots P[S_{n_k - n_{k-1}} = y_k - y_{k-1}]. \tag{9.29}$$

If the $X_n$ are continuous-valued random variables, then it can be shown that *the joint density of $S_n$ at times $n_1, n_2, \ldots, n_k$ is:*

$$f_{S_{n_1}, S_{n_2}, \ldots, S_{n_k}}(y_1, y_2, \ldots, y_k) = f_{S_{n_1}}(y_1) f_{S_{n_2 - n_1}}(y_2 - y_1) \ldots f_{S_{n_k - n_{k-1}}}(y_k - y_{k-1}). \tag{9.30}$$

---

### Example 9.18    Joint pmf of Binomial Counting Process

Find the joint pmf for the binomial counting process at times $n_1$ and $n_2$. Find the probability that $P[S_{n_1} = 0, S_{n_2} = n_2 - n_1]$, that is, the first $n_1$ trials are failures and the remaining trials are all successes.

Following the above approach we have

$$P[S_{n_1} = y_1, S_{n_2} = y_2] = P[S_{n_1} = y_1] P[S_{n_2} - S_{n_1} = y_2 - y_1]$$

$$= \binom{n_2 - n_1}{y_2 - y_1} p^{y_2 - y_1} (1 - p)^{n_2 - n_1 - y_2 + y_1} \binom{n_1}{y_1} p^{y_1} (1 - p)^{n_1 - y_1}$$

$$= \binom{n_2 - n_1}{y_2 - y_1} \binom{n_1}{y_1} p^{y_2} (1 - p)^{n_2 - y_2}.$$

The requested probability is then:

$$P[S_{n_1} = 0, S_{n_2} = n_2 - n_1] = \binom{n_2 - n_1}{n_2 - n_1} \binom{n_1}{0} p^{n_2 - n_1} (1 - p)^{n_1} = p^{n_2 - n_1} (1 - p)^{n_1}$$

which is what we would obtain from a direct calculation for Bernoulli trials.

---

### Example 9.19    Joint pdf of Sum of iid Gaussian Sequence

Let $X_n$ be a sequence of iid Gaussian random variables with zero mean and variance $\sigma^2$. Find the joint pdf of the corresponding sum process at times $n_1$ and $n_2$.

From Example 7.3, we know that $S_n$ is a Gaussian random variable with mean zero and variance $n\sigma^2$. The joint pdf of $S_n$ at times $n_j$ and $n_2$ is given by

$$f_{S_{n_1}, S_{n_2}}(y_1, y_2) = f_{S_{n_2 - n_1}}(y_2 - y_1) f_{S_{n_1}}(y_1)$$

$$= \frac{1}{\sqrt{2\pi(n_2 - n_1)\sigma^2}} e^{-(y_2 - y_1)^2 / [2(n_2 - n_1)\sigma^2]} \frac{1}{\sqrt{2\pi n_1 \sigma^2}} e^{-y_1^2 / 2n_1 \sigma^2}.$$

---

Since the sum process $S_n$ is the sum of $n$ iid random variables, it has mean and variance:

$$m_S(n) = E[S_n] = nE[X] = nm \tag{9.31}$$

$$\text{VAR}[S_n] = n \, \text{VAR}[X] = n\sigma^2. \tag{9.32}$$

The property of independent increments allows us to compute the autocovariance in an interesting way. Suppose $n \leq k$ so $n = \min(n, k)$, then

$$
\begin{aligned}
C_S(n, k) &= E[(S_n - nm)(S_k - km)] \\
&= E[(S_n - nm)\{(S_n - nm) + (S_k - km) - (S_n - nm)\}] \\
&= E[(S_n - nm)^2] + E[(S_n - nm)(S_k - S_n - (k - n)m)].
\end{aligned}
$$

Since $S_n$ and the increment $S_k - S_n$ are independent,

$$
\begin{aligned}
C_S(n, k) &= E[(S_n - nm)^2] + E[(S_n - nm)]E[(S_k - S_n - (k - n)m)] \\
&= E[(S_n - nm)^2] \\
&= \text{VAR}[S_n] = n\sigma^2,
\end{aligned}
$$

since $E[S_n - nm] = 0$. Similarly, if $k = \min(n, k)$, we would have obtained $k\sigma^2$. Therefore the *autocovariance of the sum process* is

$$
C_S(n, k) = \min(n, k)\sigma^2. \tag{9.33}
$$

---

**Example 9.20 Autocovariance of Random Walk**

Find the autocovariance of the one-dimensional random walk.

From Example 9.14 and Eqs. (9.32) and (9.33), $S_n$ has mean $n(2p - 1)$ and variance $4np(1 - p)$. Thus its autocovariance is given by

$$
C_s(n, k) = \min(n, k)4p(1 - p).
$$

---

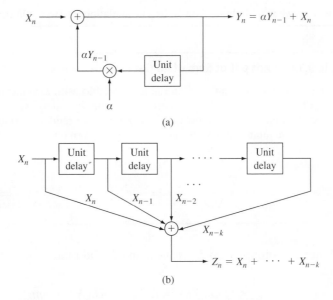

**FIGURE 9.8**
(a) First-order autoregressive process; (b) Moving average process.

The sum process can be generalized in a number of ways. For example, the recursive structure in Fig. 9.6 can be modified as shown in Fig. 9.8(a). We then obtain first-order *autoregressive random processes*, which are of interest in time series analysis and in digital signal processing. If instead we use the structure shown in Fig. 9.8(b), we obtain an example of a *moving average process*. We investigate these processes in Chapter 10.

## 9.4    POISSON AND ASSOCIATED RANDOM PROCESSES

In this section we develop the Poisson random process, which plays an important role in models that involve counting of events and that find application in areas such as queueing systems and reliability analysis. We show how the continuous-time Poisson random process can be obtained as the limit of a discrete-time process. We also introduce several random processes that are derived from the Poisson process.

### 9.4.1    Poisson Process

Consider a situation in which events occur at random instants of time at an average rate of $\lambda$ events per second. For example, an event could represent the arrival of a customer to a service station or the breakdown of a component in some system. Let $N(t)$ be the number of event occurrences in the time interval $[0, t]$. $N(t)$ is then a nondecreasing, integer-valued, continuous-time random process as shown in Fig. 9.9.

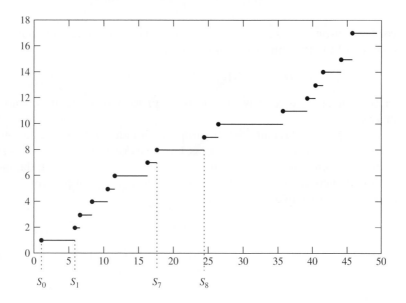

**FIGURE 9.9**

A sample path of the Poisson counting process. The event occurrence times are denoted by $S_1, S_2, \ldots$. The $j$th interevent time is denoted by $X_j = S_j - S_{j-1}$.

Suppose that the interval $[0, t]$ is divided into $n$ subintervals of very short duration $\delta = t/n$. Assume that the following two conditions hold:

1. The probability of more than one event occurrence in a subinterval is negligible compared to the probability of observing one or zero events.
2. Whether or not an event occurs in a subinterval is independent of the outcomes in other subintervals.

The first assumption implies that the outcome in each subinterval can be viewed as a Bernoulli trial. The second assumption implies that these Bernoulli trials are independent. The two assumptions together imply that the counting process $N(t)$ *can be approximated by the binomial counting process* discussed in the previous section.

If the probability of an event occurrence in each subinterval is $p$, then the expected number of event occurrences in the interval $[0, t]$ is $np$. Since events occur at a rate of $\lambda$ events per second, the average number of events in the interval $[0, t]$ is $\lambda t$. Thus we must have that

$$\lambda t = np.$$

If we now let $n \rightarrow \infty$ (i.e., $\delta = t/n \rightarrow 0$) and $p \rightarrow 0$ while $np = \lambda t$ remains fixed, then from Eq. (3.40) the binomial distribution approaches a Poisson distribution with parameter $\lambda t$. We therefore conclude that the number of event occurrences $N(t)$ in the interval $[0, t]$ has a Poisson distribution with mean $\lambda t$:

$$P[N(t) = k] = \frac{(\lambda t)^k}{k!}e^{-\lambda t} \qquad \text{for } k = 0, 1, \ldots . \qquad (9.34a)$$

For this reason $N(t)$ is called the **Poisson process**. The mean function and the variance function of the Poisson process are given by:

$$m_N(t) = E[N(t) = k] = \lambda t \quad \text{and} \quad \text{VAR}[N(t)] = \lambda t. \qquad (9.34b)$$

In Section 11.3 we rederive the Poisson process using results from Markov chain theory.

The process $N(t)$ inherits the property of independent and stationary increments from the underlying binomial process. First, *the distribution for the number of event occurrences in any interval of length t is given by Eq. (9.34a)*. Next, the independent and stationary increments property allows us to write the joint pmf for $N(t)$ at any number of points. For example, for $t_1 < t_2$,

$$
\begin{aligned}
P[N(t_1) = i, N(t_2) = j] &= P[N(t_1) = i]P[N(t_2) - N(t_1) = j - i] \\
&= P[N(t_1) = i]P[N(t_2 - t_1) = j - i] \\
&= \frac{(\lambda t_1)^i e^{-\lambda t_1}}{i!} \frac{(\lambda(t_2 - t_1))^j e^{-\lambda(t_2 - t_1)}}{(j - i)!} .
\end{aligned}
\qquad (9.35a)
$$

The independent increments property also allows us to calculate the autocovariance of $N(t)$. For $t_1 \leq t_2$:

$$C_N(t_1, t_2) = E[(N(t_1) - \lambda t_1)(N(t_2) - \lambda t_2)]$$
$$= E[(N(t_1) - \lambda t_1)\{N(t_2) - N(t_1) - \lambda t_2 + \lambda t_1 + (N(t_1) - \lambda t_1)\}]$$
$$= E[(N(t_1) - \lambda t_1)]E[(N(t_2) - N(t_1) - \lambda(t_2 - t_1)] + \text{VAR}[N(t_1)]$$
$$= \text{VAR}[N(t_1)] = \lambda t_1. \tag{9.35b}$$

---

### Example 9.21

Inquiries arrive at a recorded message device according to a Poisson process of rate 15 inquiries per minute. Find the probability that in a 1-minute period, 3 inquiries arrive during the first 10 seconds and 2 inquiries arrive during the last 15 seconds.

The arrival rate in seconds is $\lambda = 15/60 = 1/4$ inquiries per second. Writing time in seconds, the probability of interest is

$$P[N(10) = 3 \text{ and } N(60) - N(45) = 2].$$

By applying first the independent increments property, and then the stationary increments property, we obtain

$$P[N(10) = 3 \text{ and } N(60) - N(45) = 2]$$
$$= P[N(10) = 3]P[N(60) - N(45) = 2]$$
$$= P[N(10) = 3]P[N(60 - 45) = 2]$$
$$= \frac{(10/4)^3 e^{-10/4}}{3!} \frac{(15/4)^2 e^{-15/4}}{2!}.$$

---

Consider the time $T$ between event occurrences in a Poisson process. Again suppose that the time interval $[0, t]$ is divided into $n$ subintervals of length $\delta = t/n$. The probability that the interevent time $T$ exceeds $t$ seconds is equivalent to no event occurring in $t$ seconds (or in $n$ Bernoulli trials):

$$P[T > t] = P[\text{no events in } t \text{ seconds}]$$
$$= (1 - p)^n$$
$$= \left(1 - \frac{\lambda t}{n}\right)^n$$
$$\rightarrow e^{-\lambda t} \qquad \text{as } n \rightarrow \infty. \tag{9.36}$$

Equation (9.36) implies that $T$ is an exponential random variable with parameter $\lambda$. Since the times between event occurrences in the underlying binomial process are independent geometric random variables, it follows that the sequence of interevent times in a Poisson process is composed of independent random variables. We therefore conclude that the *interevent times in a Poisson process form an iid sequence of exponential random variables with mean* $1/\lambda$.

Another quantity of interest is the time $S_n$ at which the $n$th event occurs in a Poisson process. Let $T_j$ denote the iid exponential interarrival times, then

$$S_n = T_1 + T_2 + \cdots + T_n.$$

In Example 7.5, we saw that the sum of $n$ iid exponential random variables has an Erlang distribution. Thus the pdf of $S_n$ is an *Erlang random variable*:

$$f_{S_n}(y) = \frac{(\lambda y)^{n-1}}{(n-1)!} \lambda e^{-\lambda y} \qquad \text{for } y \geq 0. \tag{9.37}$$

---

**Example 9.22**

Find the mean and variance of the time until the tenth inquiry in Example 9.20.

The arrival rate is $\lambda = 1/4$ inquiries per second, so the interarrival times are exponential random variables with parameter $\lambda$. From Table 4.1, the mean and variance of exponential interarrival times then $1/\lambda$ and $1/\lambda^2$, respectively. The time of the tenth arrival is the sum of ten such iid random variables, thus

$$E[S_{10}] = 10E[T] = \frac{10}{\lambda} = 40 \text{ sec}$$

$$\text{VAR}[S_{10}] = 10 \text{ VAR}[T] = \frac{10}{\lambda^2} = 160 \text{ sec}^2.$$

---

In applications where the Poisson process models customer interarrival times, it is customary to say that arrivals occur "at random." We now explain what is meant by this statement. Suppose that we are *given* that only one arrival occurred in an interval $[0, t]$ and we let $X$ be the arrival time of the single customer. For $0 < x < t$, $N(x)$ is the number of events up to time $x$, and $N(t) - N(x)$ is the increment in the interval $(x, t]$, then:

$$
\begin{aligned}
P[X \leq x] &= P[N(x) = 1 \mid N(t) = 1] \\
&= \frac{P[N(x) = 1 \text{ and } N(t) = 1]}{P[N(t) = 1]} \\
&= \frac{P[N(x) = 1 \text{ and } N(t) - N(x) = 0]}{P[N(t) = 1]} \\
&= \frac{P[N(x) = 1]P[N(t) - N(x) = 0]}{P[N(t) = 1]} \\
&= \frac{\lambda x e^{-\lambda x} e^{-\lambda(t-x)}}{\lambda t e^{-\lambda t}} \\
&= \frac{x}{t}. \tag{9.38}
\end{aligned}
$$

Equation (9.38) implies that given that one arrival has occurred in the interval $[0, t]$, then the customer arrival time is uniformly distributed in the interval $[0, t]$. It is in this sense that customer arrival times occur "at random." It can be shown that *if the number of arrivals in the interval $[0, t]$ is $k$, then the individual arrival times are distributed independently and uniformly in the interval.*

**Example 9.23**

Suppose two customers arrive at a shop during a two-minute period. Find the probability that both customers arrived during the first minute.

The arrival times of the customers are independent and uniformly distributed in the two-minute interval. Each customer arrives during the first minute with probability 1/2. Thus the probability that both arrive during the first minute is $(1/2)^2 = 1/4$. This answer can be verified by showing that $P[N(1) = 2 \,|\, N(2) = 2] = 1/4$.

## 9.4.2    Random Telegraph Signal and Other Processes Derived from the Poisson Process

Many processes are derived from the Poisson process. In this section, we present two examples of such random processes.

### Example 9.24    Random Telegraph Signal

Consider a random process $X(t)$ that assumes the values $\pm 1$. Suppose that $X(0) = +1$ or $-1$ with probability 1/2, and suppose that $X(t)$ changes polarity with each occurrence of an event in a Poisson process of rate $\alpha$. Figure 9.10 shows a sample function of $X(t)$.

The pmf of $X(t)$ is given by

$$P[X(t) = \pm 1] = P[X(t) = \pm 1 \,|\, X(0) = 1]P[X(0) = 1]$$
$$+ P[X(t) = \pm 1 \,|\, X(0) = -1]P[X(0) = -1]. \quad (9.39)$$

The conditional pmf's are found by noting that $X(t)$ will have the same polarity as $X(0)$ only when an even number of events occur in the interval $(0, t]$. Thus

$$P[X(t) = \pm 1 \,|\, X(0) = \pm 1] = P[N(t) = \text{even integer}]$$

$$= \sum_{j=0}^{\infty} \frac{(\alpha t)^{2j}}{(2j)!} e^{-\alpha t}$$

$$= e^{-\alpha t} \frac{1}{2} \{e^{\alpha t} + e^{-\alpha t}\}$$

$$= \frac{1}{2}(1 + e^{-2\alpha t}). \quad (9.40)$$

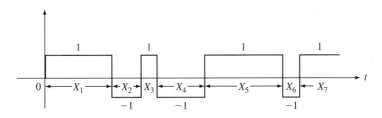

**FIGURE 9.10**

Sample path of a random telegraph signal. The times between transitions $X_j$ are iid exponential random variables.

$X(t)$ and $X(0)$ will differ in sign if the number of events in $t$ is odd:

$$P[X(t) = \pm 1 | X(0) = \mp 1] = \sum_{j=0}^{\infty} \frac{(\alpha t)^{2j+1}}{(2j+1)!} e^{-\alpha t}$$

$$= e^{-\alpha t} \frac{1}{2} \{ e^{\alpha t} - e^{-\alpha t} \}$$

$$= \frac{1}{2}(1 - e^{-2\alpha t}). \tag{9.41}$$

We obtain the pmf for $X(t)$ by substituting into Eq. (9.40):

$$P[X(t) = 1] = \frac{1}{2}\frac{1}{2}\{1 + e^{-2\alpha t}\} + \frac{1}{2}\frac{1}{2}\{1 - e^{-2\alpha t}\} = \frac{1}{2}$$

$$P[X(t) = -1] = 1 - P[X(t) = 1] = \frac{1}{2}. \tag{9.42}$$

Thus the random telegraph signal is equally likely to be $\pm 1$ at any time $t > 0$.

The mean and variance of $X(t)$ are

$$m_X(t) = 1P[X(t) = 1] + (-1)P[X(t) = -1] = 0$$

$$\text{VAR}[X(t)] = E[X(t)^2] = (1^2)P[X(t) = 1] + (-1)^2 P[X(t) = -1] = 1. \tag{9.43}$$

The autocovariance of $X(t)$ is found as follows:

$$C_X(t_1, t_2) = E[X(t_1)X(t_2)]$$

$$= 1P[X(t_1) = X(t_2)] + (-1)P[X(t_1) \neq X(t_2)]$$

$$= \frac{1}{2}\{1 + e^{-2\alpha|t_2 - t_1|}\} - \frac{1}{2}\{1 - e^{-2\alpha|t_2 - t_1|}\}$$

$$= e^{-2\alpha|t_2 - t_1|}. \tag{9.44}$$

Thus time samples of $X(t)$ become less and less correlated as the time between them increases.

---

The Poisson process and the random telegraph processes are examples of the continuous-time Markov chain processes that are discussed in Chapter 11.

---

**Example 9.25 Filtered Poisson Impulse Train**

The Poisson process is zero at $t = 0$ and increases by one unit at the random arrival times $S_j, j = 1, 2, \ldots$. Thus the Poisson process can be expressed as the sum of randomly shifted step functions:

$$N(t) = \sum_{i=1}^{\infty} u(t - S_i) \qquad N(0) = 0,$$

where the $S_i$ are the arrival times.

Since the integral of a delta function $\delta(t - S)$ is a step function $u(t - S)$, we can view $N(t)$ as the result of integrating a train of delta functions that occur at times $S_n$, as shown in Fig. 9.11(a):

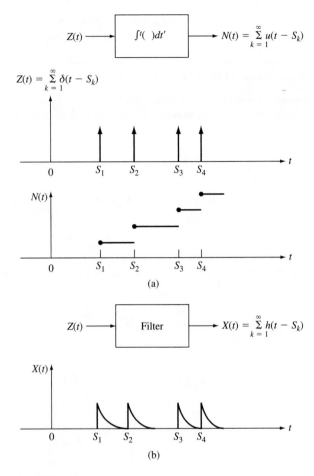

**FIGURE 9.11**
(a) Poisson process as integral of train of delta functions. (b) Filtered train of delta functions.

$$Z(t) = \sum_{i=1}^{\infty} \delta(t - S_i).$$

We can obtain other continuous-time processes by replacing the step function by another function $h(t)$,[1] as shown in Fig. 9.11(b):

$$X(t) = \sum_{i=1}^{\infty} h(t - S_i). \tag{9.45}$$

For example, $h(t)$ could represent the current pulse that results when a photoelectron hits a detector. $X(t)$ is then the total current flowing at time $t$. $X(t)$ is called a **shot noise** process.

---

[1]This is equivalent to passing $Z(t)$ through a linear system whose response to a delta function is $h(t)$.

The following example shows how the properties of the Poisson process can be used to evaluate averages involving the filtered process.

---

**Example 9.26    Mean of Shot Noise Process**

Find the expected value of the shot noise process $X(t)$.

We condition on $N(t)$, the number of impulses that have occurred up to time $t$:

$$E[X(t)] = E[E[X(t)|N(t)]].$$

Suppose $N(t) = k$, then

$$E[X(t)|N(t) = k] = E\left[\sum_{j=1}^{k} h(t - S_j)\right]$$

$$= \sum_{j=1}^{k} E[h(t - S_j)].$$

Since the arrival times, $S_1, \ldots, S_k$, when the impulses occurred are independent, uniformly distributed in the interval $[0, t]$,

$$E[h(t - S_j)] = \int_0^t h(t - s)\frac{ds}{t} = \frac{1}{t}\int_0^t h(u)\, du.$$

Thus

$$E[X(t)|N(t) = k] = \frac{k}{t}\int_0^t h(u)\, du,$$

and

$$E[X(t)|N(t)] = \frac{N(t)}{t}\int_0^t h(u)\, du.$$

Finally, we obtain

$$E[X(t)] = E[E[X(t)|N(t)]]$$

$$= \frac{E[N(t)]}{t}\int_0^t h(u)\, du$$

$$= \lambda \int_0^t h(u)\, du, \qquad (9.46)$$

where we used the fact that $E[N(t)] = \lambda t$. Note that $E[X(t)]$ approaches a constant value as $t$ becomes large if the above integral is finite.

---

## 9.5    GAUSSIAN RANDOM PROCESSES, WIENER PROCESS, AND BROWNIAN MOTION

In this section we continue the introduction of important random processes. First, we introduce the class of Gaussian random processes which find many important applications in electrical engineering. We then develop an example of a Gaussian random process: the Wiener random process which is used to model Brownian motion.

### 9.5.1    Gaussian Random Processes

A random process $X(t)$ is a **Gaussian random process** if the samples $X_1 = X(t_1)$, $X_2 = X(t_2), \ldots, X_k = X(t_k)$ are jointly Gaussian random variables for all $k$, and all choices of $t_1, \ldots, t_k$. This definition applies to both discrete-time and continuous-time processes. Recall from Eq. (6.42) that the joint pdf of jointly Gaussian random variables is determined by the vector of means and by the covariance matrix:

$$f_{X_1, X_2, \ldots, X_k}(x_1, x_2, \ldots, x_k) = \frac{e^{-1/2(\mathbf{x}-\mathbf{m})^{\mathrm{T}} K^{-1}(\mathbf{x}-\mathbf{m})}}{(2\pi)^{k/2}|K|^{1/2}}. \tag{9.47a}$$

In the case of Gaussian random processes, the mean vector and the covariance matrix are the values of the mean function and covariance function at the corresponding time instants:

$$\mathbf{m} = \begin{bmatrix} m_X(t_1) \\ \vdots \\ m_X(t_k) \end{bmatrix} \qquad K = \begin{bmatrix} C_X(t_1, t_1) & C_X(t_1, t_2) & \cdots & C_X(t_1, t_k) \\ C_X(t_2, t_1) & C_X(t_2, t_2) & \cdots & C_X(t_2, t_k) \\ \vdots & \vdots & & \vdots \\ C_X(t_k, t_1) & \cdots & & C_X(t_k, t_k) \end{bmatrix}. \tag{9.47b}$$

*Gaussian random processes therefore have the very special property that their joint pdf's are completely specified by the mean function of the process $m_X(t)$ and by the covariance function $C_X(t_1, t_2)$.* In Chapter 6 we saw that the linear transformations of jointly Gaussian random vectors result in jointly Gaussian random vectors as well. We will see in Chapter 10 that Gaussian random processes also have the property that the linear operations on a Gaussian process (e.g., a sum, derivative, or integral) results in another Gaussian random process. These two properties, combined with the fact that many signal and noise processes are accurately modeled as Gaussian, make Gaussian random processes the most useful model in signal processing.

---

### Example 9.27    iid Discrete-Time Gaussian Random Process

Let the discrete-time random process $X_n$ be a sequence of independent Gaussian random variables with mean $m$ and variance $\sigma^2$. The covariance matrix for the times $n_1, \ldots, n_k$ is

$$\{C_X(n_1, n_2)\} = \{\sigma^2 \delta_{ij}\} = \sigma^2 I,$$

where $\delta_{ij} = 1$ when $i = j$ and 0 otherwise, and $I$ is the identity matrix. Thus the joint pdf for the vector $\mathbf{X}_n = (X_{n_1}, \ldots, X_{n_k})$ is

$$f_{\mathbf{X}_n}(x_1, x_2, \ldots, x_k) = \frac{1}{(2\pi\sigma^2)^{k/2}} \exp\left\{ -\sum_{i=1}^{k} (x_i - m)^2/2\sigma^2 \right\}.$$

The Gaussian iid random process has the property that the value at every time instant is independent of the value at all other time instants.

---

## Example 9.28    Continuous-Time Gaussian Random Process

Let $X(t)$ be a continuous-time Gaussian random process with mean function and covariance function given by:

$$m_X(t) = 3t \qquad C_X(t_1, t_2) = 9e^{-2|t_1 - t_2|}.$$

Find $P[X(3) < 6]$ and $P[X(1) + X(2) > 2]$.

The sample $X(3)$ has a Gaussian pdf with mean $m_X(3) = 3(3) = 9$ and variance $\sigma_X^2(3) = C_X(3, 3) = 9e^{-2|3-3|} = 9$. To calculate $P[X(3) < 6]$ we put $X(3)$ in standard form:

$$P[X(3) < 6] = P\left[\frac{X(3) - 9}{\sqrt{9}} < \frac{6 - 9}{\sqrt{9}}\right] = 1 - Q(-1) = Q(1) = 0.16.$$

From Example 6.24 we know that the sum of two Gaussian random variables is also a Gaussian random variable with mean and variance given by Eq. (6.47). Therefore the mean and variance of $X(1) + X(2)$ are given by:

$$E[X(1) + X(2)] = m_X(1) + m_X(2) = 3 + 6 = 9$$

$$\begin{aligned}
\text{VAR}[X(1) + X(2)] &= C_X(1, 1) + C_X(1, 2) + C_X(2, 1) + C_X(2, 2) \\
&= 9\{e^{-2|1-1|} + e^{-2|2-1|} + e^{-2|1-2|} + e^{-2|2-2|}\} \\
&= 9\{2 + 2e^{-2}\} = 20.43.
\end{aligned}$$

To calculate $P[X(1) + X(2) > 2]$ we put $X(1) + X(2)$ in standard form:

$$P[X(1) + X(2) > 15] = P\left[\frac{X(1) + X(2) - 9}{\sqrt{20.43}} > \frac{15 - 9}{\sqrt{20.43}}\right] = Q(1.327) = 0.0922.$$

### 9.5.2    Wiener Process and Brownian Motion

We now construct a continuous-time Gaussian random process as a limit of a discrete-time process. Suppose that the symmetric random walk process (i.e., $p = 1/2$) of Example 9.16 takes steps of magnitude $\pm h$ every $\delta$ seconds. We obtain a continuous-time process by letting $X_\delta(t)$ be the accumulated sum of the random step process up to time $t$. $X_\delta(t)$ is a staircase function of time that takes jumps of $\pm h$ every $\delta$ seconds. At time $t$, the process will have taken $n = [t/\delta]$ jumps, so it is equal to

$$X_\delta(t) = h(D_1 + D_2 + \cdots + D_{[t/\delta]}) = hS_n. \tag{9.48}$$

The mean and variance of $X_\delta(t)$ are

$$E[X_\delta(t)] = hE[S_n] = 0$$

$$\text{VAR}[X_\delta(t)] = h^2 n \, \text{VAR}[D_n] = h^2 n,$$

where we used the fact that $\text{VAR}[D_n] = 4p(1 - p) = 1$ since $p = 1/2$.

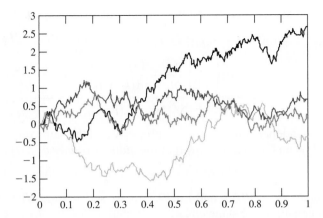

**FIGURE 9.12**
Four sample functions of the Wiener process.

Suppose that we take a limit where we simultaneously shrink the size of the jumps and the time between jumps. In particular let $\delta \to 0$ and $h \to 0$ with $h = \sqrt{\alpha\delta}$ and let $X(t)$ denote the resulting process.

$X(t)$ then has *mean* and *variance* given by

$$E[X(t)] = 0 \tag{9.49a}$$

$$\text{VAR}[X(t)] = (\sqrt{\alpha\delta})^2(t/\delta) = \alpha t. \tag{9.49b}$$

Thus we obtain a continuous-time process $X(t)$ that begins at the origin, has zero mean for all time, but has a variance that increases linearly with time. Figure 9.12 shows four sample functions of the process. Note the similarities in fluctuations to the realizations of a symmetric random walk in Fig. 9.7(b). $X(t)$ is called the **Wiener random process**. It is used to model *Brownian motion*, the motion of particles suspended in a fluid that move under the rapid and random impact of neighboring particles.

As $\delta \to 0$, Eq. (9.48) implies that $X(t)$ approaches the sum of an infinite number of random variables since $n = \lceil t/\delta \rceil \to \infty$:

$$X(t) = \lim_{\delta \to 0} hS_n = \lim_{n \to \infty} \sqrt{\alpha t}\,\frac{S_n}{\sqrt{n}}. \tag{9.50}$$

By the central limit theorem the pdf of $X(t)$ therefore approaches that of a Gaussian random variable with mean zero and variance $\alpha t$:

$$f_{X(t)}(x) = \frac{1}{\sqrt{2\pi\alpha t}}e^{-x^2/2\alpha t}. \tag{9.51}$$

$X(t)$ inherits the property of independent and stationary increments from the random walk process from which it is derived. As a result, the *joint pdf of X(t)* at several times $t_1, t_2, \ldots, t_k$ can be obtained by using Eq. (9.30):

$$f_{X(t_1), \ldots, X(t_k)}(x_1, \ldots, x_k) = f_{X(t_1)}(x_1) f_{X(t_2-t_1)}(x_2 - x_1) \ldots f_{X(t_k-t_{k-1})}(x_k - x_{k-1})$$

$$= \frac{\exp\left\{-\frac{1}{2}\left[\frac{x_1^2}{\alpha t_1} + \frac{(x_2 - x_1)^2}{\alpha(t_2 - t_1)} + \cdots + \frac{(x_k - x_{k-1})^2}{\alpha(t_k - t_{k-1})}\right]\right\}}{\sqrt{(2\pi\alpha)^k t_1 (t_2 - t_1) \ldots (t_k - t_{k-1})}}. \tag{9.52}$$

The independent increments property and the same sequence of steps that led to Eq. (9.33) can be used to show that the *autocovariance of X(t)* is given by

$$C_X(t_1, t_2) = \alpha \min(t_1, t_2) = \alpha\, t_1 \text{ for } t_1 < t_2. \tag{9.53}$$

By comparing Eq. (9.53) and Eq. (9.35b), we see that the Wiener process and the Poisson process have the same covariance function despite the fact that the two processes have very different sample functions. This underscores the fact that the mean and autocovariance functions are only partial descriptions of a random process.

---

**Example 9.29**

Show that the Wiener process is a Gaussian random process.

Equation (9.52) shows that the random variables $X(t_1), X(t_2) - X(t_1), X(t_3) - X(t_2), \ldots, X(t_k) - X(t_{k-1})$, are independent Gaussian random variables. The random variables $X(t_1), X(t_2), X(t_3), \ldots, X(t_k)$, can be obtained from the $X(t_1)$ and the increments by a linear transformation:

$$X(t_1) = X(t_1)$$

$$X(t_2) = X(t_1) + (X(t_2) - X(t_1))$$

$$X(t_3) = X(t_1) + (X(t_2) - X(t_1)) + (X(t_3) - X(t_2))$$

$$\vdots$$

$$X(t_k) = X(t_1) + (X(t_2) - X(t_1)) + \cdots + (X(t_k) - X(t_{k-1})). \tag{9.54}$$

It then follows (from Eq. 6.45) that $X(t_1), X(t_2), X(t_3), \ldots, X(t_k)$ are jointly Gaussian random variables, and that $X(t)$ is a Gaussian random process.

---

## 9.6 STATIONARY RANDOM PROCESSES

Many random processes have the property that the nature of the randomness in the process does not change with time. An observation of the process in the time interval $(t_0, t_1)$ exhibits the same type of random behavior as an observation in some other time interval $(t_0 + \tau, t_1 + \tau)$. This leads us to postulate that the probabilities of samples of the process do not depend on the instant when we begin taking observations, that is, probabilities involving samples taken at times $t_1, \ldots, t_k$ will not differ from those taken at $t_1 + \tau, \ldots, t_k + \tau$.

---

**Example 9.30 Stationarity and Transience**

An urn has 6 white balls each with the label "0" and 5 white balls with the label "1". The following sequence of experiments is performed: A ball is selected and the number noted; the first time a white ball is selected it is not put back in the urn, but otherwise balls are always put back in the urn.

The random process that results from this sequence of experiments clearly has a transient phase and a stationary phase. The transient phase consists of a string of $n$ consecutive 1's and it ends with the first occurrence of a "0". During the transient phase $P[I_n = 0] = 6/11$, and the mean duration of the transient phase is geometrically distributed with mean 11/6. After the first occurrence of a "0", the process enters a "stationary" phase where the process is a binary equiprobable iid sequence. The statistical behavior of the process does not change once the stationary phase is reached.

---

If we are dealing with random processes that began at $t = -\infty$, then the above condition can be stated precisely as follows. *A discrete-time or continuous-time random process* $X(t)$ *is* **stationary** *if the joint distribution of any set of samples does not depend on the placement of the time origin.* This means that the joint cdf of $X(t_1), X(t_2), \ldots, X(t_k)$ is the same as that of $X(t_1 + \tau), X(t_2 + \tau), \ldots, X(t_k + \tau)$:

$$F_{X(t_1),\ldots,X(t_k)}(x_1,\ldots,x_k) = F_{X(t_1+\tau),\ldots,X(t_k+\tau)}(x_1,\ldots,x_k), \tag{9.55}$$

for all time shifts $\tau$, all $k$, and all choices of sample times $t_1, \ldots, t_k$. If a process begins at some definite time (i.e., $n = 0$ or $t = 0$), then we say it is stationary if its joint distributions do not change under time shifts to the right.

Two processes $X(t)$ and $Y(t)$ are said to be **jointly stationary** if the joint cdf's of $X(t_1), \ldots, X(t_k)$ and $Y(t_1'), \ldots, Y(t_j')$ do not depend on the placement of the time origin for all $k$ and $j$ and all choices of sampling times $t_1, \ldots, t_k$ and $t_1', \ldots, t_j'$.

The *first-order cdf of a stationary random process must be independent of time*, since by Eq. (9.55),

$$F_{X(t)}(x) = F_{X(t+\tau)}(x) = F_X(x) \qquad \text{all } t, \tau. \tag{9.56}$$

This implies that the mean and variance of $X(t)$ are constant and independent of time:

$$m_X(t) = E[X(t)] = m \qquad \text{for all } t \tag{9.57}$$

$$\text{VAR}[X(t)] = E[(X(t) - m)^2] = \sigma^2 \qquad \text{for all } t. \tag{9.58}$$

The *second-order cdf of a stationary random process can depend only on the time difference between the samples* and not on the particular time of the samples, since by Eq. (9.55),

$$F_{X(t_1), X(t_2)}(x_1, x_2) = F_{X(0), X(t_2-t_1)}(x_1, x_2) \qquad \text{for all } t_1, t_2. \tag{9.59}$$

This implies that the autocorrelation and the autocovariance of $X(t)$ can depend only on $t_2 - t_1$:

$$R_X(t_1, t_2) = R_X(t_2 - t_1) \qquad \text{for all } t_1, t_2 \tag{9.60}$$

$$C_X(t_1, t_2) = C_X(t_2 - t_1) \qquad \text{for all } t_1, t_2. \tag{9.61}$$

---

### Example 9.31    iid Random Process

Show that the iid random process is stationary.

The joint cdf for the samples at any $k$ time instants, $t_1, \ldots, t_k$, is

$$F_{X(t_1),\ldots,X(t_k)}(x_1, x_2, \ldots, x_k) = F_X(x_1)F_X(x_2)\ldots F_X(x_k)$$

$$= F_{X(t_1+\tau),\ldots,X(t_k+\tau)}(x_1, \ldots, x_k),$$

for all $k$, $t_1, \ldots, t_k$. Thus Eq. (9.55) is satisfied, and so the iid random process is stationary.

---

### Example 9.32

Is the sum process a discrete-time stationary process?

The sum process is defined by $S_n = X_1 + X_2 + \cdots + X_n$, where the $X_i$ are an iid sequence. The process has mean and variance

$$m_S(n) = nm \qquad \text{VAR}[S_n] = n\sigma^2,$$

where $m$ and $\sigma^2$ are the mean and variance of the $X_n$. It can be seen that the mean and variance are not constant but grow linearly with the time index $n$. Therefore the sum process cannot be a stationary process.

---

### Example 9.33    Random Telegraph Signal

Show that the random telegraph signal discussed in Example 9.24 is a stationary random process when $P[X(0) = \pm 1] = 1/2$. Show that $X(t)$ settles into stationary behavior as $t \to \infty$ even if $P[X(0) = \pm 1] \neq 1/2$.

We need to show that the following two joint pmf's are equal:

$$P[X(t_1) = a_1, \ldots, X(t_k) = a_k] = P[X(t_1 + \tau) = a_1, \ldots, X(t_k + \tau) = a_k],$$

for any $k$, any $t_1 < \cdots < t_k$, and any $a_j = \pm 1$. The independent increments property of the Poisson process implies that

$$P[X(t_1) = a_1, \ldots, X(t_k) = a_k] = P[X(t_1) = a_1]$$
$$\times P[X(t_2) = a_2 \mid X(t_1) = a_1] \ldots P[X(t_k) = a_k \mid X(t_{k-1}) = a_{k-1}],$$

since the values of the random telegraph at the times $t_1, \ldots, t_k$ are determined by the number of occurrences of events of the Poisson process in the time intervals $(t_j, t_{j+1})$. Similarly,

$$P[X(t_1 + \tau) = a_1, \ldots, X(t_k + \tau) = a_k]$$
$$= P[X(t_1 + \tau) = a_1]P[X(t_2 + \tau) = a_2 \mid X(t_1 + \tau) = a_1]\ldots$$
$$\times P[X(t_k + \tau) = a_k \mid X(t_{k-1} + \tau) = a_{k-1}].$$

The corresponding transition probabilities in the previous two equations are equal since

$$P[X(t_{j+1}) = a_{j+1} \mid X(t_j) = a_j] = \begin{cases} \dfrac{1}{2}\{1 + e^{-2\alpha(t_{j+1}-t_j)}\} & \text{if } a_j = a_{j+1} \\[2mm] \dfrac{1}{2}\{1 - e^{-2\alpha(t_{j+1}-t_j)}\} & \text{if } a_j \neq a_{j+1} \end{cases}$$

$$= P[X(t_{j+1} + \tau) = a_{j+1} \mid X(t_j + \tau) = a_j].$$

Thus the two joint probabilities differ only in the first term, namely, $P[X(t_1) = a_1]$ and $P[X(t_1 + \tau) = a_1]$.

From Example 9.24 we know that if $P[X(0) = \pm 1] = 1/2$ then $P[X(t) = \pm 1] = 1/2$, for all $t$. Thus $P[X(t_1) = a_1] = 1/2$, $P[X(t_1 + \tau) = a_1] = 1/2$, and

$$P[X(t_1) = a_1, \ldots, X(t_k) = a_k] = P[X(t_1 + \tau) = a_1, \ldots, X(t_k + \tau) = a_k].$$

Thus we conclude that the process is stationary when $P[X(0) = \pm 1] = 1/2$.

If $P[X(0) = \pm 1] \neq 1/2$, then the two joint pmf's are not equal because $P[X(t_1) = a_1] \neq P[X(t_1 + \tau) = a_1]$. Let's see what happens if we know that the process started at a specific value, say $X(0) = 1$, that is, $P[X(0) = 1] = 1$. The pmf for $X(t)$ is obtained from Eqs. (9.39) through (9.41):

$$P[X(t) = a] = P[X(t) = a \,|\, X(0) = 1]1$$

$$= \begin{cases} \dfrac{1}{2}\{1 + e^{-2\alpha t}\} & \text{if } a = 1 \\[2mm] \dfrac{1}{2}\{1 - e^{-2\alpha t}\} & \text{if } a = -1. \end{cases}$$

For very small $t$, the probability that $X(t) = 1$ is close to 1; but as $t$ increases, the probability that $X(t) = 1$ becomes 1/2. Therefore as $t_1$ becomes large, $P[X(t_1) = a_1] \rightarrow 1/2$ and $P[X(t_1 + \tau) = a_1] \rightarrow 1/2$ and the two joint pmf's become equal. In other words, the process "forgets" the initial condition and settles down into "steady state," that is, stationary behavior.

---

### 9.6.1    Wide-Sense Stationary Random Processes

In many situations we cannot determine whether a random process is stationary, but we can determine whether the mean is a constant:

$$m_X(t) = m \qquad \text{for all } t, \tag{9.62}$$

and whether the autocovariance (or equivalently the autocorrelation) is a function of $t_1 - t_2$ only:

$$C_X(t_1, t_2) = C_X(t_1 - t_2) \qquad \text{for all } t_1, t_2. \tag{9.63}$$

*A discrete-time or continuous-time random process $X(t)$ is **wide-sense stationary** (WSS) if it satisfies Eqs. (9.62) and (9.63).* Similarly, we say that the processes $X(t)$ and $Y(t)$ are **jointly wide-sense stationary** if they are both wide-sense stationary and if their cross-covariance depends only on $t_1 - t_2$. When $X(t)$ is wide-sense stationary, we write

$$C_X(t_1, t_2) = C_X(\tau) \qquad \text{and} \qquad R_X(t_1, t_2) = R_X(\tau),$$

where $\tau = t_1 - t_2$.

*All stationary random processes are wide-sense stationary* since they satisfy Eqs. (9.62) and (9.63). The following example shows that some wide-sense stationary processes are not stationary.

---

### Example 9.34

Let $X_n$ consist of two interleaved sequences of independent random variables. For $n$ even, $X_n$ assumes the values $\pm 1$ with probability 1/2; for $n$ odd, $X_n$ assumes the values 1/3 and $-3$ with probabilities 9/10 and 1/10, respectively. $X_n$ is not stationary since its pmf varies with $n$. It is easy to show that $X_n$ has mean

$$m_X(n) = 0 \qquad \text{for all } n$$

and covariance function

$$C_X(i,j) = \begin{cases} E[X_i]E[X_j] = 0 & \text{for } i \neq j \\ E[X_i^2] = 1 & \text{for } i = j. \end{cases}$$

$X_n$ is therefore wide-sense stationary.

---

We will see in Chapter 10 that the autocorrelation function of wide-sense stationary processes plays a crucial role in the design of linear signal processing algorithms. We now develop several results that enable us to deduce properties of a WSS process from properties of its autocorrelation function.

First, *the autocorrelation function at $\tau = 0$ gives the* **average power** (second moment) of the process:

$$R_X(0) = E[X(t)^2] \qquad \text{for all } t. \tag{9.64}$$

Second, *the autocorrelation function is an even function of $\tau$* since

$$R_X(\tau) = E[X(t+\tau)X(t)] = E[X(t)X(t+\tau)] = R_X(-\tau). \tag{9.65}$$

Third, *the autocorrelation function is a measure of the rate of change of a random process* in the following sense. Consider the change in the process from time $t$ to $t + \tau$:

$$
\begin{aligned}
P[|X(t+\tau) - X(t)| > \varepsilon] &= P[(X(t+\tau) - X(t))^2 > \varepsilon^2] \\
&\leq \frac{E[(X(t+\tau) - X(t))^2]}{\varepsilon^2} \\
&= \frac{2\{R_X(0) - R_X(\tau)\}}{\varepsilon^2}, \tag{9.66}
\end{aligned}
$$

where we used the Markov inequality, Eq. (4.75), to obtain the upper bound. Equation (9.66) states that if $R_X(0) - R_X(\tau)$ is small, that is, $R_X(\tau)$ drops off slowly, then the probability of a large change in $X(t)$ in $\tau$ seconds is small.

Fourth, *the autocorrelation function is maximum at $\tau = 0$.* We use the Cauchy-Schwarz inequality:[2]

$$E[XY]^2 \leq E[X^2]E[Y^2], \tag{9.67}$$

for any two random variables $X$ and $Y$. If we apply this equation to $X(t+\tau)$ and $X(t)$, we obtain

$$R_X(\tau)^2 = E[X(t+\tau)X(t)]^2 \leq E[X^2(t+\tau)]E[X^2(t)] = R_X(0)^2.$$

Thus

$$|R_X(\tau)| \leq R_X(0). \tag{9.68}$$

---

[2]See Problem 5.74 and Appendix C.

Fifth, *if $R_X(0) = R_X(d)$, then $R_X(\tau)$ is periodic with period d and X(t) is* **mean square periodic**, that is, $E[(X(t + d) - X(t))^2] = 0$. If we apply Eq. (9.67) to $X(t + \tau + d) - X(t + \tau)$ and $X(t)$, we obtain

$$E[(X(t + \tau + d) - X(t + \tau))X(t)]^2$$
$$\leq E[(X(t + \tau + d) - X(t + \tau))^2]E[X^2(t)],$$

which implies that

$$\{R_X(\tau + d) - R_X(\tau)\}^2 \leq 2\{R_X(0) - R_X(d)\}R_X(0).$$

Thus $R_X(d) = R_X(0)$ implies that the right-hand side of the equation is zero, and thus that $R_X(\tau + d) = R_X(\tau)$ for all $\tau$. Repeated applications of this result imply that $R_X(\tau)$ is periodic with period $d$. The fact that $X(t)$ is mean square periodic follows from

$$E[(X(t + d) - X(t))^2] = 2\{R_X(0) - R_X(d)\} = 0.$$

Sixth, let $X(t) = m + N(t)$, where $N(t)$ is a zero-mean process for which $R_N(\tau) \rightarrow 0$ as $\tau \rightarrow \infty$, then

$$R_X(\tau) = E[(m + N(t + \tau))(m + N(t))] = m^2 + 2mE[N(t)] + R_N(\tau)$$
$$= m^2 + R_N(\tau) \rightarrow m^2 \quad \text{as } \tau \rightarrow \infty.$$

In other words, *$R_X(\tau)$ approaches the square of the mean of X(t) as $\tau \rightarrow \infty$.*

In summary, the autocorrelation function can have three types of components: (1) a component that approaches zero as $\tau \rightarrow \infty$; (2) a periodic component; and (3) a component due to a nonzero mean.

---

**Example 9.35**

Figure 9.13 shows several typical autocorrelation functions. Figure 9.13(a) shows the autocorrelation function for the random telegraph signal $X(t)$ (see Eq. (9.44)):

$$R_X(\tau) = e^{-2\alpha|\tau|} \quad \text{for all } \tau.$$

$X(t)$ is zero mean and $R_X(\tau) \rightarrow 0$ as $|\tau| \rightarrow \infty$.

Figure 9.13(b) shows the autocorrelation function for a sinusoid $Y(t)$ with amplitude $a$ and random phase (see Example 9.10):

$$R_Y(\tau) = \frac{a^2}{2}\cos(2\pi f_0\tau) \quad \text{for all } \tau.$$

$Y(t)$ is zero mean and $R_Y(\tau)$ is periodic with period $1/f_0$.

Figure 9.13(c) shows the autocorrelation function for the process $Z(t) = X(t) + Y(t) + m$, where $X(t)$ is the random telegraph process, $Y(t)$ is a sinusoid with random phase, and $m$ is a constant. If we assume that $X(t)$ and $Y(t)$ are independent processes, then

$$R_Z(\tau) = E[\{X(t + \tau) + Y(t + \tau) + m\}\{X(t) + Y(t) + m\}]$$
$$= R_X(\tau) + R_Y(\tau) + m^2.$$

---

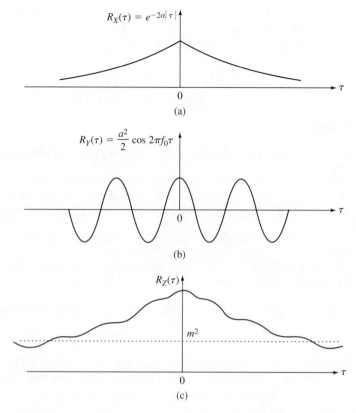

**FIGURE 9.13**
(a) Autocorrelation function of a random telegraph signal. (b) Autocorrelation function of a sinusoid with random phase. (c) Autocorrelation function of a random process that has nonzero mean, a periodic component, and a "random" component.

### 9.6.2 Wide-Sense Stationary Gaussian Random Processes

*If a Gaussian random process is wide-sense stationary, then it is also stationary.* Recall from Section 9.5, Eq. (9.47), that the joint pdf of a Gaussian random process is completely determined by the mean $m_X(t)$ and the autocovariance $C_X(t_1, t_2)$. If $X(t)$ is wide-sense stationary, then its mean is a constant $m$ and its autocovariance depends only on the difference of the sampling times, $t_i - t_j$. It then follows that the joint pdf of $X(t)$ depends only on this set of differences, and hence it is invariant with respect to time shifts. Thus the process is also stationary.

The above result makes WSS Gaussian random processes particularly easy to work with since all the information required to specify the joint pdf is contained in $m$ and $C_X(\tau)$.

---

**Example 9.36 A Gaussian Moving Average Process**

Let $X_n$ be an iid sequence of Gaussian random variables with zero mean and variance $\sigma^2$, and let $Y_n$ be the average of two consecutive values of $X_n$:

$$Y_n = \frac{X_n + X_{n-1}}{2}.$$

The mean of $Y_n$ is zero since $E[X_i] = 0$ for all $i$. The covariance is

$$C_Y(i, j) = E[Y_i Y_j] = \frac{1}{4} E[(X_i + X_{i-1})(X_j + X_{j-1})]$$

$$= \frac{1}{4}\{E[X_i X_j] + E[X_i X_{j-1}] + E[X_{i-1} X_j] + E[X_{i-1} X_{j-1}]\}$$

$$= \begin{cases} \dfrac{1}{2}\sigma^2 & \text{if } i = j \\ \dfrac{1}{4}\sigma^2 & \text{if } |i - j| = 1 \\ 0 & \text{otherwise.} \end{cases}$$

We see that $Y_n$ has a constant mean and a covariance function that depends only on $|i - j|$, thus $Y_n$ is a wide-sense stationary process. $Y_n$ is a Gaussian random variable since it is defined by a linear function of Gaussian random variables (see Section 6.4, Eq. 6.45). Thus the joint pdf of $Y_n$ is given by Eq. (9.47) with zero-mean vector and with entries of the covariance matrix specified by $C_Y(i, j)$ above.

---

### 9.6.3    Cyclostationary Random Processes

Many random processes arise from the repetition of a given procedure every $T$ seconds. For example, a data modulator ("modem") produces a waveform every $T$ seconds according to some input data sequence. In another example, a "time multiplexer" interleaves $n$ separate sequences of information symbols into a single sequence of symbols. It should not be surprising that the periodic nature of such processes is evident in their probabilistic descriptions. A discrete-time or continuous-time random process $X(t)$ is said to be **cyclostationary** if the joint cumulative distribution function of any set of samples is invariant with respect to shifts of the origin by *integer multiples of some period T.* In other words, $X(t_1), X(t_2), \ldots, X(t_k)$ and $X(t_1 + mT), X(t_2 + mT), \ldots, X(t_k + mT)$ have the same joint cdf for all $k, m$, and all choices of sampling times $t_1, \ldots, t_k$:

$$F_{X(t_1), X(t_2), \ldots, X(t_k)}(x_1, x_2, \ldots, x_k)$$
$$= F_{X(t_1+mT), X(t_2+mT), \ldots, X(t_k+mT)}(x_1, x_2, \ldots, x_k). \tag{9.69}$$

We say that $X(t)$ is **wide-sense cyclostationary** if the mean and autocovariance functions are invariant with respect to shifts in the time origin by integer multiples of $T$, that is, for every integer $m$,

$$m_X(t + mT) = m_X(t) \tag{9.70a}$$

$$C_X(t_1 + mT, t_2 + mT) = C_X(t_1, t_2). \tag{9.70b}$$

Note that if $X(t)$ is cyclostationary, then it follows that $X(t)$ is also wide-sense cyclostationary.

**Example 9.37**

Consider a random amplitude sinusoid with period $T$:

$$X(t) = A \cos(2\pi t/T).$$

Is $X(t)$ cyclostationary? wide-sense cyclostationary?
Consider the joint cdf for the time samples $t_1, \ldots, t_k$:

$$
\begin{aligned}
P[X(t_1) &\leq x_1, X(t_2) \leq x_2, \ldots, X(t_k) \leq x_k)] \\
&= P[A \cos(2\pi t_1/T) \leq x_1, \ldots, A \cos(2\pi t_k/T) \leq x_k] \\
&= P[A \cos(2\pi(t_1 + mT)/T) \leq x_1, \ldots, A \cos(2\pi(t_k + mT)/T) \leq x_k] \\
&= P[X(t_1 + mT) \leq x_1, X(t_2 + mT) \leq x_2, \ldots, X(t_k + mT) \leq x_k].
\end{aligned}
$$

Thus $X(t)$ is a cyclostationary random process and hence also a wide-sense cyclostationary process.

In the above example, the sample functions of the random process are always periodic. The following example shows that, in general, the sample functions of a cyclostationary random process need not be periodic.

**Example 9.38   Pulse Amplitude Modulation**

A modem transmits a binary iid equiprobable data sequence as follows: To transmit a binary 1, the modem transmits a rectangular pulse of duration $T$ seconds and amplitude 1; to transmit a binary 0, it transmits a rectangular pulse of duration $T$ seconds and amplitude $-1$. Let $X(t)$ be the random process that results. Is $X(t)$ wide-sense cyclostationary?
Figure 9.14(a) shows a rectangular pulse of duration $T$ seconds, and Fig. 9.14(b) shows the waveform that results for a particular data sequence. Let $A_i$ be the sequence of amplitudes ($\pm 1$)

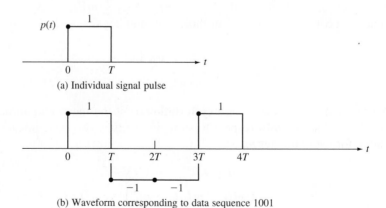

(a) Individual signal pulse

(b) Waveform corresponding to data sequence 1001

**FIGURE 9.14**
Pulse amplitude modulation.

corresponding to the binary sequence, then $X(t)$ can be represented as the sum of amplitude-modulated time-shifted rectangular pulses:

$$X(t) = \sum_{n=-\infty}^{\infty} A_n p(t - nT). \tag{9.71}$$

The mean of $X(t)$ is

$$m_X(t) = E\left[\sum_{n=-\infty}^{\infty} A_n p(t - nT)\right] = \sum_{n=-\infty}^{\infty} E[A_n]p(t - nT) = 0$$

since $E[A_n] = 0$. The autocovariance function is

$$C_X(t_1, t_2) = E[X(t_1)X(t_2)] - 0$$

$$= \begin{cases} E[X(t_1)^2] = 1 & \text{if } nT \le t_1, t_2 < (n+1)T \\ E[X(t_1)]E[X(t_2)] = 0 & \text{otherwise.} \end{cases}$$

Figure 9.15 shows the autocovariance function in terms of $t_1$ and $t_2$. It is clear that $C_X(t_1 + mT, t_2 + mT) = C_X(t_1, t_2)$ for all integers $m$. Therefore the process is wide-sense cyclostationary.

---

We will now show how a stationary random process can be obtained from a cyclostationary process. Let $X(t)$ be a cyclostationary process with period $T$. We "stationarize" $X(t)$ by observing a randomly phase-shifted version of $X(t)$:

$$X_s(t) = X(t + \Theta) \qquad \Theta \text{ uniform in } [0, T], \tag{9.72}$$

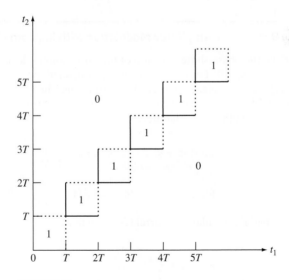

**FIGURE 9.15**
Autocovariance function of pulse amplitude-modulated random process.

where $\Theta$ is independent of $X(t)$. $X_s(t)$ can arise when the phase of $X(t)$ is either unknown or not of interest. *If $X(t)$ is a cyclostationary random process, then $X_s(t)$ is a stationary random process.* To show this, we first use conditional expectation to find the joint cdf of $X_s(t)$:

$$P[X_s(t_1) \leq x_1, X_s(t_2) \leq x_2, \ldots, X_s(t_k) \leq x_k]$$

$$= P[X(t_1 + \Theta) \leq x_1, X(t_2 + \Theta) \leq x_2, \ldots, X(t_k + \Theta) \leq x_k]$$

$$= \int_0^T P[X(t_1 + \Theta) \leq x_1, \ldots, X(t_k + \Theta) \leq x_k | \Theta = \theta] f_\Theta(\theta) \, d\theta$$

$$= \frac{1}{T} \int_0^T P[X(t_1 + \theta) \leq x_1, \ldots, X(t_k + \theta) \leq x_k] \, d\theta. \tag{9.73}$$

Equation (9.73) shows that the joint cdf of $X_s(t)$ is obtained by integrating the joint cdf of $X(t)$ over one time period. It is easy to then show that a time-shifted version of $X_s(t)$, say $X_s(t_1 + \tau), X_s(t_2 + \tau), \ldots, X_s(t_k + \tau)$, will have the same joint cdf as $X_s(t_1)$, $X_s(t_2), \ldots, X_s(t_k)$ (see Problem 9.80). Therefore $X_s(t)$ is a stationary random process.

By using conditional expectation (see Problem 9.81), it is easy to show that *if $X(t)$ is a wide-sense cyclostationary random process, then $X_s(t)$ is a wide-sense stationary random process*, with mean and autocorrelation given by

$$E[X_s(t)] = \frac{1}{T} \int_0^T m_X(t) \, dt \tag{9.74a}$$

$$R_{X_s}(\tau) = \frac{1}{T} \int_0^T R_X(t + \tau, t) \, dt. \tag{9.74b}$$

---

**Example 9.39    Pulse Amplitude Modulation with Random Phase Shift**

Let $X_s(t)$ be the phase-shifted version of the pulse amplitude–modulated waveform $X(t)$ introduced in Example 9.38. Find the mean and autocorrelation function of $X_s(t)$.

$X_s(t)$ has zero mean since $X(t)$ is zero-mean. The autocorrelation of $X_s(t)$ is obtained from Eq. (9.74b). From Fig. 9.15, we can see that for $0 < t + \tau < T, R_X(t + \tau, t) = 1$ and $R_X(t + \tau, t) = 0$ otherwise. Therefore:

$$\text{for } 0 < \tau < T: \quad R_{X_s}(\tau) = \frac{1}{T} \int_0^{T-\tau} dt = \frac{T - \tau}{T};$$

$$\text{for } -T < \tau < 0: \quad R_{X_s}(\tau) = \frac{1}{T} \int_{-\tau}^T dt = \frac{T + \tau}{T}.$$

Thus $X_s(t)$ has a triangular autocorrelation function:

$$R_{X_s}(\tau) = \begin{cases} 1 - \dfrac{|\tau|}{T} & |\tau| \leq T \\ 0 & |\tau| > T. \end{cases}$$

---

## 9.7   CONTINUITY, DERIVATIVES, AND INTEGRALS OF RANDOM PROCESSES

Many of the systems encountered in electrical engineering have dynamics that are described by linear differential equations. When the input signals to these systems are deterministic, the solutions of the differential equations give the output signals of the systems. In developing these solutions we make use of the results of calculus for deterministic functions. Since each sample function of a random process can be viewed as a deterministic signal, it is only natural to apply continuous-time random processes as input signals to the above systems. The output of the systems then consists of a sample function of another random process. On the other hand, if we view a system as acting on an input random process to produce an output random process, we find that we need to develop a new "calculus" for continuous-time random processes. In particular we need to develop probabilistic methods for addressing the continuity, differentiability, and integrability of random processes, that is, of the ensemble of sample functions as a whole. In this section we develop these concepts.

### 9.7.1   Mean Square Continuity

A natural way of viewing a random process is to imagine that each point $\zeta$ in $S$ produces a particular deterministic sample function $X(t, \zeta)$. The standard methods from calculus can be used to determine the continuity of the sample function at a point $t_0$ for each point $\zeta$. Intuitively, we say that $X(t, \zeta)$ is continuous at $t_0$ if the difference $|X(t, \zeta) - X(t_0, \zeta)|$ approaches zero as $t$ approaches $t_0$. More formally, we say that:

> $X(t, \zeta)$ is continuous at $t_0$ if given any $\varepsilon > 0$ there exists a $\delta > 0$ such that $|t - t_0| < \delta$ implies that $|X(t, \zeta) - X(t_0, \zeta)| < \varepsilon$, and we write:
>
> $$\lim_{t \to t_0} X(t, \zeta) = X(t_0, \zeta).$$

In some simple cases, such as the random sinusoid discussed in Example 9.2, we can establish that all sample functions of the random process are continuous at a point $t_0$, and so we can conclude that the random process is continuous at $t_0$. In general, however, we can only address the continuity of a random process in a probabilistic sense. In this section, we concentrate on convergence in the mean square sense, introduced in Section 7.4, because of its tractability and its usefulness in the study of linear systems subject to random inputs.

> **Mean Square Continuity:**   The random process $X(t)$ is continuous at the point $t_0$ *in the mean square sense* if
>
> $$E[(X(t) - X(t_0))^2] \to 0 \qquad \text{as } t \to t_0. \tag{9.75}$$

We denote mean square continuity by (l̲imit i̲n the m̲ean)

$$\operatorname*{l.i.m.}_{t \to t_0} X(t) = X(t_0).$$

We say that $X(t)$ is mean square continuous if it is mean square continuous for all $t_0$. Note that if all sample functions of a random process are continuous at a point $t_0$, then

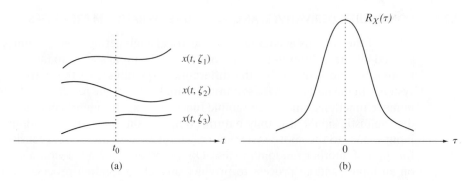

**FIGURE 9.16**
(a) Mean square continuity at $t_0$ does not imply all sample functions are continuous at $t_0$. (b) If $X(t)$ is WSS and $R_X(\tau)$ is continuous at $\tau = 0$, then $X(t)$ is mean square continuous for all $t$.

the process will also be mean square continuous at the point $t_0$. In the examples we will see that mean square continuity does not imply that all the sample functions are continuous. Thus, in general, we may have the situation in Fig. 9.16.

In order to determine what conditions are required for mean square continuity, consider the mean square difference between $X(t)$ and $X(t_0)$:

$$E[(X(t) - X(t_0))^2] = R_X(t, t) - R_X(t_0, t)$$
$$- R_X(t, t_0) + R_X(t_0, t_0). \tag{9.76}$$

Hence, if the autocorrelation function $R_X(t_1, t_2)$ is continuous at the point $(t_0, t_0)$, then letting $t \to t_0$, the right-hand side of Eq. (9.76) will vanish. Thus we conclude that *if $R_X(t_1, t_2)$ is continuous in both $t_1$ and $t_2$ at the point $(t_0, t_0)$, then $X(t)$ is mean square continuous at the point $t_0$.*

At this point it is worth recalling that a function of two variables $f(x, y)$ is continuous at a point $(a, b)$ if the limit $f(x, y)$ reaches the *same* value for *any* mode of approach from $(x, y)$ to $(a, b)$. In particular, in order for $R_X(t_1, t_2)$ to be continuous at $(t_0, t_0)$, $R_X(t_1, t_2)$ must approach the same value as $t_1$ and $t_2$ approach $(t_0, t_0)$ from *any* direction.

A discontinuity in the mean function $m_X(t)$ at some point $t_0$ indicates that the sample functions must be discontinuous at $t_0$ with nonzero probability. Therefore, we must have that *if $X(t)$ is mean square continuous at $t_0$, then the mean function $m_X(t)$ must be continuous at $t_0$*:

$$\lim_{t \to t_0} m_X(t) = m_X(t_0). \tag{9.77a}$$

To show this, we note that the variance of the difference $X(t) - X(t_0)$ is nonnegative, thus

$$0 \le \text{VAR}[X(t) - X(t_0)] = E[(X(t) - X(t_0))^2]$$
$$- E[X(t) - X(t_0)]^2.$$

Therefore

$$E[(X(t) - X(t_0))^2] \geq E[X(t) - X(t_0)]^2 = (m_X(t) - m_X(t_0))^2.$$

If $X(t)$ is mean square continuous at $t_0$, then as $t \to t_0$ the left-hand side of the above equation approaches zero. This implies that the right-hand side approaches zero, and hence $m_X(t) \to m_X(t_0)$. Equation (9.77a) can be rewritten as follows:

$$\lim_{t \to t_0} E[X(t)] = E\left[\underset{t \to t_0}{\text{l.i.m.}}\ X(t)\right]. \tag{9.77b}$$

Therefore if $X(t)$ is mean square continuous at $t_0$, then we can interchange the order of the limit and the expected value.

If the random process $X(t)$ is wide-sense stationary, then Eq. (9.76) becomes

$$E[(X(t_0 + \tau) - X(t_0))^2] = 2(R_X(0) - R_X(\tau)). \tag{9.78}$$

Therefore *if $R_X(\tau)$ is continuous at $\tau = 0$, then the wide-sense stationary random process $X(t)$ is mean square continuous at every point $t_0$.*

---

### Example 9.40    Wiener and Poisson Processes

Are the Wiener and Poisson processes mean square continuous?

The autocorrelation of the Wiener process $X(t)$ is given by

$$R_X(t_1, t_2) = \alpha \min(t_1, t_2).$$

Consider the limit as $t_1$ and $t_2$ approach $(t_0, t_0)$:

$$|R_X(t_0 + \varepsilon_1, t_0 + \varepsilon_2) - R_X(t_0, t_0)|$$
$$= \alpha |\min(t_0 + \varepsilon_1, t_0 + \varepsilon_2) - t_0| \leq \alpha \max(\varepsilon_1, \varepsilon_2).$$

As $\varepsilon_1$ and $\varepsilon_2$ approach zero, the above difference vanishes. Therefore the autocorrelation function is continuous at the point $(t_0, t_0)$, and the Wiener process is mean square continuous.

The autocorrelation of the Poisson process $N(t)$ is given by

$$R_N(t_1, t_2) = \lambda \min(t_1, t_2).$$

This is exactly the same as that of the Wiener process. Therefore the Poisson process is also mean square continuous.

---

The above example shows clearly how mean square continuity does not imply continuity of the sample functions. The Poisson and Wiener processes have the same autocorrelation function and are both mean square continuous. However, the Poisson process has a countably infinite number of discontinuities, while it can be shown that almost all sample functions of the Wiener process are continuous.

---

### Example 9.41    Pulse Amplitude Modulation

Let $X(t)$ be the pulse amplitude modulation random process introduced in Example 9.38. Is $X(t)$ mean square continuous?

The process has discontinuity at $t = mT$ with nonzero probability, so we expect the process not to be mean square continuous. The autocorrelation function of $X(t)$ is shown in Fig. 9.15 and is given by

$$R_X(t_1, t_2) = \begin{cases} 1 & nT \leq t_1 < (n+1)T \text{ and } nT \leq t_2 < (n+1)T \\ 0 & \text{otherwise.} \end{cases}$$

The autocorrelation function is continuous at all points $t_1 = t_0 \neq nT$, and hence $X(t)$ is mean square continuous at all points within the signaling intervals, $nT < t < (n+1)T$. However, the autocorrelation function is not continuous at the points $t_1 = t_0 = nT$, which correspond to the points where the transitions between pulses occur. For example, if we approach the point $(nT, nT)$ along the line $t_1 = t_2$, we obtain the limit 1; if we approach $(nT, nT)$ along a line perpendicular to the above, the limit is zero. Thus $X(t)$ is not mean square continuous at the point $t = nT$.

---

### 9.7.2 Mean Square Derivatives

Suppose we take a sample function of a random process $X(t, \zeta)$ and carry out the limiting procedure that defines the derivative of a deterministic function:

$$\lim_{\varepsilon \to 0} \frac{X(t + \varepsilon, \zeta) - X(t, \zeta)}{\varepsilon}.$$

This limit may exist for some sample functions and it may fail to exist for other sample functions of the same random process. We define the derivative of a random process in terms of mean square convergence:

**Mean Square Derivative:** The random process $X(t)$ has *mean square derivative* $X'(t)$ at $t$ defined by

$$\underset{\varepsilon \to 0}{\text{l.i.m.}} \frac{X(t + \varepsilon) - X(t)}{\varepsilon}, \tag{9.79}$$

provided that the mean square limit exists, that is,

$$\lim_{\varepsilon \to 0} E\left[ \left( \frac{X(t + \varepsilon) - X(t)}{\varepsilon} - X'(t) \right)^2 \right] = 0. \tag{9.80}$$

We also denote the mean square derivative by $dX(t)/dt$. Note that if all sample functions of $X(t)$ are differentiable at the point $t$, then the mean square derivative exists because Eq. (9.80) is satisfied. However, the existence of the mean square derivative does not imply the existence of the derivative for all sample functions.

It can be shown that *the mean square derivative of $X(t)$ at the point $t$ exists if*

$$\frac{\partial^2}{\partial t_1 \partial t_2} R_X(t_1, t_2)$$

*exists at the point* $(t_1, t_2) = (t, t)$. We examine the special case where $X(t)$ is WSS. Consider the mean square value of the first difference in $X(t)$:

$$E\left[\left(\frac{X(t+h) - X(t)}{h}\right)^2\right] = \frac{1}{h^2}(R_X(0) - R_X(h) - R_X(-h) + R_X(0))$$

$$= -\frac{1}{h}\left\{\frac{R_X(h) - R_X(0)}{h} - \frac{R_X(0) - R_X(-h)}{h}\right\}$$

$$\rightarrow )-\frac{d^2}{d\tau^2}R_X(\tau)\bigg|_{\tau=0}. \tag{9.81}$$

Therefore *the mean square derivative of a WSS random process $X(t)$ exists for all $t$ if $R_X(\tau)$ has derivatives up to order two at $\tau = 0$.*

If $X(t)$ is a Gaussian random process for which the mean square derivative $X'(t)$ exists, then $X'(t)$ must also be a Gaussian random process. To show this, consider $Y_\varepsilon(t) = (X(t + \varepsilon) - X(t))/\varepsilon$. The $k$ time samples $Y_\varepsilon(t_1), Y_\varepsilon(t_2), \ldots, Y_\varepsilon(t_k)$ are given by a linear transformation of the jointly Gaussian random variables $X(t_1 + \varepsilon)$, $X(t_1), X(t_2 + \varepsilon), X(t_2), \ldots, X(t_k + \varepsilon), X(t_k)$. It then follows that $Y_\varepsilon(t_1), Y_\varepsilon(t_2), \ldots, Y_\varepsilon(t_k)$ are jointly Gaussian random variables and hence that $Y_\varepsilon(t)$ is a Gaussian random process. $X'(t)$, the limit of $Y_\varepsilon(t)$ as $\varepsilon$ approaches zero, is then also a Gaussian random process since (from Section 7.4) mean square convergence implies convergence in distribution.

Once we have determined the existence of the mean square derivative $X'(t)$, we can proceed to find its mean and autocorrelation functions. Using the same reasoning that led to Eq. (9.77b), we can show that we can interchange the order of expectation and mean square differentiation. Therefore

$$E[X'(t)] = E\left[\underset{\varepsilon \to 0}{\text{l.i.m.}} \frac{X(t+\varepsilon) - X(t)}{\varepsilon}\right]$$

$$= \lim_{\varepsilon \to 0} E\left[\frac{X(t+\varepsilon) - X(t)}{\varepsilon}\right]$$

$$= \lim_{\varepsilon \to 0} \frac{m_X(t+\varepsilon) - m_X(t)}{\varepsilon} = \frac{d}{dt}m_X(t). \tag{9.82}$$

Note that if $X(t)$ is a wide-sense stationary process, then $m_X(t) = m$, a constant, and therefore $E[X'(t)] = 0$.

Next we find the cross-correlation between $X(t)$ and $X'(t)$:

$$R_{X,X'}(t_1, t_2) = E\left[X(t_1) \underset{\varepsilon \to 0}{\text{l.i.m.}} \frac{X(t_2+\varepsilon) - X(t_2)}{\varepsilon}\right]$$

$$= \lim_{\varepsilon \to 0} \frac{R_X(t_1, t_2 + \varepsilon) - R_X(t_1, t_2)}{\varepsilon}$$

$$= \frac{\partial}{\partial t_2}R_X(t_1, t_2).$$

Finally, we obtain the autocorrelation of $X'(t)$:

$$R_{X'}(t_1, t_2) = E\left[ \operatorname*{l.i.m.}_{\varepsilon \to 0} \left\{ \frac{X(t_1 + \varepsilon) - X(t_1)}{\varepsilon} \right\} X'(t_2) \right]$$

$$= \lim_{\varepsilon \to 0} \frac{R_{X,X'}(t_1 + \varepsilon, t_2) - R_{X,X'}(t_1, t_2)}{\varepsilon}$$

$$= \frac{\partial}{\partial t_1} R_{X,X'}(t_1, t_2) \qquad = \frac{\partial^2}{\partial t_1\, \partial t_2} R_X(t_1, t_2). \qquad (9.83)$$

If $X(t)$ is a wide-sense stationary process, we have

$$R_{X,X'}(\tau) = \frac{\partial}{\partial t_2} R_X(t_1 - t_2) = -\frac{d}{d\tau} R_X(\tau), \qquad (9.84)$$

where $\tau = t_1 - t_2$, and then

$$R_{X'}(\tau) = \frac{\partial}{\partial t_1} \left\{ \frac{\partial}{\partial t_2} R_X(t_1 - t_2) \right\} = \frac{\partial}{\partial t_1} - \frac{d}{d\tau} R_X(t_1 - t_2)$$

$$= -\frac{d^2}{d\tau^2} R_X(\tau). \qquad (9.85)$$

---

### Example 9.42

Let $X(t)$ be the random amplitude sinusoid introduced in Example 9.9. Does $X(t)$ have a mean square derivative?

The autocorrelation function for $X(t)$ is

$$R_X(t_1, t_2) = E[A^2] \cos 2\pi t_1 \cos 2\pi t_2.$$

The second mixed partial derivative with respect to $t_1$ and $t_2$ exists at every point $(t, t)$, and is given by

$$\frac{\partial^2}{\partial t_1\, \partial t_2} R_X(t_1, t_2)\big|_{t_1 = t_2 = t} = 4\pi^2 E[A^2] \sin^2 2\pi t.$$

Therefore $X(t)$ has a mean square derivative at every point $t$.

---

### Example 9.43    Wiener Process and White Gaussian Noise

Does the Wiener process have a mean square derivative?

Recall that the Wiener process is Gaussian, so we expect that its derivative is also Gaussian. We first show that this process does not have a mean square derivative. The Wiener process has autocorrelation function given by

$$R_X(t_1, t_2) = \alpha \min(t_1, t_2) = \begin{cases} \alpha t_2 & t_2 < t_1 \\ \alpha t_1 & t_2 \geq t_1. \end{cases}$$

The first derivative with respect to $t_2$ is

$$\frac{\partial}{\partial t_2} R_X(t_1, t_2) = \begin{cases} \alpha & t_2 < t_1 \\ 0 & t_2 > t_1 \end{cases} = \alpha u(t_1 - t_2).$$

The derivative of a step function does not exist at its point of discontinuity. We therefore conclude that the second mixed partial derivative does not exist at any point $t$, and hence the Wiener process does not have a mean square derivative at any point.

We can generalize the notion of derivative of a random process if we use delta functions. Recall that the delta function is defined so that its integral is a unit step function (see Eq. 4.18). We can therefore interpret the derivative of a unit step function as yielding a delta function. This suggests that the process $X'(t)$ has autocorrelation function given by

$$R_{X'}(t_1, t_2) = \frac{\partial}{\partial t_1} \alpha u(t_1 - t_2) = \alpha \delta(t_1 - t_2). \tag{9.86}$$

The properties of the delta function give the random process $X'(t)$ some unusual properties. First, since the delta function is infinite at $t_1 = t_2$, it follows that the mean square value of $X'(t)$ is infinite, that is, $X'(t)$ has infinite power. Also, since the delta function is zero whenever $t_1 \neq t_2$, it follows that any two distinct time samples, $X'(t_1)$ and $X'(t_2)$, are uncorrelated regardless of how close $t_1$ is to $t_2$. This suggests that $X'(t)$ varies extremely rapidly in time. Recall that the Wiener process was obtained in Section 9.5 as the limit of the random walk process. Thus it is not surprising that the derivative of the process has these properties.

The random process that results from taking the derivative of the Wiener process is called **white Gaussian noise**. It is very useful in modeling broadband noise in communication and radar systems. We discuss it further in the next chapter.

### 9.7.3    Mean Square Integrals

The integral of a continuous-time random process arises naturally when computing time averages. It also arises as the solution to systems described by linear differential equations. In this section, we develop the notion of the integral of a random process in the sense of mean square convergence.

Suppose we are interested in the integral of the random process $X(t)$ over the interval $(t_0, t)$. We partition the interval into $n$ subintervals and form the sum

$$I_n = \sum_{k=1}^{n} X(t_k) \, \Delta_k.$$

We define the integral of $X(t)$ as the mean square limit of the sequence $I_n$ as the width of the subintervals approaches zero. When the limit exists, we denote the limiting random process by

$$Y(t) = \int_{t_0}^{t} X(t') \, dt' = \operatorname*{l.i.m.}_{\Delta_k \to 0} \sum_k X(t_k) \Delta_k. \tag{9.87}$$

The Cauchy criterion provides us with conditions that ensure the existence of the mean square integral in Eq. (9.87):

$$E\left[ \left\{ \sum_j X(t_j) \, \Delta_j - \sum_k X(t_k) \, \Delta_k \right\}^2 \right] \to 0 \qquad \text{as } \Delta_j, \Delta_k \to 0. \tag{9.88}$$

As in the case of the mean square derivative, we obtain three terms when we expand the square inside the expected value. Each of these terms leads to an expression of the form

$$E\left[ \sum_j \sum_k X(t_j) X(t_k) \, \Delta_j \, \Delta_k \right] = \sum_j \sum_k R_X(t_j, t_k) \, \Delta_j \, \Delta_k. \tag{9.89}$$

If the limit of the expression on the right-hand side exists, then it can be shown that the three terms resulting from Eq. (9.88) add to zero. On the other hand, the limit of the right-hand side of Eq. (9.89) approaches a double integral of the autocorrelation function. We have thus shown that *the mean square integral of X(t) exists if the following double integral exists:*

$$\int_{t_0}^{t} \int_{t_0}^{t} R_X(u, v) \, du \, dv. \tag{9.90}$$

It can be shown that if $X(t)$ is a mean square continuous random process, then its integral exists.

If $X(t)$ is a Gaussian random process, then its integral $Y(t)$ is also a Gaussian random process. This follows from the fact that the $I_n$'s are linear combinations of jointly Gaussian random variables.

The mean and autocorrelation function of $Y(t)$ are given by

$$m_Y(t) = E\left[ \int_{t_0}^{t} X(t') \, dt' \right] = \int_{t_0}^{t} E[X(t')] \, dt'$$

$$= \int_{t_0}^{t} m_X(t') \, dt' \tag{9.91}$$

and

$$R_Y(t_1, t_2) = E\left[ \int_{t_0}^{t_1} X(u) \, du \int_{t_0}^{t_2} X(v) \, dv \right]$$

$$= \int_{t_0}^{t_1} \int_{t_0}^{t_2} R_X(u, v) \, du \, dv. \tag{9.92}$$

Finally, we note that if $X(t)$ is wide-sense stationary, then the integrands in Eqs. (9.90) and (9.92) are replaced by $R_X(u - v)$.

---

### Example 9.44    Moving Average of X(t)

Find the mean and variance of $M(t)$, the moving average over half a period of a random amplitude sinusoid $X(t)$ with period $T$:

$$M(t) = \frac{2}{T} \int_{t-T/2}^{t} X(t') \, dt'.$$

The mean of $M(t)$ is given by

$$E[M(t)] = \frac{2}{T} \int_{t-T/2}^{t} E[A] \cos\frac{2\pi t'}{T} \, dt' = E[A]\frac{2}{\pi} \sin\frac{2\pi t}{T}.$$

Its second moment at time $t$ is given by

$$E[M^2(t)] = R_M(t, t) = \frac{4}{T^2} \int_{t-T/2}^{t} \int_{t-T/2}^{t} E[A^2] \times \cos\frac{2\pi u}{T} \cos\frac{2\pi v}{T} \, du \, dv = E[A^2]\frac{4}{\pi^2} \sin^2\frac{2\pi t}{T}.$$

The variance is then

$$\text{VAR}[M(t)] = E[A^2]\frac{4}{\pi^2}\sin^2\frac{2\pi t}{T} - E[A]^2\frac{4}{\pi^2}\sin^2\frac{2\pi t}{T}$$

$$= \text{VAR}[A]\frac{4}{\pi^2}\sin^2\frac{2\pi t}{T}.$$

---

### Example 9.45    Integral of White Gaussian Noise

Let $Z(t)$ be the white Gaussian noise process introduced in Example 9.43. Find the autocorrelation function of $X(t)$, the integral of $Z(t)$ over the interval $(0, t)$.

From Example 9.43, the white Gaussian noise process has autocorrelation function

$$R_Z(t_1, t_2) = \alpha\delta(t_1 - t_2).$$

The autocorrelation function of $X(t)$ is then given by

$$R_X(t_1, t_2) = \int_0^{t_1}\int_0^{t_2} \alpha\delta(w - v)\, dw\, dv = \alpha\int_0^{t_2} u(t_1 - v)\, dv$$

$$= \alpha\int_0^{\min(t_1, t_2)} dv = \alpha\min(t_1, t_2).$$

We thus find that $X(t)$ has the same autocorrelation as the Wiener process. In addition we have that $X(t)$ must be a Gaussian random process since $Z(t)$ is Gaussian. It then follows that $X(t)$ must be the Wiener process because it has the joint pdf given by Eq. (9.52).

---

### 9.7.4    Response of a Linear System to Random Input

We now apply the results developed in this section to develop the solution of a linear system described by a first-order differential equation. The method can be generalized to higher-order equations. In the next chapter we develop transform methods to solve the general problem.

Consider a linear system described by the first-order differential equation:

$$X'(t) + \alpha X(t) = Z(t) \qquad t \geq 0,\, X(0) = 0. \tag{9.93}$$

For example, $X(t)$ may represent the voltage across the capacitor of an RC circuit with current input $Z(t)$. We now show how to obtain $m_X(t)$ and $R_X(t_1, t_2)$. If the input process $Z(t)$ is Gaussian, then the output process will also be Gaussian. Therefore, in the case of Gaussian input processes, we can then characterize the joint pdf of the output process.

We obtain a differential equation for $m_X(t)$ by taking the expected value of Eq. (9.93):

$$E[X'(t)] + E[X(t)] = m'_X(t) + m_X(t) = m_Z(t) \qquad t \geq 0 \qquad (9.94)$$

with initial condition $m_X(0) = E[X(0)] = 0$.

As an intermediate step we next find a differential equation for $R_{Z,X}(t_1, t_2)$. If we multiply Eq. (9.93) by $Z(t_1)$ and take the expected value, we obtain

$$E[Z(t_1)X'(t_2)] + \alpha E[Z(t_1)X(t_2)] = E[Z(t_1)Z(t_2)] \qquad t_2 \geq 0$$

with initial condition $E[Z(t_1)X(0)] = 0$ since $X(0) = 0$. The same derivation that led to the cross-correlation between $X(t)$ and $X'(t)$ (see Eq. 9.83) can be used to show that

$$E[Z(t_1)X'(t_2)] = \frac{\partial}{\partial t_2} R_{Z,X}(t_1, t_2).$$

Thus we obtain the following differential equation:

$$\frac{\partial}{\partial t_2} R_{Z,X}(t_1, t_2) + \alpha R_{Z,X}(t_1, t_2) = R_Z(t_1, t_2) \qquad t_2 \geq 0 \qquad (9.95)$$

with initial condition $R_{Z,X}(t_1, 0) = 0$.

Finally we obtain a differential equation for $R_Z(t_1, t_2)$. Multiply Eq. (9.93) by $X(t_2)$ and take the expected value:

$$E[X'(t_1)X(t_2)] + \alpha E[X(t_1)X(t_2)] = E[Z(t_1)X(t_2)] \qquad t_1 \geq 0$$

with initial condition $E[X(0)X(t_2)] = 0$. This leads to the differential equation

$$\frac{\partial}{\partial t_1} R_X(t_1, t_2) + \alpha R_X(t_1, t_2) = R_{Z,X}(t_1, t_2) \qquad t_1 \geq 0 \qquad (9.96)$$

with initial condition $R_{Z,X}(0, t_2) = 0$. Note that the solution to Eq. (9.95) appears as the forcing function in Eq. (9.96). Thus we conclude that by solving the differential equations in Eqs. (9.94), (9.95), and (9.96) we obtain the mean and autocorrelation function for $X(t)$.

---

### Example 9.46    Ornstein-Uhlenbeck Process

Equation (9.93) with the input given by a zero-mean, white Gaussian noise process is called the *Langevin equation*, after the scientist who formulated it in 1908 to describe the Brownian motion of a free particle. In this formulation $X(t)$ represents the velocity of the particle, so that Eq. (9.93) results from equating the acceleration of the particle $X'(t)$ to the force on the particle due to friction $-\alpha X(t)$ and the force due to random collisions $Z(t)$. We present the solution developed by Uhlenbeck and Ornstein in 1930.

First, we note that since the input process $Z(t)$ is Gaussian, the output process $X(t)$ will also be a Gaussian random process. Next we recall that the first-order differential equation

$$x'(t) + ax(t) = g(t) \qquad t \geq 0, x(0) = 0$$

has solution

$$x(t) = \int_0^t e^{-a(t-\tau)} g(\tau)\, d\tau \qquad t \geq 0.$$

Therefore the solution to Eq. (9.94) is

$$m_X(t) = \int_0^t e^{-\alpha(t-\tau)} m_Z(\tau)\, d\tau = 0.$$

The autocorrelation of the white Gaussian noise process is

$$R_Z(t_1, t_2) = \sigma^2 \delta(t_1 - t_2).$$

Equation (9.95) is also a first-order differential equation, and it has solution

$$R_{Z,X}(t_1, t_2) = \int_0^{t_2} e^{-\alpha(t_2-\tau)} R_Z(t_1, \tau)\, d\tau$$

$$= \int_0^{t_2} e^{-\alpha(t_2-\tau)} \sigma^2 \delta(t_1 - \tau)\, d\tau$$

$$= \begin{cases} 0 & 0 \leq t_2 < t_1 \\ \sigma^2 e^{-\alpha(t_2-t_1)} & t_2 \geq t_1 \end{cases}$$

$$= \sigma^2 e^{-\alpha(t_2-t_1)} u(t_2 - t_1),$$

where $u(x)$ is the unit step function.

The autocorrelation function of the output process $X(t)$ is the solution to the first-order differential equation Eq. (9.96). The solution is given by

$$R_X(t_1, t_2) = \int_0^{t_1} e^{-\alpha(t_1-\tau)} R_{Z,X}(\tau, t_2)\, d\tau$$

$$= \sigma^2 \int_0^{t_1} e^{-\alpha(t_1-\tau)} e^{-\alpha(t_2-\tau)} u(t_2 - \tau)\, d\tau$$

$$= \sigma^2 \int_0^{\min(t_1, t_2)} e^{-\alpha(t_1-\tau)} e^{-\alpha(t_2-\tau)}\, d\tau$$

$$= \frac{\sigma^2}{2\alpha} \left( e^{-\alpha|t_1-t_2|} - e^{-\alpha(t_1+t_2)} \right) \qquad t_1 \geq 0, t_2 \geq 0. \tag{9.97a}$$

A Gaussian random process with this autocorrelation function is called an **Ornstein-Uhlenbeck process**. Thus we conclude that the output process $X(t)$ is an Ornstein-Uhlenbeck process.

If we let $t_1 = t$ and $t_2 = t + \tau$, then as $t$ approaches infinity,

$$R_X(t + \tau, t) \rightarrow \frac{\sigma^2}{2\alpha} e^{-\alpha|\tau|}. \tag{9.97b}$$

This shows that the effect of the zero initial condition dies out as time progresses, and the process becomes wide-sense stationary. Since the process is Gaussian, this also implies that the process becomes strict-sense stationary.

**9.8 TIME AVERAGES OF RANDOM PROCESSES AND ERGODIC THEOREMS**

At some point, the parameters of a random process must be obtained through measurement. The results from Chapter 7 and the statistical methods of Chapter 8 suggest that we repeat the random experiment that gives rise to the random process a large number of times and take the arithmetic average of the quantities of interest. For example, to estimate the mean $m_X(t)$ of a random process $X(t, \zeta)$, we repeat the random experiment and take the following average:

$$\hat{m}_X(t) = \frac{1}{N} \sum_{i=1}^{N} X(t, \zeta_i), \qquad (9.98)$$

where $N$ is the number of repetitions of the experiment, and $X(t, \zeta_i)$ is the realization observed in the $i$th repetition.

In some situations, we are interested in estimating the mean or autocorrelation functions from the **time average** of a single realization, that is,

$$\langle X(t) \rangle_T = \frac{1}{2T} \int_{-T}^{T} X(t, \zeta) \, dt. \qquad (9.99)$$

An **ergodic theorem** states conditions under which a time average converges as the observation interval becomes large. In this section, we are interested in ergodic theorems that state when time averages converge to the ensemble average (expected value).

The strong law of large numbers, presented in Chapter 7, is one of the most important ergodic theorems. It states that if $X_n$ is an iid discrete-time random process with finite mean $E[X_n] = m$, then the time average of the samples converges to the ensemble average with probability one:

$$P\left[ \lim_{n \to \infty} \frac{1}{n} \sum_{i=1}^{n} X_i = m \right] = 1. \qquad (9.100)$$

This result allows us to estimate $m$ by taking the time average of a single realization of the process. We are interested in obtaining results of this type for a larger class of random processes, that is, for non-iid, discrete-time random processes, and for continuous-time random processes.

The following example shows that, in general, time averages do not converge to ensemble averages.

---

**Example 9.47**

Let $X(t) = A$ for all $t$, where $A$ is a zero-mean, unit-variance random variable. Find the limiting value of the time average.

The mean of the process is $m_X(t) = E[X(t)] = E[A] = 0$. However, Eq. (9.99) gives

$$\langle X(t) \rangle_T = \frac{1}{2T} \int_{-T}^{T} A \, dt = A.$$

Thus the time-average mean does not always converge to $m_X(t) = 0$. Note that this process is stationary. Thus this example shows that stationary processes need not be ergodic.

---

Consider the estimate given by Eq. (9.99) for $E[X(t)] = m_X(t)$. The estimate yields a single number, so obviously it only makes sense to consider processes for which $m_X(t) = m$, a constant. We now develop an ergodic theorem for the time average of wide-sense stationary processes.

Let $X(t)$ be a WSS process. The expected value of $\langle X(t) \rangle_T$ is

$$E[\langle X(t) \rangle_T] = E\left[ \frac{1}{2T} \int_{-T}^{T} X(t)\, dt \right] = \frac{1}{2T} \int_{-T}^{T} E[X(t)]\, dt = m. \qquad (9.101)$$

Equation (9.101) states that $\langle X(t) \rangle_T$ is an unbiased estimator for $m$.

Consider the variance of $\langle X(t) \rangle_T$:

$$\text{VAR}[\langle X(t) \rangle_T] = E[(\langle X(t) \rangle_T - m)^2]$$

$$= E\left[ \left\{ \frac{1}{2T} \int_{-T}^{T} (X(t) - m)\, dt \right\} \left\{ \frac{1}{2T} \int_{-T}^{T} (X(t') - m)\, dt' \right\} \right]$$

$$= \frac{1}{4T^2} \int_{-T}^{T} \int_{-T}^{T} E[(X(t) - m)(X(t') - m)]\, dt\, dt'$$

$$= \frac{1}{4T^2} \int_{-T}^{T} \int_{-T}^{T} C_X(t, t')\, dt\, dt'. \qquad (9.102)$$

Since the process $X(t)$ is WSS, Eq. (9.102) becomes

$$\text{VAR}[\langle X(t) \rangle_T] = \frac{1}{4T^2} \int_{-T}^{T} \int_{-T}^{T} C_X(t - t')\, dt\, dt'. \qquad (9.103)$$

Figure 9.17 shows the region of integration for this integral. The integrand is constant along the line $u = t - t'$ for $-2T < u < 2T$, so we can evaluate the integral as the

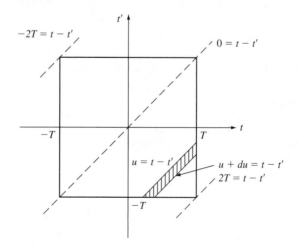

**FIGURE 9.17**
Region of integration for integral in Eq. (9.102).

sums of infinitesimal strips as shown in the figure. It can be shown that each strip has area $(2T - |u|)\,du$, so the contribution of each strip to the integral is $(2T - |u|)C_X(u)\,du$. Thus

$$\text{VAR}[\langle X(t)\rangle_T] = \frac{1}{4T^2}\int_{-2T}^{2T}(2T - |u|)C_X(u)\,du$$

$$= \frac{1}{2T}\int_{-2T}^{2T}\left(1 - \frac{|u|}{2T}\right)C_X(u)\,du. \tag{9.104}$$

Therefore, $\langle X(t)\rangle_T$ will approach $m$ in the mean square sense, that is, $E[(\langle X(t)\rangle_T - m)^2] \to 0$, if the expression in Eq. (9.104) approaches zero with increasing $T$. We have just proved the following ergodic theorem.

### Theorem

Let $X(t)$ be a WSS process with $m_X(t) = m$, then

$$\lim_{T\to\infty}\langle X(t)\rangle_T = m$$

in the mean square sense, if and only if

$$\lim_{T\to\infty}\frac{1}{2T}\int_{-2T}^{2T}\left(1 - \frac{|u|}{2T}\right)C_X(u)\,du = 0.$$

In keeping with engineering usage, we say that a WSS process is **mean ergodic** if it satisfies the conditions of the above theorem.

The above theorem can be used to obtain ergodic theorems for the time average of other quantities. For example, if we replace $X(t)$ with $Y(t + \tau)Y(t)$ in Eq. (9.99), we obtain a time-average estimate for the autocorrelation function of the process $Y(t)$:

$$\langle Y(t + \tau)Y(t)\rangle_T = \frac{1}{2T}\int_{-T}^{T}Y(t + \tau)Y(t)\,dt. \tag{9.105}$$

It is easily shown that $E[\langle Y(t + \tau)Y(t)\rangle_T] = R_Y(\tau)$ if $Y(t)$ is WSS. The above ergodic theorem then implies that the time-average autocorrelation converges to $R_Y(\tau)$ in the mean square sense if the term in Eq. (9.104) with $X(t)$ replaced by $Y(t)Y(t + \tau)$ converges to zero.

---

### Example 9.48

Is the random telegraph process mean ergodic?

The covariance function for the random telegraph process is $C_X(\tau) = e^{-2\alpha|\tau|}$, so the variance of $\langle X(t)\rangle_T$ is

$$\text{VAR}[\langle X(t)\rangle_T] = \frac{2}{2T}\int_0^{2T}\left(1 - \frac{u}{2T}\right)e^{-2\alpha u}\,du$$

$$< \frac{1}{T}\int_0^{2T}e^{-2\alpha u}\,du = \frac{1 - e^{-4\alpha T}}{2\alpha T}.$$

The bound approaches zero as $T \to \infty$, so $\text{VAR}[\langle X(t)\rangle_T] \to 0$. Therefore the process is mean ergodic.

---

If the random process under consideration is discrete-time, then the time-average estimate for the mean and the autocorrelation functions of $X_n$ are given by

$$\langle X_n \rangle_T = \frac{1}{2T + 1} \sum_{n=-T}^{T} X_n \tag{9.106}$$

$$\langle X_{n+k} X_n \rangle_T = \frac{1}{2T + 1} \sum_{n=-T}^{T} X_{n+k} X_n. \tag{9.107}$$

If $X_n$ is a WSS random process, then $E[\langle X_n \rangle_T] = m$, and so $\langle X_n \rangle_T$ is an unbiased estimate for $m$. It is easy to show that the variance of $\langle X_n \rangle_T$ is

$$\text{VAR}[\langle X_n \rangle_T] = \frac{1}{2T + 1} \sum_{k=-2T}^{2T} \left( 1 - \frac{|k|}{2T + 1} \right) C_X(k). \tag{9.108}$$

Therefore, $\langle X_n \rangle_T$ approaches $m$ in the mean square sense and is mean ergodic if the expression in Eq. (9.108) approaches zero with increasing $T$.

---

### Example 9.49    Ergodicity and Exponential Correlation

Let $X_n$ be a wide-sense stationary discrete-time process with mean $m$ and covariance function $C_X(k) = \sigma^2 \rho^{-|k|}$, for $|\rho| < 1$ and $k = 0, \pm 1, +2, \dots$. Show that $X_n$ is mean ergodic.

The variance of the sample mean (Eq. 9.106) is:

$$\text{VAR}[\langle X_n \rangle_T] = \frac{1}{2T + 1} \sum_{k=-2T}^{2T} \left( 1 - \frac{|k|}{2T + 1} \right) \sigma^2 \rho^{|k|}$$

$$< \frac{2}{2T + 1} \sum_{k=0}^{\infty} \sigma^2 \rho^k = \frac{2\sigma^2}{2T + 1} \frac{1}{1 - \rho}.$$

The bound on the right-hand side approaches zero as $T$ increases and so $X_n$ is mean ergodic.

---

### Example 9.50    Ergodicity of Self-Similar Process and Long-Range Dependence

Let $X_n$ be a wide-sense stationary discrete-time process with mean $m$ and covariance function

$$C_X(k) = \frac{\sigma^2}{2} \{|k + 1|^{2H} - 2|k|^{2H} + |k - 1|^{2H}\} \tag{9.109}$$

for $1/2 < H < 1$ and $k = 0, \pm 1, +2, \dots$ $X_n$ is said to be **second-order self-similar**. We will investigate the ergodicity of $X_n$.

We rewrite the variance of the sample mean in (Eq. 9.106) as follows:

$$\text{VAR}[\langle X_n \rangle_T] = \frac{1}{(2T + 1)^2} \sum_{k=-2T}^{2T} (2T + 1 - |k|) C_X(k)$$

$$= \frac{1}{(2T + 1)^2} \{(2T + 1) C_X(0) + (22T C_X(1)) + \dots + 2 C_X(2T)\}.$$

It is easy to show (See Problem 9.132) that the sum inside the braces is $\sigma^2(2T + 1)^{2H}$. Therefore the variance becomes:

$$\text{VAR}[\langle X_n \rangle_T] = \frac{1}{(2T + 1)^2}\sigma^2(2T + 1)^{2H} = \sigma^2(2T + 1)^{2H-2}. \tag{9.110}$$

The value of $H$, which is called the **Hurst parameter**, affects the convergence behavior of the sample mean. Note that if $H = 1/2$, the covariance function becomes $C_X(k) = 1/2\sigma^2\delta_k$ which corresponds to an iid sequence. In this case, the variance becomes $\sigma^2/(2T + 1)$ which is the convergence rate of the sample mean for iid samples. However, for $H > 1/2$, the variance becomes:

$$\text{VAR}[\langle X_n \rangle_T] = \frac{\sigma^2}{2T + 1}(2T + 1)^{2H-1}, \tag{9.111}$$

so the convergence of the sample mean is slower by a factor of $(2T + 1)^{2H-1}$ than for iid samples.

The slower convergence of the sample mean when $H > 1/2$ results from the long-range dependence of $X_n$. It can be shown that for large $k$, the covariance function is approximately given by:

$$C_X(k) = \sigma^2 H(2H - 1)k^{2H-2}. \tag{9.112}$$

For $1/2 < H < 1$, $C(k)$ decays as $1/k^\alpha$ where $0 < \alpha < 1$, which is a very slow decay rate. Thus the dependence between values of $X_n$ decreases slowly and the process is said to have a long memory or long-range dependence.

---

## *9.9    FOURIER SERIES AND KARHUNEN-LOEVE EXPANSION

Let $X(t)$ be a wide-sense stationary, mean square periodic random process with period $T$, that is, $E[(X(t + T) - X(t))^2] = 0$. In order to simplify the development, we assume that $X(t)$ is zero mean. We show that $X(t)$ can be represented in a mean square sense by a **Fourier series**:

$$X(t) = \sum_{k=-\infty}^{\infty} X_k e^{j2\pi kt/T}, \tag{9.113}$$

where the coefficients are random variables defined by

$$X_k = \frac{1}{T}\int_0^T X(t')e^{-j2\pi kt'/T}\,dt'. \tag{9.114}$$

Equation (9.114) implies that, in general, the coefficients are complex-valued random variables. *For complex-valued random variables, the correlation between two random variables X and Y is defined by $E[XY^*]$.* We also show that *the coefficients are orthogonal random variables,* that is, $E[X_k X_m^*] = 0$ for $k \neq m$.

Recall that if $X(t)$ is mean square periodic, then $R_X(\tau)$ is a periodic function in $\tau$ with period $T$. Therefore, it can be expanded in a Fourier series:

$$R_X(\tau) = \sum_{k=-\infty}^{\infty} a_k e^{j2\pi k\tau/T}, \tag{9.115}$$

where the coefficients $a_k$ are given by

$$a_k = \frac{1}{T}\int_0^T R_X(t')e^{-j2\pi kt'/T}\,dt'. \tag{9.116}$$

The coefficients $a_k$ appear in the following derivation.

First, we show that the coefficients in Eq. (9.113) are orthogonal random variables, that is, $E[X_k X_m^*] = 0$:

$$E[X_k X_m^*] = E\left[ X_k \frac{1}{T} \int_0^T X^*(t') e^{j2\pi mt'/T}\, dt' \right]$$

$$= \frac{1}{T} \int_0^T E[X_k X^*(t')] e^{j2\pi mt'/T}\, dt'.$$

The integrand of the above equation has

$$E[X_k X^*(t)] = E\left[ \frac{1}{T} \int_0^T X(u) e^{-j2\pi ku/T}\, du\, X^*(t) \right]$$

$$= \frac{1}{T} \int_0^T R_X(u - t) e^{-j2\pi ku/T}\, du$$

$$= \left\{ \frac{1}{T} \int_{-t}^{T-t} R_X(v) e^{-j2\pi kv/T}\, dv \right\} e^{-j2\pi kt/T}$$

$$= a_k e^{-j2\pi kt/T},$$

where we have used the fact that the Fourier coefficients can be calculated over any full period. Therefore

$$E[X_k X_m^*] = \frac{1}{T} \int_0^T a_k e^{-j2\pi kt'/T} e^{j2\pi mt'/T}\, dt' = a_k \delta_{k,m}, \tag{9.117}$$

where $\delta_{k,m}$ is the Kronecker delta function. Thus $X_k$ and $X_m$ are orthogonal random variables. Note that the above equation implies that $a_k = E[|X_k|^2]$, that is, the $a_k$ are real-valued.

To show that the Fourier series equals $X(t)$ in the mean square sense, we take

$$E\left[ \left| X(t) - \sum_{k=-\infty}^{\infty} X_k e^{j2\pi kt/T} \right|^2 \right]$$

$$= E[|X(t)|^2] - E\left[ X(t) \sum_{k=-\infty}^{\infty} X_k^* e^{-j2\pi kt/T} \right]$$

$$\quad - E\left[ X^*(t) \sum_{k=-\infty}^{\infty} X_k e^{j2\pi kt/T} \right] + E\left[ \sum_{k=-\infty}^{\infty} \sum_{m=-\infty}^{\infty} X_k X_m^* e^{j2\pi(k-m)t/T} \right]$$

$$= R_X(0) - \sum_{k=-\infty}^{\infty} a_k - \sum_{k=-\infty}^{\infty} a_k^* + \sum_{k=-\infty}^{\infty} a_k.$$

The above equation equals zero, since the $a_k$ are real and since $R_X(0) = \Sigma a_k$ from Eq. (9.115).

If $X(t)$ is a wide-sense stationary random process that is *not* mean square periodic, we can still expand $X(t)$ in the Fourier series in an arbitrary interval $[0, T]$. Mean square equality will hold only inside the interval. Outside the interval, the expansion repeats itself with period $T$. The Fourier coefficients will no longer be orthogonal; instead they are given by

$$E[X_k X_m^*] = \frac{1}{T^2} \int_0^T \int_0^T R_X(t - u) e^{-j2\pi kt/T} e^{j2\pi mu/T} \, dt \, du. \qquad (9.118)$$

It is easy to show that if $X(t)$ is mean square periodic, then this equation reduces to Eq. (9.117).

### 9.9.1    Karhunen-Loeve Expansion

In this section we present the **Karhunen-Loeve expansion**, which allows us to expand a (possibly nonstationary) random process $X(t)$ in a series:

$$X(t) = \sum_{k=1}^{\infty} X_k \phi_k(t) \qquad 0 \le t \le T, \qquad (9.119a)$$

where

$$X_k = \int_0^T X(t) \phi_k^*(t) \, dt, \qquad (9.119b)$$

where the equality in Eq. (9.119a) is in the mean square sense, where the coefficients $\{X_k\}$ are orthogonal random variables, and where the functions $\{\phi_k(t)\}$ are orthonormal:

$$\int_0^T \phi_i(t) \phi_j(t) \, dt = \delta_{i,j} \qquad \text{for all } i, j.$$

In other words, *the Karhunen-Loeve expansion provides us with many of the nice properties of the Fourier series for the case where $X(t)$ is not mean square periodic.* For simplicity, we again assume that $X(t)$ is zero mean.

In order to motivate the Karhunen-Loeve expansion, we review the Karhunen-Loeve transform for vector random variables as introduced in Section 6.3. Let **X** be a zero-mean, vector random variable with covariance matrix $K_X$. The eigenvalues and eigenvectors of $K_X$ are obtained from

$$K_X \mathbf{e}_i = \lambda_i \mathbf{e}_i, \qquad (9.120)$$

where the $\mathbf{e}_i$ are column vectors. The set of normalized eigenvectors are orthonormal, that is, $\mathbf{e}_i^T \mathbf{e}_j = \delta_{i,j}$. Define the matrix $P$ of eigenvectors and $\Lambda$ of eigenvalues as

$$P = [\mathbf{e}_1, \mathbf{e}_2, \ldots, \mathbf{e}_n] \qquad \Lambda = \text{diag}[\lambda_i],$$

then

$$K_X = P \Lambda P^T = [\mathbf{e}_1, \mathbf{e}_2, \ldots, \mathbf{e}_n] \begin{bmatrix} \lambda_1 & 0 & \cdots & 0 \\ 0 & \lambda_2 & \cdots & 0 \\ \cdots & \cdots & \cdots & \cdots \\ 0 & 0 & \cdots & \lambda_n \end{bmatrix} \begin{bmatrix} \mathbf{e}_1^T \\ \mathbf{e}_2^T \\ \vdots \\ \mathbf{e}_n^T \end{bmatrix}$$

$$
= [\lambda_1\mathbf{e}_1, \lambda_2\mathbf{e}_2, \ldots, \lambda_n\mathbf{e}_n]
\begin{bmatrix}
\mathbf{e}_1^{\mathrm{T}} \\
\mathbf{e}_2^{\mathrm{T}} \\
\vdots \\
\mathbf{e}_n^{\mathrm{T}}
\end{bmatrix}
$$

$$
= \sum_{k=1}^{n} \lambda_i \mathbf{e}_i \mathbf{e}_i^{\mathrm{T}}. \tag{9.121a}
$$

Therefore we find that the covariance matrix can be expanded as a weighted sum of matrices, $\mathbf{e}_i\mathbf{e}_i^{\mathrm{T}}$. In addition, if we let $\mathbf{Y} = P^{\mathrm{T}}\mathbf{X}$, then the random variables in $\mathbf{Y}$ are orthogonal. Furthermore, since $PP^{\mathrm{T}} = I$, then

$$
\mathbf{X} = P\mathbf{Y} = [\mathbf{e}_1, \mathbf{e}_2, \ldots, \mathbf{e}_n]
\begin{bmatrix}
Y_1 \\
Y_2 \\
\vdots \\
Y_n
\end{bmatrix}
= \sum_{k=1}^{n} Y_k \mathbf{e}_k. \tag{9.121b}
$$

Thus we see that the arbitrary vector random variable $\mathbf{X}$ can be expanded as a weighted sum of the eigenvectors of $K_X$, where the coefficients are orthogonal random variables. Furthermore the eigenvectors form an orthonormal set. These are exactly the properties we seek in the Karhunen-Loeve expansion for $X(t)$. If the vector random variable $\mathbf{X}$ is jointly Gaussian, then the components of $\mathbf{Y}$ are independent random variables. This results in tremendous simplification in a wide variety of problems.

In analogy to Eq. (9.120), we begin by considering the following eigenvalue equation:

$$
\int_0^T K_X(t_1, t_2)\phi_k(t_2)\, dt_2 = \lambda_k\phi_k(t_1) \qquad 0 \le t_1 \le T. \tag{9.122}
$$

The values $\lambda_k$ and the corresponding functions $\phi_k(t)$ for which the above equation holds are called the eigenvalues and eigenfunctions of the covariance function $K_X(t_1, t_2)$. Note that it is possible for the eigenfunctions to be complex-valued, e.g., complex exponentials. It can be shown that if $K_X(t_1, t_2)$ is continuous, then the normalized eigenfunctions form an orthonormal set and satisfy Mercer's theorem:

$$
K_X(t_1, t_2) = \sum_{k=1}^{\infty} \lambda_k\phi_k(t_1)\phi_k^*(t_2). \tag{9.123}
$$

Note the correspondence between Eq. (9.121) and Eq. (9.123). Equation (9.123) in turn implies that

$$
K_X(t, t) = \sum_{k=1}^{\infty} \lambda_k|\phi_k(t)|^2. \tag{9.124}
$$

We are now ready to show that the equality in Eq. (9.119a) holds in the mean square sense and that the coefficients $X_k$ are orthogonal random variables. First consider $E[X_kX_m^*]$:

$$
E[X_kX_m^*] = E\left[X_m^* \int_0^T X(t')\phi_k^*(t)\, dt'\right] = \int_0^T E[X(t')X_m^*]\phi_k^*(t')\, dt'.
$$

The integrand of the above equation has

$$E[X(t)X_m^*] = E\left[X(t)\int_0^T X^*(u)\phi_m(u)\,du\right] = \int_0^T K_X(t,u)\phi_m(u)\,du$$
$$= \lambda_m\phi_m(t).$$

Therefore

$$E[X_kX_m^*] = \int_0^T \lambda_m\phi_k^*(t')\phi_m(t')\,dt' = \lambda_k\delta_{k,m},$$

where $\delta_{k,m}$ is the Kronecker delta function. Thus $X_k$ and $X_m$ are orthogonal random variables. Note that the above equation implies that $\lambda_k = E[|X_k|^2]$, that is, the eigenvalues are real-valued.

To show that the Karhunen-Loeve expansion equals $X(t)$ in the mean square sense, we take

$$E\left[\left|X(t) - \sum_{k=-\infty}^{\infty} X_k\phi_k(t)\right|^2\right]$$

$$= E[|X(t)|^2] - E\left[X(t)\sum_{k=-\infty}^{\infty} X_k^*\phi_k^*(t)\right]$$

$$- E\left[X^*(t)\sum_{k=-\infty}^{\infty} X_k\phi_k(t)\right]$$

$$+ E\left[\sum_{k=-\infty}^{\infty}\sum_{m=-\infty}^{\infty} X_kX_m^*\phi_k(t)\phi_m^*(t)\right]$$

$$= R_X(t,t) - \sum_{k=-\infty}^{\infty} \lambda_k|\phi_k(t)|^2$$

$$- \sum_{k=-\infty}^{\infty} \lambda_k^*|\phi_k(t)|^2 + \sum_{k=-\infty}^{\infty} \lambda_k|\phi_k(t)|^2.$$

The above equation equals zero from Eq. (9.124) and from the fact that the $\lambda_k$ are real. Thus we have shown that Eq. (9.119a) holds in the mean square sense.

Finally, we note that in the important case where $X(t)$ is a Gaussian random process, then the components $X_k$ will be independent Gaussian random variables. This result is extremely useful in solving certain signal detection and estimation problems. [Van Trees.]

---

### Example 9.51 Wiener Process

Find the Karhunen-Loeve expansion for the Wiener process.

Equation (9.122) for the Wiener process gives, for $0 \le t_1 \le T$,

$$\lambda\phi(t_1) = \int_0^T \sigma^2\min(t_1,t_2)\phi(t_2)\,dt_2$$

$$= \sigma^2\int_0^{t_1} t_2\phi(t_2)\,dt_2 + \sigma^2\int_{t_1}^T t_1\phi(t_2)\,dt_2.$$

We differentiate the above integral equation once with respect to $t_1$ to obtain an integral equation and again to obtain a differential equation:

$$\sigma^2 \int_{t_1}^{T} \phi(t_2) \, dt_2 = \lambda \frac{d}{dt_1} \phi(t_1)$$

$$-\phi(t_1) = \frac{\lambda}{\sigma^2} \frac{d^2}{dt_1^2} \phi(t_1).$$

This second-order differential equation has a sinusoidal solution:

$$\phi(t_1) = a \sin \frac{\sigma t_1}{\sqrt{\lambda}} + b \cos \frac{\sigma t_1}{\sqrt{\lambda}}.$$

In order to solve the above equation for $a$, $b$, and $\lambda$, we need boundary conditions for the differential equation. We obtain these by substituting the general solution for $\phi(t)$ into the integral equation:

$$\frac{\lambda}{\sigma^2} \left( a \sin \frac{\sigma t_1}{\sqrt{\lambda}} + b \cos \frac{\sigma t_1}{\sqrt{\lambda}} \right) = \int_0^{t_1} t_2 \phi(t_2) \, dt_2 + \int_{t_1}^{T} t_1 \phi(t_2) \, dt_2.$$

As $t_1$ approaches zero, the right-hand side approaches zero. This implies that $b = 0$ in the left-hand side of the equation. A second boundary condition is obtained by letting $t_1$ approach $T$ in the equation obtained after the first differentiation of the integral equation:

$$0 = \lambda \frac{d}{dt_1} \phi(T) = \frac{\sigma a}{\sqrt{\lambda}} \cos \frac{\sigma T}{\sqrt{\lambda}}.$$

This implies that

$$\frac{\sigma T}{\sqrt{\lambda}} = \left( n - \frac{1}{2} \right) \pi \qquad n = 1, 2, \ldots.$$

Therefore the eigenvalues are given by

$$\lambda_n = \frac{\sigma^2 T^2}{\left( n - \dfrac{1}{2} \right)^2 \pi^2} \qquad n = 1, 2, \ldots.$$

The normalization requirement implies that

$$1 = \int_0^T \left( a \sin \frac{\sigma t}{\sqrt{\lambda}} \right)^2 \, dt = a^2 \frac{T}{2},$$

which implies that $a = (2/T)^{1/2}$. Thus the eigenfunctions are given by

$$\phi_n(t) = \sqrt{\frac{2}{T}} \sin \left( n - \frac{1}{2} \right) \frac{\pi}{T} t \qquad 0 \le t \le T,$$

and the Karhunen-Loeve expansion for the Wiener process is

$$X(t) = \sum_{n-1}^{\infty} X_n \sqrt{\frac{2}{T}} \sin \left( n - \frac{1}{2} \right) \frac{\pi}{T} t \qquad 0 \le t < T,$$

where the $X_n$ are zero-mean, independent Gaussian random variables with variance given by $\lambda_n$.

---

**Example 9.52    White Gaussian Noise Process**

Find the Karhunen-Loeve expansion of the white Gaussian noise process.

The white Gaussian noise process is the derivative of the Wiener process. If we take the derivative of the Karhunen-Loeve expansion of the Wiener process, we obtain

$$X'(t) = \sum_{n=1}^{\infty} \frac{\sigma}{\sqrt{\lambda}} X_n \sqrt{\frac{2}{T}} \cos\left(n - \frac{1}{2}\right)\frac{\pi}{T}t$$

$$= \sum_{n=1}^{\infty} W_n \sqrt{\frac{2}{T}} \cos\left(n - \frac{1}{2}\right)\frac{\pi}{T}t \qquad 0 \le t < T,$$

where the $W_n$ are independent Gaussian random variables with the same variance $\sigma^2$. This implies that the process has infinite power, a fact we had already found about the white Gaussian noise process. In the Problems we will see that any orthonormal set of eigenfunctions can be used in the Karhunen-Loeve expansion for white Gaussian noise.

---

## 9.10    GENERATING RANDOM PROCESSES

Many engineering systems involve random processes that interact in complex ways. It is not always possible to model these systems precisely using analytical methods. In such situations computer simulation methods are used to investigate the system dynamics and to measure the performance parameters of interest. In this section we consider two basic methods to generating random processes. The first approach involves generating the sum process of iid sequences of random variables. We saw that this approach can be used to generate the binomial and random walk processes, and, through limiting procedures, the Wiener and Poisson processes. The second approach involves taking the linear combination of deterministic functions of time where the coefficients are given by random variables. The Fourier series and Karhunen-Loeve expansion use this approach. Real systems, e.g., digital modulation systems, also generate random processes in this manner.

### 9.10.1    Generating Sum Random Processes

The generation of sample functions of the sum random process involves two steps:

1. Generate a sequence of iid random variables that drive the sum process.
2. Generate the cumulative sum of the iid sequence.

Let $D$ be an array of samples of the desired iid random variables. The function cumsum(D) in Octave and MATLAB then provides the cumulative sum, that is, the sum process, that results from the sequence in $D$.

The code below generates $m$ realizations of an $n$-step random walk process.

```
>p=1/2
>n=1000
>m=4
```

```
> V=-1:2:1;
> P=[1-p,p];
> D=discrete_rnd(V, P, m, n);
> X=cumsum (D);
> plot (X)
```

Figures 9.7(a) and 9.7(b) in Section 9.3 show four sample functions of the symmetric random walk process for $p = 1/2$. The sample functions vary over a wide range of positive and negative values. Figure 9.7(c) shows four sample functions for $p = 3/4$. The sample functions now have a strong linear trend consistent with the mean $n(2p - 1)$. The variability about this trend is somewhat less than in the symmetric case since the variance function is now $n4p(1 - p) = 3n/4$.

We can generate an approximation to a Poisson process by summing iid Bernoulli random variables. Figure 9.18(a) shows ten realizations of Poisson processes with $\lambda = 0.4$ arrivals per second. The sample functions for $T = 50$ seconds were generated using a 1000-step binomial process with $p = \lambda T/n = 0.02$. The linear increasing trend of the Poisson process is evident in the figure. Figure 9.18(b) shows the estimate of the mean and variance functions obtained by averaging across the 10 realizations. The linear trend in the sample mean function is very clear; the sample variance function is also linear but is much more variable. The mean and variance functions of the realizations are obtained using the commands mean(transpose(X)) and var(transpose(X)).

We can generate sample functions of the random telegraph signal by taking the Poisson process $N(t)$ and calculating $X(t) = 2(N(t) \text{ modulo } 2) - 1$. Figure 9.19(a) shows a realization of the random telegraph signal. Figure 9.19(b) shows an estimate of the covariance function of the random telegraph signal. The exponential decay in the covariance function can be seen in the figure. See Eq. (9.44).

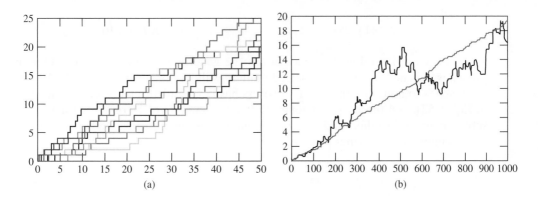

**FIGURE 9.18**
(a) Ten sample functions of a Poisson random process with $\lambda = 0.4$. (b) Sample mean and variance of ten sample functions of a Poisson random process with $\lambda = 0.4$.

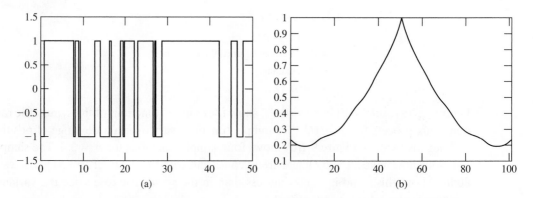

**FIGURE 9.19**
(a) Sample function of a random telegraph process with $\lambda = 0.4$. (b) Estimate of covariance function of a random telegraph process.

The covariance function is computed using the function CX_est below.

```
function [CXall]=CX_est (X, L, M_est)
N=length(X);                          % N is number of samples
CX=zeros (1,L+1);                     % L is maximum lag
M_est=mean(X)                         % Sample mean
for m=1:L+1,                          % Add product terms
   for n=1:N-m+1,
      CX(m)=CX(m) + (X(n) - M_est) * (X(n+m-1)- M_est);
   end;
   CX (m)=CX(m) / (N-m+1);            % Normalize by number of terms
end;
for i=1:L,
   CXall(i)=CX(L+2-i);               % Lags 1 to L
end
CXall(L+1:2*L+1)=CX(1:L+1);           % Lags L + 1 to 2L + 1
```

The Wiener random process can also be generated as a sum process. One approach is to generate a properly scaled random walk process, as in Eq. (9.50). A better approach is to note that the Wiener process has independent Gaussian increments, as in Eq. (9.52), and therefore, to generate the sequence $D$ of increments for the time subintervals, and to then find the corresponding sum process. The code below generates a sample of the Wiener process:

```
> a=2
> delta=0.001
> n=1000
> D=normal_rnd(0,a*delta,1,n)
> X=cumsum(D);
> plot(X)
```

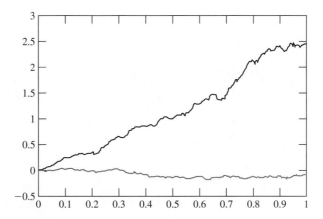

**FIGURE 9.20**
Sample mean and variance functions from 50 realizations of
Wiener process.

Figure 9.12 in Section 9.5 shows four sample functions of a Brownian motion process with $\alpha = 2$. Figure 9.20 shows the sample mean and sample variance of 50 sample functions of the Wiener process with $\alpha = 2$. It can be seen that the mean across the 50 realizations is close to zero which is the actual mean function for the process. The sample variance across the 50 realizations increases steadily and is close to the actual variance function which is $\alpha t = 2t$.

## 9.10.2    Generating Linear Combinations of Deterministic Functions

In some situations a random process can be represented as a linear combination of deterministic functions where the coefficients are random variables. The Fourier series and the Karhunen-Loeve expansions are examples of this type of representation.

In Example 9.51 let the parameters in the Karhunen-Loeve expansion for a Wiener process in the interval $0 \leq t \leq T$ be $T = 1, \sigma^2 = 1$:

$$X(t) = \sum_{n=1}^{\infty} X_n \sqrt{\frac{2}{T}} \sin\left(n - \frac{1}{2}\right)\frac{\pi t}{T} = \sum_{n=1}^{\infty} X_n \sqrt{2} \sin\left(n - \frac{1}{2}\right)\pi t$$

where the $X_n$ are zero-mean, independent Gaussian random variables with variance

$$\lambda_n = \frac{\sigma^2 T^2}{(n - 1/2)^2 \pi^2} = \frac{1}{(n - 1/2)^2 \pi^2}.$$

The following code generates the 100 Gaussian coefficients for the Karhunen-Loeve expansion for the Wiener process.

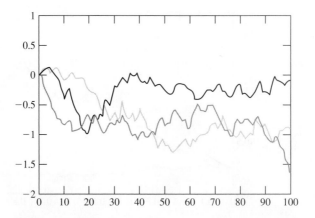

**FIGURE 9.21**
Sample functions for Wiener process using 100 terms in Karhunen-Loeve expansion.

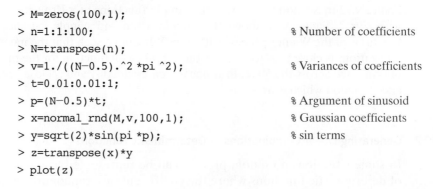

```
> M=zeros(100,1);
> n=1:1:100;                       % Number of coefficients
> N=transpose(n);
> v=1./((N-0.5).^2 *pi ^2);        % Variances of coefficients
> t=0.01:0.01:1;
> p=(N-0.5)*t;                     % Argument of sinusoid
> x=normal_rnd(M,v,100,1);         % Gaussian coefficients
> y=sqrt(2)*sin(pi *p);            % sin terms
> z=transpose(x)*y
> plot(z)
```

Figure 9.21 shows the Karhunen-Loeve expansion for the Wiener process using 100 terms. The sample functions generally exhibit the same type behavior as in the previous figures. The sample functions, however, do not exhibit the jaggedness of the other examples, which are based on the generation of many more random variables.

## SUMMARY

- A random process or stochastic process is an indexed family of random variables that is specified by the set of joint distributions of any number and choice of random variables in the family. The mean, autocovariance, and autocorrelation functions summarize some of the information contained in the joint distributions of pairs of time samples.

- The sum process of an iid sequence has the property of stationary and independent increments, which facilitates the evaluation of the joint pdf/pmf of the process at any set of time instants. The binomial and random processes are sum processes. The Poisson and Wiener processes are obtained as limiting forms of these sum processes.

- The Poisson process has independent, stationary increments that are Poisson distributed. The interarrival times in a Poisson process are iid exponential random variables.

- The mean and covariance functions completely specify all joint distributions of a Gaussian random process.

- The Wiener process has independent, stationary increments that are Gaussian distributed. The Wiener process is a Gaussian random process.

- A random process is stationary if its joint distributions are independent of the choice of time origin. If a random process is stationary, then $m_X(t)$ is constant, and $R_X(t_1, t_2)$ depends only on $t_1 - t_2$.

- A random process is wide-sense stationary (WSS) if its mean is constant and if its autocorrelation and autocovariance depend only on $t_1 - t_2$. A WSS process need not be stationary.

- A wide-sense stationary Gaussian random process is also stationary.

- A random process is cyclostationary if its joint distributions are invariant with respect to shifts of the time origin by integer multiples of some period $T$.

- The white Gaussian noise process results from taking the derivative of the Wiener process.

- The derivative and integral of a random process are defined as limits of random variables. We investigated the existence of these limits in the mean square sense.

- The mean and autocorrelation functions of the output of systems described by a linear differential equation and subject to random process inputs can be obtained by solving a set of differential equations. If the input process is a Gaussian random process, then the output process is also Gaussian.

- Ergodic theorems state when time-average estimates of a parameter of a random process converge to the expected value of the parameter. The decay rate of the covariance function determines the convergence rate of the sample mean.

## CHECKLIST OF IMPORTANT TERMS

| | |
|---|---|
| Autocorrelation function | Ergodic theorem |
| Autocovariance function | Fourier series |
| Average power | Gaussian random process |
| Bernoulli random process | Hurst parameter |
| Binomial counting process | iid random process |
| Continuous-time process | Independent increments |
| Cross-correlation function | Independent random processes |
| Cross-covariance function | Karhunen-Loeve expansion |
| Cyclostationary random process | Markov random process |
| Discrete-time process | Mean ergodic random process |

Mean function

Mean square continuity

Mean square derivative

Mean square integral

Mean square periodic process

Ornstein-Uhlenbeck process

Orthogonal random processes

Poisson process

Random process

Random telegraph signal

Random walk process

Realization, sample path, or sample function

Shot noise

Stationary increments

Stationary random process

Stochastic process

Sum random process

Time average

Uncorrelated random processes

Variance of $X(t)$

White Gaussian noise

Wide-sense cyclostationary process

Wiener process

WSS random process

## ANNOTATED REFERENCES

References [1] through [6] can be consulted for further reading on random processes. Larson and Shubert [ref 7] and Yaglom [ref 8] contain excellent discussions on white Gaussian noise and Brownian motion. Van Trees [ref 9] gives detailed examples on the application of the Karhunen-Loeve expansion. Beran [ref 10] discusses long memory processes.

1. A. Papoulis and S. Pillai, *Probability, Random Variables, and Stochastic Processes*, McGraw-Hill, New York, 2002.
2. W. B. Davenport, *Probability and Random Processes: An Introduction for Applied Scientists and Engineers*, McGraw-Hill, New York, 1970.
3. H. Stark and J. W. Woods, *Probability and Random Processes with Applications to Signal Processing*, 3d ed., Prentice Hall, Upper Saddle River, N.J., 2002.
4. R. M. Gray and L. D. Davisson, *Random Processes: A Mathematical Approach for Engineers*, Prentice Hall, Englewood Cliffs, N.J., 1986.
5. J. A. Gubner, *Probability and Random Processes for Electrical and Computer Engineering*, Cambridge University Press, Cambridge, 2006.
6. G. Grimett and D. Stirzaker, *Probability and Random Processes*, Oxford University Press, Oxford, 2006.
7. H. J. Larson and B. O. Shubert, *Probabilistic Models in Engineering Sciences*, vol. 1, Wiley, New York, 1979.
8. A. M. Yaglom, *Correlation Theory of Stationary and Related Random Functions*, vol. 1: *Basic Results*, Springer-Verlag, New York, 1987.
9. H. L. Van Trees, *Detection, Estimation, and Modulation Theory*, Wiley, New York, 1987.
10. J. Beran, *Statistics for Long-Memory Processes*, Chapman & Hall/CRC, New York, 1994.

## PROBLEMS

### Sections 9.1 and 9.2: Definition and Specification of a Stochastic Process

**9.1.** In Example 9.1, find the joint pmf for $X_1$ and $X_2$. Why are $X_1$ and $X_2$ independent?

**9.2.** A discrete-time random process $X_n$ is defined as follows. A fair die is tossed and the outcome $k$ is observed. The process is then given by $X_n = k$ for all $n$.

   **(a)** Sketch some sample paths of the process.

   **(b)** Find the pmf for $X_n$.

   **(c)** Find the joint pmf for $X_n$ and $X_{n+k}$.

   **(d)** Find the mean and autocovariance functions of $X_n$.

**9.3.** A discrete-time random process $X_n$ is defined as follows. A fair coin is tossed. If the outcome is heads, $X_n = (-1)^n$ for all $n$; if the outcome is tails, $X_n = (-1)^{n+1}$ for all $n$.

   **(a)** Sketch some sample paths of the process.

   **(b)** Find the pmf for $X_n$.

   **(c)** Find the joint pmf for $X_n$ and $X_{n+k}$.

   **(d)** Find the mean and autocovariance functions of $X_n$.

**9.4.** A discrete-time random process is defined by $X_n = s^n$, for $n \geq 0$, where $s$ is selected at random from the interval $(0, 1)$.

   **(a)** Sketch some sample paths of the process.

   **(b)** Find the cdf of $X_n$.

   **(c)** Find the joint cdf for $X_n$ and $X_{n+1}$.

   **(d)** Find the mean and autocovariance functions of $X_n$.

   **(e)** Repeat parts a, b, c, and d if $s$ is uniform in $(1, 2)$.

**9.5.** Let $g(t)$ be the rectangular pulse shown in Fig. P9.1. The random process $X(t)$ is defined as

$$X(t) = Ag(t),$$

where $A$ assumes the values $\pm 1$ with equal probability.

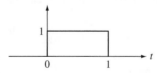

**FIGURE P9.1**

   **(a)** Find the pmf of $X(t)$.

   **(b)** Find $m_X(t)$.

   **(c)** Find the joint pmf of $X(t)$ and $X(t + d)$.

   **(d)** Find $C_X(t, t + d), d > 0$.

**9.6.** A random process is defined by

$$Y(t) = g(t - T),$$

where $g(t)$ is the rectangular pulse of Fig. P9.1, and $T$ is a uniformly distributed random variable in the interval $(0, 1)$.

**(a)** Find the pmf of $Y(t)$.

**(b)** Find $m_Y(t)$ and $C_Y(t_1, t_2)$.

**9.7.** A random process is defined by

$$X(t) = g(t - T),$$

where $T$ is a uniform random variable in the interval $(0, 1)$ and $g(t)$ is the periodic triangular waveform shown in Fig. P9.2.

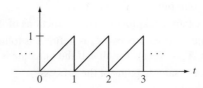

**FIGURE P9.2**

**(a)** Find the cdf of $X(t)$ for $0 < t < 1$.

**(b)** Find $m_X(t)$ and $C_X(t_1, t_2)$.

**9.8.** Let $Y(t) = g(t - T)$ as in Problem 9.6, but let $T$ be an exponentially distributed random variable with parameter $\alpha$.

**(a)** Find the pmf of $Y(t)$.

**(b)** Find the joint pmf of $Y(t)$ and $Y(t + d)$. Consider two cases: $d > 1$, and $0 < d < 1$.

**(c)** Find $m_Y(t)$ and $C_Y(t, t + d)$ for $d > 1$ and $0 < d < 1$.

**9.9.** Let $Z(t) = At^3 + B$, where $A$ and $B$ are independent random variables.

**(a)** Find the pdf of $Z(t)$.

**(b)** Find $m_Z(t)$ and $C_Z(t_1, t_2)$.

**9.10.** Find an expression for $E[|X_{t_2} - X_{t_1}|^2]$ in terms of autocorrelation function.

**9.11.** The random process $H(t)$ is defined as the "hard-limited" version of $X(t)$:

$$H(t) = \begin{cases} +1 & \text{if} \quad X(t) \geq 0 \\ -1 & \text{if} \quad X(t) < 0. \end{cases}$$

**(a)** Find the pdf, mean, and autocovariance of $H(t)$ if $X(t)$ is the sinusoid with a random amplitude presented in Example 9.2.

**(b)** Find the pdf, mean, and autocovariance of $H(t)$ if $X(t)$ is the sinusoid with random phase presented in Example 9.9.

**(c)** Find a general expression for the mean of $H(t)$ in terms of the cdf of $X(t)$.

**9.12. (a)** Are independent random processes orthogonal? Explain.

**(b)** Are orthogonal random processes uncorrelated? Explain.

**(c)** Are uncorrelated processes independent?

**(d)** Are uncorrelated processes orthogonal?

**9.13.** The random process $Z(t)$ is defined by

$$Z(t) = 2Xt - Y,$$

where $X$ and $Y$ are a pair of random variables with means $m_X, m_Y$, variances $\sigma_X^2, \sigma_Y^2$, and correlation coefficient $\rho_{X,Y}$. Find the mean and autocovariance of $Z(t)$.

**9.14.** Let $H(t)$ be the output of the hard limiter in Problem 9.11.

(a)   Find the cross-correlation and cross-covariance between $H(t)$ and $X(t)$ when the input is a sinusoid with random amplitude as in Problem 9.11a.

(b)   Repeat if the input is a sinusoid with random phase as in Problem 9.11b.

(c)   Are the input and output processes uncorrelated? Orthogonal?

**9.15.** Let $Y_n = X_n + g(n)$ where $X_n$ is a zero-mean discrete-time random process and $g(n)$ is a deterministic function of $n$.

(a)   Find the mean and variance of $Y_n$.

(b)   Find the joint cdf of $Y_n$ and $Y_{n+1}$.

(c)   Find the mean and autocovariance functions of $Y_n$.

(d)   Plot typical sample functions for $X_n$ and $Y_n$ if: $g(n) = n$; $g(n) = 1/n^2$; $g(n) = 1/n$.

**9.16.** Let $Y_n = c(n)X_n$ where $X_n$ is a zero-mean, unit-variance, discrete-time random process and $c(n)$ is a deterministic function of $n$.

(a)   Find the mean and variance of $Y_n$.

(b)   Find the joint cdf of $Y_n$ and $Y_{n+1}$.

(c)   Find the mean and autocovariance functions of $Y_n$.

(d)   Plot typical sample functions for $X_n$ and $Y_n$ if: $c(n) = n$; $c(n) = 1/n^2$; $c(n) = 1/n$.

**9.17. (a)**   Find the cross-correlation and cross-covariance for $X_n$ and $Y_n$ in Problem 9.15.

(b)   Find the joint pdf of $X_n$ and $Y_{n+1}$.

(c)   Determine whether $X_n$ and $Y_n$ are uncorrelated, independent, or orthogonal random processes.

**9.18. (a)**   Find the cross-correlation and cross-covariance for $X_n$ and $Y_n$ in Problem 9.16.

(b)   Find the joint pdf of $X_n$ and $Y_{n+1}$.

(c)   Determine whether $X_n$ and $Y_n$ are uncorrelated, independent, or orthogonal random processes.

**9.19.** Suppose that $X(t)$ and $Y(t)$ are independent random processes and let

$$U(t) = X(t) - Y(t)$$
$$V(t) = X(t) + Y(t).$$

(a)   Find $C_{UX}(t_1, t_2), C_{UY}(t_1, t_2)$, and $C_{UV}(t_1, t_2)$.

(b)   Find the $f_{U(t_1)X(t_2)}(u, x)$, and $f_{U(t_1)V(t_2)}(u, v)$. *Hint:* Use auxiliary variables.

**9.20.** Repeat Problem 9.19 if $X(t)$ and $Y(t)$ are independent discrete-time processes and $X(t)$ and $Y(t)$ have different iid random processes.

## Section 9.3: Sum Process, Binomial Counting Process, and Random Walk

**9.21. (a)**   Let $Y_n$ be the process that results when individual 1's in a Bernoulli process are erased with probability $\alpha$. Find the pmf of $S_n'$, the counting process for $Y_n$. Does $Y_n$ have independent and stationary increments?

(b)   Repeat part a if in addition to the erasures, individual 0's in the Bernoulli process are changed to 1's with probability $\beta$.

**9.22.** Let $S_n$ denote a binomial counting process.

**(a)** Show that $P[S_n = j, S_{n'} = i] \neq P[S_n = j]P[S_{n'} = i]$.

**(b)** Find $P[S_{n_2} = j \mid S_{n_1} = i]$, where $n_2 > n_1$.

**(c)** Show that $P[S_{n_2} = j \mid S_{n_1} = i, S_{n_0} = k] = P[S_{n_2} = j \mid S_{n_1} = i]$, where $n_2 > n_1 > n_0$.

**9.23. (a)** Find $P[S_n = 0]$ for the random walk process.

**(b)** What is the answer in part a if $p = 1/2$?

**9.24.** Consider the following *moving average* processes:

$$Y_n = 1/2(X_n + X_{n-1}) \qquad X_0 = 0$$

$$Z_n = 2/3\,X_n + 1/3\,X_{n-1} \qquad X_0 = 0$$

**(a)** Find the mean, variance, and covariance of $Y_n$ and $Z_n$ if $X_n$ is a Bernoulli random process.

**(b)** Repeat part a if $X_n$ is the random step process.

**(c)** Generate 100 outcomes of a Bernoulli random process $X_n$, and find the resulting $Y_n$ and $Z_n$. Are the sample means of $Y_n$ and $Z_n$ in part a close to their respective means?

**(d)** Repeat part c with $X_n$ given by the random step process.

**9.25.** Consider the following autoregressive processes:

$$W_n = 2W_{n-1} + X_n \qquad W_0 = 0$$

$$Z_n = 3/4\,Z_{n-1} + X_n \qquad Z_0 = 0.$$

**(a)** Suppose that $X_n$ is a Bernoulli process. What trends do the processes exhibit?

**(b)** Express $W_n$ and $Z_n$ in terms of $X_n, X_{n-1}, \dots, X_1$ and then find $E[W_n]$ and $E[Z_n]$. Do these results agree with the trends you expect?

**(c)** Do $W_n$ or $Z_n$ have independent increments? stationary increments?

**(d)** Generate 100 outcomes of a Bernoulli process. Find the resulting realizations of $W_n$ and $Z_n$. Is the sample mean meaningful for either of these processes?

**(e)** Repeat part d if $X_n$ is the random step process.

**9.26.** Let $M_n$ be the discrete-time process defined as the sequence of sample means of an iid sequence:

$$M_n = \frac{X_1 + X_2 + \cdots + X_n}{n}.$$

**(a)** Find the mean, variance, and covariance of $M_n$.

**(b)** Does $M_n$ have independent increments? stationary increments?

**9.27.** Find the pdf of the processes defined in Problem 9.24 if the $X_n$ are an iid sequence of zero-mean, unit-variance Gaussian random variables.

**9.28.** Let $X_n$ consist of an iid sequence of Cauchy random variables.

**(a)** Find the pdf of the sum process $S_n$. *Hint:* Use the characteristic function method.

**(b)** Find the joint pdf of $S_n$ and $S_{n+k}$.

**9.29.** Let $X_n$ consist of an iid sequence of Poisson random variables with mean $\alpha$.

**(a)** Find the pmf of the sum process $S_n$.

**(b)** Find the joint pmf of $S_n$ and $S_{n+k}$.

**9.30.** Let $X_n$ be an iid sequence of zero-mean, unit-variance Gaussian random variables.

    **(a)** Find the pdf of $M_n$ defined in Problem 9.26.

    **(b)** Find the joint pdf of $M_n$ and $M_{n+k}$. *Hint:* Use the independent increments property of $S_n$.

**9.31.** Repeat Problem 9.26 with $X_n = 1/2(Y_n + Y_{n-1})$, where $Y_n$ is an iid random process. What happens to the variance of $M_n$ as $n$ increases?

**9.32.** Repeat Problem 9.26 with $X_n = 3/4X_{n-1} + Y_n$ where $Y_n$ is an iid random process. What happens to the variance of $M_n$ as $n$ increases?

**9.33.** Suppose that an experiment has three possible outcomes, say 0, 1, and 2, and suppose that these occur with probabilities $p_0$, $p_1$, and $p_2$, respectively. Consider a sequence of independent repetitions of the experiment, and let $X_j(n)$ be the indicator function for outcome $j$. The vector

$$\mathbf{X}(n) = (X_0(n), X_1(n), X_2(n))$$

then constitutes a vector-valued Bernoulli random process. Consider the counting process for $\mathbf{X}(n)$:

$$\mathbf{S}(n) = \mathbf{X}(n) + \mathbf{X}(n - 1) + \cdots + \mathbf{X}(1) \qquad \mathbf{S}(0) = 0.$$

    **(a)** Show that $\mathbf{S}(n)$ has a multinomial distribution.

    **(b)** Show that $\mathbf{S}(n)$ has independent increments, then find the joint pmf of $\mathbf{S}(n)$ and $\mathbf{S}(n + k)$.

    **(c)** Show that components $S_j(n)$ of the vector process are binomial counting processes.

## Section 9.4: Poisson and Associated Random Processes

**9.34.** A server handles queries that arrive according to a Poisson process with a rate of 10 queries per minute. What is the probability that no queries go unanswered if the server is unavailable for 20 seconds?

**9.35.** Customers deposit \$1 in a vending machine according to a Poisson process with rate $\lambda$. The machine issues an item with probability $p$. Find the pmf for the number of items dispensed in time $t$.

**9.36.** Noise impulses occur in a radio transmission according to a Poisson process of rate $\lambda$.

    **(a)** Find the probability that no impulses occur during the transmission of a message that is $t$ seconds long.

    **(b)** Suppose that the message is encoded so that the errors caused by up to 2 impulses can be corrected. What is the probability that a $t$-second message cannot be corrected?

**9.37.** Packets arrive at a multiplexer at two ports according to independent Poisson processes of rates $\lambda_1 = 1$ and $\lambda_2 = 2$ packets/second, respectively.

    **(a)** Find the probability that a message arrives first on line 2.

    **(b)** Find the pdf for the time until a message arrives on either line.

    **(c)** Find the pmf for $N(t)$, the total number of messages that arrive in an interval of length $t$.

    **(d)** Generalize the result of part c for the "merging" of $k$ independent Poisson processes of rates $\lambda_1, \ldots, \lambda_k$, respectively:

$$N(t) = N_1(t) + \cdots + N_k(t).$$

**9.38. (a)** Find $P[N(t - d) = j \mid N(t) = k]$ with $d > 0$, where $N(t)$ is a Poisson process with rate $\lambda$.

**(b)** Compare your answer to $P[N(t + d) = j \mid N(t) = k]$. Explain the difference, if any.

**9.39.** Let $N_1(t)$ be a Poisson process with arrival rate $\lambda_1$ that is started at $t = 0$. Let $N_2(t)$ be another Poisson process that is independent of $N_1(t)$, that has arrival rate $\lambda_2$, and that is started at $t = 1$.

**(a)** Show that the pmf of the process $N(t) = N_1(t) + N_2(t)$ is given by:

$$P[N(t + \tau) - N(t) = k] = \frac{(m(t + \tau) - m(t))^k}{k!} e^{-(m(t+\tau)-m(t))} \qquad \text{for } k = 0, 1, \ldots$$

where $m(t) = E[N(t)]$.

**(b)** Now consider a Poisson process in which the arrival rate $\lambda(t)$ is a piecewise constant function of time. Explain why the pmf of the process is given by the above pmf where

$$m(t) = \int_0^t \lambda(t') \, dt'.$$

**(c)** For what other arrival functions $\lambda(t)$ does the pmf in part a hold?

**9.40. (a)** Suppose that the time required to service a customer in a queueing system is a random variable $T$. If customers arrive at the system according to a Poisson process with parameter $\lambda$, find the pmf for the number of customers that arrive during one customer's service time. *Hint:* Condition on the service time.

**(b)** Evaluate the pmf in part a if $T$ is an exponential random variable with parameter $\beta$.

**9.41. (a)** Is the difference of two independent Poisson random processes also a Poisson process?

**(b)** Let $N_p(t)$ be the number of complete pairs generated by a Poisson process up to time $t$. Explain why $N_p(t)$ is or is not a Poisson process.

**9.42.** Let $N(t)$ be a Poisson random process with parameter $\lambda$. Suppose that each time an event occurs, a coin is flipped and the outcome (heads or tails) is recorded. Let $N_1(t)$ and $N_2(t)$ denote the number of heads and tails recorded up to time $t$, respectively. Assume that $p$ is the probability of heads.

**(a)** Find $P[N_1(t) = j, N_2(t) = k \mid N(t) = k + j]$.

**(b)** Use part a to show that $N_1(t)$ and $N_2(t)$ are independent Poisson random variables of rates $p\lambda t$ and $(1 - p)\lambda t$, respectively:

$$P[N_1(t) = j, N_2(t) = k] = \frac{(p\lambda t)^j}{j!} e^{-p\lambda t} \frac{((1 - p)\lambda t)^k}{k!} e^{-(1-p)\lambda t}.$$

**9.43.** Customers play a \$1 game machine according to a Poisson process with rate $\lambda$. Suppose the machine dispenses a random reward $X$ each time it is played. Let $X(t)$ be the total reward issued up to time $t$.

**(a)** Find expressions for $P[X(t) = j]$ if $X_n$ is Bernoulli.

**(b)** Repeat part a if $X$ assumes the values $\{0, 5\}$ with probabilities $(5/6, 1/6)$.

(c)  Repeat part a if $X$ is Poisson with mean 1.

(d)  Repeat part a if with probability $p$ the machine returns all the coins.

**9.44.** Let $X(t)$ denote the random telegraph signal, and let $Y(t)$ be a process derived from $X(t)$ as follows: Each time $X(t)$ changes polarity, $Y(t)$ changes polarity with probability $p$.

(a)  Find the $P[Y(t) = \pm 1]$.

(b)  Find the autocovariance function of $Y(t)$. Compare it to that of $X(t)$.

**9.45.** Let $Y(t)$ be the random signal obtained by switching between the values 0 and 1 according to the events in a Poisson process of rate $\lambda$. Compare the pmf and autocovariance of $Y(t)$ with that of the random telegraph signal.

**9.46.** Let $Z(t)$ be the random signal obtained by switching between the values 0 and 1 according to the events in a counting process $N(t)$. Let

$$P[N(t) = k] = \frac{1}{1 + \lambda t}\left(\frac{\lambda t}{1 + \lambda t}\right)^k \qquad k = 0, 1, 2, \ldots.$$

(a)  Find the pmf of $Z(t)$.

(b)  Find $m_Z(t)$.

**9.47.** In the filtered Poisson process (Eq. (9.45)), let $h(t)$ be a pulse of unit amplitude and duration $T$ seconds.

(a)  Show that $X(t)$ is then the increment in the Poisson process in the interval $(t - T, t)$.

(b)  Find the mean and autocorrelation functions of $X(t)$.

**9.48. (a)**  Find the second moment and variance of the shot noise process discussed in Example 9.25.

(b)  Find the variance of the shot noise process if $h(t) = e^{-\beta t}$ for $t \geq 0$.

**9.49.** Messages arrive at a message center according to a Poisson process of rate $\lambda$. Every hour the messages that have arrived during the previous hour are forwarded to their destination. Find the mean of the total time waited by all the messages that arrive during the hour. *Hint:* Condition on the number of arrivals and consider the arrival instants.

## Section 9.5: Gaussian Random Process, Wiener Process and Brownian Motion

**9.50.** Let $X(t)$ and $Y(t)$ be jointly Gaussian random processes. Explain the relation between the conditions of independence, uncorrelatedness, and orthogonality of $X(t)$ and $Y(t)$.

**9.51.** Let $X(t)$ be a zero-mean Gaussian random process with autocovariance function given by

$$C_X(t_1, t_2) = 4e^{-2|t_1 - t_2|}.$$

Find the joint pdf of $X(t)$ and $X(t + s)$.

**9.52.** Find the pdf of $Z(t)$ in Problem 9.13 if $X$ and $Y$ are jointly Gaussian random variables.

**9.53.** Let $Y(t) = X(t + d) - X(t)$, where $X(t)$ is a Gaussian random process.

(a)  Find the mean and autocovariance of $Y(t)$.

(b)  Find the pdf of $Y(t)$.

(c)  Find the joint pdf of $Y(t)$ and $Y(t + s)$.

(d)  Show that $Y(t)$ is a Gaussian random process.

**9.54.** Let $X(t) = A \cos \omega t + B \sin \omega t$, where $A$ and $B$ are iid Gaussian random variables with zero mean and variance $\sigma^2$.

  **(a)** Find the mean and autocovariance of $X(t)$.

  **(b)** Find the joint pdf of $X(t)$ and $X(t + s)$.

**9.55.** Let $X(t)$ and $Y(t)$ be independent Gaussian random processes with zero means and the same covariance function $C(t_1, t_2)$. Define the "amplitude-modulated signal" by

$$Z(t) = X(t) \cos \omega t + Y(t) \sin \omega t.$$

  **(a)** Find the mean and autocovariance of $Z(t)$.

  **(b)** Find the pdf of $Z(t)$.

**9.56.** Let $X(t)$ be a zero-mean Gaussian random process with autocovariance function given by $C_X(t_1, t_2)$. If $X(t)$ is the input to a "square law detector," then the output is

$$Y(t) = X(t)^2.$$

Find the mean and autocovariance of the output $Y(t)$.

**9.57.** Let $Y(t) = X(t) + \mu t$, where $X(t)$ is the Wiener process.

  **(a)** Find the pdf of $Y(t)$.

  **(b)** Find the joint pdf of $Y(t)$ and $Y(t + s)$.

**9.58.** Let $Y(t) = X^2(t)$, where $X(t)$ is the Wiener process.

  **(a)** Find the pdf of $Y(t)$.

  **(b)** Find the conditional pdf of $Y(t_2)$ given $Y(t_1)$.

**9.59.** Let $Z(t) = X(t) - aX(t - s)$, where $X(t)$ is the Wiener process.

  **(a)** Find the pdf of $Z(t)$.

  **(b)** Find $m_Z(t)$ and $C_Z(t_1, t_2)$.

**9.60. (a)** For $X(t)$ the Wiener process with $\alpha = 1$ and $0 < t < 1$, show that the joint pdf of $X(t)$ and $X(1)$ is given by:

$$f_{X(t), X(1)}(x_1, x_2) = \frac{\exp\left\{ -\frac{1}{2}\left[ \frac{x_1^2}{t} + \frac{(x_2 - x_1)^2}{(1 - t)} \right] \right\}}{2\pi\sqrt{t(1 - t)}}.$$

  **(b)** Use part a to show that for $0 < t < 1$, the conditional pdf of $X(t)$ given $X(0) = X(1) = 0$ is:

$$f_{X(t)}(x \mid X(0) = X(1) = 0) = \frac{\exp\left\{ -\frac{1}{2}\left[ \frac{x^2}{t(1 - t)} \right] \right\}}{2\pi\sqrt{t(1 - t)}}.$$

  **(c)** Use part b to find the conditional pdf of $X(t)$ given $X(t_1) = a$ and $X(t_2) = b$ for $t_1 < t < t_2$. *Hint:* Find the equivalent process in the interval $(0, t_2 - t_1)$.

## Section 9.6: Stationary Random Processes

**9.61. (a)** Is the random amplitude sinusoid in Example 9.9 a stationary random process? Is it wide-sense stationary?

**(b)** Repeat part a for the random phase sinusoid in Example 9.10.

**9.62.** A discrete-time random process $X_n$ is defined as follows. A fair coin is tossed; if the outcome is heads then $X_n = 1$ for all $n$, and $X_n = -1$ for all $n$, otherwise.

**(a)** Is $X_n$ a WSS random process?

**(b)** Is $X_n$ a stationary random process?

**(c)** Do the answers in parts a and b change if $p$ is a biased coin?

**9.63.** Let $X_n$ be the random process in Problem 9.3.

**(a)** Is $X_n$ a WSS random process?

**(b)** Is $X_n$ a stationary random process?

**(c)** Is $X_n$ a cyclostationary random process?

**9.64.** Let $X(t) = g(t - T)$, where $g(t)$ is the periodic waveform introduced in Problem 9.7, and $T$ is a uniformly distributed random variable in the interval $(0, 1)$. Is $X(t)$ a stationary random process? Is $X(t)$ wide-sense stationary?

**9.65.** Let $X(t)$ be defined by

$$X(t) = A \cos \omega t + B \sin \omega t,$$

where $A$ and $B$ are iid random variables.

**(a)** Under what conditions is $X(t)$ wide-sense stationary?

**(b)** Show that $X(t)$ is not stationary. *Hint:* Consider $E[X^3(t)]$.

**9.66.** Consider the following moving average process:

$$Y_n = 1/2(X_n + X_{n-1}) \qquad X_0 = 0.$$

**(a)** Is $Y_n$ a stationary random process if $X_n$ is an iid integer-valued process?

**(b)** Is $Y_n$ a stationary random process if $X_n$ is a stationary process?

**(c)** Are $Y_n$ and $X_n$ jointly stationary random processes if $X_n$ is an iid process? a stationary process?

**9.67.** Let $X_n$ be a zero-mean iid process, and let $Z_n$ be an autoregressive random process

$$Z_n = 3/4 Z_{n-1} + X_n \qquad Z_0 = 0.$$

**(a)** Find the autocovariance of $Z_n$ and determine whether $Z_n$ is wide-sense stationary. *Hint:* Express $Z_n$ in terms of $X_n, X_{n-1}, \ldots, X_1$.

**(b)** Does $Z_n$ eventually settle down into stationary behavior?

**(c)** Find the pdf of $Z_n$ if $X_n$ is an iid sequence of zero-mean, unit-variance Gaussian random variables. What is the pdf of $Z_n$ as $n \to \infty$?

**9.68.** Let $Y(t) = X(t + s) - \beta X(t)$, where $X(t)$ is a wide-sense stationary random process.

**(a)** Determine whether $Y(t)$ is also a wide-sense stationary random process.

**(b)** Find the cross-covariance function of $Y(t)$ and $X(t)$. Are the processes jointly wide-sense stationary?

**(c)** Find the pdf of $Y(t)$ if $X(t)$ is a Gaussian random process.

**(d)** Find the joint pdf of $Y(t_1)$ and $Y(t_2)$ in part c.

**(e)** Find the joint pdf of $Y(t_1)$ and $X(t_2)$ in part c.

**9.69.** Let $X(t)$ and $Y(t)$ be independent, wide-sense stationary random processes with zero means and the same covariance function $C_X(\tau)$. Let $Z(t)$ be defined by

$$Z(t) = 3X(t) - 5Y(t).$$

**(a)** Determine whether $Z(t)$ is also wide-sense stationary.

**(b)** Determine the pdf of $Z(t)$ if $X(t)$ and $Y(t)$ are also jointly Gaussian zero-mean random processes with $C_X(\tau) = 4e^{-|\tau|}$.

**(c)** Find the joint pdf of $Z(t_1)$ and $Z(t_2)$ in part b.

**(d)** Find the cross-covariance between $Z(t)$ and $X(t)$. Are $Z(t)$ and $X(t)$ jointly stationary random processes?

**(e)** Find the joint pdf of $Z(t_1)$ and $X(t_2)$ in part b. *Hint:* Use auxilliary variables.

**9.70.** Let $X(t)$ and $Y(t)$ be independent, wide-sense stationary random processes with zero means and the same covariance function $C_X(\tau)$. Let $Z(t)$ be defined by

$$Z(t) = X(t) \cos \omega t + Y(t) \sin \omega t.$$

**(a)** Determine whether $Z(t)$ is a wide-sense stationary random process.

**(b)** Determine the pdf of $Z(t)$ if $X(t)$ and $Y(t)$ are also jointly Gaussian zero-mean random processes with $C_X(\tau) = 4e^{-|\tau|}$.

**(c)** Find the joint pdf of $Z(t_1)$ and $Z(t_2)$ in part b.

**(d)** Find the cross-covariance between $Z(t)$ and $X(t)$. Are $Z(t)$ and $X(t)$ jointly stationary random processes?

**(e)** Find the joint pdf of $Z(t_1)$ and $X(t_2)$ in part b.

**9.71.** Let $X(t)$ be a zero-mean, wide-sense stationary Gaussian random process with autocorrelation function $R_X(\tau)$. The output of a "square law detector" is

$$Y(t) = X(t)^2.$$

Show that $R_Y(\tau) = R_X(0)^2 + 2R_X^2(\tau)$. *Hint:* For zero-mean, jointly Gaussian random variables $E[X^2Z^2] = E[X^2]E[Z^2] + 2E[XZ]^2$.

**9.72.** A WSS process $X(t)$ has mean 1 and autocorrelation function given in Fig. P9.3.

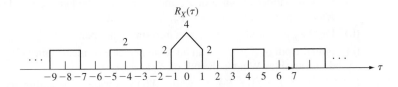

**FIGURE P9.3**

**(a)** Find the mean component of $R_X(\tau)$.

**(b)** Find the periodic component of $R_X(\tau)$.

**(c)** Find the remaining component of $R_X(\tau)$.

**9.73.** Let $X_n$ and $Y_n$ be independent random processes. A multiplexer combines these two sequences into a combined sequence $U_k$, that is,

$$U_{2n} = X_n, \qquad U_{2n+1} = Y_n.$$

(a) Suppose that $X_n$ and $Y_n$ are independent Bernoulli random processes. Under what conditions is $U_k$ a stationary random process? a cyclostationary random process?

(b) Repeat part a if $X_n$ and $Y_n$ are independent stationary random processes.

(c) Suppose that $X_n$ and $Y_n$ are wide-sense stationary random processes. Is $U_k$ a wide-sense stationary random process? a wide-sense cyclostationary random process? Find the mean and autocovariance functions of $U_k$.

(d) If $U_k$ is wide-sense cyclostationary, find the mean and correlation function of the randomly phase-shifted version of $U_k$ as defined by Eq. (9.72).

**9.74.** A ternary information source produces an iid, equiprobable sequence of symbols from the alphabet $\{a, b, c\}$. Suppose that these three symbols are encoded into the respective binary codewords 00, 01, 10. Let $B_n$ be the sequence of binary symbols that result from encoding the ternary symbols.

(a) Find the joint pmf of $B_n$ and $B_{n+1}$ for $n$ even; $n$ odd. Is $B_n$ stationary? cyclostationary?

(b) Find the mean and covariance functions of $B_n$. Is $B_n$ wide-sense stationary? wide-sense cyclostationary?

(c) If $B_n$ is cyclostationary, find the joint pmf, mean, and autocorrelation functions of the randomly phase-shifted version of $B_n$ as defined by Eq. (9.72).

**9.75.** Let $s(t)$ be a periodic square wave with period $T = 1$ which is equal to 1 for the first half of a period and $-1$ for the remainder of the period. Let $X(t) = As(t)$, where $A$ is a random variable.

(a) Find the mean and autocovariance functions of $X(t)$.

(b) Is $X(t)$ a mean-square periodic process?

(c) Find the mean and autocovariance of $X_s(t)$ the randomly phase-shifted version of $X(t)$ given by Eq. (9.72).

**9.76.** Let $X(t) = As(t)$ and $Y(t) = Bs(t)$, where $A$ and $B$ are independent random variables that assume values $+1$ or $-1$ with equal probabilities, where $s(t)$ is the periodic square wave in Problem 9.75.

(a) Find the joint pmf of $X(t_1)$ and $Y(t_2)$.

(b) Find the cross-covariance of $X(t_1)$ and $Y(t_2)$.

(c) Are $X(t)$ and $Y(t)$ jointly wide-sense cyclostationary? Jointly cyclostationary?

**9.77.** Let $X(t)$ be a mean square periodic random process. Is $X(t)$ a wide-sense cyclostationary process?

**9.78.** Is the pulse amplitude modulation random process in Example 9.38 cyclostationary?

**9.79.** Let $X(t)$ be the random amplitude sinusoid in Example 9.37. Find the mean and autocorrelation functions of the randomly phase-shifted version of $X(t)$ given by Eq. (9.72).

**9.80.** Complete the proof that if $X(t)$ is a cyclostationary random process, then $X_s(t)$, defined by Eq. (9.72), is a stationary random process.

**9.81.** Show that if $X(t)$ is a wide-sense cyclostationary random process, then $X_s(t)$, defined by Eq. (9.72), is a wide-sense stationary random process with mean and autocorrelation functions given by Eqs. (9.74a) and (9.74b).

## Section 9.7: Continuity, Derivatives, and Integrals of Random Processes

**9.82.** Let the random process $X(t) = u(t - S)$ be a unit step function delayed by an exponential random variable $S$, that is, $X(t) = 1$ for $t \geq S$, and $X(t) = 0$ for $t < S$.

(a) Find the autocorrelation function of $X(t)$.

(b) Is $X(t)$ mean square continuous?

(c) Does $X(t)$ have a mean square derivative? If so, find its mean and autocorrelation functions.

(d) Does $X(t)$ have a mean square integral? If so, find its mean and autocovariance functions.

**9.83.** Let $X(t)$ be the random telegraph signal introduced in Example 9.24.

(a) Is $X(t)$ mean square continuous?

(b) Show that $X(t)$ does not have a mean square derivative, and show that the second mixed partial derivative of its autocorrelation function has a delta function. What gives rise to this delta function?

(c) Does $X(t)$ have a mean square integral? If so, find its mean and autocovariance functions.

**9.84.** Let $X(t)$ have autocorrelation function

$$R_X(\tau) = \sigma^2 e^{-\alpha \tau^2}.$$

(a) Is $X(t)$ mean square continuous?

(b) Does $X(t)$ have a mean square derivative? If so, find its mean and autocorrelation functions.

(c) Does $X(t)$ have a mean square integral? If so, find its mean and autocorrelation functions.

(d) Is $X(t)$ a Gaussian random process?

**9.85.** Let $N(t)$ be the Poisson process. Find $E[(N(t) - N(t_0))^2]$ and use the result to show that $N(t)$ is mean square continuous.

**9.86.** Does the pulse amplitude modulation random process discussed in Example 9.38 have a mean square integral? If so, find its mean and autocovariance functions.

**9.87.** Show that if $X(t)$ is a mean square continuous random process, then $X(t)$ has a mean square integral. *Hint:* Show that

$$R_X(t_1, t_2) - R_X(t_0, t_0) = E[(X(t_1) - X(t_0))X(t_2)] + E[X(t_0)(X(t_2) - X(t_0))],$$

and then apply the Schwarz inequality to the two terms on the right-hand side.

**9.88.** Let $Y(t)$ be the mean square integral of $X(t)$ in the interval $(0, t)$. Show that $Y'(t)$ is equal to $X(t)$ in the mean square sense.

**9.89.** Let $X(t)$ be a wide-sense stationary random process. Show that $E[X(t)X'(t)] = 0$.

**9.90.** A linear system with input $Z(t)$ is described by

$$X'(t) + \alpha X(t) = Z(t) \qquad t \geq 0, X(0) = 0.$$

Find the output $X(t)$ if the input is a zero-mean Gaussian random process with autocorrelation function given by

$$R_X(\tau) = \sigma^2 e^{-\beta|\tau|}.$$

### Section 9.8: Time Averages of Random Processes and Ergodic Theorems

**9.91.** Find the variance of the time average given in Example 9.47.

**9.92.** Are the following processes WSS and mean ergodic?

    **(a)** Discrete-time dice process in Problem 9.2.

    **(b)** Alternating sign process in Problem 9.3.

    **(c)** $X_n = s^n$, for $n \geq 0$ in Problem 9.4.

**9.93.** Is the following WSS random process $X(t)$ mean ergodic?

$$R_X(\tau) = \begin{cases} 0 & |\tau| > 1 \\ 5(1 - |\tau|) & |\tau| \leq 1. \end{cases}$$

**9.94.** Let $X(t) = A \cos(2\pi ft)$, where $A$ is a random variable with mean $m$ and variance $\sigma^2$.

    **(a)** Evaluate $<X(t)>_T$, find its limit as $T \to \infty$, and compare to $m_X(t)$.

    **(b)** Evaluate $<X(t + \tau)X(t)>$, find its limit as $T \to \infty$, and compare to $R_X(t + \tau, t)$.

**9.95.** Repeat Problem 9.94 with $X(t) = A \cos(2\pi ft + \Theta)$, where $A$ is as in Problem 9.94, $\Theta$ is a random variable uniformly distributed in $(0, 2\pi)$, and $A$ and $\Theta$ are independent random variables.

**9.96.** Find an exact expression for $\mathrm{VAR}[<X(t)>_T]$ in Example 9.48. Find the limit as $T \to \infty$.

**9.97.** The WSS random process $X_n$ has mean $m$ and autocovariance $C_X(k) = (1/2)^{|k|}$. Is $X_n$ mean ergodic?

**9.98. (a)** Are the moving average processes $Y_n$ in Problem 9.24 mean ergodic?

    **(b)** Are the autoregressive processes $Z_n$ in Problem 9.25a mean ergodic?

**9.99. (a)** Show that a WSS random process is mean ergodic if

$$\int_{-\infty}^{\infty} |C(u)| < \infty.$$

    **(b)** Show that a discrete-time WSS random process is mean ergodic if

$$\sum_{k=-\infty}^{\infty} |C(k)| < \infty.$$

**9.100.** Let $<X^2(t)>_T$ denote a time-average estimate for the mean power of a WSS random process.

    **(a)** Under what conditions is this time average a valid estimate for $E[X^2(t)]$?

    **(b)** Apply your result in part a for the random phase sinusoid in Example 9.2.

**9.101. (a)** Under what conditions is the time average $<X(t + \tau)X(t)>_T$ a valid estimate for the autocorrelation $R_X(\tau)$ of a WSS random process $X(t)$?

    **(b)** Apply your result in part a for the random phase sinusoid in Example 9.2.

**9.102.** Let $Y(t)$ be the indicator function for the event $\{a < X(t) \leq b\}$, that is,

$$Y(t) = \begin{cases} 1 & \text{if } X(t) \in (a, b] \\ 0 & \text{otherwise.} \end{cases}$$

    **(a)** Show that $<Y(t)>_T$ is the proportion of time in the time interval $(-T, T)$ that $X(t) \in (a, b]$.

**(b)** Find $E[<Y(t)>_T]$.

**(c)** Under what conditions does $<Y(t)>_T \rightarrow P[a < X(t) \le b]$?

**(d)** How can $<Y(t)>_T$ be used to estimate $P[X(t) \le x]$?

**(e)** Apply the result in part d to the random telegraph signal.

**9.103. (a)** Repeat Problem 9.102 for the time average of the discrete-time $Y_n$, which is defined as the indicator for the event $\{a < X_n \le b]\}$.

**(b)** Apply your result in part a to an iid discrete-valued random process.

**(c)** Apply your result in part a to an iid continuous-valued random process.

**9.104.** For $n \ge 1$, define $Z_n = u(a - X_n)$, where $u(x)$ is the unit step function, that is, $X_n = 1$ if and only if $X_n \le a$.

**(a)** Show that the time average $<Z_n>_N$ is the proportion of $X_n$'s that are less than $a$ in the first $N$ samples.

**(b)** Show that if the process is ergodic (in some sense), then this time average is equal to $F_X(a) = P[X \le a]$.

**9.105.** In Example 9.50 show that $\text{VAR}[\langle X_n \rangle_T] = (\sigma^2)(2T + 1)^{2H-2}$.

**9.106.** Plot the covariance function vs. $k$ for the self-similar process in Example 9.50 with $\sigma^2 = 1$ for: $H = 0.5, H = 0.6, H = 0.75, H = 0.99$. Does the long-range dependence of the process increase or decrease with $H$?

**9.107. (a)** Plot the variance of the sample mean given by Eq. (9.110) vs. $T$ with $\sigma^2 = 1$ for: $H = 0.5, H = 0.6, H = 0.75, H = 0.99$.

**(b)** For the parameters in part a, plot $(2T + 1)^{2H-1}$ vs. $T$, which is the ratio of the variance of the sample mean of a long-range dependent process relative to the variance of the sample mean of an iid process. How does the long-range dependence manifest itself, especially for $H$ approaching 1?

**(c)** Comment on the width of confidence intervals for estimates of the mean of long-range dependent processes relative to those of iid processes.

**9.108.** Plot the variance of the sample mean for a long-range dependent process (Eq. 9.110) vs. the sample size $T$ in a log-log plot.

**(a)** What role does $H$ play in the plot?

**(b)** One of the remarkable indicators of long-range dependence in nature comes from a set of observations of the minimal water levels in the Nile river for the years 622–1281 [Beran, p. 22] where the log-log plot for part a gives a slope of $-0.27$. What value of $H$ corresponds to this slope?

**9.109.** Problem 9.99b gives a sufficient condition for mean ergodicity for discrete-time random processes. Use the expression in Eq. (9.112) for a long-range dependent process to determine whether the sufficient condition is satisfied. Comment on your findings.

## *Section 9.9: Fourier Series and Karhunen-Loeve Expansion

**9.110.** Let $X(t) = Xe^{j\omega t}$ where $X$ is a random variable.

**(a)** Find the correlation function for $X(t)$, which for complex-valued random processes is defined by $R_X(t_1, t_2) = E[X(t_1)X^*(t_2)]$, where * denotes the complex conjugate.

**(b)** Under what conditions is $X(t)$ a wide-sense stationary random process?

**9.111.** Consider the sum of two complex exponentials with random coefficients:

$$X(t) = X_1 e^{j\omega_1 t} + X_2 e^{j\omega_2 t} \quad \text{where } \omega_1 \neq \omega_2.$$

(a) Find the covariance function of $X(t)$.

(b) Find conditions on the complex-valued random variables $X_1$, and $X_2$ for $X(t)$ to be a wide-sense stationary random process.

(c) Show that if we let $\omega_1 = -\omega_2$, $X_1 = (U - jV)/2$ and $X_2 = (U + jV)/2$, where $U$ and $V$ are real-valued random variables, then $X(t)$ is a real-valued random process. Find an expression for $X(t)$ and for the autocorrelation function.

(d) Restate the conditions on $X_1$ and $X_2$ from part b in terms of $U$ and $V$.

(e) Suppose that in part c, $U$ and $V$ are jointly Gaussian random variables. Show that $X(t)$ is a Gaussian random process.

**9.112. (a)** Derive Eq. (9.118) for the correlation of the Fourier coefficients for a non-mean square periodic process $X(t)$.

(b) Show that Eq. (9.118) reduces to Eq. (9.117) when $X(t)$ is WSS and mean square periodic.

**9.113.** Let $X(t)$ be a WSS Gaussian random process with $R_X(\tau) = e^{-|\tau|}$.

(a) Find the Fourier series expansion for $X(t)$ in the interval $[0, T]$.

(b) What is the distribution of the coefficients in the Fourier series?

**9.114.** Show that the Karhunen-Loeve expansion of a WSS mean-square periodic process $X(t)$ yields its Fourier series. Specify the orthonormal set of eigenfunctions and the corresponding eigenvalues.

**9.115.** Let $X(t)$ be the white Gaussian noise process introduced in Example 9.43. Show that any set of orthonormal functions can be used as the eigenfunctions for $X(t)$ in its Karhunen-Loeve expansion. What are the eigenvalues?

**9.116.** Let $Y(t) = X(t) + W(t)$, where $X(t)$ and $W(t)$ are orthogonal random processes and $W(t)$ is a white Gaussian noise process. Let $\phi_n(t)$ be the eigenfunctions corresponding to $K_X(t_1, t_2)$. Show that $\phi_n(t)$ are also the eigenfunctions for $K_Y(t_1, t_2)$. What is the relation between the eigenvalues of $K_X(t_1, t_2)$ and those of $K_Y(t_1, t_2)$?

**9.117.** Let $X(t)$ be a zero-mean random process with autocovariance

$$R_X(\tau) = \sigma^2 e^{-\alpha|\tau|}.$$

(a) Write the eigenvalue integral equation for the Karhunen-Loeve expansion of $X(t)$ on the interval $[-T, T]$.

(b) Differentiate the above integral equation to obtain the differential equation

$$\frac{d^2}{dt^2} \phi(t) = \frac{\alpha^2 \left( \lambda - 2\dfrac{\sigma^2}{\alpha} \right)}{\lambda} \phi(t).$$

(c) Show that the solutions to the above differential equation are of the form $\phi(t) = A \cos bt$ and $\phi(t) = B \sin bt$. Find an expression for $b$.

**(d)** Substitute the $\phi(t)$ from part c into the integral equation of part a to show that if $\phi(t) = A \cos bt$, then $b$ is the root of $\tan bT = \alpha/b$, and if $\phi(t) = B \sin bt$, then $b$ is the root of $\tan bT = -b/\alpha$.

**(e)** Find the values of $A$ and $B$ that normalize the eigenfunctions.

*\*(f)* In order to show that the frequencies of the eigenfunctions are not harmonically related, plot the following three functions versus $bT$: $\tan bT$, $bT/\alpha T$, $-\alpha T/bT$. The intersections of these functions yield the eigenvalues. Note that there are two roots per interval of length $\pi$.

## *Section 9.10: Generating Random Processes

**9.118.** **(a)** Generate 10 realizations of the binomial counting process with $p = 1/4$, $p = 1/2$, and $p = 3/4$. For each value of $p$, plot the sample functions for $n = 200$ trials.

**(b)** Generate 50 realizations of the binomial counting process with $p = 1/2$. Find the sample mean and sample variance of the realizations for the first 200 trials.

**(c)** In part b, find the histogram of increments in the process for the interval $[1, 50]$, $[51, 100]$, $[101, 150]$, and $[151, 200]$. Compare these histograms to the theoretical pmf. How would you check to see if the increments in the four intervals are stationary?

**(d)** Plot a scattergram of the pairs consisting of the increments in the interval $[1, 50]$ and $[51, 100]$ in a given realization. Devise a test to check whether the increments in the two intervals are independent random variables.

**9.119.** Repeat Problem 9.118 for the random walk process with the same parameters.

**9.120.** Repeat Problem 9.118 for the sum process in Eq. (9.24) where the $X_n$ are iid unit-variance Gaussian random variables with mean: $m = 0$; $m = 0.5$.

**9.121.** Repeat Problem 9.118 for the sum process in Eq. (9.24) where the $X_n$ are iid Poisson random variables with $\alpha = 1$.

**9.122.** Repeat Problem 9.118 for the sum process in Eq. (9.24) where the $X_n$ are iid Cauchy random variables with $\alpha = 1$.

**9.123.** Let $Y_n = \alpha Y_{n-1} + X_n$ where $Y_0 = 0$.

**(a)** Generate five realizations of the process for $\alpha = 1/4$, $1/2$, $9/10$ and with $X_n$ given by the $p = 1/2$ and $p = 1/4$ random step process. Plot the sample functions for the first 200 steps. Find the sample mean and sample variance for the outcomes in *each* realization. Plot the histogram for outcomes in each realization.

**(b)** Generate 50 realizations of the process $Y_n$ with $\alpha = 1/2$, $p = 1/4$, and $p = 1/2$. Find the sample mean and sample variance of the realizations for the first 200 trials. Find the histogram of $Y_n$ across the realizations at times $n = 5$, $n = 50$, and $n = 200$.

**(c)** In part b, find the histogram of increments in the process for the interval $[1, 50]$, $[51, 100]$, $[101, 150]$, and $[151, 200]$. To what theoretical pmf should these histograms be compared? Should the increments in the process be stationary? Should the increments be independent?

**9.124.** Repeat Problem 9.123 for the sum process in Eq. (9.24) where the $X_n$ are iid unit-variance Gaussian random variables with mean: $m = 0$; $m = 0.5$.

**9.125. (a)** Propose a method for estimating the covariance function of the sum process in Problem 9.118. Do not assume that the process is wide-sense stationary.

**(b)** How would you check to see if the process is wide-sense stationary?

**(c)** Apply the methods in parts a and b to the experiment in Problem 9.118b.

**(d)** Repeat part c for Problem 9.123b.

**9.126.** Use the binomial process to approximate a Poisson random process with arrival rate $\lambda = 1$ customer per second in the time interval $(0, 100]$. Try different values of $n$ and come up with a recommendation on how $n$ should be selected.

**9.127.** Generate 100 repetitions of the experiment in Example 9.21.

**(a)** Find the relative frequency of the event $P[N(10) = 3$ and $N(60) - N(45) = 2]$ and compare it to the theoretical probability.

**(b)** Find the histogram of the time that elapses until the second arrival and compare it to the theoretical pdf. Plot the empirical cdf and compare it to the theoretical cdf.

**9.128.** Generate 100 realizations of the Poisson random process $N(t)$ with arrival rate $\lambda = 1$ customer per second in the time interval $(0, 10]$. Generate the pair $(N_1(t), N_2(t))$ by assigning arrivals in $N(t)$ to $N_1(t)$ with probability $p = 0.25$ and to $N_2(t)$ with probability 0.75.

**(a)** Find the histograms for $N_1(10)$ and $N_2(10)$ and compare them to the theoretical pmf by performing a chi-square goodness-of-fit test at a 5% significance level.

**(b)** Perform a chi-square goodness-of-fit test to test whether $N_1(10)$ and $N_2(10)$ are independent random variables. How would you check whether $N_1(t)$ and $N_2(t)$ are independent random processes?

**9.129.** Subscribers log on to a system according to a Poisson process with arrival rate $\lambda = 1$ customer per second. The $i$th customer remains logged on for a random duration of $T_i$ seconds, where the $T_i$ are iid random variables and are also independent of the arrival times.

**(a)** Generate the sequence $S_n$ of customer arrival times and the corresponding departure times given by $D_n = S_n + T_n$, where the connections times are all equal to 1.

**(b)** Plot: $A(t)$, the number of arrivals up to time $t$; and $D(t)$, the number of departures up to time $t$, and $N(t) = A(t) - D(t)$, the number in the system at time $t$.

**(c)** Perform 100 simulations of the system operation for a duration of 200 seconds. Assume that customer connection times are an exponential random variables with mean 5 seconds. Find the customer departure time instants and the associated departure counting process $D(t)$. How would you check whether $D(t)$ is a Poisson process? Find the histograms for $D(t)$ and the number in the system $N(t)$ at $t = 50, 100, 150, 200$. Try to fit a pmf to each histogram.

**(d)** Repeat part c if customer connection times are exactly 5 seconds long.

**9.130.** Generate 100 realizations of the Wiener process with $\alpha = 1$ for the interval $(0, 3.5)$ using the random walk limiting procedure.

**(a)** Find the histograms for increments in the intervals $(0, 0.5]$, $(0.5, 1.5]$, and $(1.5, 3.5]$ and compare these to the theoretical pdf.

**(b)** Perform a test at a 5% significance level to determine whether the increments in the first two intervals are independent random variables.

**9.131.** Repeat Problem 9.130 using Gaussian-distributed increments to generate the Wiener process. Discuss how the increment interval in the simulation should be selected.

## Problems Requiring Cumulative Knowledge

**9.132.** Let $X(t)$ be a random process with independent increments. Assume that the increments $X(t_2) - X(t_1)$ are gamma random variables with parameters $\lambda > 0$ and $\alpha = t_2 - t_1$.
  (a) Find the joint density function of $X(t_1)$ and $X(t_2)$.
  (b) Find the autocorrelation function of $X(t)$.
  (c) Is $X(t)$ mean square continuous?
  (d) Does $X(t)$ have a mean square derivative?

**9.133.** Let $X(t)$ be the pulse amplitude modulation process introduced in Example 9.38 with $T = 1$. A phase-modulated process is defined by

$$Y(t) = a \cos\left(2\pi t + \frac{\pi}{2}X(t)\right).$$

  (a) Plot the sample function of $Y(t)$ corresponding to the binary sequence 0010110.
  (b) Find the joint pdf of $Y(t_1)$ and $Y(t_2)$.
  (c) Find the mean and autocorrelation functions of $Y(t)$.
  (d) Is $Y(t)$ a stationary, wide-sense stationary, or cyclostationary random process?
  (e) Is $Y(t)$ mean square continuous?
  (f) Does $Y(t)$ have a mean square derivative? If so, find its mean and autocorrelation functions.

**9.134.** Let $N(t)$ be the Poisson process, and suppose we form the phase-modulated process

$$Y(t) = a \cos(2\pi f t + \pi N(t)).$$

  (a) Plot a sample function of $Y(t)$ corresponding to a typical sample function of $N(t)$.
  (b) Find the joint density function of $Y(t_1)$ and $Y(t_2)$. *Hint:* Use the independent increments property of $N(t)$.
  (c) Find the mean and autocorrelation functions of $Y(t)$.
  (d) Is $Y(t)$ a stationary, wide-sense stationary, or cyclostationary random process?
  (e) Is $Y(t)$ mean square continuous?
  (f) Does $Y(t)$ have a mean square derivative? If so, find its mean and autocorrelation functions.

**9.135.** Let $X(t)$ be a train of amplitude-modulated pulses with occurrences according to a Poisson process:

$$X(t) = \sum_{k=1}^{\infty} A_k h(t - S_k),$$

where the $A_k$ are iid random variables, the $S_k$ are the event occurrence times in a Poisson process, and $h(t)$ is a function of time. Assume the amplitudes and occurrence times are independent.
  (a) Find the mean and autocorrelation functions of $X(t)$.
  (b) Evaluate part a when $h(t) = u(t)$, a unit step function.
  (c) Evaluate part a when $h(t) = p(t)$, a rectangular pulse of duration $T$ seconds.

**9.136.** Consider a linear combination of two sinusoids:

$$X(t) = A_1 \cos(\omega_0 t + \Theta_1) + A_2 \cos(\sqrt{2}\omega_0 t + \Theta_2),$$

where $\Theta_1$ and $\Theta_2$ are independent uniform random variables in the interval $(0, 2\pi)$, and $A_1$ and $A_2$ are jointly Gaussian random variables. Assume that the amplitudes are independent of the phase random variables.

(a) Find the mean and autocorrelation functions of $X(t)$.

(b) Is $X(t)$ mean square periodic? If so, what is the period?

(c) Find the joint pdf of $X(t_1)$ and $X(t_2)$.

**9.137. (a)** A *Gauss-Markov random process* is a Gaussian random process that is also a Markov process. Show that the autocovariance function of such a process must satisfy

$$C_X(t_3, t_1) = \frac{C_X(t_3, t_2)C_X(t_2, t_1)}{C_X(t_2, t_2)},$$

where $t_1 \leq t_2 \leq t_3$.

(b) It can be shown that if the autocovariance of a Gaussian random process satisfies the above equation, then the process is Gauss-Markov. Is the Wiener process Gauss-Markov? Is the Ornstein-Uhlenbeck process Gauss-Markov?

**9.138.** Let $A_n$ and $B_n$ be two independent stationary random processes. Suppose that $A_n$ and $B_n$ are zero-mean, Gaussian random processes with autocorrelation functions

$$R_A(k) = \sigma_1^2 \rho_1^{|k|} \qquad R_B(k) = \sigma_2^2 \rho_2^{|k|}.$$

A block multiplexer takes blocks of two from the above processes and interleaves them to form the random process $Y_m$:

$$A_1 A_2 B_1 B_2 A_3 A_4 B_3 B_4 A_5 A_6 B_5 B_6 \ldots.$$

(a) Find the autocorrelation function of $Y_m$.

(b) Is $Y_m$ cyclostationary? wide-sense stationary?

(c) Find the joint pdf of $Y_m$ and $Y_{m+1}$.

(d) Let $Z_m = Y_{m+T}$, where $T$ is selected uniformly from the set $\{0, 1, 2, 3\}$. Repeat parts a, b, and c for $Z_m$.

**9.139.** Let $A_n$ be the Gaussian random process in Problem 9.138. A decimator takes every other sample to form the random process $V_m$:

$$A_1 A_3 A_5 A_7 A_9 A_{11}$$

(a) Find the autocorrelation function of $V_m$.

(b) Find the joint pdf of $V_m$ and $V_{m+k}$.

(c) An interpolator takes the sequence $V_m$ and inserts zeros between samples to form the sequence $W_k$:

$$A_1 0 A_3 0 A_5 0 A_7 0 A_9 0 A_{11} \ldots.$$

Find the autocorrelation function of $W_k$. Is $W_k$ a Gaussian random process?

**9.140.** Let $A_n$ be a sequence of zero-mean, unit-variance independent Gaussian random variables. A block coder takes pairs of $A$'s and linearly transforms them to form the sequence $Y_n$:

$$\begin{bmatrix} Y_{2n} \\ Y_{2n+1} \end{bmatrix} = \frac{1}{\sqrt{2}} \begin{bmatrix} 1 & 1 \\ 1 & -1 \end{bmatrix} \begin{bmatrix} A_{2n} \\ A_{2n+1} \end{bmatrix}.$$

(a) Find the autocorrelation function of $Y_n$.

(b) Is $Y_n$ stationary in any sense?

(c) Find the joint pdf of $Y_n$, $Y_{n+1}$, and $Y_{n+2}$.

**9.141.** Suppose customer orders arrive according to a Bernoulli random process with parameter $p$. When an order arrives, its size is an exponential random variable with parameter $\lambda$. Let $S_n$ be the total size of all orders up to time $n$.

(a) Find the mean and autocorrelation functions of $S_n$.

(b) Is $S_n$ a stationary random process?

(c) Is $S_n$ a Markov process?

(d) Find the joint pdf of $S_n$ and $S_{n+k}$.

# CHAPTER 10

# Analysis and Processing of Random Signals

In this chapter we introduce methods for analyzing and processing random signals. We cover the following topics:

- Section 10.1 introduces the notion of power spectral density, which allows us to view random processes in the frequency domain.
- Section 10.2 discusses the response of linear systems to random process inputs and introduce methods for filtering random processes.
- Section 10.3 considers two important applications of signal processing: sampling and modulation.
- Sections 10.4 and 10.5 discuss the design of optimum linear systems and introduce the Wiener and Kalman filters.
- Section 10.6 addresses the problem of estimating the power spectral density of a random process.
- Finally, Section 10.7 introduces methods for implementing and simulating the processing of random signals.

## 10.1 POWER SPECTRAL DENSITY

The Fourier series and the Fourier transform allow us to view deterministic time functions as the weighted sum or integral of sinusoidal functions. A time function that varies slowly has the weighting concentrated at the low-frequency sinusoidal components. A time function that varies rapidly has the weighting concentrated at higher-frequency components. Thus the rate at which a deterministic time function varies is related to the weighting function of the Fourier series or transform. This weighting function is called the "spectrum" of the time function.

The notion of a time function as being composed of sinusoidal components is also very useful for random processes. However, since a sample function of a random process can be viewed as being selected from an ensemble of allowable time functions, the weighting function or "spectrum" for a random process must refer in some way to the average rate of change of the ensemble of allowable time functions. Equation (9.66) shows that, for wide-sense stationary processes, the autocorrelation function

$R_X(\tau)$ is an appropriate measure for the average rate of change of a random process. Indeed if a random process changes slowly with time, then it remains correlated with it-self for a long period of time, and $R_X(\tau)$ decreases slowly as a function of $\tau$. On the other hand, a rapidly varying random process quickly becomes uncorrelated with itself, and $R_X(\tau)$ decreases rapidly with $\tau$.

We now present the **Einstein-Wiener-Khinchin theorem**, which states that the power spectral density of a wide-sense stationary random process is given by the Fourier transform of the autocorrelation function.[1]

### 10.1.1 Continuous-Time Random Processes

Let $X(t)$ be a continuous-time WSS random process with mean $m_X$ and autocorrelation function $R_X(\tau)$. Suppose we take the Fourier transform of a sample of $X(t)$ in the interval $0 < t < T$ as follows

$$\widetilde{x}(f) = \int_0^T X(t')e^{-j2\pi ft'}\, dt'. \tag{10.1}$$

We then approximate the power density as a function of frequency by the function:

$$\widetilde{p}_T(f) = \frac{1}{T}|\widetilde{x}(f)|^2 = \frac{1}{T}\widetilde{x}(f)\widetilde{x}^*(f) = \frac{1}{T}\left\{\int_0^T X(t')e^{-j2\pi ft'}\, dt'\right\}\left\{\int_0^T X(t')e^{j2\pi ft'}\, dt'\right\}, \tag{10.2}$$

where * denotes the complex conjugate. $X(t)$ is a random process, so $\widetilde{p}_T(f)$ is also a random process but over a different index set. $\widetilde{p}_T(f)$ is called the **periodogram esti-mate** and we are interested in the **power spectral density** of $X(t)$ which is defined by:

$$S_X(f) = \lim_{T \to \infty} E[\widetilde{p}_T(f)] = \lim_{T \to \infty} \frac{1}{T}E[\,|\widetilde{x}(f)|^2]. \tag{10.3}$$

We show at the end of this section that *the power spectral density of X(t) is given by the Fourier transform of the autocorrelation function:*

$$S_X(f) = \mathscr{F}\{R_X(\tau)\} = \int_{-\infty}^{\infty} R_X(\tau)e^{-j2\pi f\tau}\, d\tau. \tag{10.4}$$

A table of Fourier transforms and its properties is given in Appendix B.

For real-valued random processes, the autocorrelation function is an even function of $\tau$:

$$R_X(\tau) = R_X(-\tau). \tag{10.5}$$

---

[1]This result is usually called the Wiener-Khinchin theorem, after Norbert Wiener and A. Ya. Khinchin, who proved the result in the early 1930s. Later it was discovered that this result was stated by Albert Einstein in a 1914 paper (see Einstein).

Substitution into Eq. (10.4) implies that

$$S_X(f) = \int_{-\infty}^{\infty} R_X(\tau)\{\cos 2\pi f\tau - j\sin 2\pi f\tau\}\, d\tau$$

$$= \int_{-\infty}^{\infty} R_X(\tau)\cos 2\pi f\tau\, d\tau, \tag{10.6}$$

since the integral of the product of an even function $(R_X(\tau))$ and an odd function $(\sin 2\pi f\tau)$ is zero. Equation (10.6) implies that $S_X(f)$ *is real-valued and an even function of f.* From Eq. (10.2) we have that $S_X(f)$ *is nonnegative:*

$$S_X(f) \geq 0 \qquad \text{for all } f. \tag{10.7}$$

The autocorrelation function can be recovered from the power spectral density by applying the inverse Fourier transform formula to Eq. (10.4):

$$R_X(\tau) = \mathscr{F}^{-1}\{S_X(f)\}$$

$$= \int_{-\infty}^{\infty} S_X(f)e^{j2\pi f\tau}\, df. \tag{10.8}$$

Equation (10.8) is identical to Eq. (4.80), which relates the pdf to its corresponding characteristic function. The last section in this chapter discusses how the FFT can be used to perform numerical calculations for $S_X(f)$ and $R_X(\tau)$.

In electrical engineering it is customary to refer to the second moment of $X(t)$ as the **average power of $X(t)$**.[2] Equation (10.8) together with Eq. (9.64) gives

$$E[X^2(t)] = R_X(0) = \int_{-\infty}^{\infty} S_X(f)\, df. \tag{10.9}$$

Equation (10.9) states that the average power of $X(t)$ is obtained by integrating $S_X(f)$ over all frequencies. This is consistent with the fact that $S_X(f)$ is the "density of power" of $X(t)$ at the frequency $f$.

Since the autocorrelation and autocovariance functions are related by $R_X(\tau) = C_X(\tau) + m_X^2$, the power spectral density is also given by

$$S_X(f) = \mathscr{F}\{C_X(\tau) + m_X^2\}$$

$$= \mathscr{F}\{C_X(\tau)\} + m_X^2\, \delta(f), \tag{10.10}$$

where we have used the fact that the Fourier transform of a constant is a delta function. We say the $m_X$ is the "dc" component of $X(t)$.

The notion of power spectral density can be generalized to two jointly wide-sense stationary processes. The **cross-power spectral density $S_{X,Y}(f)$** is defined by

$$S_{X,Y}(f) = \mathscr{F}\{R_{X,Y}(\tau)\}, \tag{10.11}$$

---

[2]If $X(t)$ is a voltage or current developed across a 1-ohm resistor, then $X^2(t)$ is the instantaneous power absorbed by the resistor.

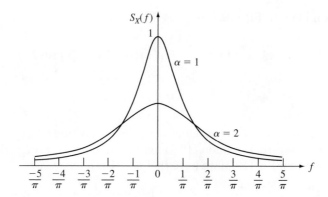

**FIGURE 10.1**
Power spectral density of a random telegraph signal with $\alpha = 1$ and $\alpha = 2$ transitions per second.

where $R_{X,Y}(\tau)$ is the cross-correlation between $X(t)$ and $Y(t)$:

$$R_{X,Y}(\tau) = E[X(t + \tau)Y(t)].\tag{10.12}$$

In general, $S_{X,Y}(f)$ is a complex function of $f$ even if $X(t)$ and $Y(t)$ are both real-valued.

---

### Example 10.1   Random Telegraph Signal

Find the power spectral density of the random telegraph signal.

In Example 9.24, the autocorrelation function of the random telegraph process was found to be

$$R_X(\tau) = e^{-2\alpha|\tau|},$$

where $\alpha$ is the average transition rate of the signal. Therefore, the power spectral density of the process is

$$S_X(f) = \int_{-\infty}^{0} e^{2\alpha\tau} e^{-j2\pi f\tau}\, d\tau + \int_{0}^{\infty} e^{-2\alpha\tau} e^{-j2\pi f\tau}\, d\tau$$

$$= \frac{1}{2\alpha - j2\pi f} + \frac{1}{2\alpha + j2\pi f}$$

$$= \frac{4\alpha}{4\alpha^2 + 4\pi^2 f^2}.\tag{10.13}$$

Figure 10.1 shows the power spectral density for $\alpha = 1$ and $\alpha = 2$ transitions per second. The process changes two times more quickly when $\alpha = 2$; it can be seen from the figure that the power spectral density for $\alpha = 2$ has greater high-frequency content.

---

### Example 10.2   Sinusoid with Random Phase

Let $X(t) = a\cos(2\pi f_0 t + \Theta)$, where $\Theta$ is uniformly distributed in the interval $(0, 2\pi)$. Find $S_X(f)$.

From Example 9.10, the autocorrelation for $X(t)$ is

$$R_X(\tau) = \frac{a^2}{2} \cos 2\pi f_0 \tau.$$

Thus, the power spectral density is

$$S_X(f) = \frac{a^2}{2} \mathcal{F}\{\cos 2\pi f_0 \tau\}$$

$$= \frac{a^2}{4} \delta(f - f_0) + \frac{a^2}{4} \delta(f + f_0), \qquad (10.14)$$

where we have used the table of Fourier transforms in Appendix B. The signal has average power $R_X(0) = a^2/2$. All of this power is concentrated at the frequencies $\pm f_0$, so the power density at these frequencies is infinite.

### Example 10.3    White Noise

The power spectral density of a WSS white noise process whose frequency components are limited to the range $-W \leq f \leq W$ is shown in Fig. 10.2(a). The process is said to be "white" in analogy to white light, which contains all frequencies in equal amounts. The average power in this

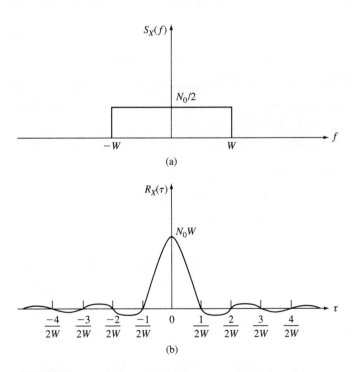

(a)

(b)

**FIGURE 10.2**
Bandlimited white noise: (a) power spectral density, (b) autocorrelation function.

process is obtained from Eq. (10.9):

$$E[X^2(t)] = \int_{-W}^{W} \frac{N_0}{2} df = N_0 W. \tag{10.15}$$

The autocorrelation for this process is obtained from Eq. (10.8):

$$\begin{aligned}
R_X(\tau) &= \frac{1}{2} N_0 \int_{-W}^{W} e^{j2\pi f \tau} df \\
&= \frac{1}{2} N_0 \frac{e^{-j2\pi W\tau} - e^{j2\pi W\tau}}{-j2\pi\tau} \\
&= \frac{N_0 \sin(2\pi W_\tau)}{2\pi\tau}. \tag{10.16}
\end{aligned}$$

$R_X(\tau)$ is shown in Fig. 10.2(b). Note that $X(t)$ and $X(t + \tau)$ are uncorrelated at $\tau = \pm k/2W$, $k = 1, 2, \ldots$.

The term white noise usually refers to a random process $W(t)$ whose power spectral density is $N_0/2$ for *all* frequencies:

$$S_W(f) = \frac{N_0}{2} \quad \text{for all } f. \tag{10.17}$$

Equation (10.15) with $W = \infty$ shows that such a process must have infinite average power. By taking the limit $W \to \infty$ in Eq. (10.16), we find that the autocorrelation of such a process approaches

$$R_W(\tau) = \frac{N_0}{2} \delta(\tau). \tag{10.18}$$

If $W(t)$ is a Gaussian random process, we then see that $W(t)$ is the white Gaussian noise process introduced in Example 9.43 with $\alpha = N_0/2$.

---

### Example 10.4 Sum of Two Processes

Find the power spectral density of $Z(t) = X(t) + Y(t)$, where $X(t)$ and $Y(t)$ are jointly WSS processes.

The autocorrelation of $Z(t)$ is

$$\begin{aligned}
R_Z(\tau) &= E[Z(t + \tau)Z(t)] = E[(X(t + \tau) + Y(t + \tau))(X(t) + Y(t))] \\
&= R_X(\tau) + R_{YX}(\tau) + R_{XY}(\tau) + R_Y(\tau).
\end{aligned}$$

The power spectral density is then

$$\begin{aligned}
S_Z(f) &= \mathcal{F}\{R_X(\tau) + R_{YX}(\tau) + R_{XY}(\tau) + R_Y(\tau)\} \\
&= S_X(f) + S_{YX}(f) + S_{XY}(f) + S_Y(f). \tag{10.19}
\end{aligned}$$

---

### Example 10.5

Let $Y(t) = X(t - d)$, where $d$ is a constant delay and where $X(t)$ is WSS. Find $R_{YX}(\tau)$, $S_{YX}(f)$, $R_Y(\tau)$, and $S_Y(f)$.

The definitions of $R_{YX}(\tau)$, $S_{YX}(f)$, and $R_Y(\tau)$ give

$$R_{YX}(\tau) = E[Y(t + \tau)X(t)] = E[X(t + \tau - d)X(t)] = R_X(\tau - d). \qquad (10.20)$$

The time-shifting property of the Fourier transform gives

$$S_{YX}(f) = \mathcal{F}\{R_X(\tau - d)\} = S_X(f)e^{-j2\pi fd}$$
$$= S_X(f)\cos(2\pi fd) - jS_X(f)\sin(2\pi fd). \qquad (10.21)$$

Finally,

$$R_Y(\tau) = E[Y(t + \tau)Y(t)] = E[X(t + \tau - d)X(t - d)] = R_X(\tau). \qquad (10.22)$$

Equation (10.22) implies that

$$S_Y(f) = \mathcal{F}\{R_Y(\tau)\} = \mathcal{F}\{R_X(\tau)\} = S_X(f). \qquad (10.23)$$

Note from Eq. (10.21) that the cross-power spectral density is complex. Note from Eq. (10.23) that $S_X(f) = S_Y(f)$ despite the fact that $X(t) \neq Y(t)$. Thus, $S_X(f) = S_Y(f)$ *does not imply that* $X(t) = Y(t)$.

---

## 10.1.2    Discrete-Time Random Processes

Let $X_n$ be a discrete-time WSS random process with mean $m_X$ and autocorrelation function $R_X(k)$. The **power spectral density of $X_n$** is defined as the Fourier transform of the autocorrelation sequence

$$S_X(f) = \mathcal{F}\{R_X(k)\}$$

$$= \sum_{k=-\infty}^{\infty} R_X(k)e^{-j2\pi fk}. \qquad (10.24)$$

Note that we need only consider frequencies in the range $-1/2 < f \leq 1/2$, since $S_X(f)$ is periodic in $f$ with period 1. As in the case of continuous random processes, $S_X(f)$ can be shown to be a real-valued, nonnegative, even function of $f$.

The inverse Fourier transform formula applied to Eq. (10.23) implies that[3]

$$R_X(k) = \int_{-1/2}^{1/2} S_X(f)e^{j2\pi fk} \, df. \qquad (10.25)$$

Equations (10.24) and (10.25) are similar to the discrete Fourier transform. In the last section we show how to use the FFT to calculate $S_X(f)$ and $R_X(k)$.

The **cross-power spectral density $S_{X,Y}(f)$** of two jointly WSS discrete-time processes $X_n$ and $Y_n$ is defined by

$$S_{X,Y}(f) = \mathcal{F}\{R_{X,Y}(k)\}, \qquad (10.26)$$

where $R_{X,Y}(k)$ is the cross-correlation between $X_n$ and $Y_n$:

$$R_{X,Y}(k) = E[X_{n+k}Y_n]. \qquad (10.27)$$

---

[3]You can view $R_X(k)$ as the coefficients of the Fourier series of the periodic function $S_X(f)$.

---

### Example 10.6    White Noise

Let the process $X_n$ be a sequence of uncorrelated random variables with zero mean and variance $\sigma_X^2$. Find $S_X(f)$.

The autocorrelation of this process is

$$
R_X(k) = \begin{cases} \sigma_X^2 & k = 0 \\ 0 & k \neq 0. \end{cases}
$$

The power spectral density of the process is found by substituting $R_X(k)$ into Eq. (10.24):

$$
S_X(f) = \sigma_X^2 \qquad -\frac{1}{2} < f < \frac{1}{2}. \tag{10.28}
$$

Thus the process $X_n$ contains all possible frequencies in equal measure.

---

### Example 10.7    Moving Average Process

Let the process $Y_n$ be defined by

$$
Y_n = X_n + \alpha X_{n-1}, \tag{10.29}
$$

where $X_n$ is the white noise process of Example 10.6. Find $S_Y(f)$.

It is easily shown that the mean and autocorrelation of $Y_n$ are given by

$$
E[Y_n] = 0,
$$

and

$$
E[Y_n Y_{n+k}] = \begin{cases} (1 + \alpha^2)\sigma_X^2 & k = 0 \\ \alpha \sigma_X^2 & k = \pm 1 \\ 0 & \text{otherwise.} \end{cases} \tag{10.30}
$$

The power spectral density is then

$$
\begin{aligned}
S_Y(f) &= (1 + \alpha^2)\sigma_X^2 + \alpha \sigma_X^2 \{ e^{j2\pi f} + e^{-j2\pi f} \} \\
&= \sigma_X^2 \{ (1 + \alpha^2) + 2\alpha \cos 2\pi f \}.
\end{aligned} \tag{10.31}
$$

$S_Y(f)$ is shown in Fig. 10.3 for $\alpha = 1$.

---

### Example 10.8    Signal Plus Noise

Let the observation $Z_n$ be given by

$$
Z_n = X_n + Y_n,
$$

where $X_n$ is the signal we wish to observe, $Y_n$ is a white noise process with power $\sigma_Y^2$, and $X_n$ and $Y_n$ are independent random processes. Suppose further that $X_n = A$ for all $n$, where $A$ is a random variable with zero mean and variance $\sigma_A^2$. Thus $Z_n$ represents a sequence of noisy measurements of the random variable $A$. Find the power spectral density of $Z_n$.

The mean and autocorrelation of $Z_n$ are

$$
E[Z_n] = E[A] + E[Y_n] = 0
$$

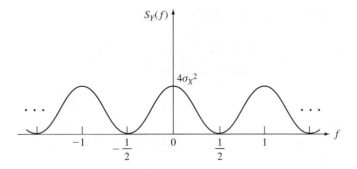

**FIGURE 10.3**
Power spectral density of moving average process discussed in Example 10.7.

and

$$E[Z_n Z_{n+k}] = E[(X_n + Y_n)(X_{n+k} + Y_{n+k})]$$
$$= E[X_n X_{n+k}] + E[X_n]E[Y_{n+k}]$$
$$+ E[X_{n+k}]E[Y_n] + E[Y_n Y_{n+k}]$$
$$= E[A^2] + R_Y(k).$$

Thus $Z_n$ is also a WSS process.

The power spectral density of $Z_n$ is then

$$S_Z(f) = E[A^2]\delta(f) + S_Y(f),$$

where we have used the fact that the Fourier transform of a constant is a delta function.

---

### 10.1.3    Power Spectral Density as a Time Average

In the above discussion, we simply stated that the power spectral density is given as the Fourier transform of the autocorrelation without supplying a proof. We now show how the power spectral density arises naturally when we take Fourier transforms of realizations of random processes.

Let $X_0, \ldots, X_{k-1}$ be $k$ observations from the discrete-time, WSS process $X_n$. Let $\tilde{x}_k(f)$ denote the discrete Fourier transform of this sequence:

$$\tilde{x}_k(f) = \sum_{m=0}^{k-1} X_m e^{-j2\pi f m}. \tag{10.32}$$

Note that $\tilde{x}_k(f)$ is a complex-valued random variable. The magnitude squared of $\tilde{x}_k(f)$ is a measure of the "energy" at the frequency $f$. If we divide this energy by the total "time" $k$, we obtain an estimate for the "power" at the frequency $f$:

$$\tilde{p}_k(f) = \frac{1}{k}|\tilde{x}_k(f)|^2. \tag{10.33}$$

$\tilde{p}_k(f)$ is called the **periodogram estimate** for the power spectral density.

Consider the expected value of the periodogram estimate:

$$E[\widetilde{p}_k(f)] = \frac{1}{k} E[\widetilde{x}_k(f)\widetilde{x}_k^*(f)]$$

$$= \frac{1}{k} E\left[ \sum_{m=0}^{k-1} X_m e^{-j2\pi fm} \sum_{i=0}^{k-1} X_i e^{j2\pi fi} \right]$$

$$= \frac{1}{k} \sum_{m=0}^{k-1}\sum_{i=0}^{k-1} E[X_m X_i] e^{-j2\pi f(m-i)}$$

$$= \frac{1}{k} \sum_{m=0}^{k-1}\sum_{i=0}^{k-1} R_X(m-i) e^{-j2\pi f(m-i)}. \tag{10.34}$$

Figure 10.4 shows the range of the double summation in Eq. (10.34). Note that all the terms along the diagonal $m' = m - i$ are equal, that $m'$ ranges from $-(k-1)$ to $k-1$, and that .here are $k - |m'|$ terms along the diagonal $m' = m - i$. Thus Eq. (10.34) becomes

$$E[\widetilde{p}_k(f)] = \frac{1}{k} \sum_{m'=-(k-1)}^{k-1} \{k - |m'|\} R_X(m') e^{-j2\pi fm'}$$

$$= \sum_{m'=-(k-1)}^{k-1} \left\{ 1 - \frac{|m'|}{k} \right\} R_X(m') e^{-j2\pi fm'}. \tag{10.35}$$

Comparison of Eq. (10.35) with Eq. (10.24) shows that the mean of the periodogram estimate is not equal to $S_X(f)$ for two reasons. First, Eq. (10.34) does not have the term in brackets in Eq. (10.25). Second, the limits of the summation in Eq. (10.35) are not $\pm\infty$. We say that $\widetilde{p}_k(f)$ is a "biased" estimator for $S_X(f)$. However, as $k \to \infty$, we see

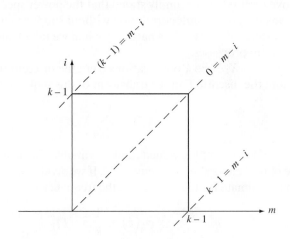

**FIGURE 10.4**
Range of summation in Eq. (10.34).

that the term in brackets approaches one, and that the limits of the summation approach $\pm\infty$. Thus

$$E[\widetilde{p}_k(f)] \to S_X(f) \qquad \text{as } k \to \infty, \tag{10.36}$$

that is, the mean of the periodogram estimate does indeed approach $S_X(f)$. Note that Eq. (10.36) shows that $S_X(f)$ is nonnegative for all $f$, since $\widetilde{p}_k(f)$ is nonnegative for all $f$.

In order to be useful, the variance of the periodogram estimate should also approach zero. The answer to this question involves looking more closely at the problem of power spectral density estimation. We defer this topic to Section 10.6.

All of the above results hold for a continuous-time WSS random process $X(t)$ after appropriate changes are made from summations to integrals. The periodogram estimate for $S_X(f)$, for an observation in the interval $0 < t < T$, was defined in Eq. 10.2. The same derivation that led to Eq. (10.35) can be used to show that the mean of the periodogram estimate is given by

$$E[\widetilde{p}_T(f)] = \int_{-T}^{T}\left\{1 - \frac{|\tau|}{T}\right\}R_X(\tau)e^{-j2\pi f\tau}\, d\tau. \tag{10.37a}$$

It then follows that

$$E[\widetilde{p}_T(f)] \to S_X(f) \qquad \text{as } T \to \infty. \tag{10.37b}$$

## 10.2    RESPONSE OF LINEAR SYSTEMS TO RANDOM SIGNALS

Many applications involve the processing of random signals (i.e., random processes) in order to achieve certain ends. For example, in prediction, we are interested in predicting future values of a signal in terms of past values. In filtering and smoothing, we are interested in recovering signals that have been corrupted by noise. In modulation, we are interested in converting low-frequency information signals into high-frequency transmission signals that propagate more readily through various transmission media.

Signal processing involves converting a signal from one form into another. Thus a signal processing method is simply a transformation or mapping from one time function into another function. If the input to the transformation is a random process, then the output will also be a random process. In the next two sections, we are interested in determining the statistical properties of the output process when the input is a wide-sense stationary random process.

### 10.2.1    Continuous-Time Systems

Consider a **system** in which an input signal $x(t)$ is mapped into the output signal $y(t)$ by the transformation

$$y(t) = T[x(t)].$$

The system is **linear** if superposition holds, that is,

$$T[\alpha x_1(t) + \beta x_2(t)] = \alpha T[x_1(t)] + \beta T[x_2(t)],$$

where $x_1(t)$ and $x_2(t)$ are arbitrary input signals, and $\alpha$ and $\beta$ are arbitrary constants.[4] Let $y(t)$ be the response to input $x(t)$, then the system is said to be **time-invariant** if the response to $x(t - \tau)$ is $y(t - \tau)$. The **impulse response** $h(t)$ of a linear, time-invariant system is defined by

$$h(t) = T[\delta(t)]$$

where $\delta(t)$ is a unit delta function input applied at $t = 0$. The response of the system to an arbitrary input $x(t)$ is then

$$y(t) = h(t) * x(t) = \int_{-\infty}^{\infty} h(s)x(t - s)\, ds = \int_{-\infty}^{\infty} h(t - s)x(s)\, ds. \quad (10.38)$$

Therefore a linear, time-invariant system is completely specified by its impulse response. The impulse response $h(t)$ can also be specified by giving its Fourier transform, the **transfer function** of the system:

$$H(f) = \mathcal{F}\{h(t)\} = \int_{-\infty}^{\infty} h(t)e^{-j2\pi ft}\, dt. \quad (10.39)$$

A system is said to be **causal** if the response at time $t$ depends only on past values of the input, that is, if $h(t) = 0$ for $t < 0$.

If the input to a linear, time-invariant system is a random process $X(t)$ as shown in Fig. 10.5, then the output of the system is the random process given by

$$Y(t) = \int_{-\infty}^{\infty} h(s)X(t - s)\, ds = \int_{-\infty}^{\infty} h(t - s)X(s)\, ds. \quad (10.40)$$

We assume that the integrals exist in the mean square sense as discussed in Section 9.7. We now show that if $X(t)$ is a wide-sense stationary process, then $Y(t)$ is also wide-sense stationary.[5]

The mean of $Y(t)$ is given by

$$E[Y(t)] = E\left[ \int_{-\infty}^{\infty} h(s)X(t - s)\, ds \right] = \int_{-\infty}^{\infty} h(s)E[X(t - s)]\, ds.$$

**FIGURE 10.5**
A linear system with a random input signal.

---

[4]For examples of nonlinear systems see Problems 9.11 and 9.56.

[5]Equation (10.40) supposes that the input was applied at an infinite time in the past. If the input is applied at $t = 0$, then $Y(t)$ is not wide-sense stationary. However, it becomes wide-sense stationary as the response reaches "steady state" (see Example 9.46 and Problem 10.29).

Now $m_X = E[X(t - \tau)]$ since $X(t)$ is wide-sense stationary, so

$$E[Y(t)] = m_X \int_{-\infty}^{\infty} h(\tau) \, d\tau = m_X H(0), \tag{10.41}$$

where $H(f)$ is the transfer function of the system. Thus the mean of the output $Y(t)$ is the constant $m_Y = H(0)m_X$.

The autocorrelation of $Y(t)$ is given by

$$E[Y(t)Y(t + \tau)] = E\left[ \int_{-\infty}^{\infty} h(s)X(t - s) \, ds \int_{-\infty}^{\infty} h(r)X(t + \tau - r) \, dr \right]$$

$$= \int_{-\infty}^{\infty} \int_{-\infty}^{\infty} h(s)h(r)E[X(t - s)X(t + \tau - r)] \, ds \, dr$$

$$= \int_{-\infty}^{\infty} \int_{-\infty}^{\infty} h(s)h(r)R_X(\tau + s - r) \, ds \, dr, \tag{10.42}$$

where we have used the fact that $X(t)$ is wide-sense stationary. The expression on the right-hand side of Eq. (10.42) depends only on $\tau$. Thus the autocorrelation of $Y(t)$ depends only on $\tau$, and since the $E[Y(t)]$ is a constant, we conclude that $Y(t)$ is a wide-sense stationary process.

We are now ready to compute the power spectral density of the output of a linear, time-invariant system. Taking the transform of $R_Y(\tau)$ as given in Eq. (10.42), we obtain

$$S_Y(f) = \int_{-\infty}^{\infty} R_Y(\tau)e^{-j2\pi f\tau} \, d\tau$$

$$= \int_{-\infty}^{\infty} \int_{-\infty}^{\infty} \int_{-\infty}^{\infty} h(s)h(r)R_X(\tau + s - r)e^{-j2\pi f\tau} \, ds \, dr \, d\tau.$$

Change variables, letting $u = \tau + s - r$:

$$S_Y(f) = \int_{-\infty}^{\infty} \int_{-\infty}^{\infty} \int_{-\infty}^{\infty} h(s)h(r)R_X(u)e^{-j2\pi f(u-s+r)} \, ds \, dr \, du$$

$$= \int_{-\infty}^{\infty} h(s)e^{j2\pi fs} \, ds \int_{-\infty}^{\infty} h(r)e^{-j2\pi fr} \, dr \int_{-\infty}^{\infty} R_X(u)e^{-j2\pi fu} \, du$$

$$= H^*(f)H(f)S_X(f)$$

$$= |H(f)|^2 S_X(f), \tag{10.43}$$

where we have used the definition of the transfer function. *Equation (10.43) relates the input and output power spectral densities to the system transfer function.* Note that $R_Y(\tau)$ can also be found by computing Eq. (10.43) and then taking the inverse Fourier transform.

Equations (10.41) through (10.43) only enable us to determine the mean and autocorrelation function of the output process $Y(t)$. In general this is not enough to determine probabilities of events involving $Y(t)$. However, if the input process is a

Gaussian WSS random process, then as discussed in Section 9.7 the output process will also be a Gaussian WSS random process. Thus the mean and autocorrelation function provided by Eqs. (10.41) through (10.43) are enough to determine all joint pdf's involving the Gaussian random process $Y(t)$.

The cross-correlation between the input and output processes is also of interest:

$$R_{Y,X}(\tau) = E[Y(t + \tau)X(t)]$$

$$= E\left[ X(t) \int_{-\infty}^{\infty} X(t + \tau - r)h(r)\, dr \right]$$

$$= \int_{-\infty}^{\infty} E[X(t)X(t + \tau - r)]h(r)\, dr$$

$$= \int_{-\infty}^{\infty} R_X(\tau - r)h(r)\, dr$$

$$= R_X(\tau) * h(\tau). \tag{10.44}$$

By taking the Fourier transform, we obtain the cross-power spectral density:

$$S_{Y,X}(f) = H(f)S_X(f). \tag{10.45a}$$

Since $R_{X,Y}(\tau) = R_{Y,X}(-\tau)$, we have that

$$S_{X,Y}(f) = S_{Y,X}^*(f) = H^*(f)S_X(f). \tag{10.45b}$$

---

### Example 10.9 Filtered White Noise

Find the power spectral density of the output of a linear, time-invariant system whose input is a white noise process.

Let $X(t)$ be the input process with power spectral density

$$S_X(f) = \frac{N_0}{2} \quad \text{for all } f.$$

The power spectral density of the output $Y(t)$ is then

$$S_Y(f) = |H(f)|^2 \frac{N_0}{2}. \tag{10.46}$$

Thus the transfer function completely determines the shape of the power spectral density of the output process.

---

Example 10.9 provides us with a method for generating WSS processes with arbitrary power spectral density $S_Y(f)$. We simply need to filter white noise through a filter with transfer function $H(f) = \sqrt{S_Y(f)}$. In general this filter will be noncausal. We can usually, but not always, obtain a *causal* filter with transfer function $H(f)$ such that $S_Y(f) = H(f)H^*(f)$. For example, if $S_Y(f)$ is a rational function, that is, if it consists of the ratio of two polynomials, then it is easy to factor $S_X(f)$ into the above form, as shown in the next example. Furthermore any power spectral density can be approximated by a rational function. Thus filtered white noise can be used to synthesize WSS random processes with arbitrary power spectral densities, and hence arbitrary autocorrelation functions.

---

### Example 10.10   Ornstein-Uhlenbeck Process

Find the impulse response of a causal filter that can be used to generate a Gaussian random process with output power spectral density and autocorrelation function

$$S_Y(f) = \frac{\sigma^2}{\alpha^2 + 4\pi^2 f^2} \quad \text{and} \quad R_Y(\tau) = \frac{\sigma^2}{2\alpha} e^{-\alpha|\tau|}$$

This power spectral density factors as follows:

$$S_Y(f) = \frac{1}{(\alpha - j2\pi f)} \frac{1}{(\alpha + j2\pi f)} \sigma^2.$$

If we let the filter transfer function be $H(f) = 1/(\alpha + j2\pi f)$, then the impulse response is

$$h(t) = e^{-\alpha t} \quad \text{for } t \geq 0,$$

which is the response of a causal system. Thus if we filter white Gaussian noise with power spectral density $\sigma^2$ using the above filter, we obtain a process with the desired power spectral density.

In Example 9.46, we found the autocorrelation function of the transient response of this filter for a white Gaussian noise input (see Eq. (9.97a)). As was already indicated, when dealing with power spectral densities we assume that the processes are in steady state. Thus as $t \to \infty$ Eq. (9.97a) approaches Eq. (9.97b).

---

### Example 10.11   Ideal Filters

Let $Z(t) = X(t) + Y(t)$, where $X(t)$ and $Y(t)$ are independent random processes with power spectral densities shown in Fig. 10.6(a). Find the output if $Z(t)$ is input into an ideal lowpass filter with transfer function shown in Fig. 10.6(b). Find the output if $Z(t)$ is input into an ideal bandpass filter with transfer function shown in Fig. 10.6(c).

The power spectral density of the output $W(t)$ of the lowpass filter is

$$S_W(f) = |H_{LP}(f)|^2 S_X(f) + |H_{LP}(f)|^2 S_Y(f) = S_X(f),$$

since $H_{LP}(f) = 1$ for the frequencies where $S_X(f)$ is nonzero, and $H_{LP}(f) = 0$ where $S_Y(f)$ is nonzero. Thus $W(t)$ has the same power spectral density as $X(t)$. As indicated in Example 10.5, this does not imply that $W(t) = X(t)$.

To show that $W(t) = X(t)$, in the mean square sense, consider $D(t) = W(t) - X(t)$. It is easily shown that

$$R_D(\tau) = R_W(\tau) - R_{WX}(\tau) - R_{XW}(\tau) + R_X(\tau).$$

The corresponding power spectral density is

$$\begin{aligned} S_D(f) &= S_W(f) - S_{WX}(f) - S_{XW}(f) + S_X(f) \\ &= |H_{LP}(f)|^2 S_X(f) - H_{LP}(f)S_X(f) - H^*_{LP}(f)S_X(f) + S_X(f) \\ &= 0. \end{aligned}$$

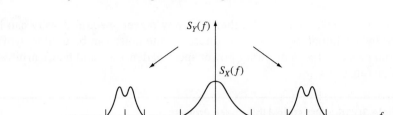

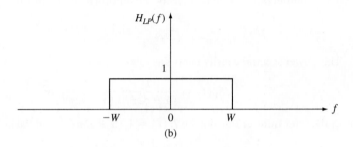

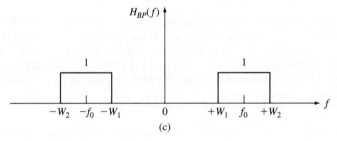

**FIGURE 10.6**
(a) Input signal to filters is $X(t) + Y(t)$, (b) lowpass filter, (c) bandpass filter.

Therefore $R_D(\tau) = 0$ for all $\tau$, and $W(t) = X(t)$ in the mean square sense since

$$E[(W(t) - X(t))^2] = E[D^2(t)] = R_D(0) = 0.$$

Thus we have shown that the lowpass filter removes $Y(t)$ and passes $X(t)$. Similarly, the bandpass filter removes $X(t)$ and passes $Y(t)$.

---

**Example 10.12**

A random telegraph signal is passed through an RC lowpass filter which has transfer function

$$H(f) = \frac{\beta}{\beta + j2\pi f},$$

where $\beta = 1/RC$ is the time constant of the filter. Find the power spectral density and autocorrelation of the output.

In Example 10.1, the power spectral density of the random telegraph signal with transition rate $\alpha$ was found to be

$$S_X(f) = \frac{4\alpha}{4\alpha^2 + 4\pi^2 f^2}.$$

From Eq. (10.43) we have

$$S_Y(f) = \left(\frac{\beta^2}{\beta^2 + 4\pi^2 f^2}\right)\left(\frac{4\alpha}{4\alpha^2 + 4\pi^2 f^2}\right)$$

$$= \frac{4\alpha\beta^2}{\beta^2 - 4\alpha^2}\left\{\frac{1}{4\alpha^2 + 4\pi^2 f^2} - \frac{1}{\beta^2 + 4\pi^2 f^2}\right\}.$$

$R_Y(\tau)$ is found by inverting the above expression:

$$R_Y(\tau) = \frac{1}{\beta^2 - 4\alpha^2}\{\beta^2 e^{-2\alpha|\tau|} - 2\alpha\beta e^{-\beta|\tau|}\}.$$

## 10.2.2  Discrete-Time Systems

The results obtained above for continuous-time signals also hold for discrete-time signals after appropriate changes are made from integrals to summations.

Let the **unit-sample response** $h_n$ be the response of a discrete-time, linear, time-invariant system to a unit-sample input $\delta_n$:

$$\delta_n = \begin{cases} 1 & n = 0 \\ 0 & n \neq 0. \end{cases} \tag{10.47}$$

The response of the system to an arbitrary input random process $X_n$ is then given by

$$Y_n = h_n * X_n = \sum_{j=-\infty}^{\infty} h_j X_{n-j} = \sum_{j=-\infty}^{\infty} h_{n-j} X_j. \tag{10.48}$$

Thus discrete-time, linear, time-invariant systems are determined by the unit-sample response $h_n$. The **transfer function** of such a system is defined by

$$H(f) = \sum_{i=-\infty}^{\infty} h_i e^{-j2\pi f i}. \tag{10.49}$$

The derivation from the previous section can be used to show that if $X_n$ is a wide-sense stationary process, then $Y_n$ is also wide-sense stationary. The mean of $Y_n$ is given by

$$m_Y = m_X \sum_{j=-\infty}^{\infty} h_j = m_X H(0). \tag{10.50}$$

The autocorrelation of $Y_n$ is given by

$$R_Y(k) = \sum_{j=-\infty}^{\infty} \sum_{i=-\infty}^{\infty} h_j h_i R_X(k + j - i). \tag{10.51}$$

By taking the Fourier transform of $R_Y(k)$ it is readily shown that the power spectral density of $Y_n$ is

$$S_Y(f) = |H(f)|^2 S_X(f). \tag{10.52}$$

This is the same equation that was found for continuous-time systems.

Finally, we note that if the input process $X_n$ is a Gaussian WSS random process, then the output process $Y_n$ is also a Gaussian WSS random whose statistics are completely determined by the mean and autocorrelation function provided by Eqs. (10.50) through (10.52).

---

### Example 10.13    Filtered White Noise

Let $X_n$ be a white noise sequence with zero mean and average power $\sigma_X^2$. If $X_n$ is the input to a linear, time-invariant system with transfer function $H(f)$, then the output process $Y_n$ has power spectral density:

$$S_Y(f) = |H(f)|^2 \sigma_X^2. \tag{10.53}$$

---

Equation (10.53) provides us with a method for generating discrete-time random processes with arbitrary power spectral densities or autocorrelation functions. If the power spectral density can be written as a rational function of $z = e^{j2\pi f}$ in Eq. (10.24), then a causal filter can be found to generate a process with the power spectral density. Note that this is a generalization of the methods presented in Section 6.6 for generating vector random variables with arbitrary covariance matrix.

---

### Example 10.14    First-Order Autoregressive Process

A first-order autoregressive (AR) process $Y_n$ with zero mean is defined by

$$Y_n = \alpha Y_{n-1} + X_n, \tag{10.54}$$

where $X_n$ is a zero-mean white noise input random process with average power $\sigma_X^2$. Note that $Y_n$ can be viewed as the output of the system in Fig. 10.7(a) for an iid input $X_n$. Find the power spectral density and autocorrelation of $Y_n$.

The unit-sample response can be determined from Eq. (10.54):

$$h_n = \begin{cases} 0 & n < 0 \\ 1 & n = 0 \\ \alpha^n & n > 0. \end{cases}$$

Note that we require $|\alpha| < 1$ for the system to be stable.[6] Therefore the transfer function is

$$H(f) = \sum_{n=0}^{\infty} \alpha^n e^{-j2\pi f n} = \frac{1}{1 - \alpha e^{-j2\pi f}}.$$

---

[6] A system is said to be **stable** if $\sum_n |h_n| < \infty$. The response of a stable system to any bounded input is also bounded.

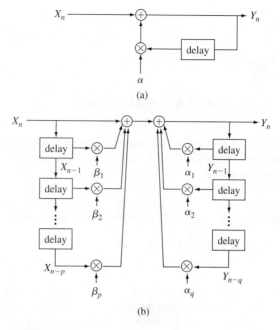

**FIGURE 10.7**
(a) Generation of AR process; (b) Generation of ARMA process.

Equation (10.52) then gives

$$S_Y(f) = \frac{\sigma_X^2}{(1 - \alpha e^{-j2\pi f})(1 - \alpha e^{j2\pi f})}$$

$$= \frac{\sigma_X^2}{1 + \alpha^2 - (\alpha e^{-j2\pi f} + \alpha e^{j2\pi f})}$$

$$= \frac{\sigma_X^2}{1 + \alpha^2 - 2\alpha \cos 2\pi f}.$$

Equation (10.51) gives

$$R_Y(k) = \sum_{j=0}^{\infty}\sum_{i=0}^{\infty} h_j h_i \sigma_X^2 \delta_{k+j-i} = \sigma_X^2 \sum_{j=0}^{\infty} \alpha^j \alpha^{j+k} = \frac{\sigma_X^2 \alpha^k}{1 - \alpha^2}.$$

## Example 10.15    ARMA Random Process

An **autoregressive moving average (ARMA) process** is defined by

$$Y_n = -\sum_{i=1}^{q} \alpha_i Y_{n-i} + \sum_{i'=0}^{p} \beta_{i'} W_{n-i'}, \qquad (10.55)$$

where $W_n$ is a WSS, white noise input process. $Y_n$ can be viewed as the output of the recursive system in Fig. 10.7(b) to the input $X_n$. It can be shown that the transfer function of the linear system defined by the above equation is

$$H(f) = \frac{\sum_{i'=0}^{p} \beta_{i'} e^{-j2\pi f i'}}{1 + \sum_{i=1}^{q} \alpha_{i} e^{-j2\pi f i}}.$$

The power spectral density of the ARMA process is

$$S_Y(f) = |H(f)|^2 \sigma_W^2.$$

ARMA models are used extensively in random time series analysis and in signal processing. The general **autoregressive process** is the special case of the ARMA process with $\beta_1 = \beta_2 = \cdots = \beta_p = 0$. The general **moving average process** is the special case of the ARMA process with $\alpha_1 = \alpha_2 = \cdots = \alpha_q = 0$. Octave has a function `filter(b, a, x)` which takes a set of coefficients $b = (\beta_1, \beta_2, \ldots, \beta_{p+1})$ and $a = (\alpha_1, \alpha_2, \ldots, \alpha_q)$ as coefficient for a filter as in Eq. (10.55) and produces the output corresponding to the input sequence $x$. The choice of $a$ and $b$ can lead to a broad range of discrete-time filters.

For example, if we let $a = (1/N, 1/N, \ldots, 1/N)$ we obtain a moving average filter:

$$Y_n = (W_n + W_{n-1} + \cdots + W_{n-N+1})/N.$$

Figure 10.8 shows a zero-mean, unit-variance Gaussian iid sequence $W_n$ and the outputs from an $N = 3$ and an $N = 10$ moving average filter. It can be seen that the $N = 3$ filter moderates the extreme variations but generally tracks the fluctuations in $X_n$. The $N = 10$ filter on the other hand severely limits the variations and only tracks slower longer-lasting trends.

Figures 10.9(a) and (b) show the result of passing an iid Gaussian sequence $X_n$ through first-order autoregressive filters as in Eq. (10.54). The AR sequence with $\alpha = 0.1$ has low correlation between adjacent samples and so the sequence remains similar to the underlying iid random process. The AR sequence with $\alpha = 0.75$ has higher correlation between adjacent samples which tends to cause longer lasting trends as evident in Fig. 10.9(b).

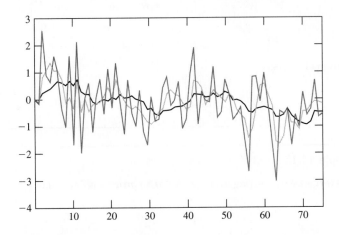

**FIGURE 10.8**
Moving average process showing iid Gaussian sequence and corresponding $N = 3, N = 10$ moving average processes.

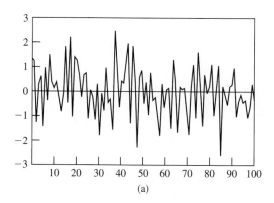

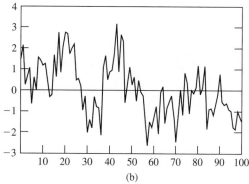

**FIGURE 10.9**
(a) First-order autoregressive process with $\alpha = 0.1$; (b) with $\alpha = 0.75$.

## 10.3    BANDLIMITED RANDOM PROCESSES

In this section we consider two important applications that involve random processes with power spectral densities that are nonzero over a finite range of frequencies. The first application involves the sampling theorem, which states that bandlimited random processes can be represented in terms of a sequence of their time samples. This theorem forms the basis for modern digital signal processing systems. The second application involves the modulation of sinusoidal signals by random information signals. Modulation is a key element of all modern communication systems.

### 10.3.1    Sampling of Bandlimited Random Processes

One of the major technology advances in the twentieth century was the development of digital signal processing technology. All modern multimedia systems depend in some way on the processing of digital signals. Many information signals, e.g., voice, music, imagery, occur naturally as analog signals that are continuous-valued and that vary continuously in time or space or both. The two key steps in making these signals amenable to digital signal processing are: (1). Convert the continuous-time signals into discrete-time signals by sampling the amplitudes; (2) Representing the samples using a fixed number of bits. In this section we introduce the sampling theorem for wide-sense stationary bandlimited random processes, which addresses the conversion of signals into discrete-time sequences.

Let $x(t)$ be a deterministic, finite-energy time signal that has Fourier transform $\tilde{X}(f) = \mathcal{F}\{x(t)\}$ that is nonzero only in the frequency range $|f| \leq W$. Suppose we sample $x(t)$ every $T$ seconds to obtain the sequence of sample values: $\{\ldots, x(-2T), x(-T), x(0), x(T), \ldots\}$. *The sampling theorem for deterministic signals states that $x(t)$ can be recovered exactly from the sequence of samples if $T \leq 1/2W$ or equivalently $1/T \geq 2W$,* that is, the sampling rate is at least twice the bandwidth of the signal. The minimum sampling rate $1/2W$ is called the **Nyquist sampling rate**. The sampling

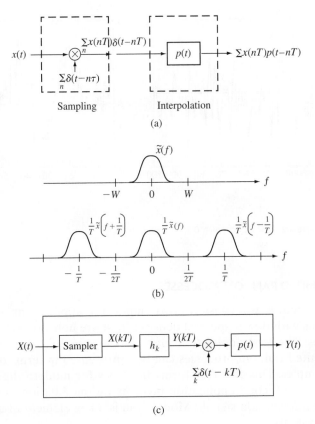

**FIGURE 10.10**
(a) Sampling and interpolation; (b) Fourier transform of sampled deterministic signal; (c) Sampling, digital filtering, and interpolation.

theorem provides the following interpolation formula for recovering $x(t)$ from the samples:

$$x(t) = \sum_{n=-\infty}^{\infty} x(nT)p(t - nT) \quad \text{where} \quad p(t) = \frac{\sin(\pi t/T)}{\pi t/T}. \tag{10.56}$$

Eq. (10.56) provides us with the interesting interpretation depicted in Fig. 10.10(a). The process of sampling $x(t)$ can be viewed as the multiplication of $x(t)$ by a train of delta functions spaced $T$ seconds apart. The sampled function is then represented by:

$$x_s(t) = \sum_{n=-\infty}^{\infty} x(nT)\delta(t - nT). \tag{10.57}$$

Eq. (10.56) can be viewed as the response of a linear system with impulse response $p(t)$ to the signal $x_s(t)$. It is easy to show that the $p(t)$ in Eq. (10.56) corresponds to the ideal lowpass filter in Fig. 10.6:

$$P(f) = \mathscr{F}\{p(t)\} = \begin{cases} 1 & -W \le f \le W \\ 0 & |f| > W. \end{cases}$$

The proof of the sampling theorem involves the following steps. We show that

$$\mathcal{F}\left\{\sum_{n=-\infty}^{\infty} x(nT)p(t - nT)\right\} = \frac{1}{T}P(f) \sum_{k=-\infty}^{\infty} \tilde{X}(f - \frac{k}{T}), \qquad (10.58)$$

which consists of the sum of translated versions of $\tilde{X}(f) = \mathcal{F}\{x(t)\}$, as shown in Fig. 10.10(b). We then observe that as long as $1/T \geq 2W$, then $P(f)$ in the above expressions selects the $k = 0$ term in the summation, which corresponds to $X(f)$. See Problem 10.45 for details.

---

### Example 10.16    Sampling a WSS Random Process

Let $X(t)$ be a WSS process with autocorrelation function $R_X(\tau)$. Find the mean and covariance functions of the discrete-time sampled process $X_n = X(nT)$ for $n = 0, \pm1, \pm2, \ldots$.

Since $X(t)$ is WSS, the mean and covariance functions are:

$$m_X(n) = E[X(nT)] = m$$

$$E[X_{n_1}X_{n_2}] = E[X(n_1T)X(n_2T)] = R_X(n_1T - n_2T) = R_X((n_1 - n_2)T).$$

This shows $X_n$ is a WSS discrete-time process.

---

Let $X(t)$ be a WSS process with autocorrelation function $R_X(\tau)$ and power spectral density $S_X(f)$. Suppose that $S_X(f)$ is bandlimited, that is,

$$S_X(f) = 0 \quad |f| > W.$$

We now show that the sampling theorem can be extended to $X(t)$. Let

$$\hat{X}(t) = \sum_{n=-\infty}^{\infty} X(nT)p(t - nT) \quad \text{where} \quad p(t) = \frac{\sin(\pi t/T)}{\pi t/T}, \qquad (10.59)$$

*then* $\hat{X}(t) = X(t)$ *in the mean square sense*. Recall that equality in the mean square sense does not imply equality for all sample functions, so this version of the sampling theorem is weaker than the version in Eq. (10.56) for finite energy signals.

To show Eq. (10.59) we first note that since $S_X(f) = \mathcal{F}\{R_X(\tau)\}$, we can apply the sampling theorem for deterministic signals to $R_X(\tau)$:

$$R_X(\tau) = \sum_{n=-\infty}^{\infty} R_X(nT)p(\tau - nT). \qquad (10.60)$$

Next we consider the mean square error associated with Eq. (10.59):

$$E[\{X(t) - \hat{X}(t)\}^2] = E[\{X(t) - \hat{X}(t)\}X(t)] - E[\{X(t) - \hat{X}(t)\}\hat{X}(t)]$$

$$= \{E[X(t)X(t)] - E[\hat{X}(t)X(t)]\} -$$
$$\{E[X(t)\hat{X}(t)] - E[\hat{X}(t)\hat{X}(t)]\}.$$

It is easy to show that Eq. (10.60) implies that each of the terms in braces is equal to zero. (See Problem 10.48.) We then conclude that $\hat{X}(t) = X(t)$ in the mean square sense.

## Example 10.17    Digital Filtering of a Sampled WSS Random Process

Let $X(t)$ be a WSS process with power spectral density $S_X(f)$ that is nonzero only for $|f| \leq W$. Consider the sequence of operations shown in Fig. 10.10(c): (1) $X(t)$ is sampled at the Nyquist rate; (2) the samples $X(nT)$ are input into a digital filter in Fig. 10.7(b) with $\alpha_1 = \alpha_2 = \cdots = \alpha_q = 0$; and (3) the resulting output sequence $Y_n$ is fed into the interpolation filter. Find the power spectral density of the output $Y(t)$.

The output of the digital filter is given by:

$$Y(kT) = \sum_{n=0}^{p} \beta_n X((k-n)T)$$

and the corresponding autocorrelation from Eq. (10.51) is:

$$R_Y(kT) = \sum_{n=0}^{p} \sum_{i=0}^{p} \beta_n \beta_i R_X((k+n-i)T).$$

The autocorrelation of $Y(t)$ is found from the interpolation formula (Eq. 10.60):

$$R_Y(\tau) = \sum_{k=-\infty}^{\infty} R_Y(kT)p(\tau - kT) = \sum_{k=-\infty}^{\infty} \sum_{n=0}^{p} \sum_{i=0}^{p} \beta_n \beta_i R_X((k+n-i)T)p(\tau - kT)$$

$$= \sum_{n=0}^{p} \sum_{i=0}^{p} \beta_n \beta_i \left\{ \sum_{k=-\infty}^{\infty} R_X((k+n-i)T)p(\tau - kT) \right\}$$

$$= \sum_{n=0}^{p} \sum_{i=0}^{p} \beta_n \beta_i R_X(\tau + (n-i)T).$$

The output power spectral density is then:

$$S_Y(f) = \mathscr{F}\{R_Y(\tau)\} = \sum_{n=0}^{p} \sum_{i=0}^{p} \beta_n \beta_i \mathscr{F}\{R_X(\tau + (n-i)T)\}$$

$$= \sum_{n=0}^{p} \sum_{i=0}^{p} \beta_n \beta_i S_X(f) e^{-j2\pi f(n-i)T}$$

$$= \left\{ \sum_{n=0}^{p} \beta_n e^{-j2\pi fnT} \right\} \left\{ \sum_{i=0}^{p} \beta_i e^{j2\pi fiT} \right\} S_X(f)$$

$$= |H(fT)|^2 S_X(f) \tag{10.61}$$

where $H(f)$ is the transfer function of the digital filter as per Eq. (10.49). The key finding here is the appearance of $H(f)$ *evaluated at* $fT$. We have obtained a very nice result that characterizes the overall system response in Fig. 10.8 to the continuous-time input $X(t)$. This result is true for more general digital filters, see [Oppenheim and Schafer].

The sampling theorem provides an important bridge between continuous-time and discrete-time signal processing. It gives us a means for implementing the real as well as the simulated processing of random signals. First, we must sample the random process above its Nyquist sampling rate. We can then perform whatever digital processing is necessary. We can finally recover the continuous-time signal by interpolation. The only difference between real signal processing and simulated signal processing is that the former usually has real-time requirements, whereas the latter allows us to perform our processing at whatever rate is possible using the available computing power.

### 10.3.2    Amplitude Modulation by Random Signals

Many of the transmission media used in communication systems can be modeled as linear systems and their behavior can be specified by a transfer function $H(f)$, which passes certain frequencies and rejects others. Quite often the information signal $A(t)$ (i.e., a speech or music signal) is not at the frequencies that propagate well. The purpose of a **modulator** is to map the information signal $A(t)$ into a transmission signal $X(t)$ that is in a frequency range that propagates well over the desired medium. At the receiver, we need to perform an inverse mapping to recover $A(t)$ from $X(t)$. In this section, we discuss two of the amplitude modulation methods.

Let $A(t)$ be a WSS random process that represents an information signal. In general $A(t)$ will be "lowpass" in character, that is, its power spectral density will be concentrated at low frequencies, as shown in Fig. 10.11(a). An **amplitude modulation** (AM) system produces a transmission signal by multiplying $A(t)$ by a "carrier" signal $\cos(2\pi f_c t + \Theta)$:

$$X(t) = A(t)\cos(2\pi f_c t + \Theta), \tag{10.62}$$

where we assume $\Theta$ is a random variable that is uniformly distributed in the interval $(0, 2\pi)$, and $\Theta$ and $A(t)$ are independent.

The autocorrelation of $X(t)$ is

$$E[X(t + \tau)X(t)]$$
$$= E[A(t + \tau)\cos(2\pi f_c(t + \tau) + \Theta)A(t)\cos(2\pi f_c t + \Theta)]$$
$$= E[A(t + \tau)A(t)]E[\cos(2\pi f_c(t + \tau) + \Theta)\cos(2\pi f_c t + \Theta)]$$

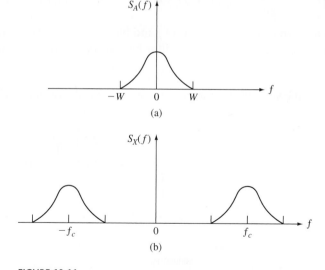

**FIGURE 10.11**
(a) A lowpass information signal; (b) an amplitude-modulated signal.

$$= R_A(\tau)E\left[\frac{1}{2}\cos(2\pi f_c\tau) + \frac{1}{2}\cos(2\pi f_c(2t + \tau) + 2\Theta)\right]$$

$$= \frac{1}{2}R_A(\tau)\cos(2\pi f_c\tau), \tag{10.63}$$

where we used the fact that $E[\cos(2\pi f_c(2t + \tau) + 2\Theta)] = 0$ (see Example 9.10). Thus $X(t)$ is also a wide-sense stationary random process.

The power spectral density of $X(t)$ is

$$S_X(f) = \mathscr{F}\left\{\frac{1}{2}R_A(\tau)\cos(2\pi f_c\tau)\right\}$$

$$= \frac{1}{4}S_A(f + f_c) + \frac{1}{4}S_A(f - f_c), \tag{10.64}$$

where we used the table of Fourier transforms in Appendix B. Figure 10.11(b) shows $S_X(f)$. It can be seen that the power spectral density of the information signal has been shifted to the regions around $\pm f_c$. $X(t)$ is an example of a **bandpass signal**. Bandpass signals are characterized as having their power spectral density concentrated about some frequency much greater than zero.

The transmission signal is demodulated by multiplying it by the carrier signal and lowpass filtering, as shown in Fig. 10.12. Let

$$Y(t) = X(t)2\cos(2\pi f_c t + \Theta). \tag{10.65}$$

Proceeding as above, we find that

$$S_Y(f) = \frac{1}{2}S_X(f + f_c) + \frac{1}{2}S_X(f - f_c)$$

$$= \frac{1}{2}\{S_A(f + 2f_c) + S_A(f)\} + \frac{1}{2}\{S_A(f) + S_A(f - 2f_c)\}.$$

The ideal lowpass filter passes $S_A(f)$ and blocks $S_A(f \pm 2f_c)$, which is centered about $\pm f$, so the output of the lowpass filter has power spectral density

$$S_Y(f) = S_A(f).$$

In fact, from Example 10.11 we know the output is the original information signal, $A(t)$.

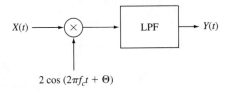

**FIGURE 10.12**
AM demodulator.

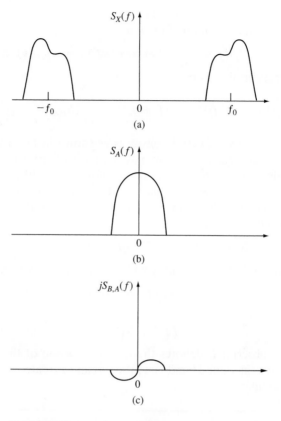

**FIGURE 10.13**
(a) A general bandpass signal. (b) a real-valued even function
of $f$. (c) an imaginary odd function of $f$.

The modulation method in Eq. (10.56) can only produce bandpass signals for which $S_X(f)$ is locally symmetric about $f_c$, $S_X(f_c + \delta f) = S_X(f_c - \delta f)$ for $|\delta f| < W$, as in Fig. 10.11(b). The method cannot yield real-valued transmission signals whose power spectral density lack this symmetry, such as shown in Fig. 10.13(a). The following **quadrature amplitude modulation** (QAM) method can be used to produce such signals:

$$X(t) = A(t) \cos(2\pi f_c t + \Theta) + B(t) \sin(2\pi f_c t + \Theta), \qquad (10.66)$$

where $A(t)$ and $B(t)$ are real-valued, jointly wide-sense stationary random processes, and we require that

$$R_A(\tau) = R_B(\tau) \qquad (10.67a)$$

$$R_{B,A}(\tau) = -R_{A,B}(\tau). \qquad (10.67b)$$

Note that Eq. (10.67a) implies that $S_A(f) = S_B(f)$, a real-valued, even function of $f$, as shown in Fig. 10.13(b). Note also that Eq. (10.67b) implies that $S_{B,A}(f)$ is a purely imaginary, odd function of $f$, as also shown in Fig. 10.13(c) (see Problem 10.57).

Proceeding as before, we can show that $X(t)$ is a wide-sense stationary random process with autocorrelation function

$$R_X(\tau) = R_A(\tau) \cos(2\pi f_c \tau) + R_{B,A}(\tau) \sin(2\pi f_c \tau) \qquad (10.68)$$

and power spectral density

$$S_X(f) = \frac{1}{2}\{S_A(f - f_c) + S_A(f + f_c)\} + \frac{1}{2j}\{S_{BA}(f - f_c) - S_{BA}(f + f_c)\}. \qquad (10.69)$$

The resulting power spectral density is as shown in Fig. 10.13(a). Thus QAM can be used to generate real-valued bandpass signals with arbitrary power spectral density.

Bandpass random signals, such as those in Fig. 10.13(a), arise in communication systems when wide-sense stationary white noise is filtered by bandpass filters. Let $N(t)$ be such a process with power spectral density $S_N(f)$. It can be shown that $N(t)$ can be represented by

$$N(t) = N_c(t) \cos(2\pi f_c t + \Theta) - N_s(t) \sin(2\pi f_c t + \Theta), \qquad (10.70)$$

where $N_c(t)$ and $N_s(t)$ are jointly wide-sense stationary processes with

$$S_{N_c}(f) = S_{N_s}(f) = \{S_N(f - f_c) + S_N(f + f_c)\}_L \qquad (10.71)$$

and

$$S_{N_c,N_s}(f) = j\{S_N(f - f_c) - S_N(f + f_c)\}_L, \qquad (10.72)$$

where the subscript $L$ denotes the lowpass portion of the expression in brackets. In words, every real-valued bandpass process can be treated as if it had been generated by a QAM modulator.

---

### Example 10.18    Demodulation of Noisy Signal

The received signal in an AM system is

$$Y(t) = A(t) \cos(2\pi f_c t + \Theta) + N(t),$$

where $N(t)$ is a bandlimited white noise process with spectral density

$$S_N(f) = \begin{cases} \dfrac{N_0}{2} & |f \pm f_c| < W \\ 0 & \text{elsewhere.} \end{cases}$$

Find the signal-to-noise ratio of the recovered signal.

Equation (10.70) allows us to represent the received signal by

$$Y(t) = \{A(t) + N_c(t)\} \cos(2\pi f_c t + \Theta) - N_s(t) \sin(2\pi f_c t + \Theta).$$

The demodulator in Fig. 10.12 is used to recover $A(t)$. After multiplication by $2\cos(2\pi f_c t + \Theta)$, we have

$$2Y(t) \cos(2\pi f_c t + \Theta) = \{A(t) + N_c(t)\}2\cos^2(2\pi f_c t + \Theta)$$
$$- N_s(t)2\cos(2\pi f_c t + \Theta)\sin(2\pi f_c t + \Theta)$$
$$= \{A(t) + N_c(t)\}(1 + \cos(4\pi f_c t + 2\Theta))$$
$$- N_s(t)\sin(4\pi f_c t + 2\Theta).$$

After lowpass filtering, the recovered signal is

$$A(t) + N_c(t).$$

The power in the signal and noise components, respectively, are

$$\sigma_A^2 = \int_{-W}^{W} S_A(f)\, df$$

$$\sigma_{N_c}^2 = \int_{-W}^{W} S_{N_c}(f)\, df = \int_{-W}^{W} \left( \frac{N_0}{2} + \frac{N_0}{2} \right) df = 2WN_0.$$

The output signal-to-noise ratio is then

$$\text{SNR} = \frac{\sigma_A^2}{2WN_0}.$$

## 10.4    OPTIMUM LINEAR SYSTEMS

Many problems can be posed in the following way. We observe a discrete-time, zero-mean process $X_\alpha$ over a certain time interval $I = \{t - a, \ldots, t + b\}$, and we are required to use the $a + b + 1$ resulting observations $\{X_{t-a}, \ldots, X_t, \ldots, X_{t+b}\}$ to obtain an estimate $Y_t$ for some other (presumably related) zero-mean process $Z_t$. The estimate $Y_t$ is required to be linear, as shown in Fig. 10.14:

$$Y_t = \sum_{\beta=t-a}^{t+b} h_{t-\beta} X_\beta = \sum_{\beta=-b}^{a} h_\beta X_{t-\beta}. \tag{10.73}$$

The figure of merit for the estimator is the mean square error

$$E[e_t^2] = E[(Z_t - Y_t)^2], \tag{10.74}$$

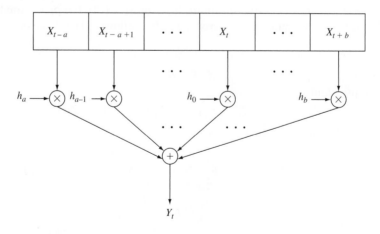

**FIGURE 10.14**
A linear system for producing an estimate $Y_t$.

and we seek to find the **optimum filter**, which is characterized by the impulse response $h_\beta$ that minimizes the mean square error.

Examples 10.19 and 10.20 show that different choices of $Z_t$ and $X_\alpha$ and of observation interval correspond to different estimation problems.

---

### Example 10.19     Filtering and Smoothing Problems

Let the observations be the sum of a "desired signal" $Z_\alpha$ plus unwanted "noise" $N_\alpha$:

$$X_\alpha = Z_\alpha + N_\alpha \qquad \alpha \in I.$$

We are interested in estimating the desired signal at time $t$. The relation between $t$ and the observation interval $I$ gives rise to a variety of estimation problems.

If $I = (-\infty, t)$, that is, $a = \infty$ and $b = 0$, then we have a **filtering** problem where we estimate $Z_t$ in terms of noisy observations of the past and present. If $I = (t - a, t)$, then we have a filtering problem in which we estimate $Z_t$ in terms of the $a + 1$ most recent noisy observations.

If $I = (-\infty, \infty)$, that is, $a = b = \infty$, then we have a **smoothing** problem where we are attempting to recover the signal from its entire noisy version. There are applications where this makes sense, for example, if the entire realization $X_\alpha$ has been recorded and the estimate $Z_t$ is obtained by "playing back" $X_\alpha$.

---

### Example 10.20     Prediction

Suppose we want to predict $Z_t$ in terms of its recent past: $\{Z_{t-a}, \ldots, Z_{t-1}\}$. The general estimation problem becomes this **prediction** problem if we let the observation $X_\alpha$ be the past $a$ values of the signal $Z_\alpha$, that is,

$$X_\alpha = Z_\alpha \qquad t - a \le \alpha \le t - 1.$$

The estimate $Y_t$ is then a linear prediction of $Z_t$ in terms of its most recent values.

---

## 10.4.1   The Orthogonality Condition

It is easy to show that the optimum filter must satisfy the **orthogonality condition** (see Eq. 6.56), which states that the error $e_t$ must be orthogonal to all the observations $X_\alpha$, that is,

$$0 = E[e_t X_\alpha] \qquad \text{for all } \alpha \in I$$
$$= E[(Z_t - Y_t)X_\alpha] = 0, \tag{10.75}$$

or equivalently,

$$E[Z_t X_\alpha] = E[Y_t X_\alpha] \qquad \text{for all } \alpha \in I. \tag{10.76}$$

If we substitute Eq. (10.73) into Eq. (10.76) we find

$$E[Z_t X_\alpha] = E\left[ \sum_{\beta=-b}^{a} h_\beta X_{t-\beta} X_\alpha \right] \qquad \text{for all } \alpha \in I$$

$$= \sum_{\beta=-b}^{a} h_\beta E[X_{t-\beta} X_\alpha]$$

$$= \sum_{\beta=-b}^{a} h_\beta R_X(t - \alpha - \beta) \qquad \text{for all } \alpha \in I. \tag{10.77}$$

Equation (10.77) shows that $E[Z_t X_\alpha]$ depends only on $t - \alpha$, and thus $X_\alpha$ and $Z_t$ are jointly wide-sense stationary processes. Therefore, we can rewrite Eq. (10.77) as follows:

$$R_{Z,X}(t - \alpha) = \sum_{\beta=-b}^{a} h_\beta R_X(t - \beta - \alpha) \qquad t - a \le \alpha \le t + b.$$

Finally, letting $m = t - \alpha$, we obtain the following key equation:

$$R_{Z,X}(m) = \sum_{\beta=-b}^{a} h_\beta R_X(m - \beta) \qquad -b \le m \le a. \tag{10.78}$$

*The optimum linear filter must satisfy the set of $a + b + 1$ linear equations given by Eq. (10.78).* Note that Eq. (10.78) is identical to Eq. (6.60) for estimating a random variable by a linear combination of several random variables. The wide-sense stationarity of the processes reduces this estimation problem to the one considered in Section 6.5.

In the above derivation we deliberately used the notation $Z_t$ instead of $Z_n$ to suggest that the same development holds for *continuous-time estimation*. In particular, suppose we seek a linear estimate $Y(t)$ for the continuous-time random process $Z(t)$ in terms of observations of the continuous-time random process $X(\alpha)$ in the time interval $t - a \le \alpha \le t + b$:

$$Y(t) = \int_{t-a}^{t+b} h(t - \beta) X(\beta) \, d\beta = \int_{-b}^{a} h(\beta) X(t - \beta) \, d\beta.$$

It can then be shown that the filter $h(\beta)$ that minimizes the mean square error is specified by

$$R_{Z,X}(\tau) = \int_{-b}^{a} h(\beta) R_X(\tau - \beta) \, d\beta \qquad -b \le \tau \le a. \tag{10.79}$$

Thus in the time-continuous case we obtain an integral equation instead of a set of linear equations. The analytic solution of this integral equation can be quite difficult, but the equation can be solved numerically by approximating the integral by a summation.[7]

We now determine the mean square error of the optimum filter. First we note that for the optimum filter, the error $e_t$ and the estimate $Y_t$ are orthogonal since

$$E[e_t Y_t] = E\left[e_t \sum h_{t-\beta} X_\beta\right] = \sum h_{t-\beta} E[e_t X_\beta] = 0,$$

where the terms inside the last summation are 0 because of Eq. (10.75). Since $e_t = Z_t - Y_t$, the mean square error is then

$$E[e_t^2] = E[e_t(Z_t - Y_t)]$$
$$= E[e_t Z_t],$$

---

[7]Equation (10.79) can also be solved by using the Karhunen-Loeve expansion.

since $e_t$ and $Y_t$ are orthogonal. Substituting for $e_t$ yields

$$E[e_t^2] = E[(Z_t - Y_t)Z_t] = E[Z_t Z_t] - E[Y_t Z_t]$$

$$= R_Z(0) - E[Z_t Y_t]$$

$$= R_Z(0) - E\left[ Z_t \sum_{\beta=-b}^{a} h_\beta X_{t-\beta} \right]$$

$$= R_Z(0) - \sum_{\beta=-b}^{a} h_\beta R_{Z,X}(\beta). \tag{10.80}$$

Similarly, it can be shown that the mean square error of the optimum filter in the continuous-time case is

$$E[e^2(t)] = R_Z(0) = \int_{-b}^{a} h(\beta) R_{Z,X}(\beta) \, d\beta. \tag{10.81}$$

The following theorems summarize the above results.

---

**Theorem**

Let $X_t$ and $Z_t$ be discrete-time, zero-mean, jointly wide-sense stationary processes, and let $Y_t$ be an estimate for $Z_t$ of the form

$$Y_t = \sum_{\beta=t-a}^{t+b} h_{t-\beta} X_\beta = \sum_{\beta=-b}^{a} h_\beta X_{t-\beta}.$$

The filter that minimizes $E[(Z_t - Y_t)^2]$ satisfies the equation

$$R_{Z,X}(m) = \sum_{\beta=-b}^{a} h_\beta R_X(m - \beta) \qquad -b \le m \le a$$

and has mean square error given by

$$E[(Z_t - Y_t)^2] = R_Z(0) - \sum_{\beta=-b}^{a} h_\beta R_{Z,X}(\beta).$$

---

**Theorem**

Let $X(t)$ and $Z(t)$ be continuous-time, zero-mean, jointly wide-sense stationary processes, and let $Y(t)$ be an estimate for $Z(t)$ of the form

$$Y(t) = \int_{t-a}^{t+b} h(t - \beta) X(\beta) \, d\beta = \int_{-b}^{a} h(\beta) X(t - \beta) \, d\beta.$$

The filter $h(\beta)$ that minimizes $E[(Z(t) - Y(t))^2]$ satisfies the equation

$$R_{Z,X}(\tau) = \int_{-b}^{a} h(\beta) R_X(\tau - \beta) \, d\beta \qquad -b \le \tau \le a$$

and has mean square error given by

$$E[(Z(t) - Y(t))^2] = R_Z(0) - \int_{-b}^{a} h(\beta)R_{Z,X}(\beta)\,d\beta.$$

---

### Example 10.21    Filtering of Signal Plus Noise

Suppose we are interested in estimating the signal $Z_n$ from the $p + 1$ most recent noisy observations:

$$X_\alpha = Z_\alpha + N_\alpha \qquad \alpha \in I = \{n - p, \ldots, n - 1, n\}.$$

Find the set of linear equations for the optimum filter if $Z_\alpha$ and $N_\alpha$ are independent random processes.

For this choice of observation interval, Eq. (10.78) becomes

$$R_{Z,X}(m) = \sum_{\beta=0}^{p} h_\beta R_X(m - \beta) \qquad m \in \{0, 1, \ldots, p\}. \tag{10.82}$$

The cross-correlation terms in Eq. (10.82) are given by

$$R_{Z,X}(m) = E[Z_n X_{n-m}] = E[Z_n(Z_{n-m} + N_{n-m})] = R_Z(m).$$

The autocorrelation terms are given by

$$\begin{aligned}
R_X(m - \beta) &= E[X_{n-\beta}X_{n-m}] = E[(Z_{n-\beta} + N_{n-\beta})(Z_{n-m} + N_{n-m})] \\
&= R_Z(m - \beta) + R_{Z,N}(m - \beta) \\
&\quad + R_{N,Z}(m - \beta) + R_N(m - \beta) \\
&= R_Z(m - \beta) + R_N(m - \beta),
\end{aligned}$$

since $Z_\alpha$ and $N_\alpha$ are independent random processes. Thus Eq. (10.82) for the optimum filter becomes

$$R_Z(m) = \sum_{\beta=0}^{p} h_\beta\{R_Z(m - \beta) + R_N(m - \beta)\} \quad m \in \{0, 1, \ldots, p\}. \tag{10.83}$$

This set of $p + 1$ linear equations in $p + 1$ unknowns $h_\beta$ is solved by matrix inversion.

---

### Example 10.22    Filtering of AR Signal Plus Noise

Find the set of equations for the optimum filter in Example 10.21 if $Z_\alpha$ is a first-order autoregressive process with average power $\sigma_Z^2$ and parameter $r$, $|r| < 1$, and $N_\alpha$ is a white noise process with average power $\sigma_N^2$.

The autocorrelation for a first-order autoregressive process is given by

$$R_Z(m) = \sigma_Z^2 r^{|m|} \qquad m = 0, \pm 1, \pm 2, \ldots.$$

(See Problem 10.42.) The autocorrelation for the white noise process is

$$R_N(m) = \sigma_N^2\,\delta(m).$$

Substituting $R_Z(m)$ and $R_N(m)$ into Eq. (10.83) yields the following set of linear equations:

$$\sigma_Z^2 r^{|m|} = \sum_{\beta=0}^{p} h_\beta(\sigma_Z^2 r^{|m-\beta|} + \sigma_N^2 \delta(m - \beta)) \qquad m \in \{0, \ldots, p\}. \tag{10.84}$$

If we divide both sides of Eq. (10.84) by $\sigma_Z^2$ and let $\Gamma = \sigma_N^2/\sigma_Z^2$, we obtain the following matrix equation:

$$
\begin{bmatrix}
1+\Gamma & r & r^2 & \cdots & r^p \\
r & 1+\Gamma & r & \cdots & r^{p-1} \\
r^2 & r & 1+\Gamma & \cdots & r^{p-2} \\
\cdot & \cdot & \cdot & \cdots & \cdot \\
r^p & r^{p-1} & r^{p-2} & \cdots & 1+\Gamma
\end{bmatrix}
\begin{bmatrix}
h_0 \\ h_1 \\ \cdot \\ \cdot \\ h_p
\end{bmatrix}
=
\begin{bmatrix}
1 \\ r \\ \cdot \\ \cdot \\ r^p
\end{bmatrix}.
\tag{10.85}
$$

Note that when the noise power is zero, i.e., $\Gamma = 0$, then the solution is $h_0 = 1, h_j = 0$, $j = 1, \ldots, p$, that is, no filtering is required to obtain $Z_n$.

Equation (10.85) can be readily solved using Octave. The following function will compute the optimum linear coefficients and the mean square error of the optimum predictor:

```
function [mse]= Lin_Est_AR (order,rho,varsig,varnoise)
n=[0:1:order-1]
r=varsig*rho.^n;
R=varnoise*eye(order)+toeplitz(r);
H=inv(R)*transpose(r)
mse=varsig-transpose(H)*transpose(r);
endfunction
```

Table 10.1 gives the values of the optimal predictor coefficients and the mean square error as the order of the estimator is increased for the first-order autoregressive process with $\sigma_Z^2 = 4$, $r = 0.9$, and noise variance $\sigma_N^2 = 4$. It can be seen that the predictor places heavier weight on more recent samples, which is consistent with the higher correlation of such samples with the current sample. For smaller values of $r$, the correlation for distant samples drops off more quickly and the coefficients place even lower weighting on them. The mean square error can also be seen to decrease with increasing order $p + 1$ of the estimator. Increasing the first few orders provides significant improvements, but a point of diminishing returns is reached around $p + 1 = 3$.

### 10.4.2 Prediction

The linear prediction problem arises in many signal processing applications. In Example 6.31 in Chapter 6, we already discussed the linear prediction of speech signals. In general, we wish to predict $Z_n$ in terms of $Z_{n-1}, Z_{n-2}, \ldots, Z_{n-p}$:

$$
Y_n = \sum_{\beta=1}^{p} h_\beta Z_{n-\beta}.
$$

**TABLE 10.1** Effect of predictor order on MSE performance.

| $p + 1$ | MSE | Coefficients | | | | |
|---|---|---|---|---|---|---|
| 1 | 2.0000 | 0.5 | | | | |
| 2 | 1.4922 | 0.37304 | 0.28213 | | | |
| 3 | 1.3193 | 0.32983 | 0.22500 | 0.17017 | | |
| 4 | 1.2549 | 0.31374 | 0.20372 | 0.13897 | 0.10510 | |
| 5 | 1.2302 | 0.30754 | 0.19552 | 0.12696 | 0.08661 | 0.065501 |

For this problem, $X_\alpha = Z_\alpha$, so Eq. (10.79) becomes

$$R_Z(m) = \sum_{\beta=1}^{p} h_\beta R_Z(m - \beta) \qquad m \in \{1, \dots, p\}. \tag{10.86a}$$

In matrix form this equation becomes

$$
\begin{bmatrix} R_Z(1) \\ R_Z(2) \\ . \\ . \\ . \\ R_Z(p) \end{bmatrix} =
\begin{bmatrix}
R_Z(0) & R_Z(1) & R_Z(2) & \cdots & R_Z(p-1) \\
R_Z(1) & R_Z(0) & R_Z(1) & \cdots & R_Z(p-2) \\
. & & . & & . \\
. & & . & & R_Z(1) \\
R_Z(p-1) & . & . & R_Z(1) & R_Z(0)
\end{bmatrix}
\begin{bmatrix} h_1 \\ h_2 \\ . \\ . \\ h_p \end{bmatrix}
$$

$$= \mathbf{R_Z h}. \tag{10.86b}$$

Equations (10.86a) and (10.86b) are called the **Yule-Walker equations**. Equation (10.80) for the mean square error becomes

$$E[e_n^2] = R_Z(0) - \sum_{\beta=1}^{p} h_\beta R_Z(\beta). \tag{10.87}$$

By inverting the $p \times p$ matrix $\mathbf{R_Z}$, we can solve for the vector of filter coefficients $h$.

---

**Example 10.23    Prediction for Long-Range and Short-Range Dependent Processes**

Let $X_1(t)$ be a discrete-time first-order autoregressive process with $\sigma_X^2 = 1$ and $r = 0.7411$, and let $X_2(t)$ be a discrete-time long-range dependent process with autocovariance given by Eq. (9.109), $\sigma_X^2 = 1$, and $H = 0.9$. Both processes have $C_X(1) = 0.7411$, but the autocovariance of $X_1(t)$ decreases exponentially while that of $X_2(t)$ has long-range dependence. Compare the performance of the optimal linear predictor for these processes for short-term as well as long-term predictions.

The optimum linear coefficients and the associated mean square error for the long-range dependent process can be calculated using the following code. The function can be modified for the autoregressive case.

```
function mse= Lin_Pred_LR(order,Hurst,varsig)
n=[0:1:order-1]
H2=2*Hurst
r=varsig*((1+n).^H2-2*(n.^H2)+abs(n-1).^H2)/2
rz=varsig*((2+n).^H2-2*((n+1).^H2)+(n).^H2)/2
R=toeplitz(r);
H=transpose(inv(R)*transpose(rz))
mse=varsig-H*transpose(rz)
endfunction
```

Table 10.2 below compares the mean square errors and the coefficients of the two processes in the case of short-term prediction. The predictor for $X_1(t)$ attains all of the benefit of prediction with a $p = 1$ system. The optimum predictors for higher-order systems set the other coefficients to zero, and the mean square error remains at 0.4577. The predictor for $X_2(t)$

**TABLE 10.2(a)** Short-term prediction: autoregressive, $r = 0.7411, \sigma_X^2 = 1, C_X(1) = 0.7411$.

| $p$ | MSE | Coefficients | |
|---|---|---|---|
| 1 | 0.45077 | 0.74110 | |
| 2 | 0.45077 | 0.74110 | 0 |

**TABLE 10.2(b)** Short-term prediction: long-range dependent process, Hurst $= 0.9, \sigma_X^2 = 1, C_X(1) = 0.7411$.

| $p$ | MSE | Coefficients | | | |
|---|---|---|---|---|---|
| 1 | 0.45077 | 0.74110 | | | |
| 2 | 0.43625 | 0.60809 | 0.17948 | | |
| 3 | 0.42712 | 0.582127 | 0.091520 | 0.144649 | |
| 4 | 0.42253 | 0.567138 | 0.082037 | 0.084329 | 0.103620 |
| 5 | 0.41964 | 0.558567 | 0.075061 | 0.077543 | 0.056707 | 0.082719 |

achieves most of the possible performance with a $p = 1$ system, but small reductions in mean square error do accrue by adding more coefficients. This is due to the persistent correlation among the values in $X_2(t)$.

Table 10.3 shows the dramatic impact of long-range dependence on prediction performance. We modified Eq. (10.86) to provide the optimum linear predictor for $X_t$ based on two observations $X_{t-10}$ and $X_{t-20}$ that are in the relatively remote past. $X_1(t)$ and its previous values are almost uncorrelated, so the best predictor has a mean square error of almost 1, which is the variance of $X_1(t)$. On the other hand, $X_2(t)$ retains significant correlation with its previous values and so the mean square error provides a significant reduction from the unit variance. Note that the second-order predictor places significant weight on the observation 20 samples in the past.

**TABLE 10.3(a)** Long-term prediction: autoregressive, $r = 0.7411, \sigma_X^2 = 1, C_X(1) = 0.7411$.

| $p$ | MSE | Coefficients | |
|---|---|---|---|
| 1 | 0.99750 | 0.04977 | |
| 2 | 0.99750 | 0.04977 | 0 |

**TABLE 10.3(b)** Long-term prediction: long-range dependent process, Hurst $= 0.9, \sigma_X^2 = 1, C_X(1) = 0.7411$.

| $p$ | MSE | Coefficients | |
|---|---|---|---|
| 10 | 0.79354 | 0.45438 | |
| 10;20 | 0.74850 | 0.34614 | 0.23822 |

### 10.4.3   Estimation Using the Entire Realization of the Observed Process

Suppose that $Z_t$ is to be estimated by a linear function $Y_t$ of the entire realization of $X_t$, that is, $a = b = \infty$ and Eq. (10.73) becomes

$$Y_t = \sum_{\beta=-\infty}^{\infty} h_\beta X_{t-\beta}.$$

In the case of continuous-time random processes, we have

$$Y(t) = \int_{-\infty}^{\infty} h(\beta) X(t - \beta)\, d\beta.$$

The optimum filters must satisfy Eqs. (10.78) and (10.79), which in this case become

$$R_{Z,X}(m) = \sum_{\beta=-\infty}^{\infty} h_\beta R_X(m - \beta) \qquad \text{for all } m \tag{10.88a}$$

$$R_{Z,X}(\tau) = \int_{-\infty}^{\infty} h(\beta) R_X(\tau - \beta)\, d\beta \qquad \text{for all } \tau. \tag{10.88b}$$

The Fourier transform of the first equation and the Fourier transform of the second equation both yield the same expression:

$$S_{Z,X}(f) = H(f) S_X(f),$$

which is readily solved for the transfer function of the optimum filter:

$$H(f) = \frac{S_{Z,X}(f)}{S_X(f)}. \tag{10.89}$$

The impulse response of the optimum filter is then obtained by taking the appropriate inverse transform. In general the filter obtained from Eq. (10.89) will be noncausal, that is, its impulse response is nonzero for $t < 0$. We already indicated that there are applications where this makes sense, namely, in situations where the entire realization $X_\alpha$ is recorded and the estimate $Z_t$ is obtained in "nonreal time" by "playing back" $X_\alpha$.

---

### Example 10.24   Infinite Smoothing

Find the transfer function for the optimum filter for estimating $Z(t)$ from $X(\alpha) = Z(\alpha) + N(\alpha)$, $\alpha \in (-\infty, \infty)$, where $Z(\alpha)$ and $N(\alpha)$ are independent, zero-mean random processes.

The cross-correlation between the observation and the desired signal is

$$R_{Z,X}(\tau) = E[Z(t + \tau)X(t)] = E[Z(t + \tau)(Z(t) + N(t))]$$

$$= E[Z(t + \tau)Z(t)] + E[Z(t + \tau)N(t)]$$

$$= R_Z(\tau),$$

since $Z(t)$ and $N(t)$ are zero-mean, independent random processes. The cross-power spectral density is then

$$S_{Z,X}(t) = S_Z(f). \tag{10.90}$$

The autocorrelation of the observation process is

$$R_X(\tau) = E[(Z(t + \tau) + N(t + \tau))(Z(t) + N(t))]$$
$$= R_Z(\tau) + R_N(\tau).$$

The corresponding power spectral density is

$$S_X(f) = S_Z(f) + S_N(f). \tag{10.91}$$

Substituting Eqs. (10.90) and (10.91) into Eq. (10.89) gives

$$H(f) = \frac{S_Z(f)}{S_Z(f) + S_N(f)}. \tag{10.92}$$

Note that the optimum filter $H(f)$ is nonzero only at the frequencies where $S_Z(f)$ is nonzero, that is, where the signal has power content. By dividing the numerator and denominator of Eq. (10.92) by $S_Z(f)$, we see that $H(f)$ emphasizes the frequencies where the ratio of signal to noise power density is large.

---

### *10.4.4 Estimation Using Causal Filters

Now, suppose that $Z_t$ is to be estimated using only the past and present of $X_\alpha$, that is, $I = (-\infty, t)$. Equations (10.78) and (10.79) become

$$R_{Z,X}(m) = \sum_{\beta=0}^{\infty} h_\beta R_X(m - \beta) \qquad \text{for all } m \tag{10.93a}$$

$$R_{Z,X}(\tau) = \int_0^{\infty} h(\beta) R_X(\tau - \beta)\, d\beta \qquad \text{for all } \tau. \tag{10.93b}$$

Equations (10.93a) and (10.93b) are called the **Wiener-Hopf equations** and, though similar in appearance to Eqs. (10.88a) and (10.88b), are considerably more difficult to solve.

First, let us consider the special case where the observation process is white, that is, for the discrete-time case $R_X(m) = \delta_m$. Equation (10.93a) is then

$$R_{Z,X}(m) = \sum_{\beta=0}^{\infty} h_\beta\, \delta_{m-\beta} = h_m \qquad m \ge 0. \tag{10.94}$$

Thus in this special case, the optimum causal filter has coefficients given by

$$h_m = \begin{cases} 0 & m < 0 \\ R_{Z,X}(m) & m \ge 0. \end{cases}$$

The corresponding transfer function is

$$H(f) = \sum_{m=0}^{\infty} R_{Z,X}(m) e^{-j2\pi fm}. \tag{10.95}$$

Note Eq. (10.95) is *not* $S_{Z,X}(f)$, since the limits of the Fourier transform in Eq. (10.95) do not extend from $-\infty$ to $+\infty$. However, $H(f)$ can be obtained from $S_{Z,X}(f)$ by finding $h_m = \mathscr{F}^{-1}[S_{Z,X}(f)]$, keeping the causal part (i.e., $h_m$ for $m \ge 0$) and setting the noncausal part to 0.

We now show how the solution of the above special case can be used to solve the general case. It can be shown that under very general conditions, the power spectral density of a random process can be factored into the form

$$S_X(f) = |G(f)|^2 = G(f)G^*(f), \tag{10.96}$$

where $G(f)$ and $1/G(f)$ are *causal* filters.[8] This suggests that we can find the optimum filter in two steps, as shown in Fig. 10.15. First, we pass the observation process through a "whitening" filter with transfer function $W(f) = 1/G(f)$ to produce a white noise process $X'_n$, since

$$S_{X'}(f) = |W(f)|^2 S_X(f) = \frac{|G(f)|^2}{|G(f)|^2} = 1 \qquad \text{for all } f.$$

Second, we find the best estimator for $Z_n$ using the whitened observation process $X'_n$ as given by Eq. (10.95). The filter that results from the tandem combination of the whitening filter and the estimation filter is the solution to the Wiener-Hopf equations.

The transfer function of the second filter in Fig. 10.15 is

$$H_2(f) = \sum_{m=0}^{\infty} R_{Z,X'}(m)e^{-j2\pi fm} \tag{10.97}$$

by Eq. (10.95). To evaluate Eq. (10.97) we need to find

$$R_{Z,X'}(k) = E[Z_{n+k}X'_n]$$

$$= \sum_{i=0}^{\infty} w_i E[Z_{n+k}X_{n-i}]$$

$$= \sum_{i=0}^{\infty} w_i R_{Z,X}(k+i), \tag{10.98}$$

where $w_i$ is the impulse response of the whitening filter. The Fourier transform of Eq. (10.98) gives an expression that is easier to work with:

$$S_{Z,X'}(f) = W^*(f)S_{Z,X}(f) = \frac{S_{Z,X}(f)}{G^*(f)}. \tag{10.99}$$

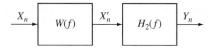

**FIGURE 10.15**
Whitening filter approach for solving Wiener-Hopf equations.

[8]The method for factoring $S_X(f)$ as specified by Eq. (10.96) is called **spectral factorization**. See Example 10.10 and the references at the end of the chapter.

The inverse Fourier transform of Eq. (10.99) yields the desired $R_{Z,X'}(k)$, which can then be substituted into Eq. (10.97) to obtain $H_2(f)$.

In summary, the optimum filter is found using the following procedure:

1. Factor $S_X(f)$ as in Eq. (10.96) and obtain a causal whitening filter $W(f) = 1/G(f)$.
2. Find $R_{Z,X'}(k)$ from Eq. (10.98) or from Eq. (10.99).
3. $H_2(f)$ is then given by Eq. (10.97).
4. The optimum filter is then

$$H(f) = W(f)H_2(f). \tag{10.100}$$

This procedure is valid for the continuous-time version of the optimum causal filter problem, after appropriate changes are made from summations to integrals. The following example considers a continuous-time problem.

---

**Example 10.25    Wiener Filter**

Find the optimum causal filter for estimating a signal $Z(t)$ from the observation $X(t) = Z(t) + N(t)$, where $Z(t)$ and $N(t)$ are independent random processes, $N(t)$ is zero-mean white noise density 1, and $Z(t)$ has power spectral density

$$S_Z(f) = \frac{2}{1 + 4\pi^2 f^2}.$$

The optimum filter in this problem is called the **Wiener filter**.

The cross-power spectral density between $Z(t)$ and $X(t)$ is

$$S_{Z,X}(f) = S_Z(f),$$

since the signal and noise are independent random processes. The power spectral density for the observation process is

$$S_X(f) = S_Z(f) + S_N(f)$$

$$= \frac{3 + 4\pi^2 f^2}{1 + 4\pi^2 f^2}$$

$$= \left( \frac{j2\pi f + \sqrt{3}}{j2\pi f + 1} \right)\left( \frac{-j2\pi f + \sqrt{3}}{-j2\pi f + 1} \right).$$

If we let

$$G(f) = \frac{j2\pi f + \sqrt{3}}{j2\pi f + 1},$$

then it is easy to verify that $W(f) = 1/G(f)$ is the whitening causal filter.

Next we evaluate Eq. (10.99):

$$S_{Z,X'}(f) = \frac{S_{Z,X}(f)}{G^*(f)} = \frac{2}{1 + 4\pi^2 f^2} \frac{1 - j2\pi f}{\sqrt{3} - j2\pi f}$$

$$= \frac{2}{(1 + j2\pi f)(\sqrt{3} - j2\pi f)}$$

$$= \frac{c}{1 + j2\pi f} + \frac{c}{\sqrt{3} - j2\pi f}, \tag{10.101}$$

where $c = 2/(1 + \sqrt{3})$. If we take the inverse Fourier transform of $S_{Z,X'}(f)$, we obtain

$$R_{Z,X'}(\tau) = \begin{cases} ce^{-\tau} & \tau > 0 \\ ce^{\sqrt{3}\tau} & \tau < 0. \end{cases}$$

Equation (10.97) states that $H_2(f)$ is given by the Fourier transform of the $\tau > 0$ portion of $R_{Z,X'}(\tau)$:

$$H_2(f) = \mathcal{F}\{ce^{-\tau}u(\tau)\} = \frac{c}{1 + j2\pi f}.$$

Note that we could have gotten this result directly from Eq. (10.101) by noting that only the first term gives rise to the positive-time (i.e., causal) component.

The optimum filter is then

$$H(f) = \frac{1}{G(f)}H_2(f) = \frac{c}{\sqrt{3} + j2\pi f}.$$

The impulse response of this filter is

$$h(t) = ce_t^{-\sqrt{3}} \qquad t > 0.$$

## 10.5    THE KALMAN FILTER

The optimum linear systems considered in the previous section have two limitations: (1) They assume wide-sense stationary signals; and (2) The number of equations grows with the size of the observation set. In this section, we consider an estimation approach that assumes signals have a certain structure. This assumption keeps the dimensionality of the problem fixed even as the observation set grows. It also allows us to consider certain nonstationary signals.

We will consider the class of signals that can be represented as shown in Fig. 10.16(a):

$$Z_n = a_{n-1}Z_{n-1} + W_{n-1} \qquad n = 1, 2, \ldots, \tag{10.102}$$

where $Z_0$ is the random variable at time 0, $a_n$ is a known sequence of constants, and $W_n$ is a sequence of zero-mean uncorrelated random variables with possibly time-varying variances $\{E[W_n^2]\}$. The resulting process $Z_n$ is nonstationary in general. We assume that the process $Z_n$ is not available to us, and that instead, as shown in Fig. 10.16(a), we observe

$$X_n = Z_n + N_n \qquad n = 0, 1, 2, \ldots, \tag{10.103}$$

where the observation noise $N_n$ is a zero-mean, uncorrelated sequence of random variables with possibly time-varying variances $\{E[N_n^2]\}$. We assume that $W_n$ and $N_n$ are uncorrelated at all times $n_1$ and $n_2$. In the special case where $W_n$ and $N_n$ are Gaussian random processes, then $Z_n$ and $X_n$ will also be Gaussian random processes. We will develop the Kalman filter, which has the structure in Fig. 10.16(b).

Our objective is to find *for each time n* the minimum mean square estimate (actually prediction) of $Z_n$ based on the observations $X_0, X_1, \ldots, X_{n-1}$ using a linear estimator that possibly varies with time:

$$Y_n = \sum_{j=i}^{n} h_j^{(n-1)} X_{n-j}. \tag{10.104}$$

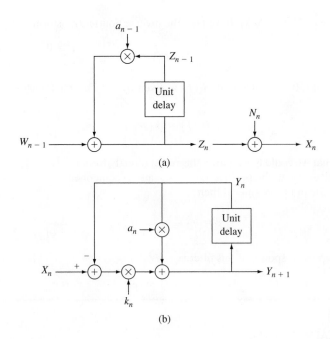

**FIGURE 10.16**
(a) Signal structure. (b) Kalman filter.

The orthogonality principle implies that the optimum filter $\{h_j^{(n-1)}\}$ satisfies

$$E\left[\left(Z_n - \sum_{j=1}^{n}h_j^{(n-1)}X_{n-j}\right)X_l\right] = 0 \qquad \text{for } l = 0, 1, \ldots, n-1,$$

which leads to a set of $n$ equations in $n$ unknowns:

$$R_{Z,X}(n, l) = \sum_{j=1}^{n}h_j^{(n-1)}R_X(n-j, l) \qquad \text{for } l = 0, 1, \ldots, n-1. \qquad (10.105)$$

At the next time instant, we need to find

$$Y_{n+1} = \sum_{j=1}^{n+1}h_j^{(n)}X_{n+1-j} \qquad (10.106)$$

by solving a system of $(n+1) \times (n+1)$ equations:

$$R_{Z,X}(n+1, l) = \sum_{j=1}^{n+1}h_j^{(n)}R_X(n+1-j, l) \qquad \text{for } l = 0, 1, \ldots, n. \qquad (10.107)$$

Up to this point we have followed the procedure of the previous section and we find that the dimensionality of the problem grows with the number of observations. We now use the signal structure to develop a recursive method for solving Eq. (10.106).

We first need the following two results: For $l < n$, we have

$$R_{Z,X}(n + 1, l) = E[Z_{n+1}X_l] = E[(a_nZ_n + W_n)X_l]$$
$$= a_nR_{Z,X}(n, l) + E[W_nX_l] = a_nR_{Z,X}(n, l), \quad (10.108)$$

since $E[W_nX_l] = E[W_n]E[X_l] = 0$, that is, $W_n$ is uncorrelated with the past of the process and the observations prior to time $n$, as can be seen from Fig. 10.16(a). Also for $l < n$, we have

$$R_{Z,X}(n, l) = E[Z_nX_l] = E[(X_n - N_n)X_l]$$
$$= R_X(n, l) - E[N_nX_l] = R_X(n, l), \quad (10.109)$$

since $E[N_nX_l] = E[N_n]E[X_l] = 0$, that is, the observation noise at time $n$ is uncorrelated with prior observations.

We now show that the set of equations in Eq. (10.107) can be related to the set in Eq. (10.105). For $l < n$, we can equate the right-hand sides of Eqs. (10.108) and (10.107):

$$a_nR_{Z,X}(n, l) = \sum_{j=1}^{n+1} h_j^{(n)} R_X(n + 1 - j, l)$$

$$= h_1^{(n)} R_X(n, l) + \sum_{j=2}^{n+1} h_j^{(n)} R_X(n + 1 - j, l)$$

$$\text{for } l = 0, 1, \ldots, n - 1. \ (10.110)$$

From Eq. (10.109) we have $R_X(n, l) = R_{Z,X}(n, l)$, so we can replace the first term on the right-hand of Eq. (10.110) and then move the resulting term to the left-hand side:

$$(a_n - h_1^{(n)})R_{Z,X}(n, l) = \sum_{j=2}^{n+1} h_j^{(n)} R_X(n + 1 - j, l)$$

$$= \sum_{j'=1}^{n} h_{j'+1}^{(n)} R_X(n - j', l). \quad (10.111)$$

By dividing both sides by $a_n - h_1^{(n)}$ we finally obtain

$$R_{Z,X}(n, l) = \sum_{j'=1}^{n} \frac{h_{j'+1}^{(n)}}{a_n - h_1^{(n)}} R_X(n - j', l)$$

$$\text{for } l = 0, 1, \ldots, n - 1. \ (10.112)$$

This set of equations is identical to Eq. (10.105) if we set

$$h_j^{(n-1)} = \frac{h_{j+1}^{(n)}}{a_n - h_1^{(n)}} \quad \text{for } j = 1, \ldots, n. \quad (10.113a)$$

Therefore, if at step $n$ we have found $h_1^{(n-1)}, \ldots, h_n^{(n-1)}$, and if somehow we have found $h_1^{(n)}$, then we can find the remaining coefficients from

$$h_{j+1}^{(n)} = (a_n - h_1^{(n)})h_j^{(n-1)} \quad j = 1, \ldots, n. \quad (10.113b)$$

Thus the key question is how to find $h_1^{(n)}$.

Suppose we substitute the coefficients in Eq. (10.113b) into Eq. (10.106):

$$Y_{n+1} = h_1^{(n)} X_n + \sum_{j'=1}^{n} (a_n - h_1^{(n)}) h_{j'}^{(n-1)} X_{n-j'}$$

$$= h_1^{(n)} X_n + (a_n - h_1^{(n)}) Y_n$$

$$= a_n Y_n + h_1^{(n)} (X_n - Y_n), \tag{10.114}$$

where the second equality follows from Eq. (10.104). The above equation has a very pleasing interpretation, as shown in Fig. 10.16(b). Since $Y_n$ is the prediction for time $n$, $a_n Y_n$ is the prediction for the next time instant, $n + 1$, based on the "old" information (see Eq. (10.102)). The term $(X_n - Y_n)$ is called the "innovations," and it gives the discrepancy between the old prediction and the observation. Finally, the term $h_1^{(n)}$ is called the *gain*, henceforth denoted by $k_n$, and it indicates the extent to which the innovations should be used to correct $a_n Y_n$ to obtain the "new" prediction $Y_{n+1}$. If we denote the **innovations** by

$$I_n = X_n - Y_n \tag{10.115}$$

then Eq. (10.114) becomes

$$Y_{n+1} = a_n Y_n + k_n I_n. \tag{10.116}$$

We still need to determine a means for computing the gain $k_n$.

From Eq. (10.115), we have that the innovations satisfy

$$I_n = X_n - Y_n = Z_n + N_n - Y_n = Z_n - Y_n + N_n = \varepsilon_n + N_n,$$

where $\varepsilon_n = Z_n - Y_n$ is the prediction error. A recursive equation can be obtained for the prediction error:

$$\varepsilon_{n+1} = Z_{n+1} - Y_{n+1} = a_n Z_n + W_n - a_n Y_n - k_n I_n$$

$$= a_n(Z_n - Y_n) + W_n - k_n(\varepsilon_n + N_n)$$

$$= (a_n - k_n)\varepsilon_n + W_n - k_n N_n, \tag{10.117}$$

with initial condition $\varepsilon_0 = Z_0$. Since $X_0$, $W_n$, and $N_n$ are zero-mean, it then follows that $E[\varepsilon_n] = 0$ for all $n$. A recursive equation for the mean square prediction error is obtained from Eq. (10.117):

$$E[\varepsilon_{n+1}^2] = (a_n - k_n)^2 E[\varepsilon_n^2] + E[W_n^2] + k_n^2 E[N_n^2], \tag{10.118}$$

with initial condition $E[\varepsilon_0^2] = E[Z_0^2]$. We are finally ready to obtain an expression for the gain $k_n$.

The gain $k_n$ must minimize the mean square error $E[\varepsilon_{n+1}^2]$. Therefore we can differentiate Eq. (10.118) with respect to $k_n$ and set it equal to zero:

$$0 = -2(a_n - k_n)E[\varepsilon_n^2] + 2k_n E[N_n^2].$$

Then we can solve for $k_n$:

$$k_n = \frac{a_n E[\varepsilon_n^2]}{E[\varepsilon_n^2] + E[N_n^2]}.\tag{10.119}$$

The expression for the mean square prediction error in Eq. (10.118) can be simplified by using Eq. (10.119) (see Problem 10.72):

$$E[\varepsilon_{n+1}^2] = a_n(a_n - k_n)E[\varepsilon_n^2] + E[W_n^2].\tag{10.120}$$

Equations (10.119), (10.116), and (10.120) when combined yield the recursive procedure that constitutes the Kalman filtering algorithm:

### Kalman filter algorithm:[9]

*Initialization:* $Y_0 = 0$      $E[\varepsilon_0^2] = E[Z_0^2]$
*For* $n = 0, 1, 2, \ldots$

$$k_n = \frac{a_n E[\varepsilon_n^2]}{E[\varepsilon_n^2] + E[N_n^2]}$$

$$Y_{n+1} = a_n Y_n + k_n(X_n - Y_n)$$

$$E[\varepsilon_{n+1}^2] = a_n(a_n - k_n)E[\varepsilon_n^2] + E[W_n^2].$$

Note that the algorithm requires knowledge of the signal structure, i.e., the $a_n$, and the variances $E[N_n^2]$ and $E[W_n^2]$. The algorithm can be implemented easily and has consequently found application in a broad range of detection, estimation, and signal processing problems. The algorithm can be extended in matrix form to accommodate a broader range of processes.

---

### Example 10.26   First-Order Autoregressive Process

Consider a signal defined by

$$Z_n = aZ_{n-1} + W_n \qquad n = 1, 2, \ldots \qquad Z_0 = 0,$$

where $E[W_n^2] = \sigma_W^2 = 0.36$, and $a = 0.8$, and suppose the observations are made in additive white noise

$$X_n = Z_n + N_n \qquad n = 0, 1, 2, \ldots,$$

where $E[N_n^2] = 1$. Find the form of the predictor and its mean square error as $n \to \infty$.

The gain at step $n$ is given by

$$k_n = \frac{a E[\varepsilon_n^2]}{E[\varepsilon_n^2] + 1}.$$

The mean square error sequence is therefore given by

$$E[\varepsilon_0^2] = E[Z_0^2] = 0$$

---

[9]We caution the student that there are two common ways of defining the gain. The statement of the Kalman filter algorithm will differ accordingly in various textbooks.

$$E[\varepsilon_{n+1}^2] = a(a - k_n)E[\varepsilon_n^2] + \sigma_W^2$$

$$= a\left(\frac{a}{1 + E[\varepsilon_n^2]}\right)E[\varepsilon_n^2] + \sigma_W^2 \qquad \text{for } n = 1, 2, \ldots.$$

The steady state mean square error $e_\infty$ must satisfy

$$e_\infty = \frac{a^2}{1 + e_\infty}e_\infty + \sigma_W^2.$$

For $a = 0.8$ and $\sigma_W^2 = 0.36$, the resulting quadratic equation yields $k_\infty = 0.3$ and $e_\infty = 0.6$. Thus at steady state the predictor is

$$Y_{n+1} = 0.8Y_n + 0.3(X_n - Y_n).$$

---

## *10.6    ESTIMATING THE POWER SPECTRAL DENSITY

Let $X_0, \ldots, X_{k-1}$ be $k$ observations of the discrete-time, zero-mean, wide-sense stationary process $X_n$. The periodogram estimate for $S_X(f)$ is defined as

$$\tilde{p}_k(f) = \frac{1}{k}|\tilde{x}_k(f)|^2, \tag{10.121}$$

where $\tilde{x}_k(f)$ is obtained as a Fourier transform of the observation sequence:

$$\tilde{x}_k(f) = \sum_{m=0}^{k-1} X_m e^{-j2\pi fm}. \tag{10.122}$$

In Section 10.1 we showed that the expected value of the periodogram estimate is

$$E[\tilde{p}_k(f)] = \sum_{m'=-(k-1)}^{k-1} \left\{1 - \frac{|m'|}{k}\right\} R_X(m')e^{-j2\pi fm'}, \tag{10.123}$$

so $\tilde{p}_k(f)$ is a biased estimator for $S_X(f)$. However, as $k \to \infty$,

$$E[\tilde{p}_k(f)] \to S_X(f), \tag{10.124}$$

so the mean of the periodogram estimate approaches $S_X(f)$.

Before proceeding to find the variance of the periodogram estimate, we note that the periodogram estimate is equivalent to taking the Fourier transform of an estimate for the autocorrelation sequence; that is,

$$\tilde{p}_k(f) = \sum_{m=-(k-1)}^{k-1} \hat{r}_k(m)e^{-j2\pi fm}, \tag{10.125}$$

where the estimate for the autocorrelation is

$$\hat{r}_k(m) = \frac{1}{k}\sum_{n=0}^{k-|m|-1} X_n X_{n+m}. \tag{10.126}$$

(See Problem 10.77.)

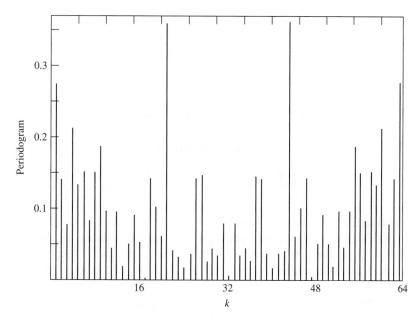

**FIGURE 10.17**
Periodogram for 64 samples of white noise sequence $X_n$ iid uniform in $(0, 1)$, $S_X(f) = \sigma_X^2 = 1/12 = 0.083$.

We might expect that as we increase the number of samples $k$, the periodogram estimate converges to $S_X(f)$. This does not happen. Instead we find that $\widetilde{p}_k(f)$ fluctuates wildly about the true spectral density, and that this random variation does not decrease with increased $k$ (see Fig. 10.17). To see why this happens, in the next section we compute the statistics of the periodogram estimate for a white noise Gaussian random process. We find that the estimates given by the periodogram have a variance that does *not* approach zero as the number of samples is increased. This explains the lack of improvement in the estimate as $k$ is increased. Furthermore, we show that the periodogram estimates are uncorrelated at uniformly spaced frequencies in the interval $-1/2 \le f < 1/2$. This explains the erratic appearance of the periodogram estimate as a function of $f$. In the final section, we obtain another estimate for $S_X(f)$ whose variance does approach zero as $k$ increases.

### 10.6.1    Variance of Periodogram Estimate

Following the approach of [Jenkins and Watts, pp. 230–233], we consider the periodogram of samples of a white noise process with $S_X(f) = \sigma_X^2$ at the frequencies $f = n/k$, $-k/2 \le n < k/2$, which will cover the frequency range $-1/2 \le f < 1/2$. (In practice these are the frequencies we would evaluate if we were using the FFT algorithm to compute $\widetilde{x}_k(f)$.) First we rewrite Eq. (10.122) at $f = n/k$ as follows:

$$\widetilde{x}_k\left(\frac{n}{k}\right) = \sum_{m=0}^{k-1} X_m\left(\cos\left(\frac{2\pi mn}{k}\right) - j\sin\left(\frac{2\pi mn}{k}\right)\right)$$

$$= A_k(n) - jB_k(n) \qquad -k/2 \le n < k/2, \qquad (10.127)$$

where

$$A_k(n) = \sum_{m=0}^{k-1} X_m \cos\left(\frac{2\pi mn}{k}\right) \tag{10.128}$$

and

$$B_k(n) = \sum_{m=0}^{k-1} X_m \sin\left(\frac{2\pi mn}{k}\right). \tag{10.129}$$

Then it follows that the periodogram estimate is

$$\tilde{p}_k\left(\frac{n}{k}\right) = \frac{1}{k}\left|\hat{x}_k\left(\frac{n}{k}\right)\right|^2 = \frac{1}{k}\{A_k^2(n) + B_k^2(n)\}. \tag{10.130}$$

We find the variance of $\tilde{p}_k(n/k)$ from the statistics of $A_k(n)$ and $B_k(n)$.

The random variables $A_k(n)$ and $B_k(n)$ are defined as linear functions of the jointly Gaussian random variables $X_0, \ldots, X_{k-1}$. Therefore $A_k(n)$ and $B_k(n)$ are also jointly Gaussian random variables. If we take the expected value of Eqs. (10.128) and (10.129) we find

$$E[A_k(n)] = 0 = E[B_k(n)] \qquad \text{for all } n. \tag{10.131}$$

Note also that the $n = -k/2$ and $n = 0$ terms are different in that

$$B_k(-k/2) = 0 = B_k(0) \tag{10.132a}$$

$$A_k(-k/2) = \sum_{i=0}^{k-1} (-1)^i X_i \qquad A_k(0) = \sum_{i=0}^{k-1} X_i. \tag{10.132b}$$

The correlation between $A_k(n)$ and $A_k(m)$ (for $n, m$ not equal to $-k/2$ or 0) is

$$
\begin{aligned}
E[A_k(n)A_k(m)] &= \sum_{i=0}^{k-1}\sum_{l=0}^{k-1} E[X_i X_l] \cos\left(\frac{2\pi ni}{k}\right) \cos\left(\frac{2\pi ml}{k}\right) \\
&= \sigma_X^2 \sum_{i=0}^{k-1} \cos\left(\frac{2\pi ni}{k}\right) \cos\left(\frac{2\pi mi}{k}\right) \\
&= \sigma_X^2 \sum_{i=0}^{k-1} \frac{1}{2}\cos\left(\frac{2\pi(n-m)i}{k}\right) + \sigma_X^2 \sum_{i=0}^{k-1} \frac{1}{2}\cos\left(\frac{2\pi(n+m)i}{k}\right),
\end{aligned}
$$

where we used the fact that $E[X_i X_l] = \sigma_X^2 \delta_{il}$ since the noise is white. The second summation is equal to zero, and the first summation is zero except when $n = m$. Thus

$$E[A_k(n)A_k(m)] = \frac{1}{2}k\sigma_X^2\, \delta_{nm} \qquad \text{for all } n, m \neq -k/2, 0. \tag{10.133a}$$

It can similarly be shown that

$$E[B_k(n)B_k(m)] = \frac{1}{2}k\sigma_X^2\, \delta_{nm} \qquad n, m \neq 0 - k/2, 0 \tag{10.133b}$$

$$E[A_k(n)B_k(m)] = 0 \qquad \text{for all } n, m. \tag{10.133c}$$

When $n = -k/2$ or $0$, we have

$$E[A_k(n)A_k(m)] = k\sigma_X^2 \, \delta_{nm} \qquad \text{for all } m. \tag{10.133d}$$

Equations (10.133a) through (10.133d) imply that $A_k(n)$ and $B_k(m)$ are uncorrelated random variables. Since $A_k(n)$ and $B_k(n)$ are jointly Gaussian random variables, this implies that they are zero-mean, *independent* Gaussian random variables.

We are now ready to find the statistics of the periodogram estimates at the frequencies $f = n/k$. Equation (10.130) gives

$$\widetilde{p}_k\left(\frac{n}{k}\right) = \frac{1}{k}\{A_k^2(n) + B_k^2(n)\} \qquad n \neq -k/2, 0$$

$$= \frac{1}{2}\sigma_X^2\left\{\frac{A_k^2(n)}{(1/2)k\sigma_X^2} + \frac{B_k^2(n)}{(1/2)k\sigma_X^2}\right\}. \tag{10.134}$$

The quantity in brackets is the sum of the squares of two zero-mean, unit-variance, independent Gaussian random variables. This is a chi-square random variable with two degrees of freedom (see Problem 7.6). From Table 4.1, we see that a chi-square random variable with $v$ degrees of freedom has variance $2v$. Thus the expression in the brackets has variance 4, and the periodogram estimate $\hat{p}_k(n/k)$ has variance

$$\text{VAR}\left[\widetilde{p}_k\left(\frac{n}{k}\right)\right] = \left(\frac{1}{2}\sigma_X^2\right)^2 4 = \sigma_X^4 = S_X(f)^2. \tag{10.135a}$$

For $n = -k/2$ and $n = 0$,

$$\widetilde{p}_k\left(\frac{n}{k}\right) = \sigma_X^2\left\{\frac{A_k^2(n)}{k\sigma_X^2}\right\}.$$

The quantity in brackets is a chi-square random variable with one degree of freedom and variance 2, so the variance of the periodogram estimate is

$$\text{VAR}\left[\widetilde{p}_k\left(\frac{n}{k}\right)\right] = 2\sigma_X^4 \qquad n = -k/2, 0. \tag{10.135b}$$

Thus we conclude from Eqs. (10.135a) and (10.135b) that *the variance of the periodogram estimate is proportional to the square of the power spectral density and does not approach zero as $k$ increases*. In addition, Eqs. (10.133a) through (10.133d) imply that *the periodogram estimates at the frequencies $f = -n/k$ are uncorrelated random variables*. A more detailed analysis [Jenkins and Watts, p. 238] shows that for arbitrary $f$,

$$\text{VAR}[\widetilde{p}_k(f)] = S_X(f)^2\left\{1 + \left(\frac{\sin(2\pi fk)}{k\sin(2\pi f)}\right)^2\right\}. \tag{10.136}$$

Thus variance of the periodogram estimate does not approach zero as the number of samples is increased.

The above discussion has only considered the spectrum estimation for a white noise, Gaussian random process, but the general conclusions are also valid for non-white, non-Gaussian processes. If the $X_i$ are not Gaussian, we note from Eqs. (10.128) and (10.129) that $A_k$ and $B_k$ are approximately Gaussian by the central limit theorem if $k$ is large. Thus the periodogram estimate is then approximately a chi-square random variable.

If the process $X_i$ is not white, then it can be viewed as filtered white noise:

$$X_n = h_n * W_n,$$

where $S_W(f) = \sigma_W^2$ and $|H(f)|^2 S_W(f) = S_X(f)$. The periodograms of $X_n$ and $W_n$ are related by

$$\frac{1}{k}\left|\tilde{x}_k\left(\frac{n}{k}\right)\right|^2 = \frac{1}{k}\left|H\left(\frac{n}{k}\right)\right|^2 \left|\tilde{w}_k\left(\frac{n}{k}\right)\right|^2. \tag{10.137}$$

Thus

$$\left|\tilde{w}_k\left(\frac{n}{k}\right)\right|^2 = \frac{|\tilde{x}_k(n/k)|^2}{|H(n/k)|^2}. \tag{10.138}$$

From our previous results, we know that $|\tilde{w}_k(n/k)|^2/k$ is a chi-square random variable with variance $\sigma_W^4$. This implies that

$$\mathrm{VAR}\left[\frac{|\tilde{x}_k(n/k)|^2}{k}\right] = \left|H\left(\frac{n}{k}\right)\right|^4 \sigma_W^4 = S_X(f)^2. \tag{10.139}$$

Thus we conclude that the variance of the periodogram estimate for nonwhite noise is also proportional to $S_X(f)^2$.

## 10.6.2  Smoothing of Periodogram Estimate

A fundamental result in probability theory is that the sample mean of a sequence of *independent* realizations of a random variable approaches the true mean with probability one. We obtain an estimate for $S_X(f)$ that goes to zero with the number of observations $k$ by taking the average of $N$ *independent* periodograms on samples of size $k$:

$$\langle \tilde{p}_k(f) \rangle_N = \frac{1}{N}\sum_{i=1}^{N} \tilde{p}_{k,i}(f), \tag{10.140}$$

where $\{\tilde{p}_{k,i}(f)\}$ are $N$ independent periodograms computed using separate sets of $k$ samples each. Figures 10.18 and 10.19 show the $N = 10$ and $N = 50$ smoothed periodograms corresponding to the unsmoothed periodogram of Fig. 10.17. It is evident that the variance of the power spectrum estimates is decreasing with $N$.

The mean of the smoothed estimator is

$$E\langle \tilde{p}_k(f) \rangle_N = \frac{1}{N}\sum_{i=1}^{N} E[\tilde{p}_{k,i}(f)] = E[\tilde{p}_k(f)]$$

$$= \sum_{m'=-(k-1)}^{k-1} \left\{1 - \frac{|m'|}{k}\right\} R_X(m')e^{-j2\pi fm'}, \tag{10.141}$$

where we have used Eq. (10.35). Thus the smoothed estimator has the same mean as the periodogram estimate on a sample of size $k$.

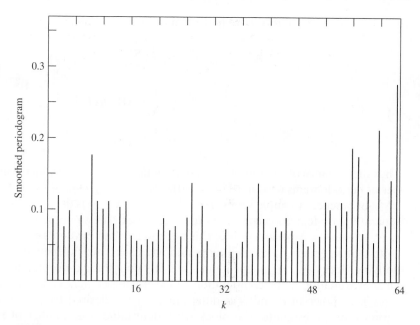

**FIGURE 10.18**
Sixty-four-point smoothed periodogram with $N = 10$, $X_n$ iid uniform in $(0, 1)$,
$S_X(f) = 1/12 = 0.083$.

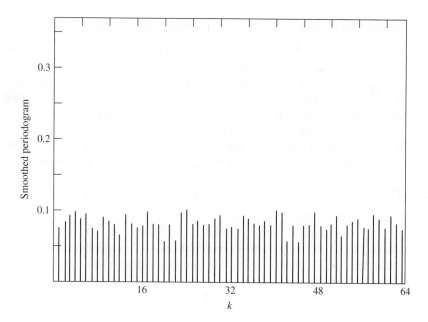

**FIGURE 10.19**
Sixty-four-point smoothed periodogram with $N = 50$, $X_n$ iid uniform in $(0, 1)$,
$S_X(f) = 1/12 = 0.083$.

The variance of the smoothed estimator is

$$\text{VAR}[\langle \tilde{p}_k(f) \rangle_N] = \frac{1}{N^2} \sum_{i=1}^{N} \text{VAR}[\tilde{p}_{k,i}(f)]$$

$$= \frac{1}{N} \text{VAR}[\tilde{p}_k(f)]$$

$$\simeq \frac{1}{N} S_X(f)^2.$$

Thus the variance of the smoothed estimator can be reduced by increasing $N$, the number of periodograms used in Eq. (10.140).

In practice, a sample set of size $Nk$, $X_0, \ldots, X_{Nk-1}$ is divided into $N$ blocks and a separate periodogram is computed for each block. The smoothed estimate is then the average over the $N$ periodograms. This method is called **Bartlett's smoothing procedure**. Note that, in general, the resulting periodograms are not independent because the underlying blocks are not independent. Thus this smoothing procedure must be viewed as an approximation to the computation and averaging of independent periodograms.

The choice of $k$ and $N$ is determined by the desired frequency resolution and variance of the estimate. The blocksize $k$ determines the number of frequencies for which the spectral density is computed (i.e., the frequency resolution). The variance of the estimate is controlled by the number of periodograms $N$. The actual choice of $k$ and $N$ depends on the nature of the signal being investigated.

## 10.7 NUMERICAL TECHNIQUES FOR PROCESSING RANDOM SIGNALS

In this chapter our discussion has combined notions from random processes with basic concepts from signal processing. The processing of signals is a very important area in modern technology and a rich set of techniques and methodologies have been developed to address the needs of specific application areas such as communication systems, speech compression, speech recognition, video compression, face recognition, network and service traffic engineering, etc. In this section we briefly present a number of general tools available for the processing of random signals. We focus on the tools provided in Octave since these are quite useful as well as readily available.

### 10.7.1 FFT Techniques

The Fourier transform relationship between $R_X(\tau)$ and $S_X(f)$ is fundamental in the study of wide-sense stationary processes and plays a key role in random signal analysis. The fast fourier transform (FFT) methods we developed in Section 7.6 can be applied to the numerical transformation from autocorrelation functions to power spectral densities and back.

Consider the computation of $R_X(\tau)$ and $S_X(f)$ for continuous-time processes:

$$R_X(\tau) = \int_{-\infty}^{\infty} S_X(f) e^{-j2\pi f\tau} \, df \approx \int_{-W}^{W} S_X(f) e^{-j2\pi f\tau} \, df.$$

First we limit the integral to the region where $S_X(f)$ has significant power. Next we restrict our attention to a discrete set of $N = 2M$ frequency values at $kf_0$ so that $-W = -Mf_0 < (-M+1)f_0 < \cdots < (M-1)f_0 < W$, and then approximate the integral by a sum:

$$R_X(\tau) \approx \sum_{m=-M}^{M-1} S_X(mf_0)e^{-j2\pi mf_0\tau} f_0.$$

Finally, we also focus on a set of discrete lag values: $kt_0$ so that $-T = -Mt_0 < (-M+1\}$ $t_0 < \cdots < (M-1)t_0 < T$. We obtain the DFT as follows:

$$R_X(kt_0) \approx f_0 \sum_{m=-M}^{M-1} S_X(mf_0)e^{-j2\pi mkt_0f_0} = f_0 \sum_{m=-M}^{M-1} S_X(mf_0)e^{-j2\pi mk/N}. \quad (10.142)$$

In order to have a discrete Fourier transform, *we must have* $t_0f_0 = 1/N$, which is equivalent to: $t_0 = 1/Nf_0$ and $T = Mt_0 = 1/2f_0$ and $W = Mf_0 = 1/2t_0$. We can use the FFT function introduced in Section 7.6 to perform the transformation in Eq. (10.142) to obtain the set of values $\{R_X(kt_0), k \in [-M, M-1]\}$ from $\{S_X(mt_0), k \in [-M, M-1]\}$. The transformation in the reverse direction is done in the same way. Since $R_X(\tau)$ and $S_X(f)$ are even functions various simplifications are possible. We discuss some of these in the problems.

Consider the computation of $S_X(f)$ and $R_X(k)$ for discrete-time processes. $S_X(f)$ spans the range of frequencies $|f| < 1/2$, so we restrict attention to $N$ points $1/N$ apart:

$$S_X\left(\frac{m}{N}\right) = \left.\sum_{k=-\infty}^{\infty} R_X(k)e^{-j2\pi kf}\right|_{f=m/N} \approx \sum_{k=-M}^{M-1} R_X(k)e^{-j2\pi km/N}. \quad (10.143)$$

The approximation here involves neglecting autocorrelation terms outside $[-M, M-1]$. Since $df \approx 1/N$, the transformation in the reverse direction is scaled differently:

$$R_X(k) = \int_{-1/2}^{1/2} S_X(f)e^{-j2\pi kf}\, df \approx \frac{1}{N}\sum_{k=-M}^{M-1} S_X\left(\frac{m}{N}\right)e^{-j2\pi km/N}. \quad (10.144)$$

We assume that the student has already tried the FFT exercises in Section 7.6, so we leave examples in the use of the FFT to the Problems.

The various frequency domain results for linear systems that relate input, output, and cross-spectral densities can be evaluated numerically using the FFT.

---

### Example 10.27   Output Autocorrelation and Cross-Correlation

Consider Example 10.12, where a random telegraph signal $X(t)$ with $\alpha = 1$ is passed through a lowpass filter with $\beta = 1$ and $\beta = 10$. Find $R_Y(\tau)$.

The random telegraph has $S_X(f) = \alpha/(\alpha^2 + \pi^2 f^2)$ and the filter has transfer function $H(f) = \beta/(\beta + j2\pi f)$, so $R_Y(\tau)$ is given by:

$$R_Y(\tau) = \mathscr{F}^{-1}\{|H(f)|^2 S_X(f)\} = \int_{-\infty}^{\infty} \frac{\beta^2}{\beta^2 + 4\pi^2 f^2} \frac{\alpha^2}{\alpha^2 + 4\pi^2 f^2}\, df.$$

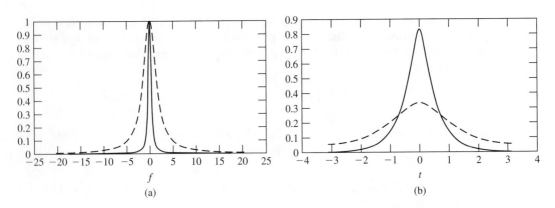

**FIGURE 10.20**
(a) Transfer function and input power spectral density; (b) Autocorrelation of filtered random telegraph with filter $\beta = 10$.

We used an $N = 256$ FFT to evaluate autocorrelation functions numerically for $\alpha = 1$ and $\beta = 1$ and $\beta = 10$. Figure 10.20(a) shows $|H(f)|^2$ and $S_X(f)$ for $\beta = 10$. It can be seen that the transfer function (the dashed line) is close to 1 in the region of $f$ where $S_X(f)$ has most of its power. Consequently we expect the output for $\beta = 10$ to have an autocorrelation similar to that of the input. For $\beta = 1$, on the other hand, the filter will attenuate more of the significant frequencies of $X(t)$ and we expect more change in the output autocorrelation. Figure 10.20(b) shows the output autocorrelation and we see that indeed for $\beta = 10$ (the solid line), $R_Y(\tau)$ is close to the double-sided exponential of $R_X(\tau)$. For $\beta = 1$ the output autocorrelation differs significantly from $R_X(\tau)$.

## 10.7.2  Filtering Techniques

The autocorrelation and power spectral density functions provide us with information about the average behavior of the processes. We are also interested in obtaining sample functions of the inputs and outputs of systems. For linear systems the principal tools for signal processing are the convolution and Fourier transform.

Convolution in discrete-time (Eq. (10.48)) is quite simple and so convolution is the workhorse in linear signal processing. Octave provides several functions for performing convolutions with discrete-time signals. In Example 10.15 we encountered the function `filter(b,a,x)` which implements filtering of the sequence $x$ with an ARMA filter with coefficients specified by vectors $b$ and $a$ in the following equation.

$$Y_n = -\sum_{i=1}^{q} \alpha_i Y_{n-i} + \sum_{j=0}^{p} \beta_j X_{n-j}.$$

Other functions use `filter(b,a,x)` to provide special cases of filtering. For example, `conv(a,b)` convolves the elements in the vectors $a$ and $b$. We can obtain the output of a linear system by letting $a$ be the impulse response and $b$ the input random sequence. The moving average example in Fig. 10.7(b) is easily obtained using this conv. Octave provides other functions implementing specific digital filters.

We can also obtain the output of a linear system in the frequency domain. We take the FFT of the input sequence $X_n$ and we then multiply it by the FFT of the transfer function. The inverse FFT will then provide $Y_n$ of the linear system. The Octave function fftconv(a,b,n) implements this approach. The size of the FFT must be equal to the total number of samples in the input sequence, so this approach is not advisable for long input sequences.

### 10.7.3   Generation of Random Processes

Finally, we are interested in obtaining discrete-time and continuous-time sample functions of the inputs and outputs of systems. Previous chapters provide us with several tools for the generation of random signals that can act as inputs to the systems of interest.

Section 5.10 provides the method for generating independent pairs of Gaussian random variables. This method forms the basis for the generation of iid Gaussian sequences and is implemented in normal_rnd=(M,V,Sz). The generation of sequences of WSS but correlated sequences of Gaussian random variables requires more work. One approach is to use the matrix approaches developed in Section 6.6 to generate individual vectors with a specified covariance matrix. To generate a vector $\mathbf{Y}$ of $n$ outcomes with covariance $\mathbf{K_Y}$, we perform the following factorization:

$$\mathbf{K_Y} = \mathbf{A}^T \mathbf{A} \mathbf{P} \boldsymbol{\lambda} \mathbf{P}^T,$$

and we generate the vector

$$\mathbf{Y} = \mathbf{A}^T \mathbf{X}$$

where $\mathbf{X}$ is vector of iid zero-mean, unit-variance Gaussian random variables. The Octave function svd(B) performs a singular value decomposition of the matrix $B$, see [Long]. When $B = \mathbf{K_Y}$ is a covariance matrix, svd returns the diagonal matrix $\mathbf{D}$ of eigenvalues of $\mathbf{K_Y}$ as well as the matrices $\mathbf{U} = \mathbf{P}$ and $\mathbf{V} = \mathbf{P}^T$.

---

### Example 10.28   Generation of Correlated Gaussian Random Variables

Generate 256 samples of the autoregressive process in Example 10.14 with $\alpha = -0.5, \sigma_X = 1$.

The autocorrelation of the process is given by $R_X(k) = (-1/2)^{|k|}$. We generate a vector $r$ of the first 256 lags of $R_X(k)$ and use the function toeplitz(r) to generate the covariance matrix. We then call the svd to obtain $A$. Finally we produce the output vector $\mathbf{Y} = \mathbf{A}^T \mathbf{X}$.

```
> n=[0:255]
> r=(-0.5).^n;
> K=toeplitz(r);
> [U,D,V]=svd(K);
> X=normal_rnd(0,1,1,256);
> y=V*(D^0.5)*transpose(X);
> plot(y)
```

Figure 10.21(a) shows a plot of $\mathbf{Y}$. To check that the sequence has the desired autocovariance we use the function autocov(X,H) which estimates the autocovariance function of the sequence $X$ for the first $H$ lag values. Figure 10.21(b) shows that the sample correlation coefficient that is obtained by dividing the autocovariance by the sample variance. The plot shows the alternating covariance values and the expected peak values of $-0.5$ and $0.25$ to the first two lags.

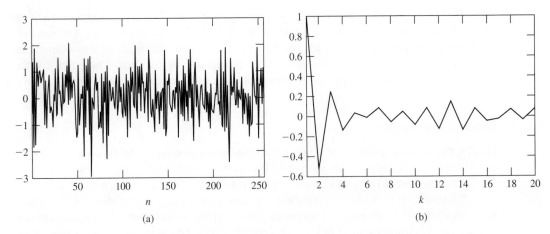

**FIGURE 10.21**
(a) Correlated Gaussian noise (b) Sample autocovariance.

An alternative approach to generating a correlated sequence of random variables with a specified covariance function is to input an uncorrelated sequence into a linear filter with a specific $H(f)$. Equation (10.46) allows us to determine the power spectral density of the output sequence. This approach can be implemented using convolution and is applicable to extremely long signal sequences. A large choice of possible filter functions is available for both continuous-time and discrete-time systems. For example, the ARMA model in Example 10.15 is capable of implementing a broad range of transfer functions. Indeed the entire discussion in Section 10.4 was focused on obtaining the transfer function of optimal linear systems in various scenarios.

### Example 10.29    Generation of White Gaussian Noise

Find a method for generating white Gaussian noise for a simulation of a continuous-time communications system.

The generation of discrete-time white Gaussian noise is trivial and involves the generation of a sequence of iid Gaussian random variables. The generation of continuous-time white Gaussian noise is not so simple. Recall from Example 10.3 that true white noise has infinite bandwidth and hence infinite power and so is impossible to realize. Real systems however are bandlimited, and hence we always end up dealing with bandlimited white noise. If the system of interest is bandlimited to $W$ Hertz, then we need to model white noise limited to $W$ Hz. In Example 10.3 we found this type of noise has autocorrelation:

$$R_X(\tau) = \frac{N_0 \sin(2\pi W \tau)}{2\pi\tau}.$$

The sampling theorem discussed in Section 10.3 allows us to represent bandlimited white Gaussian noise as follows:

$$\hat{X}(t) = \sum_{n=-\infty}^{\infty} X(nT)p(t - nT) \quad \text{where} \quad p(t) = \frac{\sin(\pi t/T)}{\pi t/T},$$

where $1/T = 2W$. The coefficients $X(nT)$ have autocorrelation $R_X(nT)$ which is given by:

$$R_X(nT) = \frac{N_0 \sin(2\pi WnT)}{2\pi nT} = \frac{N_0 \sin(2\pi Wn/2W)}{2\pi n/2W}$$

$$= \frac{N_0 W \sin(\pi n)}{\pi n} = \begin{cases} N_0 W & \text{for} \quad n = 0 \\ 0 & \text{for} \quad n \neq 0. \end{cases}$$

We thus conclude that $X(nT)$ is an iid sequence of Gaussian random variables with variance $N_0 W$. Therefore we can simulate sampled bandlimited white Gaussian noise by generating a sequence $X(nT)$. We can perform any processing required in the discrete-time domain, and we can then apply the result to an interpolator to recover the continuous-time output.

## SUMMARY

- The power spectral density of a WSS process is the Fourier transform of its autocorrelation function. The power spectral density of a real-valued random process is a real-valued, nonnegative, even function of frequency.
- The output of a linear, time-invariant system is a WSS random process if its input is a WSS random process that is applied an infinite time in the past.
- The output of a linear, time-invariant system is a Gaussian WSS random process if its input is a Gaussian WSS random process.
- Wide-sense stationary random processes with arbitrary rational power spectral density can be generated by filtering white noise.
- The sampling theorem allows the representation of bandlimited continuous-time processes by the sequence of periodic samples of the process.
- The orthogonality condition can be used to obtain equations for linear systems that minimize mean square error. These systems arise in filtering, smoothing, and prediction problems. Matrix numerical methods are used to find the optimum linear systems.
- The Kalman filter can be used to estimate signals with a structure that keeps the dimensionality of the algorithm fixed even as the size of the observation set increases.
- The variance of the periodogram estimate for the power spectral density does not approach zero as the number of samples is increased. An average of several independent periodograms is required to obtain an estimate whose variance does approach zero as the number of samples is increased.
- The FFT, convolution, and matrix techniques are basic tools for analyzing, simulating, and implementing processing of random signals.

## CHECKLIST OF IMPORTANT TERMS

Amplitude modulation
ARMA process
Autoregressive process
Bandpass signal
Causal system

Cross-power spectral density
Einstein-Wiener-Khinchin theorem
Filtering
Impulse response
Innovations

Kalman filter

Linear system

Long-range dependence

Moving average process

Nyquist sampling rate

Optimum filter

Orthogonality condition

Periodogram

Power spectral density

Prediction

Quadrature amplitude modulation

Sampling theorem

Smoothed periodogram

Smoothing

System

Time-invariant system

Transfer function

Unit-sample response

White noise

Wiener filter

Wiener-Hopf equations

Yule-Walker equations

## ANNOTATED REFERENCES

References [1] through [6] contain good discussions of the notion of power spectral density and of the response of linear systems to random inputs. References [6] and [7] give accessible introductions to the spectral factorization problem. References [7] through [9] discuss linear filtering and power spectrum estimation in the context of digital signal processing. Reference [10] discusses the basic theory underlying power spectrum estimation.

1. A. Papoulis and S. Pillai, *Probability, Random Variables, and Stochastic Processes*, McGraw-Hill, New York, 2002.
2. H. Stark and J. W. Woods, *Probability, Random Processes, and Estimation Theory for Engineers*, 3d ed., Prentice Hall, Upper Saddle River, N.J., 2002.
3. R. M. Gray and L. D. Davisson, *Random Processes: A Mathematical Approach for Engineers*, Prentice Hall, Englewood Cliffs, N.J., 1986.
4. R. D. Yates and D. J. Goodman, *Probability and Stochastic Processes*, Wiley, New York, 2005.
5. J. A. Gubner, *Probability and Random Processes for Electrical and Computer Engineering*, Cambridge University Press, Cambridge, 2006.
6. G. R. Cooper and C. D. MacGillem, *Probabilistic Methods of Signal and System Analysis*, Holt, Rinehart & Winston, New York, 1986.
7. J. A. Cadzow, *Foundations of Digital Signal Processing and Data Analysis*, Macmillan, New York, 1987.
8. A. V. Oppenheim and R. W. Schafer, *Discrete-Time Signal Processing*, Prentice Hall, Englewood Cliffs, N.J., 1989.
9. M. Kunt, *Digital Signal Processing*, Artech House, Dedham, Mass., 1986.
10. G. M. Jenkins and D. G. Watts, *Spectral Analysis and Its Applications*, Holden Day, San Francisco, 1968.
11. A. Einstein, "Method for the Determination of the Statistical Values of Observations Concerning Quantities Subject to Irregular Observations," reprinted in *IEEE ASSP Magazine,* October 1987, p. 6.
12. P. J. G. Long, "Introduction to Octave," University of Cambridge, September, 2005, available online.

**PROBLEMS**

## Section 10.1: Power Spectral Density

**10.1.** Let $g(x)$ denote the triangular function shown in Fig. P10.1.

   **(a)** Find the power spectral density corresponding to $R_X(\tau) = g(\tau/T)$.

   **(b)** Find the autocorrelation corresponding to the power spectral density $S_X(f) = g(f/W)$.

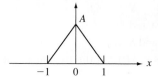

**FIGURE P10.1**

**10.2.** Let $p(x)$ be the rectangular function shown in Fig. P10.2. Is $R_X(\tau) = p(\tau/T)$ a valid autocorrelation function?

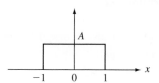

**FIGURE P10.2**

**10.3. (a)** Find the power spectral density $S_Y(f)$ of a random process with autocorrelation function $R_X(\tau) \cos(2\pi f_0 \tau)$, where $R_X(\tau)$ is itself an autocorrelation function.

   **(b)** Plot $S_Y(f)$ if $R_X(\tau)$ is as in Problem 10.1a.

**10.4. (a)** Find the autocorrelation function corresponding to the power spectral density shown in Fig. P10.3.

   **(b)** Find the total average power.

   **(c)** Plot the power in the range $|f| > f_0$ as a function of $f_0 > 0$.

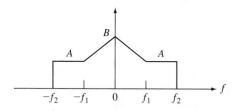

**FIGURE P10.3**

**10.5.** A random process $X(t)$ has autocorrelation given by $R_X(\tau) = \sigma_X^2 e^{-\tau^2/2\alpha^2}$, $\alpha > 0$.

    **(a)** Find the corresponding power spectral density.

    **(b)** Find the amount of power contained in the frequencies $|f| > k\,\alpha$, where $k = 1, 2, 3$.

**10.6.** Let $Z(t) = X(t) + Y(t)$. Under what conditions does $S_Z(f) = S_X(f) + S_Y(f)$?

**10.7.** Show that

    **(a)** $R_{X,Y}(\tau) = R_{Y,X}(-\tau)$.

    **(b)** $S_{X,Y}(f) = S_{Y,X}^*(f)$.

**10.8.** Let $Y(t) = X(t) - X(t - d)$.

    **(a)** Find $R_{X,Y}(\tau)$ and $S_{X,Y}(f)$.

    **(b)** Find $R_Y(\tau)$ and $S_Y(f)$.

**10.9.** Do Problem 10.8 if $X(t)$ has the triangular autocorrelation function $g(\tau/T)$ in Problem 10.1 and Fig. P 10.1.

**10.10.** Let $X(t)$ and $Y(t)$ be independent wide-sense stationary random processes, and define $Z(t) = X(t)Y(t)$.

    **(a)** Show that $Z(t)$ is wide-sense stationary.

    **(b)** Find $R_Z(\tau)$ and $S_Z(f)$.

**10.11.** In Problem 10.10, let $X(t) = a\cos(2\pi f_0 t + \Theta)$ where $\Theta$ is a uniform random variable in $(0, 2\pi)$. Find $R_Z(\tau)$ and $S_Z(f)$.

**10.12.** Let $R_X(k) = 4\alpha^{|k|}$, $|\alpha| < 1$.

    **(a)** Find $S_X(f)$.

    **(b)** Plot $S_X(f)$ for $\alpha = 0.25$ and $\alpha = 0.75$, and comment on the effect of the value of $\alpha$.

**10.13.** Let $R_X(k) = 4(\alpha)^{|k|} + 16(\beta)^{|k|}$, $\alpha < 1$, $\beta < 1$.

    **(a)** Find $S_X(f)$.

    **(b)** Plot $S_X(f)$ for $\alpha = \beta = 0.5$ and $\alpha = 0.75 = 3\beta$ and comment on the effect of value of $\alpha/\beta$.

**10.14.** Let $R_X(k) = 9(1 - |k|/N)$, for $|k| < N$ and 0 elsewhere. Find and plot $S_X(f)$.

**10.15.** Let $X_n = \cos(2\pi f_0 n + \Theta)$, where $\Theta$ is a uniformly distributed random variable in the interval $(0, 2\pi)$. Find and plot $S_X(f)$ for $f_0 = 0.5, 1, 1.75, \pi$.

**10.16.** Let $D_n = X_n - X_{n-d}$, where $d$ is an integer constant and $X_n$ is a zero-mean, WSS random process.

    **(a)** Find $R_D(k)$ and $S_D(f)$ in terms of $R_X(k)$ and $S_X(f)$. What is the impact of $d$?

    **(b)** Find $E[D_n^2]$.

**10.17.** Find $R_D(k)$ and $S_D(f)$ in Problem 10.16 if $X_n$ is the moving average process of Example 10.7 with $\alpha = 1$.

**10.18.** Let $X_n$ be a zero-mean, bandlimited white noise random process with $S_X(f) = 1$ for $|f| < f_c$ and 0 elsewhere, where $f_c < 1/2$.

    **(a)** Show that $R_X(k) = \sin(2\pi f_c k)/(\pi k)$.

    **(b)** Find $R_X(k)$ when $f_c = 1/4$.

**10.19.** Let $W_n$ be a zero-mean white noise sequence, and let $X_n$ be independent of $W_n$.

    **(a)** Show that $Y_n = W_n X_n$ is a white sequence, and find $\sigma_Y^2$.

    **(b)** Suppose $X_n$ is a Gaussian random process with autocorrelation $R_X(k) = (1/2)^{|k|}$. Specify the joint pmf's for $Y_n$.

**10.20.** Evaluate the periodogram estimate for the random process $X(t) = a \cos(2\pi f_0 t + \Theta)$, where $\Theta$ is a uniformly distributed random variable in the interval $(0, 2\pi)$. What happens as $T \to \infty$?

**10.21. (a)** Show how to use the FFT to calculate the periodogram estimate in Eq. (10.32).

**(b)** Generate four realizations of an iid zero-mean Gaussian sequence of length 128. Calculate the periodogram.

**(c)** Calculate 50 periodograms as in part b and show the average of the periodograms after every 10 additional realizations.

## Section 10.2: Response of Linear Systems to Random Signals

**10.22.** Let $X(t)$ be a differentiable WSS random process, and define

$$Y(t) = \frac{d}{dt} X(t).$$

Find an expression for $S_Y(f)$ and $R_Y(\tau)$. *Hint:* For this system, $H(f) = j2\pi f$.

**10.23.** Let $Y(t)$ be the derivative of $X(t)$, a bandlimited white noise process as in Example 10.3.

**(a)** Find $S_Y(f)$ and $R_Y(\tau)$.

**(b)** What is the average power of the output?

**10.24.** Repeat Problem 10.23 if $X(t)$ has $S_X(f) = \beta^2 e^{-\pi f^2}$.

**10.25.** Let $Y(t)$ be a short-term integration of $X(t)$:

$$Y(t) = \frac{1}{T} \int_{t-T}^{t} X(t') \, dt'.$$

**(a)** Find the impulse response $h(t)$ and the transfer function $H(f)$.

**(b)** Find $S_Y(f)$ in terms of $S_X(f)$.

**10.26.** In Problem 10.25, let $R_X(\tau) = (1 - |\tau|/T)$ for $|\tau| < T$ and zero elsewhere.

**(a)** Find $S_Y(f)$.

**(b)** Find $R_Y(\tau)$.

**(c)** Find $E[Y^2(t)]$.

**10.27.** The input into a filter is zero-mean white noise with noise power density $N_0/2$. The filter has transfer function

$$H(f) = \frac{1}{1 + j2\pi f}.$$

**(a)** Find $S_{Y,X}(f)$ and $R_{Y,X}(\tau)$.

**(b)** Find $S_Y(f)$ and $R_Y(\tau)$.

**(c)** What is the average power of the output?

**10.28.** A bandlimited white noise process $X(t)$ is input into a filter with transfer function $H(f) = 1 + j2\pi f$.

**(a)** Find $S_{Y,X}(f)$ and $R_{Y,X}(\tau)$ in terms of $R_X(\tau)$ and $S_X(f)$.

**(b)** Find $S_Y(f)$ and $R_Y(\tau)$ in terms of $R_X(\tau)$ and $S_X(f)$.

**(c)** What is the average power of the output?

**10.29. (a)** A WSS process $X(t)$ is applied to a linear system at $t = 0$. Find the mean and autocorrelation function of the output process. Show that the output process becomes WSS as $t \to \infty$.

**10.30.** Let $Y(t)$ be the output of a linear system with impulse response $h(t)$ and input $X(t)$. Find $R_{Y,X}(\tau)$ when the input is white noise. Explain how this result can be used to estimate the impulse response of a linear system.

**10.31. (a)** A WSS Gaussian random process $X(t)$ is applied to two linear systems as shown in Fig. P10.4. Find an expression for the joint pdf of $Y(t_1)$ and $W(t_2)$.

   **(b)** Evaluate part a if $X(t)$ is white Gaussian noise.

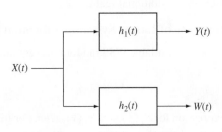

**FIGURE P10.4**

**10.32.** Repeat Problem 10.31b if $h_1(t)$ and $h_2(t)$ are ideal bandpass filters as in Example 10.11. Show that $Y(t)$ and $W(t)$ are independent random processes if the filters have nonoverlapping bands.

**10.33.** Let $Y(t) = h(t) * X(t)$ and $Z(t) = X(t) - Y(t)$ as shown in Fig. P10.5.

   **(a)** Find $S_Z(f)$ in terms of $S_X(f)$.

   **(b)** Find $E[Z^2(t)]$.

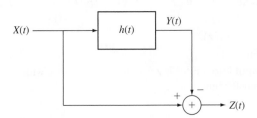

**FIGURE P10.5**

**10.34.** Let $Y(t)$ be the output of a linear system with impulse response $h(t)$ and input $X(t) + N(t)$. Let $Z(t) = X(t) - Y(t)$.

   **(a)** Find $R_{X,Y}(\tau)$ and $R_Z(\tau)$.

   **(b)** Find $S_Z(f)$.

   **(c)** Find $S_Z(f)$ if $X(t)$ and $N(t)$ are independent random processes.

**10.35.** A random telegraph signal is passed through an ideal lowpass filter with cutoff frequency $W$. Find the power spectral density of the difference between the input and output of the filter. Find the average power of the difference signal.

**10.36.** Let $Y(t) = a \cos(2\pi f_c t + \Theta) + N(t)$ be applied to an ideal bandpass filter that passes the frequencies $|f - f_c| < W/2$. Assume that $\Theta$ is uniformly distributed in $(0, 2\pi)$. Find the ratio of signal power to noise power at the output of the filter.

**10.37.** Let $Y_n = (X_{n+1} + X_n + X_{n-1})/3$ be a "smoothed" version of $X_n$. Find $R_Y(k), S_Y(f)$, and $E[Y^2{}_n]$.

**10.38.** Suppose $X_n$ is a white Gaussian noise process in Problem 10.37. Find the joint pmf for $(Y_n, Y_{n+1}, Y_{n+2})$.

**10.39.** Let $Y_n = X_n + \beta X_{n-1}$, where $X_n$ is a zero-mean, first-order autoregressive process with autocorrelation $R_X(k) = \sigma^2 \alpha^k, |\alpha| < 1$.

    **(a)** Find $R_{Y,X}(k)$ and $S_{Y,X}(f)$.

    **(b)** Find $S_Y(f), R_Y(k)$, and $E[Y_n^2]$.

    **(c)** For what value of $\beta$ is $Y_n$ a white noise process?

**10.40.** A zero-mean white noise sequence is input into a cascade of two systems (see Fig. P10.6). System 1 has impulse response $h_n = (1/2)^n u(n)$ and system 2 has impulse response $g_n = (1/4)^n u(n)$ where $u(n) = 1$ for $n \geq 0$ and 0 elsewhere.

    **(a)** Find $S_Y(f)$ and $S_Z(f)$.

    **(b)** Find $R_{W,Y}(k)$ and $R_{W,Z}(k)$; find $S_{W,Y}(f)$ and $S_{W,Z}(f)$. *Hint:* Use a partial fraction expansion of $S_{W,Z}(f)$ prior to finding $R_{W,Z}(k)$.

    **(c)** Find $E[Z_n^2]$.

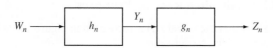

**FIGURE P10.6**

**10.41.** A moving average process $X_n$ is produced as follows:

$$X_n = W_n + \alpha_1 W_{n-1} + \cdots + \alpha_p W_{n-p},$$

where $W_n$ is a zero-mean white noise process.

    **(a)** Show that $R_X(k) = 0$ for $|k| > p$.

    **(b)** Find $R_X(k)$ by computing $E[X_{n+k}X_n]$, then find $S_X(f) = \mathcal{F}\{R_X(k)\}$.

    **(c)** Find the impulse response $h_n$ of the linear system that defines the moving average process. Find the corresponding transfer function $H(f)$, and then $S_X(f)$. Compare your answer to part b.

**10.42.** Consider the second-order autoregressive process defined by

$$Y_n = \frac{3}{4}Y_{n-1} - \frac{1}{8}Y_{n-2} + W_n,$$

where the input $W_n$ is a zero-mean white noise process.

    **(a)** Verify that the unit-sample response is $h_n = 2(1/2)^n - (1/4)^n$ for $n \geq 0$, and 0 otherwise.

    **(b)** Find the transfer function.

    **(c)** Find $S_Y(f)$ and $R_Y(k) = \mathcal{F}^{-1}\{S_Y(f)\}$.

**10.43.** Suppose the autoregressive process defined in Problem 10.42 is the input to the following moving average system:

$$Z_n = Y_n - 1/4 Y_{n-1}.$$

(a) Find $S_Z(f)$ and $R_Z(k)$.

(b) Explain why $Z_n$ is a first-order autoregressive process.

(c) Find a moving average system that will produce a white noise sequence when $Z_n$ is the input.

**10.44.** An autoregressive process $Y_n$ is produced as follows:

$$Y_n = \alpha_1 Y_{n-1} + \cdots + \alpha_q Y_{n-q} + W_n,$$

where $W_n$ is a zero-mean white noise process.

(a) Show that the autocorrelation of $Y_n$ satisfies the following set of equations:

$$R_Y(0) = \sum_{i=1}^{q} \alpha_i R_Y(i) + R_W(0)$$

$$R_Y(k) = \sum_{i=1}^{q} \alpha_i R_Y(k - i).$$

(b) Use these recursive equations to compute the autocorrelation of the process in Example 10.22.

## Section 10.3: Bandlimited Random Processes

**10.45.** (a) Show that the signal $x(t)$ is recovered in Figure 10.10(b) as long as the sampling rate is above the Nyquist rate.

(b) Suppose that a deterministic signal is sampled at a rate below the Nyquist rate. Use Fig. 10.10(b) to show that the recovered signal contains additional signal components from the adjacent bands. The error introduced by these components is called aliasing.

(c) Find an expression for the power spectral density of the sampled bandlimited random process $X(t)$.

(d) Find an expression for the power in the aliasing error components.

(e) Evaluate the power in the error signal in part c if $S_X(f)$ is as in Problem 10.1b.

**10.46.** An ideal discrete-time lowpass filter has transfer function:

$$H(f) = \begin{cases} 1 & \text{for} & |f| < f_c < 1/2 \\ 0 & \text{for} & f_c < |f| < 1/2. \end{cases}$$

(a) Show that $H(f)$ has impulse response $h_n = \sin(2\pi f_c n)/\pi n$.

(b) Find the power spectral density of $Y(kT)$ that results when the signal in Problem 10.1b is sampled at the Nyquist rate and processed by the filter in part a.

(c) Let $Y(t)$ be the continuous-time signal that results when the output of the filter in part b is fed to an interpolator operating at the Nyquist rate. Find $S_Y(f)$.

**10.47.** In order to design a differentiator for bandlimited processes, the filter in Fig. 10.10(c) is designed to have transfer function:

$$H(f) = j2\pi f/T \text{ for } |f| < 1/2.$$

**(a)** Show that the corresponding impulse response is:

$$h_0 = 0, h_n = \frac{\pi n \cos\pi n - \sin\pi n}{\pi n^2 T} = \frac{(-1)^n}{nT} \quad n \neq 0$$

**(b)** Suppose that $X(t) = a\cos(2\pi f_0 t + \Theta)$ is sampled at a rate $1/T = 4f_0$ and then input into the above digital filter. Find the output $Y(t)$ of the interpolator.

**10.48.** Complete the proof of the sampling theorem by showing that the mean square error is zero. *Hint:* First show that $E[(X(t)-(\hat{X}((t)) X(kT)] = 0$, all $k$.

**10.49.** Plot the power spectral density of the amplitude modulated signal $Y(t)$ in Example 10.18, assuming $f_c > W; f_c < W$. Assume that $A(t)$ is the signal in Problem 10.1b.

**10.50.** Suppose that a random telegraph signal with transition rate $\alpha$ is the input signal in an amplitude modulation system. Plot the power spectral density of the modulated signal assuming $f_c = \alpha/\pi$ and $f_c = 10\alpha/\pi$.

**10.51.** Let the input to an amplitude modulation system be $2\cos(2\pi f_1 + \Phi)$, where $\Phi$ is uniformly distributed in $(-\pi, \pi)$. Find the power spectral density of the modulated signal assuming $f_c > f_1$.

**10.52.** Find the signal-to-noise ratio in the recovered signal in Example 10.18 if $S_N(f) = \alpha f^2$ for $|f \pm f_c| < W$ and zero elsewhere.

**10.53.** The input signals to a QAM system are independent random processes with power spectral densities shown in Fig. P10.7. Sketch the power spectral density of the QAM signal.

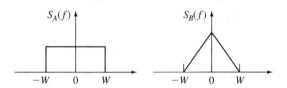

**FIGURE P10.7**

**10.54.** Under what conditions does the receiver shown in Fig. P10.8 recover the input signals to a QAM signal?

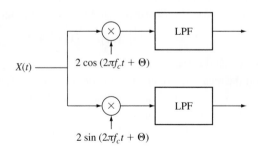

**FIGURE P10.8**

**10.55.** Show that Eq. (10.67b) implies that $S_{B,A}(f)$ is a purely imaginary, odd function of $f$.

## Section 10.4: Optimum Linear Systems

**10.56.** Let $X_\alpha = Z_\alpha + N_\alpha$ as in Example 10.22, where $Z_\alpha$ is a first-order process with $R_Z(k) = 4(3/4)^{|k|}$ and $N_\alpha$ is white noise with $\sigma_N^2 = 1$.

    **(a)** Find the optimum $p = 1$ filter for estimating $Z_\alpha$.

    **(b)** Find the mean square error of the resulting filter.

**10.57.** Let $X_\alpha = Z_\alpha + N_\alpha$ as in Example 10.21, where $Z_\alpha$ has $R_Z(k) = \sigma_Z^2(r_1)^{|k|}$ and $N_\alpha$ has $R_N(k) = \sigma_N^2 r_2^{|k|}$, where $r_1$ and $r_2$ are less than one in magnitude.

    **(a)** Find the equation for the optimum filter for estimating $Z_\alpha$.

    **(b)** Write the matrix equation for the filter coefficients.

    **(c)** Solve the $p = 2$ case, if $\sigma_Z^2 = 9$, $r_1 = 2/3$, $\sigma_N^2 = 1$, and $r_2 = 1/3$.

    **(d)** Find the mean square error for the optimum filter in part c.

    **(e)** Use the matrix function of Octave to solve parts c and d for $p = 3, 4, 5$.

**10.58.** Let $X_\alpha = Z_\alpha + N_\alpha$ as in Example 10.21, where $Z_\alpha$ is the first-order moving average process of Example 10.7, and $N_\alpha$ is white noise.

    **(a)** Find the equation for the optimum filter for estimating $Z_\alpha$.

    **(b)** For the $p = 1$ and $p = 2$ cases, write and solve the matrix equation for the filter coefficients.

    **(c)** Find the mean square error for the optimum filter in part b.

**10.59.** Let $X_\alpha = Z_\alpha + N_\alpha$ as in Example 10.19, and suppose that an estimator for $Z_\alpha$ uses observations from the following time instants: $I = \{n - p, \ldots, n, \ldots, n + p\}$.

    **(a)** Solve the $p = 1$ case if $Z_\alpha$ and $N_\alpha$ are as in Problem 10.56.

    **(b)** Find the mean square error in part a.

    **(c)** Find the equation for the optimum filter.

    **(d)** Write the matrix equation for the $2p + 1$ filter coefficients.

    **(e)** Use the matrix function of Octave to solve parts a and b for $p = 2, 3$.

**10.60.** Consider the predictor in Eq. (10.86b).

    **(a)** Find the optimum predictor coefficients in the $p = 2$ case when $R_Z(k) = 9(1/3)^{|k|}$.

    **(b)** Find the mean square error in part a.

    **(c)** Use the matrix function of Octave to solve parts a and b for $p = 3, 4, 5$.

**10.61.** Let $X(t)$ be a WSS, continuous-time process.

    **(a)** Use the orthogonality principle to find the best estimator for $X(t)$ of the form

$$\hat{X}(t) = aX(t_1) + bX(t_2),$$

    where $t_1$ and $t_2$ are given time instants.

    **(b)** Find the mean square error of the optimum estimator.

    **(c)** Check your work by evaluating the answer in part b for $t = t_1$ and $t = t_2$. Is the answer what you would expect?

**10.62.** Find the optimum filter and its mean square error in Problem 10.61 if $t_1 = t - d$ and $t_2 = t + d$.

**10.63.** Find the optimum filter and its mean square error in Problem 10.61 if $t_1 = t - d$ and $t_2 = t - 2d$, and $R_X(\tau) = e^{-\alpha|\tau|}$. Compare the performance of this filter to the performance of the optimum filter of the form $\hat{X}(t) = aX(t - d)$.

**10.64.** Modify the system in Problem 10.33 to obtain a model for the estimation error in the optimum infinite-smoothing filter in Example 10.24. Use the model to find an expression for the power spectral density of the error $e(t) = Z(t) - Y(t)$, and then show that the mean square error is given by:

$$E[e^2(t)] = \int_{-\infty}^{\infty} \frac{S_Z(f)S_N(f)}{S_Z(f) + S_N(f)} df.$$

*Hint:* $E[e^2(t)] = R_e(0)$.

**10.65.** Solve the infinite-smoothing problem in Example 10.24 if $Z(t)$ is the random telegraph signal with $\alpha = 1/2$ and $N(t)$ is white noise. What is the resulting mean square error?

**10.66.** Solve the infinite-smoothing problem in Example 10.24 if $Z(t)$ is bandlimited white noise of density $N_1/2$ and $N(t)$ is (infinite-bandwidth) white noise of noise density $N_0/2$. What is the resulting mean square error?

**10.67.** Solve the infinite-smoothing problem in Example 10.24 if $Z(t)$ and $N(t)$ are as given in Example 10.25. Find the resulting mean square error.

**10.68.** Let $X_n = Z_n + N_n$, where $Z_n$ and $N_n$ are independent, zero-mean random processes.

   **(a)** Find the smoothing filter given by Eq. (10.89) when $Z_n$ is a first-order autoregressive process with $\sigma_X^2 = 9$ and $\alpha = 1/2$ and $N_n$ is white noise with $\sigma_N^2 = 4$.

   **(b)** Use the approach in Problem 10.64 to find the power spectral density of the error $S_e(f)$.

   **(c)** Find $R_e(k)$ as follows: Let $Z = e^{j2\pi f}$, factor the denominator $S_e(f)$, and take the inverse transform to show that:

$$R_e(k) = \frac{\sigma_X^2 z_1}{\alpha(1 - z_1^2)} z_1^{|k|} \quad \text{where} \quad 0 < z_1 < 1.$$

   **(d)** Find an expression for the resulting mean square error.

**10.69.** Find the Wiener filter in Example 10.25 if $N(t)$ is white noise of noise density $N_0/2 = 1/3$ and $Z(t)$ has power spectral density

$$S_z(f) = \frac{4}{4 + 4\pi^2 f^2}.$$

**10.70.** Find the mean square error for the Wiener filter found in Example 10.25. Compare this with the mean square error of the infinite-smoothing filter found in Problem 10.67.

**10.71.** Suppose we wish to estimate (predict) $X(t + d)$ by

$$\hat{X}(t + d) = \int_0^{\infty} h(\tau)X(t - \tau)\, d\tau.$$

   **(a)** Show that the optimum filter must satisfy

$$R_X(\tau + d) = \int_0^{\infty} h(x)R_X(\tau - x)\, dx \qquad \tau \geq 0.$$

   **(b)** Use the Wiener-Hopf method to find the optimum filter when $R_X(\tau) = e^{-2|\tau|}$.

**10.72.** Let $X_n = Z_n + N_n$, where $Z_n$ and $N_n$ are independent random processes, $N_n$ is a white noise process with $\sigma_N^2 = 1$, and $Z_n$ is a first-order autoregressive process with $R_Z(k) = 4(1/2)^{|k|}$. We are interested in the optimum filter for estimating $Z_n$ from $X_n, X_{n-1}, \dots$.

(a) Find $S_X(f)$ and express it in the form:

$$S_X(f) = \frac{\frac{1}{2z_1}\left(1 - \frac{1}{z_1}e^{-j2\pi f}\right)\left(1 - z_1 e^{j2\pi f}\right)}{\left(1 - \frac{1}{2}e^{-j2\pi f}\right)\left(1 - \frac{1}{2}e^{j2\pi f}\right)}.$$

(b) Find the whitening causal filter.

(c) Find the optimal causal filter.

### Section 10.5: The Kalman Filter

**10.73.** If $W_n$ and $N_n$ are Gaussian random processes in Eq. (10.102), are $Z_n$ and $X_n$ Markov processes?

**10.74.** Derive Eq. (10.120) for the mean square prediction error.

**10.75.** Repeat Example 10.26 with $a = 0.5$ and $a = 2$.

**10.76.** Find the Kalman algorithm for the case where the observations are given by

$$X_n = b_n Z_n + N_n$$

where $b_n$ is a sequence of known constants.

### *Section 10.6: Estimating the Power Spectral Density

**10.77.** Verify Eqs. (10.125) and (10.126) for the periodogram and the autocorrelation function estimate.

**10.78.** Generate a sequence $X_n$ of iid random variables that are uniformly distributed in $(0, 1)$.

(a) Compute several 128-point periodograms and verify the random behavior of the periodogram as a function of $f$. Does the periodogram vary about the true power spectral density?

(b) Compute the smoothed periodogram based on 10, 20, and 50 independent periodograms. Compare the smoothed periodograms to the true power spectral density.

**10.79.** Repeat Problem 10.78 with $X_n$ a first-order autoregressive process with autocorrelation function: $R_X(k) = (.9)^{|k|}$; $R_X(k) = (1/2)^{|k|}$; $R_X(k) = (.1)^{|k|}$.

**10.80.** Consider the following estimator for the autocorrelation function

$$\hat{r}_k'(m) = \frac{1}{k - |m|} \sum_{n=0}^{k-|m|-1} X_n X_{n+m}.$$

Show that if we estimate the power spectrum of $X_n$ by the Fourier transform of $\hat{r}_k'(m)$, the resulting estimator has mean

$$E[\widetilde{p}_k(f)] = \sum_{m'=-(k-1)}^{k-1} R_X(m')e^{-j2\pi fm'}.$$

Why is the estimator biased?

### Section 10.7: Numerical Techniques for Processing Random Signals

**10.81.** Let $X(t)$ have power spectral density given by $S_X(f) = \beta^2 e^{-f^2/2W_0^2}/\sqrt{2\pi}$.

(a) Before performing an FFT of $S_X(f)$, you are asked to calculate the power in the aliasing error if the signal is treated as if it were bandlimited with bandwidth $kW_0$.

What value of $W$ should be used for the FFT if the power in the aliasing error is to be less than 1% of the total power? Assume $W_0 = 1000$ and $\beta = 1$.

**(b)** Suppose you are to perform $N = 2M$ point FFT of $S_X(f)$. Explore how $W$, $T$, and $t_0$ vary as a function of $f_0$. Discuss what leeway is afforded by increasing $N$.

**(c)** For the value of $W$ in part a, identify the values of the parameters $f_0$, $T$, and $t_0$ for $N = 128, 256, 512, 1024$.

**(d)** Find the autocorrelation $\{R_X(kt_0)\}$ by applying the FFT to $S_X(f)$. Try the options identified in part c and comment on the accuracy of the results by comparing them to the exact value of $R_X(\tau)$.

**10.82.** Use the FFT to calculate and plot $S_X(f)$ for the following discrete-time processes:

    **(a)** $R_X(k) = 4\alpha^{|k|}$, for $\alpha = 0.25$ and $\alpha = 0.75$.

    **(b)** $R_X(k) = 4(1/2)^{|k|} + 16(1/4)^{|k|}$.

    **(c)** $X_n = \cos(2\pi f_0 n + \Theta)$, where $\Theta$ is a uniformly distributed in $(0, 2\pi]$ and $f_0 = 1000$.

**10.83.** Use the FFT to calculate and plot $R_X(k)$ for the following discrete-time processes:

    **(a)** $S_X(f) = 1$ for $|f| < f_c$ and 0 elsewhere, where $f_c = 1/8, 1/4, 3/8$.

    **(b)** $S_X(f) = 1/2 + 1/2 \cos 2\pi f$ for $|f| < 1/2$.

**10.84.** Use the FFT to find the output power spectral density in the following systems:

    **(a)** Input $X_n$ with $R_X(k) = 4\alpha^{|k|}$, for $\alpha = 0.25$, $H(f) = 1$ for $|f| < 1/4$.

    **(b)** Input $X_n = \cos(2\pi f_0 n + \Theta)$, where $\Theta$ is a uniformly distributed random variable and $H(f) = j2\pi f$ for $|f| < 1/2$.

    **(c)** Input $X_n$ with $R_X(k)$ as in Problem 10.14 with $N = 3$ and $H(f) = 1$ for $|f| < 1/2$.

**10.85. (a)** Show that

$$R_X(\tau) = 2\mathrm{Re}\left\{ \int_0^\infty S_X(f)e^{-j2\pi f\tau}\, df \right\}.$$

    **(b)** Use approximations to express the above as a DFT relating $N$ points in the time domain to $N$ points in the frequency domain.

    **(c)** Suppose we meet the $t_0 f_0 = 1/N$ requirement by letting $t_0 = f_0 = 1/\sqrt{N}$. Compare this to the approach leading to Eq. (10.142).

**10.86. (a)** Generate a sequence of 1024 zero-mean unit-variance Gaussian random variables and pass it through a system with impulse response $h_n = e^{-2n}$ for $n \geq 0$.

    **(b)** Estimate the autocovariance of the output process of the digital filter and compare it to the theoretical autocovariance.

    **(c)** What is the pdf of the continuous-time process that results if the output of the digital filter is fed into an interpolator?

**10.87. (a)** Use the covariance matrix factorization approach to generate a sequence of 1024 Gaussian samples with autocovariance $h(t) = e^{-2|\tau|}$.

    **(b)** Estimate the autocovariance of the observed sequence and compare to the theoretical result.

## Problems Requiring Cumulative Knowledge

**10.88.** Does the pulse amplitude modulation signal in Example 9.38 have a power spectral density? Explain why or why not. If the answer is yes, find the power spectral density.

**10.89.** Compare the operation and performance of the Wiener and Kalman filters for the signals discussed in Example 10.26.

**10.90. (a)** Find the power spectral density of the ARMA process in Example 10.15 by finding the transfer function of the associated linear system.

**(b)** For the ARMA process find the cross-power spectral density from $E[Y_nX_m]$, and then the power spectral density from $E[Y_nY_m]$.

**10.91.** Let $X_1(t)$ and $X_2(t)$ be jointly WSS and jointly Gaussian random processes that are input into two linear time-invariant systems as shown below:

$$X_1(t) \rightarrow \boxed{h_1(t)} \rightarrow Y_1(t)$$

$$X_2(t) \rightarrow \boxed{h_2(t)} \rightarrow Y_2(t)$$

**(a)** Find the cross-correlation function of $Y_1(t)$ and $Y_2(t)$. Find the corresponding cross-power spectral density.

**(b)** Show that $Y_1(t)$ and $Y_2(t)$ are jointly WSS and jointly Gaussian random processes.

**(c)** Suppose that the transfer functions of the above systems are nonoverlapping, that is, $|H_1(f)||H_2(f)| = 0$. Show that $Y_1(t)$ and $Y_2(t)$ are independent random processes.

**(d)** Now suppose that $X_1(t)$ and $X_2(t)$ are nonstationary jointly Gaussian random processes. Which of the above results still hold?

**10.92.** Consider the communication system in Example 9.38 where the transmitted signal $X(t)$ consists of a sequence of pulses that convey binary information. Suppose that the pulses $p(t)$ are given by the impulse response of the ideal lowpass filter in Figure 10.6. The signal that arrives at the receiver is $Y(t) = X(t) + N(t)$ which is to be sampled and processed digitally.

**(a)** At what rate should $Y(t)$ be sampled?

**(b)** How should the bit carried by each pulse be recovered based on the samples $Y(nT)$?

**(c)** What is the probability of error in this system?

# Markov Chains

In general, the random variables within the family defining a stochastic process are not independent, and in fact can be statistically dependent in very complex ways. In this chapter we introduce the class of Markov random processes that have a simple form of dependence and that are quite useful in modeling many problems found in practice. We concentrate on integer-valued Markov processes, which are called Markov chains.

- Section 11.1 introduces Markov processes and the special case of Markov chains.
- Section 11.2 considers discrete-time Markov chains and examines the behavior of their state probabilities over time.
- Section 11.3 discusses structural properties of discrete-time Markov chains that determine their long-term behavior and limiting state probabilities.
- Section 11.4 introduces continuous-time Markov chains and considers the transient as well as long-term behavior of their state probabilities.
- Section 11.5 considers time-reversed Markov chains and develops interesting properties of reversible Markov chains that look the same going forwards and backwards in time.
- Finally, Section 11.6 introduces methods for simulating discrete-time and continuous-time Markov chains.

## 11.1 MARKOV PROCESSES

A random process $X(t)$ is a **Markov process** if the future of the process given the present is independent of the past, that is, if for arbitrary times $t_1 < t_2 < \cdots < t_k < t_{k+1}$,

$$P[X(t_{k+1}) = x_{k+1} \mid X(t_k) = x_k, \ldots, X(t_1) = x_1]$$
$$= P[X(t_{k+1}) = x_{k+1} \mid X(t_k) = x_k] \qquad (11.1)$$

if $X(t)$ is discrete-valued, and

$$P[a < X(t_{k+1}) \leq b \mid X(t_k) = x_k, \ldots, X(t_1) = x_1]$$
$$= P[a < X(t_{k+1}) \leq b \mid X(t_k) = x_k] \qquad (11.2a)$$

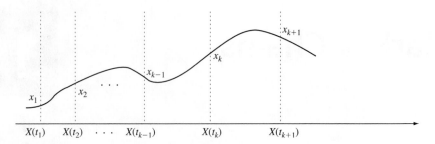

**FIGURE 11.1**
Markov property: Given $X(t_k)$, $X(t_{k+1})$ is independent of samples prior to $t_k$.

if $X(t)$ is continuous-valued. If the samples of $X(t)$ are jointly continuous, then Eq. (11.2a) is equivalent to

$$f_{X(t_{k+1})}(x_{k+1} \mid X(t_k) = x_k, \ldots, X(t_1) = x_1) = f_{X(t_{k+1})}(x_{k+1} \mid X(t_k) = x_k). \quad (11.2b)$$

We refer to Eqs. (11.1) and (11.2) as the **Markov property**. In the above expression $t_k$ is the "present," $t_{k+1}$ is the "future," and $t_1, \ldots, t_{k-1}$ is the "past," as shown in Fig. 11.1. Thus in Markov processes, pmf's and pdf's that are conditioned on several time instants always reduce to a pmf/pdf that is conditioned only on the most recent time instant. For this reason we refer to the value of $X(t)$ at time $t$ as the **state** of the process at time $t$.

---

### Example 11.1 Sum Process

Consider the sum process discussed in Section 9.3:

$$S_n = X_1 + X_2 + \cdots + X_n = S_{n-1} + X_n,$$

where the $X_i$'s are an iid sequence of random variables and where $S_0 = 0$. $S_n$ is a Markov process since

$$P[S_{n+1} = s_{n+1} \mid S_n = s_n, \ldots, S_1 = s_1] = P[X_{n+1} = s_{n+1} - s_n]$$
$$= P[S_{n+1} = s_{n+1} \mid S_n = s_n].$$

The binomial counting process and the random walk processes introduced in Section 9.3 are sum processes and therefore Markov processes.

---

### Example 11.2 Moving Average

Consider the moving average of a Bernoulli sequence:

$$Y_n = \frac{1}{2}(X_n + X_{n-1}),$$

where the $X_i$ are an independent Bernoulli sequence with $p = 1/2$. We now show that $Y_n$ is not a Markov process.

The pmf of $Y_n$ is

$$P[Y_n = 0] = P[X_n = 0, X_{n-1} = 0] = \frac{1}{4},$$

$$P\left[Y_n = \frac{1}{2}\right] = P[X_n = 0, X_{n-1} = 1] + P[X_n = 1, X_{n-1} = 0] = \frac{1}{2},$$

and

$$P[Y_n = 1] = P[X_n = 1, X_{n-1} = 1] = \frac{1}{4}.$$

Now consider the following conditional probability for two consecutive values of $Y_n$:

$$P\left[Y_n = 1 \,|\, Y_{n-1} = \frac{1}{2}\right] = \frac{P[Y_n = 1, Y_{n-1} = 1/2]}{P[Y_{n-1} = 1/2]}$$

$$= \frac{P[X_n = 1, X_{n-1} = 1, X_{n-2} = 0]}{1/2} = \frac{(1/2)^3}{1/2} = \frac{1}{4}.$$

Now suppose we have additional knowledge about the past:

$$P\left[Y_n = 1 \,|\, Y_{n-1} = \frac{1}{2}, Y_{n-2} = 1\right] = \frac{P[Y_n = 1, Y_{n-1} = 1/2, Y_{n-2} = 1]}{P[Y_{n-1} = 1/2, Y_{n-2} = 1]} = 0,$$

since no sequence of $X_n$'s leads to the sequence 1, 1/2, 1. Thus

$$P\left[Y_n = 1 \,|\, Y_{n-1} = \frac{1}{2}, Y_{n-2} = 1\right] \neq P\left[Y_n = 1 \,|\, Y_{n-1} = \frac{1}{2}\right],$$

and the process is not Markov.

---

### Example 11.3    Poisson Process

The Poisson process is a continuous-time Markov process since

$$P[N(t_{k+1}) = j \,|\, N(t_k) = i, N(t_{k-1}) = x_{k-1}, \ldots, N(t_1) = x_1]$$

$$= P[j - i \text{ events in } t_{k+1} - t_k \text{ seconds}]$$

$$= P[N(t_{k+1}) = j \,|\, N(t_k) = i].$$

---

### Example 11.4    Random Telegraph

The random telegraph signal of Example 9.24 is a continuous-time Markov process since

$$P[X(t_{k+1}) = a \,|\, X(t_k) = b, \ldots, X(t_1) = x_1]$$

$$= P[\text{even (odd) number of jumps in } t_{k+1}$$

$$- t_k \text{ seconds if } a = b(a \neq b)]$$

$$= P[X(t_{k+1}) = a \,|\, X(t_k) = b].$$

### Example 11.5    Wiener Process

The Wiener process, from Section 9.5, is a Markov process. Since it satisfies the independent increments property (Eq. 9.52), we have that:

$$f_{X(t_{k+1})}(x_{k+1} \mid X(t_k) = x_k, \ldots, X(t_1) = x_1) = f_{X(t_{k+1}-t_k)}(x_{k+1} - x_k)$$

$$= \frac{\exp\left\{-\frac{1}{2}\left[\frac{(x_{k+1} - x_k)^2}{\alpha(t_{k+1} - t_k)}\right]\right\}}{\sqrt{(2\pi\alpha)(t_{k+1} - t_k)}}.$$

The Wiener process is Gaussian and so it provides an example of a Gaussian Markov process.

---

An integer-valued Markov random process is called a **Markov chain**.[1] In the remainder of this chapter we concentrate on Markov chains.

If $X(t)$ is a Markov chain, then the joint pmf for three arbitrary time instants is

$$P[X(t_3) = x_3, X(t_2) = x_2, X(t_1) = x_1]$$
$$= P[X(t_3) = x_3 \mid X(t_2) = x_2, X(t_1) = x_1]P[X(t_2) = x_2, X(t_1) = x_1]$$
$$= P[X(t_3) = x_3 \mid X(t_2) = x_2]P[X(t_2) = x_2, X(t_1) = x_1]$$
$$= P[X(t_3) = x_3 \mid X(t_2) = x_2]P[X(t_2) = x_2 \mid X(t_1) = x_1]P[X(t_1) = x_1],$$

where we have used the definition of conditional probability and the Markov property. In general, the joint pmf for $k + 1$ arbitrary time instants is

$$P[X(t_{k+1}) = x_{k+1}, X(t_k) = x_k, \ldots, X(t_1) = x_1]$$
$$= P[X(t_{k+1}) = x_{k+1} \mid X(t_k) = x_k]$$
$$P[X(t_k) = x_k \mid X(t_{k-1}) = x_{k-1}] \ldots P[X(t_1) = x_1]$$
$$= \left\{\prod_{j=1}^{k} P[X(t_{j+1}) = x_{j+1} \mid X(t_j) = x_j]\right\}P[X(t_1) = x_1] \qquad (11.3)$$

Thus the *joint pmf of $X(t)$ at arbitrary time instants is given by the product of the pmf of the initial time instant and the probabilities for the subsequent state transitions.* Clearly, the state transition probabilities determine the statistical behavior of a Markov chain.

## 11.2    DISCRETE-TIME MARKOV CHAINS

Let $X_n$ be a discrete-time integer-valued Markov chain that starts at $n = 0$ with pmf

$$p_j(0) \triangleq P[X_0 = j] \qquad j = 0, 1, 2, \ldots. \qquad (11.4)$$

---

[1]See Cox and Miller [6] for a discussion of continuous-valued Markov processes.

We will assume that $X_n$ takes on values from a countable set of integers, usually $\{0, 1, 2, \dots\}$. We say that the Markov chain is finite state if $X_n$ takes on values from a finite set.

From Eq. (11.3), the joint pmf for the first $n + 1$ values of the process is

$$P[X_n = i_n, \dots, X_0 = i_0]$$
$$= P[X_n = i_n | X_{n-1} = i_{n-1}] \dots P[X_1 = i_1 | X_0 = i_0] P[X_0 = i_0]. \quad (11.5)$$

Thus the joint pmf for a particular sequence is simply the product of the probability for the initial state and the probabilities for the subsequent one-step state transitions.

We will assume that the one-step state transition probabilities are fixed and do not change with time, that is,

$$P[X_{n+1} = j | X_n = i] = p_{ij} \quad \text{for all } n. \quad (11.6)$$

$X_n$ is said to have **homogeneous transition probabilities**. The joint pmf for $X_n, \dots, X_0$ is then given by

$$P[X_n = i_n, \dots, X_0 = i_0] = p_{i_{n-1}, i_n} \dots p_{i_0, i_1} p_{i_0}(0). \quad (11.7)$$

Thus $X_n$ is completely specified by the *initial pmf* $p_i(0)$ and the *matrix of one-step transition probabilities P*:

$$P = \begin{bmatrix} p_{00} & p_{01} & p_{02} & \cdots \\ p_{10} & p_{11} & p_{12} & \cdots \\ . & . & . & \\ p_{i0} & p_{i1} & \cdots & \\ . & . & \cdots & \end{bmatrix}. \quad (11.8)$$

We will call $P$ the **transition probability matrix**. Note that each row of $P$ must add to one since

$$1 = \sum_j P[X_{n+1} = j | X_n = i] = \sum_j p_{ij}. \quad (11.9)$$

If the Markov chain is finite state, then the matrix $P$ will be an $n \times n$ nonnegative square with rows that add up to 1.

---

### Example 11.6 Two-State Markov Chain for Speech Activity

A Markov model for packet speech assumes that if the $n$th packet contains silence, then the probability of silence in the next packet is $1 - \alpha$ and the probability of speech activity is $\alpha$. Similarly, if the $n$th packet contains speech activity, then the probability of speech activity in the next packet is $1 - \beta$ and the probability of silence is $\beta$.

Let $X_n$ be the indicator function for speech activity in a packet at time $n$, then $X_n$ is a two-state Markov chain with the state transition diagram shown in Fig. 11.2(a), and transition probability matrix

$$P = \begin{bmatrix} 1 - \alpha & \alpha \\ \beta & 1 - \beta \end{bmatrix}. \quad (11.10)$$

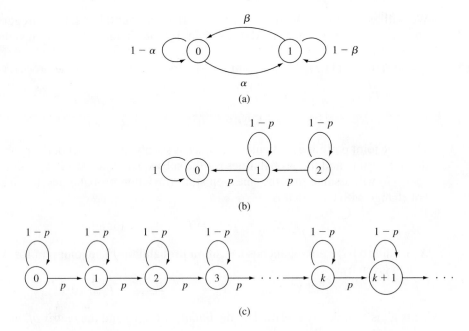

**FIGURE 11.2**
(a) State transition diagram for two-state Markov chain. (b) State transition diagram for Markov chain for light bulb inventory. (c) State transition diagram for binomial counting process.

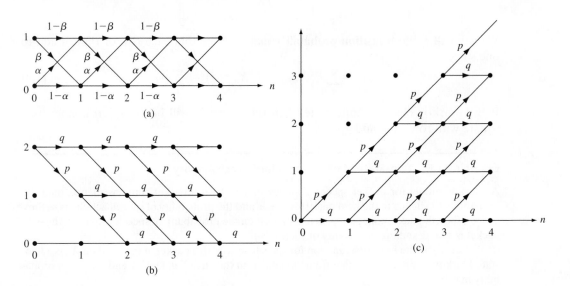

**FIGURE 11.3**
Trellis diagrams for Markov chain examples.

The sample functions of $X_n$ can be viewed as traversing the **trellis diagram** in Fig. 11.3(a) which shows the possible values of the process over time. At any give time, the process occupies the "state" that corresponds to its value. The sample function is realized as the process steps from one state at a given time instant to a state in the next time instant. The transitions are determined according to the transition probability matrix.

---

### Example 11.7

On day 0 a house has two new light bulbs in reserve. The probability that the house will need a single new light bulb during day $n$ is $p$, and the probability that it will not need any is $q = 1 - p$. Let $Y_n$ be the number of new light bulbs left in the house at the end of day $n$. $Y_n$ is a Markov chain with state transition diagram shown in Fig. 11.2(b), and transition probability matrix

$$P = \begin{bmatrix} 1 & 0 & 0 \\ p & q & 0 \\ 0 & p & q \end{bmatrix}.$$

The trellis diagram for this process in Fig. 11.3(b) shows that, unless $q = 1$, the transition probabilities bias the process towards the "trapping" state $Y_n = 0$. Thus the sample functions of $Y_n$ are nonincreasing functions of $n$.

---

### Example 11.8    Binomial Counting Process

Let $S_n$ be the binomial counting process introduced in Example 9.15. In one step, $S_n$ can either stay the same or increase by one. The state transition diagram is shown in Fig. 11.2(c), and the transition probability matrix is given by

$$P = \begin{bmatrix} 1 - p & p & 0 & 0 & \cdots \\ 0 & 1 - p & p & 0 & \cdots \\ 0 & 0 & 1 - p & p & \cdots \\ \cdot & \cdot & \cdots & \cdots \end{bmatrix}.$$

The trellis diagram for binomial process in Fig. 11.3(c) shows that, unless $q = 1$, the transition probabilities bias the process towards steady growth over time. The sample functions of $S_n$ are nondecreasing functions of $n$.

---

## 11.2.1    The *n*-Step Transition Probabilities

To evaluate the joint pmf for arbitrary time instants (see Eq. 11.3), we need to know the transition probabilities for an arbitrary number of steps. Let $P(n) = \{p_{ij}(n)\}$ *be the matrix of n-step transition probabilities,* where

$$p_{ij}(n) = P[X_{n+k} = j \mid X_k = i] \qquad n \geq 0, i, j \geq 0. \tag{11.11}$$

Note that $P[X_{n+k} = j \mid X_k = i] = P[X_n = j \mid X_0 = i]$ for all $n \geq 0$ and $k \geq 0$, since the transition probabilities do not depend on time.

First, consider the two-step transition probabilities. The probability of going from state $i$ at $t = 0$, passing through state $k$ at $t = 1$, and ending at state $j$ at $t = 2$ is

$$
\begin{aligned}
P[X_2 = j, X_1 = k \,|\, X_0 = i] &= \frac{P[X_2 = j, X_1 = k, X_0 = i]}{P[X_0 = i]} \\
&= \frac{P[X_2 = j \,|\, X_1 = k]P[X_1 = k \,|\, X_0 = i]P[X_0 = i]}{P[X_0 = i]} \\
&= P[X_2 = j \,|\, X_1 = k]P[X_1 = k \,|\, X_0 = i] \\
&= p_{ik}(1)p_{kj}(1).
\end{aligned}
$$

Note that $p_{ik}(1)$ and $p_{kj}(1)$ are components of $P$, the one-step transition probability matrix. We obtain $p_{ij}(2)$, the probability of going from $i$ at $t = 0$ to $j$ at $t = 2$, by summing over all possible intermediate states $k$:

$$
p_{ij}(2) = \sum_k p_{ik}(1)p_{kj}(1) \qquad \text{for all } i, j. \tag{11.12a}
$$

Equation (11.12a) states that the $ij$ entry of $P(2)$ is obtained by multiplying the $i$th row of $P(1)$ by the $j$th column of $P(1)$. In other words, $P(2)$ is obtained by multiplying the one-step transition probability matrices:

$$
P(2) = P(1)P(1) = P^2. \tag{11.12b}
$$

Now consider the probability of going from state $i$ at $t = 0$, passing through state $k$ at $t = m$, and ending at state $j$ at time $t = m + n$. Following the same procedure as above we obtain the **Chapman–Kolmogorov equations**:

$$
p_{ij}(m + n) = \sum_k p_{ik}(m)p_{kj}(n) \quad \text{for all } n, m \geq 0 \text{ all } i, j. \tag{11.13a}
$$

Therefore the matrix of $n + m$ step transition probabilities $P(n + m) = \{p_{ij}(n + m)\}$ is obtained by the following matrix multiplication:

$$
P(n + m) = P(n)P(m). \tag{11.13b}
$$

It is easy to show by an induction argument that this implies that:

$$
P(n) = P^n. \tag{11.14}
$$

When the Markov chain has finite state, we can use computer programs to calculate the powers of $P$ numerically.

## 11.2.2    The State Probabilities

Now consider the state probabilities at time $n$. Let $\mathbf{p}(n) = \{p_j(n)\}$ denote the row vector of **state probabilities** at time $n$. The probability $p_j(n)$ is related to $\mathbf{p}(n - 1)$ by

$$
\begin{aligned}
p_j(n) &= \sum_i P[X_n = j \,|\, X_{n-1} = i]P[X_{n-1} = i] \\
&= \sum_i p_{ij}p_i(n - 1). \tag{11.15a}
\end{aligned}
$$

Equation (11.15a) states that $\mathbf{p}(n)$ is obtained by multiplying the row vector $\mathbf{p}(n-1)$ by the matrix $P$:

$$\mathbf{p}(n) = \mathbf{p}(n-1)P. \tag{11.15b}$$

Similarly, $p_j(n)$ is related to $\mathbf{p}(0)$ by

$$p_j(n) = \sum_i P[X_n = j \,|\, X_0 = i]P[X_0 = i]$$

$$= \sum_i p_{ij}(n)p_i(0), \tag{11.16a}$$

and in matrix notation

$$\mathbf{p}(n) = \mathbf{p}(0)P(n) = \mathbf{p}(0)P^n \qquad n = 1, 2, \ldots. \tag{11.16b}$$

Thus the *state pmf at time n is obtained by multiplying the initial state pmf by $P^n$.*

---

### Example 11.9

To find the $n$-step transition probability in Example 11.7, note that

$$p_{22}(n) = P[\text{no new light bulbs needed in } n \text{ days}] = q^n$$

$$p_{21}(n) = P[1 \text{ light bulb needed in } n \text{ days}] = npq^{n-1}$$

$$p_{20}(n) = 1 - p_{22}(n) - p_{21}(n).$$

The other terms in $P(n)$ are found in similar fashion, thus

$$P(n) = \begin{bmatrix} 1 & 0 & 0 \\ 1 - q^n & q^n & 0 \\ 1 - q^n - npq^{n-1} & npq^{n-1} & q^n \end{bmatrix}.$$

Note that if $q < 1$ then, as $n \to \infty$,

$$P(n) \to \begin{bmatrix} 1 & 0 & 0 \\ 1 & 0 & 0 \\ 1 & 0 & 0 \end{bmatrix}.$$

As a result, the state pmf $\mathbf{p}(n) = (p_0(n), p_1(n), p_2(n))$ approaches

$$\mathbf{p}(n) = (p_0(0), p_1(0), p_2(0))P(n)$$

$$= (0, 0, 1)P(n)$$

$$\to (0, 0, 1)\begin{bmatrix} 1 & 0 & 0 \\ 1 & 0 & 0 \\ 1 & 0 & 0 \end{bmatrix} = (1, 0, 0),$$

where $(p_0(0), p_1(0), p_2(0))$ is the row vector of initial state probabilities and $(p_0(0), p_1(0), p_2(0)) = (0, 0, 1)$ since we start with two light bulbs. As time progresses, $p_0(n) \to 1$. In words, the above equation states that we eventually run out of light bulbs!

---

**Example 11.10**

Let $\alpha = 1/10$ and $\beta = 1/5$ in Example 11.6. Find $P(n)$ for $n = 2, 4, 8$, and $16$.

$$P^2 = \begin{bmatrix} .9 & .1 \\ .2 & .8 \end{bmatrix}^2 = \begin{bmatrix} .83 & .17 \\ .34 & .66 \end{bmatrix}$$

$$P^4 = \begin{bmatrix} .83 & .17 \\ .34 & .66 \end{bmatrix}^2 = \begin{bmatrix} .7467 & .2533 \\ .5066 & .4934 \end{bmatrix}$$

and similarly

$$P^8 = \begin{bmatrix} .6859 & .3141 \\ .6282 & .3718 \end{bmatrix} \qquad P^{16} = \begin{bmatrix} .6678 & .3322 \\ .6644 & .3356 \end{bmatrix}.$$

There is a clear trend here: It appears that as $n \to \infty$,

$$P^n \to \begin{bmatrix} 2/3 & 1/3 \\ 2/3 & 1/3 \end{bmatrix}.$$

We can use matrix diagonalization methods from linear algebra to find $P^n$ [Anton, p. 246]. First we find that the eigenvalues of $P$ are $1$ and $1 - \alpha - \beta$ from:

$$0 = \det(P - \lambda I) = \begin{vmatrix} 1 - \alpha - \lambda & \alpha \\ \beta & 1 - \beta - \lambda \end{vmatrix} = (1 - \alpha - \lambda)(1 - \beta - \lambda) - \alpha\beta$$

$$= (1 - \lambda)(1 - \alpha - \beta - \lambda).$$

The corresponding eigenvectors are:

$$\mathbf{e}_1 = \begin{bmatrix} 1 \\ 1 \end{bmatrix} \text{ and } \mathbf{e}_2 = \begin{bmatrix} \alpha \\ -\beta \end{bmatrix}$$

so the matrix with eigenvectors as columns is:

$$\mathbf{E} = [\mathbf{e}_1 \, \mathbf{e}_2] = \begin{bmatrix} 1 & \alpha \\ 1 & -\beta \end{bmatrix}.$$

We then have that:

$$P = \mathbf{E}\Lambda\mathbf{E}^{-1} = \frac{1}{\alpha + \beta} \begin{bmatrix} 1 & \alpha \\ 1 & -\beta \end{bmatrix} \begin{bmatrix} 1 & 0 \\ 0 & 1 - \alpha - \beta \end{bmatrix} \begin{bmatrix} \beta & \alpha \\ 1 & -1 \end{bmatrix}.$$

The payoff is in the calculation of $P^n$:

$$P^n = (\mathbf{E}\Lambda\mathbf{E}^{-1})(\mathbf{E}\Lambda\mathbf{E}^{-1})\ldots(\mathbf{E}\Lambda\mathbf{E}^{-1}) = \mathbf{E}\Lambda(\mathbf{E}^{-1}\mathbf{E})\Lambda\ldots\Lambda(\mathbf{E}^{-1}\mathbf{E})\Lambda\mathbf{E}^{-1}$$

$$= \mathbf{E}\Lambda\Lambda\ldots\Lambda\mathbf{E}^{-1} = \mathbf{E}\Lambda^n\mathbf{E}^{-1}$$

$$= \frac{1}{\alpha + \beta} \begin{bmatrix} 1 & \alpha \\ 1 & -\beta \end{bmatrix} \begin{bmatrix} 1 & 0 \\ 0 & (1 - \alpha - \beta)^n \end{bmatrix} \begin{bmatrix} \beta & \alpha \\ 1 & -1 \end{bmatrix}$$

$$= \begin{bmatrix} \dfrac{\beta}{\alpha + \beta} & \dfrac{\alpha}{\alpha + \beta} \\ \dfrac{\beta}{\alpha + \beta} & \dfrac{\alpha}{\alpha + \beta} \end{bmatrix} + \frac{(1 - \alpha - \beta)^n}{\alpha + \beta} \begin{bmatrix} \alpha & \alpha \\ -\beta & \beta \end{bmatrix}.$$

Equation (11.19b) is underdetermined and requires the normalization equation:

$$\sum_i \pi_i = 1. \tag{11.19c}$$

We refer to $\boldsymbol{\pi}$ as the **stationary state pmf** of the Markov chain. If we start the Markov chain with initial state pmf $\mathbf{p}(0) = \boldsymbol{\pi}$, then by Eqs. (11.16b) and (11.19b) we have that the state probability vector

$$\mathbf{p}(n) = \boldsymbol{\pi} P^n = \boldsymbol{\pi} \qquad \text{for all } n.$$

The resulting process is a stationary random process as defined in Section 9.6, since the probability of the sequence of states $i_0, i_1, \ldots, i_n$ starting at time $k$ is, by Eq. (11.5),

$$
\begin{aligned}
P[X_{n+k} &= i_n, \ldots, X_k = i_0] \\
&= P[X_{n+k} = i_n \mid X_{n+k-1} = i_{n-1}] \ldots P[X_{1+k} = i_1 \mid X_k = i_0] P[X_k = i_0] \\
&= P[X_{n+k} = i_n \mid X_{n+k-1} = i_{n-1}] \ldots P[X_{1+k} = i_1 \mid X_k = i_0] \pi_{i_0} \\
&= p_{i_{n-1}, i_n} \cdots p_{i_0, i_1} \pi_{i_0},
\end{aligned}
$$

which is independent of the initial time $k$. Thus the probabilities are independent of the choice of time origin, and the process is stationary.

---

### Example 11.13

Find the stationary state pmf in Example 11.6.
    Equation (11.19a) gives

$$\pi_0 = (1 - \alpha)\pi_0 + \beta\pi_1$$

$$\pi_1 = \alpha\pi_0 + (1 - \beta)\pi_1,$$

which imply that $\alpha\pi_0 = \beta\pi_1 = \beta(1 - \pi_0)$ since $\pi_0 + \pi_1 = 1$. Thus

$$\pi_0 = \frac{\beta}{\alpha + \beta} = \frac{2}{3} \qquad \pi_1 = \frac{\alpha}{\alpha + \beta} = \frac{1}{3}.$$

---

In this section we have shown the typical behavior of many Markov chains where the $n$-step transition probabilities and the state probabilities converge to constants that are independent of the initial conditions. These constant probabilities are found by solving the set of linear equations (11.19). It is worth noting, however, that not all Markov chains settle into stationary behavior where the process "forgets" the initial conditions. For example, the binomial counting process (Example 9.15) with $p > 0$ grows steadily so that for any fixed $j$, $p_j(n) \to 0$ as $n \to \infty$. The following example shows two atypical situations where the initial conditions determine the behavior for all time.

---

### Example 11.14    Two-State Process with Atypical Behavior

Consider the two-state process with state transition diagram shown in Fig. 11.2(a). In Example 11.10 we found that the two-state process settles into steady state behavior so long as $|1 - \alpha - \beta| < 1$. Let's see what happens when this condition is not satisfied.

Consider first the case where $\alpha = \beta = 1$, and suppose that we start the process in state 0, that is, $p_0(0) = 1$. The state probabilities at time $n$ are:

$$\mathbf{p}(n) = (p_0(0), 1 - p_0(0))P^n = (1, 0)\begin{bmatrix} 0 & 1 \\ 1 & 0 \end{bmatrix}^n.$$

The process in this case alternates between state 0 at even time instants and state 1 at odd time instants. $P^n$ does not converge, and instead alternates assuming the values $P$ and $P^2 = I$. The state probability vector alternates between the values $(1, 0)$ and $(0, 1)$ so it does not exhibit convergence.

Now consider the case $\alpha = \beta = 0$, and suppose again that we start the process in state 0, that is, $p_0(0) = 1$. The state probabilities at time $n$ are:

$$\mathbf{p}(n) = (1, 0)\begin{bmatrix} 1 & 0 \\ 0 & 1 \end{bmatrix}^n = (1, 0) \text{ for all } n.$$

In this case, the process remains fixed at state 0, which was selected at the initial time instant. Note that the process would have remained fixed at state 1 if state 1 had been selected initially. The state probability vector remains fixed at $(1, 0)$ if the initial state was 0 or $(0, 1)$ if the initial state was 1. In this case, both $P^n$ and $\mathbf{p}(n)$ converge immediately but to values that are determined by the initial condition.

---

The previous example demonstrates that we need to identify the conditions under which the state probability of Markov chains will converge to a stationary pmf that is found from Eq. (11.19). This is the topic of the next section.

## 11.3    CLASSES OF STATES, RECURRENCE PROPERTIES, AND LIMITING PROBABILITIES

In this section we take a closer look at the relation between the behavior of a Markov chain and its transition probability matrix. First we see that the states of a discrete-time Markov chain can be divided into one or more separate classes and that these classes can be of several types. We then show that the long-term behavior of a Markov chain is related to the types of its state classes. Figure 11.5 summarizes the types of classes to which a state can belong and identifies the associated long-term behavior.

### 11.3.1    Classes of States

We say that **state $j$ is accessible from state $i$** if for some $n \geq 0$, $p_{ij}(n) > 0$, that is, if there is a sequence of transitions from $i$ to $j$ that has nonzero probability. We say that **states $i$ and $j$ communicate** if they are accessible to each other; we then write $i \leftrightarrow j$. Note that a state communicates with itself since $p_{ii}(0) = 1$.

If state $i$ communicates with state $j$ and state $j$ communicates with state $k$, that is, $i \leftrightarrow j$ and $j \leftrightarrow k$, then state $i$ communicates with $k$. To see this, note that $i \leftrightarrow j$ implies that there is a nonzero probability path from $i$ to $j$ and $j \leftrightarrow k$ implies that there is a subsequent nonzero probability path from $j$ to $k$. The combined paths form a nonzero probability path from $i$ to $k$. A nonzero probability path in the reverse direction exists for the same reasons.

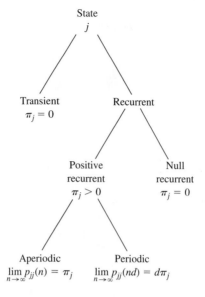

**FIGURE 11.5**
Classification of states and associated long-term behavior. The proportion of time spent in state $j$ is denoted by $\pi_j$.

We say that two states belong to the same **class** if they communicate with each other. Note that two different classes of states must be disjoint since having a state in common would imply that the states from both classes communicate with each other. Thus *the states of a Markov chain consist of one or more disjoint communication classes.* A Markov chain that consists of a single class is said to be **irreducible**.

### Example 11.15

Figure 11.6(a) shows the state transition diagram for a Markov chain with three classes: $\{0\}, \{1, 2\}$, and $\{3\}$.

### Example 11.16

Figure 11.6(b) shows the state transition diagram for a Markov chain with one class: $\{0, 1, 2, 3\}$. Thus the chain is irreducible.

### Example 11.17   Binomial Counting Process

Figure 11.6(c) shows the state transition diagram for a binomial counting process. It can be seen that the classes are: $\{0\}, \{1\}, \{2\}, \ldots$.

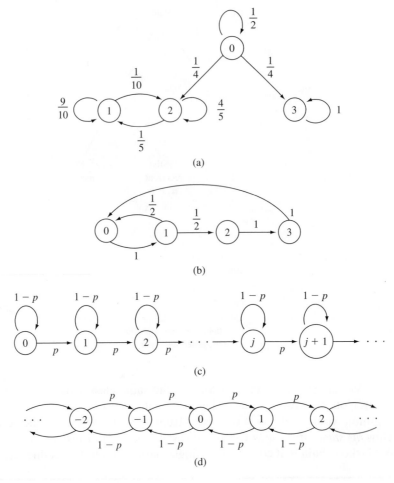

**FIGURE 11.6**
(a) A three-class Markov chain. (b) A periodic Markov chain. (c) A binomial counting
process. (d) The random walk process.

### Example 11.18    Random Walk

Figure 11.6(d) shows the state transition diagram for the random walk process. If $p > 0$, then the
process has only one class, $\{0, \pm 1, \pm 2, \dots\}$, so it is irreducible.

## 11.3.2    Recurrence Properties

Suppose we start a Markov chain in state $i$. State $i$ is said to be **recurrent** if the process
returns to the state with probability one, that is,

$$f_i = P[\text{ever returning to state } i] = 1. \tag{11.20a}$$

State $i$ is said to be **transient** if

$$f_i < 1. \tag{11.20b}$$

If we start the Markov chain in a recurrent state $i$, then the state reoccurs an infinite number of times. If we start the Markov chain in a transient state, the state does not reoccur after some finite number of returns. Each reoccurrence of the state can be viewed as a failure in a Bernoulli trial. The probability of failure is $f_i$. Thus the number of returns to state $i$ terminating with a success (no return) is a geometric random variable with mean $(1 - f_i)^{-1}$. If $f_i < 1$, then the probability of an infinite number of successes is zero. Therefore a transient state reoccurs only a finite number of times.

Let $X_n$ denote the Markov chain with initial state $i$, $X_0 = i$. Let $I_i(X)$ be the indicator function for state $i$, that is, $I_i(X)$ is equal to 1 if $X = i$ and equal to 0 otherwise. The expected number of returns to state $i$ is then

$$E\left[\sum_{n=1}^{\infty} I_i(X_n) \mid X_0 = i\right] = \sum_{n=1}^{\infty} E[I_i(X_n) \mid X_0 = i] = \sum_{n=1}^{\infty} p_{ii}(n) \tag{11.21}$$

since by Example 4.16

$$E[I_i(X_n) \mid X_0 = i] = P[X_n = i \mid X_0 = i] = p_{ii}(n).$$

A state is recurrent if and only if it reoccurs an infinite number of times, thus from Eq. (11.21) *state $i$ is recurrent if and only if*

$$\sum_{n=1}^{\infty} p_{ii}(n) = \infty. \tag{11.22}$$

Similarly, *state $i$ is transient if and only if*

$$\sum_{n=1}^{\infty} p_{ii}(n) < \infty. \tag{11.23}$$

---

## Example 11.19

In Example 11.15 (Fig. 11.6a), state 0 is transient since $p_{00}(n) = (1/2)^n$, so

$$\sum_{n=1}^{\infty} p_{00}(n) = \frac{1}{2} + \left(\frac{1}{2}\right)^2 + \left(\frac{1}{2}\right)^3 + \cdots = 1 < \infty.$$

On the other hand, if the process were started in state 1, we would have the two-state process discussed in Example 11.10. For such a process we found that

$$p_{11}(n) = \frac{\beta + \alpha(1 - \alpha - \beta)^n}{\alpha + \beta} = \frac{1/2 + 1/4(7/10)^n}{3/4}$$

so that

$$\sum_{n=1}^{\infty} p_{11}(n) = \sum_{n=1}^{\infty} \left(\frac{2}{3} + \frac{(7/10)^n}{3}\right) = \infty.$$

Therefore state 1 is recurrent.

---

### Example 11.20   Binomial Counting Process

In the binomial counting process all the states are transient since $p_{ii}(n) = (1 - p)^n$ so that for $p > 0$,

$$\sum_{n=1}^{\infty} p_{ii}(n) = \sum_{n=1}^{\infty} (1 - p)^n = \frac{1 - p}{p} < \infty.$$

### Example 11.21   Random Walk

Consider state zero in the random walk process in Fig. 11.6(d). The state reoccurs in $2n$ steps if and only if $n$ +1s and $n$ −1s occur during the $2n$ steps. This occurs with probability

$$p_{00}(2n) = \binom{2n}{n} p^n (1 - p)^n.$$

Stirling's formula for $n!$ can be used to show that

$$\binom{2n}{n} p^n (1 - p)^n \sim \frac{(4p(1 - p))^n}{\sqrt{\pi n}},$$

where $a_n \sim b_n$ when $\lim_{n \to \infty} a_n/b_n = 1$.

Thus Eq. (11.21) for state 0 is

$$\sum_{n=1}^{\infty} p_{00}(2n) \sim \sum_{n=1}^{\infty} \frac{(4p(1 - p))^n}{\sqrt{\pi n}}.$$

If $p = 1/2$, then $4p(1 - p) = 1$ and the series diverges. It then follows that state 0 is recurrent. If $p \neq 1/2$, then $(4p(1 - p)) < 1$, and the above series converges. This implies that state 0 is transient. Thus when $p = 1/2$, the random walk process maintains a precarious balance about 0. As soon as $p \neq 1/2$, a positive or negative drift is introduced and the process grows towards $\pm\infty$.

---

*Recurrence and transience are class properties*: If a state $i$ is recurrent, then all states in its class are recurrent; if a state is transient, then all the states in its class are transient. If state $i$ is recurrent, then all states in its class will be visited eventually as the process forever returns to state $i$ over and over again. Indeed all other states in its class will appear an infinite number of times.

To show the recurrence class property, let $i$ be a recurrent state and let $j$ be another state in the class, then $i \leftrightarrow j$, and there are probabilities $p_{ji}(m) > 0$ and $p_{ij}(l) > 0$ that corresponds to nonzero probability paths that lead from $j$ to $i$ in $m$ steps, and back from $i$ to $j$ in $l$ steps. We can identify many nonzero probability paths that go from $j$ to $j$ by splicing the above two paths to recurrent paths for state $i$: go from $j$ to $i$ using the above path; then from $i$ to $i$ using an $n$-step recurrent path; then back from $i$ to $j$ using the above path. The probabilities for these paths provide a lower bound to the recurrence probabilities for $j$:

$$\sum_k p_{jj}(k) > \sum_n p_{ji}(m) p_{ii}(n) p_{ij}(l) = p_{ji}(m) p_{ij}(l) \sum_n p_{ii}(n) = \infty,$$

since state $i$ is recurrent. This implies that state $j$ is also recurrent. Now suppose that state $i$ is transient, and let $j$ be another state in its class. State $j$ cannot be recurrent, for this would imply that $i$ is recurrent, in contradiction to our assumption. Therefore $j$ must be transient.

*If a Markov chain is irreducible then either all its states are transient or all its states are recurrent.* If the Markov chain has a finite state space, it is impossible for all of its states to be transient. At least some of the states must occur an infinite number of times as time progresses, implying that all states are recurrent. Therefore, *the states of a finite-state, irreducible Markov chain are all recurrent.* If the state space is countably infinite, then all the states can be transient. The random walk with $p \neq 1/2$ provides an example of such a Markov chain.

The structure of the state transition diagram and the associated nonzero transition probabilities can impose periodicity in the realizations of a discrete-time Markov chain. We say that state $i$ has **period** $d$ if it can only reoccur at times that are multiples of $d$, that is, $p_{ii}(n) = 0$ whenever $n$ is not a multiple of $d$, where $d$ is the largest integer with this property. We say that state $i$ is **aperiodic** if it has period $d = 1$.

*Periodicity is a class property*, that is, all states in a class have the same period. An irreducible Markov chain is said to be **aperiodic** if the states in its single class have period one. An irreducible Markov chain is said to be **periodic** if its states have period $d > 1$.

To show that periodicity is a class property, suppose that state $i$ has period $d$ and let $j$ be another state in the same class. Since $i \leftrightarrow j$, there are probabilities $p_{ji}(m) > 0$ and $p_{ij}(l) > 0$ that corresponds to paths that lead from $j$ to $i$ in $m$ steps, and back from $i$ to $j$ in $l$ steps. We can create a path from $j$ to $j$ by splicing the $m$-step path for $j$ to $i$ with the $l$-step path from $i$ to $j$; this path has length $m + l$ and probability $p_{ji}(m)p_{ij}(l) > 0$. The length $m + l$ must be divisible by $d'$, the period of state $j$. Now create multiple paths from $j$ to $j$ by attaching the above two paths to nonzero probability paths that go from $i$ to $i$ in $n$ steps. These paths have length $m + l + n$ and probability $p_{ji}(m)p_{ii}(n)p_{ij}(l) > 0$. All these paths go from $j$ to $j$ so $m + n + l$ must be divisible by $d'$. We already showed that $m + l$ is divisible by $d'$, so we have that $n$ must also be divisible by $d'$. But $n$ can be the length of any path that goes from $i$ to $i$, and so $d$, the period of state $i$, is the largest value that divides all such $n$. This implies that $d'$ must divide $d$. By reversing the roles of state $i$ and state $j$, the same series of arguments imply that $d$ must divide $d'$. Thus $d = d'$ and state $i$ and state $j$ have the same period.

---

### Example 11.22    Two-State Process with Atypical Behavior

Characterize the two "atypical" Markov chains in Example 11.14.

In the case where $\alpha = \beta = 1$, Fig. 11.2(a) shows that we have a single communication class with period $d = 2$. This explains why the process alternates between state 0 at even time instants and state 1 at odd time instants

In the case $\alpha = \beta = 0$, we have two communication classes: $\{0\}$ and $\{1\}$. The selection of the initial state at $t = 0$ effectively picks one of the two classes, and the process remains in that class forever.

---

### Example 11.23

In Example 11.15 (Fig 11.6a), all the states have the property that $p_{ii}(n) > 0$ for $n = 1, 2, \ldots$. Therefore all three classes in the Markov chain have period 1.

### Example 11.24

In the Markov chain in Fig 11.6(b), the states 0 and 1 can reoccur at time $2, 4, 6, \ldots$ and states 2 and 3 at times $4, 6, 8, \ldots$. Therefore the Markov chain has period 2.

### Example 11.25

In the random walk process in Fig 11.6(d), a state reoccurs when the number of successes ($+1$s) equals the number of failures ($-1$s). This can only happen after an even number of steps. The process therefore has period 2.

Figure 11.7(a) summarizes the possible structures that can be encountered for Markov chains. In the case of irreducible finite-state Markov chains, all states in the single class must be recurrent and the class can either be aperiodic or periodic. If a finite-state

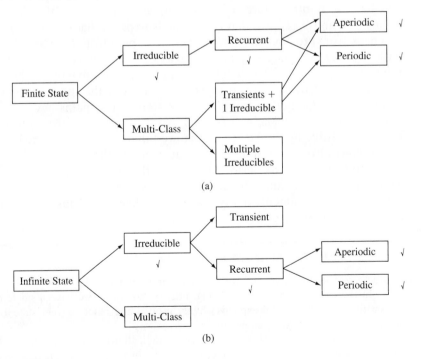

**FIGURE 11.7**
Possible structures for Markov chains.

Markov chain consists of multiple transient classes and a single irreducible class, then the chain will eventually settle in the states of the irreducible class. Thus in the long-run the behavior is the same as that of an irreducible chain. A finite-state Markov chain with multiple irreducible classes will eventually enter and remain thereafter in one of the irreducible classes. Over the long run, the chain will exhibit the behavior of an irreducible Markov chain with the given class of states. Thus the case of multi-irreducible classes can be viewed as a two stage random experiment in which the first stage involves selecting one of the irreducible classes.

Figure 11.7(b) summarizes the possible structures for Markov chains with infinite state space. The major difference from the finite case is that an irreducible class can have all of its states be transient. Consequently when a chain has multiple classes it is now possible for the chain to enter and remain in a class that is either transient or recurrent.

### 11.3.3  Limiting Probabilities

If all the states in a Markov chain are transient, then all the state probabilities approach zero as $n \to \infty$. If a Markov chain has some transient classes and some recurrent classes, as in Fig. 11.6(a), then eventually the process enters and remains thereafter in one of the recurrent classes. Therefore we can concentrate on individual recurrent classes when studying the limiting probabilities of a chain. For this reason we assume in this section that we are dealing with an irreducible Markov chain.

Suppose we start a Markov chain in a *recurrent* state $i$ at time $n = 0$. Let $T_i(1), T_i(1) + T_i(2), \ldots$ be the times when the process returns to state $i$, where $T_i(k)$ is the time that elapses between the $(k-1)$th and $k$th returns (see Fig. 11.8). The $T_i$ form an iid sequence since each return time is independent of previous return times.

The proportion of time spent in state $i$ after $k$ returns to $i$ is

$$\text{proportion of time in state } i = \frac{k}{T_i(1) + T_i(2) + \cdots + T_i(k)}. \tag{11.24}$$

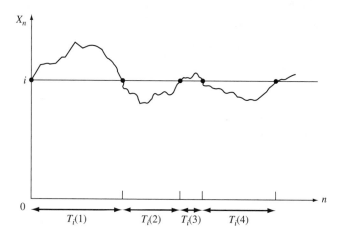

**FIGURE 11.8**
Recurrence times for state $i$.

Since the state is recurrent, the process returns to state $i$ an infinite number of times. Thus the law of large numbers implies that, with probability one, the reciprocal of the above expression approaches the **mean recurrence time** $E[T_i]$ so the long-term proportion of time spent in state $i$ approaches

$$\text{proportion of time in state } i \rightarrow \frac{1}{E[T_i]} = \pi_i, \qquad (11.25)$$

where $\pi_i$ is *the long-term proportion of time spent in state i.*

If $E[T_i] < \infty$, then we say that state $i$ is **positive recurrent**. Equation (11.25) then implies that

$$\pi_i > 0 \qquad \text{if state } i \text{ is positive recurrent.}$$

If $E[T_i] = \infty$, then we say that state $i$ is **null recurrent**. Equation (11.25) then implies that

$$\pi_i = 0 \qquad \text{if state } i \text{ is null recurrent.}$$

It can be shown that positive and null recurrence are class properties.

Positive recurrent, aperiodic states are called **ergodic**. Once a Markov chain enters an ergodic state, then the process will remain in the state's class forever. Furthermore the process will visit all states in the class sufficiently frequently that the long-term proportion of time in a given state will be governed by Eq. (11.25) and approach a nonzero value. Thus the process will reveal its underlying state probabilities through time averages. Given our previous discussion on ergodicity in Chapter 9, it is not surprising that an **ergodic Markov chain** is defined as an irreducible, aperiodic, positive recurrent Markov chain.

---

**Example 11.26**

The process in Fig. 11.6(b) returns to state 0 in two steps with probability 1/2 and in four steps with probability 1/2. Therefore the mean recurrence time for state 0 is

$$E[T_0] = \frac{1}{2}(2) + \frac{1}{2}(4) = 3.$$

Therefore state 0 is positive recurrent and the long-term proportion of time spent in state 0 is

$$\pi_0 = \frac{1}{3}.$$

---

**Example 11.27   Random Walk**

In Example 11.21 it was shown that the random walk process is recurrent if $p = 1/2$. However, the mean recurrence time can be shown to be infinite when $p = 1/2$ (Feller, 1968, p. 314). Thus all the states in the chain are null recurrent.

---

The $\pi_j$'s in Eq. (11.25) satisfy the equations that define the stationary state pmf:

$$\pi_j = \sum_i \pi_i P_{ij} \qquad \text{for all } j \qquad (11.26a)$$

and

$$1 = \sum_i \pi_i. \tag{11.26b}$$

To see this, note that since $\pi_i$ is the proportion of time spent in state $i$, then $\pi_i P_{ij}$ is the proportion of time in which state $j$ follows $i$. If we sum over all $i$, we then obtain the long-term proportion of time in state $j$, $\pi_j$.

---

### Example 11.28

The stationary state pmf for the periodic Markov chain in Fig. 11.6(b) is found from Eqs. (11.26a) and (11.26b):

$$\pi_0 = \frac{1}{2}\pi_1 + \pi_3$$

$$\pi_1 = \pi_0$$

$$\pi_2 = \frac{1}{2}\pi_1$$

$$\pi_3 = \pi_2.$$

These equations imply that $\pi_1 = \pi_0$ and $\pi_2 = \pi_3 = \pi_0/2$. Since the probabilities must add to one, we obtain

$$\pi_1 = \pi_0 = \frac{1}{3} \quad \text{and} \quad \pi_2 = \pi_3 = \frac{1}{6}.$$

Note that $\pi_0 = 1/3$ was obtained for the mean recurrence time in Example 11.26.

---

In Section 11.2 we found that for certain Markov chains, the $n$-step transition matrix approaches a fixed matrix of equal rows as $n \to \infty$ (see Eq. 11.17). We also saw that the rows of this limiting matrix consisted of a pmf that satisfied Eqs. (11.26a) and (11.26b). We are now ready to state under what conditions this occurs.

---

### Theorem 1[2]

For an irreducible aperiodic Markov chain exactly one of the following assertions holds:

**(i)** All states are transient or all states are null recurrent; $p_{ij}(n) \to 0$ as $n \to \infty$ for all $i$ and $j$ and there exists no stationary pmf

**(ii)** All states are positive recurrent, so

$$\lim_{n \to \infty} p_{ij}(n) = \pi_j \quad \text{for all } j \tag{11.27}$$

where $\{\pi_j, j = 1, 2, 3, \dots \}$ is the unique stationary pmf solution to Eq. (11.26ab).

---

[2]A proof to Theorem 1 is given by [Ross, pp. 108–110].

Theorem 1 states that for ergodic Markov chains, the $n$-step transition probabilities approach constant values given by the steady state pmf. Note that Eq. (11.27) can be written in matrix form as shown in Eq. (11.17b). From Eq. (11.18), it then follows that the state probabilities approach steady state values that are independent of the initial conditions. These steady state probabilities correspond to the stationary probabilities obtained by solving Eq. (11.26ab), and thus correspond to the long-term proportion of time spent in a given state. Theorem 1 also states that if the irreducible Markov chain is transient or null recurrent, then a stationary pmf solution to Eq. (11.26ab) does not exist. This implies that when we do find a solution, and the chain is irreducible and aperiodic, then the Markov chain must be positive recurrent and hence ergodic.

---

### Example 11.29 Age of a Device

Consider a Markov Chain that counts the age of a device in service at the end of each day. At the end of each day, the device either increases its age by 1 (with probability $a$) or fails and returns to the "1" state (with probability $1 - a$). A failed device is replaced at the beginning of the next day and the age counting processes is resumed. Determine whether the Markov chain has a stationary distribution.

The state transition diagram for the Markov chain is shown in Fig. 11.9. If $a > 0$, then every state $i$ can access any state $i + 1$, and consequently any state $i$ can access any state $j > i$. In addition every state $i$ can access state 1. This implies that there is a nonzero probability path between any two states, and so the Markov chain is irreducible. State 1 can reoccur in intervals of $1, 2, 3, 4, \ldots$, and so state 1 has period 1. Therefore all the states have period 1 and the Markov chain is aperiodic.

The equations for the stationary probabilities are:

$$\pi_1 = (1 - a)\pi_1 + (1 - a)\pi_2 + \cdots = (1 - a)(\pi_1 + \pi_2 + \cdots) = 1 - a$$

$$\pi_{i+1} = a\pi_i \quad \text{for} \quad i \geq 1.$$

By a simple induction argument we can show that:

$$\pi_i = (1 - a)a^{i-1} \quad \text{for} \quad i \geq 1.$$

Therefore the Markov chain is positive recurrent and has this stationary pmf.

---

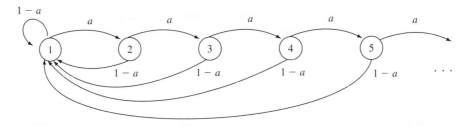

**FIGURE 11.9**
Age of a device.

**Example 11.30  Google PageRank Algorithm**

In Example 11.12 we showed the basic approach for ranking Web pages according to an associated Markov chain. The approach included a strategy to deal with the case where users become trapped in a page with no outgoing links, i.e., page 2 in Fig. 11.4(a). The approach, however, is not sufficient to ensure that the Markov chain is irreducible and aperiodic. For example, in Fig. 11.4(b) users can also become trapped in the periodic class $\{4, 5\}$. This poses a problem for the rank algorithm which uses the power of the transition probability matrix to obtain the stationary pmf. To deal with this problem, the PageRank algorithm also assumes that each time a new page is selected, the procedure in Example 11.12 is used with probability $\alpha$, but otherwise (with probability $1 - \alpha$) any of all possible Web pages is selected with equal probability. The value $\alpha = 0.85$ is usually cited as appropriate. The modified ranking method then has a transition probability matrix that is aperiodic and irreducible and the conditions of Theorem 1 are satisfied.

For the example in Fig. 11.4(b) we have:

$$P = (0.85) \begin{bmatrix} 0 & 1/2 & 1/2 & 0 & 0 \\ 1/5 & 1/5 & 1/5 & 1/5 & 1/5 \\ 1/3 & 1/3 & 0 & 1/3 & 0 \\ 0 & 0 & 0 & 0 & 1 \\ 0 & 0 & 1/2 & 0 & 1/2 \end{bmatrix} + (0.15) \begin{bmatrix} 1/5 & 1/5 & 1/5 & 1/5 & 1/5 \\ 1/5 & 1/5 & 1/5 & 1/5 & 1/5 \\ 1/5 & 1/5 & 1/5 & 1/5 & 1/5 \\ 1/5 & 1/5 & 1/5 & 1/5 & 1/5 \\ 1/5 & 1/5 & 1/5 & 1/5 & 1/5 \end{bmatrix}$$

$$= \begin{bmatrix} 0.0300 & 0.4550 & 0.4550 & 0.0300 & 0.0300 \\ 0.2000 & 0.2000 & 0.2000 & 0.2000 & 0.2000 \\ 0.3133 & 0.3133 & 0.0300 & 0.3133 & 0.0300 \\ 0.0300 & 0.0300 & 0.0300 & 0.0300 & 0.8800 \\ 0.0300 & 0.0300 & 0.4550 & 0.0300 & 0.4550 \end{bmatrix}.$$

The matrix $P$ has a stationary state pmf given by:

$$\mathbf{p}(n) = (0.13175, 0.18772, 0.24642, 0.13173, 0.30239).$$

See [Langville] for more details on the PageRank algorithm.

For periodic processes, we have the following result.

**Theorem 2**

For an irreducible, periodic, and positive recurrent Markov chain with period $d$,

$$\lim_{n \to \infty} p_{jj}(nd) = d\pi_j \text{ for all } j \tag{11.28}$$

where $\pi_j$ is the unique nonnegative solution of Eqs. (11.26a) and (11.26b).

As before, $\pi_j$ represents the proportion of time spent in state $j$. However, the fact that state $j$ is constrained to occur at multiples of $d$ steps implies that the probability of occurrence of the state $j$ is $d$ times greater at the allowable times and zero elsewhere.

### Example 11.31

In Examples 11.26 and 11.28 we found that the long-term proportion of time spent in state 0 is $\pi_0 = 1/3$. If we start in state 0, then only even states can occur at even time instants. Thus at these even time instants the probability of state 0 is 2/3 and of state 2 is 1/3. At odd time instants, the probabilities of states 0 and 2 are zero.

---

Theorems 1 and 2 only address the most important cases of irreducible, periodic and aperiodic Markov chains indicated by the checkmarks in Fig. 11.7. The following example considers a case not covered by Theorems 1 and 2.

---

### Example 11.32    Markov Chain with Multiple Irreducible Classes

Does the Markov chain in Fig. 11.6(a) have a unique stationary pmf?

The equations for the stationary probabilities are:

$$p_0 = 1/2 p_0$$
$$p_1 = 9/10 p_1 + 1/5 p_2$$
$$p_2 = 1/4 p_0 + 1/10 p_1 + 4/5 p_2$$
$$p_3 = 1/4 p_0 + p_3.$$

The first equation implies that $p_0 = 0$, which reduces the fourth equation to $p_3 = p_3$, which imposes no constraints on $p_3$. The middle two equations are equivalent and both imply that $p_1 = 2p_2$. The normalization condition requires that $1 = p_1 + p_2 + p_3 = 3p_2 + p_3$. Therefore the equations are underdetermined and there are many solutions with the form: $(0, 2p_2, p_2, 1 - 3p_2)$ where $0 \leq p_2 \leq 1/3$.

Now let's approach the problem according to its three classes: $\{0\}$, $\{1, 2\}$, and $\{3\}$. The first class is transient and the other two classes are recurrent. Suppose the initial state is 3, then the process remains in that state forever. The stationary pmf for class $\{3\}$ by itself is $(0, 0, 0, 1)$. If the initial state is 1 or 2, then the process remains in this class forever; the stationary pmf for this class in isolation is $(0, 2/3, 1/3, 0)$. Finally if the initial state is 0, then the process will eventually leave and enter one of the other two classes with equal probability. In the general case, if the initial state is selected according to the pmf $(p_0(0), p_1(0), p_2(0), p_3(0))$ then the class $\{1, 2\}$ will be entered with probability $1/2\, p_0(0) + p_1(0) + p_2(0)$, and class $\{3\}$ will be entered with probability $1/2\, p_0(0) + p_3(0)$. The stationary pmf would then have the form:

$$\left\{ 1/2\, p_0(0) + p_1(0) + p_2(0) \right\}(0, 2/3, 1/3, 0) + \left\{ 1/2\, p_0(0) + p_3(0) \right\}(0, 0, 0, 1)$$
$$= \gamma(0, 2/3, 1/3, 0) + (1 - \gamma)(0, 0, 0, 1)$$
$$= (0, 2\gamma/3, \gamma/3, 1 - \gamma).$$

If we let $\gamma/3 = p_2$ we see that this solution has the form we derived before.

For example, suppose the initial pmf was $(0, 1/3, 1/6, 1/2)$, then this pmf satisfies the condition for a stationary pmf and the repeated multiplication by $P$ will yield the same pmf. In this sense this multiclass Markov chain has a stationary pmf. Note however that the relative frequencies of the states depend on which irreducible class is actually entered. Thus if we record long-term average frequencies we will observe either $(0, 2/3, 1/3, 0)$ or $(0, 0, 0, 1)$. The stationary pmf does not correspond to either of these two pmf's; instead the stationary pmf gives us the expected value of the two pmf's:

$$(0, 1/3, 1/6, 1/2) = 1/2(0, 2/3, 1/3, 0) + 1/2(0, 0, 0, 1)$$

where 1/2 is the probability of entering the two irreducible classes for this choice of initial pmf.

---

Example 11.32 illustrates the behavior of multiclass finite-state Markov chain. In these chains the process will eventually enter and remain forever in one of its recurrent classes. Each recurrent class can be considered as a separate irreducible Markov chain with its own stationary pmf. The multiclass Markov chain will then have stationary pmf's that depend on the stationary pmf's of its constituent recurrent classes according to the initial state probabilities. These multiclass Markov chains are not ergodic since the relative frequencies of the states do not correspond to the stationary pmf.

If a multiclass chain has infinite state space, then the situation discussed above can occur as a special case: the process initially works its way through transient classes and eventually settles in one of a number of ergodic classes. However, in general, it is possible for some or all of the classes to be transient and/or null recurrent. In such case the process may never settle into stationary behavior.

## 11.4    CONTINUOUS-TIME MARKOV CHAINS

In Section 11.2 we saw that the transition probability matrix determines the behavior of a discrete-time Markov chain. In this section we see that the same is true for continuous-time Markov chains.

The joint pmf for $k + 1$ arbitrary time instants of a Markov chain is given by Eq. (11.3):

$$P[X(t_{k+1}) = x_{k+1}, X(t_k) = x_k, \ldots, X(t_1) = x_1]$$
$$= P[X(t_{k+1}) = x_{k+1} \,|\, X(t_k) = x_k] \cdots$$
$$\times P[X(t_2) = x_2 \,|\, X(t_1) = x_1] P[X(t_1) = x_1]. \quad (11.29)$$

This result holds regardless of whether the process is discrete-time or continuous-time. In the continuous-time case, Eq. (11.29) requires that we know the transition probabilities from an arbitrary time $s$ to an arbitrary time $s + t$:

$$P[X(s + t) = j \,|\, X(s) = i] \qquad t \geq 0.$$

We assume here that the transition probabilities depend only on the difference between the two times:

$$P[X(s + t) = j \,|\, X(s) = i] = P[X(t) = j \,|\, X(0) = i] = p_{ij}(t)$$
$$t \geq 0, \text{ all } s. \quad (11.30)$$

We say that $X(t)$ has **homogeneous transition probabilities**.

Let $P(t) = \{p_{ij}(t)\}$ *denote the matrix of transition probabilities in an interval of length t.* Since $p_{ii}(0) = 1$ and $p_{ij}(0) = 0$ for $i \neq j$, we have

$$P(0) = I, \tag{11.31}$$

where $I$ is the identity matrix.

---

### Example 11.33 Poisson Process

For the Poisson process, the transition probabilities satisfy

$$
\begin{aligned}
p_{ij}(t) &= P[j - i \text{ events in } t \text{ seconds}] \\
&= p_{0,\,j-i}(t) \\
&= \frac{(\alpha t)^{j-i}}{(j-i)!} e^{-\alpha t} \qquad j \geq i.
\end{aligned}
$$

Therefore

$$
P(t) = \begin{bmatrix}
e^{-\alpha t} & \alpha t e^{-\alpha t} & (\alpha t)^2 e^{-\alpha t}/2! & \cdot & \cdots \\
0 & e^{-\alpha t} & \alpha t e^{-\alpha t} & (\alpha t)^2 e^{-\alpha t}/2! & \cdots \\
0 & 0 & e^{-\alpha t} & \alpha t e^{-\alpha t} & \cdots \\
\cdot & \cdot & \cdot & \cdot & \cdots
\end{bmatrix}.
$$

As $t$ approaches zero, $e^{-\alpha t} \approx 1 - \alpha t$. Thus for a small time interval $\delta$,

$$
P(\delta) \approx \begin{bmatrix}
1 - \alpha\delta & \alpha\delta & 0 & \cdots \\
0 & 1 - \alpha\delta & \alpha\delta & \cdots \\
0 & 0 & 1 - \alpha\delta & \cdots \\
\cdot & \cdot & \cdot & \cdots
\end{bmatrix},
$$

where all terms of order $\delta^2$ or higher have been neglected. Thus the probability of more than one transition in a very short time interval is negligible. Note that this is consistent with the assumptions made in deriving the Poisson process in Section 9.4.

---

### Example 11.34 Random Telegraph

In the random telegraph example, the process $X(t)$ changes with each occurrence of an event in a Poisson process. From Eqs. (9.40) and (9.41) we see that the transition probabilities are as follows:

$$P[X(t) = a \mid X(0) = a] = \frac{1}{2}\{1 + e^{-2\alpha t}\}$$

$$P[X(t) = a \mid X(0) = b] = \frac{1}{2}\{1 - e^{-2\alpha t}\} \qquad \text{if } a \neq b.$$

Thus the transition probability matrix is

$$
P(t) = \begin{bmatrix}
1/2\{1 + e^{-2\alpha t}\} & 1/2\{1 - e^{-2\alpha t}\} \\
1/2\{1 - e^{-2\alpha t}\} & 1/2\{1 + e^{-2\alpha t}\}
\end{bmatrix}.
$$

### 11.4.1  State Occupancy Times

Since the random telegraph signal changes polarity with each occurrence of an event in a Poisson process, it follows that the time spent in each state is an exponential random variable. It turns out that this is a property of the **state occupancy time** for all continuous-time Markov chains, that is: $X(t)$ *remains at a given value (state) for an exponentially distributed random time*. To see why, let $T_i$ be the time spent in a state $i$. The probability of spending more than $t$ seconds in this state is then

$$P[T_i > t].$$

Now suppose that the process has already been in state $i$ for $s$ seconds; then the probability of spending $t$ more seconds in this state is

$$P[T_i > t + s \,|\, T_i > s] = P[T_i > t + s \,|\, X(s') = i, 0 \leq s' \leq s],$$

since the $\{T_i > s\}$ implies that the system has been in state $i$ during the time interval $(0, s)$. The Markov property implies that if $X(s) = i$, then the past is irrelevant and we can view the system as being restarted in state $i$ at time $s$:

$$P[T_i > t + s \,|\, T_i > s] = P[T_i > t]. \tag{11.32}$$

Only the exponential random variable satisfies this memoryless property (see Section 4.4). Thus the time spent in state $i$ is an exponential random variable with some mean $1/v_i$:

$$P[T_i > t] = e^{-v_i t}. \tag{11.33}$$

The *mean state occupancy time* $1/v_i$ will usually be different for each state.

The above result provides us with another way of looking at continuous-time Markov chains. Each time a state, say $i$, is entered, an exponentially distributed state occupancy time $T_i$ is selected. When the time is up, the next state $j$ is selected according to a *discrete-time* Markov chain, with transition probabilities $\widetilde{q}_{ij}$. Then the new state occupancy time is selected according to $T_j$, and so on.[3] We call $\widetilde{q}_{ij}$ an **embedded Markov chain**. We will see in the last part of this section that the properties of the continuous-time Markov chain depends on the class properties of its embedded chain.

---

### Example 11.35

The random telegraph signal in Example 11.34 spends an exponentially distributed time with mean $1/\alpha$ in each state. When a transition occurs, the transition is always from the present state to the only other state, thus the embedded Markov chain is

$$\widetilde{q}_{00} = 0 \qquad \widetilde{q}_{01} = 1$$
$$\widetilde{q}_{10} = 1 \qquad \widetilde{q}_{11} = 0.$$

---

[3]This view of Markov chains is useful in setting up computer simulation models of Markov chain processes.

## 11.4.2   Transition Rates and Time-Dependent State Probabilities

Consider the transition probabilities in a very short time interval of duration $\delta$ seconds. The probability that the process remains in state $i$ during the interval is

$$P[T_i > \delta] = e^{-v_i\delta}$$

$$= 1 - \frac{v_i\delta}{1!} + \frac{v_i^2\delta^2}{2!} - \cdots$$

$$= 1 - v_i\delta + o(\delta),$$

where $o(\delta)$ denotes terms that become negligible relative to $\delta$ as $\delta$ approaches zero.[4] The exponential distributions of the state occupancy times imply that the probability of two or more transitions in an interval of duration $\delta$ is $o(\delta)$. Thus for small $\delta$, $p_{ii}(\delta)$ is approximately equal to the probability that the process remains in state $i$ for $\delta$ seconds:

$$p_{ii}(\delta) = P[T_i > \delta] + o(\delta)$$

$$= 1 - v_i\delta + o(\delta)$$

or equivalently,

$$1 - p_{ii}(\delta) = v_i\delta + o(\delta). \tag{11.34}$$

We call $v_i$ the *rate at which the process $X(t)$ leaves state $i$.*

Once the process leaves state $i$, it will enter state $j$ with probability $\widetilde{q}_{ij}$, where $\widetilde{q}_{ij}$ is the transition probability of the embedded Markov chain. Thus

$$p_{ij}(\delta) = (1 - p_{ii}(\delta))\widetilde{q}_{ij}$$

$$= v_i\widetilde{q}_{ij}\delta + o(\delta)$$

$$= \gamma_{ij}\delta + o(\delta). \tag{11.35a}$$

We call $\gamma_{ij} = v_i\widetilde{q}_{ij}$ the *rate at which the process $X(t)$ enters state $j$ from state $i$.* For completeness, we define $\gamma_{ii} = -v_i$, so that by Eq. (11.34),

$$p_{ii}(\delta) - 1 = \gamma_{ii}\delta + o(\delta). \tag{11.35b}$$

If we divide both sides of Eqs. (11.35a) and (11.35b) by $\delta$ and take the limit $\delta \to 0$, we obtain

$$\lim_{\delta\to0}\frac{p_{ij}(\delta)}{\delta} = \gamma_{ij} \qquad i \neq j \tag{11.36a}$$

and

$$\lim_{\delta\to0}\frac{p_{ii}(\delta) - 1}{\delta} = \gamma_{ii}, \tag{11.36b}$$

since

$$\lim_{\delta\to0}\frac{o(\delta)}{\delta} = 0,$$

because $o(\delta)$ is of order higher than $\delta$.

---

[4]A function $g(h)$ is said to be $o(h)$ if $\lim_{h\to0}g(h)/h = 0$, that is, $g(h)$ goes to zero faster than $h$ does.

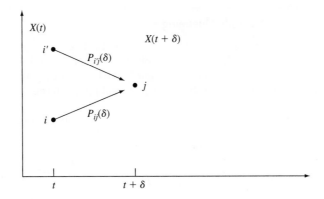

**FIGURE 11.10**
Transitions into state $j$.

We are now ready to develop a set of equations for finding the state probabilities at time $t$, which will be denoted by

$$p_j(t) \triangleq P[X(t) = j].$$

For $\delta > 0$, we have (see Fig. 11.10)

$$
\begin{aligned}
p_j(t + \delta) &= P[X(t + \delta) = j] \\
&= \sum_i P[X(t + \delta) = j \mid X(t) = i] P[X(t) = i] \\
&= \sum_i p_{ij}(\delta) p_i(t).
\end{aligned}
\tag{11.37}
$$

If we subtract $p_j(t)$ from both sides, we obtain

$$p_j(t + \delta) - p_j(t) = \sum_{i \neq j} p_{ij}(\delta) p_i(t) + (p_{jj}(\delta) - 1) p_j(t). \tag{11.38}$$

If we divide by $\delta$, apply Eqs. (11.36a) and (11.36b) and let $\delta \to 0$, we obtain

$$p_j'(t) = \sum_i \gamma_{ij} p_i(t). \tag{11.39}$$

Equation (11.39) is a form of the **Chapman–Kolmogorov equations** for continuous-time Markov chains. To find $p_j(t)$ we need to solve this system of differential equations with initial conditions specified by the initial state pmf $\{ p_j(0), j = 0, 1, \dots \}$.

Note that if we solve Eq. (11.39) under the assumption that the state at time zero was $i$, that is, with initial condition $p_i(0) = 1$ and $p_j(0) = 0$ for all $j \neq i$, then the solution is actually $p_{ij}(t)$, the $ij$ component of $P(t)$. Thus Eq. (11.39) can also be used to find the transition probability matrix.

### Example 11.36   A Simple Queueing System

A queueing system alternates between two states. In state 0, the system is idle and waiting for a customer to arrive. This idle time is an exponential random variable with mean $1/\alpha$. In state 1, the system is busy servicing a customer. The time in the busy state is an exponential random variable with mean $1/\beta$. Find the state probabilities $p_0(t)$ and $p_1(t)$ in terms of the initial state probabilities $p_0(0)$ and $p_1(0)$.

The system moves from state 0 to state 1 at a rate $\alpha$, and from state 1 to state 0 at a rate $\beta$:

$$\gamma_{00} = -\alpha \qquad \gamma_{01} = \alpha$$
$$\gamma_{10} = \beta \qquad \gamma_{11} = -\beta.$$

Equation (11.39) then gives

$$p_0'(t) = -\alpha p_0(t) + \beta p_1(t)$$
$$p_1'(t) = \alpha p_0(t) - \beta p_1(t).$$

Since $p_0(t) + p_1(t) = 1$, the first equation becomes

$$p_0'(t) = -\alpha p_0(t) + \beta(1 - p_0(t)),$$

which is a first-order differential equation:

$$p_0'(t) + (\alpha + \beta)p_0(t) = \beta \qquad p_0(0) = p_0.$$

The general solution of this equation is

$$p_0(t) = \frac{\beta}{\alpha + \beta} + Ce^{-(\alpha+\beta)t}.$$

We obtain $C$ by setting $t = 0$ and solving in terms of $p_0(0)$; then we find

$$p_0(t) = \frac{\beta}{\alpha + \beta} + \left( p_0(0) - \frac{\beta}{\alpha + \beta} \right) e^{-(\alpha+\beta)t}$$

and

$$p_1(t) = \frac{\alpha}{\alpha + \beta} + \left( p_1(0) - \frac{\alpha}{\alpha + \beta} \right) e^{-(\alpha+\beta)t}.$$

Note that as $t \to \infty$,

$$p_0(t) \to \frac{\beta}{\alpha + \beta} \qquad \text{and} \qquad p_1(t) \to \frac{\alpha}{\alpha + \beta}.$$

Thus as $t \to \infty$, the state probabilities approach constant values that are independent of the initial state probabilities.

---

### Example 11.37   The Poisson Process

Find the state probabilities for the Poisson process.

The Poisson process moves only from state $i$ to state $i + 1$ at a rate $\alpha$.

Thus

$$\gamma_{ii} = -\alpha \qquad \text{and} \qquad \gamma_{i,\,i+1} = \alpha.$$

Equation (11.39) then gives

$$p_0'(t) = -\alpha p_0(t) \qquad \text{for } j = 0$$
$$p_j'(t) = -\alpha p_j(t) + \alpha p_{j-1}(t) \qquad \text{for } j \geq 1.$$

The initial condition for the Poisson process is $p_0(0) = 1$, so the solution for the $j = 0$ equation is

$$p_0(t) = e^{-\alpha t}.$$

The equation for $j = 1$ is

$$p_1'(t) = -\alpha p_1(t) + \alpha e^{-\alpha t} \qquad p_1(0) = 0,$$

which is also a first-order differential equation for which the solution is

$$p_1(t) = \frac{\alpha t}{1!} e^{-\alpha t}.$$

It can be shown by an induction argument that the solution of the state $j$ equation is

$$p_j(t) = \frac{(\alpha t)^j}{j!} e^{-\alpha t}.$$

For any fixed time $t$, the sum of $\{p_j(t)\}$ is one. Note however, that for any $j$, $p_j(t) \to 0$ as $t \to \infty$. Figure 11.11 shows how the pmf drifts to higher values as time progresses. Thus for the Poisson process, the probability of any finite state approaches zero as $t \to \infty$. This is consistent with the fact that the process grows steadily with time.

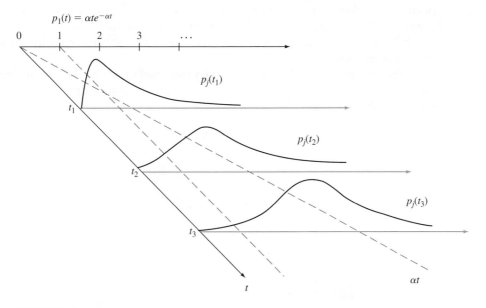

**FIGURE 11.11**
State pmf of Poisson process vs. time.

### 11.4.3 Steady State Probabilities and Global Balance Equations

As $t \to \infty$, the state probabilities in the two-state queueing system in Example 11.36 converge to a pmf that does not depend on the initial conditions. This is typical of systems that reach "equilibrium" or "steady state." For such a system, $p_j(t) \to p_j$ and $p_j'(t) \to 0$, so Eq. (11.39) becomes

$$0 = \sum_i \gamma_{ij} p_i \qquad \text{for all } j, \tag{11.40a}$$

or equivalently, recalling that $\gamma_{jj} = -v_j$,

$$v_j p_j = \sum_{i \neq j} \gamma_{ij} p_i \qquad \text{for all } j, \tag{11.40b}$$

where

$$\sum_j p_j = 1. \tag{11.40c}$$

Equation (11.40b) can be rewritten as follows:

$$p_j \left( \sum_{i \neq j} \gamma_{ji} \right) = \sum_{i \neq j} \gamma_{ij} p_i \tag{11.40d}$$

since

$$v_j = \sum_{i \neq j} \gamma_{ji}.$$

The system of linear equations given by Eq. (11.40b) or (11.40d) are called the **global balance equations**. These equations state that at equilibrium, the rate of probability flow out of state $j$, namely $v_j p_j$, is equal to the rate of flow into state $j$, as shown in Fig. 11.12. By solving this set of linear equations we can obtain the stationary state pmf of the system (when it exists).[5]

We refer to $\mathbf{p} = \{p_i\}$ as the **stationary state pmf** of the Markov chain. Since $\mathbf{p}$ satisfies Eq. (11.39), if we start the Markov chain with initial state pmf given by $\mathbf{p}$, then the state probabilities will be

$$p_i(t) = p_i \qquad \text{for all } t.$$

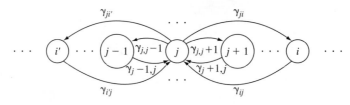

**FIGURE 11.12**
Global balance of probability flows.

---

[5]The last part of this section discusses conditions under which the stationary pmf exists.

The resulting process is a stationary random process as defined in Section 9.6 since the probability of the sequence of states $i_0, i_1, \ldots, i_n$ at times $t < t_1 + t < \cdots < t_n + t$ is, by Eq. (11.29),

$$P[X(t) = i_0, X(t_1 + t) = i_1, \ldots, X(t_n + t) = i_n]$$
$$= P[X(t_n + t) = i_n \mid X(t_{n-1} + t) = i_{n-1}] \cdots$$
$$\times P[X(t_1 + t) = i_1 \mid X(t) = i_0] P[X(t) = i_0].$$

The transition probabilities depend only on the difference between the associated times. Thus the above joint probability depends on the choice of origin only through $P[X(t) = i_0]$. But $P[X(t) = i_0] = p_{i_0}$ for all $t$. Therefore we conclude that the above joint probability is independent of the choice of time origin and thus that the process is stationary.

---

**Example 11.38**

Find the stationary state pmf for the two-state queueing system discussed in Example 11.36.
Equation (11.40b) for this system gives

$$\alpha p_0 = \beta p_1 \quad \text{and} \quad \beta p_1 = \alpha p_0.$$

Noting that $p_0 + p_1 = 1$, we obtain

$$p_0 = \frac{\beta}{\alpha + \beta} \quad \text{and} \quad p_1 = \frac{\alpha}{\alpha + \beta}.$$

---

**Example 11.39    The M/M/1 Single-Server Queueing System**

Consider a queueing system in which customers are served one at a time in order of arrival. The time between customer arrivals is exponentially distributed with rate $\lambda$, and the time required to service a customer is exponentially distributed with rate $\mu$. Find the steady state pmf for the number of customers in the system.

The state transition rates are as follows. Customers arrive at a rate $\lambda$, so

$$\gamma_{i,i+1} = \lambda \quad i = 0, 1, 2, \ldots.$$

When the system is nonempty, customers depart at the rate $\mu$. Thus

$$\gamma_{i,i-1} = \mu \quad i = 1, 2, 3, \ldots.$$

The transition rate diagram is shown in Fig. 11.13. The global balance equations are

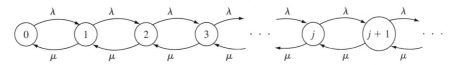

**FIGURE 11.13**
Transition rate diagram for M/M/1 queueing system.

$$\lambda p_0 = \mu p_1 \qquad \text{for } j = 0 \tag{11.41a}$$

$$(\lambda + \mu)p_j = \lambda p_{j-1} + \mu p_{j+1} \qquad \text{for } j = 1, 2, \ldots . \tag{11.41b}$$

We can rewrite Eq. (11.41b) as follows:

$$\lambda p_j - \mu p_{j+1} = \lambda p_{j-1} - \mu p_j \qquad \text{for } j = 1, 2, \ldots ,$$

which implies that

$$\lambda p_{j-1} - \mu p_j = \text{constant} \qquad \text{for } j = 1, 2, \ldots . \tag{11.42}$$

Equation (11.42) with $j = 1$ and Eq. (11.41a) together imply that

$$\text{constant} = \lambda p_0 - \mu p_1 = 0.$$

Thus Eq. (11.42) becomes

$$\lambda p_{j-1} = \mu p_j,$$

or equivalently,

$$p_j = \rho p_{j-1} \qquad j = 1, 2, \ldots$$

and by a simple induction argument

$$p_j = \rho^j p_0,$$

where $\rho = \lambda/\mu$. We obtain $p_0$ by noting that the sum of the probabilities must be one:

$$1 = \sum_{j=0}^{\infty} p_j = (1 + \rho + \rho^2 + \cdots)p_0 = \frac{1}{1 - \rho} p_0,$$

where the series converges if and only if $\rho < 1$.
Thus

$$p_j = (1 - \rho)\rho^j \qquad j = 0, 1, 2, \ldots . \tag{11.43}$$

This queueing system is discussed in detail in Section 12.3.

The condition for the existence of a steady state solution has a simple explanation. The condition $\rho < 1$ is equivalent to

$$\lambda < \mu,$$

that is, the rate at which customers arrive must be less than the rate at which the system can process them. Otherwise the queue builds up without limit as time progresses.

---

### Example 11.40    A Birth-and-Death Process

A **birth-and-death process** is a Markov chain in which only transitions between adjacent states occur as shown in Fig. 11.14. The single-server queueing system discussed in Example 11.39 is an example of a birth-and-death process.

The global balance equations for a general birth-and-death process are

$$\lambda_0 p_0 = \mu_1 p_1 \qquad j = 0 \tag{11.44a}$$

$$\lambda_j p_j - \mu_{j+1} p_{j+1} = \lambda_{j-1} p_{j-1} - \mu_j p_j \qquad j = 1, 2, \ldots . \tag{11.44b}$$

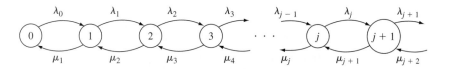

**FIGURE 11.14**
Transition rate diagram for general birth-and-death process.

As in the previous example, it then follows that

$$p_j = r_j p_{j-1} \qquad j = 1, 2, \ldots$$

and

$$p_j = r_j r_{j-1} \ldots r_1 p_0 \qquad j = 1, 2, \ldots, \tag{11.45}$$

where $r_j = (\lambda_{j-1})/\mu_j$. If we define

$$R_j = r_j r_{j-1} \ldots r_1 \quad \text{and} \quad R_0 = 1,$$

then $p_0$ is found from

$$1 = \left( \sum_{j=0}^{\infty} R_j \right) p_0.$$

If the series in the above equation converges, then the stationary pmf is given by

$$p_j = \frac{R_j}{\displaystyle\sum_{i=0}^{\infty} R_i}. \tag{11.46}$$

If the series does not converge, then a stationary pmf does not exist, and $p_j = 0$ for all $j$. In Chapter 12, we will see that many useful queueing systems can be modeled by birth-and-death processes.

## 11.4.4    Limiting Probabilities for Continuous-Time Markov Chains

We saw above that a continuous-time Markov chain $X(t)$ can be viewed as consisting of a sequence of states determined by some discrete-time Markov chain $X_n$ with transition probabilities $\widetilde{q}_{ij}$ and a corresponding sequence of exponentially distributed state occupancy times. In this section we use this approach to investigate the limiting probabilities of continuous-time Markov chains.

First we consider the construction of stationary solutions for $X(t)$ from the steady state solutions of $X_n$. Suppose that the embedded Markov chain $X_n$ is irreducible and positive recurrent, so that Eq. (11.25) holds. Let $N_i(n)$ denote the number of times state $i$ occurs in the first $n$ transitions, and let $T_i(j)$ denote the occupancy time the $j$th time state $i$ occurs. The proportion of time spent by $X(t)$ in state $i$ after the first $n$ transitions is

$$\frac{\text{time spent in state } i}{\text{time spent in all states}} = \frac{\displaystyle\sum_{j=1}^{N_i(n)} T_i(j)}{\displaystyle\sum_{i}\sum_{j=1}^{N_i(n)} T_i(j)}$$

$$= \frac{\dfrac{N_i(n)}{n}\,\dfrac{1}{N_i(n)}\displaystyle\sum_{j=1}^{N_i(n)} T_i(j)}{\displaystyle\sum_{i}\dfrac{N_i(n)}{n}\,\dfrac{1}{N_i(n)}\sum_{j=1}^{N_i(n)} T_i(j)}. \qquad (11.47)$$

As $n \to \infty$, by Eqs. (11.25) and (11.26ab), with probability one,

$$\frac{N_i(n)}{n} \to \pi_i, \qquad (11.48)$$

the stationary pmf of the embedded Markov chain. In addition, we also have that $N_i(n) \to \infty$ as $n \to \infty$, so that by the strong law of large numbers, with probability one,

$$\frac{1}{N_i(n)}\sum_{j=1}^{N_i(n)} T_i(j) \to E[T_i] = 1/v_i, \qquad (11.49)$$

where we have used the fact that the state occupancy time in state $i$ has mean $1/v_i$. Similarly the denominator in Eq. (11.47) must approach $\left(\sum \pi_j/v_j\right)$. Equations (11.48) and (11.49) when applied to Eq. (11.47) imply that if $\sum \pi_j/v_j < \infty$, with probability one, the long-term proportion of time spent in state $i$ approaches

$$p_i = \frac{\pi_i/v_i}{\displaystyle\sum_{j}\pi_j/v_j} = c\pi_i/v_i, \qquad (11.50)$$

where $\pi_j$ is the unique pmf solution to

$$\pi_j = \sum_{i}\pi_i\widetilde{q}_{ij} \qquad \text{for all } j \qquad (11.51)$$

and $c$ is a normalization constant.

We obtain the global balance equation, Eq. (11.40b), by substituting $\pi_i = v_i p_i/c$ from Eq. (11.50) and $\widetilde{q}_{ij} = \gamma_{ij}/v_i$ into Eq. (11.51):

$$v_j p_j = \sum_{i \neq j} p_i\gamma_{ij} \qquad \text{for all } j.$$

Thus the $p_i$'s are the unique solution of the global balance equations.

We have proved the following result:

---

### Theorem 3

Assume a time-continuous Markov chain, for which the embedded Markov chain is irreducible and positive recurrent with stationary pmf $\{\pi_j\}$ and $\sum_j \pi_j/v_j < \infty$, then the following assertions hold:

**(i)** $\lim\limits_{t\to\infty} p_j(t) = p_j$   for all $j$;

**(ii)** The solution $\{p_i\}$ is unique and satisfies Eqs. (11.40bc);

**(iii)** For each $j$, $p_j$ is the long-term proportion of time spent in state $j$.

---

Now assume that we know that the Markov chain is irreducible and that we have a solution $\{p_j\}$ to the global balance equations (11.40bc):

$$p_j v_j = \sum_{i \neq j} p_i \gamma_{ij}.$$

Substituting Eq. (11.50) into the above equation

$$c\pi_j = \left(\frac{c\pi_j}{v_j}\right) v_j = \sum_{i \neq j} \left(\frac{c\pi_i}{v_i}\right) \gamma_{ij} = c\sum_{i \neq j} \pi_i\left(\frac{\gamma_{ij}}{v_i}\right) = c\sum_{i \neq j} \pi_i \tilde{q}_{ij}$$

implies that the following choice of $\{\pi_j\}$ gives a solution for the stationary pmf of the embedded Markov chain:

$$\pi_j = \frac{p_j v_j}{\sum\limits_{i} p_i v_i}.$$

Note that we must require that the denominator be finite. From Theorem 1 in Section 11.4, if there is a stationary pmf then it is unique and positive recurrent. Furthermore the construction of $\{\pi_j\}$ from the $\{p_j\}$ ensures that $p_j$ is the long-term proportion of time in state $j$ as well as the limiting state probability for $X(t)$.

We have shown the following theorem:

---

### Theorem 4

Assume a time-continuous Markov chain, for which the embedded Markov chain is irreducible. Suppose that $\{p_j\}$ is a solution to the global balance equations (11.40bc), and that $\sum_j \pi_j v_j < \infty$, then the following assertions hold:

**(i)** The solution $\{p_i\}$ is unique;

**(ii)** $\lim\limits_{t\to\infty} p_j(t) = p_j$   for all $j$;

**(iii)** For each $j$, $p_j$ is the long-term proportion of time spent in state $j$;

**(iv)** The embedded Markov chain is positive recurrent.

---

**Example 11.41**

In the two-state system in Example 11.36,

$$[\tilde{q}_{ij}] = \begin{bmatrix} 0 & 1 \\ 1 & 0 \end{bmatrix}.$$

The equation $\boldsymbol{\pi} = \boldsymbol{\pi}[\tilde{q}_{ij}]$ implies that

$$\pi_0 = \pi_1 = \frac{1}{2}.$$

In addition, $v_0 = \alpha$ and $v_1 = \beta$. Thus

$$p_0 = \frac{1/2(1/\alpha)}{1/2(1/\alpha + 1/\beta)} = \frac{\beta}{\alpha + \beta}$$

and

$$p_1 = \frac{\alpha}{\alpha + \beta}.$$

---

## *11.5    TIME-REVERSED MARKOV CHAINS

We now consider the random process that results when we play a Markov chain backwards in time. We will see that the resulting process is also a Markov chain and so develop another method for obtaining the stationary probabilities of the forward and reverse processes. The insights gained by looking at the reverse process prove useful in developing certain results in queueing theory in Chapter 12.

Let $X_n$ be a stationary ergodic Markov chain[6] with one-step transition probability matrix $P = \{p_{ij}\}$ and stationary state pmf $\{\pi_j\}$. Consider the dependence of $X_{n-1}$, the "future" in the reverse process, on $X_n, X_{n+1}, \ldots, X_{n+k}$, the "present and past":

$$P[X_{n-1} = j \mid X_n = i, X_{n+1} = i_1, \ldots, X_{n+k} = i_k]$$

$$= \frac{P[X_{n-1} = j, X_n = i, X_{n+1} = i_1, \ldots, X_{n+k} = i_k]}{P[X_n = i, X_{n+1} = i_1, \ldots, X_{n+k} = i_k]}$$

$$= \frac{\pi_j p_{ji} p_{i,i_1} \cdots p_{i_{k-1}, i_k}}{\pi_i p_{i,i_1} \cdots p_{i_{k-1}, i_k}}$$

$$= \frac{\pi_j p_{ji}}{\pi_i}$$

$$= P[X_{n-1} = j \mid X_n = i]. \tag{11.52}$$

---

[6]That is, let it be an irreducible, aperiodic, stationary Markov chain.

The above equations show that *the **time-reversed process** is also a Markov chain with one-step transition probabilities*

$$P[X_{n-1} = j \mid X_n = i] = q_{ij} = \frac{\pi_j p_{ji}}{\pi_i}. \tag{11.53}$$

Since $X_n$ is irreducible and aperiodic, its stationary state probabilities $\pi_j$ represent the proportion of time that the state is in state $j$. This proportion of time does not depend on whether one goes forward or backward in time, so $\pi_j$ must also be the stationary pmf for the reverse process. Thus *the forward and reverse process must have the same stationary pmf.*

---

### Example 11.42

Suppose that a new light bulb is put in use at day $n = 0$, and suppose that each time a light bulb fails it is replaced the next day. Let $X_n$ be the age of the light bulb (in days) at the end of day $n$. If $a_i$ is the probability that the lifetime $L$ of a light bulb is $i$ days, then the probability that the light bulb fails on day $j$ given that it has not failed up to then is

$$b_j = \frac{P[L = j]}{P[L \geq j]} = \frac{a_j}{\displaystyle\sum_{k=j}^{\infty} a_k} \qquad j = 1, 2, \dots.$$

Thus the transition probabilities for $X_n$ are

$$\begin{aligned}
p_{i,i+1} &= 1 - b_i & i = 1, 2, \dots \\
p_{i1} &= b_i & i = 1, 2, \dots \\
p_{ij} &= 0 & \text{otherwise.}
\end{aligned}$$

Figure 11.15(a) shows the state transition diagram of $X_n$, and Fig. 11.16(a) shows a typical sample function that consists of a sawtooth-shaped function that increases linearly and then falls abruptly to one when a light bulb fails.

Figure 11.16(b) shows a sample function of the reverse process from which we deduce that the state transition diagram must be as shown in Fig. 11.15(b). The transition probabilities for the reverse process are obtained from Eq. (11.53):

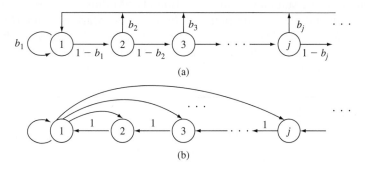

(a)

(b)

**FIGURE 11.15**
(a) Transition diagram for age of a renewal process. (b) Transition diagram for time-reversed process.

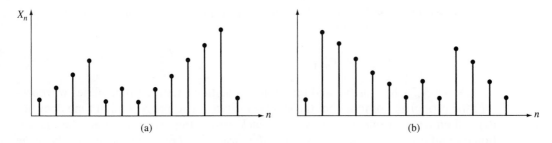

**FIGURE 11.16**
(a) Age of light bulb in use at time $n$. (b) Time-reversed process of $X_n$.

$$q_{i,i-1} = \frac{\pi_{i-1}}{\pi_i}(1 - b_{i-1}) \qquad i = 2, 3, 4, \ldots$$

$$q_{1,i} = \frac{\pi_i}{\pi_1}b_i \qquad\qquad i = 1, 2, \ldots$$

$$q_{i,j} = 0 \qquad\qquad\qquad \text{otherwise.}$$

For now we defer the problem of finding the stationary state probabilities $\pi_j$.

Example 11.42 shows that Eq. (11.53) provides us with conditions that must be satisfied by the stationary probabilities $\pi_j$. Suppose we were able to *guess* a pmf $\{\pi_j\}$ so that Eq. (11.53) holds, that is,

$$\pi_i q_{ij} = \pi_j p_{ji} \qquad \text{for all } i, j. \tag{11.54}$$

It then follows that $\{\pi_j\}$ is the stationary pmf. To see this, sum Eq. (11.54) over all $j$, then

$$\sum_j \pi_j p_{ji} = \pi_i \sum_j q_{ij} = \pi_i \qquad \text{for all } i. \tag{11.55}$$

But Eq. (11.55) is the condition for $\pi_j$ to be the stationary pmf for the forward process, thus $\pi_j$ is the stationary pmf. Equation (11.54) thus provides us with another method for finding the stationary pmf of a discrete-time Markov chain: *If we can guess a set of transition probabilities $q_{i,j}$ for the reverse process and a pmf $\pi_j$ so that Eq. (11.54) is satisfied, then it follows that the $\pi_j$ is the stationary pmf for the Markov chain and the $q_{i,j}$ are the transition probabilities for the reverse process.*

### Example 11.43

The sample function of the reverse process in Example 11.42 suggests that for $i > 1$, the process moves from state $i$ to state $i - 1$ with probability one; that is,

$$q_{i,i-1} = \frac{\pi_{i-1}(1 - b_{i-1})}{\pi_i} = 1,$$

which implies that

$$\pi_i = (1 - b_{i-1})\pi_{i-1} \qquad i = 2, 3, \ldots$$
$$= (1 - b_{i-1})(1 - b_{i-2}) \cdots (1 - b_1)\pi_1. \qquad (11.56)$$

However, from Example 11.42 for $i \geq 2$,

$$(1 - b_{i-1}) = 1 - \frac{a_{i-1}}{\displaystyle\sum_{k=i-1}^{\infty} a_k} = \frac{\displaystyle\sum_{k=i}^{\infty} a_k}{\displaystyle\sum_{k=i-1}^{\infty} a_k},$$

so in Eq. (11.56), the denominator of $(1 - b_{i-1})$ cancels the numerator of $(1 - b_{i-2})$, the denominator of $(1 - b_{i-2})$ cancels the numerator of $(1 - b_{i-3})$, and so on. Thus

$$\pi_i = \left\{ \sum_{k=i}^{\infty} a_k \right\} \pi_1 = P[L \geq i]\pi_1 \qquad i = 2, 3, \ldots.$$

We obtain $\pi_1$ by using the fact that the probabilities sum to one:

$$1 = \pi_1 \sum_{i=1}^{\infty} P[L \geq i] = \pi_1 E[L],$$

where we have used Eq. (4.29) for $E[L]$. Thus

$$\pi_i = \frac{P[L \geq i]}{E[L]} \qquad i = 1, 2, \ldots. \qquad (11.57)$$

## 11.5.1   Time-Reversible Markov Chains

A stationary ergodic Markov chain is said to be **reversible** if the one-step transition probability matrix of the forward and reverse processes are the same, that is, if

$$q_{ij} = p_{ij} \qquad \text{for all } i, j. \qquad (11.58)$$

Equations (11.53) and (11.58) together imply that a Markov chain is reversible if and only if

$$\pi_i p_{ij} = \pi_j p_{ji} \qquad \text{for all } i, j. \qquad (11.59)$$

Since $\pi_i$ and $\pi_j$ are the long-term proportion of transitions out of states $i$ and $j$, respectively, Eq. (11.59) implies that a chain is reversible if the proportion of transitions from $i$ to $j$ is equal to the proportion of transitions from $j$ to $i$.

## Example 11.44   Discrete-Time Birth-and-Death Process

Figure 11.17 shows the state transition diagram for a discrete-time birth-and-death process with transition probabilities

$$p_{00} = 0 \qquad p_{01} = 1 = a_0$$
$$p_{i,i+1} = a_i \qquad p_{i,i-1} = 1 - a_i \qquad i = 1, 2, \ldots$$
$$p_{ij} = 0 \qquad \text{otherwise.}$$

**FIGURE 11.17**
Transition diagram for a discrete-time birth-and-death process.

For any sample path, the number of transitions from $i$ to $i + 1$ can differ by at most 1 from the number of transitions from $i + 1$ to $i$ since the only way to return to $i$ is through $i + 1$. Thus the long-term proportion of transitions from $i$ to $i + 1$ is equal to that from $i + 1$ to $i$. Since these are the only possible transitions, it follows that birth-and-death processes are reversible.

Equation (11.59) implies that

$$a_j \pi_j = (1 - a_{j+1}) \pi_{j+1} \quad j = 0, 1, 2, \ldots,$$

which allows us to write all the $\pi_j$'s in terms of $\pi_0$:

$$\pi_j = \left( \frac{a_{j-1}}{1 - a_j} \right) \cdots \left( \frac{a_0}{1 - a_1} \right) \pi_0 = \frac{a_{j-1} \cdots a_0}{(1 - a_j) \cdots (1 - a_1)} \pi_0 \triangleq R_j \pi_0. \tag{11.60}$$

The probability $\pi_0$ is found from $\quad 1 = \pi_0 \sum_{j=0}^{\infty} R_j.$ $\tag{11.61}$

The series in Eq. (11.61) must converge in order for $\pi_j$ to exist.

### 11.5.2    Time-Reversible Continuous-Time Markov Chains

Now consider a stationary, continuous-time Markov chain played backward in time. If $X(t) = i$ (i.e., the process is in state $i$ at time $t$), then the probability that the reverse process remains in state $i$ for an additional $s$ seconds is

$$P[X(t') = i, \quad t - s \le t' \le t \,|\, X(t) = i] = \frac{P[X(t - s) = i, T_i > s]}{P[X(t) = i]}$$

$$= \frac{P[X(t - s) = i] P[T_i > s]}{P[X(t) = i]}$$

$$= P[T_i > s] = e^{-v_i s}, \tag{11.62}$$

where $P[X(t - s) = i] = P[X(t) = i]$ because $X(t)$ is a stationary process, and where $T_i$ is the time spent in state $i$ for the forward process. Thus *the reverse process also spends an exponentially distributed amount of time with rate $v_i$ in state $i$.*

The jumps in the forward process $X(t)$ are determined by the embedded Markov chain $\widetilde{q}_{ij}$, so the jumps in the reverse process are determined by the discrete-time Markov chain corresponding to the time-reversed embedded Markov chain given by Eq. (11.53):

$$q_{ij} = \frac{\pi_j \widetilde{q}_{ji}}{\pi_i}. \tag{11.63}$$

It follows that the transition rates for the time-reversed continuous-time process are given by

$$\gamma'_{ij} = v_i q_{ij} = \frac{\pi_j v_i \widetilde{q}_{ji}}{\pi_i}$$

$$= \frac{v_i \pi_j \gamma_{ji}}{\pi_i v_j} = \frac{p_j \gamma_{ji}}{p_i}, \tag{11.64}$$

where we used the fact that $\widetilde{q}_{ji} = \gamma_{ji}/v_j$ and $p_j = c\pi_j/v_j$. In comparing Eq. (11.64) to Eq. (11.53), note that the transition rates $\gamma'_{ij}$ have simply replaced the transition probabilities $q_{ij}$ in going from the discrete-time to the continuous-time case.

The discussion that led to Eq. (11.54) provides us with another method for determining the stationary pmf $p_j$ of $X(t)$. *If we can guess a set of transition rates $\gamma'_{i,j}$ and a pmf $p_j$ such that*

$$p_i \gamma'_{i,j} = p_j \gamma_{j,i} \qquad \text{for all } i, j \tag{11.65a}$$

*and*

$$\sum_{j \neq i} \gamma_{i,j} = \sum_{j \neq i} \gamma'_{i,j} \qquad \text{for all } i, \tag{11.65b}$$

*then $p_j$ is the stationary pmf for $X(t)$ and $\gamma'_{i,j}$ are the transition rates for the reverse process.*

Since the state occupancy times in the forward and reverse processes are exponential random variables with the same mean, the continuous-time Markov chain $X(t)$ is reversible if and only if its embedded Markov chain is reversible. Equation (11.59) implies that the following condition must be satisfied:

$$\pi_i \widetilde{q}_{ij} = \pi_j \widetilde{q}_{ji} \qquad \text{for all } i, j, \tag{11.66}$$

where $\pi_j$ is the stationary pmf of the embedded Markov chain. Recall from Eq. (11.50) that $\pi_j = cv_j p_j$, where $p_j$ is the stationary pmf of $X(t)$. Substituting into Eq. (11.66), we obtain

$$p_i v_i \widetilde{q}_{ij} = p_j v_j \widetilde{q}_{ji},$$

which is equivalent to

$$p_i \gamma_{ij} = p_j \gamma_{ji}. \tag{11.67}$$

Thus we conclude that $X(t)$ *is reversible if and only if Eq. (11.67) is satisfied.* As in the discrete-time case, Eq. (11.67) can be interpreted as stating that the rate at which $X(t)$ goes from state $i$ to state $j$ is equal to the rate at which $X(t)$ goes from state $j$ to state $i$.

---

### Example 11.45   Continuous-Time Birth-and-Death Process

Consider the general continuous-time birth-and-death process introduced in Example 11.40. The embedded Markov chain in this process is a discrete-time birth-and-death process of the type discussed in Example 11.44. It therefore follows that all continuous-time birth-and-death processes are time-reversible.

---

In Chapter 12 we will see that the time reversibility of certain Markov chains implies some remarkable properties about the departure processes of queueing systems.

## 11.6  NUMERICAL TECHNIQUES FOR MARKOV CHAINS

In this section we present several numerical techniques that are useful in the analysis of Markov chains. The first part of the section presents methods for finding the stationary as well as transient solutions for the state probabilities of Markov chains. The second part of the section addresses the simulation of discrete-time and continuous-time Markov chains.

### 11.6.1  Stationary Probabilities of Markov Chains

The most basic calculation with *finite-state discrete-time Markov chains* involves finding their stationary state probabilities. To do so, we consider the equation:

$$\boldsymbol{\pi} = \boldsymbol{\pi} P \quad \text{or equivalently} \quad \mathbf{0} = \boldsymbol{\pi}(P - I). \tag{11.68a}$$

In general the above set of linear equations is undetermined. To see this, note that the sum of the columns of the matrix $P - I$ is zero. Therefore we need the normalization equation: $\pi_1 + \pi_2 + \cdots + \pi_K = 1$. We can incorporate this equation by replacing one of the columns of $P - I$ with the all 1's column vector. Let $Q$ be the matrix that results when we replace the first column of $P - I$; the system of linear equations becomes:

$$\mathbf{b} = \boldsymbol{\pi} Q, \tag{11.68b}$$

where $\mathbf{b}$ is a row vector with 1 in the first entry and zeros elsewhere. If the Markov chain is irreducible, then a unique stationary pmf exists and is obtained by inverting the above equation.

---

### Example 11.46    Google PageRank

Find the stationary pmf for the PageRank algorithm in Example 11.30.
     After we take $P - I$ from the example and replace the first column with all 1's we obtain:

$$Q = \begin{bmatrix} 1 & 0.4550 & 0.4550 & 0.0300 & 0.0300 \\ 1 & -0.8000 & 0.2000 & 0.2000 & 0.2000 \\ 1 & 0.3133 & -0.9700 & 0.3133 & 0.0300 \\ 1 & 0.0300 & 0.0300 & -0.9700 & 0.8800 \\ 1 & 0.0300 & 0.4550 & 0.0300 & -0.5450 \end{bmatrix}.$$

We then invert $Q$ to obtain the pmf:

$$\boldsymbol{\pi} = (0.13175, 0.18772, 0.24642, 0.13172, 0.30239).$$

The Octave commands for the above procedure are given below:

```
> Q=[1 0.455 0.455 0.03 0.03
> 1 −.8 .2 .2 .2
> 1 0.3133 −.97 0.3133 0.03
> 1 0.03 0.03 −0.97 0.88
```

```
> 1 0.03 0.455 0.03 -.545];
> b=[1 0 0 0 0];
> p=b*inv(Q)
p =
    0.13175 0.18772 0.24642 0.13172 0.30239
```

In the case of infinite-state Markov chains, we can apply matrix inversion by truncating the state space at some value where the state probabilities become negligible. Another method, discussed in the next chapter, involves the application of the probability generating function for the state of the system.

To find the stationary pmf for *finite-state continuous-time Markov chains*, we need to find a pmf that satisfies Eq. (11.40a) as well as the normalization condition:

$$\mathbf{0} = \mathbf{p}\Gamma \quad \text{and} \quad 1 = \mathbf{pe} \tag{11.69a}$$

where

$$\Gamma = \begin{bmatrix} -v_0 & \gamma_{01} & \gamma_{02} & \gamma_{03} \\ \gamma_{10} & -v_1 & \cdots & \gamma_{1K-1} \\ \cdots & \cdots & \cdots & \cdots \\ \gamma_{K-10} & \gamma_{K-11} & \cdots & -v_{K-1} \end{bmatrix} \quad \text{and} \quad \mathbf{e} = \begin{bmatrix} 1 \\ 1 \\ \cdots \\ 1 \end{bmatrix}. \tag{11.69b}$$

The columns of $\Gamma$ sum to zero, so as before we need to replace a column of $\Gamma$ with $\mathbf{e}$. We obtain $\mathbf{p}$ by multiplying $\mathbf{b}$ by the inverse of the resulting matrix.

---

### Example 11.47    Cartridge Inventory

An office orders laser printer cartridges in batches of four cartridges. Suppose that each cartridge lasts for an exponentially distributed time with mean 1 month. Assume that a new batch of four cartridges becomes available as soon as the last cartridge in a batch runs out. Find the stationary pmf for $N(t)$, the number of cartridges available at time $t$.

$N(t)$ takes on values from the set $\{1, 2, 3, 4\}$ and follows a periodic sequence of values $4 \rightarrow 3 \rightarrow 2 \rightarrow 1 \rightarrow 4 \ldots$. The rate out of each state is 1 and the rate into each state from the previous state is also 1. Therefore the transition rate matrix and the modified global balance equations are:

$$\Gamma = \begin{bmatrix} -1 & 0 & 0 & 1 \\ 1 & -1 & 0 & 0 \\ 0 & 1 & -1 & 0 \\ 0 & 0 & 1 & -1 \end{bmatrix} \quad \mathbf{b} = \mathbf{p} \begin{bmatrix} 1 & 0 & 0 & 1 \\ 1 & -1 & 0 & 0 \\ 1 & 1 & -1 & 0 \\ 1 & 0 & 1 & -1 \end{bmatrix}.$$

It is easy to show that the $\mathbf{p} = (1/4, 1/4, 1/4, 1/4)$. In a more complicated case we would use numerical inversion to solve for $\mathbf{p}$.

---

## 11.6.2    Time-Dependent Probabilities of Markov Chains

We now consider finding the time-dependent probabilities of a *finite-state discrete-time Markov chain* as given by Eq. (8.16b). Example 11.9 described the general approach for finding $P^n$. First, however, we note a few facts about the transition probability matrix $P$.

A **stochastic matrix** is defined as a nonnegative matrix for which the elements of each row add to one. Thus $P$ is a stochastic matrix. A stochastic matrix always has $\lambda = 1$ as an eigenvalue and $\mathbf{e}^T = (1, \ldots, 1)$ as a right eigenvector: $1\mathbf{e} = P\mathbf{e}$. This follows from the fact that all the row elements of $P$ add to one. On the other hand, the stationary pmf $\pi$ is a left eigenvector for the $\lambda = 1$ eigenvalue of $P$: $1\pi = \pi P$. It can be shown [Gallager, pp. 116–117] that if $P$ corresponds to an aperiodic irreducible Markov chain, then $\lambda = 1$ is the largest eigenvalue and the magnitude of all other eigenvalues are less than 1.

Let $P$ correspond to an aperiodic irreducible Markov chain. Proceeding as in Example 11.19, to find $P^n$ we first find the eigenvalues $1 = \lambda_1 > |\lambda_2| > \ldots > |\lambda_K|$ and right eigenvectors of $P$: $\mathbf{e}_1, \mathbf{e}_2, \ldots, \mathbf{e}_K$. Letting $\mathbf{E}$ be the matrix with eigenvectors as columns, we then have that:

$$P^n = \mathbf{E}\Lambda^n\mathbf{E}^{-1}$$

$$= \mathbf{E}\begin{bmatrix} 1 & 0 & \ldots & 0 \\ 0 & \lambda_2^n & \ldots & 0 \\ 0 & 0 & \ldots & 0 \\ 0 & 0 & \ldots & \lambda_K^n \end{bmatrix}\mathbf{E}^{-1}. \tag{11.70}$$

Note how all but the 1-1 entry in the diagonal matrix approach zero as $n$ increases. Note as well that the first column of $\mathbf{E}$ is the all 1's vector. This implies that the first row of $\mathbf{E}^{-1}$ contains the stationary pmf $\pi$. In Octave the eigenvalues and eigenvectors of $P$ are obtained using the eig($P$) function, which was discussed previously in Section 10.7. In practice it is simpler and more convenient to use the command P^n.

Next we consider finding the time-dependent probabilities of a *finite-state continuous-time Markov chain* that are the solution to Eq. (11.39):

$$\mathbf{p}'(t) = [p_j'(t)] = \sum_{i=1}^{K} p_i(t)\gamma_{ij} = \mathbf{p}(t)\Gamma \quad \text{subject to} \quad \mathbf{p}(0) = (p_i(0), \ldots, p_K(0)). \tag{11.71}$$

We are now dealing with first-order vector differential equations. Electrical engineering students encounter this equation in an introductory linear systems course. The solution is given by:

$$\mathbf{p}(t) = \mathbf{p}(0)P(t) = \mathbf{p}(0)e^{\Gamma t} \tag{11.72a}$$

where $P(t) = e^{\Gamma t}$ is the matrix of transition probabilities in an interval of length $t$ seconds, and where the exponential matrix function is defined by:

$$P(t) = [p_{ij}(t)] = e^{\Gamma t} = \sum_{j=0}^{\infty} \frac{(\Gamma t)^j}{j!}. \tag{11.72b}$$

Furthermore, using matrix diagonalization the exponential matrix can be evaluated as:

$$P(t) = \mathbf{E}[e^{\lambda_i t}]\mathbf{E}^{-1} \tag{11.72c}$$

where $\mathbf{E}$ is a matrix whose columns are the eigenvectors of $\Gamma$ and the middle matrix is a diagonal matrix with exponential functions as its elements. [Gallager, p. 194] shows that if the Markov chain is finite state and irreducible, then $\Gamma$ has an eigenvalue $\lambda = 0$ which has right eigenvector $\mathbf{e}^T = (1, 1,...,1)$. $\Gamma$ also has a left eigenvector $\mathbf{p}$ corresponding to $\lambda = 0$ which is the unique stationary state pmf. Furthermore the remaining eigenvalues of $\Gamma$ have negative real parts. This implies that all but the $\lambda = 0$ exponential terms in the diagonal matrix decay to zero as $t$ increases. If we let $\lambda = 0$ occupy the 1-1 entry in the diagonal matrix, then as $t \to \infty$, $P(t)$ approaches the product of the $\mathbf{e}$ and the first row of $\mathbf{E}^{-1}$.

### Example 11.48    Cartridge Inventory

Find the state probabilities for $N(t)$ in Example 11.47 if $N(0) = 4$.

   We use the `eig(Γ)` function to obtain the eigenvalues and eigenvectors of $\Gamma$ and the associated matrices, $\mathbf{E}$, $\Lambda$, and $\mathbf{E}^{-1}$:

$$\mathbf{E} = \frac{1}{2}\begin{bmatrix} 1 & 1 & 1 & 1 \\ 1 & j & -j & -1 \\ 1 & -1 & -1 & 1 \\ 1 & -j & j & -1 \end{bmatrix} \quad \Lambda = \begin{bmatrix} 0 & 0 & 0 & 0 \\ 0 & -1-j & 0 & 0 \\ 0 & 0 & -1+j & 0 \\ 0 & 0 & 0 & -2 \end{bmatrix} \quad \mathbf{E}^{-1} = \frac{1}{2}\begin{bmatrix} 1 & 1 & 1 & 1 \\ 1 & -j & -1 & j \\ 1 & j & -1 & -j \\ 1 & -1 & 1 & -1 \end{bmatrix}$$

Note that two of the eigenvalues and their corresponding eigenvectors are complex. The state probabilities are given by:

$$\mathbf{p}(t) = \mathbf{p}(0)\mathbf{E}\begin{bmatrix} 1 & 0 & 0 & 0 \\ 0 & e^{-(1+j)t} & 0 & 0 \\ 0 & 0 & e^{-(1-j)t} & 0 \\ 0 & 0 & 0 & e^{-2t} \end{bmatrix}\mathbf{E}^{-1}$$

$$= (0, 0, 0, 1)\frac{1}{4}\begin{bmatrix} 1 & 1 & 1 & 1 \\ 1 & j & -j & -1 \\ 1 & -1 & -1 & 1 \\ 1 & -j & j & -1 \end{bmatrix}\begin{bmatrix} 1 & 0 & 0 & 0 \\ 0 & e^{-(1+j)t} & 0 & 0 \\ 0 & 0 & e^{-(1-j)t} & 0 \\ 0 & 0 & 0 & e^{-2t} \end{bmatrix}\begin{bmatrix} 1 & 1 & 1 & 1 \\ 1 & -j & -1 & j \\ 1 & j & -1 & -j \\ 1 & -1 & 1 & -1 \end{bmatrix}$$

$$= \frac{1}{4}(1, -j, j, -1)\begin{bmatrix} 1 & 1 & 1 & 1 \\ e^{-(1+j)t} & -je^{-(1+j)t} & -e^{-(1+j)t} & je^{-(1+j)t} \\ e^{-(1-j)t} & je^{-(1-j)t} & -e^{-(1-j)t} & -je^{-(1-j)t} \\ e^{-2t} & -e^{-2t} & e^{-2t} & -e^{-2t} \end{bmatrix}$$

$$= \frac{1}{4}(1 - 2e^{-t}\sin t - e^{-2t}, 1 - 2e^{-t}\cos t + e^{-2t}, 1 + 2e^{-t}\sin t - e^{-2t}, 1 + 2e^{-t}\cos t + e^{-2t}).$$

Figure 11.18 shows the four state probabilities vs. time. It can be seen that all of the probability mass is initially in state 4 and that the mass first transfers to state 3, then state 2, and finally to state 1. Eventually all state probabilities approach the steady state value of 1/4.

## 11.6.3    Simulation of Markov Chains

We simulate a Markov chain by emulating its underlying random experiments. We begin by selecting the initial state according to an initial state pmf. We then generate the sequence of states by producing outcomes according to the associated transition

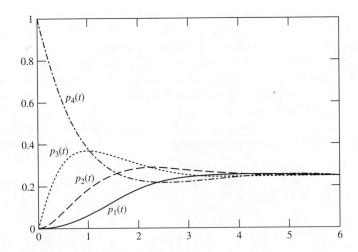

**FIGURE 11.18**
Time-dependent probabilities in cartridge inventory.

probabilities. In the case of continuous-time Markov chains we also need to generate a state occupancy time after each state transition has been determined. Figure 11.19 shows the inputs and outputs of generic modules for generating realizations of a Markov chain.

**Discrete-Time Markov Chains** The module for generating a sequence of states for a Markov chain requires the following inputs: i. The state space; ii. The matrix of state transition probabilities; iii. The initial state probability mass function; and iv. The number of steps in the simulation sequence. The module operates as follows:

**1.** Generates the initial state according to $\pi_0$.

**2.** Repeatedly generates the next state according to the transition probabilities of the current state.

**3.** Stops when the required number of steps has been simulated.

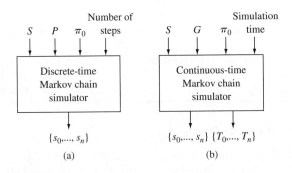

**FIGURE 11.19**
Generic modules for simulating Markov chains.

### Example 11.49    Discrete-Time Markov Chain

Develop a program to generate Markov chains with the state transition diagram as shown in Fig. 11.20(a). Note that the Markov chain is similar to that of a birth-death process except that transitions from a state to itself are allowed. Use the program to simulate 1000 time steps in a data multiplexer where in each time unit a packet is received with probability $a$, and/or a packet transmitted from its buffer with probability $b$. Assume the data multiplexer is initially empty.

For this example we wrote the function `Discrete_MC(Nmax,P,IC,L)`. The state space is $\{0, 1, \ldots, N_{max}\}$. Since Octave uses indices from 1 onwards, the array state ranges from 1 to $N_{max} + 1$. For the Markov chains under consideration we need to specify only three probabilities for the transition probabilities for each state. Therefore $P$ is an $N_{max} + 1$ row by 3 column matrix. The initial state pmf is a $N_{max} + 1$ by 1 vector. The output of the function is a vector of states of size $L$.

The Markov chain for the data multiplexer has the following transition probabilities. If $N = 0$, that is, the system is empty, the next state is either $N = 1$ with probability $a$, or $N = 0$ with probability $1 - a$, that is: $p_{00} = 1 - a$, $p_{01} = a$. If $N = n > 0$, the next state is $n + 1$ with probability $(1 - b)a$; $n$ with probability $ab$; or $n - 1$ with probability $b(1 - a)$, that is: $p_{n\,n+1} = (1 - b)a$, $p_{n\,n} = ab$, $p_{n-1\,n} = (1 - a)b$. If $N = N_{max}$, the next state is $N_{max} - 1$ with probability $(1 - a)b$; or $N_{max}$ with probability $1 - b(1 - a)$, since the system is not allowed to grow beyond $N_{max}$.

The code below prepares the inputs and then calls the function `Discrete_MC(S, P,IC,N)`. The basic step in the function involves generating a discrete random variable that determines whether the chain increases by 1, decreases by 1, or remains the same.

```
Nmax=50;
P=zeros(Nmax+1,3);
a=0.45;
b=0.50;
P(1,:)=[0,1-a,a];
r=[(1-a)*b,a*b+(1-a)*(1-b),(1-b)*a];
for n=2:Nmax;
     P(n,:)=r;
end
```

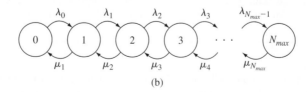

(a)

(b)

**FIGURE 11.20**
Generic Markov chains: (a) discrete-time; (b) birth-death continuous-time.

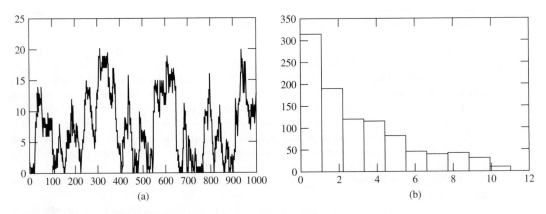

**FIGURE 11.21**
(a) Simulation of discrete-time data multiplexer; (b) histogram of number of packets in data multiplexer.

```
P(Nmax+1,:)=[(1-a)*b,1-(1-a)*b,0];
IC=zeros(Nmax+1,1);
IC(1,1)=1;
L=1000
Seq=Discrete_MC(Nmax,P,IC,L);
plot(Seq-1)

function stseq = Discrete_MC(Nmax,P,IC,L)
stseq=zeros(1,L);
s=[1:Nmax+1];
step=[-1,0,1];
InitSt=discrete_rnd(1,s,IC);
stseq(1)=InitSt;
for n=2:L+1;
    nextst=stseq(n-1)+discrete_rnd(1,step,P(stseq(n-1),:));
    stseq(n)=nextst;
end
```

Figure 11.21(a) shows a graph of a 1000-step realization of the Markov chain. The parameters in the simulation are $a = 0.45$ and $b = 0.5$. The latter parameter implies that a packet requires two time units on average of service before it departs the system. During the two time units that it takes to service the above packet, $2 \times (0.45) = 0.9$ packets arrive on average. This is an example of a "heavy traffic" situation which is characterized by the sporadic but sustained buildups of packets seen in the simulation. Figure 11.21(b) shows the histogram of the state occurrences in the simulation. It can be seen that the probability mass is concentrated at the lower state values.

**Continuous-Time Markov Chains**    The module for generating a sequence of states for a continuous-time Markov chain requires the following inputs: i. The state space; ii. The matrix of state transition rates; iii. The initial state probability mass function; and iv. The duration of the simulation. The module operates as follows:

1.  Generates the initial state according to $\pi_0$.
2.  Repeatedly generates the next state using the transition probabilities from the current state, and the state occupancy times for the new state.
3.  Stops when the elapsed time has been simulated.

---

### Example 11.50    Continuous-Time Birth-Death Process

Develop a program to generate continuous-time Markov chains with the state transition diagram shown in Figure 11.20(b). Use the program to simulate 1000 seconds of an M/M/1 queueing system. Assume the system is initially empty.

For this example we wrote the function `Continuous_MC(S,G,IC,T)`, given below. The module uses the embedded Markov chain approach and sequentially generates next state and occupancy time pairs. The transition probabilities for the embedded Markov chain are $\{\widetilde{q}_{jj-1} = \mu_j/(\lambda_j + \mu_j), \widetilde{q}_{jj+1} = \lambda_j/(\lambda_j + \mu_j)\}$ and the mean occupancy times are exponential random variables with mean $\{1/(\lambda_j + \mu_j)\}$. The basic step involves generating a binary random variable that determines whether the chain increases or decreases by 1, and then determines the occupancy time in the resulting state.

```
function [stseq,OccTime,n] = Continuous_MC(Nmax,G,IC,T)
Taggr=-1;
L=T*(G(Nmax-1,1)+G(Nmax-1,2));    % Estimate max number of state transitions.
stseq=zeros(1,L);
OccTime=zeros(1,L);
Q=zeros(1,2);
s=[1:Nmax+1];
step=[-1,1];
InitSt=discrete_rnd(1,s,IC);
stseq(1)=InitSt;
n=1;
OccTime(n)=exponential_rnd(G(stseq(n),1)+G(stseq(n),2));
Taggr=OccTime(n);
while (Taggr < T);
     n=n+1;
     Q(stseq(n-1),:)=[G(stseq(n-1),1),G(stseq(n-1),2)]/(G(stseq(n-
1),1)+G(stseq(n-1),2));
     nextst=stseq(n-1)+discrete_rnd(1,step,Q(stseq(n-1),:));
     stseq(n)=nextst;
     OccTime(n)=exponential_rnd((G(stseq(n),1)+G(stseq(n),2)));
     Taggr=Taggr+OccTime(n);
End
```

Figure 11.22 shows a graph of a realization of the Markov chain. The simulated queueing system has an arrival rate of $\lambda = 0.9$ jobs/second and a mean job service time of $\mu = 1$ second. Therefore the system is operating in heavy traffic and experiences surges in job backlogs. The

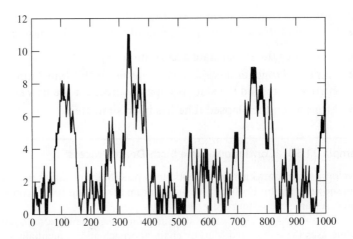

**FIGURE 11.22**
Simulation of M/M/1 continuous-time Markov chain.

calculation of the proportion of time that the system spends in each state is more complicated than for discrete-time systems because the occupancy times must be taken into account. These calculations will be addressed in the next chapter.

## SUMMARY

- A random process is said to be Markov if the future of the process, given the present, is independent of the past.
- A Markov chain is an integer-valued Markov process.
- The joint pmf for a Markov chain at several time instants is equal to the product of the probability of the state at the first time instant and the probabilities of the subsequent state transitions (Eq. 11.3).
- For discrete-time Markov chains: (1) the $n$-step transition probability matrix $P(n)$ is equal to $P^n$, where $P$ is the one-step transition probability; (2) the state probability after $n$ steps $\mathbf{p}(n)$ is equal to $\mathbf{p}(0)P^n$, where $\mathbf{p}(0)$ is the initial state probability; and (3) $P^n$ approaches a constant matrix as $n \to \infty$ for Markov chains that settle into steady state.
- The states of a discrete-time Markov chain can be divided into disjoint classes. The long-term behavior of a Markov chain is determined by the properties of its classes. In particular, for ergodic Markov chains the stationary state probabilities represent the long-term proportion of time spent in each state.
- A continuous-time Markov chain can be viewed as consisting of a discrete-time embedded Markov chain that determines the state transitions and of exponentially distributed state occupancy times.
- For continuous-time Markov chains: (1) the state probabilities and the transition probability matrix can be found by solving Eq. (11.39); (2) the steady state

probabilities can be found by solving the global balance equation, Eq. (11.40b) or (11.40c).

- A continuous-time Markov chain has a steady state if its embedded Markov chain is irreducible and positive recurrent with unique stationary pmf given by the solution of the global balance equations.

- The time-reversed version of a Markov chain is also a Markov chain. A discrete-time (continuous-time) irreducible, stationary ergodic Markov chain is reversible if the transition probability matrix (transition rate matrix) for the forward and reverse processes is the same.

- Matrix numerical methods can be used to find the time-dependent and the stationary probabilities of Markov chains.

## CHECKLIST OF IMPORTANT TERMS

Accessible state
Birth-and-death process
Chapman–Kolmogorov equations
Class of states
Embedded Markov chain
Ergodic Markov chain
Global balance equations
Homogeneous transition probabilities
Irreducible Markov chain
Markov chain
Markov process
Markov property
Mean recurrence time
Null recurrent state

Period of a state/class
Positive recurrent state
Recurrent state/class
Reversible Markov chain
State
State occupancy time
State probabilities
Stationary state pmf
Stochastic matrix
Time-reversed Markov chain
Transient state/class
Transition probability matrix
Trellis diagram

## ANNOTATED REFERENCES

References [1] and [2] contain very good discussions of discrete-time Markov chains. Feller has a rich set of classic examples that are a pleasure to read. Reference [3] gives a concise but quite complete introduction to Markov chains. Reference [4] provides an introduction to discrete-time and continuous-time Markov chains at about the same level as this chapter. References [6] and [7] give a more rigorous and complete coverage of Markov chains and processes.

1. K. L. Chung, *Elementary Probability Theory with Stochastic Processes*, Springer-Verlag, New York, 1975.
2. W. Feller, *An Introduction to Probability Theory and Its Applications*, vol. 1, Wiley, New York, 1968.
3. Y. A. Rozanov, *Probability Theory: A Concise Course*. Dover Publications, New York, 1969.
4. S. M. Ross, *Introduction to Probability Models*, Academic Press, Orlando, FL, 2003.

5. S. M. Ross, *Stochastic Processes,* Wiley, New York, 1983.

6. D. R. Cox and H. D. Miller, *The Theory of Stochastic Processes*, Chapman and Hall, London, 1972.

7. R. G. Gallager, *Discrete Stochastic Processes*, Kluwer Academic Press, Boston, 1996.

8. J. Kohlas, *Stochastic Methods of Operations Research*, Cambridge University Press, London, 1982.

9. H. Anton, *Elementary Linear Algebra*, Wiley, New York, 1981.

10. A. M. Langville and C. D. Meyer, *Google's PageRank and Beyond*, Princeton University Press, Princeton, NJ, 2006.

## PROBLEMS

### Section 11.1: Markov Processes

**11.1.** Let $M_n$ denote the sequence of sample means from an iid random process $X_n$:

$$M_n = \frac{X_1 + X_2 + \cdots + X_n}{n}.$$

**(a)** Is $M_n$ a Markov process?

**(b)** If the answer to part a is yes, find the following state transition pdf:

$$f_{M_n}(x \mid M_{n-1} = y).$$

**11.2.** An urn initially contains five black balls and five white balls. The following experiment is repeated indefinitely: A ball is drawn from the urn; if the ball is white, it is put back in the urn, otherwise it is left out. Let $X_n$ be the number of black balls remaining in the urn after $n$ draws from the urn.

**(a)** Is $X_n$ a Markov process? If so, find the appropriate transition probabilities and the corresponding Trellis diagram.

**(b)** Do the transition probabilities depend on $n$?

**(c)** Repeat part a if the urn initially has $K$ black balls and $K$ white balls.

**11.3.** An urn initially contains two black balls and two white balls. The following experiment is repeated indefinitely: A ball is drawn from the urn; with probability $a$, the color of the ball is changed to the other color and is then put back in the urn, otherwise it is put back without change. Let $X_n$ be the number of black balls in the urn after $n$ draws from the urn.

**(a)** Is $X_n$ a Markov process? If so, find the appropriate transition probabilities.

**(b)** Do the transition probabilities depend on $n$?

**(c)** Repeat part a if $a = 1$. What changes?

**(d)** Repeat parts a and c if the urn contains $K$ black balls and $K$ white balls.

**11.4.** Michael and Marisa initially have four pens each. Out of the total of eight pens, half are good and half are dry. The following experiment is repeated indefinitely: Michael and Marisa exchange a randomly selected pen from their set. Let $X_n$ be the number of good pens in Marisa's set after $n$ draws.

**(a)** Is $X_n$ a Markov process? If so, find the appropriate transition probabilities.

**(b)** Do the transition probabilities depend on $n$?

(c)   Repeat part a if Michael and Marisa initially have a total of $K$ good pens and $K$ dry pens.

**11.5.**  Does a Markov process have independent increments? *Hint:* Use the process in Problem 11.2 to support your answer.

**11.6.**  Let $X_n$ be the Bernoulli iid process, and let $Y_n$ be given by

$$Y_n = X_n + X_{n-1}.$$

It was shown in Example 11.2 that $Y_n$ is not a Markov process. Consider the vector process defined by $\mathbf{Z}_n = (X_n, X_{n-1})$.

(a)   Show that $\mathbf{Z}_n$ is a Markov process.

(b)   Find the state transition diagram for $\mathbf{Z}_n$.

**11.7.**  (a)   Show that the following autoregressive process is a Markov process:

$$Y_n = rY_{n-1} + X_n \qquad Y_0 = 0,$$

where $X_n$ is an iid process.

(b)   Find the transition pdf if $X_n$ is an iid Gaussian sequence.

**11.8.**  The amount of water in an aquifer at year end is a random variable $X_n$. The amount of water drawn from the aquifer in a year is a random variable $D_n$ and the amount restored by rainfall is $W_n$.

(a)   Find a set of equations to describe the total amount of water $X_n$ in the aquifer over time.

(b)   Under what conditions is $X_n$ a Markov process?

## Section 11.2: Discrete-Time Markov Chains

**11.9.**  Let $X_n$ be an iid random process. Show that $X_n$ is a Markov process and give its one-step transition probability matrix.

**11.10.**  An information source generates iid integer-valued bits $X_n$ for which $P[0] = a = 1 - P[1]$.

(a)   Suppose that $X_n$ is transmitted over a binary symmetric channel with error probability $\varepsilon$. Find the probabilities of the outputs of the channel.

(b)   Suppose that $X_n$ is transmitted over $K$ consecutive identical and independent binary symmetric channels. Does the sequence of channel outputs form a Markov chain?

(c)   Find the $K$-step transition probabilities that relate the input bits from the source to the outputs of the $K$th channel.

(d)   What are the probabilities of the outputs of the $K$th channel as $K \to \infty$?

**11.11.**  Each time unit a data multiplexer receives a packet with probability $a$, and/or transmits a packet from its buffer with probability $b$. Assume that the multiplexer can hold at most $N$ packets. Let $X_n$ be the number of packets in the multiplexer at time $n$.

(a)   Show that the system can be modeled by a Markov chain.

(b)   Find the transition probability matrix $P$.

(c)   Find the stationary pmf.

**11.12.**  Let $X_n$ be the Markov chain defined for the urn experiment in Problem 11.2.

(a)   Find the one-step transition probability matrix $P$ for $X_n$.

(b)   Find the two-step transition probability matrix $P^2$ by matrix multiplication. Check your answer by computing $p_{54}(2)$ and comparing it to the corresponding entry in $P^2$.

(c)   What happens to $X_n$ as $n$ approaches infinity? Use your answer to guess the limit of $P^n$ as $n \to \infty$.

**11.13.** Let $X_n$ be the Markov chain defined in Problem 11.3.

**(a)** Find the one-step transition probability matrix $P$ for $X_n$ with $a = 1/10$.

**(b)** Find $P^2$, $P^4$, and $P^8$ by matrix multiplication.

**(c)** What happens to $X_n$ as $n$ approaches infinity?

**(d)** Repeat parts a, b, and c if $a = 1$.

**11.14.** In the Ehrenfest model of heat exchange, two containers hold a total of $\rho$ particles [Feller, pp. 121]. Each time instant a particle is selected at random and moved to the other container. Let $X_n$ be the number of particles in the first container.

**(a)** Show that this model is the same as in Problem 11.3(d).

**(b)** Use the state transition diagram to explain why the model exhibits a "central force."

**(c)** Show that the stationary pmf is given by a binomial pmf with parameters $\rho$ and 1/2. Give an intuitive explanation for this result.

**11.15.** Let $X_n$ be the pen-exchange Markov chain defined in Problem 11.4.

**(a)** Find $P$.

**(b)** Use Octave or a numerical program to find $P^2$, $P^4$, and $P^8$ by matrix multiplication.

**(c)** What happens to $X_n$ as $n$ approaches infinity?

**11.16.** In the Bernoulli–Laplace model for diffusion, a total of $2\rho$ particles are distributed between two containers, and half of the particles are black and half are white [Feller, 1968, pp. 378]. Each time instant a particle is selected at random from each container and moved to the other container. Let $X_n$ be the number of white particles in the first container.

**(a)** Show that this model is the same as in Problem 11.4(c).

**(b)** Show that the stationary pmf is given by:

$$\pi_j = \binom{\rho}{j}^2 \bigg/ \binom{2\rho}{\rho} \text{ for } j = 0, 1, \dots, \rho.$$

**11.17.** The vector process $\mathbf{Z}_n$ in Problem 11.6 has four possible states, so in effect it is equivalent to a Markov chain with states $\{0, 1, 2, 3\}$.

**(a)** Find the one-step transition probability matrix $P$.

**(b)** Find $P^2$ and check your answer by computing the probability of going from state $(0, 1)$ to state $(0, 1)$ in two steps.

**(c)** Show that $P^n = P^2$ for all $n > 2$. Give an intuitive justification for why this is true for this random process.

**(d)** Find the steady state probabilities for the process.

**11.18.** Consider a sequence of Bernoulli trials with probability of success $p$ and let $X_n$ denote the number of consecutive successes in a streak up to time $n$.

**(a)** Show that $X_n$ is a Markov chain.

**(b)** Find the one-step transition probability and draw the corresponding state transition diagram.

**(c)** Find the stationary pmf assuming $p < 1$.

**11.19.** Two gamblers play the following game. A fair coin is flipped; if the outcome is heads, player $A$ pays player $B$ \$1, and if the outcome is tails player $B$ pays player $A$ \$1. The game is continued until one of the players goes broke. Suppose that initially player $A$ has \$1 and player $B$ has \$2, so a total of \$3 is up for grabs. Let $X_n$ denote the number of dollars held by player $A$ after $n$ trials.

**(a)** Show that $X_n$ is a Markov chain.

**(b)** Sketch the state transition diagram for $X_n$ and give the one-step transition probability matrix $P$.

**(c)** Use the state transition diagram to help you show that for $n$ even (i.e., $n = 2k$),

$$p_{ii}(n) = \left(\frac{1}{2}\right)^n \text{ for } i = 1, 2 \text{ and } p_{10}(n) = \frac{2}{3}\left(1 - \left(\frac{1}{4}\right)^k\right) = p_{23}(n).$$

**(d)** Find the $n$-step transition probability matrix for $n$ even using part c.

**(e)** Find the limit of $P^n$ as $n \to \infty$.

**(f)** Find the probability that player $A$ eventually wins.

**11.20.** A certain part of a machine can be in two states: working or undergoing repair. A working part fails during the course of a day with probability $a$. A part undergoing repair is put into working order during the course of a day with probability $b$. Let $X_n$ be the state of the part.

**(a)** Show that $X_n$ is a two-state Markov chain and give its one-step transition probability matrix $P$.

**(b)** Find the $n$-step transition probability matrix $P^n$.

**(c)** Find the steady state probability for each of the two states.

**11.21.** A machine consists of two parts that fail and are repaired independently. A working part fails during any given day with probability $a$. A part that is not working is repaired by the next day with probability $b$. Let $X_n$ be the number of working parts in day $n$.

**(a)** Show that $X_n$ is a three-state Markov chain and give its one-step transition probability matrix $P$.

**(b)** Show that the steady state pmf $\pi$ is binomial with parameter $p = b/(a + b)$.

**(c)** What do you expect is the steady state pmf for a machine that consists of $n$ parts?

**11.22.** A stochastic matrix is defined as a nonnegative matrix for which the elements of each row add to one.

**(a)** Show that the transition probability matrix $P$ for a Markov chain is a stochastic matrix.

**(b)** Show that if $P$ and $Q$ are stochastic matrices, then $PQ$ is also a stochastic matrix.

**(c)** Show that if $P$ is a stochastic matrix, then $P^n$ is also a stochastic matrix.

**11.23.** Show that if $P^k$ has identical rows, then $P^j$ has identical rows for all $j \geq k$.

**11.24.** Prove Eq. (11.14) by induction.

## Section 11.3: Classes of States, Recurrence Properties, and Limiting Probabilities

**11.25. (a)** Sketch the state-transition diagrams for the Markov chains with the following transition probability matrices.

**(b)** Specify the classes of the Markov chains and classify them as recurrent or transient.

**(c)** Use Octave to calculate the first few powers of each matrix. Note any interesting behavior.

$$
\text{(i)} \begin{bmatrix} 0 & 1 & 0 \\ 1/2 & 0 & 1/2 \\ 1 & 0 & 0 \end{bmatrix}
\qquad
\text{(ii)} \begin{bmatrix} 1 & 0 & 0 \\ 0 & 0 & 1 \\ 0 & 1 & 0 \end{bmatrix}
\qquad
\text{(iii)} \begin{bmatrix} 1/2 & 1/2 & 0 \\ 0 & 1 & 0 \\ 1/2 & 0 & 1/2 \end{bmatrix}
$$

$$
\text{(iv)} \begin{bmatrix} 0 & 1/2 & 1/2 & 0 \\ 0 & 0 & 1 & 0 \\ 0 & 0 & 1 & 0 \\ 1 & 0 & 0 & 0 \end{bmatrix}
\qquad
\text{(v)} \begin{bmatrix} 1/2 & 1/2 & 0 & 0 \\ 1 & 0 & 0 & 0 \\ 1/2 & 0 & 1/4 & 1/4 \\ 0 & 1/4 & 1/4 & 1/2 \end{bmatrix}
$$

**11.26.** Characterize the long-term behavior of the Markov chains in Problem 11.25. Find the long-term proportion of time spent in each state. Find the stationary pmf where applicable and determine whether it is unique.

**11.27.** Consider a three-state Markov chain. Select transition probabilities and sketch the associated transition diagram to produce the following attributes:

**(a)** $X_n$ is irreducible.

**(b)** $X_n$ is has one transient class and one recurrent class.

**(c)** $X_n$ is has two recurrent classes.

**11.28. (a)** Find the transition probability matrices for the Markov chains with the state transition diagrams shown in Fig. P11.1.

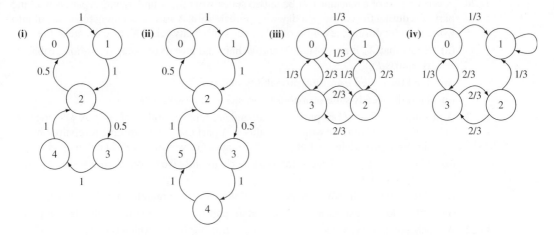

**FIGURE P11.1**

**(b)** Specify the classes of the Markov chains and classify them as recurrent or transient; periodic or aperiodic.

**(c)** Characterize the long-term behavior of the Markov chains and find the long-term proportion of time spent in each state, and the stationary pmf where applicable.

**(d)** Use Octave to evaluate $P^n$ for $n = 1, 2, 3, 4, 5$. Explain any interesting results you may find.

**11.29. (a)** Apply the PageRank modeling procedure to the Markov chains in Problem 11.28 to find the transition probability matrix.

**(b)** Find the PageRank value for each node.

**11.30.** Consider a random walk in the set $\{0, 1, \ldots, M\}$ with transition probabilities

$$p_{01} = 1, \ p_{M,M-1} = 1, \text{ and } \quad p_{i,i-1} = q \qquad p_{i,i+1} = p \text{ for } \quad i = 1, \ldots, M - 1.$$

**(a)** Sketch the state transition diagram.

**(b)** Find the long-term proportion of time spent in each state, and the limit of $p_{ii}(n)$ as $n \to \infty$. Evaluate the special case when $p = 1/2$.

**11.31.** Repeat Problem 11.30 if the random walk is modified so that

$$p_{01} = p, \ p_{00} = q, \ p_{M,M-1} = q, \text{ and } p_{M,M} = p.$$

**11.32.** For a finite-state, irreducible Markov chain, explain why none of the states can have zero probability.

**11.33.** Suppose that state $i$ belongs to a recurrent class of a finite-state Markov chain and that $p_{ii}(1) > 0$. Show that $i$ belongs to a class which is aperiodic.

**11.34.** Prove that positive and null recurrence are class properties.

**11.35.** In this problem we develop expressions for recurrence probabilities and expectations. Let $a_n = f_{ii}(n)$ be the probability that a first return to state $i$ from state $i$ occurs after $n$ steps; and let $b_n = p_{ii}(n)$ be the probability of a return to state $i$ from state $i$ after $n$ steps.

(a) Show that: $b_n = \sum_{j=0}^{n} b_j a_{n-j}$ where $b_0 = 1, a_0 = 0$. *Hint:* Use conditional probability.

(b) Let $A(z)$ and $B(z)$ be the generating functions of $\{a_n\}$ and $\{b_n\}$ as defined in Eq. (4.84). Explain why the series converge for $|z| < 1$, and show that $B(z) = \dfrac{1}{1 - A(z)}$.

(c) Show that $f_i = \lim_{z \to 1} A(z)$.

(d) Show that state $i$ is recurrent if and only if $\lim_{z \to 1} B(z) = \infty$.

**11.36.** Consider a Markov chain with state space $\{0, 1, 2, \dots\}$ and the following transition probabilities:

$$p_{0j} = f_j \text{ and } p_{jj-1} = 1 \text{ where } 1 = f_1 + f_2 + \cdots + f_j + \cdots.$$

(a) Sketch the state transition diagram.

(b) Determine whether the Markov chain is irreducible.

(c) Determine whether state 0 is transient, or null/positive recurrent.

(d) Find an expression for the stationary pmf, if it exists.

(e) Provide specific answers to parts c and d if $\{f_i\}$ is given by the following pmfs: **(i)** geometric; **(ii)** Zipf. (See Eq. (3.51).)

**11.37.** Consider a Markov chain with state space $\{1, 2, \dots\}$ and the following transition probabilities:

$$p_{jj+1} = a_j \text{ and } p_{j1} = 1 - a_j \text{ where } 0 < a_j < 1.$$

(a) Sketch the state transition diagram.

(b) Determine whether the Markov chain is irreducible.

(c) Determine whether state 1 is transient, or null/positive recurrent.

(d) Find an expression for the stationary pmf, if it exists.

(e) Provide specific answers to parts c and d if:

    **(i)**  $a_j = 1/2$ all $j$      **(ii)**  $a_j = (j - 1)/j$      **(iii)**  $a_j = 1/j$

    **(iv)**  $a_j = (1/2)^j$      **(v)**  $a_j = 1 - (1/2)^j$.

**11.38.** Let $X_n$ and $Y_n$ be two ergodic Markov chains with the same state space but different transition probability matrices, $P_1$ and $P_2$, respectively, and different stationary pmf's.

(a) A new process is constructed as follows. A coin is flipped and if the outcome is heads, $P_1$ is used to generate the entire sequence; but if the outcome is tails, $P_2$ is used instead. Is the resulting process Markov and does it have a stationary pmf? Is it ergodic?

(b) Repeat part a if the process is constructed as follows. A coin is flipped before every time instant and the associated transition probability matrix is used to determine the next state.

(c) Repeat part a if the state for odd (even) time instants is determined according to $P_1$ $(P_2)$.

**11.39.** Characterize the processes in Problem 11.38(a–c) if $X_n$ and $Y_n$ are two processes from Problem 11.36(e) with two different geometric pmfs.

**11.40.** Construct a multiclass infinite-state Markov chain that has the following attributes:

    **(a)**  One class is transient and one class is null recurrent.

    **(b)**  One class is null recurrent and one class is positive recurrent.

### Section 11.4: Continuous-Time Markov Chains

**11.41.** Consider the simple queueing system discussed in Example 11.36.

    **(a)**  Use the results in Example 11.36 to find the state transition probability matrix.

    **(b)**  Find the following probabilities:

$$P[X(1.5) = 1, X(3) = 1 \,|\, X(0) = 0]$$
$$P[X(1.5) = 1, X(3) = 1].$$

**11.42.** A rechargeable battery in a depot is in one of three states: fully charged, in use, or recharging. Assume the mean time in each of these states is: $1/\lambda$; 1 hour; 3 hours. Batteries are not put into use unless they are fully charged.

    **(a)**  Find a Markov model for the battery states and sketch the state transition diagram.

    **(b)**  Find the stationary pmf. Explain how the pmf varies with $\lambda$.

**11.43.** Suppose that the depot in Problem 11.42 has two batteries. Define the state at time $t$ by $\{N_F(t), N_U(t), N_C(t)\}$, that is, by the number of batteries in each state.

    **(a)**  Sketch the state transition diagram for a six-state Markov chain for the system.

    **(b)**  Find the stationary pmf and evaluate it for various values of $\lambda$.

**11.44.** Rolo, a Chihuahua, spends most of the daytime sleeping in the kitchen. When a person enters the kitchen, Rolo greets him or her and wags her tail for an average time of one minute. At the end of this period Rolo is fed with probability 1/4, patted briefly with probability 5/8, or taken for a walk with probability 1/8. If fed, Rolo spends an average of two minutes eating. The walks take 15 minutes on average. After eating, being patted, or walking, she returns to sleep. Assume that people enter the kitchen on average every hour.

    **(a)**  Find a Markov chain model with four states: {sleep, greet, eat, walk}. Specify the transition rate matrix.

    **(b)**  Find the steady state probabilities.

**11.44.** A critical part of a machine has an exponentially distributed lifetime with parameter $\alpha = 1$. Suppose that $n = 4$ spare parts are initially in stock, and let $N(t)$ be the number of spares left at time $t$.

    **(a)**  Find $p_{ij}(t) = P[N(s + t) = j \,|\, N(s) = i]$.

    **(b)**  Find the transition probability matrix.

    **(c)**  Find $p_j(t)$.

    **(d)**  Plot $p_j(t)$ versus time for $j = 0, 1, 2, 3, 4$.

    **(e)**  Give the general solution for $p_j(t)$ for arbitrary $\alpha > 0$ and $n$.

**11.45.** A machine shop initially has $n = 3$ identical machines in operation. Assume that the time until breakdown for each machine is an exponentially distributed random variable with parameter $\alpha = 2$. Let $N(t)$ denote the number of machines in working order at time $t$.

    **(a)**  Find $p_{ij}(t) = P[N(s + t) = j \,|\, N(s) = i]$.

    **(b)**  Find the transition probability matrix.

    **(c)** Show that $N(t)$ is a binomial random variable with parameter $p = e^{-\alpha t}$.

    **(d)** Plot $p_j(t)$ versus time for $j = 0, 1, 2, 3, 4$.

    **(e)** Give the general solution for $p_j(t)$ for arbitrary $\alpha > 0$ and $n$.

**11.46.** A shop has $n = 3$ machines and one technician to repair them. A machine remains in the working state for an exponentially distributed time with parameter $\mu = 1/3$. The technician works on one machine at a time, and it takes him an exponentially distributed time of rate $\alpha = 1$ to repair each machine. Let $X(t)$ be the number of working machines at time $t$.

    **(a)** Show that if $X(t) = k$, then the time until the next machine breakdown is an exponentially distributed random variable with rate $k\mu$.

    **(b)** Find the transition rate matrix $[\gamma_{ij}]$ and sketch the transition rate diagram for $X(t)$.

    **(c)** Write the global balance equations and find the steady state probabilities for $X(t)$.

    **(d)** Redo parts b and c if the number of technicians is increased to 2.

    **(e)** Find the steady state probabilities for arbitrary values of $n$, $\alpha$, and $\mu$.

**11.47.** A speaker alternates between periods of speech activity and periods of silence. Suppose that the former are exponentially distributed with mean $1/\alpha = 200$ ms and the latter exponentially distributed with mean $1/\beta = 400$ ms. Consider a group of $n = 4$ independent speakers and let $N(t)$ denote the number of speakers in speech activity at time $t$.

    **(a)** Find the transition rate diagram and the transition rate matrix for this system.

    **(b)** Write the global balance equations and show that the steady state pmf is given by a binomial distribution. Why is this solution not surprising?

    **(c)** Find the steady state probabilities for arbitrary values of $n$, $\alpha$, and $\beta$.

**11.48.** A continuous-time Markov chain $X(t)$ can be approximated by a sampled-time discrete-time Markov chain $X_n = X(n\delta)$ where the sampling interval is $\delta$ seconds.

    **(a)** Find the transition probabilities for $X_n$ if $X(t)$ is the M/M/1 queue in Example 11.39.

    **(b)** Find the stationary pmf for part a. Compare to the answer in the example.

**11.49.** Consider the single-server queueing system in Example 11.39. Suppose that at most $K$ customers can be in the system at any time. Let $N(t)$ be the number of customers in the system at time $t$. Find the steady state probabilities for $N(t)$.

**11.50.** **(a)** Find the embedded Markov chain for the process described in Example 11.39.

    **(b)** Find the stationary pmf of the embedded Markov chain.

    **(c)** Characterize the long-term probabilities of the process using Eq. (11.50).

**11.51.** Repeat Problem 11.50 for the process described in Example 11.40.

**11.52.** Suppose that the embedded Markov chain for the process $N(t)$ is given by the discrete-time Markov chain in Problem 11.36 with $\{f_i\}$ given by a geometric pmf. Find the steady state probabilities of $N(t)$, if they exist, in the following cases:

    **(a)** The occupancy times of all states are exponentially distributed with mean 1.

    **(b)** The occupancy time of state $j$ is exponentially distributed with mean $j$.

    **(c)** The occupancy time of state $j$ is exponentially distributed with mean $2^j$.

## *Section 11.5: Time-Reversed Markov Chains

**11.53.** $N$ balls are distributed in two urns. At time $n$, a ball is selected at random, removed from its present urn, and placed in the other urn. Let $X_n$ denote the number of balls in urn 1.

    **(a)** Find the transition probabilities for $X_n$.

    **(b)** Argue that the process is time reversible and then obtain the steady state probabilities for $X_n$.

**11.54.** A point moves in the unit circle in jumps of $\pm 90°$. Suppose that the process is initially at $0°$, and that the probability of $+90°$ is $p$.

   **(a)** Find the transition probabilities for the resulting Markov chain and obtain the steady state probabilities.

   **(b)** Is the process reversible? Why or why not?

**11.55.** Find the transition probabilities for the time-reversed version of the random walk discussed in Problem 11.31. Is the process reversible?

**11.56.** Is the Markov chain in Problem 11.16 time reversible?

**11.57.** Is the Markov chain in Problem 11.17 time reversible?

**11.58.** **(a)** Specify the time-reversed version of the process defined in Problem 11.49. Is the process reversible?

   **(b)** Find the steady state probabilities of the process using Eq. (11.67).

**11.59.** Use the results of Example 11.42 to find the stationary pmf of the Markov chains in Problem 11.37(i).

**11.60.** Determine whether the simple queueing system in Example 11.36 is reversible.

**11.61.** Determine whether the machine repair model in Problem 11.46 is reversible.

**11.62.** **(a)** Is the speech activity model in Problem 11.47 reversible?

   **(b)** Is the model reversible if $\alpha = \beta$?

## *Section 11.6: Numerical Techniques for Markov Chains

**11.63.** Consider the urn experiment in Problem 11.2.

   **(a)** Use matrix diagonalization to find an expression for the state pmf as a function of time. Plot the state pmf vs. time.

   **(b)** Run a simulation for this urn experiment 100 times and build a histogram of the number of steps that take place until the last black ball is removed.

   **(c)** Derive the pmf for the number of steps that elapse until the last black ball is removed. Compare the theoretical pmf with the observed histogram in part b.

**11.64.** Consider the Bernoulli–Laplace diffusion model from Problem 11.16 with $\rho = 5$.

   **(a)** Use matrix diagonalization to obtain an expression for the time-dependent state pmf. Plot the state pmf vs. time for different initial conditions.

   **(b)** Write a simulation for the model and make several observations of 200-step sample functions. Is the process ergodic? Is it necessary to perform multiple realizations of the process, or does it suffice to collect statistics from one long realization?

   **(c)** Compare histograms of the state occupancy and compare to the theoretical result for: 5 separate realizations of 200 steps; 1 realization of 1000 steps.

   **(d)** Use the autocov function in Octave to estimate the covariance function of the process.

**11.65.** Consider the data multiplexer in Problem 11.11.

   **(a)** Derive the transition probabilities for the multiplexer assuming a maximum state of $N = 100$. Find the steady state pmf for the following parameters: $b = 0.5$ and $a = 0.1, a = 0.25, a = 0.50$.

   **(b)** Simulate the data multiplexer for each of the cases in part a. Run the simulation for 1000 steps.

   **(c)** For each realization record a histogram of the length of idle periods (when the system remains continuously empty) and the length of the busy periods (when the system remains continuously nonempty). Which of the three choices of parameters above correspond to "heavy traffic"; "light traffic?"

**11.66.** Consider the gamblers' experiment in Problem 11.19 with player $A$ beginning with \$6 and player $B$ with \$3.

  **(a)** Find the transition probability $P$ and obtain an expression for $P^n$. What is the probability that player $A$ wins? What is the average time until player $A$ wins (when he wins)?

  **(b)** Simulate 500 trials of the experiment. Find the relative frequency of player $A$ winning and compare to the theoretical result.

  **(c)** Find the mean time until player $A$ wins; until player $B$ wins. Compare to the theoretical results.

**11.67.** Consider the residual lifetime process in Problem 11.36. Assume a machine state of 100.

  **(a)** Simulate 1000 steps of the process with a geometric random variable with mean 5. Record histograms of the state pmf and obtain the autocovariance of the realization.

  **(b)** Repeat part a with a Zipf random variable of mean 5. Compare the histogram and autocovariance to those found in part a.

**11.68.** Consider the age process in Problem 11.37. Assume a machine state of 100.

  **(a)** Simulate 1000 steps of the process with $a_j = (j - 1)/j$. Does the process behave as expected?

  **(b)** Repeat part a with $a_j = 1 - (1/2)^j$.

**11.69.** Consider the battery experiment in Problem 11.43.

  **(a)** Use matrix diagonalization to obtain the time-dependent state transition probabilities for $\lambda = 0.1, 1, 10$. What are the steady state probabilities? What are the corresponding embedded state probabilities?

  **(b)** Simulate 500 hours of operation and observe the histogram of the embedded state occupancies. Compare to the theoretical results.

**11.70.** Consider the machine repair model in Problem 11.46. Assume $n = 10$ machines, $\mu = 1/10$ average working time, and $\alpha = 1$.

  **(a)** Obtain the time-dependent state transition probabilities for 1 and 2 technicians. What are the steady state probabilities? What are the corresponding embedded state probabilities?

  **(b)** Simulate 1000 hours of operation and observe the histogram of the embedded state occupancies. Compare to the theoretical results.

**11.71.** Use the simulator developed in Example 11.49 to simulate a sampled-time approximation to the birth-death process shown in Figure 11.20(b). Simulate 200 seconds of an M/M/1 queue in which jobs arrive at rate $\lambda = 0.9$ jobs per second and jobs complete processing at a rate of 1 job every second. Assume the system is initially empty. Show the realizations of the sampled process and measure the proportion of time spent in each state. Compare these to the theoretical values.

## Problems Requiring Cumulative Knowledge

**11.72. (a)** The Markov chain in Fig. 11.6(b) is started in state 0 at time 0. Find the $n$-step transition probability matrix for even and odd numbers of steps. What happens as $n \to \infty$?

  **(b)** Let $X_n$ be an irreducible, periodic, positive recurrent Markov chain in steady state. Is $X_n$ a cyclostationary random process?

**11.73.** Let $X_n$ be an ergodic Markov chain. Let $I_j(n)$ be the indicator function for state $j$ at time $n$, that is, $I_j(n)$ is 1 if the state at time $n$ is $j$, and 0 otherwise. What is the limiting value of the time average of $I_j(n)$? Is this result an ergodic theorem?

**11.74.** Let $X(t)$ be a continuous-time model for speech activity, in which a speaker is active (state 1) for an exponentially distributed time with rate $\alpha$ and is silent (state 0) for an exponentially distributed time with rate $\beta$. Assume all active and silence durations are independent random variables.

    **(a)** Find a two-state Markov chain for $X(t)$.

    **(b)** Find $p_0(t)$ and $p_1(t)$.

    **(c)** Find the autocorrelation function of $X(t)$.

    **(d)** If $X(t)$ is asymptotically wide-sense stationary, find its power spectral density.

    **(e)** Suppose we have $n$ independent speakers, and let $N(t)$ be the total number of speakers active at time $t$. Find the autocorrelation function of $N(t)$, and its power spectral density if it is asymptotically wide-sense stationary.

**11.75.** Let $X_n$ be a continuous-valued discrete-time Markov process.

    **(a)** Find the expression for the joint pdf corresponding to Eq. (11.5).

    **(b)** Find the expression for the two-step transition pdf corresponding to Eq. (11.12a).

**11.76.** Consider the aquifer in Problem 11.8.

    **(a)** Find a recursive equation for the amount of water in the aquifer $X_{n+1}$ in year $n + 1$ in terms of the amount of water in year $n$, the amount withdrawn from use $D_n$, and the amount restored by rainfall $W_n$. Note that the amount of water must be nonnegative.

    **(b)** Find an integral expression relating the steady state pdf of $X$ to the pdf's of $W$ and $D$. Assume that $W$ and $D$ are independent and Gaussian random variables. Propose possible approaches to solving these equations.

    **(c)** Write a computer simulation to investigate the distribution of $X$ as a function of $W$ and $D$ assuming: $W_n$ and $D_n$ are iid random variables with the same mean; $D_n$ is iid random variable, but $W_n$ is independent with a slowly varying mean (with period 100 years) that is equal to that of $D_n$ when averaged over the entire period.

# Introduction to Queueing Theory

In many applications, scarce resources such as computers and communication systems are shared among a community of users. Users place demands for these resources at random times, and they require use of these resources for time periods whose durations are random. Inevitably requests for the resource arrive while the resource is occupied, and a mechanism to provide an orderly access to the resource is required. The most common access control mechanism is to file user requests in a waiting line or "queue" such as might be formed at a bank by customers waiting to be served. Resource sharing can also take place in systems of very large scale, e.g., peer-to-peers networks, where the "queues" are not as readily apparent.

Queueing theory deals with the study of waiting lines and resource sharing. The random nature of the demand behavior of customers implies that probabilistic measures such as average delay, average throughput, and delay percentiles are required to assess the performance of such systems. Queueing theory provides us with the probability tools needed to evaluate these measures.

This chapter is organized as follows:

- Section 12.1 introduces the basic structure of a queueing system.
- Section 12.2 develops Little's formula which provides a fundamental relationship that is applicable in most queueing systems.
- In Section 12.3 we examine the M/M/1 queue and use it to develop many of the basic insights into queueing systems.
- Sections 12.4 and 12.5 develop multiserver systems and finite-source systems which can both be represented by Markov chains.
- Sections 12.6 and 12.7 develop M/G/1 queues which require more complex modeling.
- Section 12.8 and 12.9 presents Burke's and Jackson's theorems which allow us to model networks of queues.
- Finally Section 12.10 considers the simulation of queueing systems.

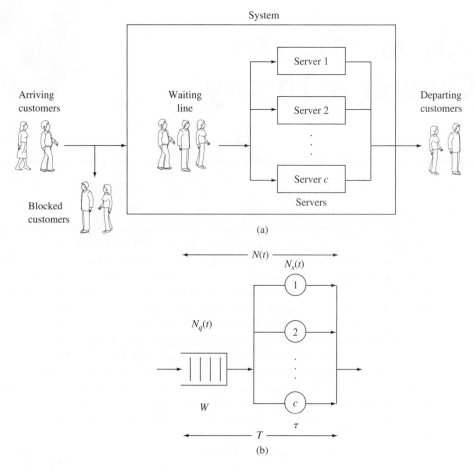

**FIGURE 12.1**
(a) Elements of a queueing system. (b) Elements of a queueing system model: $N(t)$, number in system; $N_q(t)$, number in queue; $N_s(t)$, number in service; $W$, waiting time in queue; $\tau$, service time; and $T$, total time in the system.

## 12.1 THE ELEMENTS OF A QUEUEING SYSTEM

Figure 12.1(a) shows a typical queueing system and Fig. 12.1(b) shows the elements of a queueing system model. Customers from some population arrive at the system at the random *arrival times* $S_1, S_2, S_3, \ldots, S_i, \ldots$, where $S_i$ denotes the arrival time of the *i*th customer. We denote the customer **arrival rate** by $\lambda$.

The queueing system has one or more identical servers, as shown in Fig. 12.1(a). The *i*th customer arrives at the system seeking a service that will require $\tau_i$ seconds of **service time** from one server. If all the servers are busy, then the arriving customer joins a queue where he remains until a server becomes available. Sometimes, only a limited number of waiting spaces are available so customers that arrive when there is no room are turned away. Such customers are called "blocked" and we will denote the rate at which customers are turned away by $\lambda_b$.

The **queue** or **service discipline** specifies the order in which customers are selected from the queue and allowed into service. For example, some common queueing disciplines are *first come, first served*, and *last come, first served*. The queueing discipline affects the **waiting time** $W_i$ that elapses from the arrival time of the $i$th customer until the time when it enters service. The **total delay** $T_i$ of the $i$th customer in the system is the sum of its waiting time and service time:

$$T_i = W_i + \tau_i. \tag{12.1}$$

From the customer's point of view, the performance of the system is given by the statistics of the waiting time $W$ and the total delay $T$, and the proportion of customers that are blocked, $\lambda_b/\lambda$. From the point of view of resource allocation, the performance of the system is measured by the proportion of time that each server is utilized and the rate at which customers are serviced by the system, $\lambda_d = \lambda - \lambda_b$. These quantities are a function of $N(t)$, the number of customers in the system at time $t$, and $N_q(t)$, the number of customers in queue at time $t$.

The notation $a/b/m/K$ is used to describe a queueing system, where $a$ specifies the type of arrival process, $b$ denotes the service time distribution, $m$ specifies the number of servers, and $K$ denotes the maximum number of customers allowed in the system at any time. If $a$ is given by M, then the arrival process is Poisson and the interarrival times are independent, identically distributed (iid) exponential random variables. If $b$ is given by M, then the service times are iid exponential random variables. If $b$ is given by D, then the service times are constant, that is, deterministic. If $b$ is given by G, then the service times are iid according to some general distribution. For example, in this chapter we deal with M/M/1, M/M/1/$K$, M/M/$c$, M/M/$c$/$c$, M/D/1, and M/G/1 queues.

Queueing system models find many applications in electrical and computer engineering. The "servers" in Fig. 12.1 can represent a variety of resources that perform "work." For example, in communication networks, the server can represent a communications line that transmits packets of information. In computer systems, the servers could represent processes in a computer that each handles Web queries from a particular client. Modern distributed applications combine these communications and computing resources into vast networks of interacting queueing systems.

## 12.2    LITTLE'S FORMULA

We now develop **Little's formula**, which states that, for systems that reach steady state, the average number of customers in a system is equal to the product of the average arrival rate and the average time spent in the system:

$$E[N] = \lambda E[T]. \tag{12.2}$$

This formula is valid under very general conditions, so it is applicable in an amazing number of situations.

Consider the queueing system shown in Fig. 12.2. The system begins empty at time $t = 0$, and the customer arrival times are denoted by $S_1, S_2, \ldots$. Let $A(t)$ be the number of customer arrivals up to time $t$. The $i$th customer spends time $T_i$ in the system and then

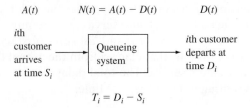

$$A(t) \qquad N(t) = A(t) - D(t) \qquad D(t)$$

$$T_i = D_i - S_i$$

**FIGURE 12.2**
Time in system is departure time minus arrival time.
Number in system at time $t$ is number of arrivals
minus number of departures.

departs at time $D_i = S_i + T_i$. We will let $D(t)$ be the number of customer departures up to time $t$. The **number of customers in the system** at time $t$ is the number of arrivals that have not yet left the system:

$$N(t) = A(t) - D(t). \tag{12.3}$$

Figure 12.3 shows a possible sample path for $A(t)$, $D(t)$, and $N(t)$ in a queueing system with "first come, first served" service discipline.

Consider the time average of the number of customers in the system $N(t)$ during the interval $(0, t]$:

$$\langle N \rangle_t = \frac{1}{t} \int_0^t N(t') \, dt'. \tag{12.4}$$

In Fig. 12.3, $N(t)$ is the region between $A(t)$ and $D(t)$, so the above integral is given by the area of the enclosed region up to time $t$. It can be seen that each customer who has

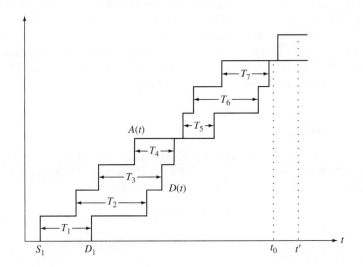

**FIGURE 12.3**
Total time spent by the first seven customers is the area in $A(t) - D(t)$ up to time $t_0$.

departed the system by time $t$ contributes $T_i$ to the integral, and thus the integral is simply the total time all customers have spent in the system up to time $t$.

Consider, for now, a time instant $t = t_0$ for which $N(t) = 0$ as in Fig. 12.3, then the integral is exactly given by the sum of the $T_i$ of the first $A(t)$ customers:

$$\langle N \rangle_t = \frac{1}{t} \sum_{i=1}^{A(t)} T_i. \tag{12.5}$$

The average arrival rate up to time $t$ is given by

$$\langle \lambda \rangle_t = \frac{A(t)}{t}. \tag{12.6}$$

If we solve Eq. (12.6) for $t$ and substitute into Eq. (12.5), we obtain

$$\langle N \rangle_t = \langle \lambda \rangle_t \frac{1}{A(t)} \sum_{i=1}^{A(t)} T_i. \tag{12.7}$$

Let $\langle T \rangle_t$ be the average of the times spent in the system by the first $A(t)$ customers, then

$$\langle T \rangle_t = \frac{1}{A(t)} \sum_{i=1}^{A(t)} T_i. \tag{12.8}$$

Comparing Eqs. (12.7) and (12.8), we conclude that

$$\langle N \rangle_t = \langle \lambda \rangle_t \langle T \rangle_t. \tag{12.9}$$

Finally, we assume that as $t \to \infty$, with probability one, the above time averages converge to the expected value of the corresponding steady state random processes, that is,

$$\langle N \rangle_t \to E[N]$$
$$\langle \lambda \rangle_t \to \lambda$$
$$\langle T \rangle_t \to E[T]. \tag{12.10}$$

Equations (12.9) and (12.10) then imply Little's formula:

$$E[N] = \lambda E[T]. \tag{12.11}$$

The restriction of $t$ to instants $t_0$ where $N(t_0) = 0$ is not necessary. The time average of $N(t)$ up to an arbitrary time $t'$ as shown in Fig. 12.3 is given by the average up to time $t_0$ plus a contribution from the interval from $t_0$ to $t'$. If $E[N] < \infty$, then as $t$ becomes large, this contribution becomes negligible.

The assumption of first come, first served service discipline is not necessary. It turns out that Little's formula holds for many service disciplines. See Problem 12.2 for examples. In addition, Little's formula holds for systems with an arbitrary number of servers.

Up to this point we have implicitly assumed that the "system" is the entire queueing system, so $N$ is the number in the queueing system and $T$ is the time spent in the

queueing system. However, Little's formula is so general that it applies to many interpretations of "system." Examples 12.1 and 12.2 show other designations for "system."

---

### Example 12.1    Mean Number in Queue

Let $N_q(t)$ be the number of customers waiting in queue for the server to become available, and
let the random variable $W$ denote the waiting time. If we designate the queue to be the "system,"
then Little's formula becomes

$$E[N_q] = \lambda E[W]. \tag{12.12}$$

---

### Example 12.2    Server Utilization

Let $N_s(t)$ be the number of customers that are being served at time $t$, and let $\tau$ denote the service
time. If we designate the set of servers to be the "system," then Little's formula becomes

$$E[N_s] = \lambda E[\tau]. \tag{12.13}$$

$E[N_s]$ is the average number of busy servers for a system in steady state.

For single-server systems, $N_s(t)$ can only be 0 or 1, so $E[N_s]$ represents the proportion of
time that the server is busy. If $p_0 = P[N(t) = 0]$ denotes the steady state probability that the
system is empty, then we must have that

$$1 - p_0 = E[N_s] = \lambda E[\tau] \tag{12.14}$$

or

$$p_0 = 1 - \lambda E[\tau], \tag{12.15}$$

since $1 - p_0$ is the proportion of time that the server is busy. For this reason, the **utilization of a
single-server system** is defined by

$$\rho = \lambda E[\tau]. \tag{12.16}$$

We similarly define **utilization of a $c$-server system** by

$$\rho = \frac{\lambda E[\tau]}{c}. \tag{12.17}$$

From Eq. (12.13), $\rho$ represents the average fraction of busy servers.

---

## 12.3    THE M/M/1 QUEUE

Consider a single-server system in which customers arrive according to a Poisson process
of rate $\lambda$ so the **interarrival times** are iid exponential random variables with mean $1/\lambda$.
Assume that the service times are iid exponential random variables with mean $1/\mu$, and
that the interarrival and service times are independent. In addition, assume that the system can accommodate an unlimited number of customers. The resulting system is an
M/M/1 queueing system. In this section we find the steady state pmf of $N(t)$, the number
of customers in the system, and the pdf of $T$, the total customer delay in the system.

### 12.3.1   Distribution of Number in the System

The number of customers $N(t)$ in an M/M/1 system is a continuous-time Markov chain. To see why, suppose we are given that $N(t) = k$, and consider the next possible change in the number in the system. The time until the next arrival is an exponential random variable that is independent of the service times of customers already in the system. The memoryless property of the exponential random variable implies that this interarrival time is independent of the present and past history of $N(t)$. If the system is nonempty (i.e., $N(t) > 0$) the time until the next departure is also an exponential random variable. The memoryless property implies that the time until the next departure is independent of the time already spent in service. Thus if we know that $N(t) = k$, then the past history of the system is irrelevant as far as the probabilities of future states are concerned. This is the property required of a Markov chain.

To find the transition rates for $N(t)$, consider the probabilities of the various ways in which $N(t)$ can change.

**(i)** Since $A(t)$, the number of arrivals in an interval of length $t$, is a Poisson process, the probability of one arrival in an interval of length $\delta$ is

$$P[A(\delta) = 1] = \frac{\lambda\delta}{1!}e^{-\lambda\delta} = \lambda\delta\left\{1 - \frac{\lambda\delta}{1!} + \frac{(\lambda\delta)^2}{2!} - \cdots\right\}$$

$$= \lambda\delta + o(\delta). \tag{12.18}$$

**(ii)** Similarly, the probability of more than one arrival is

$$P[A(\delta) \geq 2] = o(\delta). \tag{12.19}$$

**(iii)** Since the service time is an exponential random variable $\tau$, the time a customer has spent in service is independent of how much longer he will remain in service because of the memoryless property of $\tau$. In particular, the probability of a customer in service completing his service in the next $\delta$ seconds is

$$P[\tau \leq \delta] = 1 - e^{-\mu\delta} = \mu\delta + o(\delta). \tag{12.20}$$

**(iv)** Since service times and the arrival process are independent, the probability of one arrival and one departure in an interval of length $\delta$ is

$$P[A(\delta) = 1, \tau \leq \delta] = P[A(\delta) = 1]P[\tau \leq \delta] = o(\delta) \tag{12.21}$$

from Eqs. (12.18) and (12.20). Similarly, the probability of any change that involves more than a single arrival or a single departure is $o(\delta)$.

Properties (i) through (iv) imply that $N(t)$ has the transition rate diagram shown in Fig. 12.4. The global balance equations for the steady state probabilities are

$$\lambda p_0 = \mu p_1$$

$$(\lambda + \mu)p_j = \lambda p_{j-1} + \mu p_{j+1} \qquad j = 1, 2, \ldots. \tag{12.22}$$

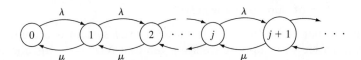

**FIGURE 12.4**
Transition rate diagram for M/M/1 system.

In Example 11.39, we saw that a steady state solution exists when $\rho = \lambda/\mu < 1$:

$$P[N(t) = j] = (1 - \rho)\rho^j \qquad j = 0, 1, 2, \ldots. \tag{12.23}$$

The condition $\rho = \lambda/\mu < 1$ must be met if the system is to be stable in the sense that $N(t)$ does not grow without bound. Since $\mu$ is the maximum rate at which the server can process customers, the condition $\rho < 1$ is equivalent to

$$\text{Arrival rate} = \lambda < \mu = \text{Maximum service rate.} \tag{12.24}$$

If the inequality is violated, we have customers arriving at the system faster than they can be processed and sent out. This is an unstable situation in which the number in the queue will grow steadily without bound.

The mean number of customers in the system is given by

$$E[N] = \sum_{j=0}^{\infty} jP[N(t) = j] = \frac{\rho}{1 - \rho}, \tag{12.25}$$

where we have used the fact that $N$ has a geometric distribution (see Table 3.1).

The mean total customer delay in the system is found from Eq. (12.25) and Little's formula:

$$E[T] = \frac{E[N]}{\lambda} = \frac{\rho/\lambda}{1 - \rho}$$

$$= \frac{1/\mu}{1 - \rho} = \frac{E[\tau]}{1 - \rho} = \frac{1}{\mu - \lambda}. \tag{12.26}$$

The mean waiting time in queue is given by the mean of the total time in the system minus the service time:

$$E[W] = E[T] - E[\tau]$$

$$= \frac{E[\tau]}{1 - \rho} - E[\tau]$$

$$= \frac{\rho}{1 - \rho}E[\tau]. \tag{12.27}$$

Little's formula then gives the mean number in queue:

$$E[N_q] = \lambda E[W]$$

$$= \frac{\rho^2}{1 - \rho}. \tag{12.28}$$

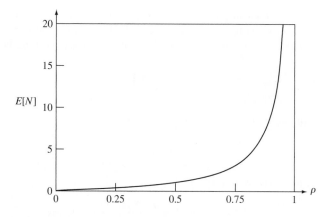

**FIGURE 12.5**
Mean number of customers in the system versus utilization for M/M/1 queue.

The server utilization (defined in Example 12.2) is given by

$$1 - p_0 = 1 - (1 - \rho) = \rho = \frac{\lambda}{\mu}. \tag{12.29}$$

Figures 12.5 and 12.6 show $E[N]$ and $E[T]$ versus $\rho$. It can be seen that as $\rho$ approaches one, the mean number in the system and the system delay become arbitrarily large.

---

### Example 12.3

A router receives packets from a group of users and transmits them over a single transmission line. Suppose that packets arrive according to a Poisson process at a rate of one packet every 4 ms, and suppose that packet transmission times are exponentially distributed with mean 3 ms.

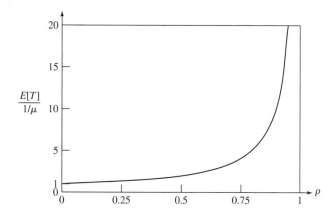

**FIGURE 12.6**
Mean total customer delay versus utilization for M/M/1 system. The delay is expressed in multiples of mean service times.

Find the mean number of packets in the system and the mean total delay in the system. What percentage increase in arrival rate results in a doubling of the above mean total delay?

The arrival rate is 1/4 packets/ms and the mean service time is 3 ms. The utilization is therefore

$$\rho = \frac{1}{4}(3) = \frac{3}{4}.$$

The mean number of packets in the system is then

$$E[N] = \frac{\rho}{1 - \rho} = 3.$$

The mean time in the system is

$$E[T] = \frac{E[N]}{\lambda} = \frac{3}{1/4} = 12 \text{ ms}.$$

The mean time in the system will be doubled to 24 ms when

$$24 = \frac{E[\tau]}{1 - \rho'} = \frac{3}{1 - \rho'}.$$

The resulting utilization is $\rho' = 7/8$ and the corresponding arrival rate is $\lambda' = \rho'\mu = 7/24$. The original arrival rate was 6/24. Thus an increase in arrival rate of $1/6 = 17\%$ leads to a 100% increase in mean system delay.

The point of this example is that *the onset of congestion is swift.* The mean delay increases rapidly once the utilization increases beyond a certain point.

---

### Example 12.4   Concentration and Effect of Scale

A large processor handles transactions at a rate of $K\mu$ transactions per second. Suppose transactions arrive according to a Poisson process of rate $K\lambda$ transactions/second, and that transactions require an exponentially distributed amount of processing time. Suppose that a proposal is made to eliminate the large processor and to replace it with $K$ processors, each with a processing rate of $\mu$ transactions per second and an arrival rate of $\lambda$. Compare the mean delay performance of the existing and the proposed systems.

The large processor system is an M/M/1 queue with arrival rate $K\lambda$, service rate $K\mu$, and utilization $\rho = K\lambda/K\mu = \lambda/\mu$. The mean delay is given by Eq. (12.26):

$$E[T] = \frac{E[\tau]}{1 - \rho} = \frac{1/K\mu}{1 - \rho}.$$

Each of the small processors is an M/M/1 system with arrival rate $\lambda$, service rate $\mu$, and utilization $\rho = \lambda/\mu$. The mean delay is

$$E[T'] = \frac{E[\tau']}{1 - \rho} = \frac{1/\mu}{1 - \rho} = KE[T].$$

Thus, the system with the single large processor with processing rate $K\mu$ has a smaller mean delay than the system with $K$ small processors each of rate $\mu$. In other words, the concentration of customer demand into a single system results in significant delay performance improvement.

### 12.3.2 Delay Distribution in M/M/1 System and Arriving Customer's Distribution

Let $N_a$ denote the number of customers found in the system by a customer arrival. We call $P[N_a = k]$ the **arriving customer's distribution**. We now show that if arrivals are Poisson and independent of the system state and customer service times, then the arriving customer's distribution is equal to the steady state distribution for the number in the system. A customer that arrives at time $t + \delta$ finds $k$ in the system if $N(t) = k$, thus

$$P[N_a(t) = k] = \lim_{\delta \to 0} P[N(t) = k \mid A(t + \delta) - A(t) = 1]$$

$$= \lim_{\delta \to 0} \frac{P[N(t) = k, A(t + \delta) - A(t) = 1]}{P[A(t + \delta) - A(t) = 1]}$$

$$= \lim_{\delta \to 0} \frac{P[A(t + \delta) - A(t) = 1 \mid N(t) = k]P[N(t) = k]}{P[A(t + \delta) - A(t) = 1]},$$

where we have used the definition of conditional probability. The probability of an arrival in the interval $(t, t + \delta]$ is independent of $N(t)$, thus

$$P[N_a(t) = k] = \lim_{\delta \to 0} \frac{P[A(t + \delta) - A(t) = 1]P[N(t) = k]}{P[A(t + \delta) - A(t) = 1]}$$

$$= P[N(t) = k].$$

Thus the probability that $N_a = k$ is simply the proportion of time during which the system has $k$ customers in the system. For the M/M/1 queueing system under consideration we have

$$P[N_a = k] = P[N(t) = k] = (1 - \rho)\rho^k. \tag{12.30}$$

We are now ready to compute the distribution for the total time $T$ that a customer spends in an M/M/1 system. Suppose that an arriving customer finds $k$ in the system, that is, $N_a = k$. If the service discipline is "first come, first served," then $T$ is the residual service time of the customer found in service, the service times of the $k - 1$ customers found in queue, and the service time of the arriving customer. The memoryless property of the exponential service time implies that the residual service time of the customer found in service has the same distribution as a full service time. Thus $T$ is the sum of $k + 1$ iid exponential random variables. In Example 7.5 we saw that this sum has the gamma pdf

$$f_T(x \mid N_a = k) = \frac{(\mu x)^k}{k!} \mu e^{-\mu x} \qquad x > 0. \tag{12.31}$$

The pdf of $T$ is found by averaging over the probability of an arriving customer finding $k$ messages in the system, $P[N_a = k]$. Thus the pdf of $T$ is

$$f_T(x) = \sum_{k=0}^{\infty} \frac{(\mu x)^k}{k!} \mu e^{-\mu x} P[N(t) = k]$$

$$= \sum_{k=0}^{\infty} \frac{(\mu x)^k}{k!} \mu e^{-\mu x} (1 - \rho)\rho^k$$

$$= (1 - \rho)\mu e^{-\mu x} \sum_{k=0}^{\infty} \frac{(\mu \rho x)^k}{k!}$$

$$= (1 - \rho)\mu e^{-\mu x} e^{\mu \rho x}$$

$$= (\mu - \lambda)e^{-(\mu - \lambda)x} \qquad x > 0. \tag{12.32}$$

Thus $T$ is an exponential random variable with mean $1/(\mu - \lambda)$. Note that this is in agreement with Eq. (12.26) for the mean of $T$ obtained through Little's formula.

We can similarly show that the pdf for the waiting time is

$$f_W(x) = (1 - \rho)\delta(x) + \lambda(1 - \rho)e^{-\mu(1-\rho)x} \qquad x > 0. \tag{12.33}$$

---

**Example 12.5**

Find the 95% percentile of the total delay.

The $p$th percentile of $T$ is that value of $x$ for which

$$p = P[T \le x]$$

$$= \int_0^x (\mu - \lambda)e^{-(\mu - \lambda)y} \, dy = 1 - e^{-(\mu - \lambda)x},$$

which yields

$$x = \frac{1}{\mu - \lambda}\ln\frac{1}{1 - p} = -E[T]\ln(1 - p). \tag{12.34}$$

The 95% percentile is obtained by substituting $p = .95$ above. The result is $x = 3.0 \, E[T]$.

---

### 12.3.3 The M/M/1 System with Finite Capacity

Real systems can only accommodate a finite number of customers, but the assumption of infinite capacity is convenient when the probability of having a full system is negligible. Consider the M/M/1/$K$ queueing system that is identical to the M/M/1 system with the exception that it can only hold a maximum of $K$ customers in the system. Customers that arrive when the system is full are turned away.

The process $N(t)$ for this system is a continuous-time Markov chain that takes on values from the set $\{0, 1, \ldots, K\}$ with transition rate diagram as shown in Fig. 12.7. It can be seen that the arrival rate *into* the system is now zero when $N(t) = K$. The transition rates from the other states are the same as for the M/M/1 system.

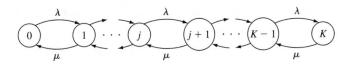

**FIGURE 12.7**
Transition rate diagram for M/M/1/K system.

The global balance equations are now

$$\lambda p_0 = \mu p_1$$

$$(\lambda + \mu)p_j = \lambda p_{j-1} + \mu p_{j+1} \qquad j = 1, 2, \ldots, K - 1$$

$$\mu p_K = \lambda p_{K-1}. \tag{12.35}$$

Let $\rho = \lambda/\mu$. It can be readily shown (see Problem 12.14) that the steady state probabilities are

$$P[N = j] = \frac{(1 - \rho)\rho^j}{1 - \rho^{K+1}} \qquad j = 0, 1, 2, \ldots, K \tag{12.36}$$

for $\rho < 1$ or $\rho > 1$. When $\rho = 1$ all the states are equiprobable. Figure 12.8 shows the steady state probabilities for various values of $\rho$.

The mean number of customers in the system is given by

$$E[N] = \sum_{j=0}^{K} jP[N(t) = j]$$

$$= \begin{cases} \dfrac{\rho}{1 - \rho} - \dfrac{(K + 1)\rho^{K+1}}{1 - \rho^{K+1}} & \text{for } \rho \neq 1 \\[2ex] \dfrac{K}{2} & \text{for } \rho = 1. \end{cases} \tag{12.37}$$

The mean total time spent by customers in the system is found from Eq. (12.37) by using Little's formula with $\lambda_a$, the rate of arrivals that actually enter the system. The proportion of time when the system turns away customers is $P[N(t) = K] = p_K$. Thus the system turns away customers at the rate

$$\lambda_b = \lambda p_K, \tag{12.38}$$

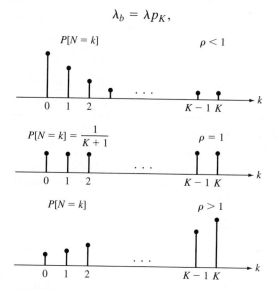

**FIGURE 12.8**
Typical pmf's for $N(t)$ of M/M/1/K system.

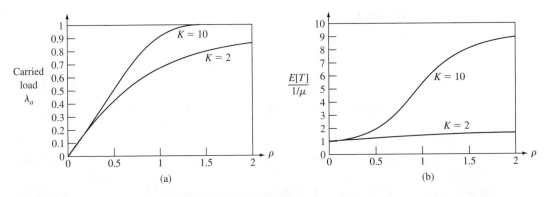

**FIGURE 12.9**
(a) Carried load versus offered load for M/M/1/$K$ system with $K = 2$ and $K = 10$. (b) Mean customer delay versus offered load in M/M/1/$K$ system with $K = 2$ and $K = 10$.

and the actual arrival rate *into* the system is

$$\lambda_a = \lambda(1 - p_K). \tag{12.39}$$

Applying Little's formula to Eq. (12.37) we obtain

$$E[T] = \frac{E[N]}{\lambda_a} = \frac{E[N]}{\lambda(1 - p_K)}. \tag{12.40}$$

In finite-capacity systems, it is necessary to distinguish between the traffic load offered to a system and the actual load carried by the system. The **offered load**, or **traffic intensity**, is a measure of the demand made on the system and is defined as

$$\lambda \frac{\text{customers}}{\text{second}} \times E[\tau] \frac{\text{seconds of service}}{\text{customer}}. \tag{12.41}$$

The **carried load** is the actual demand met by the system:

$$\lambda_a \frac{\text{customers}}{\text{second}} \times E[\tau] \frac{\text{seconds of service}}{\text{customer}}. \tag{12.42}$$

---

### Example 12.6    Mean Delay and Carried Load Versus $K$

Figure 12.9(a) gives a comparison of the carried load versus the offered load $\rho$ for two values of $K$. It can be seen that increasing the capacity $K$ results in an increase in carried load since more customers are allowed into the system. Figure 12.9(b) gives the corresponding values for the mean delay. We see that increasing $K$ results in increased delays, again because more customers are allowed into the system.

---

### Example 12.7

Suppose that an M/M/1 model is used for a system that has capacity $K$, and that the probability of rejecting customers is approximated by $P[N = K]$. Compare this approximation to the exact probability given by the M/M/1/$K$ model.

For the M/M/1 system the above probability is given by

$$P[N = K] = (1 - \rho)\rho^K.$$

For $\rho < 1$, the probability of rejecting a customer in the M/M/1/K system is

$$P[N' = K] = \frac{(1 - \rho)\rho^K}{1 - \rho^{K+1}} = (1 - \rho)\rho^K\{1 + \rho^{K+1} + (\rho^{K+1})^2 + \cdots\}.$$

For $\rho < 1$ and $K$ large, $P[N = k] \simeq P[N' = K]$. For $\rho > 1$, the M/M/1 approximation breaks down and gives a negative probability.

## 12.4    MULTI SERVER SYSTEMS: M/M/c, M/M/c/c, AND M/M/∞

We now modify the M/M/1 system to consider queueing systems with multiple servers. In particular, we consider systems with iid exponential interarrival times and iid exponential service times. As in the case of the M/M/1 system, the resulting systems can be modeled by continuous-time Markov chains.

### 12.4.1    Distribution of Number in the M/M/c System

The transition rate diagram for an M/M/c system is shown in Fig. 12.10. As before, arrivals occur at a rate $\lambda$. The difference now is that the departure rate is $k\mu$ when $k$ servers are busy. To see why, suppose that $k$ of the servers are busy, then the time until the next departure is given by

$$X = \min(\tau_1, \tau_2, \ldots, \tau_k),$$

where $\tau_i$ are iid exponential random variables with parameter $\mu$. The complementary cdf of this random variable is

$$\begin{aligned}
P[X > t] &= P[\min(\tau_1, \tau_2, \ldots, \tau_k) > t] \\
&= P[\tau_1 > t, \tau_2 > t, \ldots, \tau_k > t] \\
&= P[\tau_1 > t]P[\tau_2 > t] \ldots P[\tau_k > t] \\
&= e^{-\mu t}e^{-\mu t} \ldots e^{-\mu t} \\
&= e^{-k\mu t}.
\end{aligned} \tag{12.43}$$

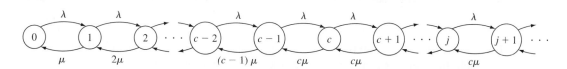

**FIGURE 12.10**
Transition rate diagram for M/M/c system.

Thus the time until the next departure is an exponential random variable with mean $1/k\mu$. So when $k$ servers are busy, customers depart at rate $k\mu$. When the number of customers in the system is greater than $c$, all $c$ servers are busy and the departure rate is $c\mu$.

We obtain the steady state probabilities for the M/M/c system from the general solution for birth-and-death processes found in Example 11.40. The probabilities of the first $c$ states are obtained from the following recursion (see Eq. 11.45):

$$p_j = \frac{\lambda}{j\mu} p_{j-1} \qquad j = 1, \ldots, c,$$

which leads to

$$p_j = \frac{a^j}{j!} p_0 \qquad j = 0, 1, \ldots, c, \tag{12.44}$$

where

$$a = \frac{\lambda}{\mu}. \tag{12.45}$$

The probabilities for states equal to or greater than $c$ are obtained from the following recursion:

$$p_j = \frac{\lambda}{c\mu} p_{j-1} \qquad j = c, c+1, c+2, \ldots,$$

which leads to

$$p_j = \rho^{j-c} p_c \qquad j = c, c+1, c+2, \ldots \tag{12.46a}$$

$$= \frac{\rho^{j-c} a^c}{c!} p_0, \tag{12.46b}$$

where we have used Eq. (12.44) with $j = c$ and where

$$\rho = \frac{\lambda}{c\mu}. \tag{12.47}$$

Finally $p_0$ is obtained from the normalization condition:

$$1 = \sum_{j=0}^{\infty} p_j = p_0 \left\{ \sum_{j=0}^{c-1} \frac{a^j}{j!} + \frac{a^c}{c!} \sum_{j=c}^{\infty} \rho^{j-c} \right\}.$$

The system is stable and has a steady state if the term inside the brackets is finite. This is the case if the second series converges, which in turn requires that $\rho < 1$, or equivalently,

$$\lambda < c\mu. \tag{12.48}$$

In other words, the system is stable if the customer arrival rate is less than the total rate at which the $c$ servers can process customers. The final form for $p_0$ is

$$p_0 = \left\{ \sum_{j=0}^{c-1} \frac{a^j}{j!} + \frac{a^c}{c!} \frac{1}{1-\rho} \right\}^{-1}. \tag{12.49}$$

The probability that an arriving customer finds all servers busy and has to wait in queue is an important parameter of the M/M/c system:

$$P[W > 0] = P[N \geq c] = \sum_{j=c}^{\infty} \rho^{j-c} p_c = \frac{p_c}{1 - \rho}. \qquad (12.50)$$

This probability is called the **Erlang C formula** and is denoted by $C(c, a)$:

$$C(c, a) = \frac{p_c}{1 - \rho} = P[W > 0]. \qquad (12.51)$$

The mean number of customers in queue is given by

$$E[N_q] = \sum_{j=c}^{\infty} (j - c)\rho^{j-c} p_c = p_c \sum_{j'=0}^{\infty} j' \rho^{j'}$$

$$= \frac{\rho}{(1 - \rho)^2} p_c$$

$$= \frac{\rho}{1 - \rho} C(c, a). \qquad (12.52)$$

The mean waiting time is found from Little's formula:

$$E[W] = \frac{E[N_q]}{\lambda}$$

$$= \frac{1/\mu}{c(1 - \rho)} C(c, a). \qquad (12.53)$$

The mean total time in the system is

$$E[T] = E[W] + E[\tau] = E[W] + \frac{1}{\mu}. \qquad (12.54)$$

Finally, the mean number in the system is found from Little's formula:

$$E[N] = \lambda E[T] = E[N_q] + a, \qquad (12.55)$$

where we have used Equation (12.54).

---

### Example 12.8

A company has two 1 Megabit/second lines connecting two of its sites. Suppose that packets for these lines arrive according to a Poisson process at a rate of 150 packets per second, and that packets are exponentially distributed with mean 10 kbits. When both lines are busy, the system queues the packets and transmits them on the first available line. Find the probability that a packet has to wait in queue.

First we need to compute $p_0$. The system parameters are $c = 2$, $\lambda = 150$ packets/sec, $1/\mu = 10$ kbit/1 Mbit/s $= 10$ ms, $a = \lambda/\mu = 1.5$ and $\rho = \lambda/c\mu = 3/4$. Therefore:

$$p_0 = \left\{ 1 + 1.5 + \frac{(1.5)^2}{2!} \frac{1}{1 - 3/4} \right\}^{-1} = \frac{1}{7}.$$

The probability of having to wait is then

$$C(2, 1.5) = \frac{(1.5)^2}{2!} p_0 \frac{1}{1 - \rho} = \frac{9}{14}.$$

### Example 12.9   M/M/1 Versus M/M/c

Compare the mean delay and mean waiting time performance of the two systems shown in Fig. 12.11. Note that both systems have the same processing rate.

For the M/M/1 system, $\rho = \lambda/\mu = (1/2)/1 = 1/2$, so the mean waiting time is

$$E[W] = \frac{\rho/\mu}{1 - \rho} = 1 \text{ s},$$

and the mean total delay is

$$E[T] = \frac{1/\mu}{1 - \rho} = 2 \text{ s}.$$

For the M/M/2 system, $a = \lambda/\mu' = 1$, and $\rho = \lambda/2\mu' = 1/2$. The probability of an empty system is

$$p_0 = \left\{ 1 + a + \frac{a^2/2}{1 - 1/2} \right\}^{-1} = \frac{1}{3}.$$

The Erlang $C$ formula is

$$C(2, 1) = \frac{a^2/2}{1 - \rho} p_0 = \frac{1}{3}.$$

System 1: M/M/1

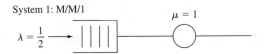

System 2: M/M/2

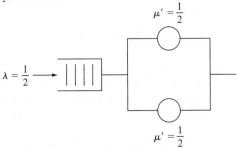

**FIGURE 12.11**
M/M/1 and M/M/2 systems with the same arrival rate and the same maximum processing rate.

The mean waiting time is then

$$E[W'] = \frac{1/\mu'}{2(1-\rho)}C(2,1) = \frac{2}{3},$$

and the mean delay is

$$E[T'] = \frac{2}{3} + \frac{1}{\mu'} = \frac{8}{3}.$$

Thus the M/M/1 system has a smaller total delay but a larger waiting time than the M/M/2. In general, increasing the number of servers decreases the waiting time but increases the total delay.

---

### 12.4.2  Waiting Time Distribution for M/M/c

Before we compute the pdf of the waiting time, consider the conditional probability that there are $j - c > 0$ customers in queue given that all servers are busy (i.e., $N(t) \geq c$):

$$P[N(t) = j \,|\, N(t) \geq c] = \frac{P[N(t) = j, N(t) \geq c]}{P[N(t) \geq c]} = \frac{P[N(t) = j]}{P[N(t) \geq c]} \qquad j \geq c$$

$$= \frac{\rho^{j-c}p_c}{p_c/(1-\rho)} = (1 - \rho)\rho^{j-c} \qquad j \geq c. \tag{12.56}$$

This geometric pmf suggests that when all the servers are busy, the M/M/c system behaves like an M/M/1 system. We use this fact to compute the cdf of $W$.

Suppose that a customer arrives when there are $k$ customers in queue. There must be $k + 1$ service completions before our customer enters service. From Eq. (12.43), each service completion is exponentially distributed with rate $c\mu$. Thus the waiting time for our customer is the sum of $k + 1$ iid exponential random variables with parameter $c\mu$, which we know is a gamma random variable with parameter $c\mu$:

$$f_W(x \,|\, N = c + k) = \frac{(c\mu x)^k}{k!}c\mu e^{-c\mu x}. \tag{12.57}$$

The cdf for $W$ given that $W > 0$, or equivalently $N \geq c$, is obtained by combining Eqs. (12.56) and (12.57):

$$F_W(x \,|\, W > 0) = \sum_{k=0}^{\infty} F_W(x \,|\, N = c + k)P[N = c + k \,|\, N \geq c]$$

$$= \sum_{k=0}^{\infty} \int_0^x \frac{(c\mu y)^k}{k!}c\mu e^{-c\mu y}\,dy(1-\rho)\rho^k$$

$$= (1-\rho)\int_0^x \sum_{k=0}^{\infty} \frac{(c\mu y)^k}{k!}\rho^k c\mu e^{-c\mu y}\,dy$$

$$= (1-\rho)c\mu \int_0^x e^{-c\mu(1-\rho)y}\,dy$$

$$= 1 - e^{-c\mu(1-\rho)x}.$$

The cdf of $W$ is then

$$P[W \le x] = P[W = 0] + F_W(x \mid W > 0)P[W > 0] \qquad x > 0$$
$$= (1 - C(c, a)) + (1 - e^{-c\mu(1-\rho)x})C(c, a)$$
$$= 1 - C(c, a)e^{-c\mu(1-\rho)x}. \tag{12.58}$$

Since $T = W + \tau$, where $W$ and $\tau$ are independent random variables, it is easy to show that if $a \ne c - 1$, the cdf of $T$ is

$$P[T \le x] = 1 + \frac{a - c + P[W = 0]}{c - 1 - a}e^{-\mu x} + \frac{C(c, a)}{c - 1 - a}e^{-c\mu(1-\rho)x}. \tag{12.59}$$

### Example 12.10

What is the probability that a packet has to wait more than one minute in the system discussed in Example 12.8?

In Example 12.8 we found that $p_0 = 1/7$ and that the probability of having to wait is

$$C(2, 1.5) = \frac{9}{14}.$$

The probability of having to wait more than one minute is

$$P[W > 1] = 1 - P[W \le 1]$$
$$= C(c, a)e^{-c\mu(1-\rho)1} = \frac{9}{14}e^{-200(1/4)(0.040)}$$
$$= \frac{9}{14}e^{-2} = 0.3045.$$

### 12.4.3 The M/M/c/c Queueing System

The M/M/$c$/$c$ queueing system has $c$ servers but no waiting room. Customers that arrive when all servers are busy are turned away. The transition rate diagram for this system is shown in Fig. 12.12, where it can be seen that the arrival rate is zero when $N(t) = c$.

The steady state probabilities for this system have the same form as those for states $0, \ldots, c$ in the M/M/$c$ system:

$$p_j = \frac{a^j}{j!}p_0 \qquad j = 0, \ldots, c, \tag{12.60}$$

where

$$a = \frac{\lambda}{\mu} \tag{12.61}$$

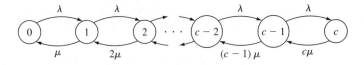

**FIGURE 12.12**
Transition rate diagram for M/M/c/c system.

is the offered load and

$$p_0 = \left\{ \sum_{j=0}^{c} \frac{a^j}{j!} \right\}^{-1}. \tag{12.62}$$

The **Erlang $B$ formula** is defined as the probability that all servers are busy:

$$B(c, a) = P[N = c] = p_c = \frac{a^c/c!}{1 + a + a^2/2! + \cdots + a^c/c!}. \tag{12.63}$$

The actual arrival rate *into* the system is then

$$\lambda_a = \lambda(1 - B(c, a)). \tag{12.64}$$

The average number in the system is obtained from Little's formula:

$$E[N] = \lambda_a E[\tau] = \frac{\lambda}{\mu}(1 - B(c, a)). \tag{12.65}$$

Note that $E[N]$ is also equal to the carried load as defined by Eq. (12.42).

The Erlang $B$ formula depends only on the arrival rate $\lambda$, the mean service time $E[\tau] = 1/\mu$, and the number of servers $c$. It turns out that Eq. (12.63) also gives the probability of blocking for M/G/$c$/$c$ systems (see Ross, 1983).

---

### Example 12.11

A company has five 1 Megabit per second lines to carry videoconferences between two company sites. Suppose that each videoconference requires 1 Mbps and lasts for an average of 1 hour. Assume that requests for videoconferences arrive according to a Poisson process with rate 3 calls per hour. Find the probability that a call request is blocked due to lack of lines.

The offered load is $a = \lambda/\mu = 3$ calls/hr $\times$ 1 hr/call = 3. The blocking probability is then:

$$B(5, 3) = \frac{3^5/5!}{1 + 3 + 9/2 + 27/6 + 81/24 + 243/120} = 0.11.$$

---

### The M/M/∞ Queueing System

Consider a system with Poisson arrivals and exponential service times, and suppose that the number of servers is so large that arriving customers always find a server available. In effect we have a system with an infinite number of servers. If we allow $c$ to approach infinity for the M/M/$c$/$c$ system, we obtain the M/M/∞ system with the transition rate diagram shown in Fig. 12.13.

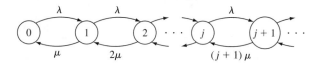

**FIGURE 12.13**
Transition rate diagram for M/M/∞ system.

The steady state probabilities are also found by letting $c$ approach infinity in the equations for the M/M/$c$/$c$ system:

$$p_j = \frac{a^j}{j!}e^{-a} \qquad j = 0, 1, 2, \ldots, \tag{12.66}$$

where $a = \lambda/\mu$. Thus the number of customers in the system is a Poisson random variable. The mean number of customers in the system is

$$E[N] = a.$$

---

**Example 12.12**

Subscribers connect to a university's online catalog at a rate of 4 subscribers per minute. Sessions have an average duration of 5 minutes. Find the probability that there are more than 25 users online.

The offered load is $a = \lambda/\mu = 4$ subscribers/minute $\times$ 5 minutes/subscriber $= 20$. The pmf for the number of users connected is a Poisson random variable with mean 20. The probability that there are more than 25 in the system is:

$$P[N > 25] = 1 - \sum_{j=0}^{25}\frac{25^j}{j!}e^{-25} = 0.888$$

where we used the Octave function poisson_cdf(25,20).

---

## 12.5 FINITE-SOURCE QUEUEING SYSTEMS

Consider a single-server queueing system that serves $K$ sources as shown in Fig. 12.14(a). Each source can be in one of two states: In the first state, the source is preparing a request for service from the server; in the second state, the source has generated a request that is either waiting in queue or being served. For example, the sources could represent $K$ machines and the server could represent a repairman who repairs machines when they break down. In another example, the $K$ sources could represent clients that generate queries for a Web server as shown in Fig. 12.14(b).

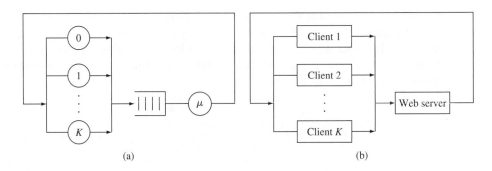

(a) (b)

**FIGURE 12.14**
(a) A finite-source single-server system. (b) A multi-user computer system.

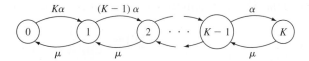

**FIGURE 12.15**
Transition rate diagram for a finite-source single-server system.

Let $N(t)$ be the number of requests in the system. We assume that each source spends an exponentially distributed amount of time with mean $1/\alpha$ preparing each service request. Thus when idle, a source generates a request for service in the interval $(t, t + \delta)$ with probability $\alpha\delta + o(\delta)$. If the state of the system is $N(t) = k$, then the number of idle sources is $K - k$, so the rate at which service requests are generated is $(K - k)\alpha$. We also assume that the time required to service each request is an exponentially distributed amount of time with mean $1/\mu$. $N(t)$ is then the continuous-time Markov chain with the transition rate diagram shown in Fig. 12.15.

The steady state probabilities are found using the results obtained in Example 11.40:

$$p_k = \frac{K!}{(K - k)!}\left(\frac{\alpha}{\mu}\right)^k p_0 \qquad k = 0, 1, \ldots, K, \tag{12.67}$$

where

$$p_0 = \left\{ \sum_{k=0}^{K} \frac{K!}{(K - k)!}\left(\frac{\alpha}{\mu}\right)^k \right\}^{-1}. \tag{12.68}$$

We first compute the mean arrival rate $\lambda$ and the mean delay $E[T]$ indirectly. In the last part of the section we show how they can be calculated directly. The server utilization $\rho$ is the proportion of time when the system is busy, thus

$$\rho = 1 - p_0, \tag{12.69}$$

where $p_0$ is given by Eq. (12.68). The mean arrival rate to the queue can then be found from Little's formula with "system" defined as the server:

$$\lambda E[\tau] = \rho = 1 - p_0,$$

which implies

$$\lambda = \frac{\rho}{E[\tau]} = \mu\rho = \mu(1 - p_0). \tag{12.70}$$

A source takes an average time of $1/\alpha$ to generate a request and then spends time $E[T]$ having it serviced in the queueing system. Thus each source generates a request at the rate $(1/\alpha + E[T])^{-1}$ requests per second. Since the actual arrival rate must equal the rate at which the $K$ sources generate requests, we have

$$\lambda = \frac{K}{1/\alpha + E[T]}. \tag{12.71}$$

The mean delay in the system for each request is found by solving for $E[T]$:

$$E[T] = \frac{K}{\lambda} - \frac{1}{\alpha}. \tag{12.72}$$

Finally, we can apply Little's formula to Eq. (12.72) to obtain the mean number in the system:

$$E[N] = \lambda E[T] = K - \frac{\lambda}{\alpha}. \tag{12.73}$$

Note that this implies that $\lambda/\alpha$ is the mean number of idle sources. The mean waiting time is obtained by subtracting the mean service time from $E[T]$:

$$E[W] = E[T] - \frac{1}{\mu}. \tag{12.74}$$

The proportion of time that a source spends waiting for the completion of a service request is the ratio of the time spent in the system to the mean cycle time:

$$P[\text{source busy}] = \frac{E[T]}{E[T] + 1/\alpha}. \tag{12.75}$$

---

**Example 12.13    Web Server System**

Some Web server designs place a limit $K$ on the number of clients that can interact with it at any given time. The set of $K$ clients generate queries to the Web server as follows. Each client spends an exponentially distributed "think" time preparing a transaction request, and the server takes an exponentially distributed time processing each request. The "throughput" of the server is defined as the rate at which it completes transactions. The response time is the total time a transaction spends in the server. Find expressions for the throughput and response time for two extreme cases: $K$ small and $K$ large.

When $K$ is sufficiently small, there is no waiting in queue, so

$$E[T] \simeq \frac{1}{\mu} \qquad \text{for } K \text{ small,} \tag{12.76}$$

and by Eq. (12.71),

$$\lambda = \frac{K}{1/\alpha + 1/\mu} \qquad \text{for } K \text{ small.} \tag{12.77}$$

Thus $\lambda$ grows linearly with $K$. As $K$ increases, the server eventually becomes fully utilized, and then answers queries at its maximum rate, namely $\mu$ transactions per second. Thus

$$\lambda \simeq \mu \qquad \text{for } K \text{ large,} \tag{12.78}$$

and Eq. (12.72) becomes

$$E[T] = \frac{K}{\mu} - \frac{1}{\alpha} \qquad \text{for } K \text{ large.} \tag{12.79}$$

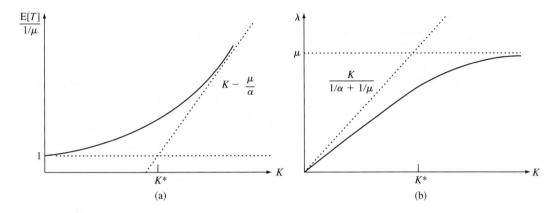

**FIGURE 12.16**
Delay and throughput for finite-source system as a function of number of sources. Dashed lines show small-*K* and large-*K* asymptotes.

These asymptotic expressions for the throughput and response time are shown in Fig. 12.16(a) and (b). The value of $K$ where the two asymptotes for $E[T]$ intersect is called the *system saturation point*,

$$K^* = \frac{1/\mu + 1/\alpha}{1/\mu}. \tag{12.80}$$

When $K$ becomes larger than $K^*$, the queries from different clients are certain to interfere with one another and the response time increases accordingly.

### 12.5.1   *Arriving Customer's Distribution

In the above discussion, we found $\lambda$, $E[N]$, and $E[T]$ in a roundabout way (see Eqs. 12.70, 12.71, and 12.72). To calculate $E[T]$ directly, we argue as follows. If we assume a first-come, first-served service discipline, then a customer who arrives when there are $N_a = k$ requests in the queueing system spends a total time in the system equal to the sum of 1 residual service time, $k - 1$ service times, and the customer's own service time. Since all of these times are iid exponential random variables with mean $1/\mu$, the mean time in the system for our request is

$$E[T \mid N_a = k] = \frac{k + 1}{\mu}.$$

The mean time in the system is then found by averaging over $N_a$:

$$E[T] = \frac{1}{\mu} \sum_{k=0}^{K-1} (k + 1) P[N_a = k]. \tag{12.81}$$

The difficulty with the above equation is that arrivals are not Poisson—remember that the arrival rate is $(K - N(t))\alpha$, and thus depends on the state of the system. Consequently, the distribution of states seen by an arriving customer is not the same as

$P[N = k]$, the proportion of time that there are $k$ requests in the queueing system. For example, a service request cannot be generated when all sources have requests in the system, that is, $N(t) = K$, so $P[N_a = K] = 0$. However, $P[N = K]$ is nonzero since it is possible for all sources to have requests in the queueing system simultaneously.

To find $P[N_a = k]$ we need to find the long-term proportion of time that arriving customers find $k$ customers in the system. Since $p_k = P[N(t) = k]$ is the long-term proportion of time the system is in state $k$, then in a very long time interval of duration $T'$ approximately $p_k T'$ seconds are spent in state $k$. The arrival rate when $N(t) = k$ is $(K - k)\alpha$ requests per second, so the number of arrivals that find $k$ requests is approximately

$$(K - k)\alpha \text{ customers/second} \times p_k T' \text{ seconds in state } k. \tag{12.82}$$

The total number of arrivals in time $T'$ is obtained by summing over all states:

$$\sum_{j=0}^{K} (K - j)\alpha p_j T'. \tag{12.83}$$

Thus *the proportion of arrivals that find k requests in the system is*

$$
\begin{aligned}
P[N_a = k] &= \frac{(K - k)\alpha p_k T'}{\sum\limits_{j=0}^{K}(K - j)\alpha p_j T'} = \frac{(K - k)p_k}{\sum\limits_{j=0}^{K}(K - j)p_j} \\[2mm]
&= \frac{(K - k)[K!/(K - k)!](\alpha/\mu)^k p_0}{\sum\limits_{j=0}^{K}(K - j)[K!/(K - j)!](\alpha/\mu)^j p_0} \\[2mm]
&= \frac{[(K - 1)!/(K - k - 1)!](\alpha/\mu)^k}{\sum\limits_{j=0}^{K-1}[(K - 1)!/(K - j - 1)!](\alpha/\mu)^j} \quad 0 \le k \le K - 1. \tag{12.84}
\end{aligned}
$$

If we compare Eq. (12.84) with Eq. (12.67), we see that Eq. (12.84) is the steady state probability of having $k$ customers in a system with $K - 1$ sources. In other words, *a source when placing a request "sees" a queueing system that behaves as if the source were not present at all!*

We leave it up to you in Problem 12.37 to show that Eqs. (12.84) and (12.81) give $E[T]$ as given in Eq. (12.72). Indeed, this same approach can be used to find the pdf of $T$.

## 12.6    M/G/1 QUEUEING SYSTEMS

We now consider single-server queueing systems in which the arrivals follow a Poisson process but in which the service times need not be exponentially distributed. We assume that the service times are independent, identically distributed random variables with general pdf $f_\tau(x)$. The resulting queueing system is denoted by M/G/1.

The number of customers $N(t)$ in an M/G/1 system is a continuous-time random process. Recall that the "state" of the system is the information about the past history

**FIGURE 12.17**
Sequence of service times and a residual service time.

of the system that is relevant to the probabilities of future events. In the preceding sections, customer interarrival times and service times were exponential distributions, so $N(t)$ was always the state of the system. This is no longer the case for M/G/1 systems. For example, if service times are constant, then knowledge about when a customer began service specifies the customer's future departure time. Thus the state of an M/G/1 system at time $t$ is specified by $N(t)$ together with the remaining ("residual") service time of the customer being served at time $t$.

In this section we present a simple approach based on Little's formula that gives the mean waiting time and mean delay in an M/G/1 system. We also use this simple approach to find the mean waiting times in M/G/1 systems that have priority classes.

### 12.6.1    The Residual Service Time

Suppose that an arriving customer finds the server busy, and consider the residual time of the customer found in service. Let $\tau_1, \tau_2, \ldots$ be the iid sequence of service times of customers in this M/G/1 system, and suppose we divide the positive time axis into segments of length $\tau_1, \tau_2, \ldots$ as shown in Fig. 12.17. We can then view customers who arrive when the server is busy as picking a point at random on this time axis. The **residual service time** is then the remainder of time in the segment that is intercepted as shown in Fig. 12.17.

In Example 7.21 we showed that the long-term proportion of time that the residual service time exceeds $x$ is given by

$$\frac{1}{E[\tau]} \int_x^{\infty} (1 - F_{\tau}(y)) \, dy. \tag{12.85}$$

Since the arrival times of Poisson customers are independent of the system state, Eq. (12.85) is also the probability that the residual service time $R$ of a customer found in service exceeds $x$, that is,

$$P[R > x] = \frac{1}{E[\tau]} \int_x^{\infty} (1 - F_{\tau}(y)) \, dy. \tag{12.86}$$

The pdf of $R$ is then

$$f_R(x) = -\frac{d}{dx} P[R > x] = \frac{1 - F_{\tau}(x)}{E[\tau]}. \tag{12.87}$$

The mean residual time is

$$E[R] = \int_0^{\infty} x \frac{1 - F_{\tau}(x)}{P[\tau]} \, dx.$$

Integrating by parts with $u = (1 - F_\tau(x))/E[\tau]$ and $dv = x\,dx$, we obtain

$$E[R] = (1 - F_\tau(x))\frac{x^2}{2E[\tau]}\Big|_0^\infty + \frac{1}{2E[\tau]}\int_0^\infty x^2 f_\tau(x)\,dx$$

$$= \frac{E[\tau^2]}{2E[\tau]}. \tag{12.88}$$

---

### Example 12.14

Compare the residual service times of two systems with exponential service times of mean $m$ and constant service times of mean $m$, respectively.

For an exponential service time of mean $m$, the second moment is $2m^2$, thus the mean residual service time is, from Eq. (12.88),

$$E[R_{\text{exp}}] = \frac{2m^2}{2m} = m.$$

Thus the mean residual time is the same as the full service time of a customer. This is consistent with the memoryless property of the exponential random variable.

The second moment of a constant random variable of value $m$ is $m^2$. Thus the mean residual service time is

$$E[R_{\text{const}}] = \frac{m^2}{2m} = \frac{m}{2},$$

which is what one would expect; on the average we expect to wait half a service time.

---

### 12.6.2 Mean Delay in M/G/1 Systems

Consider the time $W$ spent by a customer waiting for service in an M/G/1 system. If the service discipline is first come, first served, then $W$ is the sum of the residual service time $R'$ of the customer (if any) found in service and the $N_q(t) = k - 1$ service times of the customers (if any) found in queue. Thus the mean waiting time is then

$$E[W] = E[R'] + E[N_q(t)]E[\tau], \tag{12.89}$$

since the service times are iid with mean $E[\tau]$ (see Eq. 7.13). From Little's formula we have that $E[N_q(t)] = \lambda E[W]$, so

$$E[W] = E[R'] + \lambda E[W]E[\tau] = E[R'] + \rho E[W]. \tag{12.90}$$

The residual service time $R'$ encountered by an arriving customer is zero when the system is found empty, and $R$, as defined in the previous section, when a customer is found in service. Thus

$$E[R'] = 0P[N(t) = 0] + E[R](1 - P[N(t) = 0])$$

$$= \frac{E[\tau^2]}{2E[\tau]}\lambda E[\tau]$$

$$= \frac{\lambda E[\tau^2]}{2}, \tag{12.91}$$

where we have used Eq. (12.88) for $E[R]$ and Eq. (12.14) for the fact that $1 - P[N(t) = 0] = \rho = \lambda E[\tau]$.

The **mean waiting time $E[W]$** of a customer in an M/G/1 system is found by substituting Eq. (12.91) into Eq. (12.90) and solving for $E[W]$:

$$E[W] = \frac{\lambda E[\tau^2]}{2(1 - \rho)}. \tag{12.92}$$

We can obtain another expression for $E[W]$ by noting that $E[\tau^2] = \sigma_\tau^2 + E[\tau]^2$:

$$E[W] = \frac{\lambda(\sigma_\tau^2 + E[\tau]^2)}{2(1 - \rho)} = \lambda E[\tau]^2 \frac{(1 + C_\tau^2)}{2(1 - \rho)}$$

$$= \frac{\rho(1 + C_\tau^2)}{2(1 - \rho)} E[\tau], \tag{12.93}$$

where $C_\tau^2 = \sigma_\tau^2 / E[\tau]^2$ is the coefficient of variation of the service time. Equation (12.93) is called the **Pollaczek–Khinchin mean value formula**.

The **mean delay $E[T]$** is found by adding the mean service time to $E[W]$:

$$E[T] = E[\tau] + E[\tau] \frac{\rho(1 + C_\tau^2)}{2(1 - \rho)}. \tag{12.94}$$

From Eqs. (12.93) and (12.94) we can see that the mean waiting time and mean delay time are affected not only by the mean service time and the server utilization but also by the coefficient of variation of the service time. Thus the degree of randomness of the service times as measured by $C_\tau^2$ affects these delays.[1]

---

### Example 12.15

Compare $E[W]$ for the M/M/1 and M/D/1 systems. The second moments of the exponential and constant random variables were found in Example 12.14. The exponential service time has a coefficient of variation equal to one. Thus Eq. (12.93) implies

$$E[W_{M/M/1}] = \frac{\rho}{(1 - \rho)} E[\tau]. \tag{12.95}$$

The constant service time has zero variance, so its coefficient of variation is zero. Thus

$$E[W_{M/D/1}] = \frac{\rho}{2(1 - \rho)} E[\tau]. \tag{12.96}$$

Thus we see that the waiting time in an M/D/1 is half that in an M/M/1 system.

---

[1]On the other hand, it is rather surprising that only the first two moments of the distribution of the service time affect $E[W]$ and $E[T]$.

### 12.6.3   Mean Delay in M/G/1 Systems with Priority Service Discipline

Consider a queueing system that handles $K$ priority classes of customers. Type $k$ customers arrive according to a Poisson process of rate $\lambda_k$ and have service times with pdf $f_{\tau_k}(x)$ and mean $E[\tau_k]$. A separate queue is kept for each priority class, and each time the server becomes available it selects the next customer from the highest-priority nonempty queue. This service discipline is often referred to as **"head-of-line priority service."** We assume that customers cannot be preempted once their service has begun.

The server utilization from type $k$ customers is

$$\rho_k = \lambda_k E[\tau_k].$$

We assume that the total server utilization is less than 1:

$$\rho = \rho_1 + \cdots + \rho_K < 1. \tag{12.97}$$

If this is not the case, one or more of the lower-priority queues become unstable, that is, grow without bound.

Consider the mean waiting time $W_1$ of the highest-priority (type 1) customer. If an arriving type 1 customer finds $N_{q_1}(t) = k_1$ type 1 customers in queue and if the service discipline is first come, first served within each class, then $W_1$ is the sum of the residual service time $R''$ of the customer (if any) found in service and the $N_{q_1}(t) = k_1$ service times of the type 1 customers (if any) found in queue. Thus

$$E[W_1] = E[R''] + E[N_{q_1}]E[\tau_1].$$

Following the same development that followed Eq. (12.89) in the previous section, we arrive at the following expression for the **mean waiting time for type 1 customers**:

$$E[W_1] = \frac{E[R'']}{1 - \rho_1}. \tag{12.98}$$

If an arriving type 2 customer finds $N_{q_1}(t) = k_1$ type 1 and $N_{q_2}(t) = k_2$ type 2 customers waiting in queue, then $W_2$ is the sum of the residual service time $R''$ of the customer (if any) found in service, the $k_1$ service times of the type 1 customers (if any) found in queue, the service times of the $k_2$ type 2 customers found in queue, *and* the service times of the higher-priority type 1 customers who arrive while our customer is waiting in queue. Thus

$$E[W_2] = E[R''] + E[N_{q_1}]E[\tau_1] + E[N_{q_2}]E[\tau_2] + E[M_1]E[\tau_1], \tag{12.99}$$

where $M_1$ denotes the number of type 1 arrivals during our customer's waiting time. By Little's formula we have $E[N_{q_1}] = \lambda_1 E[W_1]$ and $E[N_{q_2}] = \lambda_2 E[W_2]$. In addition, the mean number of type 1 arrivals during $E[W_2]$ seconds is $E[M_1] = \lambda_1 E[W_2]$. Substituting these expressions in Eq. (12.99) gives

$$E[W_2] = E[R''] + \rho_1 E[W_1] + \rho_2 E[W_2] + \rho_1 E[W_2].$$

Solving for $E[W_2]$,

$$E[W_2] = \frac{E[R''] + \rho_1 E[W_1]}{1 - \rho_1 - \rho_2}$$

$$= \frac{E[R'']}{(1 - \rho_1)(1 - \rho_1 - \rho_2)}, \qquad (12.100)$$

where we have used Eq. (12.98) for $E[W_1]$.

If there are more than two classes of customers, the above method can be used to show that the mean waiting time for a type $k$ customer is

$$E[W_k] = \frac{E[R'']}{(1 - \rho_1 - \cdots - \rho_{k-1})(1 - \rho_1 - \cdots - \rho_k)}. \qquad (12.101)$$

The customer found in service by an arriving customer can be of any type, so $R''$ is the residual service time of customers of all types:

$$E[R''] = \frac{\lambda E[\tau^2]}{2}, \qquad (12.102)$$

where $\lambda$ is the total arrival rate,

$$\lambda = \lambda_1 + \cdots + \lambda_K, \qquad (12.103)$$

and $E[\tau^2]$ is the second moment of the service time of customers of all types. The fraction of customers who are type $k$ is $\lambda_k/\lambda$, thus

$$E[\tau^2] = \frac{\lambda_1}{\lambda} E[\tau_1^2] + \cdots + \frac{\lambda_K}{\lambda} E[\tau_K^2]. \qquad (12.104)$$

We finally arrive at the following expression for the **mean waiting time for type $k$ customers**:

$$E[W_k] = \frac{\sum_{j=1}^{K} \lambda_j E[\tau_j^2]}{2(1 - \rho_1 - \cdots - \rho_{k-1})(1 - \rho_1 - \cdots - \rho_k)}. \qquad (12.105)$$

The **mean delay for type $k$ customers** is then

$$E[T_k] = E[W_k] + E[\tau_k]. \qquad (12.106)$$

Equation (12.105) reveals the effect of the priority classes on one another. Class $k$ customers are affected by lower-priority customers only through the residual-service-time term in the numerator. On the other hand, if the server utilization of the first $k - 1$ classes exceeds one, then the queue for class $k$ customers is unstable.

## Example 12.16

A computer handles two types of jobs. Type 1 jobs require a constant service time of 1 ms, and type 2 jobs require an exponentially distributed amount of time with mean 10 ms. Find the mean waiting time if the system operates as follows: (1) an ordinary M/G/1 system and (2) a two-priority M/G/1 system with priority given to type 1 jobs. Assume that the arrival rates of the two classes are Poisson with the same rate.

The first two moments of the service time are

$$E[\tau] = \frac{1}{2}E[\tau_1] + \frac{1}{2}E[\tau_2] = 5.5$$

$$E[\tau^2] = \frac{1}{2}E[\tau_1^2] + \frac{1}{2}E[\tau_2^2] = \frac{1}{2}(1^2 + 2(10^2)) = 100.5.$$

The traffic intensity for each class and the total traffic intensity are

$$\rho_1 = 1\frac{\lambda}{2}, \qquad \rho_2 = 10\frac{\lambda}{2}, \quad \text{and}$$
$$\rho = \lambda E[\tau] = 5.5\lambda,$$

where $\lambda$ is the total arrival rate. The mean residual service time is then

$$E[R] = \frac{\lambda E[\tau^2]}{2} = 50.25\lambda.$$

From Eq. (12.92), the mean waiting time for an M/G/1 system is

$$E[W] = \frac{E[R]}{1 - \rho} = \frac{50.25\lambda}{1 - 5.5\lambda}. \tag{12.107}$$

For the priority system we have

$$E[W_1] = \frac{E[R]}{1 - \rho_1} = \frac{50.25\lambda}{1 - 0.5\lambda} \tag{12.108}$$

and

$$E[W_2] = \frac{E[R]}{(1 - \rho_1)(1 - \rho)} = \frac{50.25\lambda}{(1 - 0.5\lambda)(1 - 5.5\lambda)}. \tag{12.109}$$

Comparison of Eqs. (12.108) and (12.109) with Eq. (12.107) shows that the waiting time of type 1 customers is improved by a factor of $(1 - \rho)/(1 - \rho_1)$ and that of type 2 is worsened by the factor $1/(1 - \rho_1)$.

The overall mean waiting for the priority system is

$$E[W_p] = \frac{1}{2}E[W_1] + \frac{1}{2}E[W_2] = \frac{1}{2}\left(\frac{E[R]}{1 - \rho_1}\right)\left(1 + \frac{1}{1 - \rho}\right)$$

$$= \left(\frac{1 - \rho/2}{1 - \rho_1}\right)\left(\frac{E[R]}{1 - \rho}\right)$$

$$= \frac{1 - 2.75\lambda}{1 - 0.5\lambda}E[W],$$

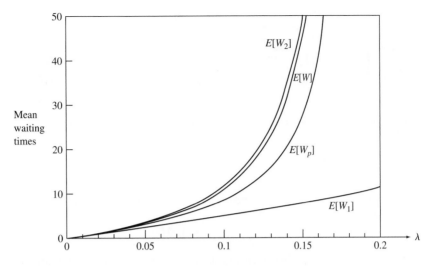

**FIGURE 12.18**

Relative mean waiting times in priority and nonpriority M/G/1 systems: $E[W]$, mean waiting time in M/G/1 system; $E[W_1]$, $E[W_2]$, mean waiting time for type 1 and type 2 customers in priority system; $E[W_p]$, overall mean waiting time in priority system.

where $E[W]$ is the mean waiting time of the M/G/1 system without priorities. Figure 12.18 shows $E[W]$, $E[W_p]$, $E[W_1]$, and $E[W_2]$. It can be seen that the discipline "short-job type first" used here improves the average waiting time. The graphs for $E[W_1]$ and $E[W_2]$ also show that at $\lambda = 2/11$ the lower-priority queue becomes unstable but the higher-priority remains stable up to $\lambda = 2$.

## 12.7    M/G/1 ANALYSIS USING EMBEDDED MARKOV CHAINS

In the previous section we noted that the state of an M/G/1 queueing system is given by the number of customers in the system $N(t)$ and the residual service time of the customer in service. Suppose we observe $N(t)$ at the instants when the residual service time becomes zero (i.e., at the instants $D_j$ when the $j$th service completion occurs); then all of the information relevant to the probability of future events is embodied in $N_j = N(D_j)$, *the number of customers left behind by the $j$th departing customer.* We will show that the sequence $N_j$ is a discrete-time Markov chain and that the steady state pmf at customer departure instants is equal to the steady state pmf of the system at arbitrary time instants. Thus we can find the steady state pmf of $N(t)$ if we can find the steady state pmf for the chain $N_j$.

### 12.7.1    The Embedded Markov Chain

First we show that the sequence $N_j = N(D_j)$ is a Markov chain. Consider the relation between $N_j$ and $N_{j-1}$. If $N_{j-1} \geq 1$, then a customer enters service immediately at time $D_j$, as shown in Fig. 12.19(a), and $N_j$ equals $N_{j-1}$, minus the customer that is served in

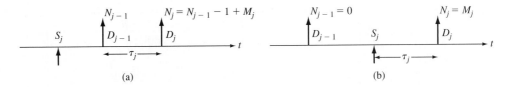

**FIGURE 12.19**
(a) Customer $j - 1$ leaves the system nonempty at time $D_{j-1}$. (b) Customer $j - 1$ leaves the system empty at time $D_{j-1}$.

between, plus the number of customers $M_j$ that arrive during the service time of the $j$th customer:

$$N_j = N_{j-1} - 1 + M_j \qquad \text{if } N_{j-1} \geq 1. \tag{12.110a}$$

If $N_{j-1} = 0$, then as shown in Fig. 12.19(b), there are no departures until the $j$th customer arrives and completes his service; $N_j$ then is the number of customers who arrive during this service time:

$$N_j = M_j \qquad \text{if } N_{j-1} = 0. \tag{12.110b}$$

Thus we see that $N_j$ depends on the past only through $N_{j-1}$ and $M_j$. The $M_j$ form an iid sequence because the service times are iid and because of the memoryless property of Poisson arrivals. Thus $N_j$ depends on the past of the system only through $N_{j-1}$. We therefore conclude that the sequence $N_j$ is a Markov chain.

Next we need to show that the steady state pmf of $N(t)$ is the same as the steady state pmf of $N_j$. We do so in two steps: first, we show that in M/G/1 systems, the distribution of customers found by arriving customers is the same as that left behind by departing customers; second, we show that in M/G/1 systems, the distribution of customers found by arriving customers is the same as the steady state distribution of $N(t)$. It then follows that the steady state pmf's of $N(t)$ and $N_j$ are the same.

First we need to show that *for systems in which customers arrive one at a time and depart one at a time (i.e., M/G/1 systems) the distribution found by arriving customers is the same as that left behind by departing customers.* Let $U_n(t)$ be the number of times the system goes from $n$ to $n + 1$ in the interval $(0, t)$; then $U_n(t)$ is the number of times an arriving customer finds $n$ customers in the system. Similarly, let $V_n(t)$ be the number of times that the system goes from $n + 1$ to $n$; then $V_n(t)$ is the number of times a departing customer leaves $n$. Note that the transition $n$ to $n + 1$ cannot reoccur until after the number in the system drops to $n$ once more (i.e., until after the transition $n + 1$ to $n$ reoccurs). Thus $U_n(t)$ and $V_n(t)$ can differ by at most 1. As $t$ becomes large, both of these transitions occur a large number of times, so the rate of transitions from $n$ to $n + 1$ equals the rate from $n + 1$ to $n$. Thus the rate at which customer arrivals find $n$ in the system equals the rate at which departures leave $n$ in the system. It then follows that the probability that an arrival finds $n$ in the system is equal to the probability that a departure leaves $n$ behind.

Since the arrivals in an M/G/1 system are Poisson and independent of the customer service times, the customer arrival times are independent of the state of the system. Thus the probability that an arrival finds $n$ customers in the system is equal to the proportion of time the system has $n$ customers, that is, the steady state probability $P[N(t) = n]$. Thus *the distribution of states seen by arriving customers is the same as the steady state distribution*.

By combining the results from the two previous paragraphs, we have that for an M/G/1 system, the pmf of $N_j$, the state at customer departure points, is the same as the steady state pmf of $N(t)$. In the next section, we find the generating function of $N_j$ and thus of $N(t)$.

## 12.7.2   The Number of Customers in an M/G/1 System

We now find the generating function for the steady state pmf of $N_j$. The transition probabilities for $N_j$ can be deduced from Eqs. (12.110a) and (12.110b):

$$p_{ik} = P[N_j = k \,|\, N_{j-1} = i] = P[M_j = k - i + 1] \qquad i > 0 \qquad (12.111a)$$

$$p_{0k} = P[N_j = k \,|\, N_{j-1} = 0] = P[M_j = k]. \qquad (12.111b)$$

Note that $p_{ik} = 0$ for $k - i + 1 < 0$. The probability that there are $N_j = k$ customers in the system at time $j$ is

$$
\begin{aligned}
P[N_j = k] &= \sum_{i=0}^{\infty} P[N_{j-1} = i]p_{ik} \\
&= P[N_{j-1} = 0]P[M_j = k] \\
&\quad + \sum_{i=1}^{k+1} P[N_{j-1} = i]P[M_j = k + 1 - i] \qquad (12.112a) \\
&= P[N_{j-1} = 0]P[M_j = k] \\
&\quad + \sum_{i=1}^{\infty} P[N_{j-1} = i]P[M_j = k + 1 - i], \qquad (12.112b)
\end{aligned}
$$

where we have used the fact that $P[M_j = k + 1 - i] = 0$ for $i > k + 1$.

If the process $N_j$ reaches a steady state as $j \to \infty$, then $P[N_j = k] \to P[N_d = k]$ and the above equation becomes

$$
\begin{aligned}
P[N_d = k] &= P[N_d = 0]P[M = k] \\
&\quad + \sum_{i=1}^{\infty} P[N_d = i]P[M = k + 1 - i], \qquad (12.113)
\end{aligned}
$$

where $N_d$ denotes the number of customers left behind by a departing customer.

Since the steady state pmf of $N_j$ is equal to that of $N(t)$, Eq. (12.113) also holds for the steady state pmf of $N(t)$. Equation (12.113) is readily solved for the generating function of $N(t)$ by using the probability generating function. The generating functions for $N$ and for $M$ are given by

$$G_N(z) = \sum_{k=0}^{\infty} P[N = k]z^k \quad \text{and} \quad G_M(z) = \sum_{k=0}^{\infty} P[M = k]z^k.$$

We multiply both sides of Eq. (12.113) (with $N_d$ replaced by $N$) by $z^k$ and sum from 0 to infinity:

$$\sum_{k=0}^{\infty} P[N = k]z^k = \sum_{k=0}^{\infty} P[N = 0]P[M = k]z^k$$

$$+ \sum_{k=0}^{\infty}\sum_{i=1}^{\infty} P[N = i]P[M = k + 1 - i]z^k. \quad (12.114)$$

The generating functions for $N$ and $M$ are immediately recognizable in the first two summations:

$$G_N(z) = P[N = 0]G_M(z)$$

$$+ z^{-1}\sum_{i=1}^{\infty} P[N = i]z^i \sum_{k=0}^{\infty} P[M = k + 1 - i]z^{k+1-i}.$$

The first summation is the generating function for $N$ with the $i = 0$ term missing. Let $k' = k + 1 - i$ in the second summation and note that $P[M = k'] = 0$ for $k' < 0$, then

$$G_N(z) = P[N = 0]G_M(z) + z^{-1}\{G_N(z) - P[N = 0]\}\left\{\sum_{k'=0}^{\infty} P[M = k']z^{k'}\right\}$$

$$= P[N = 0]G_M(z) + z^{-1}(G_N(z) - P[N = 0])G_M(z). \quad (12.115)$$

The generating function for $N$ is found by solving for $G_N(z)$:

$$G_N(z) = \frac{P[N = 0](z - 1)G_M(z)}{z - G_M(z)}. \quad (12.116)$$

We can find $P[N = 0]$ by noting that as $z \to 1$, we must have

$$G_N(z) = \sum_{k=0}^{\infty} P[N = k]z^k \to 1. \quad (12.117)$$

When we take the limit $z \to 1$ in Eq. (12.116) we obtain zero for the numerator and the denominator. By applying L'Hopital's rule, we obtain

$$1 = P[N = 0]\frac{G_M(z) + (z - 1)G'_M(z)}{1 - G'_M(z)}\bigg|_{z=1} = \frac{P[N = 0]}{1 - E[M]}. \quad (12.118)$$

Thus

$$P[N = 0] = 1 - E[M] \quad (12.119)$$

and

$$G_N(z) = \frac{(1 - E[M])(z - 1)G_M(z)}{z - G_M(z)}. \quad (12.120)$$

Note from Eq. (12.119) that we must have $E[M] < 1$ since $P[N = 0] \geq 0$. This stability condition makes sense since it implies that on the average less than one customer should arrive during the time it takes to service a customer.

We now determine $G_M(z)$, the generating function for the number of arrivals during a service time:

$$G_M(z) = \sum_{k=0}^{\infty} P[M = k]z^k$$

$$= \sum_{k=0}^{\infty} \int_0^{\infty} P[M = k \mid \tau = t]f_\tau(t)\,dt\,z^k. \qquad (12.121a)$$

Noting that the number of arrivals in $t$ seconds is a Poisson random variable,

$$G_M(z) = \sum_{k=0}^{\infty} \int_0^{\infty} \frac{(\lambda t)^k}{k!} e^{-\lambda t} f_\tau(t)\,dt\,z^k$$

$$= \int_0^{\infty} e^{-\lambda t} f_\tau(t) \sum_{k=0}^{\infty} \frac{(\lambda t)^k}{k!} z^k\,dt$$

$$= \int_0^{\infty} e^{-\lambda t} f_\tau(t) e^{\lambda t z}\,dt$$

$$= \int_0^{\infty} e^{-\lambda(1-z)t} f_\tau(t)\,dt$$

$$= \hat{\tau}(\lambda(1 - z)), \qquad (12.121b)$$

where $\hat{\tau}(s)$ is the Laplace transform of the pdf of $\tau$:

$$\hat{\tau}(s) = \int_0^{\infty} e^{-st} f_\tau(t)\,dt. \qquad (12.122)$$

We can obtain the moments of $M$ by taking derivatives of $G_M(z)$:

$$E[M] = \frac{d}{dz} G_M(z)\bigg|_{z=1} = \frac{d}{du}\hat{\tau}(u)\frac{d}{dz}\lambda(1 - z)\bigg|_{z=1}$$

$$= \hat{\tau}'(\lambda(1 - z))(-\lambda)|_{z=1}$$

$$= -\lambda\hat{\tau}'(0) = \lambda E[\tau] = \rho, \qquad (12.123)$$

where we used the chain rule in the second equality. Similarly,

$$E[M(M - 1)] = \lambda^2\hat{\tau}''(0) = \lambda^2 E[\tau^2].$$

Thus

$$\sigma_M^2 = E[M^2] - E[M]^2 = \lambda^2 E[\tau^2] + \lambda E[\tau] - (\lambda E[\tau])^2$$

$$= \lambda^2\sigma_\tau^2 + \lambda E[\tau]. \qquad (12.124)$$

If we substitute Eqs. (12.123) and (12.121b) into Eq. (12.120), we obtain the **Pollaczek–Khinchin transform equation,**

$$G_N(z) = \frac{(1 - \rho)(z - 1)\hat{\tau}(\lambda(1 - z))}{z - \hat{\tau}(\lambda(1 - z))}. \tag{12.125}$$

Note that $G_N(z)$ depends on the utilization $\rho$, the arrival rate $\lambda$, and the Laplace transform of the service time pdf.

---

### Example 12.17    M/M/1 System

Use the Pollaczek–Khinchin transform formula to find the pmf for $N(t)$ for an M/M/1 system. The Laplace transform for the pdf of an exponential service of mean $1/\mu$ is

$$\hat{\tau}(s) = \frac{\mu}{s + \mu}.$$

Thus the Pollaczek–Khinchin transform formula is

$$\begin{aligned}
G_N(z) &= \frac{(1 - \rho)(z - 1)[\mu/(\lambda(1 - z) + \mu)]}{z - [\mu/(\lambda(1 - z) + \mu)]} \\
&= \frac{(1 - \rho)(z - 1)\mu}{(\lambda - \lambda z + \mu)z - \mu} = \frac{1 - \rho}{1 - \rho z},
\end{aligned}$$

where we canceled the $z - 1$ term from the numerator and denominator and noted that $\rho = \lambda/\mu$. By expanding $G_N(z)$ in a power series, we have

$$G_N(z) = \sum_{k=0}^{\infty}(1 - \rho)\rho^k z^k = \sum_{k=0}^{\infty}P[N = k]z^k,$$

which implies that the steady state pmf is

$$P[N = k] = (1 - \rho)\rho^k \qquad k = 0, 1, 2, \ldots,$$

which is in agreement with our previous results for the M/M/1 system.

---

### Example 12.18    M/H₂/1 System

Find the pmf for the number of customers in an M/G/1 system that has arrivals of rate $\lambda$ and where the service times are hyperexponential random variables of degree two, as shown in Fig. 12.20. In other words, with probability 1/9 the service time is exponentially distributed with mean $1/\lambda$, and with probability 8/9 the service time is exponentially distributed with mean $1/2\lambda$.

In order to find $\hat{\tau}(s)$ we note that the pdf of $\tau$ is

$$f_\tau(x) = \frac{1}{9}\lambda e^{-\lambda x} + \frac{8}{9}2\lambda e^{-2\lambda x} \qquad x > 0.$$

Thus the mean service time is

$$E[\tau] = \frac{1}{9\lambda} + \frac{8}{9(2\lambda)} = \frac{5}{9\lambda},$$

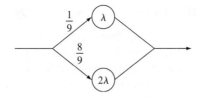

**FIGURE 12.20**
A hyperexponential service time results if
we select an exponential service time of
rate $\lambda$ with probability 1/9 and an
exponential service time of rate $2\lambda$ with
probability 8/9.

and the server utilization is $\rho = \lambda E[\tau] = 5/9$. The Laplace transform of $f_\tau(x)$ is

$$\hat{\tau}(s) = \frac{1}{9}\frac{\lambda}{s + \lambda} + \frac{8}{9}\frac{2\lambda}{s + 2\lambda} = \frac{18\lambda^2 + 17\lambda s}{9(s + \lambda)(s + 2\lambda)}.$$

Substitution of $\hat{\tau}(\lambda(1 - z))$ into Eq. (12.125) gives

$$G_N(z) = \frac{(1 - \rho)(z - 1)(18\lambda^2 + 17\lambda^2(1 - z))}{9(\lambda - \lambda z + \lambda)(\lambda - \lambda z + 2\lambda)z - (18\lambda^2 + 17\lambda^2(1 - z))}$$

$$= \frac{(1 - \rho)(z - 1)(35 - 17z)}{9(2 - z)(3 - z)z - (35 - 17z)},$$

where we have canceled $\lambda^2$ from the numerator and denominator. If we factor the denominator we obtain

$$G_N(z) = \frac{(1 - \rho)(35 - 17z)(z - 1)}{9(z - 1)(z - 7/3)(z - 5/3)}$$

$$= (1 - \rho)\left\{\frac{1/3}{1 - 3z/7} + \frac{2/3}{1 - 3z/5}\right\},$$

where we have carried out a partial fraction expansion. Finally we note that since $G_N(z)$ converges for $|z| < 1$, we can expand $G_N(z)$ as follows:

$$G_N(z) = (1 - \rho)\left\{\frac{1}{3}\sum_{k=0}^{\infty}\left(\frac{3}{7}\right)^k z^k + \frac{2}{3}\sum_{k=0}^{\infty}\left(\frac{3}{5}\right)^k z^k\right\}.$$

Since the coefficient of $z^k$ is $P[N = k]$, we finally have that

$$P[N = k] = \frac{4}{27}\left(\frac{3}{7}\right)^k + \frac{8}{27}\left(\frac{3}{5}\right)^k \qquad k = 0, 1, \ldots,$$

where we used the fact that $\rho = 5/9$.

### 12.7.3  Delay and Waiting Time Distribution in an M/G/1 System

We now find the delay and waiting time distributions for an M/G/1 system with first-come, first-served service discipline. If a customer spends $T_j$ seconds in the queueing system, then the number of customers $N_d$ it leaves behind in the system is the number of customers that arrive during these $T$ seconds, since customers are served in order of arrival. An expression for the generating function for $N_d$ is found by proceeding as in Eq. (12.121a):

$$
G_{N_d}(z) = \sum_{k=0}^{\infty} \int_0^\infty P[N_d = k \,|\, T = t] f_T(t)\, dt\; z^k
$$
$$
= \hat{T}(\lambda(1 - z)), \tag{12.126}
$$

where $\hat{T}(s)$ is the Laplace transform of the pdf of $T$, the total delay in the system. Since the steady state distributions of $N_d(t)$ and $N(t)$ are equal, we have that $G_N(z) = G_{N_d}(z)$ and thus combining Eqs. (12.125) and (12.126):

$$
\hat{T}(\lambda(1 - z)) = \frac{(1 - \rho)(z - 1)\hat{\tau}(\lambda(1 - z))}{z - \hat{\tau}(\lambda(1 - z))}. \tag{12.127}
$$

If we let $s = \lambda(1 - z)$, Eq. (12.127) yields an expression for $\hat{T}(s)$:

$$
\hat{T}(s) = \frac{(1 - \rho)s\hat{\tau}(s)}{s - \lambda + \lambda\hat{\tau}(s)}. \tag{12.128}
$$

The pdf of $T$ is found from the inverse transform of $\hat{T}(s)$ either analytically or numerically.

Since $T = W + \tau$, where $W$ and $\tau$ are independent random variables, we have that

$$
\hat{T}(s) = \hat{W}(s)\hat{\tau}(s). \tag{12.129}
$$

Equations (12.128) and (12.129) can then be solved for the Laplace transform of the waiting time pdf:

$$
\hat{W}(s) = \frac{(1 - \rho)s}{s - \lambda + \lambda\hat{\tau}(s)}. \tag{12.130}
$$

Equations (12.128) and (12.130) are also referred to as the **Pollaczek–Khinchin transform equations**.

---

### Example 12.19    M/M/1

Find the pdf's of $W$ and $T$ for an M/M/1 system. Substituting $\hat{\tau}(s) = \mu/(s + \mu)$ into Eq. (12.128) gives

$$
\hat{T}(s) = \frac{(1 - \rho)s\mu}{(s + \mu)(s - \lambda) + \lambda\mu} = \frac{(1 - \rho)\mu}{s - (\lambda - \mu)}, \tag{12.131}
$$

which is readily inverted to obtain

$$f_T(x) = \mu(1 - \rho)e^{-\mu(1-\rho)x} \qquad x > 0. \tag{12.132}$$

Similarly, Eq. (9.130) gives

$$\hat{W}(s) = \frac{(1 - \rho)s}{s - \lambda + \lambda\mu/(s + \mu)} = (1 - \rho)\frac{s + \mu}{s + \mu - \lambda}.$$

In order to invert this expression, the numerator polynomial must have order lower than that of the denominator polynomial. We achieve this by dividing the denominator into the numerator:

$$\hat{W}(s) = (1 - \rho)\frac{s + \mu - \lambda + \lambda}{s + \mu - \lambda} = (1 - \rho)\left\{1 + \frac{\lambda}{s + \mu - \lambda}\right\}. \tag{12.133}$$

We then obtain

$$f_W(x) = (1 - \rho)\delta(x) + \lambda(1 - \rho)e^{-\mu(1-\rho)x} \qquad x > 0. \tag{12.134}$$

The delta function at zero corresponds to the fact that a customer has zero wait with probability $(1 - \rho)$. Equations (12.132) and (12.134) were previously obtained as Eqs. (12.32) and (12.33) in Section 12.3 by a different method.

---

## Example 12.20   M/H$_2$/1

Find the pdf of the waiting time in the M/H$_2$/1 system discussed in Example 12.18.
    Substitution of $\hat{\tau}(s)$ from Example 12.18 into Eq. (12.130) gives

$$\begin{aligned}
\hat{W}(s) &= \frac{9s(1 - \rho)(s + \lambda)(s + 2\lambda)}{9(s - \lambda)(s + \lambda)(s + 2\lambda) + \lambda(18\lambda^2 + 17\lambda s)} \\
&= \frac{(1 - \rho)(s + \lambda)(s + 2\lambda)}{s^2 + 2\lambda s + 8\lambda^2/9} \\
&= (1 - \rho)\frac{9s^2 + 27\lambda s + 18\lambda^2}{9s^2 + 18\lambda s + 8\lambda^2} \\
&= (1 - \rho)\left\{1 + \frac{9\lambda s + 10\lambda^2}{9s^2 + 18\lambda s + 8\lambda^2}\right\} \\
&= (1 - \rho)\left\{1 + \frac{2\lambda/3}{s + 2\lambda/3} + \frac{\lambda/3}{s + 4\lambda/3}\right\},
\end{aligned}$$

where we have followed the same sequence of steps as in Example 12.18 and then done a partial fraction expansion.
    The inverse Laplace transform then yields

$$f_W(x) = \frac{4}{9}\left\{\delta(x) + \frac{2\lambda}{3}e^{-2\lambda x/3} + \frac{1}{4}\frac{4\lambda}{3}e^{-4\lambda x/3}\right\} \qquad x > 0.$$

Examples 12.18 and 12.19 demonstrate that the Pollaczek–Khinchin transform equations can be used to obtain closed-form expressions for the pmf of $N(t)$ and the pdf's of $W$ and $T$ when the Laplace transform of the service time pdf is a rational function of $s$, that is, a ratio of polynomials in $s$. This result is particularly important because it can be shown that the Laplace transform of any service time pdf can be approximated arbitrarily closely by a rational function of $s$. Thus in principle we can obtain exact expressions for the pmf of $N(t)$ and pdf's of $W$ and $T$.

In addition it should be noted that *the Pollaczek–Khinchin transform expressions can always be inverted numerically* using fast Fourier transform methods such as those discussed in Section 7.6. This numerical approach does not require that the Laplace transform of the pdf be a rational function of $s$.

## 12.8    BURKE'S THEOREM: DEPARTURES FROM M/M/c SYSTEMS

In many problems, a customer requires service from several service stations before a task is completed. These problems require that we consider a *network* of queueing systems. In such networks, the departures from some queues become the arrivals to other queues. This is the reason why we are interested in the statistical properties of the departure process from a queue.

Consider two queues in tandem as shown in Fig. 12.21, where the departures from the first queue become the arrivals at the second queue. Assume that the arrivals to the first queue are Poisson with rate $\lambda$ and that the service time at queue 1 is exponentially distributed with rate $\mu_1 > \lambda$. Assume that the service time in queue 2 is also exponentially distributed with rate $\mu_2 > \lambda$.

The state of this system is specified by the number of customers in the two queues, $(N_1(t), N_2(t))$. This state vector forms a Markov process with the transition rate diagram shown in Fig. 12.22, and global balance equations:

$$\lambda P[N_1 = 0, N_2 = 0] = \mu_2 P[N_1 = 0, N_2 = 1] \tag{12.135a}$$

$$(\lambda + \mu_1)P[N_1 = n, N_2 = 0] = \mu_2 P[N_1 = n, N_2 = 1]$$
$$+ \lambda P[N_1 = n - 1, N_2 = 0] \qquad n > 0 \tag{12.135b}$$

$$(\lambda + \mu_2)P[N_1 = 0, N_2 = m] = \mu_2 P[N_1 = 0, N_2 = m + 1]$$
$$+ \mu_1 P[N_1 = 1, N_2 = m - 1] \qquad m > 0 \tag{12.135c}$$

$$(\lambda + \mu_1 + \mu_2)P[N_1 = n, N_2 = m] = \mu_2 P[N_1 = n, N_2 = m + 1]$$
$$+ \mu_1 P[N_1 = n + 1, N_2 = m - 1]$$
$$+ \lambda P[N_1 = n - 1, N_2 = m]$$
$$n > 0, m > 0. \tag{12.135d}$$

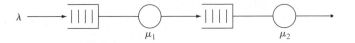

**FIGURE 12.21**
Two tandem exponential queues with Poisson input.

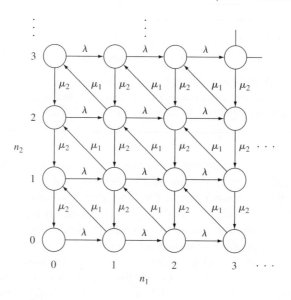

**FIGURE 12.22**
Transition rate diagram for two tandem exponential queues with
Poisson input.

It is easy to verify that the following joint state pmf satisfies Eqs. (12.135a)
through (12.135d):

$$P[N_1 = n, N_2 = m] = (1 - \rho_1)\rho_1^n (1 - \rho_2)\rho_2^m \qquad n \geq 0, m \geq 0, \quad (12.136)$$

where $\rho_i = \lambda/\mu_i$. We know that the first queue is an M/M/1 system, so

$$P[N_1 = n] = (1 - \rho_1)\rho_1^n \qquad n = 0, 1, \ldots. \tag{12.137}$$

By summing Eq. (12.136) over all $n$, we obtain the marginal state pmf of the second queue:

$$P[N_2 = m] = (1 - \rho_2)\rho_2^m \qquad m \geq 0. \tag{12.138}$$

Equations (12.136) through (12.138) imply that

$$P[N_1 = n, N_2 = m] = P[N_1 = n]P[N_2 = m] \qquad \text{for all } n, m. \tag{12.139}$$

In words, *the number of customers at queue 1 and the number at queue 2 at the same time in-stant are independent random variables.* Furthermore, *the steady state pmf at the second queue is that of an M/M/1 system with Poisson arrival rate $\lambda$ and exponential service time $\mu_2$.*

We say that a network of queues has a **product-form solution** when the joint pmf of the vector of numbers of customers at the various queues is equal to the product of the marginal pmf's of the number in the individual queues. We now discuss Burke's theorem, which states the fundamental result underlying the product-form solution in Eq. (12.139).

## Burke's Theorem

Consider an M/M/1, M/M/c, or M/M/$\infty$ queueing system at steady state with arrival rate $\lambda$, then

1. The departure process is Poisson with rate $\lambda$.
2. At each time $t$, the number of customers in the system $N(t)$ is independent of the sequence of departure times prior to $t$.

The product-form solution for the two tandem queues follows from Burke's theorem. Queue 1 is an M/M/1 queue, so from part 1 of the theorem the departures from queue 1 form a Poisson process. Thus the arrivals to queue 2 are a Poisson process, so the second queue is also an M/M/1 system with steady state pmf given by Eq. (12.138). It remains to show that the numbers of customers in the two queues at the same time instant are independent random variables.

The arrivals to queue 2 prior to time $t$ are the departures from queue 1 prior to time $t$. By part 2 of Burke's theorem the departures from queue 1, and hence the arrivals to queue 2, prior to time $t$ are independent of $N_1(t)$. Since $N_2(t)$ is determined by the sequence of arrivals from queue 1 prior to time $t$ and the independent sequence of service times, it then follows that $N_1(t)$ and $N_2(t)$ are independent. Equation (12.139) then follows. Note that Burke's theorem does not state that $N_1(t)$ and $N_2(t)$ are independent random processes. This would require that $N_1(t_1)$ and $N_2(t_2)$ be independent random variables for all $t_1$ and $t_2$. This is clearly not the case.

Burke's theorem implies that the generalization of Eq. (12.139) holds for the tandem combination of any number of M/M/1, M/M/c, or M/M/$\infty$ queues. Indeed, the result holds for any "feedforward" network of queues in which a customer cannot visit any queue more than once.

## Example 12.21

Find the joint state pmf for the network of queues shown in Fig. 12.23, where queue 1 is driven by a Poisson process of rate $\lambda_1$, where the departures from queue 1 are randomly routed to queues 2 and 3, and where queue 3 also has an additional independent Poisson arrival stream of rate $\lambda_2$.

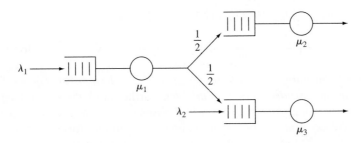

**FIGURE 12.23**
A feedforward network of queues.

From Burke's theorem $N_1(t)$ and $N_2(t)$ are independent, as are $N_1(t)$ and $N_3(t)$. Since the random split of a Poisson process yields independent Poisson processes, we have that the inputs to queues 2 and 3 are independent. The input to queue 2 is Poisson with rate $\lambda_1/2$. The input to queue 3 is Poisson of rate $\lambda_1/2 + \lambda_2$ since the merge of two independent Poisson processes is also Poisson. Thus

$$P[N_1(t) = k, N_2(t) = m, N_3(t) = n]$$

$$= (1 - \rho_1)\rho_1^k(1 - \rho_2)\rho_2^m(1 - \rho_3)\rho_3^n \qquad k, m, n \geq 0,$$

where $\rho_1 = \lambda_1/\mu_1$, $\rho_2 = \lambda_1/2\mu_2$, and $\rho_3 = (\lambda_1/2 + \lambda_2)/\mu_3$, and where we have assumed that all of the queues are stable.

---

## *12.8.1 Proof of Burke's Theorem Using Time Reversibility

Consider the sample path of an M/M/1, M/M/c, or M/M/$\infty$ system as shown in Fig. 12.24(a). Note that the arrivals in the forward process correspond to the departures in the time-reversed process. In Section 11.5, we showed that birth-and-death Markov chains in steady state are time-reversible processes; that is, the sample functions of the process played backward in time have the same statistics as the forward process. Since M/M/1, M/M/c, and M/M/$\infty$ systems are birth-and-death Markov chains, we

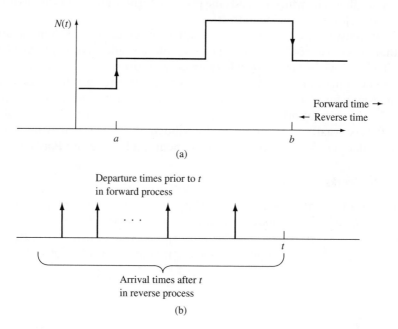

(a)

(b)

**FIGURE 12.24**

(a) Time instant $a$ is an arrival time in the forward process and a departure time in the reverse process. Time instant $b$ is a departure in the forward process and an arrival in the reverse process. (b) The departure times prior to time $t$ in the forward process correspond exactly to the arrival times after time $t$ in the reverse process.

have that their states are reversible processes. Thus the sample functions of these systems played backward in time correspond to the sample functions of queueing systems of the same type. It then follows that the arrival process of the time-reversed system is a Poisson process.

To prove part 1 of Burke's theorem, we note that the interdeparture times of the forward-time system are the interarrival times of the time-reversed system. Since the arrival process of the time-reversed system is Poisson, it then follows that the departure process of the forward system is also Poisson. Thus we have shown that the departure process of an M/M/1, M/M/c, or M/M/∞ system is Poisson.

To prove part 2 of Burke's theorem, fix a time $t$ as shown in Fig. 12.24(b). The departures before time $t$ from the forward system are the arrivals after time $t$ in the reverse system. In the reverse system, the arrivals are Poisson and thus the arrival times after time $t$ do not depend on $N(t)$. These arrival instants of the reverse process are exactly the departure instants before $t$ in the forward process. It then follows that $N(t)$ and the departure instants prior to $t$ are independent, so part 2 is proved.

## 12.9    NETWORKS OF QUEUES: JACKSON'S THEOREM

In many queueing networks, a customer is allowed to visit a particular queue more than once. Burke's theorem does not hold for such systems. In this section we discuss Jackson's theorem, which extends the product-form solution for the steady state pmf to a broader class of queueing networks.

If a customer is allowed to visit a queue more than once, then the arrival process at that queue will not be Poisson. For example, consider the simple M/M/1 queue with feedback shown in Fig. 12.25, where external customers arrive according to a Poisson process of rate $\lambda$ and where departures are instantaneously fed back into the system with probability .9. If the arrival rate is much less than the departure rate, then we have that the net arrival process (i.e., external and feedback arrivals) typically consists of isolated external arrivals followed by a burst of feedback arrivals. Thus the arrival process does not have independent increments and so it is not Poisson.

### 12.9.1    Open Networks of Queues

Consider a network of $K$ queues in which customers arrive from outside the network to queue $k$ according to independent Poisson processes of rate $\alpha_k$. We assume that the service time of a customer in queue $k$ is exponentially distributed with rate $\mu_k$ and independent of all other service times and arrival processes. We also suppose that queue

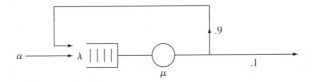

**FIGURE 12.25**
A queue with feedback.

$k$ has $c_k$ servers. After completion of service in queue $k$, a customer proceeds to queue $i$ with probability $P_{ki}$ and exits the network with probability

$$1 - \sum_{i=1}^{K} P_{ki}.$$

The total arrival rate $\lambda_k$ into queue $k$ is the sum of the external arrival rate and the internal arrival rates:

$$\lambda_k = \alpha_k + \sum_{j=1}^{K} \lambda_j P_{jk} \qquad k = 1, \ldots, K. \tag{12.140}$$

It can be shown that Eq. (12.140) has a unique solution if no customer remains in the network indefinitely. We call such networks **open queueing networks**.

The vector of the number of customers in all the queues,

$$\mathbf{N}(t) = (N_1(t), N_2(t), \ldots, N_K(t)),$$

is a Markov process. Jackson's theorem gives the steady state pmf for $\mathbf{N}(t)$.

---

### Jackson's Theorem

If $\lambda_k < c_k \mu_k$, then for any possible state $\mathbf{n} = (n_1, n_2, \ldots, n_K)$,

$$P[\mathbf{N}(t) = \mathbf{n}] = P[N_1 = n_1] P[N_2 = n_2] \ldots P[N_K = n_K], \tag{12.141}$$

where $P[N_k = n_k]$ is the steady state pmf of an M/M/$c_k$ system with arrival rate $\lambda_k$ and service rate $\mu_k$.

---

Jackson's theorem states that the numbers of customers in the queues at time $t$ are *independent* random variables. In addition, it states that the steady state probabilities of the individual queues are those of an M/M/$c_k$ system. This is an amazing result because in general the input process to a queue is not Poisson, as was demonstrated in the simple queue with feedback discussed in the beginning of this section.

---

### Example 12.22

Messages arrive at a concentrator according to a Poisson process of rate $\alpha$. The time required to transmit a message and receive an acknowledgment is exponentially distributed with mean $1/\mu$. Suppose that a message needs to be retransmitted with probability $p$. Find the steady state pmf for the number of messages in the concentrator.

The overall system can be represented by the simple queue with feedback shown in Fig. 12.25. The net arrival rate into the queue is $\lambda = \alpha + \lambda p$, that is,

$$\lambda = \frac{\alpha}{1 - p}.$$

Thus, the pmf for the number of messages in the concentrator is

$$P[N = n] = (1 - \rho)\rho^n \qquad n = 0, 1, \ldots,$$

where $\rho = \lambda/\mu = \alpha/(1 - p)\mu$.

---

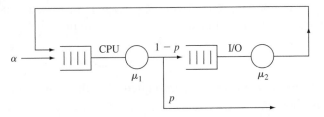

**FIGURE 12.26**
An open queueing network model for a computer system.

## Example 12.23

New programs arrive at a CPU according to a Poisson process of rate $\alpha$ as shown in Fig. 12.26. A program spends an exponentially distributed execution time of mean $1/\mu_1$ in the CPU. At the end of this service time, the program execution is complete with probability $p$ or it requires retrieving additional information from secondary storage with probability $1 - p$. Suppose that the retrieval of information from secondary storage requires an exponentially distributed amount of time with mean $1/\mu_2$. Find the mean time that each program spends in the system.

The net arrival rates into the two queues are

$$\lambda_1 = \alpha + \lambda_2 \qquad \text{and} \qquad \lambda_2 = (1 - p)\lambda_1.$$

Thus

$$\lambda_1 = \frac{\alpha}{p} \qquad \text{and} \qquad \lambda_2 = \frac{(1 - p)\alpha}{p}.$$

Each queue behaves like an M/M/1 system, so

$$E[N_1] = \frac{\rho_1}{1 - \rho_1} \qquad \text{and} \qquad E[N_2] = \frac{\rho_2}{1 - \rho_2},$$

where $\rho_1 = \lambda_1/\mu_1$ and $\rho_2 = \lambda_2/\mu_2$. Little's formula then gives the mean for the total time spent in the system:

$$E[T] = \frac{E[N_1 + N_2]}{\alpha} = \frac{1}{\alpha}\left[\frac{\rho_1}{1 - \rho_1} + \frac{\rho_2}{1 - \rho_2}\right].$$

## *12.9.2 Proof of Jackson's Theorem

Jackson's theorem can be proved by writing the global balance equations for the queueing network and verifying that the solution is given by Eq. (12.141). We present an alternative proof of the theorem using a result from time-reversed Markov chains. For notational simplicity we consider only the case of a network of single-server queues.

Let $\mathbf{n}$ and $\mathbf{n}'$ be two possible states of the network, and let $v_{\mathbf{n},\mathbf{n}'}$ denote the transition rate from $\mathbf{n}$ to $\mathbf{n}'$. In Section 11.5, we found that if we can guess a state pmf $P[\mathbf{n}]$ and a set of transition rates $\hat{v}_{\mathbf{n}',\mathbf{n}}$ for the reverse process such that (Eq. 11.65)

$$P[\mathbf{n}]v_{\mathbf{n},\mathbf{n}'} = P[\mathbf{n}']\hat{v}_{\mathbf{n}',\mathbf{n}} \tag{12.142a}$$

and such that the total rate out of state $\mathbf{n}$ is the same in the forward and reverse processes (Eq. 11.64 summed over $j$)

$$\sum_{\mathbf{m}} v_{\mathbf{n},\mathbf{m}} = \sum_{\mathbf{m}} \hat{v}_{\mathbf{n},\mathbf{m}}, \qquad (12.142b)$$

then $P[\mathbf{n}]$ is the steady state pmf of the process.

For the case under consideration our guess for the pmf is

$$P[\mathbf{n}] = \prod_{j=1}^{K} (1 - \rho_j)\rho_j^{n_j}, \qquad (12.143)$$

so the proof reduces to finding a consistent set of transition rates for the reverse process that satisfy Eqs. (12.142a) and (12.142b). Noting that $v_{\mathbf{n},\mathbf{n}'}$ is known and that $P[\mathbf{n}]$ and $P[\mathbf{n}']$ are specified by Eq. (12.143), Eq. (12.142a) can be solved for the transition rates of the reverse process:

$$\hat{v}_{\mathbf{n}',\mathbf{n}} = \frac{P[\mathbf{n}]v_{\mathbf{n},\mathbf{n}'}}{P[\mathbf{n}']}. \qquad (12.144)$$

Let $\mathbf{n} = (n_1, \ldots, n_k)$ denote a state for the network, and let $\mathbf{e}_k = (0, \ldots, 0, 1, 0, \ldots, 0)$, where the 1 is located in the $k$th component. Only three types of transitions in the state of the queueing network have nonzero probabilities. In the first type of transition, an external arrival to queue $k$ takes the state from $\mathbf{n}$ to $\mathbf{n} + \mathbf{e}_k$. In the second type of transition, a departure from queue $k$ exits the network and takes the state from $\mathbf{n}$ to $\mathbf{n} - \mathbf{e}_k$, where $n_k > 0$. In the third type of transition, a customer leaves queue $k$ and proceeds to queue $j$, thus taking the state from $\mathbf{n}$ to $\mathbf{n} - \mathbf{e}_k + \mathbf{e}_j$, where $n_k > 0$. Table 12.1 shows three types of transitions and their corresponding rates for the forward process.

A consistent set of transition rates for the reverse process is obtained by solving Eq. (12.144) for the three types of transitions possible. For example, if we let $\mathbf{n}' = \mathbf{n} + \mathbf{e}_k$, then the transition $\mathbf{n} \rightarrow \mathbf{n} + \mathbf{e}_k$ in the forward process corresponds to the transition $\mathbf{n} + \mathbf{e}_k \rightarrow \mathbf{n}$ in the reverse process. Equation (12.144) gives

$$\hat{v}_{\mathbf{n}',\mathbf{n}} = \frac{\alpha_k \prod_{j=1}^{K} (1 - \rho_j)\rho_j^{n_j}}{\rho_k \prod_{j=1}^{K} (1 - \rho_j)\rho_j^{n_j}}$$

$$= \frac{\alpha_k}{\rho_k} = \frac{\alpha_k}{\lambda_k/\mu_k} = \frac{\alpha_k \mu_k}{\lambda_k}.$$

The other reverse process transition rates are found in similar manner. Table 12.1 shows the results for the transition rates of the reverse process that are implied by Eq. (12.144).

The proof that the pmf in Eq. (12.143) gives the steady state pmf of the network of queues is completed by showing that the total transition rate out of any state $\mathbf{n}$ is the same in the forward and in the reverse process, that is, Eq. (12.142b) holds. In the

**TABLE 12.1**    Allowable transitions in Jackson network and their corresponding rates in the forward and reverse processes

**Forward Process**

| Transition | Rate | |
|---|---|---|
| $\mathbf{n} \to \mathbf{n} + \mathbf{e}_k$ | $\alpha_k$ | all $k$ |
| $\mathbf{n} \to \mathbf{n} - \mathbf{e}_k$ | $\mu_k\left(1 - \sum\limits_{j=1}^{K} P_{kj}\right)$ | all $k: n_k > 0$ |
| $\mathbf{n} \to \mathbf{n} - \mathbf{e}_k + \mathbf{e}_j$ | $\mu_k P_{kj}$ | all $k: n_k > 0$, all $j$ |

**Reverse Process**

| Transition | Rate | |
|---|---|---|
| $\mathbf{n} \to \mathbf{n} + \mathbf{e}_k$ | $\lambda_k\left(1 - \sum\limits_{j} P_{kj}\right)$ | all $k$ |
| $\mathbf{n} \to \mathbf{n} - \mathbf{e}_k$ | $\dfrac{\alpha_k \mu_k}{\lambda_k}$ | all $k: n_k > 0$ |
| $\mathbf{n} \to \mathbf{n} - \mathbf{e}_k + \mathbf{e}_j$ | $\dfrac{\lambda_j P_{jk} \mu_k}{\lambda_k}$ | all $k: n_k > 0$, all $j$ |

forward process, the total transition rate out of state $\mathbf{n}$ is obtained by adding the entries for the forward process in Table 12.1:

$$\sum_{\mathbf{m}} v_{\mathbf{n},\mathbf{m}} = \sum_{k} \alpha_k + \sum_{k:\, n_k > 0} \mu_k. \tag{12.145a}$$

For the reverse process, we have from Table 12.1 that

$$\sum_{\mathbf{m}} \hat{v}_{\mathbf{n},\mathbf{m}} = \sum_{k} \lambda_k\left(1 - \sum_{j} P_{kj}\right) + \sum_{k:\, n_k > 0}\left\{\frac{\alpha_k \mu_k}{\lambda_k} + \sum_{j}\frac{\lambda_j P_{jk}\mu_k}{\lambda_k}\right\}. \tag{12.145b}$$

We need to show that the right-hand sides of Eqs. (12.145a) and (12.145b) are equal. First, note that Eq. (12.140) implies that

$$\lambda_k - \alpha_k = \sum_{j=1}^{K} \lambda_j P_{jk}.$$

The right-hand side of Eq. (12.145b) then becomes

$$\left(\sum_{k} \lambda_k - \sum_{j}\sum_{k} \lambda_k P_{kj}\right) + \sum_{k:\, n_k > 0}\left\{\frac{\alpha_k \mu_k}{\lambda_k} + \frac{\mu_k}{\lambda_k}\sum_{j}\lambda_j P_{jk}\right\}$$

$$= \sum_{k} \lambda_k - \sum_{j}(\lambda_j - \alpha_j) + \sum_{k:\, n_k > 0}\left\{\frac{\alpha_k \mu_k}{\lambda_k} + \frac{\mu_k}{\lambda_k}(\lambda_k - \alpha_k)\right\}$$

$$= \sum_{k} \alpha_k + \sum_{k:\, n_k > 0} \mu_k.$$

Thus the right-hand sides of Eqs. (12.145a) and (12.145b) are equal and thus Eq. (12.143) is the steady state pmf of the network of queues. This completes the proof of Jackson's theorem for a network of single-server queues.

### 12.9.3   Closed Networks of Queues

In some problems, a *fixed* number of customers, say $I$, circulate endlessly in a **closed network of queues**. For example, some computer system models assume that at any time a fixed number of processes use the CPU and input/output (I/O) resources of a computer as shown in Fig. 12.27. We now consider queueing networks that are identical to the previously discussed **open networks** except that the external arrival rates are zero and the networks always contain a fixed number of customers $I$. We show that the steady state pmf for such systems is product form but that the states of the queues are no longer independent.

The net arrival rate into queue $k$ is now given by

$$\lambda_k = \sum_{j=1}^{K} \lambda_j P_{jk} \qquad k = 1, \ldots, K. \tag{12.146}$$

Note that these equations have the same form as the set of equations that define the stationary pmf for a discrete-time Markov chain with transition probabilities $P_{jk}$. The only difference is that the sum of the $\lambda_k$'s need not be one. Thus the solution vector to Eq. (12.146) must be proportional to the stationary pmf $\{\pi_j\}$ corresponding to $\{P_{jk}\}$:

$$\lambda_k = \lambda(I)\pi_k, \tag{12.147}$$

where

$$\pi_k = \sum_{j=1}^{K} \pi_j P_{jk} \tag{12.148}$$

and where $\lambda(I)$ is a constant that depends on $I$, the number of customers in the queueing network. If we sum both sides of Eq. (12.147) over $k$, we see that $\lambda(I)$ is the sum of the arrival rates in all the queues in the network, and $\pi_k = \lambda_k/\lambda(I)$ is the fraction of total arrivals to queue $k$.

---

### Theorem

Let $\lambda_k = \lambda(I)\pi_k$ be a solution to Eq. (12.146), and let $\mathbf{n} = (n_1, n_2, \ldots, n_K)$ be any state of the network for which $n_1, \ldots, n_K \geq 0$ and

$$n_1 + n_2 + \cdots + n_K = I, \tag{12.149}$$

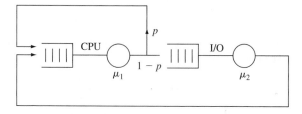

**FIGURE 12.27**
A closed queueing network model for a computer system.

then

$$P[\mathbf{N}(t) = \mathbf{n}] = \frac{P[N_1 = n_1]P[N_2 = n_2]\dots P[N_K = n_K]}{S(I)}, \qquad (12.150)$$

where $P[N_k = n_k]$ is the steady state pmf of an $M/M/c_k$ system with arrival rate $\lambda_k$ and service rate $\mu_k$, and where $S(I)$ is the normalization constant given by

$$S(I) = \sum_{\mathbf{n}:n_1+\dots+n_K=I} P[N_1 = n_1]P[N_2 = n_2]\dots P[N_K = n_K]. \qquad (12.151)$$

Equation (12.150) states that $P[\mathbf{N}(t) = \mathbf{n}]$ has a product form. However, $P[\mathbf{N}(t) = \mathbf{n}]$ is no longer equal to the product of the marginal pmf's because of the normalization constant $S(I)$. This constant arises because the fact that there are always $I$ customers in the network implies that the allowable states $\mathbf{n}$ must satisfy Eq. (12.149). The theorem can be proved by taking the approach used to prove Jackson's theorem above.

### Example 12.24

Suppose that the computer system in Example 12.23 is operated so that there are always $I$ programs in the system. The resulting network of queues is shown in Fig. 12.27. Note that the feedback loop around the CPU signifies the completion of one job and its instantaneous replacement by another one. Find the steady state pmf of the system. Find the rate at which programs are completed.

The stationary probabilities associated with Eq. (9.146) are found by solving

$$\pi_1 = p\pi_1 + \pi_2, \qquad \pi_2 = (1-p)\pi_1, \qquad \text{and} \qquad \pi_1 + \pi_2 = 1.$$

The stationary probabilities are then

$$\pi_1 = \frac{1}{2-p} \qquad \text{and} \qquad \pi_2 = \frac{1-p}{2-p} \qquad (12.152)$$

and the arrival rates are

$$\lambda_1 = \lambda(I)\pi_1 = \frac{\lambda(I)}{2-p} \qquad \text{and} \qquad \lambda_2 = \frac{(1-p)\lambda(I)}{2-p}. \qquad (12.153)$$

The stationary pmf for the network is then

$$P[N_1 = i, N_2 = I - i] = \frac{(1-\rho_1)\rho_1^i(1-\rho_2)\rho_2^{I-i}}{S(I)} \qquad 0 \le i \le I, \qquad (12.154)$$

where $\rho_1 = \lambda_1/\mu_1$ and $\rho_2 = \lambda_2/\mu_2$, and where we have used the fact that if $N_1 = i$ then $N_2 = I - i$. The normalization constant is then

$$S(I) = (1-\rho_1)(1-\rho_2)\sum_{i=0}^{I}\rho_1^i\rho_2^{I-i}$$

$$= (1-\rho_1)(1-\rho_2)\rho_2^I\frac{1-(\rho_1/\rho_2)^{I+1}}{1-(\rho_1/\rho_2)}. \qquad (12.155)$$

Substitution of Eq. (12.155) into Eq. (12.154) gives

$$P[N_1 = i, N_2 = I - i] = \frac{1 - \beta}{1 - \beta^{I+1}} \beta^i \qquad 0 \le i \le I, \tag{12.156}$$

where

$$\beta = \frac{\rho_1}{\rho_2} = \frac{\pi_1 \mu_2}{\pi_2 \mu_1} = \frac{\mu_2}{(1 - p)\mu_1}. \tag{12.157}$$

Note that the form of Eq. (12.156) suggests that queue 1 behaves like an M/M/1/$K$ queue. The apparent load to this queue is $\beta$, which is proportional to the ratio of I/O to CPU service rates and inversely proportional to the probability of having to go to I/O.

The rate at which programs are completed is $p\lambda_1$. We find $\lambda_1$ from the relation between server utilization and probability of an empty system:

$$1 - \lambda_1/\mu_1 = P[N_1 = 0] = \frac{1 - \beta}{1 - \beta^{I+1}},$$

which implies that

$$p\lambda_1 = p\mu_1 \frac{\beta(1 - \beta^I)}{1 - \beta^{I+1}}.$$

## Example 12.25

A transmitter (queue 1 in Fig. 12.28) has two permits for message transmission. As long as the transmitter has a permit ($N_1 > 0$), it generates messages with exponential interarrival times of rate $\lambda$. The messages enter the transmission system and require an exponential service time at station 2. As soon as a message arrives at the other side of the transmission system, the corresponding permit is sent back via station 3. Thus the transmitter can have at most two messages outstanding in the network at any given time. Find the steady state pmf for the network of queues. Find the rate at which messages enter the transmission system.

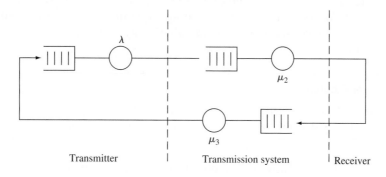

**FIGURE 12.28**
A closed queueing network model for a message transmission system.

We can view the two permits as two customers circulating the queueing network. Since $P_{1,2} = P_{2,3} = P_{3,1} = 1$, we have that $\pi_1 = \pi_2 = \pi_3 = 1/3$ and thus

$$\lambda_1 = \lambda_2 = \lambda_3 = \frac{\lambda(2)}{3}.$$

The steady state pmf for the network is

$$P[N_1 = i, N_2 = j, N_3 = 2 - i - j] = \frac{(1 - \rho_1)\rho_1^i(1 - \rho_2)\rho_2^j(1 - \rho_3)\rho_3^{I-i-j}}{S(2)}$$

for $0 \leq i \leq 2, 0 \leq j \leq 2 - i$,

where $\rho_1 = \lambda(2)/3\lambda$ and $\rho_2 = \rho_3 = \lambda(2)/3\mu$. The normalization constant $S(2)$ is obtained by summing the above joint pmf over all possible states and equating the result to one. There are six possible network states: $(2, 0, 0), (0, 2, 0), (0, 0, 2), (1, 1, 0), (1, 0, 1), (0, 1, 1)$. Thus the normalization constant is given by

$$S(2) = (1 - \rho_1)(1 - \rho_2)(1 - \rho_3)\{\rho_1^2 + \rho_2^2 + \rho_3^2 + \rho_1\rho_2 + \rho_1\rho_3 + \rho_2\rho_3\}$$
$$= (1 - \rho_1)(1 - \rho_2)^2\{\rho_1^2 + 2\rho_2^2 + 2\rho_1\rho_2 + \rho_2^2\},$$

where we have used the fact that $\rho_2 = \rho_3$.

The rate at which messages enter the system is

$$\lambda_1 = \lambda(1 - P[N_1 = 0]),$$

where

$$P[N_1 = 0] = P[\mathbf{N} = (0, 2, 0)] + P[\mathbf{N} = (0, 0, 2)] + P[\mathbf{N} = (0, 1, 1)]$$
$$= \frac{3\rho_2^2}{\rho_1^2 + 2\rho_1\rho_2 + 3\rho_2^2} = \frac{3/\mu^2}{1/\lambda^2 + 2/\lambda\mu + 3/\mu^2}.$$

---

### 12.9.4  Mean Value Analysis

Example 12.25 shows that the evaluation of the normalization constant is the fundamental difficulty with closed queueing networks. Fortunately, a method has been developed for obtaining certain average quantities of interest without having to evaluate this constant. This **mean value analysis** method is based on the following theorem.

---

### Arrival Theorem

In a closed queueing network with $I$ customers, the system as seen by a customer arrival to queue $j$ is the steady state pmf of the same network with one fewer customer.

---

We have already encountered this result in the discussion of finite-source queueing systems in Section 12.5. We prove the result in the last part of this section. We now use the result to develop the mean value analysis method.

Let $E[N_j(I)]$ be the mean number of customers in the $j$th queue for a network that has $I$ customers, let $E[T_j(I)]$ denote the mean time spent by a customer in queue $j$, and let $\lambda_j(I)$ denote the average customer arrival rate at queue $j$. The mean time spent by a customer in queue $j$ is his service time plus the service times of the customers he finds in the queue upon arrival:

$$E[T_j(I)] = E[\tau_j] + E[\tau_j] \times \text{mean number found upon arrival}$$

$$= E[\tau_j] + E[\tau_j]E[N_j(I-1)]$$

$$= \frac{1 + E[N_j(I-1)]}{\mu_j}, \tag{12.158}$$

where $E[N_j(I-1)]$ is the mean number found upon arrival by the arrival theorem. By Little's formula, the mean number of customers in queue $j$ when there are $I$ in the network is

$$E[N_j(I)] = \lambda_j(I)E[T_j(I)] = \lambda(I)\pi_j E[T_j(I)]. \tag{12.159}$$

Since the sum of the customers in all queues is $I$ in the previous equation, we have that

$$I = \sum_{j=1}^{K} E[N_j(I)] = \lambda(I)\sum_{j=1}^{K}\pi_j E[T_j(I)]. \tag{12.160}$$

Thus

$$\lambda(I) = \frac{I}{\sum\limits_{j=1}^{K}\pi_j E[T_j(I)]}. \tag{12.161}$$

The *mean value analysis* method combines Eqs. (12.158) through (12.161) in the following way. First compute $\pi_j$ by solving Eq. (12.148), then for $I = 0$:

$$E[N_j(0)] = 0 \qquad \text{for } j = 1, \ldots, K.$$

For $I = 1, 2, \ldots$:

$$E[T_j(I)] = \frac{1}{\mu_j} + \frac{E[N_j(I-1)]}{\mu_j} \qquad j = 1, \ldots, K \tag{12.158}$$

$$\lambda(I) = \frac{I}{\sum\limits_{i=0}^{K}\pi_i E[T_j(I)]} \tag{12.161}$$

$$E[N_j(I)] = \lambda(I)\pi_j E[T_j(I)] \qquad j = 1, \ldots, K. \tag{12.159}$$

Thus the mean value algorithm begins with an empty system and by use of the above three equations builds up to a network with the desired number of customers. This method has considerably simplified the numerical solution of closed queueing networks and extended the range of network sizes that can be analyzed.

## Example 12.26

In Example 12.24, let $\mu_1 = \mu_2 = 1$, and $p = 1/2$. Find the rate at which programs are completed if $I = 2$.

It was already indicated in Example 12.24 that the rate of program completion is $p\lambda_1(2) = p\pi_1\lambda(2)$. From Eq. (12.152), we have that $\pi_1 = 1/(2 - p) = 2/3$. Thus we only need to find $\lambda(2)$, the total arrival rate of the network with $I = 2$.

Starting the mean value method with $I = 1$, we have

$$E[T_1(1)] = \frac{1}{\mu_1} = 1 \qquad E[T_2(1)] = \frac{1}{\mu_2} = 1$$

$$\lambda(1) = \frac{1}{\pi_1 T_1(1) + \pi_2 T_2(1)} = 1$$

$$E[N_1(1)] = \lambda(1)\pi_1 E[T_1(1)] = \frac{2}{3}$$

$$E[N_2(1)] = \lambda(1)\pi_2 E[T_2(1)] = \frac{1}{3}.$$

Continuing with $I = 2$, we have

$$E[T_1(2)] = \frac{1}{\mu_1} + \frac{E[N_1(1)]}{\mu_1} = \frac{5}{3}$$

$$E[T_2(2)] = \frac{1}{\mu_2} + \frac{E[N_2(1)]}{\mu_2} = \frac{4}{3}$$

$$\lambda(2) = \frac{2}{\pi_1 E[T_1(2)] + \pi_2 E[T_2(2)]} = \frac{9}{7}.$$

Thus the program completion rate is

$$p\pi_1\lambda(2) = \frac{3}{7}.$$

You should verify that this is consistent with the results of Example 12.24.

## Example 12.27

In Example 12.25, let $1/\lambda = a$ and $\mu = 1$. Find the rate at which messages enter the system when $I = 2$.

We previously found that $\pi_1 = \pi_2 = \pi_3 = 1/3$ and

$$\lambda_1(I) = \lambda_2(I) = \lambda_3(I) = \frac{\lambda(I)}{3}.$$

Starting the mean value method with $I = 1$, we have

$$E[T_1(1)] = a \qquad E[T_2(1)] = E[T_3(1)] = 1$$

$$\lambda(1) = \frac{1}{\pi_1 E[T_1(1)] + \pi_2 E[T_2(1)] + \pi_3 E[T_3(1)]} = \frac{3}{a + 2}$$

$$E[N_1(1)] = \lambda(1)\pi_1 E[T_1(1)] = \frac{a}{a+2}$$

$$E[N_2(1)] = \lambda(1)\pi_2 E[T_2(1)] = \frac{1}{a+2} = E[N_3(1)].$$

Continuing with $I = 2$, we have

$$E[T_1(2)] = a + aE[N_1(1)] = \frac{2a^2 + 2a}{a+2}$$

$$E[T_2(2)] = 1 + 1E[N_2(1)] = \frac{a+3}{a+2} = E[T_3(2)]$$

$$\lambda_2(2) = \frac{2}{(1/3)\{(2a^2 + 2a)/(a+2) + [2(a+3)/(a+2)]\}}$$

$$= \frac{3(a+2)}{a^2 + 2a + 3}.$$

Finally, messages enter the transmission network at a rate $\lambda_1(2) = \lambda(2)/3$, so

$$\lambda_1(2) = \frac{a+2}{a^2 + 2a + 3}.$$

You should verify that this is consistent with the results obtained in Example 12.25.

---

### *12.9.5  Proof of the Arrival Theorem

Consider the instant when a customer leaves queue $j$ and is proceeding to queue $k$. We are interested in the pmf of the system state at these arrival instants. Suppose that at this instant, with the customer removed from the system, the customer sees the network in state $\mathbf{n} = (n_1, \ldots, n_K)$. This occurs only when the network state goes from the state $\mathbf{n}' = (n_1, \ldots, n_j + 1, \ldots, n_K)$ to the state $\mathbf{n}'' = (n_1, \ldots, n_j, \ldots, n_k + 1, \ldots, n_K)$. Thus:

$$P[\text{customer sees } \mathbf{n} \mid \text{customer goes from } j \text{ to } k]$$

$$= \frac{P[\text{customer sees } \mathbf{n}, \text{customer goes from } j \text{ to } k]}{P[\text{customer goes from } j \text{ to } k]}$$

$$= \frac{P[\text{customer goes from } j \text{ to } k \mid \text{state is } \mathbf{n}']P[\mathbf{N}(I) = \mathbf{n}']}{P[\text{customer goes from } j \text{ to } k]}$$

$$= \frac{\mu_j P_{jk} P[\mathbf{N}(I) = \mathbf{n}']}{\mu_j P_{jk} P[N_j(I) > 0]}$$

$$= \frac{P[\mathbf{N}(I) = \mathbf{n}']}{P[N_j(I) > 0]}. \tag{12.162}$$

To simplify the notation, let us assume that we are dealing with a network of M/M/1 queues, then

$$P[\mathbf{N}(I) = \mathbf{n}'] = \frac{P[N_1 = n_1]\dots P[N_j = n_j + 1]\dots P[N_K = n_K]}{S(I)}$$

$$= \rho_j \prod_{m=1}^{K} \frac{\rho_m^{n_m}}{S'(I)}, \tag{12.163}$$

where $S'(I)$ absorbs all the constants associated with the $P[N_m = n_m]$:

$$S'(I) = \sum_{\mathbf{n}:n_1+\dots+n_K=I} \prod_{m=1}^{K} \rho_m^{n_m}. \tag{12.164}$$

Next, consider the probability that queue $j$ is not empty:

$$P[N_j(I) > 0] = \sum_{\mathbf{n}:n_1+\dots+n_K=I-1} P[N_1 = n_1]\dots P[N_j = n_j + 1]\dots P[N_k = n_k]$$

$$= \sum_{\mathbf{n}:n_1+\dots+n_K=I-1} \rho_j \frac{\prod_{m=1}^{K} \rho_m^{n_m}}{S'(I)}$$

$$= \frac{\rho_j}{S'(I)} \sum_{\mathbf{n}:n_1+\dots+n_K=I-1} \prod_{m=1}^{K} \rho_m^{n_m}$$

$$= \frac{\rho_j S'(I - 1)}{S'(I)}, \tag{12.165}$$

where we have noted that the above summation is the normalization constant for a network with $I - 1$ customers $S'(I - 1)$.

Finally, we substitute Eqs. (12.165) and (12.163) into Eq. (12.162):

$$P[\text{customer sees } \mathbf{n} \mid \text{customer goes from } j \text{ to } k]$$

$$= \frac{\rho_j \prod_{m=1}^{K} \rho_m^{n_m}/S'(I)}{[\rho_j S'(I - 1)]/S'(I)}$$

$$= \prod_{m=1}^{K} \frac{\rho_m^{n_m}}{S'(I - 1)}$$

$$= P[\mathbf{N}(I - 1) = \mathbf{n}],$$

which is the steady state probability for $\mathbf{n}$ in a network with $I - 1$ customers. This completes the proof of the arrival theorem.

## 12.10   SIMULATION AND DATA ANALYSIS OF QUEUEING SYSTEMS

In this section we present a basic introduction to the simulation of queueing systems. Analytical methods are valuable due to the ease with which they allow us to explore the issues and tradeoffs in a given model. Numerical techniques can supplement analytical methods and provide additional detailed information, especially when transient and dynamic behavior is of interest. However, in many situations analytical and numerical methods are not sufficient and simulation provides us with a flexible means to investigate the behavior of complex systems. In this section we introduce the basic approaches available for simulating queueing systems. Throughout our discussion we emphasize the need for *careful design of the simulation experiment* as well as the need for *careful application of statistical methods* on the observations to draw valid conclusions.

### 12.10.1   Approaches to Simulation

The dynamics of a queueing system are represented by one or more random processes, so the usual considerations in simulating random processes apply. A very basic option is whether a *single realization* or *multiple realizations* of the random process are used.

Multiple realizations that are statistically independent allow us to use the standard statistical methods introduced in Chapter 8 to analyze iid random variables, for example, to obtain confidence intervals and fit distributions. A single realization of a random process allows us a more restricted set of statistical tools and frequently leads to methods that attempt to provide a set of observations that are iid so that we can use standard tools. In some real experimental situations we may only have one realization of the process to work with and so we may have no choice. However in computer simulation with proper design, we can usually conduct multiple replications of an experiment to produce independent observations.[4] In general, we recommend a pragmatic approach that uses some replication when possible.

A simulation study based on a single realization usually involves *assumptions about stationarity and ergodicity* so that the behavior of the process over time reveals its ensemble averages and probabilities. Examples of such processes are processes with stationary independent increments and processes that involve ergodic Markov chains. Both of these classes of processes involve initial transient behavior and so we must decide whether to keep or discard the observations obtained during the initial portion of the simulation. If we decide to discard, then we need to somehow *identify when the transient phase is over* and the process has reached steady state. This is not an easy task, as discussed extensively in [Pawlikowski], and there are a variety of criteria that can be applied for declaring that a system has reached steady state. We note that the use of replicated simulations can help characterize the transient phase of a process. (See Problem 12.67.)

---

[4]Care should be taken to ensure that the seed in the random number generator is different in each replication.

The design of a simulation must take into account the behavior and parameters that we are interested in measuring and observing. Seemingly easy questions such as determining state probabilities are not so straightforward. We could be interested in the long-term proportion of time the system spends in state, or the states seen by arriving customers, or even the state left behind by a departing customer. We have seen that these quantities need not be the same. The design of the simulation can ease or make difficult the measurement of a particular parameter.

In the remainder of the section we are interested in the parameters of the system when it is in steady state, usually either the mean number of customers in the system or the long-term proportion of time the system has a certain number of customers. We cover the following approaches to simulating a queueing system.

- Simulation through independent replication;
- Time-sampled process: $\{N(k\delta)\}$;
- Embedded Markov chain and state occupancies: $\{N(t_k), T_k\}$;
- Replication through regenerative cycles.

### 12.10.2  Simulation through Independent Replications

**Simulation through independent replications** involves simulating a process $R$ times to obtain a set of $R$ independent observations $\{X(t, \zeta_1), X(t, \zeta_2), \ldots, X(t, \zeta_R)\}$. We use a function of the observations to estimate a parameter $\theta$ of the random process:

$$\hat{\Theta}(\mathbf{X}_R) = g(X(t, \zeta_1), X(t, \zeta_2), \ldots, X(t, \zeta_R)).$$

For example, to estimate the mean of the process at time $t$ we use:

$$\overline{X}_R(t) = \frac{1}{R} \sum_{r=1}^{R} X(t, \zeta_r). \tag{12.166}$$

To estimate the variance of the process at time $t$ we use:

$$\hat{\sigma}_R^2(t) = \frac{1}{R-1} \sum_{r=1}^{R} (X(t, \zeta_r) - \overline{X}_R(t))^2. \tag{12.167}$$

By design the observations are independent random variables. In order to proceed, we also need to assume that the observations are Gaussian random variables. The usual approach of taking the sum of a sufficiently large number of variables and using the central limit theorem applies. We can also use a statistical test to check that the samples are close to Gaussian distributed. Once we have Gaussian observations, we can provide the confidence intervals from Eq. (8.58):

$$(\overline{X}_R - t_{\alpha/2, n-1}\hat{\sigma}_R/\sqrt{n}, \overline{X}_R + t_{\alpha/2, n-1}\hat{\sigma}_R/\sqrt{n}). \tag{12.168}$$

Equation (12.168) is used widely to provide approximate confidence intervals.

We note that the sample mean and variance estimators in Eqs. (12.166) and (12.167) and the associated confidence intervals allow us to identify time dependencies in the behavior of the random process. In particular, in the next example, we use them to identify the transient phase of a random process that has a steady state.

When the random process is a continuous function of time, the estimator can take the form of an integral. For example, for a Markov chain process we can estimate either the time average of the process or the proportion of time in state $j$ in the $r$th replication by an integral over an interval of time $T$:

$$\hat{N}_r = \frac{1}{T} \int_0^T N(t, \zeta_r)\, dt \quad \text{and} \quad \hat{p}_j^{(r)} = \frac{1}{T} \int_0^T I_j(N(t, \zeta_r))\, dt. \quad (12.169)$$

$\{\hat{N}_r\}$ and $\{\hat{p}_j^{(r)}\}$ provide the independent random variables that can be used to obtain a confidence interval for the time average of $N(t)$ and the proportion of time that $N(t) = j$.

### 12.10.3  Time-Sampled Process Simulation

A simple approach to simulating continuous-time queueing systems is to use **time-sampled process simulation**. The time axis is divided into small intervals of length $\delta$ and a discrete-time process is simulated. The following example demonstrates the approach.

---

**Example 12.28    Transient of M/M/1 Queue Using Sampled-Time Approximation**

Investigate the transient behavior of $N(t)$, the number of customers in an M/M/1 queueing system, using a sampled-time approach. Assume the system is initially empty. Generate 2000 steps of $\delta = 0.1$ seconds with $\mu = 1$ job/second and run two cases: $\lambda = 0.5$ and $\lambda = 0.9$ jobs/second. Replicate the simulation 20 times and plot the sample mean of the process across the 20 replications (Eq. 12.166). Find the covariance function for each realization and plot the average of the covariance functions across the 20 replications.

The sampled-time approximation involves simulating a system in small steps of $\delta$ seconds. For a birth-death process (such as the M/M/1 queue) in state $j > 0$, three outcomes can occur in $\delta$ seconds: (1.) no arrival and no departure occur with probability $1 - (\lambda_j + \mu_j)\delta$; (2.) one arrival occurs with probability $\lambda_j\delta$; (3.) one departure occurs with probability $\mu_j\delta$. We can adjust for the $j = 0$ state by letting $\mu_0 = 0$, and the $j = N_{max}$ state by letting $\lambda_{Nmax} = 0$. Note that the state-transition diagram of this sampled-time queueing system has the structure of the discrete-time Markov chain in Example 11.49. We use the code for that example to generate 20 realizations of 2000 steps of $N(k\delta)$, which corresponds to 200 seconds of time.

Figure 12.29(a) shows the sample mean of 20 realizations of $N(t)$. Note that this sample mean averages over 20 processes that can each exhibit a lot of variation, see Figs. 11.20 and 11.21. Consequently the averaged realizations still exhibit quite a bit of variation. The lower curve corresponds to $\rho = 0.5$, which can be seen to reach and vary about the true mean of $E[N] = 1$ after about 100 steps (10 seconds). The higher curve corresponds to $\rho = 0.9$, which is a much higher utilization. The true mean in this case is $E[N] = 9$ and it can be seen that the average of the realizations does not reach the area of the mean until about 1400 steps. Thus we see that the transient period increases dramatically as the utilization approaches 1.

Figure 12.29(b) shows the sample mean of the normalized covariance functions of the 20 realizations of $N(t)$. For $\rho = 0.5$, the autocovariance does not reach 0 until about 200 steps. Furthermore, for $\rho = 0.9$, the autocovariance is approximately 0.6 after 200 steps. This much longer sustained correlation is another indicator of the increase in transient time as utilization is increased.

---

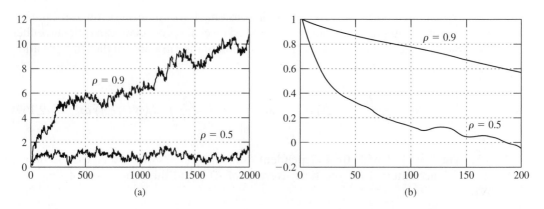

**FIGURE 12.29**
(a) Transient of M/M/1 queue using sampled-time approach, $\rho = 0.5, 0.9$; (b) normalized covariance of M/M/1 queue,
$\rho = 0.5, 0.9$.

In order to approximate the queueing process accurately, the time-sampled approach requires that we use a small step size. In addition to possibly increasing the amount of computation required to perform the simulation size, a small step size has the effect of making more adjacent samples highly correlated. This is clearly evident in the observed autocovariance function in the above example.

The correlation of samples poses a problem in estimating parameters of a queueing process from a single realization. Suppose we are interested in estimating the mean of $\{N(k\delta)\}$ from a *single realization* of the process:

$$\overline{N}_n = \frac{1}{n}\sum_{k=1}^{n} N(k\delta). \tag{12.170}$$

The terms in the series $\{N(k\delta)\}$ are correlated, so from Eq. (9.108), assuming that the process is wide sense stationary, the variance of the sample mean is then larger than it would be for iid samples:

$$\mathrm{VAR}[\overline{N}_n] = \frac{1}{n}\left[C_N(0) + 2\sum_{k=1}^{n-1}\left(1 - \frac{k}{n}\right)C_N(k)\right], \tag{12.171}$$

where $C_N(k)$ is the covariance function of $N(t)$. Only $C_N(0)$, which corresponds to the variance of $N$, would be present if the observations were uncorrelated. Example 12.28 demonstrated how $N(t)$ in queueing systems can maintain significant correlation for significant periods of time. The example also illustrated how the process $N(t)$ becomes more correlated as the utilization increases. As discussed in Examples 9.49 and 9.50, the net effect is that the convergence of the sample mean to $E[N]$ is slower than if the samples were independent. This larger variance can be taken into account by gathering estimates for the covariance terms $C_N(k)$ and using Eq. (12.168) in the calculation of confidence intervals. (See [Law, p. 556] for a discussion on such confidence intervals).

The relative frequencies of the states provide estimates for the long-range proportion of time spent in each state:

$$\hat{p}_j = \frac{1}{n} \sum_{k=1}^{n} I_j(k\delta)$$  (12.172)

where $I_j$ is the indicator function for the event $\{N(k\delta)\} = j\}$. Relative frequencies are a special case of sample means so the same cautions regarding the variance of the estimates and convergence rates apply.

The **method of batch means**, introduced in Section 8.4, provides an approach to dealing with the correlation among samples. A long simulation run is divided into multiple segments that are sufficiently long that the samples from different segments have low correlation. The parameter estimates from different segments, e.g., sample mean or relative frequencies, are treated as independent random variables and the standard statistical tools are applied to the batch means and batch relative frequencies.

---

### Example 12.29    Confidence Intervals Using Batch Means

Use the method of batch means to estimate the mean of the M/M/1 queue when $\lambda = 0.5$ and $\mu = 1$ job per second. Each realization should consist of 8 batches of 600 steps. Replicate each simulation five times.

Five replications of 5000-step realizations were carried out. The first 200 samples from each realization were discarded to remove bias from the initial transient. The remaining 4800 samples in each realization were divided into 8 batches. Table 12.2(a) shows the means for each of the resulting 40 batches. For each realization the sample mean and sample standard deviation for the 8 batch means were calculated and are shown in Table 12.2(b). Confidence intervals were then calculated for each realization. For a 90% confidence level ($a = 10\%$), $t_{a/2} = 1.8946$ and $\delta = t_{a/2}\sigma/\sqrt{8}$. The upper and lower limits of the confidence interval for the mean of the process are given in the two rightmost columns of Table 12.2(b). Every confidence interval contains the value 1, which is the expected value of the M/M/1 queue when $\rho = 1/2$.

**TABLE 12.2a**    Sequence of batch means for five replications

| r/b | 1 | 2 | 3 | 4 | 5 | 6 | 7 | 8 |
|-----|---------|---------|---------|---------|---------|---------|---------|---------|
| 1 | 0.84500 | 0.70667 | 0.51500 | 4.57167 | 0.30500 | 3.56000 | 1.75167 | 0.91167 |
| 2 | 0.83000 | 0.66000 | 0.97667 | 1.21833 | 1.14667 | 1.16333 | 2.39833 | 0.61000 |
| 3 | 0.96000 | 0.55333 | 0.89833 | 0.62500 | 0.31000 | 3.39167 | 0.86167 | 0.43333 |
| 4 | 2.73333 | 1.06167 | 0.62167 | 0.45667 | 2.17333 | 1.30000 | 0.57667 | 0.88167 |
| 5 | 1.14000 | 0.85667 | 0.82500 | 1.07167 | 0.67833 | 1.02167 | 1.08833 | 1.44667 |

**TABLE 12.2b**    Confidence interval for mean for each of five replications

| r/b | Mean | $\sigma$ | $\delta$ | Lower | Upper |
|-----|--------|---------|---------|---------|--------|
| 1 | 1.6458 | 1.57547 | 1.05532 | 0.59052 | 2.7011 |
| 2 | 1.1254 | 0.56347 | 0.37744 | 0.74798 | 1.5029 |
| 3 | 1.0042 | 0.99199 | 0.66448 | 0.33969 | 1.6686 |
| 4 | 1.2256 | 0.81934 | 0.54883 | 0.67679 | 1.7745 |
| 5 | 1.0160 | 0.23455 | 0.15711 | 0.85893 | 1.1732 |

**TABLE 12.2c**  Sequence of batch confidence intervals across five replications

| r/b | 1 | 2 | 3 | 4 | 5 | 6 | 7 | 8 |
|---|---|---|---|---|---|---|---|---|
| Mean | 1.3017 | 0.7677 | 0.7673 | 1.5887 | 0.9227 | 2.0873 | 1.3353 | 0.8567 |
| $\sigma$ | 0.8099 | 0.1972 | 0.1931 | 1.6965 | 0.7796 | 1.2727 | 0.7356 | 0.3846 |
| $\delta$ | 0.7721 | 0.1880 | 0.1841 | 1.6174 | 0.7432 | 1.2134 | 0.7013 | 0.3667 |
| Upper | 2.0738 | 0.9557 | 0.9515 | 3.2061 | 1.6659 | 3.3007 | 2.0366 | 1.2234 |
| Lower | 0.5296 | 0.5796 | 0.5832 | −0.0287 | 0.1795 | 0.8739 | 0.6340 | 0.4900 |

Table 12.2(c) gives the 90% confidence interval that is calculated for the batch means *across* different replications. These batches are truly independent and will not be affected by correlation effects. It is important to determine whether any evidence of bias exists in the earlier batches due to the initial transient phase. It can be seen that the second and third columns do not include the value 1 by a small margin.

We also calculated a 90% confidence interval for the combined 40 batches and obtained $(1.2034 - 0.24575, 1.2034 + 0.24575) = (0.95765, 1.449)$. Finally, we calculated a 90% confidence interval based on the sample means of the 5 realizations, and obtained $(1.2034 - 0.25096, 1.2034 + 0.25096) = (0.95244, 1.4544)$. Note that the latter 5 realizations are truly independent and constitute a pure application (no batching) of the replication method.

### 12.10.4 Simulation Using Embedded Markov Chains

Many queueing systems have natural embedding points that lead to discrete-time Markov chains. We saw in Chapter 11 that queueing systems that are modeled by continuous-time Markov chains can be defined in terms of an embedded Markov chain and exponentially distributed state occupancy times. In this chapter we saw that the distribution of the steady state number of customers in an M/G/1 system can also be observed through an embedded Markov chain. In this section we discuss **simulation based on embedded Markov chains**.

First, let $N(t)$ be the number of customers in a queueing system that is modeled by a continuous-time Markov chain. The transition rate matrix $\Gamma$ for the process provides us with the transition probabilities of the embedded chain as well as the state occupancy times (see Eq. 11.35). In Example 11.50 we used this approach to generate realizations of an M/M/1 queue. The output of this simulation is a sequence of states $\{N_i\}$ and the corresponding state occupancy times $\{T_i\}$. The relative frequencies obtained from the sequence of states provide us with an estimate for the state probabilities $\{\pi_j\}$ of the embedded Markov chain. The occupancy times according to their corresponding state, e.g., $\{T_k(j), k = 1, \ldots, n_j\}$ for state $j$, can also provide us with an estimate for the state occupancy times. We can obtain an estimate for the mean of $N(t)$ directly:

$$\hat{N} = \frac{1}{T} \int_0^T N(t)\, dt = \frac{1}{T} \sum_{k=1}^n N_k T_k. \tag{12.173}$$

An estimate for long-term proportion of time in state $j$ is obtained similarly:

$$\hat{p}_j = \frac{1}{T}\int_0^T I_j(t)\, dt = \frac{1}{T}\sum_{k=1}^{n_j} T_k(j).\tag{12.174}$$

If the Markov chains that model the system are ergodic, then the above estimates will converge to the correct steady state values.

---

### Example 12.30 M/M/1 Steady State Probabilities Using Embedded Markov Chain

Use the embedded Markov chain approach to estimate the state probabilities in an M/M/1 system with $\lambda = 0.75$ and $\mu = 1$. Calculate the proportion of time spent in each state and obtain confidence intervals for these values by using replication.

The code in Example 11.50 can be modified to calculate Eq. (12.174) by accumulating the total time spent in each state as the simulator generates each new state and occupancy time. Each realization was 1800 seconds in duration, but no data was gathered during the first 300 seconds of the simulation. Eight pmf estimates were obtained and the sample mean and standard deviation as well as a 90% confidence interval for each state probability were computed using the eight independent estimates from the replication. The results are shown in Fig. 12.30. It can be seen that there is generally good agreement between the theoretical pmf and the confidence intervals.

---

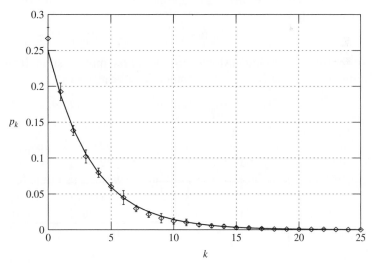

**FIGURE 12.30**
Confidence intervals for steady state M/M/1 pmf.

The following example shows that we can simulate an M/G/1 system using another type of embedded Markov chain.

---

**Example 12.31    Simulating M/G/1 Using Embedded Markov Chains**

Section 12.7 showed that the steady state distribution for the number of customers in an M/G/1 system is the same as the distribution for the number left behind by a customer departure. Furthermore, the number of customers left behind by the $j$th customer departure, $N_j$, forms a discrete-time Markov chain as follows:

$$N_j = (N_{j-1} - 1)^+ + M_j \tag{12.175}$$

where $M_j$ is the number of arrivals during the service time of the $j$th customer and where

$$(x)^+ \triangleq \max(0, x).$$

Therefore we can obtain the steady state pmf for $N(t)$ in an M/G/1 system by finding the transition probability matrix associated with Eq. (12.175) and applying the methods developed in Section 11.6. We explore this approach further in the problems.

---

Next we introduce *Lindley's recursion for the waiting time in a G/G/1 system* as a final application of embedded Markov chain methods. Assume that the customer interarrival times and service times are independent random variables with arbitrary distributions. We focus on the waiting time experienced by an arriving customer and we show that the sequence of waiting times forms a Markov chain.

Let $a_1, a_2, \ldots$ denote the customer interarrival times and let $\tau_1, \tau_2, \ldots$ be their corresponding service times. Let $W_n$ be the waiting time of the $n$th customer. Suppose the $(n + 1)$st customer arrives to a nonempty system, as shown in Fig. 12.31(a). Note that we must have:

$$W_n + \tau_n = a_{n+1} + W_{n+1}$$

in order for the arriving customer to find a nonempty system. It then follows that the waiting time for the $(n + 1)$st customer must be given by:

$$W_{n+1} = W_n + \tau_n - a_{n+1} \text{ if } W_n + \tau_n - a_{n+1} \geq 0. \tag{12.176a}$$

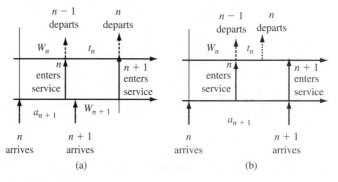

**FIGURE 12.31**
Customer arrivals and departures in G/G/1 queue.

On the other hand, the arriving customer finds an empty system (Fig. 12.31b) under the following conditions:

$$W_{n+1} = 0 \quad \text{if} \quad W_n + \tau_n - a_{n+1} < 0. \tag{12.176b}$$

Therefore we conclude that the sequence of waiting times is given by **Lindley's recursion**:

$$W_{n+1} = \max(0, W_n + \tau_n - a_{n+1}). \tag{12.177}$$

$W_{n+1}$ depends on the past only through $W_n$ and $\tau_n$ and $a_{n+1}$. Since $\tau_n$ and $a_{n+1}$ are from iid sequences and are independent of each other, we conclude that $W_{n+1}$ is a Markov process with stationary transition probabilities. Note that $W_n$ assumes a continuum of values. We can generate the sequence of total delays experienced by the sequence of customers as follows: $T_n = W_n + a_n$.

Equation (12.177) can be used to derive an integral equation for the steady state waiting time of customers in a G/G/1 system [Kleinrock, p. 282]. The equation is similar to the Wiener–Hopf equation we encountered in Section 10.4 and usually requires transform methods to solve. However, *Eq. (12.177) is remarkably simple to use in simulations.*

---

### Example 12.32    Estimating Waiting Time Distribution Using Lindley's Recursion

Estimate the distribution of the customer waiting times in an M/M/1 queue when $\lambda = 0.9$ and $\mu = 1$ job per second. Compare the empirical cdf of the observed total time in the system with the theoretical distribution.

Lindley's recursion can be readily implemented in Octave. Arrays of exponential interarrival times with $\lambda = 0.9$ and service times with $\mu = 1$ job per second are generated initially. Lindley's recursion is then used to compute the sequence of waiting times and total delays for the sequence of customers. The Octave function `empirical_cdf` is used to obtain the cdf of the observations. In the simulation a sequence of 2000 waiting and total times were collected and no data was deleted to allow for an initial transient period. Figure 12.32 compares the empirical cdf with the distribution for waiting time in an M/M/1 system with $\rho = 0.9$. A test such as the Kolmogorov–Smirnov test can be applied to assess goodness of fit of the empirical distribution to the hypothetical distribution.

---

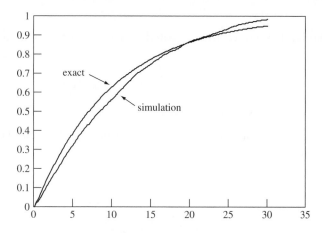

**FIGURE 12.32**
Empircial cdf of M/M/1 queue using Lindley's recursion, $\rho = 0.9$.

### 12.10.5 Replication through Regenerative Cycles

In Section 7.5 we considered renewal processes where time is divided into intervals according to an iid sequence of positive random variables $\{X_i\}$. We associated with each interval $X_i$ a cost $C_i$. We then proved the following result Eq. (7.47):

$$\lim_{t \to \infty} \frac{1}{t} \sum_{j=1}^{M(t)} C_j = \frac{E[C]}{E[X]} \tag{12.178}$$

where $E[C]$ is the average cost per cycle and $E[X]$ is the mean cycle length.

The **regenerative method for simulation** involves finding renewal points in a queueing system where the process "restarts" itself so that its future is independent of the past. For example, in many queueing systems this renewal or regeneration occurs when a customer arrives to an empty system. Measurements taken during different cycles are then independent random variables. Thus in effect the regenerative method partitions a single simulation into a number of independent replications.

The long-term time average of $C(t)$ in Eq. (12.178) is given by the ratio of the sample mean for the measurements for $C$ and the sample mean for $X$. For example, if we are interested in the probability that the system is in state $j$, then we let $C_j$ be the time the system is in state $j$ during the $j$th cycle:

$$C_i = \int_{R_{i-1}}^{R_i} I_j(t) \, dt = \sum_{k=1}^{n_i(j)} T_k^i(j) \tag{12.179}$$

where $n_i(j)$ is the number of times state $j$ occurred during the $i$th cycle and $T_k^i(j)$ is the occupancy time of the $j$th occurrence of state $j$ during the $i$th cycle. The corresponding estimate for the proportion of time in state $j$ is:

$$\hat{p}_j = \frac{\dfrac{1}{n} \sum_{k=1}^{n_i(j)} T_k^i(j)}{\dfrac{1}{n} \sum_{i=1}^{n} X_i}. \tag{12.180}$$

On the other hand if we are interested in the mean of $N(t)$, we let

$$C_i = \int_{R_{i-1}}^{R_i} N(t) \, dt = \sum_{k=1}^{n_i} N_k^i T_k^i \tag{12.181}$$

where $n_i$ is the number of states visited during the $i$th cycle. The corresponding estimate for the mean is:

$$\hat{N} = \frac{\dfrac{1}{n} \sum_{i=1}^{n} \sum_{k=1}^{n_i} N_k^i T_k^i}{\dfrac{1}{n} \sum_{i=1}^{n} X_i}. \tag{12.182}$$

The numerators and denominators in Eqs. (12.180) and (12.182) individually are strongly consistent estimators for their corresponding parameters. Therefore the estimators formed by taking their ratios in Eqs. (12.180) and (12.182) are also strongly consistent. Note, however, that the ratios provide biased estimates. We discuss confidence intervals after the following example.

---

### Example 12.33  Regenerative Method for M/M/1 Simulation

Estimate the mean waiting time of customers in the system in Example 12.28 using the regenerative method to analyze the sequence of waiting times produced by Lindley's recursion.

Let a cycle consist of the time from when a customer arrives to an empty system until the next time a customer arrives to an empty system. We are interested in the average waiting time experienced by customers over a long period of time. Suppose we measure the number of customers serviced in a sequence of cycles $\{N_c(i)\}$, and the total of the waiting times of all customers in the cycle $\{W_{agg}(i)\}$. Each of these sequences is iid and so each one will converge to its respective mean. The ratio of the two expressions provides an estimate for the mean waiting time (see Problem 12.78):

$$\hat{W} = \frac{\dfrac{1}{n}\sum_{i=1}^{n} W_{agg}(i)}{\dfrac{1}{n}\sum_{i=1}^{n} N_c(i)}. \tag{12.183}$$

It is easy to prepare a simulation to gather $\{N_c(i)\}$, $\{W_{agg}(i)\}$, and the sequence of cycle durations $\{X_i\}$ using Lindley's recursion because each regeneration point is marked by arriving customers that have zero waiting time. The resulting sequences can be parsed according to their respective cycles and the above cycle statistics can then be gathered.

A simulation with 4000 customer arrivals to an M/M/1 systems with $\lambda = 0.9$ and $\mu = 1$ was conducted and the results in Table 12.3 were obtained. The 4000 arrivals produced 366 cycles. The ratio of the mean number of customers serviced in a cycle to the mean cycle duration gives the following estimate for the arrival rate:

$$\text{Arrival Rate Estimate} = 10.842/11.913 = 0.91,$$

which is close to $\lambda = 0.9$. The estimate for the mean waiting time obtained from the ratio in Eq. (12.183) was 8.80. From Eq. (9.27) the mean waiting time for this M/M/1 queue is $E[W] = 9$, which again is quite close.

---

**TABLE 12.3**  Per regenerative cycle statistics for M/M/1 queue

| M/M/1 Mean Waiting Time | |
|---|---|
| L = 4000 | TotCycle = 366 |
| MeanCycle = 11.913 | STDCycle = 41.374 |
| MeanCount = 10.842 | STDCount = 39.236 |
| MeanCycleWait = 95.424 | STDCycleWait = 612.20 |
| MeanWait = 8.8017 | |

Of course the whole point of striving to get independent observations is to produce confidence intervals. In [Law, p. 559] an approximate confidence interval is developed for an estimator of the form in Eq. (12.183). The pair $(W_{agg}(i), N_c(i))$ form an iid sequence but in general $W_{agg}(i)$ and $N_c(i)$ are correlated. It can be shown that for large $n$ the estimator in Eq. (12.183) is asymptotically Gaussian with mean $E[W]$ and variance:

$$\hat{\sigma}_{\hat{W}}^2(n) = \hat{\sigma}_{W_{agg}}^2(n) - 2\hat{W}(n)\hat{\sigma}_{W_{agg}, N_c}^2 + (\hat{W}(n))^2\hat{\sigma}_{N_c}^2(n) \tag{12.184}$$

where $\hat{\sigma}_{W_{agg}, N_c}^2$ is the estimator for the covariance of $W_{agg}(i)$ and $N_c(i)$. This result leads to the following confidence interval:

$$\left( \hat{W} - \frac{z_{1-\alpha/2}\hat{\sigma}_{\hat{W}}\sqrt{n}}{\hat{N}_c}, \hat{W} + \frac{z_{1-\alpha/2}\hat{\sigma}_{\hat{W}}\sqrt{n}}{\hat{N}_c} \right). \tag{12.185}$$

The required estimates for the variances and covariances of $W_{agg}(i)$, $N_c(i)$ can be made from the per-cycle statistics.

In practice the regenerative method is difficult to apply because the occurrence of regenerative instances is not controllable. For example, the busy periods of queueing systems under heavy traffic vary dramatically and so the occurrence of regeneration points can be quite unpredictable.

In conclusion, simulation straddles the space between theoretical models and the real world. The basic introduction to simulation methods for queueing systems provides an excellent opportunity to illustrate the role of statistical techniques in the application of probability models to real world problems. The presence of transient effects and correlations in the observed data provide an excellent opportunity to emphasize the need to apply probability models and statistical tools with care. But we should end this book on a positive note: the availability of plentiful and inexpensive computing allows us to extend the reach of our theoretical and simulation models into new frontiers!

## SUMMARY

- A queueing system is specified by the arrival process, the service time distribution, the number of servers, the waiting room, and the queue discipline.

- Little's formula states that under very general conditions: The mean number in a system is equal to the product of the mean arrival rate and the mean time spent in the system.

- In M/M/1, M/M/1/$K$, M/M/$c$, M/M/$c$/$c$, and M/M/$\infty$ queueing systems, the number of customers in the system is a continuous-time Markov chain. The steady state distribution for the number in the system is found by solving the global balance equations for the Markov chain. The waiting time and delay distribution when the service discipline is first come, first served is found by using the arriving customer's distribution.

- If the arrival process in a queueing system is a Poisson process and if the customer interarrival times are independent of the service times, then the arriving customer's distribution is the same as the steady state distribution of the queueing system.

- In M/G/1 queueing systems the arriving customer's distribution and the departing customer's distribution are both equal to the steady state distribution of the queueing system. The steady state distribution for the number of customers in an M/G/1 system can be found by embedding a discrete-time Markov chain at the customer departure instants.

- Burke's theorem states that the output process of M/M/1, M/M/$c$, and M/M/$\infty$ systems at steady state are Poisson processes, and that the departure instants prior to time $t$ are independent of the state of the system at time $t$. As a result, feedforward combinations of queueing systems with exponential service times have a product-form solution.

- Jackson's theorem states that for networks of queueing systems with exponential service times and external Poisson input processes, the joint state pmf is of product form. If the network of queues is open, the marginal state pmf of each queue is the same as that of a queue in isolation that has Poisson arrivals of the same rate. If the network of queues is closed, finding the joint state pmf requires finding a normalization constant. The mean value analysis method allows us to find the mean number in each queue, the mean time spent in each queue, and the arrival rate in each queue in a closed network of queues.

- Approaches to simulating queueing systems include replication, time sampling, and embedded Markov chains. The analysis of observations must deal with the effect of transient behavior as well as the correlation of observations.

## CHECKLIST OF IMPORTANT TERMS

*a/b/m/K*
Arrival rate
Arriving customer's distribution
Burke's theorem
Carried load
Closed networks of queues
Departing customer's distribution
Erlang $B$ formula
Erlang $C$ formula
Finite-source queueing system
Head-of-line priority service
Interarrival times
Jackson's theorem
Lindley's recursion
Little's formula
Mean value analysis
Method of batch means
M/G/1 queueing system
M/M/$c$ queueing system
M/M/$c/c$ queueing system
M/M/1 queueing system

M/M/1/$K$ queueing system
Offered load
Open networks of queues
Pollaczek–Khinchin mean value formula
Pollaczek–Khinchin transform equation
Product-form solution
Queue discipline
Regenerative method for simulation
Residual service time
Server utilization
Service discipline
Service time
Simulation based on embedded Markov chains
Simulation through independent replication
Time-sampled process simulation
Total delay
Traffic intensity
Waiting time

## ANNOTATED REFERENCES

References [1] and [2] provide an introduction to queueing theory at a level slightly higher than that given here. Reference [2] is an invaluable source of classical queueing theory results in telephony problems. Reference [3] demonstrates the application of queueing theory to data communication networks. References [1–7] discuss techniques for simulating queueing systems and for analyzing the resulting data. [8–10] presents excellent discussions on reversible processes and M/G/c/c and M/G/$\infty$.

1. L. Kleinrock, *Queueing Systems*, vol. 1, Wiley, New York, 1975.
2. R. B. Cooper, *Introduction to Queueing Theory*, 2nd ed. North Holland, 1981. Reprinted by CEE Press of the George Washington University.
3. D. Bertsekas and R. Gallager, *Data Networks*, Prentice-Hall, Englewood Cliffs, NJ, 1987.
4. A. M. Law and W. D. Kelton, *Simulation, Modeling, and Analysis*, 2nd ed. McGraw-Hill, New York, 1999.
5. J. Banks, J. S. Carson II, and B. L. Nelson, *Discrete-Event System Simulation*, Prentice-Hall, Upper Saddle River, NJ, 1996.
6. G. S. Fishman, *Discrete-Event Simulation: Modeling, Programming, and Analysis*, Springer-Verlag, New York, 2001.
7. S. M. Ross, *Stochastic Processes*, Wiley, New York, 1983.
8. M. Reiser and S. S. Lavenberg, "Mean-value analysis of closed multichain queueing networks," *J. Assoc. Comput. Mach.* 27: 313–322, 1980.
9. S. S. Lavenberg, *Computer Performance Modeling Handbook*, Academic Press, New York, 1983.
10. K. Pawlikowski, "Steady-state simulation of queueing processes: survey of problems and solutions," *ACM Computing Surveys*, Vol. 22, No. 2, pp. 123–170, 1990.

## PROBLEMS

### Sections 12.1 and 12.2: The Elements of a Queueing Network and Little's Formula

**12.1.** Describe the following queueing systems: M/M/1, M/D/1/$K$, M/G/3, D/M/2, G/D/1, D/D/2.

**12.2.** Suppose that a queueing system is empty at time $t = 0$, let the arrival times of the first six customers be 1, 3, 4, 7, 8, 15, and let their respective service times be 3.5, 4, 2, 1, 1.5, 4. Find $S_i$, $\tau_i$, $D_i$, $W_i$, and $T_i$ for $i = 1, \ldots, 5$; sketch $N(t)$ versus $t$; and check Little's formula by computing $\langle N \rangle_t$, $\langle \lambda \rangle_t$, and $\langle T \rangle_t$ for each of the following three service disciplines:

    **(a)** First come, first served.

    **(b)** Last come, first served.

    **(c)** Shortest job first (assume that the precise service time of each job is known before it enters service).

**12.3.** A data communication line delivers a block of information every 10 $\mu$s. A decoder checks each block for errors and corrects the errors if necessary. It takes 1 $\mu$s to determine whether a block has any errors. If the block has one error, it takes 5 $\mu$s to correct it, and if it has more than one error it takes 20 $\mu$s to correct the error. Blocks wait in a queue when the decoder falls behind. Suppose that the decoder is initially empty and that the numbers of errors in the first ten blocks are 0, 1, 3, 1, 0, 4, 0, 1, 0, 0.

**(a)** Plot the number of blocks in the decoder as a function of time.

**(b)** Find the mean number of blocks in the decoder.

**(c)** What percentage of the time is the decoder empty?

**12.4.** Three queues are arranged in a loop as shown in Fig. P12.1. Assume that the mean service time in queue $i$ is $m_i = 1/\mu_i$.

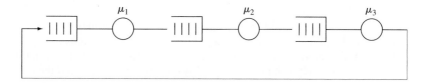

**FIGURE P12.1**

**(a)** Suppose the queue has a single customer circulating in the loop. Find the mean time $E[T]$ it takes the customer to cycle around the loop. Deduce from $E[T]$ the mean arrival rate $\lambda$ at each of the queues. Verify that Little's formula holds for these two quantities.

**(b)** If there are $N$ customers circulating in the loop, how are the mean arrival rate and the mean cycle time related?

**12.5.** A very popular barbershop is always full. The shop has two barbers and three chairs for waiting, and as soon as a customer completes his service and leaves the shop, another enters the shop. Assume the mean service time is $m$.

**(a)** Use Little's formula to relate the arrival rate and the mean time spent in the shop.

**(b)** Use Little's formula to relate the arrival rate and the mean time spent in service.

**(c)** Use the above formulas to find an expression for the mean time spent in the system in terms of the mean service time.

**12.6.** In Problem 12.3, suppose that the probabilities of zero, one, and more than one errors are $p_0$, $p_1$, and $p_2$, respectively. Use Little's formula to find the mean number of blocks in the decoder.

**12.7.** A communication network receives messages from $R$ sources with mean arrival rates $\lambda_1, \ldots, \lambda_R$. On the average there are $E[N_i]$ messages from source $i$ in the network.

**(a)** Use Little's formula to find the average time $E[T_i]$ spent by type $i$ customers in the network.

**(b)** Let $\lambda$ denote the total arrival rate into the network. Use Little's formula to find an expression for the mean time $E[T]$ spent by customers (of all types) in the network in terms of the $E[N_i]$.

**(c)** Combine the results of part a and part b to obtain an expression for $E[T]$ in terms of $E[T_i]$. Derive the same expression using $A(t)$ the arrival processes for each type.

## Section 12.3: The M/M/1 Queue

**12.8. (a)** Find $P[N \geq n]$ for an M/M/1 system.

**(b)** What is the maximum allowable arrival rate in a system with service rate $\mu$, if we require that $P[N \geq 10] = 10^{-3}$?

**12.9.** A decision to purchase one of two machines is to be made. Machine 1 has a processing rate of $\mu$ transactions/hour and it costs $B$ dollars/hour to operate whether idle or not; machine 2 is twice as fast but costs twice as much to operate. Suppose that transactions arrive at the system according to a Poisson process of rate $\lambda$ and that the transaction processing times are exponentially distributed. The total cost of the system is the operation cost plus a cost of $A$ dollars for each hour a customer has to wait.

    **(a)** Find expressions for the total cost per hour for each of the systems. Plot this cost versus the arrival rate.

    **(b)** If $A = B/10$, for what range of arrival rates is machine 1 cheaper? Repeat for $A = 10B$.

**12.10.** Consider an M/M/1 queueing system in which each customer arrival brings in a profit of $5 but in which each unit time of delay costs the system $1. Find the range of arrival rates for which the system makes a net profit.

**12.11.** Consider an M/M/1 queueing system with arrival rate $\lambda$ customers/second.

    **(a)** Find the service rate required so that the average queue is five customers (i.e., $E[N_q] = 5$).

    **(b)** Find the service rate required so that the queue that forms from time to time has mean 5 (i.e., $E[N_q \mid N_q > 0] = 5$).

    **(c)** Which of the two criteria, $E[N_q]$ or $E[N_q \mid N_q > 0]$, do you consider the more appropriate?

**12.12.** Show that the $p$th percentile of the waiting time for an M/M/1 system is given by

$$x = \frac{1/\mu}{1 - \rho} \ln\left(\frac{\rho}{1 - p}\right).$$

**12.13.** Consider an M/M/1 queueing system with service rate two customers per second.

    **(a)** Find the maximum allowable arrival rate if 90% of customers should not have a delay of more than 3 seconds.

    **(b)** Find the maximum allowable arrival rate if 90% of customers should not have to wait for service for more than 2 seconds. *Hint:* Use the result from Problem 12.12, and then find $\lambda$ by trial and error.

**12.14.** Verify Eq. (12.36) for the steady state pmf of an M/M/1/$K$ system.

**12.15.** Consider an M/M/1/2 queueing system in which each customer accepted into the system brings in a profit of $5 and each customer rejected results in a loss of $1. Find the arrival rate at which the system breaks even.

**12.16.** For an M/M/1/$K$ system show that

$$P[N = k \mid N < K] = \frac{P[N = k]}{1 - P[N = K]} \qquad 0 \le k < K.$$

Why does this probability represent the proportion of arriving customers who actually enter the system and find exactly $k$ customers in the system?

**12.17.** **(a)** Use the matrix exponential method of Eq. (11.72) to find the transient solution for the state pmfs for an M/M/1/5 queue under the following conditions:

        **(i)** $\rho = 0.5$ and $N(0) = 0$, $N(0) = 2$, $N(0) = 5$;

        **(ii)** $\rho = 1$ and $N(0) = 0$, $N(0) = 2$, $N(0) = 5$.

    **(b)** Plot $E[N(t)]$ vs. $t$ for the cases considered in part a.

**12.18.** Suppose that two types of customers arrive at a queueing system according to independent Poisson process of rate $\lambda/2$. Both types of customers require exponentially distributed service times of rate $\mu$. Type 1 customers are always accepted into the system, but type 2 customers are turned away when the total number of customers in the system exceeds $K$.

    **(a)** Sketch the transition rate diagram for $N(t)$, the total number of customers in the system.

    **(b)** Find the steady state pmf of $N(t)$.

**12.19.** Consider the queueing system in Problem 12.18 with $K = 5$ and with a maximum system occupancy of 10 customers. In this problem we use the matrix exponential method of Eq. (11.72) to explore how the system adjusts to sudden increases in load.

    **(a)** Find the transient state pmf for the system with $\lambda = 1/2$ and $\mu = 1$, assuming that initially there are 5 customers in the system.

    **(b)** Suppose that at time 20, the $\lambda$ increases to 1. Find the transient state pmf after this surge in traffic.

## Section 12.4: Multiserver Systems: M/M/c, M/M/c/c, and M/M/$\infty$

**12.20.** Find $P[N \geq c + k]$ for an M/M/c system.

**12.21.** Customers arrive at a shop according to a Poisson process of rate 12 customers per hour. The shop has two clerks to attend to the customers. Suppose that it takes a clerk an exponentially distributed amount of time with mean 5 minutes to service one customer.

    **(a)** What is the probability that an arriving customer must wait to be served?

    **(b)** Find the mean number of customers in the system and the mean time spent in the system.

    **(c)** Find the probability that there are more than 4 customers in the system.

**12.22.** Little's formula applied to the servers implies that the mean number of busy servers is $\lambda E[\tau]$. Verify this by explicit calculation of the mean number of busy servers in an M/M/c system.

**12.23.** Inquiries arrive at an information center according to a Poisson process of rate 10 inquiries per second. It takes a server 1/2 second to answer each query.

    **(a)** How many servers are needed if we require that the mean total delay for each inquiry should not exceed 4 seconds, and 90% of all queries should wait less than 8 seconds?

    **(b)** What is the resulting probability that all servers are busy? Idle?

**12.24.** Consider a queueing system in which the maximum processing rate is $c\mu$ customers per second. Let $k$ be the number of customers in the system. When $k \geq c$, $c$ customers are served at a rate $\mu$ each. When $0 < k \leq c$, these $k$ customers are served at a rate $c\mu/k$ each. Assume Poisson arrivals of rate $\lambda$ and exponentially distributed times.

    **(a)** Find the transition rate diagram for this system.

    **(b)** Find the steady state pmf for the number in the system.

    **(c)** Find $E[W]$ and $E[T]$.

    **(d)** For $c = 2$, compare $E[W]$ and $E[T]$ for this system to those of M/M/1 and M/M/2 systems of the same maximum processing rate.

**12.25. (a)** Suppose that the queueing system in Problem 12.24 models a Web server where $c$ is the maximum number of clients allowed to place queries at the same time. Discuss the impact of the choice of the parameter $c$ on queueing and total delay performance.

    **(b)** Consider the fact that while connected to the Web server, clients spend their time in three states: sending the query, waiting for the response, and thinking after each response. How does this affect the choice of $c$? Should the system impose a timeout limit on the customer's connection time?

**12.26.** Show that the Erlang $B$ formula satisfies the following recursive equation:

$$B(c, a) = \frac{aB(c - 1, a)}{c + aB(c - 1, a)},$$

where $a = \lambda E[\tau]$.

**12.27.** Consider an M/M/5/5 system in which the arrival rate is 10 customers per minute and the mean service time is 1/2 minute.

(a) Find the probability of blocking a customer. *Hint:* Use the result from the Problem 12.26.

(b) How many more servers are required to reduce the blocking probability to 10%?

**12.28.** A tool rental shop has four floor sanders. Customers for floor sanders arrive according to a Poisson process at a rate of one customer every two days. The average rental time is exponentially distributed with mean two days. If the shop has no floor sanders available, the customers go to the shop across the street.

(a) Find the proportion of customers that go to the shop across the street.

(b) What is the mean number of floor sanders rented out?

(c) What is the increase in lost customers if one of the sanders breaks down and is not replaced?

**12.29.** (a) Show that the Erlang $C$ formula is related to the Erlang $B$ formula by

$$C(c, a) = \frac{cB(c, a)}{c - a\{1 - B(c, a)\}} \qquad \text{for } c > a.$$

(b) Show that this implies that $C(c, a) > B(c, a)$.

**12.30.** Suppose that department A in a certain company has three private videoconference lines connecting two sites. Calls arrive according to a Poisson process of rate 1 call/hour, and have an exponentially distributed holding time of 2 hours. Calls that arrive when the three lines are busy are automatically redirected to public video lines. Suppose that department B also has three private videoconference lines connecting the same sites, and that it has the same arrival and service statistics.

(a) Find the proportion of calls that are redirected to public lines.

(b) Suppose we consolidate the videoconference traffic from the two departments and allow all calls to share the six lines. What proportion of calls are redirected to public lines?

**12.31.** A $c = 10$ server blocking system handles two streams of customers that each arrive at rate $\lambda/2$. Type 1 customers have a mean service time of 1 time unit, and Type 2 customers have a service time of 3 time units. Compare the blocking performance of a system that allows customers to access any available server against one that allocates half the servers to each class. Does scale matter? Does the answer change if $c = 100$?

**12.32.** Suppose we use $P[N = c]$ from an M/M/$\infty$ system to approximate $B(c, a)$ in selecting the number of servers in an M/M/c/c system. Is the resulting design optimistic or pessimistic?

**12.33.** During the evening rush hour, users log onto a peer-to-peer network at a rate of 10 users per second. Each user stays connected to the network an average of 1 hour.

(a) What is the steady state pmf for the number of customers logged onto the peer-to-peer network?

(b) Is steady state ever achieved?

(c) Is it reasonable to assume a Gaussian distribution for the number of customers in the system?

## Section 12.5: Finite-Source Queueing Systems

**12.34.** A computer is shared by 15 users as shown in Fig. 12.14(b). Suppose that the mean service time is 2 seconds and the mean think time is 30 seconds, and that both of these times are exponentially distributed.

    **(a)** Find the mean delay and mean throughput of the system.

    **(b)** What is the system saturation point $K^*$ for this system?

    **(c)** Repeat part a if 5 users are added to the system.

**12.35.** A Web server that has the maximum number of clients connected is modeled by the system in Figure 12.14(b). Suppose that the system can handle a query in 10 milliseconds and the users click new queries at a rate of 1 every 5 seconds.

    **(a)** Find the value of $K^*$ for this system.

    **(b)** Find the pmf for the number of requests found in queue by arriving queries.

**12.36.** Find the transition rate diagram and steady state pmf for a two-server finite-source queueing system.

**12.37.** Verify that Eqs. (12.84) and (12.81) give $E[T]$ as given in Eq. (12.72).

**12.38.** Consider a $c$-server, finite-source queueing system that allows no queueing for service. Requests that arrive when all servers are busy are turned away, and the corresponding source immediately returns to the "think" state, and spends another exponentially distributed think time before submitting another request for service.

    **(a)** Find the transition rate diagram and show that the steady state pmf for the state of the system is

$$P_K[N=j] = \frac{\binom{K}{j} p^j (1-p)^{K-j}}{\sum_{i=0}^{c} \binom{K}{i} p^i (1-p)^{K-i}} \qquad i = 0, \ldots, c,$$

    where $c$ is the number of servers, $K$ is the number of sources, and

$$p = \frac{\alpha/\mu}{1 + \alpha/\mu}.$$

    **(b)** Find the probability that all servers are busy.

    **(c)** Use the fact that arriving customers "see" the steady state pmf of a system with one less source to show that the fraction of arrivals that are turned away is given by $P_{K-1}(c)$. The resulting expression is called the Engset formula.

**12.39.** A video-on-demand system is modeled as a $c = 10$ server system that handles video chunk requests from $K$ clients. Suppose that the system is modeled by the Engset system from Problem 12.38. Suppose that users generate requests at a rate of one per second and the each server can meet the request within 100 ms. Find the number of clients that can be connected if the probability of turning away a request is 10%? 1%?

## Section 12.6: M/G/1 Queueing Systems

**12.40.** Find the mean waiting time and mean delay in an M/G/1 system in which the service time is a $k$-Erlang random variable (see Table 4.1) with mean $1/\mu$. Compare the results to M/M/1 and M/D/1 systems.

**12.41.** A $k = 2$ hyperexponential random variable is obtained by selecting a service time at random from one of two exponential random variables as shown in Fig. P12.2. Find the mean delay in an M/G/1 system with this hyperexponential service time distribution.

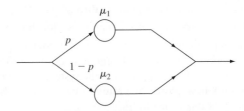

**FIGURE P12.2**

**12.42.** Customers arrive at a queueing system according to a Poisson process of rate $\lambda$. A fraction $\alpha$ of the customers require a fixed service time $d$, and a fraction $1 - \alpha$ require an exponential service time of mean $1/\mu$. Find the mean waiting time and mean delay in the resulting M/G/1 system.

**12.43.** Find the mean waiting time and mean delay in an M/G/1 system in which the service time consists of a fixed time $d$ plus an exponentially distributed time of mean $1/\mu$.

**12.44.** Fixed-length messages arrive at a transmitter according to a Poisson process of rate $\lambda$. The time required to transmit a message and to receive an acknowledgment is $d$ seconds. If a message is acknowledged as having been received correctly, then the transmitter proceeds with the next message. If the message is acknowledged as having been received in error, the transmitter retransmits the message. Assume that a message undergoes errors in transmission with probability $p$, and that transmission errors are independent.

    **(a)** Find the mean and variance of the effective message service time.

    **(b)** Find the mean message delay.

**12.45.** Packets at a router with a 1 Gigabit/second transmission line arrive at a rate of $\lambda$ packets per second. Suppose that half the packets are 40 bytes long and half the packets are 1500 bytes long. Find the mean packet delay as a function of $\lambda$.

**12.46.** A file server receives requests at a rate of $\lambda$ requests per second. The server can transmit files at a rate of 12.5 Megabytes per second. Suppose that file lengths have a Pareto distribution with mean 1 Megabyte.

    **(a)** Find the average delay in meeting a file request.

    **(b)** Discuss the effect of the Pareto distribution parameter on system performance.

**12.47.** Jobs arrive at a machine according to a Poisson process of rate $\lambda$. The service times for the jobs are exponentially distributed with mean $1/\mu$. The machine has a tendency to break down while it is serving customers; if a particular service time is $t$, then the probability that it will break down $k$ times during this service time is a Poisson random variable with mean $\alpha t$. It takes an exponentially distributed time with mean $1/\beta$ to repair the machine. Assume a machine is always working when it begins a job.

    **(a)** Find the mean and variance of the total time required to complete a job. *Hint:* Use conditional expectation.

    **(b)** Find the mean job delay for this system.

**12.48.** Consider a two-class nonpreemptive priority queueing system, and suppose that the lower-priority class is saturated (i.e., $\lambda_1 E[\tau_1] + \lambda_2 E[\tau_2] > 1$).

**(a)** Show that the rate of low-priority customers served by the system is $\lambda_2' = (1 - \lambda_1 E[\tau_1])/E[\tau_2]$. *Hint:* What proportion of time is the server busy with class two customers?

**(b)** Show that the mean waiting time for class 1 customers is

$$E[W_1] = \frac{(1/2)\lambda_1 E[\tau_1^2]}{1 - \lambda_1 E[\tau_1]} + \frac{E[\tau_2^2]}{2E[\tau_2]}.$$

**12.49.** Consider an M/G/1 system in which the server goes on vacations (becomes unavailable) whenever it empties the queue. If upon returning from vacation the system is still empty, the server takes another vacation, and so on until it finds customers in the system. Suppose that vacation times are independent of each other and of the other variables in the system. Show that the mean waiting time for customers in this system is

$$E[W] = \frac{(1/2)\lambda E[\tau^2]}{1 - \lambda E[\tau]} + \frac{E[V^2]}{2E[V]},$$

where $V$ is the vacation time. *Hint:* Show that this system is equivalent to a nonpreemptive priority system and use the result of Problem 12.48.

**12.50.** Fixed-length packets arrive at a concentrator that feeds a synchronous transmission system. The packets arrive according to a Poisson process of rate $\lambda$, but the transmission system will only begin packet transmissions at times $id$, $i = 1, 2, \ldots$, where $d$ is the transmission time for a single packet. Find the mean packet waiting time. *Hint:* Show that this is an M/D/1 queue with vacations as in Problem 12.49.

**12.51.** A queueing system handles two types of traffic. Type $i$ traffic arrives according to a Poisson process and has exponentially distributed service times with mean $1/\mu_i$ for $i = 1, 2$. Suppose that type 1 customers are given nonpreemptive priority. Plot the overall and per-class mean waiting time versus $\lambda$ if $\lambda_1 = \lambda_2 = \lambda$, $\mu_1 = 1$, $\mu_2 = 1/10$.

**12.52.** Consider a two-class priority M/G/1 system in which high-priority customer arrivals preempt low-priority customers who are found in service. Preempted low-priority customers are placed at the head of their queue, and they resume service when the server again becomes available to low-priority customers.

**(a)** What is the mean waiting time and the mean delay for the high-priority customers?

**(b)** Show that the time required to service all customers found by a type 2 arrival to the system is

$$\frac{R_2}{1 - \rho_1 - \rho_2},$$

where $\rho_j = \lambda_j E[\tau_j]$, and

$$R_2 = \frac{1}{2}\sum_{j=1}^{2}\lambda_j E[\tau_j^2].$$

**(c)** Show that the time required to service all type 1 customers who arrive during the time a type 2 customer spends in the system is $\rho_1 E[T_2]$.

**(d)** Use parts b and c to show that

$$E[T_2] = \frac{(1 - \rho_1 - \rho_2)/\mu_2 + R_2}{(1 - \rho_1)(1 - \rho_1 - \rho_2)}.$$

**12.53.** Evaluate and plot the formulas developed in Problem 12.52 using the two traffic classes described in Problem 12.51.

### Section 12.7: M/G/1 Analysis Using Embedded Markov Chain

**12.54.** The service time in an M/G/1 system has a $k = 2$ Erlang distribution with mean $1/\mu$ and $\lambda = \mu/2$.

  **(a)** Find $G_N(z)$ and $P[N = j]$.

  **(b)** Find $\hat{W}(s)$ and $\hat{T}(s)$ and the corresponding pdf's.

**12.55. (a)** In Problem 12.47, show that the Laplace transform of the pdf for the total time $\tau$ required to complete the service of a customer is

$$\hat{\tau}(s) = \frac{\mu(s + \beta)}{(s + \beta)(s + \mu) + \alpha s}.$$

  *Hint:* Use conditional expectation in evaluating $E[e^{-s\tau}]$, and note that the number of breakdowns depends on the service time of the customer.

  **(b)** Find $\hat{W}(s)$ and $\hat{T}(s)$ and the corresponding pdf's.

**12.56. (a)** Show that Eqs. (12.110a) and (12.110b) can be written as

$$N_j = N_{j-1} - U(N_{j-1}) + M_j, \tag{12.186}$$

  where

$$U(x) = \begin{cases} 1 & x > 0 \\ 0 & x \le 0. \end{cases}$$

  **(b)** Take the expected value of both sides of Eq. (12.186) to obtain an expression for $P[N > 0]$.

  **(c)** Square both sides of Eq. (12.186) and take the expected value to obtain the Pollaczek–Khinchin formula for $E[N]$.

**12.57. (a)** Show that for an M/D/1 system,

$$G_N(z) = \frac{(1 - \rho)(1 - z)}{1 - ze^{\rho(1-z)}}.$$

  **(b)** Expand the denominator in a geometric series, and then identify the coefficient of $z^k$ to obtain

$$P[N = k] = (1 - \rho)\sum_{j=0}^{k} \frac{(-j\rho)^{k-j-1}(-j\rho - k + 1)e^{j\rho}}{(k - j)!}.$$

**12.58. (a)** Show that Eq. (12.130) can be rewritten as

$$\hat{W}(s) = \frac{1 - \rho}{1 - \rho\hat{R}(s)}, \tag{12.87}$$

where

$$\hat{R}(s) = \frac{1 - \hat{\tau}(s)}{sE[\tau]}$$

is the Laplace transform of the pdf of the residual service time.

**(b)** Expand the denominator of Eq. (12.187) in a geometric series and invert the resulting transform expression to show that

$$f_W(x) = \sum_{k=0}^{\infty} (1 - \rho)\rho^k f^{(k)}(x), \tag{12.188}$$

where $f^{(k)}(x)$ is the $k$th-order convolution of the residual service time.

**12.59.** Approximate $f_W(x)$ for an M/D/1 system using the $k = 0, 1, 2$ terms of Eq. (12.188). Sketch the resulting pdf for $\rho = 1/2$.

## Section 12.8: Burke's Theorem: Departures from M/M/c Systems

**12.60.** Consider the interdeparture times from a stable M/M/1 system in steady state.

**(a)** Show that if a departure leaves the system nonempty, then the time to the next departure is an exponential random variable with mean $1/\mu$.

**(b)** Show that if a departure leaves the system empty, then the time to the next departure is the sum of two independent exponential random variables of means $1/\lambda$ and $1/\mu$, respectively.

**(c)** Combine the results of parts a and b to show that the interdeparture times are exponential random variables with mean $1/\lambda$.

**12.61.** Find the joint pmf for the number of customers in the queues in the network shown in Fig. P12.3.

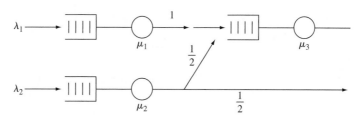

**FIGURE P12.3**

**12.62.** Write the balance equations for the feedforward network shown in Fig. P12.4 and verify that the joint state pmf is of product form.

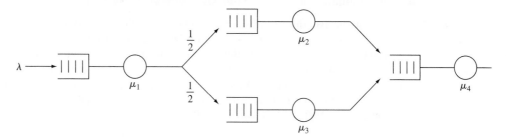

**FIGURE P12.4**

**12.63.** Verify that Eqs. (12.137) through (12.139) satisfy Eq. (12.135).

## Section 12.9: Networks of Queues: Jackson's Theorem

**12.64.** Find the joint state pmf for the open network of queues shown in Fig. P12.5.

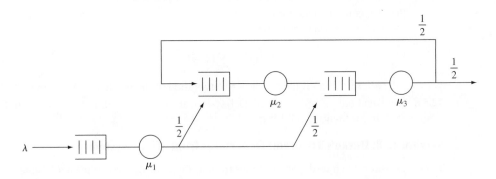

**FIGURE P12.5**

**12.65.** A computer system model has three programs circulating in the network of queues shown in Fig. P12.6.

   **(a)** Find the joint state pmf of the system.

   **(b)** Find the average program completion rate.

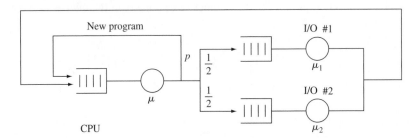

**FIGURE P12.6**

**12.66.** Use the mean value analysis algorithm to answer Problem 12.65, part b.

## Section 12.10: Simulation and Data Analysis of Queueing Systems

**12.67.** **(a)** Repeat the experiment in Example 12.28 for an M/M/1 system with $\rho = 0.5, 0.7$, and 0.9. Use sample means for $N(t)$ based on 25 replications to characterize the transient behavior. Try out smoothing the sample means using a moving average filter over time. Give an estimate of the time to reach steady state in each of these systems.

   **(b)** Now investigate the effect of initial condition on the duration of the transient phase. For each of the utilizations above compare the transient duration when the initial condition is: $N(0) = 0$; $N(0) = 5$; $N(0) = 10$.

**12.68.** For the experiment in Problem 12.67, calculate the sample covariance for each realization and then average over the 25 replications. Find the number of lags required for each value of $r$ until the correlation drops to zero. Comment on the implications for the size of the batches if a method of batch means approach is to be used.

**12.69.** The correlation of $N(t)$ for an M/M/1 system has the following geometric upper bound [Fishman]:

$$\rho_j \le \left[ \frac{4\rho}{(1 + \rho)^2} \right]^j \quad \text{for} \quad j = 0, 1, 2, \dots.$$

Evaluate the ratio of the variance of the sample mean estimator for this process to that of an iid process when $\rho = 0.5, 0.75, 0.9, 0.99$.

**12.70.** Run the simulation for the experiment in Example 12.29 50 times. For each simulation produce a confidence interval using the method of batch means. Determine the fraction of the confidence intervals that covered the actual mean $E[N]$. Comment on the accuracy of the confidence intervals given by Eq. (12.168).

**12.71.** Develop a simulation model for an M/M/3 system with $\lambda = 2$ customers per second and $\mu = 1$ customer per second. Use the method of batch means as in Example 12.29 to estimate the probability that an arriving customer has to queue for service. Provide appropriate confidence intervals.

**12.72. (a)** Consider the simulation in Example 12.30 where the embedded Markov chain approach is used to estimate the steady state pmf. For $\rho = 0.5$ and $\rho = 0.9$, use different warm-up periods to investigate the effect of the initial transient on the pmf estimates.

**(b)** Double the number of replications and observe the impact on the confidence intervals.

**12.73.** Develop a simulation for an M/D/1 system with $\rho = 0.7$ using the embedded Markov chain in Eq. (12.172). Design the simulation to estimate the pmf for the number of customers in the system as well as the mean number in the system.

**(a)** Discuss what transient effects can be expected in this approach.

**(b)** Use the method of batch means to develop estimates for the mean number of customers in the system. Discuss the choice of batch size and warm-up period. Evaluate the confidence intervals produced by several realizations.

**12.74.** Use Lindley's recursion to estimate the waiting-time distribution for customers in an M/D/1 system with $\rho = 0.5$ and $\rho = 0.7$. Is there anything peculiar about the distribution?

**12.75.** Use Lindley's recursion to estimate the waiting-time distribution for customers in a D/M/1 system with $\rho = 0.5$ and $\rho = 0.7$.

**12.76.** Use Lindley's recursion to estimate the waiting-time distribution for customers in an M/G/1 system with $\rho = 0.5$ and $\rho = 0.7$ where the service-time distribution is Pareto with parameter $\alpha = 2.5$. Try a simulation with $\alpha = 1.5$. Does anything peculiar happen?

**12.77.** Repeat the experiment in Example 12.33, but use the method of batch means to provide confidence intervals for the mean waiting time.

**12.78.** Explain why the estimator in Eq. (12.183) will converge to the expected value of the waiting time.

**12.79.** Use the regenerative method to estimate the mean number in the system and the probability that the system is empty in an M/D/1 system. Evaluate the confidence interval provided by Eq. (12.185).

## Problems Requiring Cumulative Knowledge

**12.80.** Consider an M/M/2/2 system in which one server is twice as fast as the other server.

(a) What definition of "state" of the system results in a continuous-time Markov chain?

(b) Find the steady state pmf for the system if customers arriving at an empty system are always routed to the faster server.

(c) Find the steady state pmf for the system if customers arriving at an empty system are equally likely to be routed to either server.

**12.81.** (a) Find the transient pmf, $P[N(t) = j]$, for an M/M/1/2 system which is in the empty state at time 0.

(b) Repeat part a if the system is full at time 0.

**12.82.** (a) In an M/G/1 system, why are the set of times when customers arrive to an empty system renewal instants?

(b) How would you apply the results from renewal theory in Section 7.5 to estimate the pmf for the number of customers in the system?

(c) How would you obtain a confidence interval for $P[N(t) = j]$?

**12.83.** Let $N(t)$ be a Poisson random process with parameter $\lambda$. Suppose that each time an event occurs, a coin is flipped and the outcome is recorded. Assume that the probability of heads depends on the time of the arrival and is denoted by $p(t)$. Let $N_1(t)$ and $N_2(t)$ denote the number of heads and tails recorded up to time $t$, respectively.

(a) Show that $N_1(t)$ and $N_2(t)$ are independent Poisson random variables with rates $p\lambda$ and $(1 - p)\lambda$, where

$$p = \frac{1}{t} \int_0^t p(t') \, dt'.$$

(b) Are $N_1(t)$ and $N_2(t)$ independent Poisson random processes? If so, how would you show this?

**12.84.** Consider an M/G/$\infty$ system in which customers arrive at rate $\lambda$ and in which the customer service times have distribution $F_X(x)$. Suppose that the system is empty at time 0. Let $N_1(t)$ be the number of customers who have completed their service by time $t$, and let $N_2(t)$ be the number of customers still in the system at time $t$.

(a) Use the result of Problem 12.83 to find the joint pmf of $N_1(t)$ and $N_2(t)$.

(b) What is the steady state pmf for the number of customers in an M/G/$\infty$ system?

(c) Apply Little's formula to compute the average number of customers in the system. Is the result consistent with your result in part b?

# Mathematical Tables

**A.    TRIGONOMETRIC IDENTITIES**

$$\sin^2 \alpha + \cos^2 \alpha = 1$$

$$\sin(\alpha + \beta) = \sin \alpha \cos \beta + \cos \alpha \sin \beta$$

$$\sin(\alpha - \beta) = \sin \alpha \cos \beta - \cos \alpha \sin \beta$$

$$\cos(\alpha + \beta) = \cos \alpha \cos \beta - \sin \alpha \sin \beta$$

$$\cos(\alpha - \beta) = \cos \alpha \cos \beta + \sin \alpha \sin \beta$$

$$\sin 2\alpha = 2 \sin \alpha \cos \alpha$$

$$\cos 2\alpha = \cos^2 \alpha - \sin^2 \alpha = 2 \cos^2 \alpha - 1 = 1 - 2 \sin^2 \alpha$$

$$\sin \alpha \sin \beta = \frac{1}{2}\cos(\alpha - \beta) - \frac{1}{2}\cos(\alpha + \beta)$$

$$\cos \alpha \cos \beta = \frac{1}{2}\cos(\alpha - \beta) + \frac{1}{2}\cos(\alpha + \beta)$$

$$\sin \alpha \cos \beta = \frac{1}{2}\sin(\alpha + \beta) + \frac{1}{2}\sin(\alpha - \beta)$$

$$\cos \alpha \sin \beta = \frac{1}{2}\sin(\alpha + \beta) - \frac{1}{2}\sin(\alpha - \beta)$$

$$\sin^2 \alpha = \frac{1}{2}(1 - \cos 2\alpha)$$

$$\cos^2 \alpha = \frac{1}{2}(1 + \cos 2\alpha)$$

$$e^{j\alpha} = \cos \alpha + j \sin \alpha$$

$$\cos \alpha = (e^{j\alpha} + e^{-j\alpha})/2$$

$$\sin \alpha = (e^{j\alpha} - e^{-j\alpha})/2j$$

$$\sin \alpha = \cos(\alpha - \pi/2)$$

## B.    INDEFINITE INTEGRALS

$$\int u \, dv = uv - \int v \, du \qquad \text{where } u \text{ and } v \text{ are functions of } x$$

$$\int x^n \, dx = x^{n+1}/(n+1) \qquad \text{except for } n = -1$$

$$\int x^{-1} \, dx = \ln x$$

$$\int e^{ax} \, dx = e^{ax}/a$$

$$\int \ln x \, dx = x \ln x - x$$

$$\int (a^2 + x^2)^{-1} \, dx = (1/a) \tan^{-1}(x/a)$$

$$\int (\ln x)^n/x \, dx = (1/(n+1))(\ln x)^{n+1}$$

$$\int x^n \ln ax \, dx = (x^{n+1}/(n+1)) \ln ax - x^{n+1}/(n+1)^2$$

$$\int x e^{ax} \, dx = e^{ax}(ax - 1)/a^2$$

$$\int x^2 e^{ax} \, dx = e^{ax}(a^2x^2 - 2ax + 2)/a^3$$

$$\int \sin ax \, dx = -(1/a) \cos ax$$

$$\int \cos ax \, dx = (1/a) \sin ax$$

$$\int \sin^2 ax \, dx = x/2 - \sin(2ax)/4a$$

$$\int x \sin ax \, dx = (1/a^2)(\sin ax - ax \cos ax)$$

$$\int x^2 \sin ax \, dx = \{2ax \sin ax + 2 \cos ax - a^2x^2 \sin ax\}/a^3$$

$$\int \cos^2 ax \, dx = x/2 + \sin(2ax)/4a$$

$$\int x \cos ax \, dx = (1/a^2)(\cos ax + ax \sin ax)$$

$$\int x^2 \cos ax \, dx = (1/a^3)\{2ax \cos ax - 2 \sin ax + a^2x^2 \sin ax\}$$

## C.    DEFINITE INTEGRALS

$$\int_0^\infty t^{n-1}e^{-(a+1)t}\,dt = \frac{\Gamma(n)}{(a+1)^n} \qquad n > 0, a > -1$$

$\Gamma(n) = (n-1)!$    if $n$ is an integer, $n > 0$

$$\Gamma\left(\frac{1}{2}\right) = \sqrt{\pi}$$

$$\Gamma\left(n + \frac{1}{2}\right) = \frac{1 \cdot 3 \cdot 5 \cdots (2n-1)}{2^n}\sqrt{\pi} \qquad n = 1, 2, 3, \ldots$$

$$\int_0^\infty e^{-\alpha^2 x^2}\,dx = \sqrt{\pi}/2\alpha$$

$$\int_0^\infty xe^{-\alpha^2 x^2}\,dx = 1/2\alpha^2$$

$$\int_0^\infty x^2 e^{-\alpha^2 x^2}\,dx = \sqrt{\pi}/4\alpha^3$$

$$\int_0^\infty x^n e^{-\alpha^2 x^2}\,dx = \Gamma((n+1)/2)/(2\alpha^{n+1})$$

$$\int_0^\infty a/(a^2 + x^2)\,dx = \pi/2 \qquad \text{if } a > 0$$

$$\int_0^\infty \frac{\sin^2 ax}{x^2}\,dx = |a|\pi/2 \qquad \text{if } a > 0$$

$$\int_0^1 x^{a-1}(1-x)^{b-1}\,dx = B(a, b) = \frac{\Gamma(a)\Gamma(b)}{\Gamma(a+b)}$$

# Tables of Fourier Transforms

## A. FOURIER TRANSFORM DEFINITION

$$G(f) = \mathcal{F}\{g(t)\} = \int_{-\infty}^{\infty} g(t)e^{-j2\pi ft}\, dt$$

$$g(t) = \mathcal{F}^{-1}\{G(f)\} = \int_{-\infty}^{\infty} G(f)e^{j2\pi ft}\, df$$

## B. PROPERTIES

Linearity: $\mathcal{F}\{ag_1(t) + bg_2(t)\} = aG_1(f) + bG_2(f)$

Time scaling: $\mathcal{F}\{g(at)\} = G(f/a)/|a|$

Duality: If $\mathcal{F}\{g(t)\} = G(f)$, then $\mathcal{F}\{G(t)\} = g(-f)$

Time shifting: $\mathcal{F}\{g(t - t_0)\} = G(f)e^{-j2\pi ft_0}$

Frequency shifting: $\mathcal{F}\{g(t)e^{j2\pi f_0 t}\} = G(f - f_0)$

Differentiation: $\mathcal{F}\{g'(t)\} = j2\pi f G(f)$

Integration: $\mathcal{F}\left\{ \int_{-\infty}^{t} g(s)ds \right\} = G(f)/(j2\pi f) + (G(0)/2)\delta(f)$

Multiplication in time: $\mathcal{F}\{g_1(t)g_2(t)\} = G_1(f) * G_2(f)$

Convolution in time: $\mathcal{F}\{g_1(t) * g_2(t)\} = G_1(f)G_2(f)$

## C. TRANSFORM PAIRS

| $g(t)$ | $G(f)$ |
|---|---|

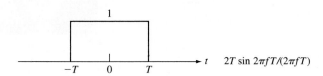 $2T \sin 2\pi fT/(2\pi fT)$

$2W \sin(2\pi Wt)/2\pi Wt$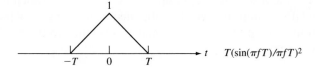

 $T(\sin(\pi fT)/\pi fT)^2$

$e^{-at}u(t), \quad a > 0$       $1/(a + j2\pi f)$

$e^{-a|t|}, \quad a > 0$       $2a/(a^2 + (2\pi f)^2)$

$e^{-\pi t^2}$       $e^{-\pi f^2}$

$\delta(t)$       $1$

$1$       $\delta(f)$

$\delta(t - t_0)$       $e^{-j2\pi ft_0}$

$e^{j2\pi f_0 t}$       $\delta(f - f_0)$

$\cos(2\pi f_0 t)$       $\dfrac{1}{2}\delta(f - f_0) + \dfrac{1}{2}\delta(f + f_0)$

$\sin(2\pi f_0 t)$       $(1/2j)\{\delta(f - f_0) - \delta(f + f_0)\}$

$u(t)$       $\dfrac{1}{2}\delta(f) + 1/(j2\pi f)$

# Matrices and Linear Algebra

## A.    BASIC DEFINITIONS

Let $\mathbf{A} = [a_{ij}]$ be an $m$ row by $n$ column matrix with element $a_{ij}$ in the $i$th row and $j$th column. A matrix is **square** if $m = n$.

The **transpose** of $\mathbf{A}$ is the $n$ row by $m$ column matrix $\mathbf{A}^T = [a_{ij}]^T$ which has element $a_{ij}$ in the $j$th row and $i$th column, and which is obtained by interchanging the rows and columns of $\mathbf{A}$. The transpose of the product of matrices is equal to the product of the transposes in reverse order:

$$(\mathbf{AB})^T = \mathbf{B}^T\mathbf{A}^T \quad \text{and} \quad (\mathbf{ABC})^T = \mathbf{C}^T\mathbf{B}^T\mathbf{A}^T.$$

The **identity** matrix $\mathbf{I}$ is a square matrix whose diagonal elements equal 1 and off-diagonal elements equal zero. For any square matrix $\mathbf{A}$:

$$\mathbf{AI} = \mathbf{IA} = \mathbf{A}.$$

The **inverse** of a square matrix $\mathbf{A}$ is a square matrix $\mathbf{A}^{-1}$ for which

$$\mathbf{AA}^{-1} = \mathbf{A}^{-1}\mathbf{A} = \mathbf{I}.$$

We say that $\mathbf{A}$ is **invertible** if $\mathbf{A}^{-1}$ exists, and **singular** otherwise.

## B.    DIAGONALIZATION

A nonzero vector $\mathbf{e} = (\mathbf{e}_1, \mathbf{e}_2, \ldots, \mathbf{e}_n)^T$ is an **eigenvector** of an $n \times n$ matrix if it satisfies:

$$\mathbf{Ae} = \lambda\mathbf{e}$$

for some scalar $\lambda$. $\lambda$ is called an **eigenvalue** of $\mathbf{A}$ and $\mathbf{e}$ an eigenvector of A corresponding to $\lambda$.

The eigenvalues of $\mathbf{A}$ are found by finding the roots of the polynomial equation:

$$\det(\lambda\mathbf{I} - \mathbf{A}) = 0.$$

An $n \times n$ matrix $\mathbf{A}$ is said to be **diagonalizable** if there exists an invertible matrix $\mathbf{P}$ such that $\mathbf{P}^{-1}\mathbf{AP} = \mathbf{D}$, a diagonal matrix, or equivalently $\mathbf{AP} = \mathbf{PD}$.

**Theorem:**

$\mathbf{A}$ is diagonalizable if and only if $\mathbf{A}$ has $n$ linearly independent eigenvectors.

A square matrix $\mathbf{P}$ is **orthogonal** if $\mathbf{P}^{-1} = \mathbf{P}^{\mathrm{T}}$, or equivalently, $\mathbf{A}\mathbf{A}^{\mathrm{T}} = \mathbf{A}^{\mathrm{T}}\mathbf{A} = \mathbf{I}$.

A set of vectors $\{\mathbf{e}_1, \mathbf{e}_2, \dots, \mathbf{e}_n\}$ is said to be **orthonormal** if distinct vectors are orthogonal, that is, $\mathbf{e}_i{}^{\mathrm{T}}\mathbf{e}_j = 0$ for $i \neq j$, and $\mathbf{e}_i{}^{\mathrm{T}}\mathbf{e}_i = 1$ for $i = 1, \dots, n$.

**Theorem:**

If the set of vectors $\{\mathbf{e}_1, \mathbf{e}_2, \dots, \mathbf{e}_n\}$ are nonzero and orthogonal then they are also linearly independent.

An $n \times n$ matrix $\mathbf{A}$ is said to be **orthogonally diagonalizable** if there exists an orthogonal matrix $\mathbf{P}$ such that $\mathbf{P}^{\mathrm{T}}\mathbf{A}\mathbf{P} = \mathbf{D}$, a diagonal matrix, or equivalently $\mathbf{A}\mathbf{P} = \mathbf{P}\mathbf{D}$.

An $n \times n$ matrix $\mathbf{A}$ is **symmetric** if $\mathbf{A} = \mathbf{A}^{\mathrm{T}}$.

**Theorem:**

A symmetric matrix $\mathbf{A}$ has only real eigenvalues.

**Theorem:**

The following conditions are equivalent:
  **a.** $\mathbf{A}$ is orthogonally diagonalizable,
  **b.** $\mathbf{A}$ has an orthonormal set of $n$ eigenvectors,
  **c.** $\mathbf{A}$ is a symmetric matrix.

## C.  QUADRATIC FORMS

The $n \times n$ real symmetric matrix $\mathbf{A}$ and the $n \times 1$ column vector $\mathbf{x} = (x_1, x_2, \dots, x_n)^{\mathrm{T}}$ have the quadratic form given by:

$$\mathbf{x}^{\mathrm{T}}\mathbf{A}\mathbf{x} = \sum_{i=1}^{n} \sum_{j=1}^{n} a_{ij} x_i x_j.$$

$\mathbf{A}$ is nonnegative definite if $\mathbf{x}^{\mathrm{T}}\mathbf{A}\mathbf{x} \geq 0$ for all $\mathbf{x}$, and positive definite if $\mathbf{x}^{\mathrm{T}}\mathbf{A}\mathbf{x} > 0$ for all nonzero $\mathbf{x}$.

Let $\mathbf{A} = [a_{ij}]$ be an $n \times n$ matrix, then the $k$th principal submatrix of $\mathbf{A}$ is the $k \times k$ matrix $\mathbf{A}_k = [a_{ij}]$ with element $a_{ij}$ in the $i$th row and $j$th column.

**Theorem:**

A symmetric matrix $\mathbf{A}$ is positive definite (nonnegative definite) if and only if

  **a.** All eigenvalues are positive (nonnegative) and
  **b.** The determinant of all principal submatrices are positive (nonnegative).

If $\mathbf{A}$ is a positive definite matrix then $\mathbf{x}^{\mathrm{T}}\mathbf{A}^{-1}\mathbf{x} = 1$ is the equation of an ellipsoid with center at the origin. The $k$th semiaxis of the ellipsoid is given by $\mathbf{e}_k / \sqrt{\lambda_k}$, that is, the eigenvectors determine the direction of the semiaxes and the eigenvalues determine the corresponding length.

# Index

## A

Almost-sure convergence, 381–382, 385
Amplitude modulation (AM):
  bandpass signal, 602
  quadrature amplitude modulation (QAM)
    method, 603–604
  by random signals, 601–605
Aperiodic state, 667
ARMA random process, 595–596
Arrival rate, 714
Arrival theorem, 766–770
  proof of, 769–770
Associative properties, 28
Autocorrelation function, 494–495
Autocovariance function, 494–495
Autoregressive moving average (ARMA)
    process, 595–596
Autoregressive processes, 595
  random, 507
Average power, 522, 579
Axioms of probability, 21, 30–41, 79
  continuous sample spaces, 37–41
  discrete sample spaces, 35–37

## B

Bandlimited random processes, 597–605
  amplitude modulation by random
    signals, 601–605
  sampling of, 597–601
Bandpass signal, 602
  amplitude modulation (AM), 602
Bartlett's smoothing procedure, 628
Batch means:
  confidence intervals using, 775–776
  method of, 775–776
Bayes estimation, 461–462
Bayes hypothesis testing, 455–460
  binary communications, 457–458
    MAP receiver for, 458–459
  minimum cost hypothesis test, 457
  server allocation, 459–460
Bayes' rule, 52–53, 79

Bayesian decision methods, 455–462
  Bayes hypothesis testing, 455–460
  minimum cost theorem
    proof of, 460–461
Bernoulli random variables, 102
  coin toss, 117
  estimation, 428
    of $p$ for, 421
  Fisher information for, 424–425
  mean of, 105
  properties of, 115
  variance of, 110
Bernoulli trials, 60
  and binomial probabilities, 70
  estimating $p$ in, 461–462
Beta random variables, 165, 172–173
  generating, 198
Bias, estimators, 416
Binary communication system, 50, 52
Binary random variable:
  entropy of, 203–205
Binary transmission system, probabilities of
    input-output pairs in, 50
Binomial counting process, 493, 501–502
  independent and stationary increments of, 504
  joint pmf of, 505
  Markov chains, 663
  transient state, 666
Binomial probability law, 60–62
Binomial random variables, 103
  Chernoff bound for, 375–377
  coin toss, 118
  defined, 117–118
  mean of, 118–119
  negative
    properties of, 116
  properties of, 115
  redundant systems, 119
  sampling distribution of, 414–415
  three coin tosses and, 105
  variance of, 119
Binomial theorem, 61–62
Birth-and-death process, 682–683
Borel fields, 30, 38, 75–77

Brownian motion, 517
Burke's theorem, 754–758
    proof of, using time reversibility, 757–758

# C

Cauchy random variables, 165, 173
Causal filters, 615
    estimation using, 614–617
Causal system, 588
Central limit theorem, 167fn, 369–378
    Chernoff bound for binomial random
        variable, 375–377
    Gaussian approximation for binomial
        probabilities, 373–375
    proof of, 377–378
Certain event, 24
Chapman–Kolmogorov equations, 654, 677
Characteristic function, 184–187
    for an exponentially distributed random variable, 185
    for a geometric random variable, 185
Chebyshev inequality, 181–183
Chernoff bound, 183
    for binomial random variable, 375–377
    for Gaussian random variable, 187
Chi-square goodness-of-fit test, 465
Chi-square random variable, 170
Chi-square test, 463–468
    for exponential random variable:
        equal-length intervals (table), 467
        equiprobable intervals (table), 468
    for Poisson random variable (table), 468
Circuit theory, 4
Circuit theory models, 4
Classes of states, 660–662
Closed networks of queues, 763–766
Combinatorial formulas, 41, 44, 79
Communication over unreliable channels, 12–13
Communication system design, 9
Commutative properties, 28
Complement, of a set, 27
Complement operation, 27
Composite hypotheses, testing, 449–455
Compression of signals, 13
Computer simulation models, 3–4, 79
Conditional cdf's, 152–155
Conditional expectation, 268–271, 336
Conditional pdf's, 153–155, 307
Conditional pmf's, 306
Conditional probability, 21, 47–53, 79, 261–268
Conditional probability mass function, 111–114
    conditional expected value, 113–114
        device lifetimes, 114
    device lifetimes, 113
    random clock, 112
    residual waiting times, 112–113

Conditional variance of $X$ given $B$:
    defined, 114
Confidence intervals, 430–441
    batch means method (example), 435
    cases, 431–435
    confidence level, 431
    and hypothesis testing, 455
    for the variance of a Gaussian random
        variable, 436–437
Consistent estimators, 418
Continuity of probability, 76–77
Continuous random variables, 146–149, 163–174
    beta, 165, 172–173
    calculating distributions using the discrete Fourier
        transform, 398–400
    Cauchy, 165, 173
    exponential, 163–167
    gamma, 164, 170–172
    Gaussian, 164, 167–170
    Laplacian, 165
    Pareto, 165, 173–174
        mean and variance of, 174
    Rayleigh, 165
    two, joint pdf of, 248–254
    uniform, 163
Continuous sample spaces, 24, 37–41, 79
Continuous-time Gaussian random processes, 516
Continuous-time Markov chains, 673–686, 690–691
    global balance equations, 680–683
        birth-and-death process, 682–683
    homogeneous transition probabilities, 673–674
    limiting probabilities for, 683–686
    mean state occupancy time, 675
    Poisson process, 674, 678–679
    queueing system, 678
        M/M/1 single-server queueing system, 681–683
    random telegraph signal, 674
    simulation of, 698–700
    state occupancy times, 675
    steady state probabilities and, 680–683
    transition rates and time-dependent state
        probabilities, 676–679
Continuous-time random processes:
    power spectral density, 578–583
        random telegraph signal, 580
        sinusoid with random phase, 580–581
        sum of two processes, 582–583
        white noise, 581–582
Continuous-time stochastic process, defined, 488
Continuous-time systems:
    filtered white noise, 590
    response to random signals, 587–593
    transfer function, 588
Convergence:
    almost-sure, 381–382, 385
    Cauchy criterion, 384

in distribution, 387
  mean square convergence, 384
  in probability, 384–385
  sure, 381
Correlated Gaussian random variables, generation of, 631–632
Correlated vector random variables, generation of, 342–345
Correlation, 258
Correlation coefficient, 259, 494
Correlation matrix, 319
Cost accumulation rate, 390–392
Covariance, 258
Covariance matrix, 319
  diagonalization of, 324–325
  generating random vectors with, 342–344
Cramer-Rao inequality, 423–428
  Fisher information, 423–424
    for Bernoulli random variable, 424–425
    for an exponential random variable, 425
  lower bound for Bernoulli random variable, 426
  proof of, 426–428
  score function, 423–424
  statement of, 425
Critical region, 442
Cross-correlation, 496
Cross-covariance, 497
  matrix, 321
Cross-power spectral density, 579
Cumulative distribution function (cdf), 141–146
  conditional, 152–155
  defined, 141–142
  limiting properties of, 147
  proof of properties of, 146
  three coin tosses, 142
  uniform random variable in the unit interval, 143
Cyclostationary random processes, 525–529
  pulse amplitude modulation, 526–527
    with random phase shift, 528


**D**

Decision rule, 442
Decreasing sequence of events, 76
Delta function, 151–152
Demodulation of noisy signal, 604–605
DeMorgan's Rules, 28
Deterministic models, 4
Diagonalization, of covariance matrix, 324–325
Difference, of sets, 27
Differential entropy, 206
  of a Gaussian random variable, 207
  of a uniform random variable, 206
Discrete Fourier transform (DFT):
  calculating distributions using, 392–400
  defined, 394

Discrete random variables, 99–104, 146
  calculating distributions using the discrete Fourier transform, 393–398
  expected value and moments of, 104–111
  generation of, 127–129
    generation of Poisson random variable, 128
    generation of tosses of a die, 128
  pairs of, 236–241
  pdf for, 151
  probability mass function (pmf), 99–100
  properties of, 115
  uniform, mean of, 105–106
Discrete sample spaces, 24, 35–37, 79
Discrete-time birth-and-death process, 689–690
Discrete-time Markov chains, 650–660
  binomial counting process, 653
  Google PageRank, 657–658
  homogeneous transition probabilities, 651
  $n$-step transition probabilities, 653–654
  simulation of, 696–698
  state probabilities, 654–658
  steady state probabilities, 658–660
Discrete-time random process, 495, 582–583
  binomial counting and random walk processes, 501–507
  cross-power spectral density, 583
  iid random process, 498–500
  independent increments and Markov properties of random processes, 500–501
  moving average process, 584
  power spectral density, 583–585
  signal plus noise, 584–585
  white noise, 584
Discrete-time systems:
  filtered white noise, 594
  response to random signals, 593–597
  transfer function, 593
discrete_rnd function, 128
Disjoint sets, 27
Distribution, convergence in, 387
Distribution to data, testing the fit of, 462–468
Distributive properties, 28


**E**

Eigenfunctions, 547
Eigenvalues, 547
80/20 rule, and the Lorenz curve, 126–127
Einstein, Albert, 578fn
Einstein-Wiener-Khinchin theorem, 578
Elementary events, 25
  probability of, 35
Elements, 25
Embedded Markov chains, 675
  simulation using, 776–779
Empty set, 26

Engset formula, 789
Entropy, 202–212
    of a binary random variable, 203–204
    defined, 202
    differential, 206
    of a geometric random variable, 205
    maximum
        method of, 211–212
    as a measure of information, 207–210
    of a quantized continuous random variable, 206
    of a random variable, 202–207
    reduction of, through partial information, 204
    relative, 204
Equally likely outcomes, 35
Ergodic Markov chain, 668–670
Ergodic theorem, 540
Ergodicity:
    and exponential correlation, 543
    of self-similar process and long-range
        dependence, 543–544
Error control by retransmission, 64
Error control system, 12
Error correction coding, 62–63
Error detection and correction methods, 13
Estimation:
    Bernoulli random variable, 421
    Cramer-Rao inequality, 423–428
    maximum likelihood, 419–430
    of mean and variance for Gaussian random
        variable, 422–423
    parameter, 415–419
    Poisson random variable, 421–422
    and sample mean, 416–417
    using causal filters, 614–617
    using the entire realization of the observed
        process, 613–614
Estimation error, 334
Estimation of random variables, 332–342
    MAP and ML estimators, 332–334
    minimum MSE estimator, 336–338
    minimum MSE linear estimator, 334–335
    using a vector of observations, 338–342
Estimators:
    bias, 416
    consistent, 418
    for the exponential random variable, 417–418
    finding, 419
    properties of, 416–419
    sample mean, consistency of, 418
    sample variance, consistency of, 418–419
    strongly consistent, 418
    unbiased, 417
Event classes, 29–30, 70–75
    Lisa and Homer's urn experiment, 72–73
Events:

certain, 24
    elementary, 25
    impossible, 24
    null, 24
    product form, 304
Expected value(s), 11
    betting game, 106
    discrete random variables, 104–111
    of the indicator function, 159
    of a random variable, 155–163
    of a sinusoid with random phase, 158
    of $Y = g(X)$, 157–159
Exponential failure law, 190–191
Exponential random variables, 163–167
    estimators for, 417–418
    example, 150
    Fisher information for, 425

**F**

Failure rate function, 189–192
Fast Fourier transform (FFT):
    algorithms, 396–397
    and random processes, 628–630
Filtered noisy signal, 493
Filtered Poisson impulse train, 512–513
Filtered white noise:
    continuous-time systems, 590
    discrete-time systems, 594
Filtering problem, 606
Filtering techniques, random processes, 628–630
Finite sample space, 30
Finite-source queueing systems, 734–738
    arriving customer's distribution, 737–738
    Web server system, 736–737
Finite-state continuous-time Markov chains, 694
    stationary pmf for, 693
Finite-state discrete-time Markov chain, 693–694
Finite-state Markov chains, 667
First-order autoregressive (AR) process, 594–595
Fisher information, 423–424
    for Bernoulli random variable, 424–425
Fourier series, 544–546
    and Karhunen-Loeve expansion, 544–550
Fourier transform, 184–185

**G**

Gamma random variables, 164, 170–172
    generating, 199–200, 201
    implementing rejection method for, 200
    Laplace transform of, 189
    pdf of, 170
Gaussian random processes, 515–518
    continuous-time, 516

iid discrete-time, 515–516
moving average process, 524–525
Gaussian random variables, 164, 167–170
  cdf for, 167
  Chernoff bound for, 187
  and communications systems, 168
  conditional pdf of, 327–328
  confidence intervals:
    summary of, 437
    for the variance of, 436–437
  differential entropy of, 207
  estimation of mean and variance for, 422–423
  joint characteristic function of, 331–332
  jointly, 278–284
  linear transformation of, 328–330
  one-sided test for mean of, 449–450
    as UMP, 451
  pdf for, 167
  sampling distribution for the sample mean
    of, 413–414
  sampling distributions for, 437–441
  testing the variance of, 454–455
  two, testing the means of, 446–447
  two-sided test for mean of:
    known variance, 452–453
    unknown variance, 453–454
  variance of, 160
Geometric probability law, 63–64
Geometric random variables, 103, 119–120
  defined, 119
  entropy of, 205
  mean of, 106
  properties of, 115
  variance of, 110–111
Global balance equations, 680–683
Google PageRank, 657–658, 692–693
  algorithm, 671

**H**

Homogeneous transition probabilities, 651, 673–674
Hurst parameter, 544
Hyperexponential random variable, 202
Hypothesis testing, 441–455
  alternative hypothesis, 444
  Bayes hypothesis testing, 455–460
  composite hypotheses, testing, 449–455
  composite hypothesis, 444
  confidence intervals and, 455
  critical region, 442
  decision rule, 442
  fair coin, testing, 442–443
  improved battery, testing, 443
  likelihood ratio function, 446
  maximum likelihood test, 448

Neyman-Pearson, 446–448
null hypothesis, 441–442
*p*-value of the test statistic, 443
rejection region, 435, 442, 445–446
significance level, 442
significance testing, 441–443
  objective of, 441–442
simple hypotheses:
  defined, 444
  testing, 444–449
summary of, 455
testing the means of two Gaussian random
  variables, 446–447

**I**

Ideal filters, 591–592
iid Bernoulli random variables, 383, 492–493
iid discrete-time Gaussian random processes, 515–516
iid Gaussian random variables, 493
iid Gaussian sequence, joint pdf of, 505
iid interarrivals, arrival rate for, 389
iid random process, 498–500
  autocorrelation function of, 498
  autocovariance of, 498
  Bernoulli random process, 499
  mean of, 498
  random step process, 499–500
Impossible event, 24
Impulse response, 588
Increasing sequence of events, 76
Independence of events, 53–59
Independent events, 79
  examples of, 55
Independent experiments, 57
Independent Gaussian random variables:
  generating, 284–286
  radius and angle of, 275–276
  sum of, 362
Independent, identically distributed (iid) random
  variables, 361
  iid Bernoulli random variables, 383
  pdf of, 365
  relative frequency, 365–366
  sum of, 362–363
Independent increments, 502–504
Independent Poisson arrivals, merging of, 310–311
Independent random processes, 496
Independent random variables, 254–257
  covariance of, 259
  product of functions of, 258
Independent replications, simulation through, 772–773
Indexed family of random variables, *See* Random
  processes
Indicator function, 102

Infinite smoothing, 613–614
Initial probability assignment, 34, 79
    satisfying axioms of probability, 41
Innovations, 620
Interarrival (cycle) times, 387–392
Internet scale systems, 15–16
Intersection, 27
Irreducible class, 663, 667

**J**

Jackson's theorem, 758–762
    proof of, 760–762
    statement of, 759
Joint characteristic function, 322–324
    of Gaussian random variables, 331–332
Joint cumulative distribution function, 243, 305
Joint distribution functions, 305–309
    vector random variables, 305–309
        joint cumulative distribution function, 305
        joint probability density function, 307
        joint probability mass function, 305–306
Joint moments, 258
Joint probability density function, 307
Joint probability mass function, 236, 305–306
Jointly Gaussian random variables:
    generating vectors of, 344–345
    linear transformations of, 277–278
    MAP and ML estimators, 333–334
    minimum mean square error, 338
    pairs of, 278–284
        estimation of signal in noise, 282–283
    rotation of, 283–284
    sum of, 330
Jointly Gaussian random vectors, 325–328
Jointly stationary processes, 519
Jointly wide-sense stationary processes, 521

**K**

Kalman filter, 617–622
    algorithm, 621
Karhunen-Loeve expansion, 325, 546–550, 607fn
    defined, 546
    and Fourier series, 544–550
    of Weiner process, 548–549, 550
Khinchin, A. Ya., 578fn
Kirchhoff's voltage and current laws, 4
Kronecker delta function, 545, 548

**L**

Langevin equation, 538
Laplace transform, 188–189
Laplacian random variables, 165
    example, 150

Laws of large numbers:
    and sample mean, 365–366
    strong law, 368–369
    weak law, 367
Likelihood function, 420
Likelihood ratio function, 446, 457
Lindley's recursion, 778–779
Linear combinations of deterministic functions,
        generating, 553–554
Linear prediction problem, 610–611
Linear systems:
    optimum, 605–617
    response to random signals, 587–593
        continuous-time systems, 587–593
        discrete-time systems, 593–597
Linear transformations:
    of Gaussian random variables, 330
    of jointly Gaussian random variables, 277–278
    pdf of, 276–278
    of random vectors, 320–322
Little's formula, 715–718
    mean number in queue, 718
    server utilization, 718
Long-term arrival rates, 387–392
Long-term averages, 359–410
    time, 390–392
Long-term proportion of "up"time, 390–391
Lorenz curve, 126–127

**M**

$m$-Erlang random variables, 170–172, 202
M/G/1 analysis, embedded Markov
        chains, 745–750
M/G/1 queueing systems, 738–745
    delay and waiting time distribution in, 752–754
    mean delay, 740–741
        with priority service discipline, 742–745
        for type $k$ customers, 743
    mean waiting time, 741
        for type 1 customers, 742
        for type 2 customers, 743
    mean waiting time for type 1 customers, 742
    mean waiting time for type 2 customers, 743
    number of customers in, 747–750
    Pollaczek–Khinchin mean value formula, 741
    Pollaczek–Khinchin transform equation, 750, 754
    residual service time, 739–740
M/H$_2$/1 queueing system, 750–751, 753
M/M/$\infty$ queueing system, 733–734
    transition rate diagram for, 733
M/M/1 queue, 718–727
    arriving customer's distribution, 723–724
    carried load, 726
    delay distribution, 723–724
    distribution of number in the system, 719–722

interarrival times, 718
offered load, 726
system with finite capacity, 724–727
traffic intensity, 726
M/M/1 simulation, regenerative method for, 781
M/M/c queueing system, 727–732
distribution of number in, 727–731
waiting time distribution for, 731–732
M/M/c/c queueing system, 732–733
Erlang B formula, 733
transition rate diagram for, 732
MAP estimator, 332–334
compared to ML estimator, 333
for X given the observation Y, 333
Marginal cdf's, 305
Marginal cumulative distribution functions, 243
Marginal pdf's, 307
Marginal pmf's, 306
Marginal probability mass functions, 241–242
Markov chains, 79, 647–712
age of a device, 670
binomial counting process, 661
cartridge inventory (example), 693–694
classes of states, 660–662
continuous-time, 674–686
defined, 66, 650
discrete-time, 650–660, 675
n-step transition probabilities, 653–654
state probabilities, 654–658
steady state probabilities, 658–660
embedded, 675
finite-state, 667
Google PageRank algorithm, 671
irreducible class, 661, 665
limiting probabilities, 667–673
with multiple irreducible classes, 672–673
numerical techniques for, 692–700
random walk, 660
recurrence properties, 660–665
simulation of, 695–700
continuous-time Markov chains, 698–700
discrete-time Markov chains, 696–698
states of, 661
stationary probabilities of, 692–693
structures for, 666
time-dependent probabilities of, 693–694
time-reversed, 686–692
trellis diagram for, 65
two-state, for speech activity, 651–653
Markov inequality, 181, 183
Markov processes, 647–648
defined, 647
moving average, 648–649
Poisson process as, 649
random telegraph signal, 649
state of, 648

sum processes, 648
Wiener process as, 650
Markov property, 648
Mathematical models:
defined, 2
predictions of, 3
and system design/modification decisions, 2
as tools in analysis/design, 2–4
Matlab®, 67, 70, 129, 200, 285, 393
Maximum a posteriori (MAP)
estimator, 332–334
Maximum likelihood estimation, 419–430
defined, 419
likelihood function, 420
log likelihood function, 420
maximum likelihood method, 420
Poisson distributed typos (example), 419
Maximum likelihood (ML) estimators, 333–334
asymptotic properties of, 428–430
Mean:
of random variables, 155–163
discrete, 104–111
exponential, 156–157
Gaussian, 156
uniform, 156
of shot noise process, 514
Mean ergodic:
defined, 542
Mean function, 494
Mean recurrence time, 668
Mean square continuity, 529–532
Mean square convergence, 384
Mean square derivatives, 532–535
Mean square error (MSE), 338
Mean square estimation error, 417
Mean square integrals, 535–537
Mean square periodic, 523
Mean state occupancy time, 677
Mean time to failure (MTTF), 190
Mean value analysis, 766–769
arrival theorem, 767–770
proof of, 769–770
Mean vector, 318–319
Memoryless property, 166–167
Mersenne Twister, 67
Message transmissions, 102–103
Minimum mean square error (MMSE) linear
estimator, 334
Minimum MSE estimator, 336–338
Minimum MSE linear estimator, 334–335
compared to linear MSE estimator, 336–337
Mixed type, random variables of, 147
ML estimator, 333–334
compared to MAP estimator, 333
for X given the observation Y, 333
Modeling process, 3

Models:
 defined, 2
 usefulness of, 2–3
Modulator, 601
Moment theorem, 185–186
Moving average process, 507, 595
Multinomial probability law, 63
Multiple realizations, 771
Multiple server systems, 727
 M/M/∞ queueing system, 733–734
 M/M/c/c queueing system, 732–733
 M/M/c queueing system, 727–732
Mutually exclusive sets, 27

**N**

$n$ factorial, 44
Negative recurrent state, 668
Neyman-Pearson hypothesis testing, 446–448
Nonindependent events, 79
 examples of, 55
Nonindependent Gaussian random variables, sum of, 272
Normal random variables, 411
Null event, 24
Numerical techniques:
 for Markov chains, 692–700
 for processing random signals, 628–633
  fast Fourier transform (FFT) methods, 628–630
  filtering techniques, 630–631
Nyquist sampling rate, 597–598, 600

**O**

Octave, 67, 70, 129, 200, 285, 393
Ohm's law, 4
One-dimensional random walk, 502–504
 autocovariance of, 505
 independent and stationary increments of, 504
Optimum filter, defined, 606
Optimum linear systems, 605–617
 estimation:
  using causal filters, 614–617
  using the entire realization of the observed
   process, 613–614
 orthogonality condition, 606–610
 prediction, 610–612
Optimum minimum mean square estimator, 338
 diversity receiver, 340–341
 second-order prediction of speech, 341–342
Ornstein-Uhlenbeck process, 538–539, 591
Orthogonal random processes, 496
Orthogonal random variables, 258
Orthogonality condition, 335, 339, 606–610
Outcome, experiments, 4–5
 defined, 22

**P**

Packet voice transmission system, 9–11, 391
Parameter estimation, 415–419
Pareto distribution, 173
Pareto random variables, 165, 173–174
 mean and variance of, 174
Partition, 73
Periodic state, 665
Periodogram estimate, 585–587
 defined, 578
 smoothing of, 626–628
 variance of, 623–626
Point estimator, 415
Points, 25
Poisson distributed types, 415–416
Poisson process, 531
 defined, 508
 as Markov processes, 651
Poisson random variables, 120–124
 arrivals at a packet multiplexer, 122
 defined, 120
 errors in optical transmission, 123
 estimation of $p$ for, 421–422
 mean/variance of, 122
 pmf for, 120, 123
 for a probability generating function, 188
 properties of, 116
 queries at a call center, 122
poisson_rnd function, 129
Pollaczek–Khinchin mean value formula, 741
Pollaczek–Khinchin transform
  equation, 750, 754
Population, defined, 412
Positive recurrent state, 668
Power set of S, 30
Power spectral density, 577–587
 continuous-time random processes, 578–583
 cross-power spectral density, 579
 defined, 578
 discrete-time random processes, 583–585
 estimating, 622–628
 periodogram estimate:
  smoothing of, 626–628
  variance of, 623–626
 as time average, 585–587
Prediction problem, 606
 for long-range and short-range dependent
  processes, 611–612
Probability:
 a posteriori, 52
 axiomatic approach to a theory of, 8, 411
 axioms of, 21, 30–41, 79
  continuous sample spaces, 37–41
  discrete sample spaces, 35–37

convergence in, 384–385
of an outcome, 5
of sequences of events, 75–78
using counting methods to compute, 41–47
Probability density function of X (pdf), 148–155
conditional, 152–155
defined, 148
of discrete random variables, 150–151
of exponential random variables, 150
of Laplacian random variables, 150
of uniform random variables, 149–150
Probability generating function, 187–189
for a Poisson random variable, 188
Probability law, 79
for a random experiment, 30–31
Probability mass function (pmf), discrete random
    variables, 99–100
Probability models, 1–20, 4, 79
building, 8–9
defined, 1
Probability theory, 13–14, 411
basic concepts of, 21–79
Product form, 236
Product-form events, 304
Pseudo-random number generators, 67–69, 79
Pulse amplitude modulation, 526–527, 531–532
with random phase shift, 528

**Q**

Quadrature amplitude modulation (QAM)
    method, 603–604
Quality control, 52–53
Quantized continuous random variables, entropy of, 206
Queue discipline, 715
Queueing theory, 713–796
arrival theorem, 766–770
    proof of, 769–770
Burke's theorem, 754–758
closed networks of queues, 763–766
    theorem, 763–764
finite-source queueing systems, 734–738
    arriving customer's distribution, 737–738
    Web server system, 736–737
Jackson's theorem, 758–762
    proof of, 760–762
    statement of, 759
Little's formula, 715–718
    mean number in queue, 718
    server utilization, 718
M/G/1 analysis, embedded Markov chains, 745–750
M/G/1 queueing systems, 738–745
    delay and waiting time distribution in, 752–754
    mean delay for type $k$ customers, 743
    mean delay in, 740–741

mean delay with priority service discipline, 743–745
mean waiting time, 741
mean waiting time for type 1 customers, 742
mean waiting time for type 2 customers, 743
number of customers in, 747–750
Pollaczek–Khinchin mean value formula, 741
Pollaczek–Khinchin transform equation, 750, 754
residual service time, 739–740
M/H$_2$/1 queueing system, 750–751, 753
M/M/1 queue, 718–727
    arriving customer's distribution, 723–724
    delay distribution, 723–724
    distribution of number in the system, 719–722
    interarrival times, 718
    system with finite capacity, 724–727
mean value analysis, 766–769
multiple server systems, 727
    M/M/$\infty$ queueing system, 733–734
    M/M/c/c queueing system, 732–733
    M/M/c queueing system, 727–732
open queueing networks, 758–760, 763
queueing system:
    elements of, 714–715
    models, 715
    number of customers in, 716–717
    simulation and data analysis of, 771–782

**R**

Random amplitude, sinusoid with, 495
Random experiments, 4
events, 24–25
probability law for, 30–31
sample space, 22–24
sequential, 21
simulation of, 70
specifying, 21–30
Random input, response of a linear system to, 537–539
Random number generators, 67–70, 101
generation of numbers from the unit interval, 68–69
pseudo-, 67–69
simulation of random experiments, 70
Random phase, sinusoid with, 495–496
Random processes, 487–576
continuity, 529–532
defined, 488–491
derivatives, 532–535
discrete-time processes, 498–507
filtered Poisson impulse train, 512–513
Gaussian, 515–518
generation of, 550–554, 631–633
independent increments and Markov properties
    of, 500–501
integrals, 535–537
mean of shot noise process, 514

mean square continuity, 529–532
mean square derivatives, 532–535
mean square integrals, 535–537
multiple, 496–497
Poisson process, 507–511
random binary sequence, 489
random sinusoids, 489
random telegraph signal (process), 511–512
specifying, 491–497
stationary, 518–528
time averages of, 540–544
time samples, joint distributions of, 492–493
Random sample, 412, 415
Random signals:
    amplitude modulation by, 601–605
    analysis/processing of, 577–646
    bandlimited random processes, 597–605
        amplitude modulation by random signals, 601–605
        sampling of, 597–601
    discrete-time systems, 593–597
    Kalman filter, 617–622
        algorithm, 621
    numerical techniques for processing, 628–633
        fast Fourier transform (FFT) methods, 628–630
        filtering techniques, 630–631
    optimum linear systems, 605–617
        estimation using causal filters, 614–617
        estimation using the entire realization of the
            observed process, 613–614
        orthogonality condition, 606–610
        prediction, 610–612
    power spectral density, 577–587
        continuous-time random processes, 578–583
        defined, 578
        discrete-time random processes, 583–585
        estimating, 622–628
        as time average, 585–587
    response of linear systems to, 587–593
Random telegraph signal (process), 511–512
Random variables:
    Bernoulli, 102
        coin toss, 117
        estimation, 421, 428
        Fisher information for, 424–425
        mean of, 105
        properties of, 115
        variance of, 110
    beta, 165, 172–173
        generating, 198
    betting games, 101
    binomial, 103
        Chernoff bound for, 375–377
        coin toss, 118
        coin tosses and, 101
        defined, 117–118

        mean of, 118–119
        negative, properties of, 116
        properties of, 115
        redundant systems, 119
        sampling distribution of, 414–415
        three coin tosses and, 105
        variance of, 119
    Cauchy, 165, 173
    computer methods for generating, 194–202
        rejection method, 196–201
        transformation method, 195–196
    continuous, 146–149, 163–174
        beta, 165, 172–173
        calculating distributions using the discrete Fourier
            transform, 398–400
        Cauchy, 165, 173
        exponential, 163–167
        gamma, 164, 170–172
        Gaussian, 164, 167–170
        Laplacian, 165
        Pareto, 165, 173–174
        Rayleigh, 165
        two, joint pdf of, 248–254
        uniform, 163
    convergence of sequences of, 378–387
    correlated vector random variables, generating,
        342–345
    cumulative distribution function (cdf), 141–146
    defined, 96
    with differences in type, 247–248
        communication channel with discrete input and
            continuous output, 247–248
    discrete, 99–104, 146
        calculating distributions using the discrete Fourier
            transform, 393–398
        expected value and moments of, 104–111
        generation of, 127–129
        pairs of, 236–241
        pdf for, 151
        probability mass function (pmf), 99–100
        properties of, 115
        uniform, mean of, 105–106
    discrete random variables, pairs of, 236–241
    estimation of, 332–342
    expected value, 155–163
        of functions of, 107–109
    exponential, 163–167
        estimators for, 417–418
        example, 150
        Fisher information for, 425
    formal definition of, 99, 141
    functions of, 174–181
    gamma, 164, 170–172, 425
        generating, 199–200, 201
        implementing rejection method for, 200

Laplace transform of, 189
pdf of, 170
Gaussian, 167–170
cdf for, 167
Chernoff bound for, 187
and communications systems, 168
conditional pdf of, 327–328
confidence intervals, 436–437
differential entropy of, 207
estimation of mean and variance for, 422–423
joint characteristic function of, 331–332
jointly, 278–284
linear transformation of, 328–330
one-sided test for mean of, 449–450, 451
pdf for, 167
sampling distribution for the sample mean
of, 413–414
sampling distributions for, 437–441
testing the variance of, 454–455
two-sided test for mean of, 452–454
two, testing the means of, 446–447
variance of, 160
Gaussian random variables, 164
generation of functions of, 201–202
generation of mixtures of, 202
$m$-Erlang random variable, 202
geometric, 103, 119–120
defined, 119
entropy of, 205
mean of, 106
properties of, 115
variance of, 110–111
hyperexponential, 202
iid Bernoulli, 383, 492–493
iid discrete-time Gaussian, 515–516
iid Gaussian, 493
independent, 254–257
covariance of, 259
product of functions of, 258
independent, identically distributed (iid), 361
joint cdf of $x$ and $y$, 242–247
jointly Gaussian:
generating vectors of, 344–345
linear transformations of, 277–278
MAP and ML estimators, 333–334
minimum mean square error, 338
pairs of, 278–284
rotation of, 283–284
sum of, 330
Laplacian, 165
example, 150
$m$-Erlang, 170–172, 202
marginal probability mass functions, 241–242
maximum/minimum of, 310
mean of, 155–163

of mixed type, 147
notion of, 96–99
$n$th moment of, 161
orthogonal, 258
pairs of, 233–302
Pareto, 165, 173–174
mean and variance of, 174
Poisson, 120–124
arrivals at a packet multiplexer, 122
defined, 120
errors in optical transmission, 123
estimation of $p$ for, 421–422
mean/variance of, 122
pmf for, 120, 123
for a probability generating function, 188
properties of, 116
queries at a call center (example), 122
square-law device, 107–108
St. Petersburg paradox, 107
standard deviation of, 109
sums of, 257–258, 359–410
mean and variance of, 360–361
pdf of, 361–363
random number of variables, 364–365
transformations of, 274–275
two, 233–236
expected value of a function of, 257–258
functions of, 271–278
joint moments and expected values of a function
of, 257–261
sum of, 271–272
types of, 146–147
uncorrelated, 260–261
uniform, 101, 124–125, 163–164
differential entropy of, 206
example, 149–150
properties of, 116
in unit interval, 124–125, 143
variance of, 160
variance of, 109–111, 160–163
Gaussian, 160
three coin tosses, 110
uniform, 160
voice packet multiplexer, 108–109
Zipf, 125–127
80/20 rule and the Lorenz curve, 126–127
properties of, 116
rare events and long tails, 126
Random vectors:
linear transformations of, 320–322
transformations of, 311–312
Random walk:
autocovariance of, 506
independent and stationary increments of, 504
Markov chains, 664

Rayleigh continuous random variables, 165
Realization, 488
Recurrence properties, 662–667
Recurrent state, 667–669
    random walk, 668
Redundant systems, reliability of, 311
Regression curve, 336
Rejection method, 196–201
    implementing for gamma random variables, 200
Rejection region, 442, 445–446
Relative complement, of sets, 27
Relative entropy, 204
Relative frequency, 5–6, 365–366, 412
    properties of, 7
Reliability, 13
    defined, 189
    of redundant systems, 311
Reliability calculations, 189–194
    exponential failure law, 190–191
    failure rate function, 189–192
    mean time to failure (MTTF), 190
    system reliability, 192–194
    Weibull failure law, 192
Renewal counting process, 387
Repair cycles, 389
Replication through regenerative cycles, 780–782
Residual lifetime, 391–392
Residual service time, 739–740
Resource-sharing systems, 14–15

# S

Sample function, 488
Sample mean, 10, 365–366, 412
    and estimation, 416–417
    mean and variance of, 413
Sample mean estimators, consistency of, 418
Sample path, 488
Sample point, 22
Sample space, 4, 22, 79
    continuous, 24, 37–41, 79
    discrete, 24, 35–37, 79
Sample variance, 416–417, 437
Sample variance estimators, consistency of, 418–419
Sampling:
    permutations of $n$ distinct objects, 43–47
        sampling with replacement/with ordering, 47
        sampling without replacement/without
            ordering, 44–46
    using counting methods to compute:
        sampling with replacement/with ordering, 42
        sampling without replacement/without
            ordering, 42–43
Sampling distribution:
    of binomial random variable, 414–415

defined, 412
    for Gaussian random variables, 437–441
    for the sample mean:
        large $n$, 414
        of Gaussian random variables, 413–414
Scattergram, 259
Scattergram plot, 236
Second moment of $X$, 109
Sequence of random variables, 378–387
Sequences of events, probability of, 75–78
Sequential experiments, 59–66
    binomial probability law, 60–62
    geometric probability law, 63–64
    independent experiments, sequences of, 59
    multinomial probability law, 63
    sequences of dependent experiments, 64–66
Sequential random experiments, 21
Service discipline, 717
Service time, 716
Set operations/set relations, 26
Set theory, 21
    review of, 25–29
Shot noise process, 501
Signal plus noise, 497
    autoregressive, filtering of, 609–610
    filtering of, 609
Signal-to-noise ratio (SNR), defined, 283
Significance level, 442
Significance testing, 441–443
    objective of, 441–442
Simple hypotheses:
    defined, 444
    radar detection problem, 444–445
    testing, 444–449
    Type I and Type II error probabilities, using sample
        size to select, 445
Simulation:
    of queueing systems, 771–782
        approaches to, 771–772
    regenerative method for, 780
    replication through regenerative cycles, 780–782
    through independent replications, 772–773
    time-sampled process, 773–776
    using embedded Markov chains, 776–779
Simulation based Markov chains, 776–779
Single realization, 771, 774
Smoothing, 606
    infinite, 613–614
    of periodogram estimate, 626–628
Spectral factorization, defined, 615fn
Square-law device, 107–108
St. Petersburg paradox, 107
Stable system, 594fn
Standard deviation, of a random variable, 109, 160
Standby redundancy, 272–273

State, of Markov processes, 648
State occupancy times, 675
State probabilities, 654–658
State transition diagram, two-state process
    with, 659–660
Stationary probabilities, of Markov chains, 692–693
Stationary random processes, 518–528
    cyclostationary, 525–529
    iid random process, 519–520
    jointly stationary processes, 519
    random telegraph signal, 520–521
    stationarity and transience, 518–519
    wide-sense, 521–524
        Gaussian random processes, 524–525
Stationary state pmf, of Markov chains, 659, 680
Statistical inferences, 412
Statistical regularity, 5–6
Statistics, 411–486
    defined, 411
    origin of, 411–412
    samples, 411–415
    sampling distributions, 411–415
Steady state probabilities, 658–660
Stirling's formula, 44
Stochastic matrix, 694
Stochastic processes, *See* Random processes
Strong law of large numbers, 368–369
Strongly consistent estimators, 418
Subset, 25, 79
Sum processes, 501–507, 648
    binomial counting process, 501–502
    defined, 501
    one-dimensional random walk, 502–504
Sum random processes, generating, 550–553
Sure convergence, 381
System reliability, 58–59
System saturation point, 737

**T**

Theorem on total probability, 50
Time averages, of random processes, 540–544
Time-dependent probabilities of Markov chains,
    693–694
    cartridge inventory, 695
Time-invariant systems, 588
Time-reversed Markov chains, 686–692
    continuous-time Markov chains, 690–691
    discrete-time birth-and-death process, 689–690
Time-reversed process, 687
Time-sampled process simulation, 773–776
    method of batch means, 775
    transient of M/M/1 queue using, 773
Time samples, joint distributions of, 492–493
Total delay, 715

Total probability, theorem on, 50
Transfer function:
    continuous-time systems, 588
    discrete-time systems, 593
Transform methods, 184–189
    characteristic function, 184–187
    Laplace transform, 188–189
    probability generating function, 187–189
Transformation method, 195–196
Transformations:
    pdf of, 312–317
    of uncorrelated random vector, 321
    to uncorrelated random vector, 321–322
Transient state, 663
    binomial counting process, 664
    random walk, 664
Transition pdf, 501
Transition pmf, 501
Translated unit step function, 151
Transmission errors, 103
Tree diagram, 49

**U**

Unbiased estimators, 366, 417
Uncorrelated jointly Gaussian random variables,
    independence of, 327
Uncorrelated random processes, 497
Uncorrelated random variables, 260–261
Uncorrelated random vector:
    transformation of, 321
    transformation to, 321–322
Uniform random variables, 101, 124–125, 163–164
    differential entropy of, 206
    example, 149–150
    properties of, 116
    in unit interval, 124–125
    in the unit interval, 143
    variance of, 160
Uniformly most powerful (UMP) test, 451
Union, 27
Unit-sample response, 593
Unit step function, 151
Universal set, 25

**V**

Variance:
    analog-to-digital conversion, 161–163
    of random variables, 109–111, 160–163
        Gaussian, 160
        three coin tosses, 110
        uniform, 160
Variance function, 494
Vector random variables, 303–358

arrivals at a packet switch, 304, 306–307
audio signal samples, 304
covariance matrix, 319
defined, 303
events, 304–305
expected values of, 318–325
functions of, 309–317
independence, 309
joint distribution functions, 305–309
    joint cumulative distribution function, 305
    joint probability density function, 307
    joint probability mass function, 305–306
joint Poisson counts, 304
jointly continuous random variables, 307
mean vector, 318–319
multiplicative sequences, 308–309
probabilities, 304–305
Voice packet multiplexer, 108–109

**W**

Waiting time, 715
Weak law of large numbers, 367
Web server systems, 14–15
    configuration of, 15
    simple model for, 14
Weibull failure law, 192
White Gaussian noise:
    defined, 535
    generation of, 632–633

integral of, 537
and Wiener random process, 534–535
White Gaussian noise process, 550
Wide-sense stationary Gaussian random
        processes, 524–525
Wide-sense stationary random processes, 521–524
Wiener filter, 616–617
Wiener-Hopf equations, 614
Wiener-Khinchin theorem, 578fn
Wiener, Norbert, 578fn
Wiener process, 516–517, 531
    as Markov processes, 652
    sample functions of, 517
Wiener random process, 517
    and white Gaussian noise, 534–535
WSS random process:
    sampled, digital filtering of, 600
    sampling, 599

**Y**

Yule-Walker equations, 611

**Z**

Zipf, George, 125
Zipf random variables, 125–127
    80/20 rule and the Lorenz curve, 126–127
    properties of, 116
    rare events and long tails, 126